Everyday Mathematics®

The University of Chicago School Mathematics Project

Teacher's Lesson Guide
Volume 2

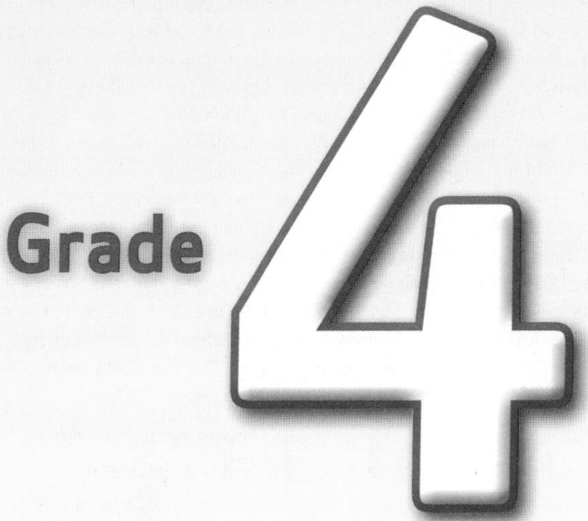

Grade 4

McGraw Hill Education

Chicago, IL • Columbus, OH • New York, NY

The University of Chicago School Mathematics Project (UCSMP)

Max Bell, Director, UCSMP Elementary Materials Component; Director, *Everyday Mathematics* First Edition; James McBride, Director, *Everyday Mathematics* Second Edition; Andy Isaacs, Director, *Everyday Mathematics* Third Edition; Amy Dillard, Associate Director, *Everyday Mathematics* Third Edition; Rachel Malpass McCall, Associate Director, *Everyday Mathematics* Common Core State Standards Edition

Authors

Max Bell, John Bretzlauf, Amy Dillard, Robert Hartfield, Andy Isaacs, Rebecca W. Maxcy†, James McBride, Kathleen Pitvorec, Peter Saecker, Robert Balfanz*, William Carroll*, Sheila Sconiers*
**First Edition only †Common Core State Standards Edition only*

Technical Art

Diana Barrie

ELL Consultant

Kathryn B. Chval

Third Edition Teachers in Residence

Rebecca W. Maxcy
Carla L. LaRochelle

Mathematics and Technology Advisor

James Flanders

UCSMP Editorial

Laurie K. Thrasher
Kathryn M. Rich

Contributors

Carla LaRochelle, Regina Littleton (Office Manager), Kriszta Miner (Project Manager), David B. Spangler; Deborah Karen Cohen, Maureen Dando, Joseph Dunlap, Serena Hohmann, Joanna Jolly, Carrie Kamm, Colleen Kelly, Sarah Elizabeth Martinek, Claire Doremus Ruch, Laurel Serleth, Nancy Smith, Cynthia G. Somerville, Ingrid Stressenger, Martha Ayala, Virginia J. Bates, Randee Blair, Donna R. Clay, Vanessa Day, Jean Faszholz, Patti Haney, Margaret Phillips Holm, Nancy Kay Hubert, Sybil Johnson, Judith Kiehm, Deborah Arron Leslie, Laura Ann Luczak, Mary O'Boyle, William D. Pattison, Beverly Pilchman, Denise Porter, Judith Ann Robb, Sheila Sconiers, Mary Seymour, Laura A. Sunseri-Driscoll

Photo Credits

Cover (l)Tony Hamblin/Frank Lane Picture Agency/CORBIS, (r)Gregory Adams/Lonely Planet Images/Getty Images, (bkgd)John W Banagan/Iconica/Getty Images; **Back Cover** Gregory Adams/Lonely Planet Images/Getty Images; **iii** (t c)The McGraw-Hill Companies, (b)George Diebold Photography/Iconica/Getty Images; **iv** (t)The McGraw-Hill Companies, (b)Photodisc/Getty Images; **v** (t)The McGraw-Hill Companies, Stockbyte/Getty Images; **vi** (t)The McGraw-Hill Companies, (b)Zedcor Wholly Owned/PhotoObjects.net/Getty Images; **vii** The McGraw-Hill Companies; **554** (l)The McGraw-Hill Companies, (r)TM_Design/Alamy; **555** The McGraw-Hill Companies; **565** C Squared Studios/Photodisc/Getty Images; **566** (t)Roberto Gerometta/Lonely Planet Images/Getty Images, (b)Luis Veiga/The Image Bank/Getty Images; **567** The McGraw-Hill Companies; **568** Sandra Baker/Stone/Getty Images; **569** Stockbyte/Getty Images; **577** The McGraw-Hill Companies; **642** SOMOS/SuperStock; **643** Sean Ellis/Stone/Getty Images; **653** (t)Getty Images, (b)Jim Wark/Lonely Planet Images/Getty Images; **654** (t)Andy Sacks/Photographer's Choice/Getty Images, (b)Peter Cade/Stone/Getty Images; **655** (t)Learning Resources, (b)Steve Taylor/Digital Vision/Getty Images; **656** MAPS.com/CORBIS; **657** (tl)Stockbyte/Getty Images, (others)PNC/Photodisc/Getty Images; **708** (l)Stockbyte/Getty Images, (r)Ryan McVay/Photodisc/Getty Images; **719** (t)Digital Vision/Getty Images, (b)The McGraw-Hill Companies; **720** (t)Walter Bibikow/Getty Images, (b)Photodisc/Getty Images; **721** (l)Mike Powell/Getty Images Sport/Getty Images, (r)Capture +/Alamy; **767 773** (l)The McGraw-Hill Companies; **778** Mark Downey/Digital Vision/Getty Images; **779** (l)Photos.com/Jupiterimages, (c tr br)SHIGERU TANAKA/amana images/Getty Images; **789** Todd Gipstein/CORBIS; **790** William Manning/CORBIS; **791** (tr)Travel Ink/Photodisc/Getty Images; (others)William Morris/The Bridgeman Art Library/Getty Images; **792** (tl)Creasource/CORBIS, (cl)Ciaran Griffin/Stockbyte/Getty Images, (b)Jim Craigmyle/CORBIS; **832** Pixtal/SuperStock; **833** The McGraw-Hill Companies; **843** (t to b)C Squared Studios/Photodisc/Getty Images, (2)George Doyle/Stockbyte/Getty Images, (3)Stockbyte/Getty Images, (4)Dave Schiefelbein/The Image Bank/Getty Images; **844** (l)Blue Line Pictures/Photographer's Choice/Getty Images, (r)The McGraw-Hill Companies; **845** John Schwieder/Alamy; **846** (t)The McGraw-Hill Companies, (b)Zena Holloway/CORBIS; **847** (t)Paula Hible/Foodpix/Getty Images, (b)Harald Sund/Stone/Getty Images; **894** (tr)PNC/Photodisc/Getty Images, (b)Russ Widstrand/Workbook Stock/Getty Images; **895** Aaron Flaum/Alamy; **905** (t)Medioimages/Superstock, (b)Rich Frishman/Stone/Getty Images; **906** CSA Plastock/CSA Images/Getty Images; **907** David Chasey/Photodisc/Getty Images; **Icons** (NCTM l-r)Sharon Hoogstraten/Courtesy of Dave Wyman, Jules Frazier/Photodisc/Getty Images, Comstock/PunchStock, Sundell Larsen/Getty Images, PhotoAlto/PunchStock, Four Elements/V262/CORBIS, Juan Silva/Stockbyte/Getty Images, Digital Vision/Getty Images; (iTLG)C Squared Studios/Getty Images; (Online Content Support)Image Source; (Objective)Brand X Pictures/PunchStock/Getty Images.

This material is based upon work supported by the National Science Foundation under Grant No. ESI-9252984. Any opinions, findings, conclusions, or recommendations expressed in this material are those of the authors and do not necessarily reflect the views of the National Science Foundation.

everyday**math**.com

Education

Send all inquiries to:
McGraw-Hill Education
STEM Learning Solutions Center
P.O. Box 812960
Chicago, IL 60681

ISBN: 978-0-07-657690-6
MHID: 0-07-657690-6

Printed in the United States of America.

1 2 3 4 5 6 7 8 9 RMN 17 16 15 14 13 12 11

McGraw-Hill is committed to providing instructional materials in Science, Technology, Engineering, and Mathematics (STEM) that give all students a solid foundation, one that prepares them for college and careers in the 21st century.

Contents

Volume 1

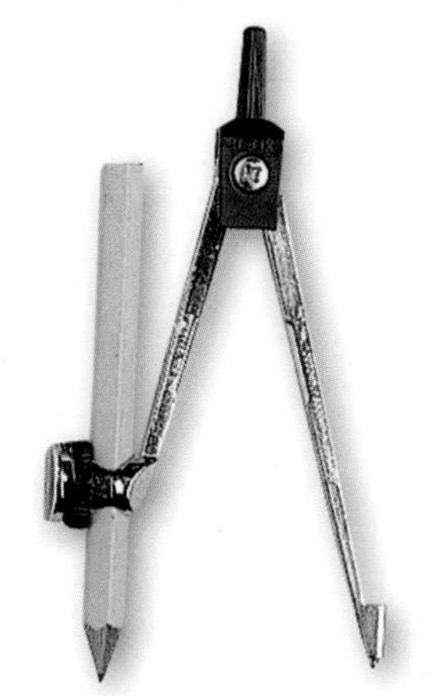

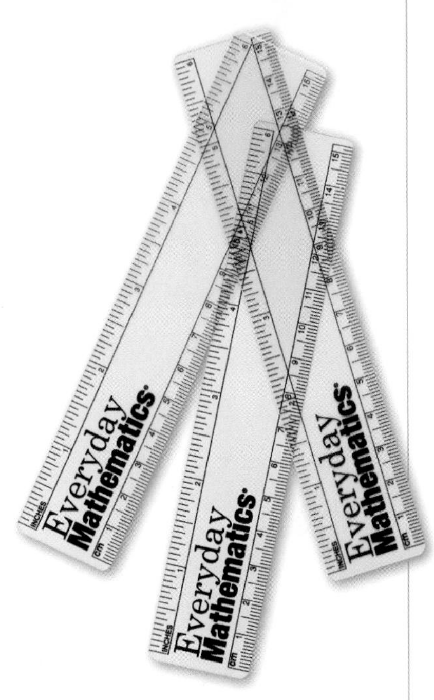
Everyday Mathematics
Everyday Mathematics

Everyday Mathematics

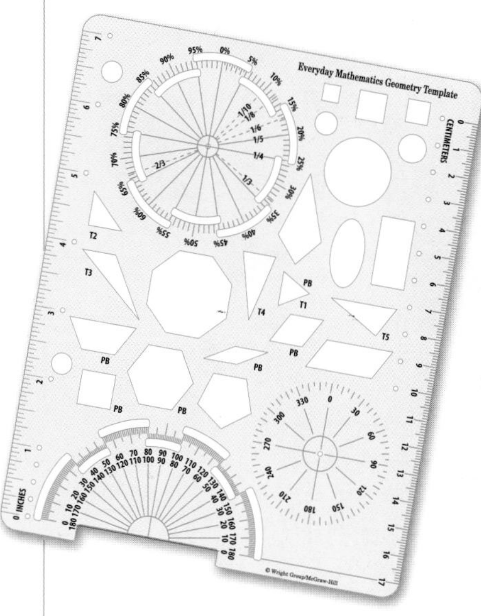
Everyday Mathematics Geometry Template
CENTIMETERS
INCHES

Volume 2

12
1
2
3
4
5
6
7
8
9
10
11

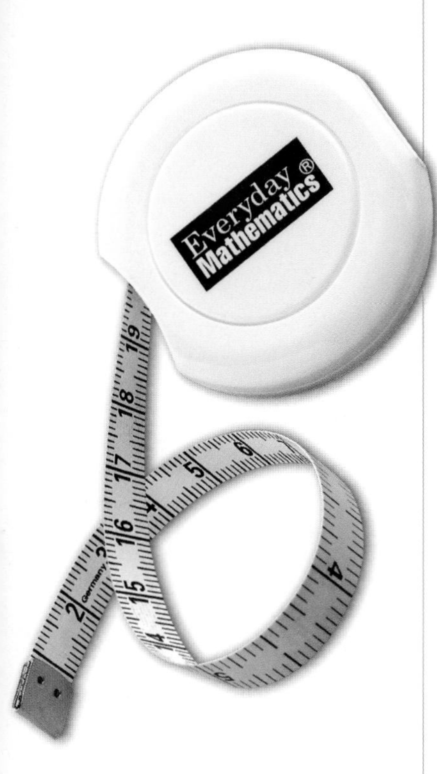
Everyday
Mathematics®

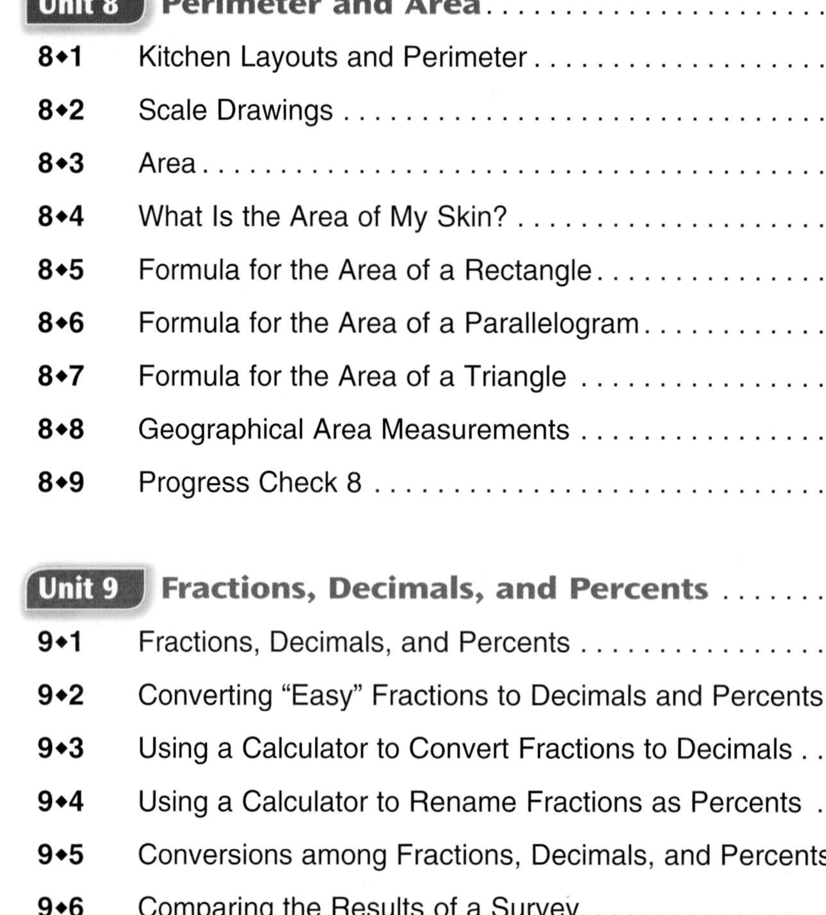

Unit 7 Organizer

Fractions and Their Uses; Chance and Probability

Overview

Unit 7 begins with a review of fraction ideas previously introduced and extends knowledge by developing a good understanding of equivalent fractions. Unit 7 also provides informal activities related to chance and probability. Unit 7 has four main areas of focus:

- To review fractions as parts of a whole (ONE), fractions on number lines, and uses of fractions,
- To guide students as they order fractions and find fractional parts of sets and regions,
- To provide practice identifying equivalent fractions, and
- To review basic ideas of probability, comparing predicted and actual results, and guiding the application of fractions to chance experiments.

Linking to the Common Core State Standards

The content of Unit 7 addresses the Common Core State Standards for Mathematics in *Number and Operations–Fractions.* The correlation of the Common Core State Standards to the *Everyday Mathematics* Grade 4 Lessons begins on page CS1.

Contents

Learning In Perspective

	Lesson Objectives	Links to the Past	Links to the Future
7·1	To review fractions as parts of a whole (ONE), fractions on number lines, and uses of fractions.	Grades 1–3: Name parts of a whole as fractions.	Grade 5: Find the whole, given a fraction or percent of the whole.
7·2	To provide practice finding fractional parts of sets.	Grade 3: Name fractional parts of collections and regions as fractions and mixed numbers.	Grade 5: Solve parts and whole problems. Review concept of whole or ONE as applied to sets.
7·3	To review basic vocabulary and concepts of probability; and to introduce finding probabilities for events when all the possible outcomes are equally likely.	Grade 3: Introduce the vocabulary of chance events. Conduct probability experiments: predict outcomes; test predictions; make frequency tables and bar graphs.	Grade 5: Perform experiments to estimate the probability of a chance event; record probabilities on a Probability Meter Poster.
7·4	To guide students as they find fractional parts of polygonal regions.	Grade 3: Name fractional parts of collections and regions as fractions and mixed numbers.	Grade 5: Solve parts and whole problems. Review concept of whole or ONE as applied to sets.
7·5	To guide students in the use of pattern blocks to add and subtract fractions and mixed numbers.	Grade 3: Review basic fraction concepts and notation. Make a number-line poster for fractions.	Grade 5: Use common denominators to + and − fractions with unlike denominators. Grade 6: +, −, *, and ÷ fractions and mixed numbers with like or unlike denominators.
7·6	To provide practice identifying equivalent fractions.	Grade 2: Identify equivalent fractions with fraction cards. Play *Equivalent Fractions.* Grade 3: Create name-collection boxes for fractions.	Grade 5: Rename fractions and mixed numbers in simplest form. Grade 6: Applications and maintenance.
7·7	To guide the development and use of a rule for generating equivalent fractions.	Grade 2: Identify equivalent fractions with fraction cards. Play *Equivalent Fractions.* Grade 3: Create name-collection boxes for fractions.	Grade 5: Formulate a division rule for finding equivalent fractions.
7·8	To provide experience renaming fractions as decimals and decimals as fractions; and to develop an understanding of the relationship between fractions and division.	Grades 1 and 2: Model decimals through hundredths with base-10 blocks, 10-by-10 grids, and money. Grade 3: Use place-value tools to display decimals through thousandths.	Grade 5: Rename fractions as decimals. Grade 6: Rename numbers expressed by fractions, mixed numbers, decimals, and percents.
7·9	To provide practice ordering sets of fractions.	Grades 2 and 3: Sort fractions by size (relative to $\frac{1}{2}$). Play *Fraction Top-It* to compare fractions.	Grade 5: Compare fractions by renaming them with a common denominator. Grade 6: Compare fractions by renaming them as decimals. Compare ratios by renaming them as *n*-to-1 ratios.
7·10	To guide students as they find the whole, or the ONE, for given fractions.	Grades 1–3: Name parts of a whole as fractions.	Grade 5: Find the whole, given a fraction or percent of the whole.
7·11	To review basic ideas of probability, including fairness and expected results; and to guide the application of fractions to spinners.	Grade 3: Introduce the vocabulary of chance events. Conduct probability experiments: predict outcomes; test predictions; make frequency tables and bar graphs.	Grade 5: Perform experiments to estimate the probability of a chance event; record probabilities on a Probability Meter Poster.
7·12	To guide students in comparing predicted and actual results from an experiment with equally likely outcomes.	Grade 3: Introduce the vocabulary of chance events. Conduct probability experiments: predict outcomes; test predictions; make frequency tables and bar graphs.	Grade 5: Perform experiments to estimate the probability of a chance event; record probabilities on a Probability Meter Poster.
7·12a	To apply and extend previous understandings of multiplication to multiply a fraction by a whole number.	Grade 3: Skip count by multiples.	Grade 5: Use an area model to represent the product of a fraction and a whole number; apply an algorithm to multiply a fraction and a whole number.

	Key Concepts and Skills	Grade 4 Goals*
7•1	Identify fractions as equal parts of a whole or the ONE and solve problems involving fractional parts of regions.	Number and Numeration Goal 2
	Identify equivalent fractions and mixed numbers.	Number and Numeration Goal 5
	Identify a triangle, hexagon, trapezoid, and rhombus.	Geometry Goal 2
	Find fractions and mixed numbers on number lines.	Patterns, Functions, and Algebra Goal 1
7•2	Solve problems involving fractional parts of collections.	Number and Numeration Goal 2
	Identify the whole or the ONE when given the "fraction-of."	Number and Numeration Goal 2
	Identify equivalent fractions.	Number and Numeration Goal 5
	Use an equal-sharing division strategy.	Operations and Computation Goal 4
7•3	Add fractions with like denominators.	Operations and Computation Goal 5
	Use basic probability terms to describe and compare the likelihood of an event; explain the choice of term.	Data and Chance Goal 3
	Predict the outcomes of an experiment.	Data and Chance Goal 4
	Express the probability of an event as a fraction.	Data and Chance Goal 4
7•4	Identify the whole or the ONE.	Number and Numeration Goal 2
	Find fractional parts of polygonal regions.	Number and Numeration Goal 2
	Identify equivalent fractions.	Number and Numeration Goal 5
	Model fraction addition with pattern blocks.	Operations and Computation Goal 5
	Identify a triangle, hexagon, trapezoid, and rhombus.	Geometry Goal 2
7•5	Identify the whole or the ONE.	Number and Numeration Goal 2
	Represent fractions and mixed numbers with pattern blocks.	Number and Numeration Goal 2
	Identify equivalent fractions.	Number and Numeration Goal 5
	Model fraction and mixed-number addition and subtraction with pattern blocks.	Operations and Computation Goal 5
	Identify a triangle, hexagon, trapezoid, and rhombus.	Geometry Goal 2
7•6	Identify fractional parts of regions.	Number and Numeration Goal 2
	Name equivalent fractions.	Number and Numeration Goal 5
	Use patterns in a table to find equivalent fractions.	Patterns, Functions, and Algebra Goal 1
7•7	Identify fractional parts of regions.	Number and Numeration Goal 2
	Name equivalent fractions.	Number and Numeration Goal 5
	Use a rule for generating equivalent fractions.	Number and Numeration Goal 5
	Develop a rule for generating equivalent fractions.	Patterns, Functions, and Algebra Goal 1
7•8	Read and write decimals through hundredths.	Number and Numeration Goal 1
	Represent a shaded region as a fraction and a decimal.	Number and Numeration Goal 2
	Rename fractions with 10 and 100 in the denominator as decimals.	Number and Numeration Goal 5
	Use equal sharing to solve division problems.	Operations and Computation Goal 4
7•9	Compare fractions.	Number and Numeration Goal 6
	Order fractions.	Number and Numeration Goal 6
	Explain strategies used to compare and order fractions.	Number and Numeration Goal 6
	Use patterns to compare and order fractions.	Patterns, Functions, and Algebra Goal 1
7•10	Given a fractional part of a region, name the ONE.	Number and Numeration Goal 2
	Given a fractional part of a collection, name the ONE.	Number and Numeration Goal 2
	Identify a hexagon, trapezoid, and rhombus.	Geometry Goal 2
7•11	Name fractional parts of regions.	Number and Numeration Goal 2
	Use equivalent fractions to design spinners.	Number and Numeration Goal 5
	Use probability language to describe the likelihood of events.	Data and Chance Goal 3
	Conduct experiments and calculate expected probability.	Data and Chance Goal 4
7•12	Rename fractions as percents.	Number and Numeration Goal 5
	Use basic probability terms to describe the likelihood of events.	Data and Chance Goal 3
	Conduct a cube-drop experiment.	Data and Chance Goal 4
	Use fractions and percents to predict the outcomes of an experiment.	Data and Chance Goal 4
	Compare predicted outcomes and actual results.	Data and Chance Goal 4
7•12a	Use a number line to represent a fraction.	Number and Numeration Goal 2
	Understand a fraction $\frac{a}{b}$ as a multiple of $\frac{1}{b}$.	Number and Numeration Goal 3
	Determine between which two whole numbers a fraction lies.	Number and Numeration Goal 6
	Solve number stories involving multiplication of a fraction by a whole number.	Operations and Computation Goal 7
	Write equations to model number stories.	Patterns, Functions, and Algebra Goal 2

*See the Appendix for a complete list of Grade 4 Goals.

A Balanced Curriculum

Ongoing Practice

Everyday Mathematics provides numerous opportunities for ongoing practice. These activities are embedded throughout the lessons:

Mental Math and Reflexes activities promote speed and accuracy in mental computation.

Math Boxes offer mixed practice and are paired across lessons as shown in the brackets below. This makes them useful as assessment tools. The last one or two boxes on each page preview the next unit's content.

Mixed practice	[7•1, 7•3], [7•2, 7•4], [7•5, 7•7], [7•6, 7•8], [7•9, 7•11, 7•12a], [7•10, 7•12]
Mixed practice with multiple choice	7•2, 7•3, 7•6, 7•7, 7•9, 7•10
Mixed practice with writing/reasoning	7•1, 7•2, 7•4, 7•7, 7•8, 7•9, 7•10, 7•12

Study Links are daily homework assignments that review the content of the lesson and often contain ongoing facts practice or computation practice.

5-Minute Math problems are offered for additional practice in Lessons 7•7, 7•12, and 7•12a.

EM Facts Workshop Game provides online practice of basic facts and computation.

EXTRA PRACTICE **Extra Practice** activities are included in Lessons 7•2, 7•3, 7•5, 7•6, 7•7, 7•8, 7•9, 7•12, and 7•12a.

Practice through Games

Games are an essential component of practice in the *Everyday Mathematics* program. Games offer skills practice and promote strategic thinking. See the *Differentiation Handbook* for ways to adapt games to meet students' needs.

Lesson	Game	Skill Practiced
7•1	*Product Pile-Up*	Maintaining automaticity with multiplication facts [OC Goal 3]
7•2, 7•3	*Fraction Of*	Identifying fractions of collections [NN Goal 2]
7•3, 7•6	*Grab Bag*	Calculating the probability of an event [DC Goal 4]
7•5	*Angle Tangle*	Measuring and estimating the measures of angles [MRF Goal 1]
7•6, 7•7	*Fraction Match*	Identifying equivalent fractions [NN Goal 5]
7•9	*Over and Up Squares*	Plotting ordered number pairs [MRF Goal 4]
7•9	*Angle Add-Up*	Solving addition and subtraction problems to find the measures of unknown angles [OC Goal 2]
7•9, 7•10	*Fraction Top-It*	Comparing and ordering fractions [NN Goal 6]
7•10	*Getting to One*	Applying proportional reasoning skills [NN Goal 2]
7•11	*Chances Are*	Using basic probability terms [DC Goal 3]

[NN] Number and Numeration [OC] Operations and Computation [DC] Data and Chance
[MRF] Measurement and Reference Frames [GEO] Geometry [PFA] Patterns, Functions, and Algebra

Problem Solving 

Experts at problem solving and mathematical modeling generally do these things:

- Identify the problem.
- Decide what information is needed to solve the problem.
- Play with and study the data to find patterns and meaning.
- Identify and use mathematical procedures to solve the problem.
- Decide whether the solution makes sense and whether it can be applied to other problems.

The table below lists some of the opportunities in this unit for students to practice these strategies.

Lessons that teach *through* problem solving, not just *about* problem solving

Lesson	Activity
7•1	Identify fractional parts of number lines.
7•2	Use pennies to model "fraction-of" problems.
7•4	Explore fractional parts of regions with pattern blocks.
7•5	Model fraction and mixed-number sums and differences with pattern blocks.
7•6	Collect fraction names.
7•10	Use pattern blocks to find the ONE.
7•11	Design spinners.
7•12	Make predictions for a cube-drop experiment.

See Chapter 18: Problem Solving in the *Teacher's Reference Manual* for more information.

The Language of Mathematics

Everyday Mathematics provides lesson-specific suggestions to help all students acquire, process, and express mathematical ideas. Throughout Unit 7, there are lesson-specific language development notes that address the needs of English language learners, indicated by ELL.

ELL SUPPORT Activities to support English language learners are in Part 3 of Lessons 7•1, 7•3, 7•11, and 7•12.

The *English Learners Handbook* and the *Differentiation Handbook* have suggestions for promoting language development and acquisition of mathematics vocabulary. See Unit 7 in each handbook.

Unit 7 Vocabulary

denominator
equal chance
equally (more, less) likely
equation
equivalent fractions
Equivalent Fractions Rule
event
expect
fair (die or spinner)
favorable outcome
mixed number
multiple
numerator
outcome
probability
"whole" box
whole (or ONE or unit)

Literacy Connection

Lesson 7•5 *Full House: An Invitation to Fractions,* by Dayle Ann Dodds, Candlewick Press, 2009

Lesson 7•11 *Do You Wanna Bet? Your Chance to Find Out About Probability,* by Jean Cushman, Houghton Mifflin, 2007

For more literacy connections, see the *Home Connection Handbook,* Grades 4–6.

Cross-Curricular Links 

Art – Lesson 7•1
Social Studies – Lesson 7•2
Technology – Lesson 7•11
Literature – Lessons 7•5, 7•11

Balanced Assessment

Daily Assessments

- **Recognizing Student Achievement** – A daily assessment that is included in every lesson to evaluate students' progress toward the Grade 4 Grade-Level Goals.
- **Informing Instruction** – Notes that appear throughout the unit to help anticipate students' common errors and suggest appropriate problem-solving strategies.

Lesson	Recognizing Student Achievement	Informing Instruction
7•1	Describe fractions as equal parts of a whole. [NN Goal 2]	
7•2	Solve "fraction-of" problems. [NN Goal 2]	Rename fractions to solve "fraction-of" problems.
7•3	Use basic probability terms to indicate the likelihood of an event. [DC Goal 3]	
7•4	Describe the relationship between the whole and its fractional parts. [NN Goal 2]	Emphasize that the ONE or the whole can change.
7•5	Use pattern blocks to solve fraction addition problems. [OC Goal 5]	
7•6	Estimate the measure of an angle. [MRF Goal 1]	Understand what the numerator and denominator in a fraction represent.
7•7	Describe a method for determining fraction equivalency. [NN Goal 5]	Find equivalent names for fractions.
7•8	Rename tenths and hundredths as decimals with the assistance of a visual model. [NN Goal 5]	
7•9	Compare fractions and explain strategies. [NN Goal 6]	Understand that the denominator represents the number of pieces in the whole.
7•10	Compare fractions and write a number model to illustrate the comparison. [NN Goal 6]	
7•11	Express the probability of an event as a fraction. [DC Goal 4]	Understand the term *expect.*
7•12	Predict the outcomes of an experiment and test the predictions using manipulatives. [DC Goal 4]	Convert fractions to percents.
7•12a	Solve mixed-number addition problems. [OC Goal 5]	Eliminate irrelevant information in number stories.

[NN] Number and Numeration [OC] Operations and Computation [DC] Data and Chance
[MRF] Measurement and Reference Frames [GEO] Geometry [PFA] Patterns, Functions, and Algebra

Portfolio Opportunities

The following lessons provide opportunities to gather samples of students' mathematical writings, drawings, and creations to add balance to the assessment process: Lessons 7•1, 7•2, 7•4, 7•7, 7•9, 7•10, 7•12, and 7•13.

See pages 16 and 17 in the *Assessment Handbook* for more information about portfolios and how to use them.

Unit Assessment

Progress Check 7 – A cumulative assessment of concepts and skills taught in Unit 7 and in previous units, providing information for evaluating students' progress and planning for future instruction. These assessments include oral/slate, written, and open-response activities, as shown below in the sample Progress Check lesson opener.

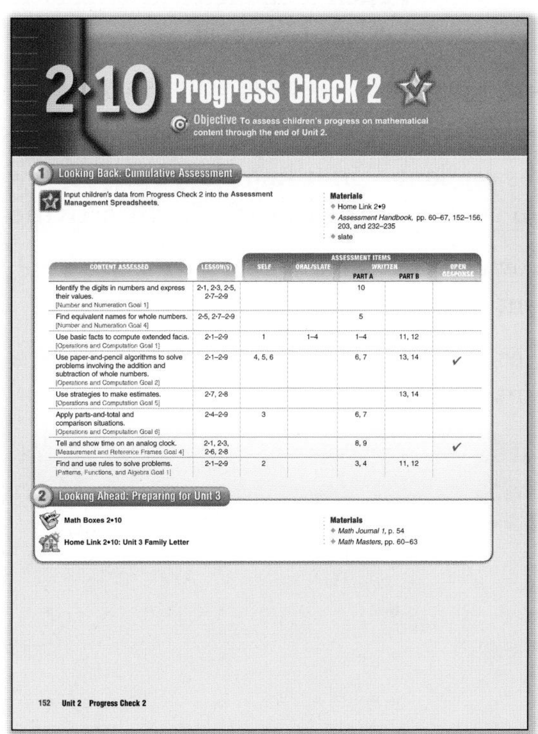

2•10 Progress Check 2

Objective To assess children's progress on mathematical content through the end of Unit 2.

1 Looking Back: Cumulative Assessment

Input children's data from Progress Check 2 into the **Assessment Management Spreadsheets.**

Materials
- Home Link 2•9
- *Assessment Handbook,* pp. 60–67, 152–156, 203, and 232–235
- slate

Content Assessed	Lesson(s)	Assessment Items: Self	Oral/Slate	Written: Part A	Written: Part B	Open Response
Identify the digits in numbers and express their values. [Number and Numeration Goal 1]	2•1, 2•3, 2•5, 2•7–2•9			10		
Find equivalent names for whole numbers. [Number and Numeration Goal 4]	2•5, 2•7–2•9			5		
Use basic facts to compute extended facts. [Operations and Computation Goal 1]	2•1–2•9	1	1–4	1–4	11, 12	
Use paper-and-pencil algorithms to solve problems involving the addition and subtraction of whole numbers. [Operations and Computation Goal 2]	2•1–2•9	4, 5, 6		6, 7	13, 14	✓
Use strategies to make estimates. [Operations and Computation Goal 5]	2•7, 2•8				13, 14	
Apply parts-and-total and comparison situations. [Operations and Computation Goal 6]	2•4–2•9	3		6, 7		
Tell and show time on an analog clock. [Measurement and Reference Frames Goal 4]	2•1, 2•3, 2•6, 2•8			8, 9		✓
Find and use rules to solve problems. [Patterns, Functions, and Algebra Goal 1]	2•1–2•9	2		3, 4	11, 12	

2 Looking Ahead: Preparing for Unit 3

Math Boxes 2•10

Home Link 2•10: Unit 3 Family Letter

Materials
- *Math Journal 1,* p. 54
- *Math Masters,* pp. 60–63

152 **Unit 2 Progress Check 2**

Core Assessment Resources

Assessment Handbook

- **Unit 7 Assessment Overview,** pages 102–109
- **Unit 7 Assessment Masters,** pages 184–188
- **Unit 7 Individual Profiles of Progress,** pages 270, 271, and 302
- **Unit 7 Class Checklists,** pages 272, 273, and 303
- **Math Logs,** pages 306–308
- **Exit Slip,** page 311
- **Other Student Assessment Forms,** pages 304, 305, 309, and 310

Assessment Management Spreadsheets

The Assessment Management Spreadsheets consist of the Digital Class Checklists and Individual Profile of Progress Checklists. Use them to monitor, record, and report student progress.

Addressing All Needs

Differentiated Instruction

Adjusting the Activity – suggests adaptations that target advanced learners, English language learners, or learners who need additional instructional support.

ELL SUPPORT / ELL – provides lesson-specific suggestions to help English language learners understand and process the mathematical content.

READINESS – accesses students' prior knowledge or previews content that prepares students to engage in the lesson's Part 1 activities.

EXTRA PRACTICE – provides additional opportunities to apply the mathematical content of the lesson.

ENRICHMENT – enables students to apply or further explore the mathematical content of the lesson.

Lesson	Adjusting the Activity	ELL Support/ ELL	Readiness	Extra Practice	Enrichment
7•1	•	•	•		•
7•2	•	•	•	•	•
7•3	•	•	•	•	•
7•4	•	•	•		•
7•5	•	•	•	•	
7•6	•	•	•	•	•
7•7	•	•	•	•	•
7•8	•	•	•	•	•
7•9	•	•	•	•	•
7•10	•	•			•
7•11	•	•	•		•
7•12	•	•	•	•	•
7•12a	•		•	•	•

Additional Resources

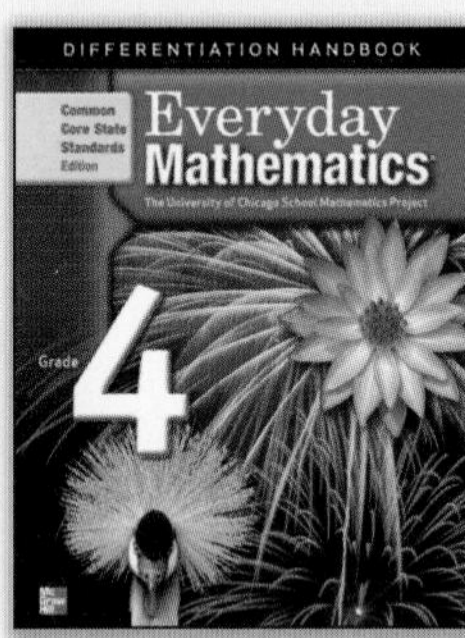

Differentiation Handbook
Provides ideas and strategies for differentiating instruction.
Pages 90–96

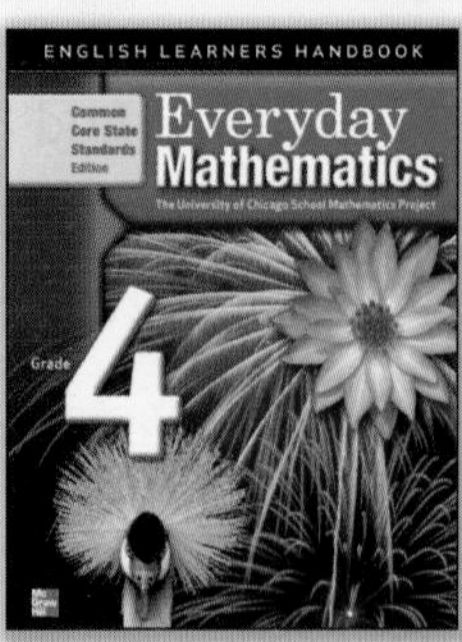

English Learners Handbook
Contains lesson-specific comprehension strategies.
Pages 60–71a

Multilingual Handbook
Previews concepts and vocabulary. It is written in six languages.
Pages 119–142b

Planning Tips

Multiage Classroom

Companion Lessons from Grades 3 and 5 can help you meet instructional needs of a multiage classroom. The full Scope and Sequence can be found in the Appendix.

Grade 3	8•1, 8•3	8•1				8•5		8•6	8•6		11•4	1•3, 11•3	
Grade 4	**7•1**	**7•2**	**7•3**	**7•4**	**7•5**	**7•6**	**7•7**	**7•8**	**7•9**	**7•10**	**7•11**	**7•12**	**7•12a**
Grade 5	5•1			6•8	6•9	6•10	5•4	5•5–5•7	5•3				8•7

Pacing for Success

Pacing depends on a number of factors, such as students' individual needs and how long your school has been using *Everyday Mathematics*. At the beginning of Unit 7, you may want to use tools available at www.everydaymathonline.com to help you set your pace.

Home Support

Unit 7 Family Letter (English/Spanish) provides families with an overview, Do-Anytime Activities, Building Skills through Games, a list of vocabulary, and answers to the daily homework (Study Links). Family Letters in English, Spanish, and seven other languages are also available online.

Study Links are the daily homework assignments. They consist of active projects and ongoing review problems.

Home Support Resources

Home Connection Handbook
Offers ideas and reproducible masters for communicating with families. See Table of Contents for unit information.

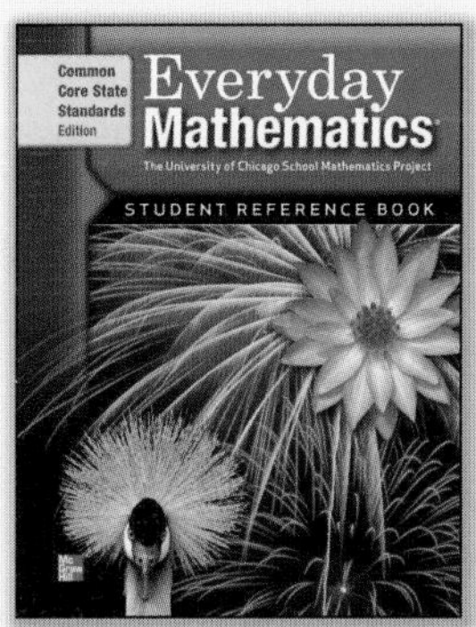

Student Reference Book
Provides a resource for students and parents.

Pages 43, 46, 58, 230, 236, 237, 243–245, 247–249, 257, 259, 276, 277, 280, 286, 287, 297, 302–305

Technology Resources

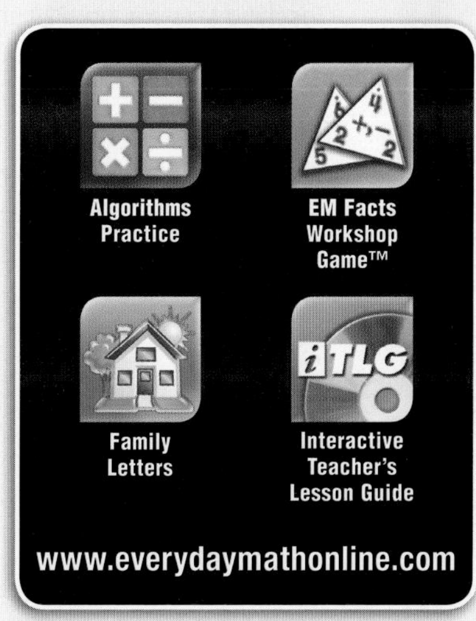

Materials

www.everydaymathonline.com

ePresentations

eToolkit

Algorithms Practice
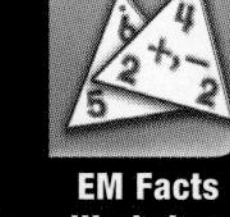
EM Facts Workshop Game™

Family Letters

Assessment Management

Common Core State Standards

Curriculum Focal Points

Interactive Teacher's Lesson Guide

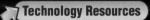

Lesson	Masters	Manipulative Kit	Other Items
7•1	Study Link Master, p. 203 Teaching Masters, pp. 204–206 *Differentiation Handbook,* p. 140	per group: 8 each of number cards 1–10; pattern blocks; slate; compass	straightedge; scissors; tape; crayons or colored pencils; calculator; Geometry Template
7•2	Teaching Aid Masters, pp. 388 or 389 and 419–421*; Study Link Master, p. 207 Teaching Master, p. 208 Game Masters, pp. 477–480	straws*; slate	20 pennies or other counters; quarter-sheets of paper*; pencils*
7•3	Teaching Masters, pp. 210 and 211 Study Link Master, p. 209 Game Masters, pp. 477–480 and 483–485	per group: 3 six-sided dice; slate	per partnership: 1 deck of regular playing cards, scissors; 1 large grocery bag; chart paper*; counters*
7•4	Teaching Masters, pp. 212, 214, and 215 Teaching Aid Masters, pp. 388* or 389* and 441; Transparency of *Math Masters,* p. 212*; Study Link Master, p. 213	pattern blocks; slate	overhead pattern blocks*; red pencil or marker*; straightedge; chart paper*; red, blue, and green crayons; scissors; red, blue, and green colored tiles*
7•5	Study Link Master, p. 216; Game Master, p. 457; Teaching Master, p. 217 Teaching Aid Master p. 393	pattern blocks; slate	overhead pattern blocks*; colored chalk*; protractor; straightedge; *Full House: An Invitation to Fractions;* calculator
7•6	Study Link Master, p. 218 Game Masters, pp. 473–476 and 483–485 Teaching Masters, pp. 219–222 Teaching Aid Master, p. 389	pattern blocks; per partnership: 3 six-sided dice	Fraction Cards (Activity Sheets 5 and 6); scissors; glue
7•7	Teaching Masters, pp. 224 and 225 Study Link Master, p. 223; Game Masters, pp. 473–476; Teaching Aid Masters, pp. 388* or 389 and 397	pattern blocks; slate	colored chalk; straightedge; calculator; Fraction Number-Line Poster (*Math Masters,* pp. 204–205)
7•8	Transparency of *Math Masters,* p. 426 Study Link Master, p. 226; Teaching Aid Masters, pp. 412, 414, 416*, 426*, and 442; Teaching Masters, pp. 227–227B	base-10 blocks; slate	overhead base-10 blocks*; pen or colored pencil; calculator
7•9	Transparency of *Math Masters,* p. 439 Study Link Master, p. 228 Game Masters, pp. 494 and 506–509 Teaching Masters, pp. 229 and 230	per partnership: 2 six-sided dice, 4 each of number cards 1–8, 1 each of number cards 0 and 9; slate; pattern blocks*	Fraction Cards (Activity Sheets 5 and 6); colored pencils; scissors; tape; calculator*; dry-erase markers; straightedge
7•10	Study Link Master, p. 231 Game Master, p. 506 Teaching Master, p. 232	pattern blocks; slate	Geometry Template; overhead pattern blocks*; beans, pennies, or other counters; Fraction Cards; calculator
7•11	Teaching Masters, pp. 233 and 237 Study Link Masters, pp. 234–236 Game Masters, pp. 462–466 *Differentiation Handbook,* p. 140	per partnership: 2 six-sided dice*; slate	large paper clip and 2 pieces of removable tape; crayons, markers, or colored pencils; straightedge; data pad or chart paper*; Internet*; scissors; *Do You Wanna Bet? Your Chance to Find Out About Probability*
7•12	Teaching Masters, pp. 238 and 240–242 Teaching Aid Masters, pp. 388 or 389 and 397; Study Link Master, p. 239 *Differentiation Handbook,* p. 140	slate; base-10 blocks; per partnership: 1 cm cube; pattern blocks*	colored pencils, markers, or crayons; shoe box or copier-paper box*; Geometry Template*
7•12a	Teaching Masters, pp. 242B–242D Study Link Master, p. 242A		half-sheets of paper; calculator
7•13	Assessment Masters, pp. 184–188 Study Link Masters, pp. 243–246	slate; pattern blocks	straightedge; colored pencils*

*Denotes optional materials

Mathematical Background

The discussion below highlights the major content ideas presented in Unit 7 and helps establish instructional priorities.

Fraction Concepts, Notation, and Uses (Lessons 7•1, 7•2, 7•4, and 7•10)

In today's world, people seldom add, subtract, or divide using fractional notation. But very often, they do use fractional notation to express and convey information such as the following:

- fractions of sets or collections of discrete things (things difficult to partition or break into parts)
  Examples: half-dozen eggs; $\frac{1}{4}$ of the cars in the parking lot
- fractions as parts of continuous things
  Examples: A recipe calls for $\frac{2}{3}$ cup of milk, $\frac{1}{2}$ cup of sugar, and $\frac{1}{4}$ pound of butter.
- fractions to name points between whole numbers on rulers, other measurement scales, and number lines
  Examples: rulers marked in inches and sixteenths of inches; scale on a measuring cup
- fractions to express rates
  Example: 24 miles per gallon, perhaps set up originally as the rate $\frac{240 \text{ miles}}{10 \text{ gallons}}$
- fractions to set up ratio comparisons or express scales on architectural plans, maps, or pictures
  Examples: Jan got $\frac{1}{4}$ of the vote $(\frac{53 \text{ votes}}{212 \text{ votes}})$; the scale of the encyclopedia pictures of the aardvark is $\frac{1}{12}$ or 1 to 12.
- fraction notation for division
  Example: As indicated above, information in rate or ratio comparison is often expressed first as a fraction before being divided.

Note

Except for those cases in which fractions are used to express comparisons in rates or ratios, a fraction will be a fraction of something. *Everyday Mathematics* refers to this "something" as the "whole," or the "ONE." It is important to emphasize that fractions can be meaningless unless one thinks of them in reference to the whole. Half a glass of milk is different from half a quart; and half a second is very different from half an hour.

Unit 7 Organizer

Whole
1 hour

Everyday Mathematics uses a device called the "whole" box to remind students that a fraction is a part of a whole thing ($\frac{1}{4}$ of an orange is a fraction of a whole orange). A box, pictured next to a problem or at the top of a page, contains a word or phrase that describes the whole, such as "quart of milk" or "1 hour."

In Lesson 7-2, students solve a variety of "fraction-of" problems, in which the whole is a collection of objects. Pattern blocks are used in Lesson 7-4 to partition various 2-dimensional shapes. They also provide students with practice naming fractional parts of a region. These activities reinforce the idea that fractions should always be viewed in relation to the whole, unless they are used to indicate rates or ratios.

In Lesson 7-10, students use pattern blocks and counters to find the whole for given fractions.

Section 9.3 of the *Teacher's Reference Manual* contains more information about fractions, concepts, notation, and uses.

Continuing the World Tour (Lesson 7•2)

Students continue the World Tour by flying from Budapest, Hungary, to Brasília, Brazil. They follow the established World Tour routine to update the Route Map and begin gathering information about countries in South America.

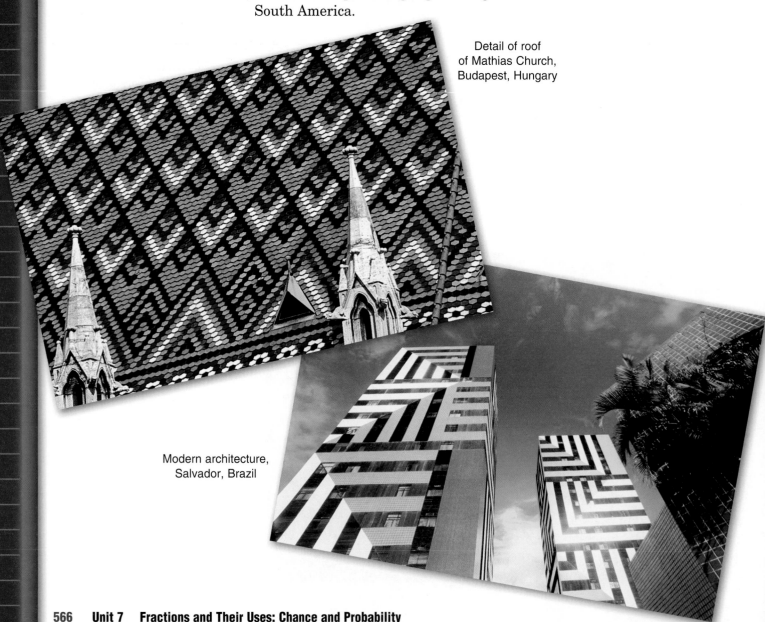

Detail of roof of Mathias Church, Budapest, Hungary

Modern architecture, Salvador, Brazil

Fraction and Mixed-Number Addition and Subtraction

(Lesson 7◆5)

In Lesson 7-5, fractional relationships between pattern blocks are applied to solve simple fraction and mixed-number addition and subtraction problems, such as $\frac{2}{3} + \frac{1}{6}$ and $1\frac{5}{6} - \frac{2}{3}$. The focus is not on using common denominators to add and subtract, but on gaining hands-on experience with these kinds of problems. Paper-and-pencil methods for fraction and mixed-number addition and subtraction are treated in detail in *Fifth Grade Everyday Mathematics.*

Consult Sections 11.3.2 and 11.3.3 of the *Teacher's Reference Manual* for additional information on fraction and mixed-number addition and subtraction.

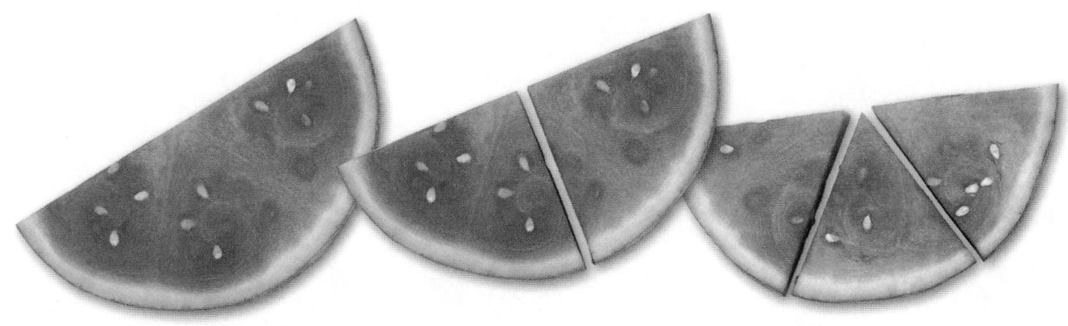

Equivalent Fractions

(Lessons 7◆6, 7◆7, and 7◆9)

By now, students should be very familiar with the idea of equivalent names for numbers. They have been filling in name-collection boxes, usually with names for whole numbers, since the middle of first grade. And in third grade, students began collecting names for equivalent fractions. However, the application of this idea to fractions will require careful teaching, time, and practice.

There is an unlimited choice of names for any fraction. For example, the number "one-half" can be written as $\frac{1}{2}$ or as $\frac{2}{4}, \frac{3}{6}, \frac{4}{8}, \frac{5}{10}, \frac{6}{12}, \ldots, \frac{100}{200}, \ldots, \frac{1{,}000}{2{,}000}, \ldots$, and so on. It can also be written in nonfraction notation, such as 0.5 and 50%. The ability to change the name or form of a number in countless ways is a very powerful tool in mathematics.

In this unit, ideas of equivalent fractions are developed with decks of Fraction Cards, which students cut out from pages in the journal. The cards show fraction symbols on one side and shaded pictures for the fractions on the other side.

In Lesson 7-6, students use their Fraction Cards to identify equivalent fractions by matching cards that have equal amounts of shading. They begin a collection of fraction names in the journal and add names to this table throughout the school year.

In Lesson 7-7, students learn that they can rename a fraction by multiplying both its numerator and denominator by the same number. Students will expand their collections of fraction names with the help of this rule.

Note

Understanding equivalent fractions is the key ingredient needed to compare and compute with fractions. By placing special emphasis on equivalent fractions, the authors hope to avoid difficulties faced by many students and even adults when working with fractions.

Fraction Cards play an important role in Lesson 7-9, where students use them to determine whether a fraction is greater or less than another fraction, to order sets of fractions from the smallest fraction to the largest fraction, and to compare fractions to $\frac{1}{2}$.

Fraction Cards are used again in Lesson 7-10 to play a game called *Fraction Top-It,* which is an adaptation of the card game *War.* Equivalent names for fractions are used to compare pairs of fractions. Players can check who has the larger fraction by comparing the amount shaded. Eventually, students who play this game frequently will not need to rely on visual confirmation as much.

To further investigate equivalent fractions, refer to section 9.3.1 in the *Teacher's Reference Manual.*

Fractions and Decimals (Lesson 7•8)

Equivalent fractions and shaded grid squares are used to rename fractions as decimals. Students add these decimal versions to their collections of fraction names.

Advantages and Disadvantages of Fractions and Decimals

Both fractions and decimals are used to represent numbers that are between whole numbers. Each form has its advantages and disadvantages. Relative size is easy to determine with decimals (for example, $0.45 > 0.0095$), but sometimes difficult with fractions (for example, is $\frac{7}{9}$ greater than or less than $\frac{5}{6}$?). Decimals are much easier to use in most calculations because the place-value structure and algorithms for decimals are closely linked to those of whole numbers. Decimals also appear in scientific notation for very large and very small numbers. Hence, decimals are universally used in science and industry. But people often want to refer to a part of something or compare one thing with another, and, for that reason, they find fractions very useful.

More information on fractions and decimals can be found in the *Teacher's Reference Manual* in Section 9.3.

Note

The authors believe that most students should be exposed to concepts and skills many times and in many different ways, often only briefly, before they can master them. The probability activities in *Everyday Mathematics* are good examples.

Project Note

Use Project 3, A Carnival Game, to provide opportunities to analyze a cube-tossing game and invent a profitable variation. See the *Differentiation Handbook* for modifications to Project 3.

Chance and Probability

(Lessons 7•3, 7•11, and 7•12)

The authors want students to feel comfortable talking about chance events. Therefore, one focus in Lessons 7-3, 7-11, and 7-12 is on vocabulary development. While many expressions are suggested (for example, *chance, unlikely, more likely, probably, certain*), they should not be taught formally. Students will gradually make these words part of their vocabulary through repeated use. Choose expressions that are meaningful to the class. Students are familiar with *expect* and *predict,* but *probability* is a difficult word which does not need to be used at this time.

Most of the probability activities follow a similar pattern: Students make predictions about the likelihood of a particular outcome and then check their predictions by performing an experiment. The authors want students to become aware of the fact that the more often they repeat an experiment, the more reliable their predictions will be. In these activities, some individual results may be very close to the expected results, but others may be far off. However, when the class data are combined, the result should be very close to the predicted results.

See Section 12.1 of the *Teacher's Reference Manual* for more information concerning chance and probability.

Multiplying Fractions by Whole Numbers (Lesson 7•12a)

A fraction $\frac{a}{b}$ can be interpreted as multiple of the fraction $\frac{1}{b}$. For example, $\frac{5}{4}$ is a multiple of $\frac{1}{4}$, because $5 * \frac{1}{4} = \frac{5}{4}$. In Lesson 7-12a, students explore this idea to develop a method for multiplying fractions by whole numbers. They use visual fraction models to discover that, in general, $n * \frac{a}{b} = \frac{(n * a)}{b}$.

See Section 11.3.4 in the *Teacher's Reference Manual* for more information about multiplying fractions by whole numbers.

7•1 Review of Basic Fraction Concepts

Objective To review fractions as parts of a whole (ONE), fractions on number lines, and uses of fractions.

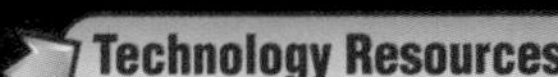

www.everydaymathonline.com

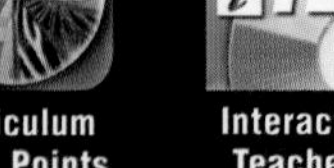

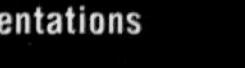

1 Teaching the Lesson

Key Concepts and Skills

- Identify fractions as equal parts of a whole or the ONE and solve problems involving fractional parts of regions.
  [Number and Numeration Goal 2]
- Identify equivalent fractions and mixed numbers.
  [Number and Numeration Goal 5]
- Identify a triangle, hexagon, trapezoid, and rhombus.
  [Geometry Goal 2]
- Find fractions and mixed numbers on number lines.
  [Patterns, Functions, and Algebra Goal 1]

Key Activities

Students review the meaning and uses of fractions. They draw various pattern-block shapes and color a fractional part of each shape.

Ongoing Assessment: Recognizing Student Achievement
Use journal page 186.
[Number and Numeration Goal 2]

Key Vocabulary

whole (or ONE or unit) ◆ mixed number ◆ denominator ◆ numerator ◆ "whole" box

Materials

Math Journal 2, pp. 185–187
Student Reference Book, p. 43
pattern blocks (optional) ◆ straightedge ◆ calculator ◆ slate

2 Ongoing Learning & Practice

Playing *Product Pile-Up*
Student Reference Book, p. 259
per group: 8 each of number cards 1–10 (from 2 Everything Math Decks, if available)
Students maintain automaticity with multiplication facts.

Math Boxes 7•1
Math Journal 2, p. 188
Students practice and maintain skills through Math Box problems.

Study Link 7•1
Math Masters, p. 203
Students practice and maintain skills through Study Link activities.

3 Differentiation Options

READINESS

Creating a Number-Line Model for Fractions
Math Masters, pp. 204 and 205
scissors ◆ tape
Students locate fractions on a number line.

ENRICHMENT

Constructing an Equilateral Triangle
Math Masters, p. 206
compass ◆ straightedge ◆ scissors ◆ crayons or colored pencils ◆ tape
Students construct an equilateral triangle using a compass and straightedge.

ENRICHMENT

Naming Fractional Parts of a Region
Geometry Template or pattern blocks ◆ crayons or colored pencils
Students make designs with pattern blocks and label each block as a fraction of the design.

ELL SUPPORT

Building a Math Word Bank
Differentiation Handbook, p. 140
Students add the terms *numerator* and *denominator* to their Math Word Banks.

Advance Preparation

***Teacher's Reference Manual,* Grades 4–6** pp. 17, 18, 60–63

Getting Started

Mental Math and Reflexes

Have students name the next three multiples in a sequence.
Suggestions:

●○○ 5, 10, 15, ... 20, 25, 30
8, 10, 12, ... 14, 16, 18
12, 15, 18, ... 21, 24, 27

●●○ 16, 20, 24, ... 28, 32, 36
24, 30, 36, ... 42, 48, 54
9, 18, 27, ... 36, 45, 54

●●● 56, 48, 40, ... 32, 24, 16
54, 45, 36, ... 27, 18, 9
56, 49, 42, ... 35, 28, 21

Math Message

List three ways that fractions are used outside of your math class.

1 Teaching the Lesson

Interactive whiteboard-ready ePresentations are available at www.everydaymathonline.com to help you teach the lesson.

▶ Math Message Follow-Up

SMALL-GROUP ACTIVITY

(*Student Reference Book,* p. 43)

Ask students to share their examples. Then have students read *Student Reference Book,* page 43 to find other uses of fractions.

Tell students that in this lesson they will review fractions as parts of wholes, measures, and counts.

Links to the Future

The use of fractions in rate and ratio comparisons is addressed in Unit 12 of *Fourth Grade Everyday Mathematics.*

▶ Reviewing Fraction Ideas and Notation

WHOLE-CLASS ACTIVITY

ELL

Write several fractions on the board, and remind students of the following:

- ▷ A fraction is always a fraction of something—for example, $\frac{1}{2}$ of an orange or $\frac{3}{5}$ of a mile. This "something" is called the **whole,** or **ONE;** for measures and counts, it is the **unit.**
- ▷ The parts into which the whole is divided must be the same size—they must be "fair shares."
- ▷ The common fraction notation is $\frac{a}{b}$, but fractions can also be written with a slash: *a/b*.
- ▷ Numbers such as $2\frac{1}{2}$ and $1\frac{3}{5}$ are called **mixed numbers.**
- ▷ The number below the fraction bar is called the **denominator.** It names the number of equal parts into which the whole is divided.

Student Page

Fractions

Here are some other examples of uses of fractions:

- ♦ Study the recipe shown at the right. Many of the amounts listed in the recipe include fractions.

Jambalaya
$\frac{3}{4}$ cup rice
4 ounces each of sausage and chicken
4 cups peppers
$1\frac{2}{3}$ cups chopped onions
$1\frac{1}{2}$ tablespoons chopped thyme
$\frac{1}{8}$ teaspoon salt

- ♦ A movie critic gave the film *Finding Nemo* a rating of $3\frac{1}{2}$ stars (on a scale of 0 to 4 stars).

Finding Nemo

- ♦ This spinner has $\frac{1}{3}$ of the circle colored red, $\frac{1}{4}$ colored blue, and $\frac{5}{12}$ colored green.

  If we spin the spinner many times, it will land on red about $\frac{1}{3}$ of the time. It will land on blue about $\frac{1}{4}$ of the time. And it will land on green about $\frac{5}{12}$ of the time.

  The probability that the spinner will land on a color that is *not* green is $\frac{7}{12}$.

- ♦ If a map includes a **scale,** you can use the scale to estimate real-world distances. The scale on the map shown here is given as 1:10,000. This means that every distance on the map is $\frac{1}{10,000}$ of the real-world distance. A 1 centimeter distance on the map stands for a real-world distance of 10,000 centimeters (100 meters).

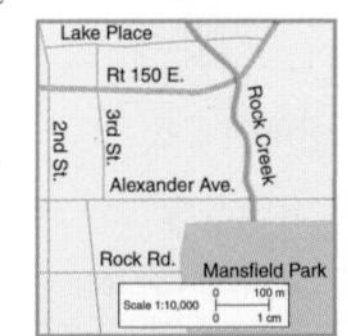

- ♦ Fractions are often used to describe clothing sizes. For example, women's shoes come in sizes 3, $3\frac{1}{2}$, 4, $4\frac{1}{2}$, and so on, up to 14.

  Part of a size chart for women's shoes is shown at the right. It gives the recommended shoe size for women whose feet are between 9 and 10 inches long.

Size Chart for Women's Shoes

Heel-to-toe length (in.)	Size
$8\frac{15}{16}$ to $9\frac{1}{16}$	6
$9\frac{2}{16}$ to $9\frac{3}{16}$	$6\frac{1}{2}$
$9\frac{4}{16}$ to $9\frac{6}{16}$	7
$9\frac{7}{16}$ to $9\frac{9}{16}$	$7\frac{1}{2}$
$9\frac{10}{16}$ to $9\frac{11}{16}$	8
$9\frac{12}{16}$ to $9\frac{14}{16}$	$8\frac{1}{2}$
$9\frac{15}{16}$ to $10\frac{1}{16}$	9

Student Reference Book, p. 43

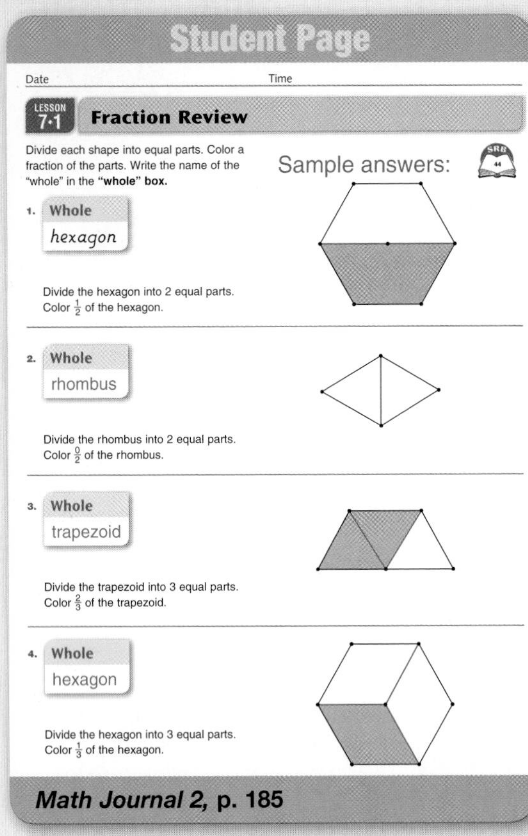

Student Page

Date Time

LESSON 7·1 **Fraction Review**

Divide each shape into equal parts. Color a fraction of the parts. Write the name of the "whole" in the **"whole" box.**

Sample answers:

1. Whole: hexagon

Divide the hexagon into 2 equal parts. Color $\frac{1}{2}$ of the hexagon.

2. Whole: rhombus

Divide the rhombus into 2 equal parts. Color $\frac{0}{2}$ of the rhombus.

3. Whole: trapezoid

Divide the trapezoid into 3 equal parts. Color $\frac{2}{3}$ of the trapezoid.

4. Whole: hexagon

Divide the hexagon into 3 equal parts. Color $\frac{1}{3}$ of the hexagon.

Math Journal 2, p. 185

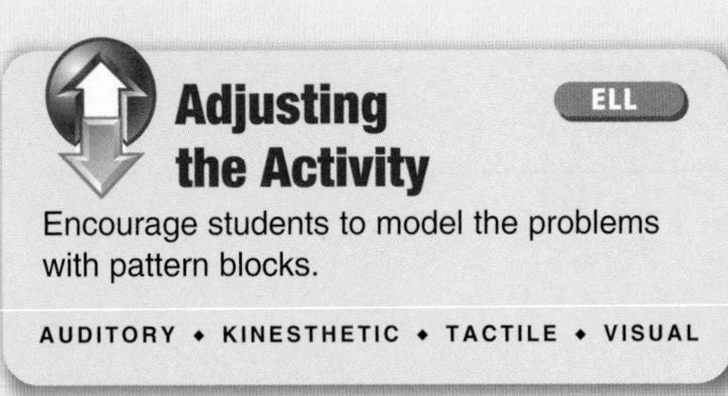

Adjusting the Activity ELL

Encourage students to model the problems with pattern blocks.

AUDITORY ◆ KINESTHETIC ◆ TACTILE ◆ VISUAL

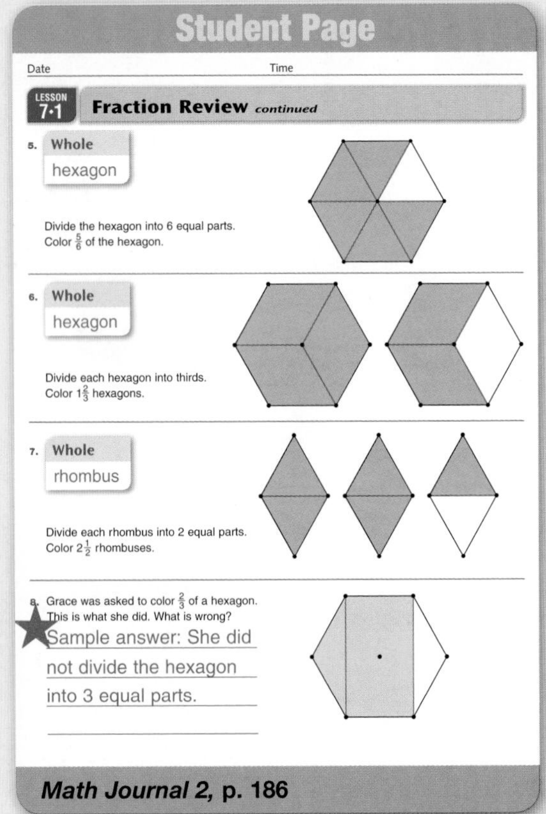

Student Page

Date Time

LESSON 7·1 **Fraction Review** *continued*

5. Whole: hexagon

Divide the hexagon into 6 equal parts. Color $\frac{5}{6}$ of the hexagon.

6. Whole: hexagon

Divide each hexagon into thirds. Color $1\frac{2}{3}$ hexagons.

7. Whole: rhombus

Divide each rhombus into 2 equal parts. Color $2\frac{1}{2}$ rhombuses.

8. Grace was asked to color $\frac{2}{3}$ of a hexagon. This is what she did. What is wrong?

Sample answer: She did not divide the hexagon into 3 equal parts.

Math Journal 2, p. 186

▷ The number above the fraction bar is called the **numerator.** It names the number of parts under consideration. For example, if Sue ate $\frac{2}{3}$ of a pizza, the pizza is the "whole." The fraction $\frac{2}{3}$ tells us that the pizza was divided into three equal parts, and Sue ate two of them.

To support English language learners, label the *numerator* and *denominator* of each fraction written on the board.

▶ Identifying Fractional Parts of Pattern-Block Shapes

PARTNER ACTIVITY

(*Math Journal 2,* pp. 185 and 186)

Students use a straightedge to divide each shape on journal pages 185 and 186 into a specified number of equal parts and color a fraction of the shape.

Do Problem 1 with the class. Remind students that the whole (or ONE) is the hexagon. Call students' attention to the **"whole" box,** which is used to write the name of the whole. As they work on Problems 2–7, students record the name of each item in the "whole" box. Have students complete Problem 8 independently.

NOTE You might ask students to identify a fraction that could describe the colored parts of the shapes in Problem 6 on journal page 186. $\frac{5}{3}$ Repeat this procedure for Problem 7. $\frac{5}{2}$ The term *improper fraction* is sometimes used to describe a fraction with a numerator that is greater than or equal to its denominator.

When students have finished, explain that it is sometimes useful to write fractions and mixed numbers as sums. This is called *decomposing* a fraction or mixed number. For example, $\frac{4}{5}$ can be decomposed into the sum $\frac{1}{5} + \frac{3}{5}$ or the sum $\frac{2}{5} + \frac{2}{5}$.

Ask students to decompose each fraction or mixed number in Problems 5, 6, and 7 into a sum of fractions. Sample answers: Problem 5: $\frac{1}{6} + \frac{1}{6} + \frac{1}{6} + \frac{1}{6} + \frac{1}{6} = \frac{5}{6}$; Problem 6: $\frac{3}{3} + \frac{2}{3} = 1\frac{2}{3}$; Problem 7: $\frac{2}{2} + \frac{2}{2} + \frac{1}{2} = 2\frac{1}{2}$ Pose additional fractions for students to decompose.

Ongoing Assessment: Recognizing Student Achievement

Journal page 186 Problem 8

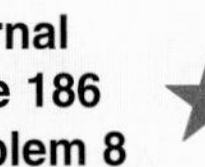

Use **journal page 186, Problem 8** to assess students' understanding of fractions as equal parts of a whole. Students are making adequate progress if their responses note that Grace did not divide the hexagon into 3 *equal* parts. Some students' responses may include correct ways to shade $\frac{2}{3}$ of the hexagon.

[Number and Numeration Goal 2]

Identifying Fractional Parts of Number Lines

PARTNER ACTIVITY

(*Math Journal 2,* p. 187)

In Problems 9–14 on journal page 187, students write fractions and mixed numbers for points on number lines. Number-line problems reinforce the concept that fractions and decimals can be used to name numbers between whole numbers.

Entering Fractions and Mixed Numbers on a Calculator

(*Math Journal 2,* p. 187)

Lead students through the appropriate steps to enter fractions and mixed numbers on their calculators.

To enter $\frac{3}{4}$:

- ▷ On a TI-15, press 3 [n] 4 [d].
- ▷ On a Casio *fx*-55, press 3 [b/c] 4.

To enter $4\frac{7}{8}$:

- ▷ On a TI-15, press 4 [Unit] 7 [n] 8 [d].
- ▷ On a Casio *fx*-55, press 4 [a] 7 [b/c] 8.

Have students practice using their calculators to enter the fractions and mixed numbers on journal page 187.

2 Ongoing Learning & Practice

Playing *Product Pile-Up*

(*Student Reference Book,* p. 259)

Students play *Product Pile-Up* to maintain automaticity with multiplication facts. See Lesson 4-3 for additonal information.

Math Boxes 7•1

(*Math Journal 2,* p. 188)

Mixed Practice Math Boxes in this lesson are paired with Math Boxes in Lesson 7-3. The skill in Problem 6 previews Unit 8 content.

Writing/Reasoning Have students write a response to the following: *How did you determine whether the angle in Problem 2 was obtuse or acute?* Sample answer: The measure of angle *POL* is greater than 90 degrees, so it is obtuse.

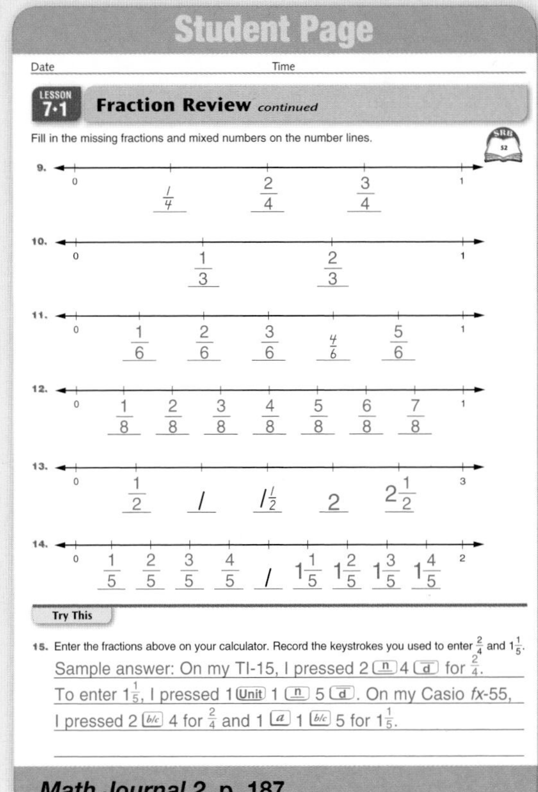

Student Page

Date Time

LESSON 7•1 **Fraction Review** *continued*

Fill in the missing fractions and mixed numbers on the number lines.

9. 0, $\frac{1}{4}$, $\frac{2}{4}$, $\frac{3}{4}$, 1

10. 0, $\frac{1}{3}$, $\frac{2}{3}$, 1

11. 0, $\frac{1}{6}$, $\frac{2}{6}$, $\frac{3}{6}$, $\frac{4}{6}$, $\frac{5}{6}$, 1

12. 0, $\frac{1}{8}$, $\frac{2}{8}$, $\frac{3}{8}$, $\frac{4}{8}$, $\frac{5}{8}$, $\frac{6}{8}$, $\frac{7}{8}$, 1

13. 0, $\frac{1}{2}$, 1, $1\frac{1}{2}$, 2, $2\frac{1}{2}$, 3

14. 0, $\frac{1}{5}$, $\frac{2}{5}$, $\frac{3}{5}$, $\frac{4}{5}$, 1, $1\frac{1}{5}$, $1\frac{2}{5}$, $1\frac{3}{5}$, $1\frac{4}{5}$, 2

Try This

15. Enter the fractions above on your calculator. Record the keystrokes you used to enter $\frac{2}{4}$ and $1\frac{1}{5}$.

Sample answer: On my TI-15, I pressed 2 [n] 4 [d] for $\frac{2}{4}$. To enter $1\frac{1}{5}$, I pressed 1 [Unit] 1 [n] 5 [d]. On my Casio *fx*-55, I pressed 2 [b/c] 4 for $\frac{2}{4}$ and 1 [a] 1 [b/c] 5 for $1\frac{1}{5}$.

Math Journal 2, p. 187

Adjusting the Activity ELL

Have students refer to their Fraction Number-Line Poster. See the optional Readiness activity in Part 3.

AUDITORY ◆ KINESTHETIC ◆ TACTILE ◆ VISUAL

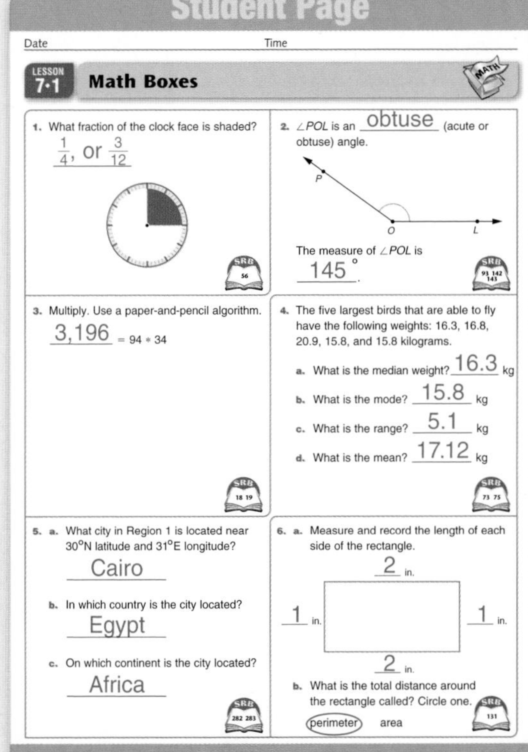

Student Page

Date Time

LESSON 7•1 **Math Boxes**

1. What fraction of the clock face is shaded? $\frac{1}{4}$, or $\frac{3}{12}$

2. ∠*POL* is an obtuse (acute or obtuse) angle.
The measure of ∠*POL* is 145°.

3. Multiply. Use a paper-and-pencil algorithm.
3,196 = 94 ∗ 34

4. The five largest birds that are able to fly have the following weights: 16.3, 16.8, 20.9, 15.8, and 15.8 kilograms.
a. What is the median weight? 16.3 kg
b. What is the mode? 15.8 kg
c. What is the range? 5.1 kg
d. What is the mean? 17.12 kg

5. a. What city in Region 1 is located near 30°N latitude and 31°E longitude? Cairo
b. In which country is the city located? Egypt
c. On which continent is the city located? Africa

6. a. Measure and record the length of each side of the rectangle. 2 in., 1 in., 1 in., 2 in.
b. What is the total distance around the rectangle called? Circle one. (perimeter) area

Math Journal 2, p. 188

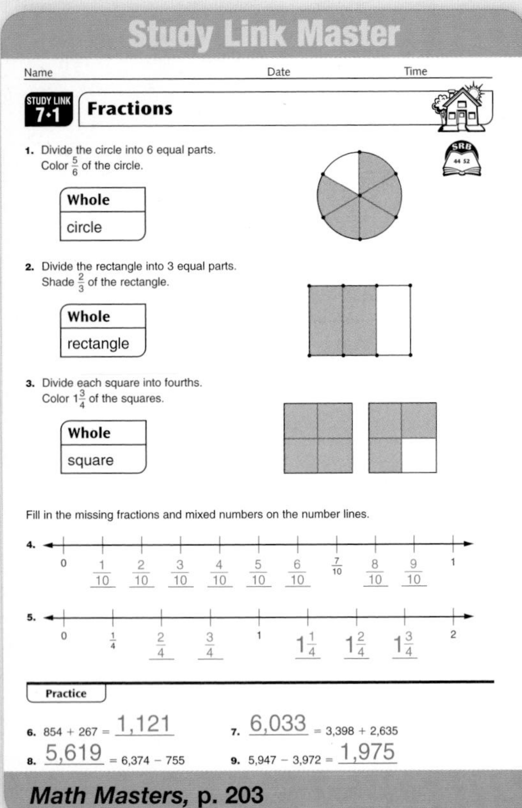

Study Link Master

Name Date Time

STUDY LINK 7·1 **Fractions**

1. Divide the circle into 6 equal parts. Color $\frac{5}{6}$ of the circle.

Whole
circle

2. Divide the rectangle into 3 equal parts. Shade $\frac{2}{3}$ of the rectangle.

Whole
rectangle

3. Divide each square into fourths. Color $1\frac{3}{4}$ of the squares.

Whole
square

Fill in the missing fractions and mixed numbers on the number lines.

4. 0, $\frac{1}{10}$, $\frac{2}{10}$, $\frac{3}{10}$, $\frac{4}{10}$, $\frac{5}{10}$, $\frac{6}{10}$, $\frac{7}{10}$, $\frac{8}{10}$, $\frac{9}{10}$, 1

5. 0, $\frac{1}{4}$, $\frac{2}{4}$, $\frac{3}{4}$, 1, $1\frac{1}{4}$, $1\frac{2}{4}$, $1\frac{3}{4}$, 2

Practice

6. 854 + 267 = 1,121
7. 6,033 = 3,398 + 2,635
8. 5,619 = 6,374 − 755
9. 5,947 − 3,972 = 1,975

Math Masters, p. 203

Teaching Master

Name Date Time

LESSON 7·1 **Fraction Strips**

Cut along the dashed lines.

1 Whole: 0, 1

Halves: $\frac{0}{2}$, $\frac{1}{2}$, $\frac{2}{2}$

Fourths: $\frac{0}{4}$, $\frac{1}{4}$, $\frac{2}{4}$, $\frac{3}{4}$, $\frac{4}{4}$

Eighths: $\frac{0}{8}$, $\frac{1}{8}$, $\frac{2}{8}$, $\frac{3}{8}$, $\frac{4}{8}$, $\frac{5}{8}$, $\frac{6}{8}$, $\frac{7}{8}$, $\frac{8}{8}$

Thirds: $\frac{0}{3}$, $\frac{1}{3}$, $\frac{2}{3}$, $\frac{3}{3}$

Sixths: $\frac{0}{6}$, $\frac{1}{6}$, $\frac{2}{6}$, $\frac{3}{6}$, $\frac{4}{6}$, $\frac{5}{6}$, $\frac{6}{6}$

Math Masters, p. 204

▶ Study Link 7·1

INDEPENDENT ACTIVITY

(*Math Masters,* p. 203)

Home Connection Students identify fractional parts of shapes and number lines.

3 Differentiation Options

READINESS

SMALL-GROUP ACTIVITY

15–30 Min

▶ Creating a Number-Line Model for Fractions

(*Math Masters,* pp. 204 and 205)

To provide experience locating fractions on a number line, have students create a Fraction Number-Line Poster.

Students cut out the fraction strips on *Math Masters,* page 204. The top strip shows a number line from 0 to 1. It represents the whole, or the ONE. Have students tape it exactly over the strip on *Math Masters,* page 205.

Ask students to fold the "Halves" strip in half, make a mark where the crease meets the number line, and label it $\frac{1}{2}$. Have students tape it to the strip on *Math Masters,* page 205.

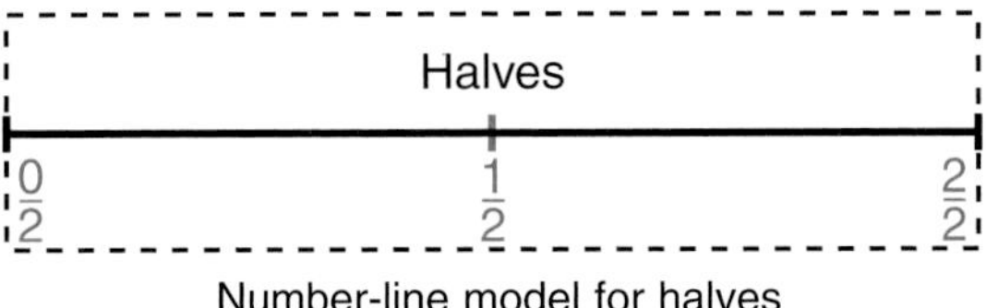

Number-line model for halves

Ask students to fold, label, and tape the remaining strips. Have them choose how to fold and label the last strip.

For each strip, have students begin with their finger on the 0 and count each fractional part until they count to one. This way, they count the number of intervals, not the number of marks.

Discuss how the number-line model is different from the region and set models for fractions. Ask: *Can you think of places in the everyday world where fraction number lines are found?* Sample answers: Rulers and measuring cups

NOTE The Fraction Number-Line Poster is also used in the Readiness activity in Lesson 7-7.

ENRICHMENT

INDEPENDENT ACTIVITY

Constructing an Equilateral Triangle

5–15 Min

(*Math Masters,* p. 206)

To apply students' understanding of fractions as equal parts of a whole, have them construct an equilateral triangle using a compass and straightedge. They cut out the triangle and divide it into six equal parts.

Possible strategy: Put two vertices together, and fold the triangle in half. Unfold it. Repeat the process twice, using a different pair of vertices each time.

ENRICHMENT

INDEPENDENT ACTIVITY

Naming Fractional Parts of a Region

15–30 Min

Portfolio Ideas

Art Link To apply students' understanding of the whole, have them use pattern blocks (hexagon, trapezoid, wide rhombus, and triangle) or the Geometry Template to draw and color a design (whole). Ask students to write the fraction of the design each shape represents. Students should compare their designs and note that the amount represented by a fraction depends on the whole, or the ONE. *For example:*

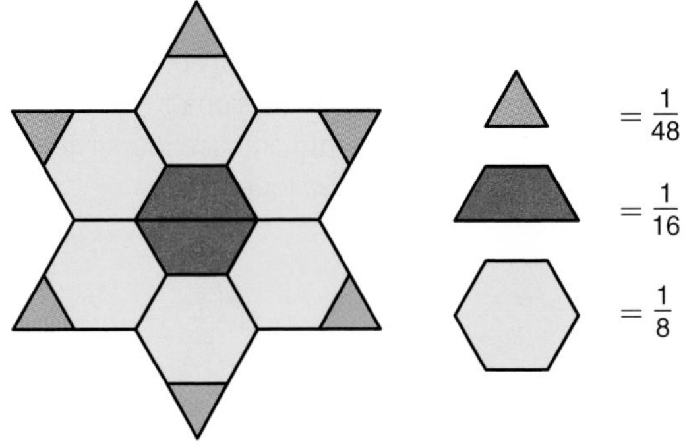

ELL SUPPORT

SMALL-GROUP ACTIVITY

Building a Math Word Bank

5–15 Min

(*Differentiation Handbook*, p. 140)

To provide language support for fractions, have students use the Word Bank Template found on *Differentiation Handbook,* page 140. Ask students to write the terms *numerator* and *denominator*, draw pictures relating to each term, and write other related words. See the *Differentiation Handbook* for more information.

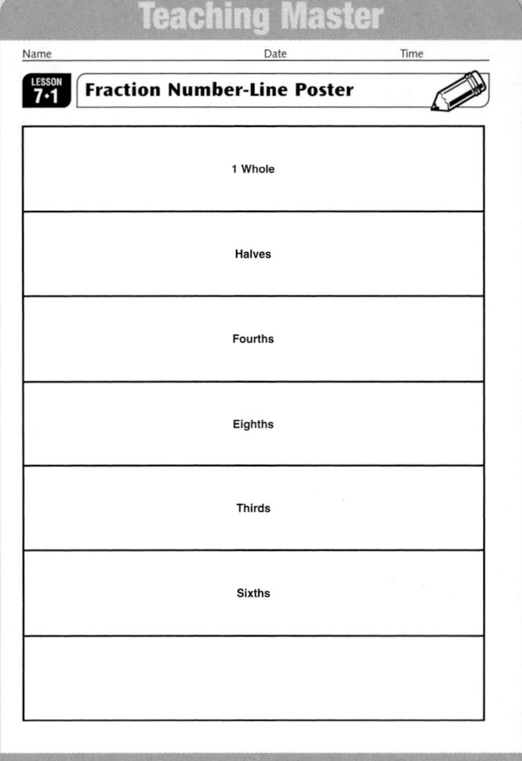

Teaching Master

Name Date Time

LESSON 7·1 **Fraction Number-Line Poster**

1 Whole
Halves
Fourths
Eighths
Thirds
Sixths

Math Masters, p. 205

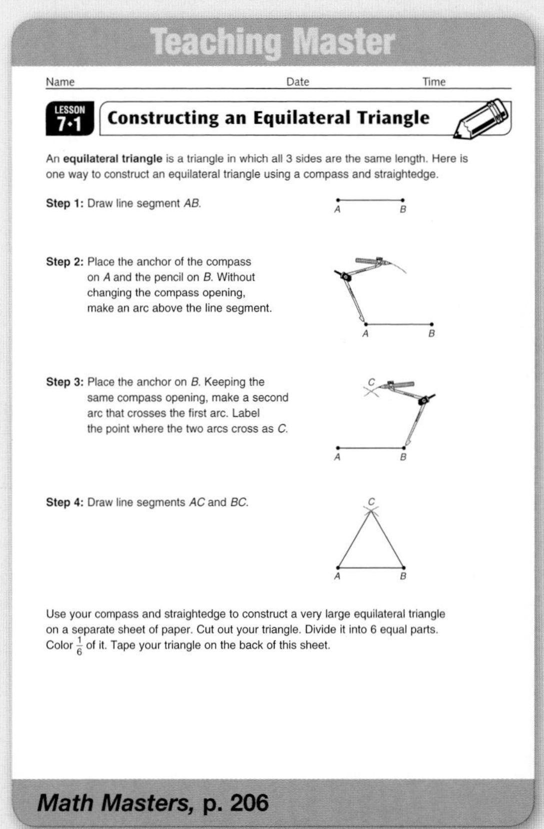

Teaching Master

Name Date Time

LESSON 7·1 **Constructing an Equilateral Triangle**

An **equilateral triangle** is a triangle in which all 3 sides are the same length. Here is one way to construct an equilateral triangle using a compass and straightedge.

Step 1: Draw line segment *AB*.

Step 2: Place the anchor of the compass on *A* and the pencil on *B*. Without changing the compass opening, make an arc above the line segment.

Step 3: Place the anchor on *B*. Keeping the same compass opening, make a second arc that crosses the first arc. Label the point where the two arcs cross as *C*.

Step 4: Draw line segments *AC* and *BC*.

Use your compass and straightedge to construct a very large equilateral triangle on a separate sheet of paper. Cut out your triangle. Divide it into 6 equal parts. Color $\frac{1}{6}$ of it. Tape your triangle on the back of this sheet.

Math Masters, p. 206

7•2 Fractions of Sets

Objective To provide practice finding fractional parts of sets.

www.everydaymathonline.com

ePresentations | eToolkit | Algorithms Practice | EM Facts Workshop Game™ | Family Letters | Assessment Management | Common Core State Standards | Curriculum Focal Points | Interactive Teacher's Lesson Guide

1 Teaching the Lesson

Key Concepts and Skills

- Solve problems involving fractional parts of collections. [Number and Numeration Goal 2]
- Identify the whole or the ONE when given the "fraction-of." [Number and Numeration Goal 2]
- Identify equivalent fractions. [Number and Numeration Goal 5]
- Use an equal-sharing division strategy. [Operations and Computation Goal 4]

Key Activities

Students find fractions of a whole when the whole is a collection of objects.

Ongoing Assessment: Recognizing Student Achievement Use journal page 190. [Number and Numeration Goal 2]

Ongoing Assessment: Informing Instruction See page 578.

Materials

Math Journal 2, pp. 189 and 190
Study Link 7•1
20 pennies or other counters ◆ slate ◆ straws or pencils ◆ quarter-sheets of paper (optional)

2 Ongoing Learning & Practice

Resuming the World Tour

Math Journal 2, pp. 329–333
Student Reference Book, pp. 276, 277, 280, 286, 287, 297, and 302–305
Math Masters, pp. 419–421 (optional)
Students continue the World Tour.

Math Boxes 7•2

Math Journal 2, p. 191
Students practice and maintain skills through Math Box problems.

Study Link 7•2

Math Masters, p. 207
Students practice and maintain skills through Study Link activities.

3 Differentiation Options

READINESS

Exploring Fractions of a Set

Math Masters, p. 388 or 389
Students act out a fraction situation.

ENRICHMENT

Solving "Fraction-of" Problems

Math Masters, p. 208
Students solve "fraction-of" hiking problems.

EXTRA PRACTICE

Playing *Fraction Of*

Student Reference Book, pp. 244 and 245
Math Masters, pp. 477–480
counters (optional)
Students practice identifying fractions of collections.

Advance Preparation

For Part 1, put a supply of pennies (or counters) next to the Math Message (at least 20 per student). For the optional Extra Practice activity in Part 3, consider copying *Math Masters,* pages 477, 478, and 480 on cardstock.

***Teacher's Reference Manual,* Grades 4–6** pp. 17, 18, 60–63

Getting Started

Mental Math and Reflexes

Pose mental addition and subtraction problems. Have students share solution strategies. *Suggestions:*

●○○ 11 + 12 = 23	●●○ 13 + 28 = 41	●●● 123 + 246 = 369
18 + 6 = 24	19 + 33 = 52	225 + 468 = 693
27 − 15 = 12	55 − 47 = 8	247 − 135 = 112
37 − 19 = 18	75 − 41 = 34	364 − 297 = 67

Math Message

Take 20 pennies. Show $\frac{1}{2}$ of 20.

Study Link 7•1 Follow-Up

Ask students to decompose the fractions in Problems 1, 2, and 3.

1 Teaching the Lesson

Math Message Follow-Up

Partners compare answers and share their thinking or strategies.

Tell students that in this lesson they will investigate different ways to divide sets into fractional parts.

Modeling "Fraction-of" Problems with Pennies

PARTNER ACTIVITY

Ask each partnership to place 24 pennies on the desk and count out $\frac{2}{3}$ of them. Emphasize that the whole is 24 pennies, or 24 cents, not 1 penny. Stress the importance of identifying the whole in any problem involving fractions.

Have students share solution strategies. If no one suggests it, model the following strategy:

Divide the 24 pennies into 3 equal groups, or 3 "fair shares." Separate the groups from one another with straws or pencils.

- How much is the whole? 24 pennies, or 24¢
- The pennies in each group represent what fraction of all the pennies? $\frac{1}{3}$
- How many pennies are in each group (or share)? 8 pennies
- How much is $\frac{2}{3}$ of 24 pennies? 16 pennies, or 16¢

Summary: One way to find $\frac{2}{3}$ of 24 is to first find $\frac{1}{3}$ of 24. 8 If $\frac{1}{3}$ of 24 is 8, $\frac{2}{3}$ of 24 must be twice as much. 16

$\frac{1}{3}$ of 24 = 8
$\frac{2}{3}$ of 24 = 16

Whole
24 pennies

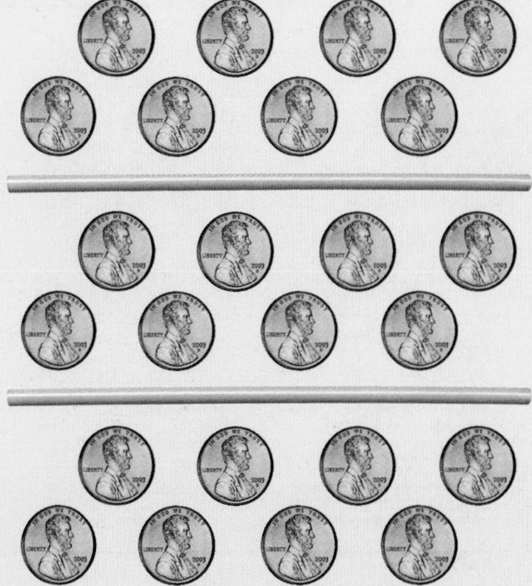

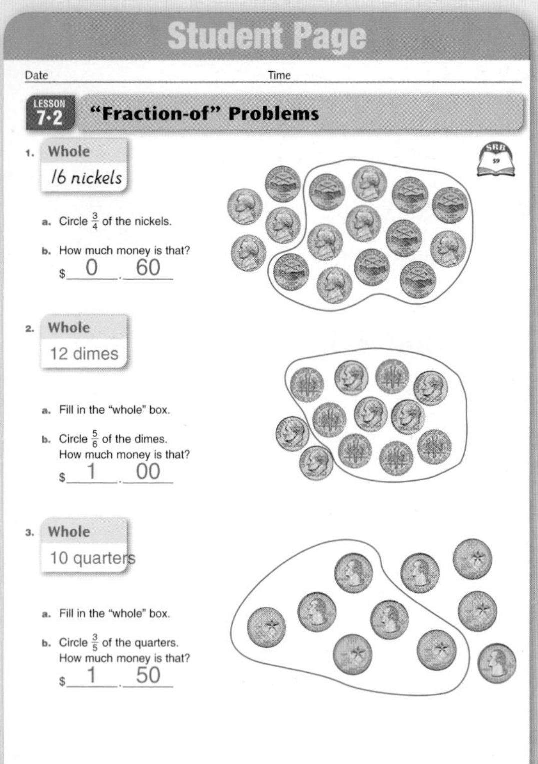
Student Page

Date Time

LESSON 7·2 **"Fraction-of" Problems**

1. Whole: 16 nickels
   a. Circle $\frac{3}{4}$ of the nickels.
   b. How much money is that? \$0.60
2. Whole: 12 dimes
   a. Fill in the "whole" box.
   b. Circle $\frac{5}{6}$ of the dimes. How much money is that? \$1.00
3. Whole: 10 quarters
   a. Fill in the "whole" box.
   b. Circle $\frac{3}{5}$ of the quarters. How much money is that? \$1.50

Math Journal 2, p. 189

Pose similar problems, and have students model the solutions with pennies. *Suggestions:*

- How much is $\frac{1}{4}$ of 32¢? 8¢ $\frac{2}{4}$ of 32¢? 16¢ $\frac{3}{4}$ of 32¢? 24¢
- How much is $\frac{1}{5}$ of 30¢? 6¢ $\frac{2}{5}$ of 30¢? 12¢ $\frac{4}{5}$ of 30¢? 24¢
- How much is $\frac{2}{3}$ of 27¢? 18¢ $\frac{5}{6}$ of 30¢? 25¢ $\frac{3}{8}$ of 40¢? 15¢

Adjusting the Activity

ELL

Have students place quarter-sheets of paper on their desks to represent the number of equal groups. Ask them to divide the pennies into equal groups by distributing them among the sheets. The total number of sheets (groups) represents the denominator of the fraction.

AUDITORY ◆ KINESTHETIC ◆ TACTILE ◆ VISUAL

▶ Solving "Fraction-of" Problems

(*Math Journal 2,* pp. 189 and 190)

Suggest that students use counters to model the "fraction-of" problems on journal pages 189 and 190.

When students have completed the page, ask them to describe a calculator strategy for solving Problem 4b. Sample answers: Enter $\frac{2}{3}$ into the calculator and multiply by 12, or divide 12 by 3 and multiply by 2.

Ongoing Assessment: Informing Instruction

Watch for the strategies students use to solve Problems 9 and 10. The strategy of first finding $\frac{1}{4}$ of 14 (or 22) and using the answer to find $\frac{2}{4}$, while possible, is not practical. Look for students to note that $\frac{2}{4}$ is another name for $\frac{1}{2}$. Renaming $\frac{2}{4}$ as $\frac{1}{2}$ makes it easier to solve the problems.

Ongoing Assessment: Recognizing Student Achievement

Journal page 190 Problems 4a–8a ★

Use **journal page 190, Problems 4a–8a** to assess students' ability to solve "fraction-of" problems. Students are making adequate progress if they are able to find the fraction of a collection when the fraction is a unit fraction. Some students may be able to solve "fraction-of" problems involving non-unit fractions (Problems 4b–8b) and fractions greater than one (Problems 4c–8c).

[Number and Numeration Goal 2]

Student Page

Date Time

LESSON 7·2 **"Fraction-of" Problems** *continued*

Solve.

4. a. $\frac{1}{3}$ of 12 = 4 b. $\frac{2}{3}$ of 12 = 8 c. $\frac{5}{3}$ of 12 = 20
5. a. $\frac{1}{5}$ of 15 = 3 b. $\frac{3}{5}$ of 15 = 9 c. $\frac{7}{5}$ of 15 = 21
6. a. $\frac{1}{4}$ of 36 = 9 b. $\frac{3}{4}$ of 36 = 27 c. $\frac{6}{4}$ of 36 = 54
7. a. $\frac{1}{8}$ of 32 = 4 b. $\frac{5}{8}$ of 32 = 20 c. $\frac{9}{8}$ of 32 = 36
8. a. $\frac{1}{6}$ of 24 = 4 b. $\frac{4}{6}$ of 24 = 16 c. $\frac{13}{6}$ of 24 = 52
9. $\frac{2}{4}$ of 14 = 7
10. $\frac{2}{4}$ of 22 = 11
11. What is $\frac{1}{2}$ of 25? $12\frac{1}{2}$ Explain.
    Sample answer: $\frac{1}{2}$ of 25 is the same as dividing 25 by 2, which is $12\frac{1}{2}$.
12. Michael had 20 baseball cards. He gave $\frac{1}{5}$ of them to his friend Alana, and $\frac{2}{5}$ to his brother Dean.
    a. How many baseball cards did he give to Alana? 4 cards
    b. How many did he give to Dean? 8 cards
    c. How many did he keep for himself? 8 cards

Try This

13. Maurice spent $\frac{1}{2}$ of his money on lunch. He has \$2.50 left. How much money did he start with? \$5.00
14. Erika spent $\frac{3}{4}$ of her money on lunch. She has \$2.00 left. How much money did she start with? \$8.00

Math Journal 2, p. 190

2 Ongoing Learning & Practice

▶ Resuming the World Tour

INDEPENDENT ACTIVITY

(*Math Journal 2,* pp. 329–333; *Student Reference Book,* pp. 276, 277, 280, 286, 287, 297, and 302–305; *Math Masters,* pp. 419–421)

Social Studies Link Students follow the established World Tour routine.

- ▷ They update the Route Map by drawing a line to connect Budapest, Hungary, and Brasília, Brazil.
- ▷ They use the World Tour section of the *Student Reference Book* to locate facts about Brazil and Brasília and then fill in the Country Notes pages for this country and capital.
- ▷ If they are keeping a Route Log, they update it.

▶ Math Boxes 7•2

INDEPENDENT ACTIVITY

(*Math Journal 2,* p. 191)

Mixed Practice Math Boxes in this lesson are paired with Math Boxes in Lesson 7-4. The skill in Problem 6 previews Unit 8 content.

Writing/Reasoning Have students write a response to the following: *Describe the relationship between the fraction you chose in Problem 1 and the minutes on the clock face.* Sample answer: The clock face is divided into 12 sections. Six of the 12 sections are shaded. Each section represents 5 minutes, so 30 minutes are shaded. $6 * 5 = 30$

▶ Study Link 7•2

INDEPENDENT ACTIVITY

(*Math Masters,* p. 207)

Home Connection Students solve "fraction-of" problems.

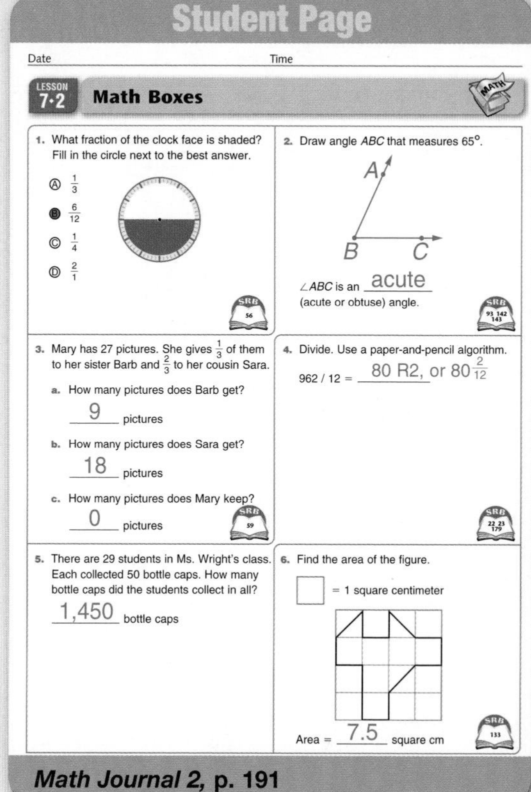

Student Page

Date Time

LESSON 7•2 **Math Boxes**

1. What fraction of the clock face is shaded? Fill in the circle next to the best answer.
   - Ⓐ $\frac{1}{3}$
   - ● $\frac{6}{12}$
   - Ⓒ $\frac{1}{4}$
   - Ⓓ $\frac{2}{1}$

2. Draw angle *ABC* that measures 65°.
   ∠*ABC* is an acute (acute or obtuse) angle.

3. Mary has 27 pictures. She gives $\frac{1}{3}$ of them to her sister Barb and $\frac{2}{3}$ to her cousin Sara.
   - a. How many pictures does Barb get? 9 pictures
   - b. How many pictures does Sara get? 18 pictures
   - c. How many pictures does Mary keep? 0 pictures

4. Divide. Use a paper-and-pencil algorithm.
   962 / 12 = 80 R2, or $80\frac{2}{12}$

5. There are 29 students in Ms. Wright's class. Each collected 50 bottle caps. How many bottle caps did the students collect in all? 1,450 bottle caps

6. Find the area of the figure.
   □ = 1 square centimeter
   Area = 7.5 square cm

Math Journal 2, p. 191

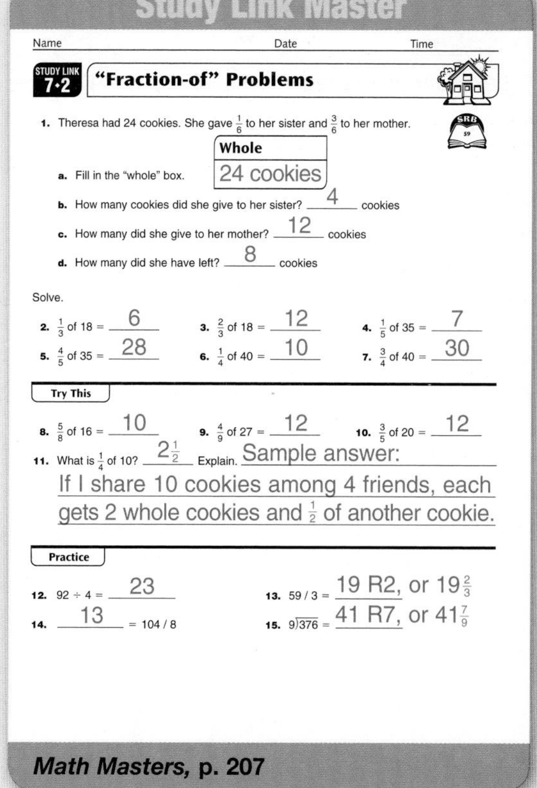

Study Link Master

Name Date Time

STUDY LINK 7•2 **"Fraction-of" Problems**

1. Theresa had 24 cookies. She gave $\frac{1}{6}$ to her sister and $\frac{3}{6}$ to her mother.
   - a. Fill in the "whole" box. Whole: 24 cookies
   - b. How many cookies did she give to her sister? 4 cookies
   - c. How many did she give to her mother? 12 cookies
   - d. How many did she have left? 8 cookies

Solve.

2. $\frac{1}{3}$ of 18 = 6
3. $\frac{2}{3}$ of 18 = 12
4. $\frac{1}{5}$ of 35 = 7
5. $\frac{4}{5}$ of 35 = 28
6. $\frac{1}{4}$ of 40 = 10
7. $\frac{3}{4}$ of 40 = 30

Try This

8. $\frac{5}{8}$ of 16 = 10
9. $\frac{4}{9}$ of 27 = 12
10. $\frac{3}{5}$ of 20 = 12
11. What is $\frac{1}{4}$ of 10? $2\frac{1}{2}$ Explain. Sample answer: If I share 10 cookies among 4 friends, each gets 2 whole cookies and $\frac{1}{2}$ of another cookie.

Practice

12. 92 ÷ 4 = 23
13. 59 / 3 = 19 R2, or $19\frac{2}{3}$
14. 13 = 104 / 8
15. 9⟌376 = 41 R7, or $41\frac{7}{9}$

Math Masters, p. 207

Teaching Master

Name Date Time

LESSON 7·2 **Hiking Trails**

Luis is staying in a large state park that has 8 hiking trails. In the table at the right, each trail is labeled *easy, moderate,* or *rugged,* depending on how difficult that trail is for hiking.

Luis figures that it would take him about 20 minutes to walk 1 mile on an easy trail, about 30 minutes on a moderate trail, and about 40 minutes on a rugged trail.

State Park Trails

Trail	Miles	Type
Ice Age	$1\frac{1}{4}$	easy
Kettle	2	moderate
Pine	$\frac{3}{4}$	moderate
Bluff	$1\frac{3}{4}$	rugged
Cliff	$\frac{3}{4}$	rugged
Oak	$1\frac{1}{2}$	easy
Sky	$1\frac{1}{2}$	moderate
Badger	$3\frac{1}{2}$	moderate

1. About how long will it take Luis to walk the following trails?
   a. Kettle Trail: About 60 minutes
   b. Cliff Trail: About 30 minutes
   c. Oak Trail: About 30 minutes
   d. Bluff Trail: About 70 minutes
2. If Luis wants to hike for about $\frac{3}{4}$ of an hour, which trail should he choose? Sky Trail
3. If he wants to hike for about 25 minutes, which trail should he choose? Ice Age (or Pine) Trail
4. About how long would it take him to complete Pine Trail? About 22–23 minutes
5. Do you think Luis could walk Badger Trail in less than 2 hours? yes
   Explain. Sample answer: Badger is a moderate trail. Luis can walk 1 mile on a moderate trail in 30 minutes. So, he can walk 4 miles in 2 hours. Badger Trail is only $3\frac{1}{2}$ miles long, so Luis could walk it in less than 2 hours.

Math Masters, p. 208

Game Master

Name Date Time

***Fraction Of* Gameboard and Record Sheet**

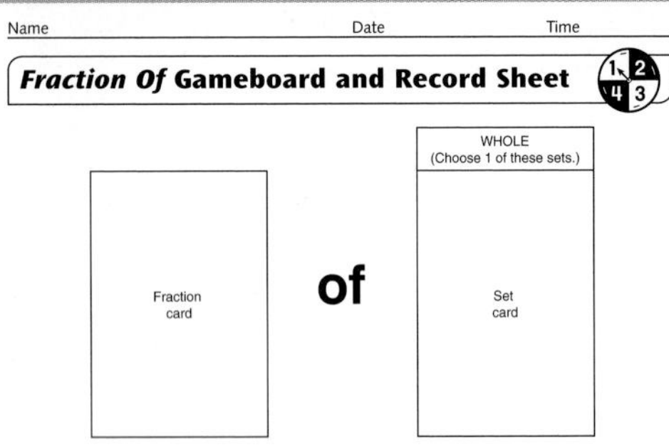

Round	"Fraction-of" Problem	Points
Sample	$\frac{1}{5}$ of 25	5
1		
2		
3		
4		
5		
6		
7		
8		
	Total Score	

Math Masters, p. 479

3 Differentiation Options

READINESS

SMALL-GROUP ACTIVITY

▶ Exploring Fractions of a Set

5–15 Min

(*Math Masters,* p. 388 or 389)

To explore fractions of a set, have students use fractions to describe various attributes of a small group of students. For example, give one student a pencil. Ask: *What fraction of the students is holding a pencil? What fraction is not holding a pencil?* Use other attributes, such as clothing or eye color, to model finding the fraction of a set.

When students have enough experience describing the group in terms of fractions, have them find objects in the room that come in sets and use fractions to describe attributes of these sets. Have them record their work in a Math Log or on an Exit Slip. For example, $\frac{1}{8}$ of the markers in a box are yellow; $\frac{1}{12}$ of a box of colored chalk is pink; $\frac{4}{4}$ of the students at our table have calculators.

ENRICHMENT

INDEPENDENT ACTIVITY

▶ Solving "Fraction-of" Problems

5–15 Min

(*Math Masters,* p. 208)

To apply students' understanding of "fraction-of" situations, have them solve the hiking trail problems on *Math Masters,* page 208. When discussing solution strategies, remind students that the trail data are estimates. The lengths of the trails are given to the nearest $\frac{1}{4}$ mile. The times Luis thinks it will take him to walk a mile are also estimates.

EXTRA PRACTICE

PARTNER ACTIVITY

▶ Playing *Fraction Of*

5–15 Min

(*Student Reference Book,* pp. 244 and 245; *Math Masters,* pp. 477–480)

To practice identifying fractions of collections, have students play *Fraction Of.* See Lesson 7-3 for additional information.

Planning Ahead

Obtain one regular deck of playing cards for every two students to use in Lesson 7-3.

7·3 Probabilities When Outcomes Are Equally Likely

Objectives To review basic vocabulary and concepts of probability; and to introduce finding probabilities for events when all the possible outcomes are equally likely.

Technology Resources www.everydaymathonline.com

ePresentations

eToolkit

Algorithms Practice

EM Facts Workshop Game™

Family Letters

Assessment Management

Common Core State Standards

Curriculum Focal Points

Interactive Teacher's Lesson Guide

1 Teaching the Lesson

Key Concepts and Skills

- Add fractions with like denominators. [Operations and Computation Goal 5]
- Use basic probability terms to describe and compare the likelihood of an event; explain the choice of term. [Data and Chance Goal 3]
- Predict the outcomes of an experiment. [Data and Chance Goal 4]
- Express the probability of an event as a fraction. [Data and Chance Goal 4]

Key Activities

Students use terms such as *certain, very likely, likely, 50-50 chance, unlikely, very unlikely,* and *impossible* to describe the likelihood of an event. They calculate the probabilities for a playing card experiment that has equally likely outcomes.

Ongoing Assessment: Recognizing Student Achievement Use journal page 192. [Data and Chance Goal 3]

Key Vocabulary

equally likely ◆ outcome ◆ event ◆ probability ◆ favorable outcome

Materials

Math Journal 2, p. 192
Study Link 7·2
Math Masters, p. 210 (optional)
per partnership: 1 deck of regular playing cards ◆ 1 large grocery bag ◆ slate ◆ chart paper (optional)

2 Ongoing Learning & Practice

Playing *Fraction Of*
Student Reference Book, pp. 244 and 245
Math Masters, pp. 477–480
counters (optional)
Students practice finding fractional parts of sets.

Math Boxes 7·3
Math Journal 2, p. 193
Students practice and maintain skills through Math Box problems.

Study Link 7·3
Math Masters, p. 209
Students practice and maintain skills through Study Link activities.

3 Differentiation Options

READINESS

Exploring a Deck of Regular Playing Cards
Math Masters, p. 210
per partnership: 1 deck of regular playing cards
Students examine a deck of regular playing cards.

ENRICHMENT

Conducting and Analyzing a Playing Card Experiment
Math Masters, p. 211
per partnership: 1 deck of regular playing cards, 1 large grocery bag
Students explore expected and actual results by conducting a playing card experiment.

EXTRA PRACTICE

Playing *Grab Bag*
Student Reference Book, p. 249
Math Masters, pp. 483–485
per partnership: 3 six-sided dice, scissors
Students practice calculating the probability of an event.

ELL SUPPORT

Building Background for Mathematics Words
Students discuss the likelihood of events in everyday life.

Advance Preparation

Place the card decks next to the Math Message. If students are unfamiliar with such cards, use the optional Readiness activity in Part 3 prior to teaching the lesson. For the optional Extra Practice activity in Part 3, consider copying *Math Masters,* pages 483 and 484 on cardstock.

***Teacher's Reference Manual,* Grades 4–6** pp. 156, 157

Getting Started

Mental Math and Reflexes

Write fractions and mixed numbers on the board for students to decompose on their slates in at least two different ways. *Suggestions:* Sample answers are given.

●○○ $\frac{6}{7}$ $\frac{6}{7} = \frac{2}{7} + \frac{4}{7}$; $\frac{6}{7} = \frac{1}{7} + \frac{5}{7}$

$\frac{4}{5}$ $\frac{4}{5} = \frac{1}{5} + \frac{3}{5}$; $\frac{4}{5} = \frac{2}{5} + \frac{2}{5}$

$\frac{3}{9}$ $\frac{3}{9} = \frac{1}{9} + \frac{1}{9} + \frac{1}{9}$; $\frac{3}{9} = \frac{2}{9} + \frac{1}{9}$

●●○ $\frac{9}{10}$ $\frac{9}{10} = \frac{3}{10} + \frac{6}{10}$; $\frac{9}{10} = \frac{5}{10} + \frac{4}{10}$

$\frac{8}{9}$ $\frac{8}{9} = \frac{6}{9} + \frac{2}{9}$; $\frac{8}{9} = \frac{3}{9} + \frac{5}{9}$

$\frac{7}{12}$ $\frac{7}{12} = \frac{2}{12} + \frac{5}{12}$; $\frac{7}{12} = \frac{3}{12} + \frac{4}{12}$

●●● $1\frac{2}{8}$ $1\frac{2}{8} = 1 + \frac{1}{8} + \frac{1}{8}$; $1\frac{2}{8} = \frac{8}{8} + \frac{2}{8}$

$2\frac{2}{5}$ $2\frac{2}{5} = 2 + \frac{1}{5} + \frac{1}{5}$; $2\frac{2}{5} = \frac{5}{5} + \frac{5}{5} + \frac{2}{5}$

$1\frac{3}{4}$ $1\frac{3}{4} = \frac{4}{4} + \frac{3}{4}$; $1\frac{3}{4} = \frac{4}{4} + \frac{2}{4} + \frac{1}{4}$

Math Message

Which phrase—extremely likely, 50-50 chance, or very unlikely—*best describes the chance of picking a red card from a regular deck of playing cards?*

Study Link 7·2 Follow-Up

Review answers. If students are having difficulty with Problem 11, suggest that they approach the problem in terms of money. Ask questions like the following:

- What is $\frac{1}{4}$ of \$1.00? 1 quarter, or 25¢
- If you have \$10.00, what is $\frac{1}{4}$ of that amount? 10 quarters, which is equal to \$2.50, or $2\frac{1}{2}$

Adjusting the Activity

Have students refer to the playing card information on *Math Masters,* page 210. See the optional Readiness activity in Part 3.

AUDITORY ◆ KINESTHETIC ◆ TACTILE ◆ VISUAL

1 Teaching the Lesson

▶ Math Message Follow-Up

WHOLE-CLASS DISCUSSION

Have volunteers share answers. Ask them to explain why they chose a particular phrase and why they thought the others were incorrect. There is a 50-50 chance of picking a red card. There are 52 cards in the deck; 26 are red and 26 are black.

▶ Reviewing Words and Phrases Associated with Chance Events

WHOLE-CLASS ACTIVITY

ELL

Many everyday expressions are used to describe the likelihood of an event. Write the words *impossible, extremely unlikely, very unlikely, unlikely, 50-50* or *even chance, likely, very likely, extremely likely,* and *certain* on the board or chart paper. To support English language learners, keep the list on display throughout this unit.

Place a deck of regular playing cards in a bag and shake it. Without looking, pick one card. Do not show it to the class. Ask: *How likely do you think it is that the card I picked is a black card?* Have students choose one of the phrases listed on the board and explain why they chose it. Sample answer: I chose *even chance* because there are equal numbers of black cards and red cards.

Ask: How likely do you think it is that the card I picked is

- a face card? (12 cards) Sample answer: I think unlikely because there are not that many face cards; there are only three in each suit.
- a heart? (13 cards) Sample answer: Unlikely; there are four suits, and hearts is only one of the four.
- a heart, diamond, or club? (39 cards) likely
- a non-face card? (40 cards) likely
- a spade face card? (3 cards) very unlikely
- not a spade face card? (49 cards) very likely
- an ace of spades? (1 card) extremely unlikely
- not the ace of spades? (51 cards) extremely likely
- the 46 of diamonds? (0 cards) impossible
- not the 46 of diamonds? (52 cards) certain

Adjusting the Activity

Highlight only the words and phrases *certain, likely, even chance, unlikely,* and *impossible.*

AUDITORY ◆ KINESTHETIC ◆ TACTILE ◆ VISUAL

Finally, have students use the phrases *more likely,* ***equally likely,*** and *less likely* to compare two events. *For example:*

▷ Picking a heart is *more likely* than picking the 9 of hearts.

▷ Picking a red card and picking a black card are *equally likely*.

▷ Picking a face card is *less likely* than picking a non-face card.

Introducing a Formula for Finding the Probability of an Event When the Outcomes Are Equally Likely

WHOLE-CLASS DISCUSSION

(*Math Journal 2,* p. 192)

When you randomly draw a single card from the deck, 52 equally likely results or **outcomes** are possible. Similarly, when you roll a die, there are 6 possible equally likely outcomes: 1, 2, 3, 4, 5, or 6. You may be interested only in a specific set or collection of outcomes, such as rolling a 3 or rolling an even number. This specific set or collection of possible outcomes is called an **event.**

A **probability** is a number from 0 to 1 that tells the chance that an event will happen. The closer a probability is to 1, the more likely the event is to happen. When the possible outcomes are equally likely, the following formula is used to find the probability of an event:

$$\text{Probability of an event} = \frac{\text{number of favorable outcomes}}{\text{number of possible outcomes}}$$

Adjusting the Activity

Have students use everyday language to reword the formula for finding the probability of an event. *For example:*

$$\frac{\text{number of outcomes I'm looking for}}{\text{number of all the outcomes}}$$

$$\frac{\text{how many things I want to happen}}{\text{how many things could happen}}$$

AUDITORY ◆ KINESTHETIC ◆ TACTILE ◆ VISUAL

Student Page

Date ______ Time ______

LESSON 7·3 **Playing Card Probabilities**

A deck of regular playing cards is placed in a bag. You shake the bag and, without looking, pick one card.

1. How many possible outcomes are there? (*Hint:* How many cards are in the bag?) 52 possible outcomes
2. Are the outcomes equally likely? (*Hint:* Does each card have an equal chance of being chosen?) yes
3. Find the probability of each event. Probability of an event = $\frac{\text{number of favorable outcomes}}{\text{number of possible outcomes}}$

Event	Favorable Outcomes	Possible Outcomes	Probability
Pick a red card	26	52	$\frac{26}{52}$
Pick a club	13	52	$\frac{13}{52}$
Pick a non-face card	40	52	$\frac{40}{52}$
Pick a diamond face card	3	52	$\frac{3}{52}$
Pick a card that is *not* a diamond face card	49	52	$\frac{49}{52}$
Pick the ace of clubs	1	52	$\frac{1}{52}$
Pick a red *or* a black card	52	52	$\frac{52}{52}$
Pick the 23 of hearts	0	52	$\frac{0}{52}$

4. Circle the word or phrase that best describes the probability of picking a 5 from a bag of 52 regular playing cards without looking.

impossible (very unlikely) even chance likely

Explain why you chose your answer. Sample answer: The probability of choosing a 5 card is only 4 out of 52.

Math Journal 2, p. 192

A **favorable outcome** is an outcome that satisfies or meets the conditions of the event or that will make the event happen.
For example:

- ▷ Picking a heart is an event. A *favorable outcome* is picking a 2, 3, 4, 5, 6, 7, 8, 9, 10, J, Q, K, or A of hearts. There are 13 favorable outcomes out of 52 possible outcomes. The probability of the event is $\frac{13}{52}$.
- ▷ Picking a face card is an event. A *favorable outcome* is picking a J, Q, or K of hearts, diamonds, spades, or clubs. There are 12 favorable outcomes out of 52 possible outcomes. The probability of the event is $\frac{12}{52}$.

Complete Problems 1 and 2 on journal page 192 with the class.

Links to the Future

In *Third Grade Everyday Mathematics,* students used "____ out of ____" language to express the probability of an event. This activity is an initial exposure to expressing probability as a fraction. Do not expect all students to be proficient with this skill at this time. Students will have additional opportunities to practice this skill in Lessons 7-11 and 7-12 and throughout *Fourth Grade Everyday Mathematics.*

▶ Finding the Probability of an Event When the Outcomes Are Equally Likely

PARTNER ACTIVITY

(*Math Journal 2,* p. 192)

For each event in Problem 3, students must identify and count the number of cards satisfying that event. After students have counted the cards, they may think in different ways to name the probability. Discuss the strategies they used.

Event: Pick a diamond face card.

- ▷ There are three diamond face cards: the jack, queen, and king. That is 3 out of 52 cards. So the probability of picking a diamond face card is $\frac{3}{52}$.
- ▷ Three cards are diamond face cards. Each one has a $\frac{1}{52}$ chance of being picked. So the total chance of picking a diamond face card is $\frac{1}{52} + \frac{1}{52} + \frac{1}{52}$ or $\frac{3}{52}$.

Event: Pick a club.

- ▷ The *favorable outcomes* are the club cards. There are 13 club cards: 2, 3, 4, 5, 6, 7, 8, 9, 10, J, Q, K, and A.
- ▷ The number of *possible outcomes* is 52, because there are 52 cards in the deck.
- ▷ The probability is the number of favorable outcomes over the number of possible outcomes, which is $\frac{13}{52}$.

Have students complete Problem 4 independently.

Ongoing Assessment: Recognizing Student Achievement

Journal page 192 Problem 4

Use **journal page 192, Problem 4** to assess students' ability to use a basic probability term to describe the likelihood of an event. Students are making adequate progress if they indicate it is very unlikely that they will pick a 5, because there are 52 cards in the deck and only four of them are 5s. Some students may be able to express the probability of the event as a fraction. $\frac{4}{52}$

[Data and Chance Goal 3]

2 Ongoing Learning & Practice

Playing *Fraction Of*

PARTNER ACTIVITY

(*Student Reference Book,* pp. 244 and 245; *Math Masters,* pp. 477–480)

Students play *Fraction Of* to practice finding fractional parts of sets.

Adjusting the Activity

To focus on unit fractions, have students use only the fraction cards marked with a hexagon in the corner. Additionally, encourage students to use counters to model the problems.

AUDITORY ◆ KINESTHETIC ◆ TACTILE ◆ VISUAL

Math Boxes 7·3

INDEPENDENT ACTIVITY

(*Math Journal 2,* p. 193)

Mixed Practice Math Boxes in this lesson are paired with Math Boxes in Lesson 7-1. The skill in Problem 6 previews Unit 8 content.

Study Link 7·3

INDEPENDENT ACTIVITY

(*Math Masters,* p. 209)

Home Connection Students determine the probabilities of picking specific colored tiles out of a bag.

Student Page

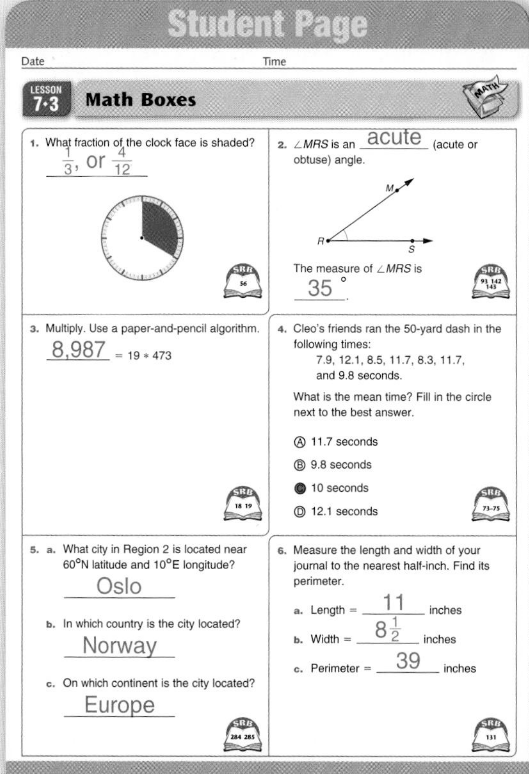

Date Time

LESSON 7·3 **Math Boxes**

1. What fraction of the clock face is shaded? $\frac{1}{3}$, or $\frac{4}{12}$

2. ∠*MRS* is an acute (acute or obtuse) angle.
The measure of ∠*MRS* is 35 °.

3. Multiply. Use a paper-and-pencil algorithm.
8,987 = 19 ∗ 473

4. Cleo's friends ran the 50-yard dash in the following times:
7.9, 12.1, 8.5, 11.7, 8.3, 11.7, and 9.8 seconds.
What is the mean time? Fill in the circle next to the best answer.
Ⓐ 11.7 seconds
Ⓑ 9.8 seconds
● 10 seconds
Ⓓ 12.1 seconds

5. a. What city in Region 2 is located near 60°N latitude and 10°E longitude? Oslo
b. In which country is the city located? Norway
c. On which continent is the city located? Europe

6. Measure the length and width of your journal to the nearest half-inch. Find its perimeter.
a. Length = 11 inches
b. Width = $8\frac{1}{2}$ inches
c. Perimeter = 39 inches

Math Journal 2, p. 193

Study Link Master

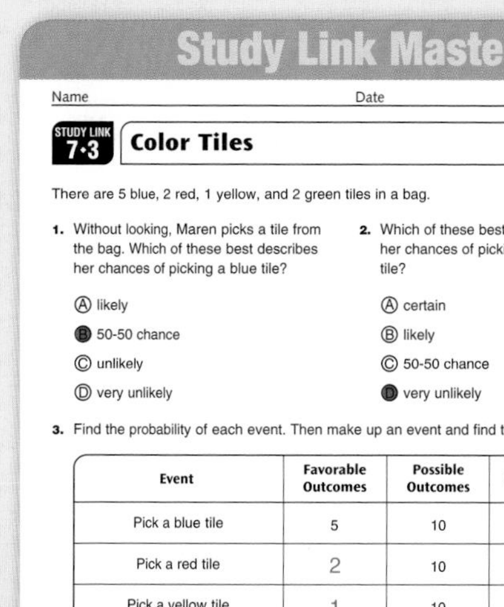

Name Date Time

STUDY LINK 7·3 **Color Tiles**

There are 5 blue, 2 red, 1 yellow, and 2 green tiles in a bag.

1. Without looking, Maren picks a tile from the bag. Which of these best describes her chances of picking a blue tile?
Ⓐ likely
● 50-50 chance
Ⓒ unlikely
Ⓓ very unlikely

2. Which of these best describes her chances of picking a yellow tile?
Ⓐ certain
Ⓑ likely
Ⓒ 50-50 chance
● very unlikely

3. Find the probability of each event. Then make up an event and find the probability.

Event	Favorable Outcomes	Possible Outcomes	Probability
Pick a blue tile	5	10	$\frac{5}{10}$
Pick a red tile	2	10	$\frac{2}{10}$
Pick a yellow tile	1	10	$\frac{1}{10}$
Pick a green tile	2	10	$\frac{2}{10}$
Pick a blue, red, or green tile	9	10	$\frac{9}{10}$
Answers vary.		10	$\frac{\ }{10}$

4. Suppose you picked a color tile from the bag 10 times. After each pick, you put the tile back in the bag. How many times would you expect to pick a blue tile? 5 times
Try the experiment. Compare your prediction with the actual results.

Practice

5. 74 ∗ 8 = 592
6. 3,948 = 4 ∗ 987
7. 1,690 = 65 ∗ 26
8. 35 ∗ 462 = 16,170

Math Masters, p. 209

3 Differentiation Options

READINESS

5–15 Min

▶ Exploring a Deck of Regular Playing Cards

(*Math Masters,* p. 210)

To explore possible outcomes for a playing card experiment, have students investigate a regular deck of playing cards. The information students record on *Math Masters,* page 210 will help them determine the probability of selecting particular cards in Part 1 of the lesson.

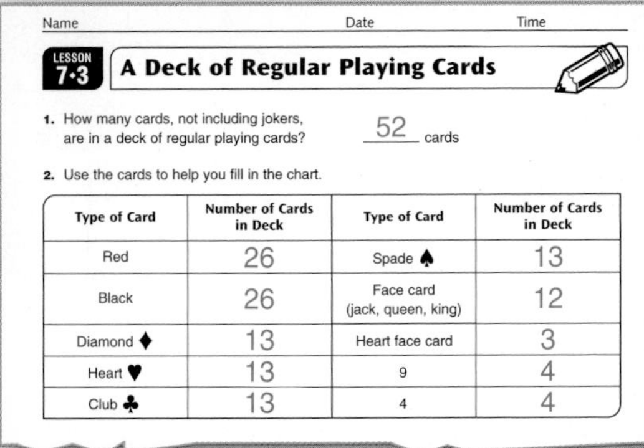

Name Date Time

LESSON 7·3 **A Deck of Regular Playing Cards**

1. How many cards, not including jokers, are in a deck of regular playing cards? 52 cards

2. Use the cards to help you fill in the chart.

Type of Card	Number of Cards in Deck	Type of Card	Number of Cards in Deck
Red	26	Spade ♠	13
Black	26	Face card (jack, queen, king)	12
Diamond ♦	13	Heart face card	3
Heart ♥	13	9	4
Club ♣	13	4	4

Math Masters, page 210

ENRICHMENT

PARTNER ACTIVITY

15–30 Min

▶ Conducting and Analyzing a Playing Card Experiment

(*Math Masters,* p. 211)

To further explore expected results and actual results, have students conduct a playing card experiment. Ask several partnerships to discuss and compare the results of their experiments. Consider having them report their results to the class.

Teaching Master

Name Date Time

LESSON 7·3 **A Playing-Card Experiment**

1. Place 52 playing cards in a bag. Shake the bag.

2. Before you begin the experiment, predict the results for each event.

Event	Predicted Results for 52 Picks	Tallies	Actual Results for 52 Picks
Pick a black card	$\frac{26}{52}$	Answers vary.	$\frac{\square}{52}$
Pick a red card	$\frac{26}{52}$		
Pick a face card	$\frac{12}{52}$		
Pick a heart	$\frac{13}{52}$		
Pick an Ace	$\frac{4}{52}$		
Pick an Ace of spades	$\frac{1}{52}$		

3. Now do the experiment.

Step 1: Pick a card from the bag.

Step 2: Record a tally for each event that applies. For example, for the king of clubs put a tally mark next to *black card* and *face card.*

Step 3: Mark an X in the grid to record the number of picks.

Step 4: Return the card to the bag and shake it.

Repeat Steps 1–4 until all 52 boxes in the grid have been filled in.

4. Describe how your actual results compare with your predicted results. Be sure to include anything that surprised you.

Answers vary.

***Math Masters,* p. 211**

EXTRA PRACTICE

PARTNER ACTIVITY

15–30 Min

▶ Playing *Grab Bag*

(*Student Reference Book,* p. 249; *Math Masters,* pp. 483–485)

Algebraic Thinking To practice calculating the probability of an event, have students play *Grab Bag*. See Lesson 7-6 for additional information.

ELL SUPPORT

5–15 Min

▶ Building Background for Mathematics Words

To provide language support for probability, have students think about the likelihood of events that occur in their everyday lives. Discuss and display the words *impossible, maybe,* and *certain* on a bulletin board or poster. Have students draw one image for each category and describe what they have drawn as they display their drawings in the appropriate categories.

7•4 Pattern-Block Fractions

Objective To guide students as they find fractional parts of polygonal regions.

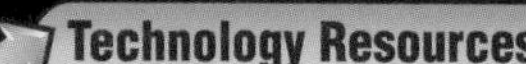

www.everydaymathonline.com

ePresentations

eToolkit

Algorithms Practice

EM Facts Workshop Game™

Family Letters

Assessment Management

Common Core State Standards

Curriculum Focal Points

Interactive Teacher's Lesson Guide

1 Teaching the Lesson

Key Concepts and Skills

- Identify the whole or the ONE. [Number and Numeration Goal 2]
- Find fractional parts of polygonal regions. [Number and Numeration Goal 2]
- Identify equivalent fractions. [Number and Numeration Goal 5]
- Model fraction addition with pattern blocks. [Operations and Computation Goal 5]
- Identify a triangle, hexagon, trapezoid, and rhombus. [Geometry Goal 2]

Key Activities

Students use pattern blocks to partition 2-dimensional shapes, and they name fractional parts of regions.

Ongoing Assessment: Informing Instruction See page 589.

Ongoing Assessment: Recognizing Student Achievement Use a Math Log or Exit Slip (*Math Masters,* page 388 or 389). [Number and Numeration Goal 2]

Materials

Math Journal 2, pp. 194–196
Study Link 7•3
Math Masters, p. 212; p. 388 or 389 (optional)
transparency of *Math Masters,* p. 212 (optional) ◆ pattern blocks ◆ straightedge ◆ slate ◆ overhead pattern blocks (optional) ◆ red pencil or marker (optional) ◆ chart paper (optional)

2 Ongoing Learning & Practice

Math Boxes 7•4

Math Journal 2, p. 197
Students practice and maintain skills through Math Box problems.

Study Link 7•4

Math Masters, p. 213
Students practice and maintain skills through Study Link activities.

3 Differentiation Options

READINESS

Building Rectangles

Math Masters, p. 214
red, blue, and green crayons ◆ scissors ◆ red, blue, and green colored tiles (optional)
Students use colored squares to build different rectangles.

ENRICHMENT

Exploring Tangrams

Math Masters, pp. 215 and 441
scissors
Students determine values of tangram pieces.

ENRICHMENT

Writing Fraction and Mixed-Number Addition Number Stories

Students decompose fractions and mixed numbers to write addition number stories with the same answer.

Advance Preparation

For Part 1, each partnership or small group needs at least 2 yellow, 4 red, 4 blue, and 6 green pattern blocks.

***Teacher's Reference Manual,* Grades 4–6** pp. 62, 63

Getting Started

Mental Math and Reflexes

Pose "fraction-of" problems. *Suggestions:*

●○○ $\frac{1}{4}$ of 20¢ = 5¢
$\frac{1}{6}$ of 24¢ = 4¢
$\frac{1}{5}$ of 45¢ = 9¢

●●○ $\frac{3}{4}$ of 20¢ = 15¢
$\frac{5}{6}$ of 24¢ = 20¢
$\frac{4}{5}$ of 45¢ = 36¢

●●● $\frac{8}{7}$ of 49¢ = 56¢
$\frac{9}{4}$ of 16¢ = 36¢
$\frac{4}{2}$ of 60¢ = 120¢ or $1.20

Math Message

$\frac{1}{2}$ of the students in Mrs. Lopez's class went to the soccer game.

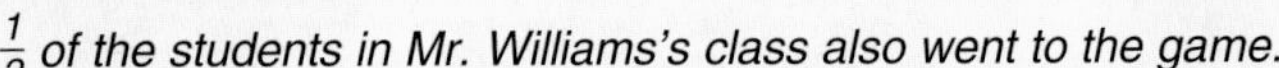

$\frac{1}{2}$ of the students in Mr. Williams's class also went to the game.

Did the same number of students from each class go to the game?

Study Link 7·3 Follow-Up

Have students pose the events they made up in Problem 3 and ask partners to find the probabilities. For Problem 4, have students describe how their predictions for the experiment compared with the actual results.

1 Teaching the Lesson

▶ Math Message Follow-Up

WHOLE-CLASS DISCUSSION

As students share their ideas, help them understand that a fraction that is used to name part of a collection is not meaningful if one does not know what it is a fraction of—that is, what the whole collection is. For example, half of each class went to the game, but the classes may have different numbers of students.

Tell students that in this lesson they will explore how the values of individual pattern blocks change when the "whole" changes.

▶ Exploring Fractional Parts of Regions with Pattern Blocks

WHOLE-CLASS ACTIVITY

Lesson 7-4 consists of three sets of problems. Each set requires the use of one of the three shapes on *Math Masters,* page 212 and a set of pattern blocks. Each shape can be completely covered by pattern blocks.

In each set of problems, students do the following:

1. Determine what fraction of the shape is covered by each pattern block.
2. Cover the shape on the master with pattern blocks, as indicated on the journal page.
3. Record a partition of the shape on journal page 194, 195, or 196.
4. Label each fractional part of the shape with a fraction.

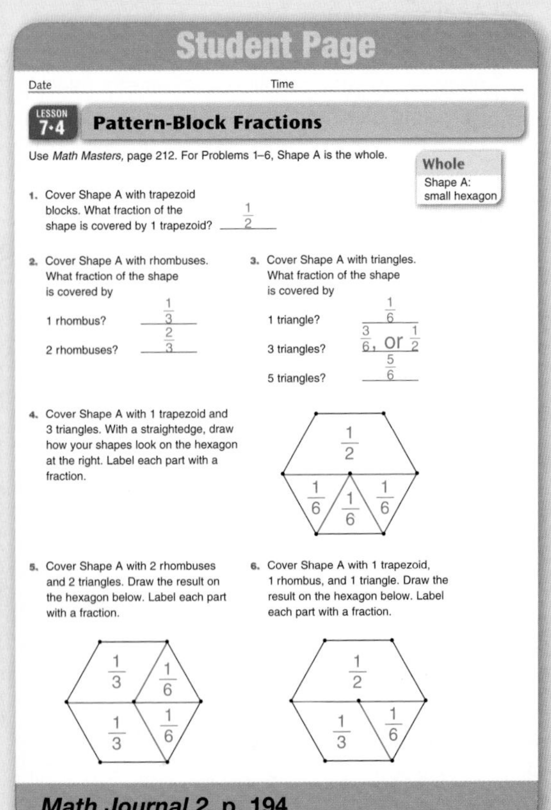

Student Page

Date Time

LESSON 7·4 **Pattern-Block Fractions**

Use *Math Masters,* page 212. For Problems 1–6, Shape A is the whole.

Whole
Shape A: small hexagon

1. Cover Shape A with trapezoid blocks. What fraction of the shape is covered by 1 trapezoid? $\frac{1}{2}$
2. Cover Shape A with rhombuses. What fraction of the shape is covered by
   1 rhombus? $\frac{1}{3}$
   2 rhombuses? $\frac{2}{3}$
3. Cover Shape A with triangles. What fraction of the shape is covered by
   1 triangle? $\frac{1}{6}$
   3 triangles? $\frac{3}{6}$, or $\frac{1}{2}$
   5 triangles? $\frac{5}{6}$
4. Cover Shape A with 1 trapezoid and 3 triangles. With a straightedge, draw how your shapes look on the hexagon at the right. Label each part with a fraction.
5. Cover Shape A with 2 rhombuses and 2 triangles. Draw the result on the hexagon below. Label each part with a fraction.
6. Cover Shape A with 1 trapezoid, 1 rhombus, and 1 triangle. Draw the result on the hexagon below. Label each part with a fraction.

Math Journal 2, p. 194

Adjusting the Activity

ELL

Write each of the pattern-block names on the board or on chart paper in the color that matches the block. For example, write *rhombus* in blue and *triangle* in green.

AUDITORY ◆ KINESTHETIC ◆ TACTILE ◆ VISUAL

Solving Problems about Shape A

WHOLE-CLASS ACTIVITY

(*Math Journal 2,* p. 194; *Math Masters,* p. 212)

Have students form partnerships or small groups, and pass out pattern blocks, but work with the whole class on Problems 1–6 on journal page 194.

Students should use Shape A on *Math Masters,* page 212 for the problems on this journal page. Ask the questions on page 194 one at a time. Have students solve them using pattern blocks and then record their answers in the journal. Consider using a transparency of the master and overhead pattern blocks as you discuss the problems and answers.

Adjusting the Activity

ELL

Have students write number models to illustrate how Shape A was covered with pattern blocks in Problems 4–6.

Problem 4: $\frac{1}{2} + \frac{1}{6} + \frac{1}{6} + \frac{1}{6} = 1$

Problem 5: $\frac{1}{3} + \frac{1}{3} + \frac{1}{6} + \frac{1}{6} = 1$

Problem 6: $\frac{1}{2} + \frac{1}{3} + \frac{1}{6} = 1$

AUDITORY ◆ KINESTHETIC ◆ TACTILE ◆ VISUAL

Solving Problems about Shape B

PARTNER ACTIVITY

PROBLEM SOLVING

(*Math Journal 2,* p. 195; *Math Masters,* p. 212)

Before students begin Problems 7–12 on journal page 195, have them observe that Shape B is not the same size as Shape A; therefore, each pattern block takes on a different fractional value. Discuss solutions.

Ongoing Assessment: Informing Instruction

Watch for students who continue to use the single hexagon as the whole. Emphasize that the whole or the ONE is different than that used for the problems on journal page 194. Encourage students to circle the whole box with a red pencil or marker to remind them of the new whole.

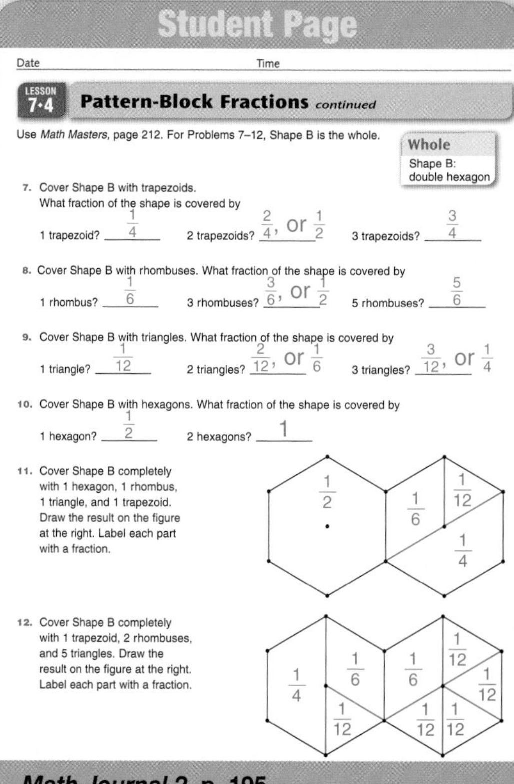

Student Page

Date Time

LESSON 7•4 **Pattern-Block Fractions** *continued*

Use *Math Masters,* page 212. For Problems 7–12, Shape B is the whole.

Whole Shape B: double hexagon

7. Cover Shape B with trapezoids. What fraction of the shape is covered by
1 trapezoid? $\frac{1}{4}$ 2 trapezoids? $\frac{2}{4}$, or $\frac{1}{2}$ 3 trapezoids? $\frac{3}{4}$

8. Cover Shape B with rhombuses. What fraction of the shape is covered by
1 rhombus? $\frac{1}{6}$ 3 rhombuses? $\frac{3}{6}$, or $\frac{1}{2}$ 5 rhombuses? $\frac{5}{6}$

9. Cover Shape B with triangles. What fraction of the shape is covered by
1 triangle? $\frac{1}{12}$ 2 triangles? $\frac{2}{12}$, or $\frac{1}{6}$ 3 triangles? $\frac{3}{12}$, or $\frac{1}{4}$

10. Cover Shape B with hexagons. What fraction of the shape is covered by
1 hexagon? $\frac{1}{2}$ 2 hexagons? 1

11. Cover Shape B completely with 1 hexagon, 1 rhombus, 1 triangle, and 1 trapezoid. Draw the result on the figure at the right. Label each part with a fraction.

12. Cover Shape B completely with 1 trapezoid, 2 rhombuses, and 5 triangles. Draw the result on the figure at the right. Label each part with a fraction.

Math Journal 2, p. 195

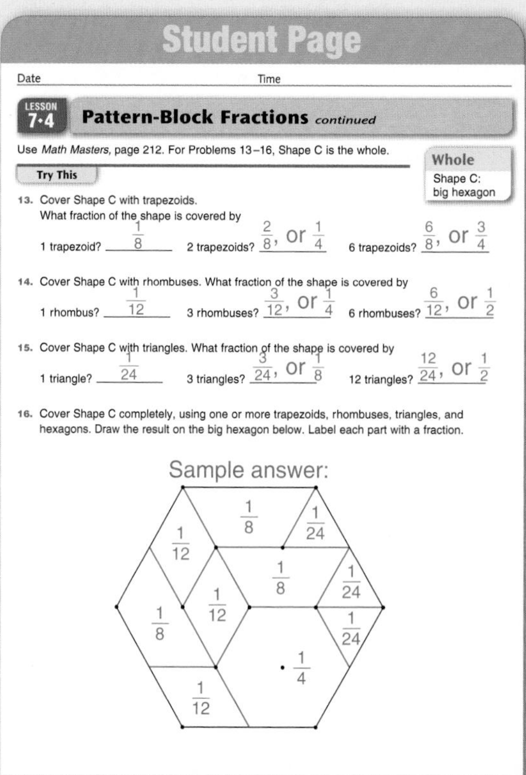

Student Page

Date Time

LESSON 7•4 **Pattern-Block Fractions** *continued*

Use *Math Masters,* page 212. For Problems 13–16, Shape C is the whole.

Whole Shape C: big hexagon

Try This

13. Cover Shape C with trapezoids. What fraction of the shape is covered by
1 trapezoid? $\frac{1}{8}$ 2 trapezoids? $\frac{2}{8}$, or $\frac{1}{4}$ 6 trapezoids? $\frac{6}{8}$, or $\frac{3}{4}$

14. Cover Shape C with rhombuses. What fraction of the shape is covered by
1 rhombus? $\frac{1}{12}$ 3 rhombuses? $\frac{3}{12}$, or $\frac{1}{4}$ 6 rhombuses? $\frac{6}{12}$, or $\frac{1}{2}$

15. Cover Shape C with triangles. What fraction of the shape is covered by
1 triangle? $\frac{1}{24}$ 3 triangles? $\frac{3}{24}$, or $\frac{1}{8}$ 12 triangles? $\frac{12}{24}$, or $\frac{1}{2}$

16. Cover Shape C completely, using one or more trapezoids, rhombuses, triangles, and hexagons. Draw the result on the big hexagon below. Label each part with a fraction.

Math Journal 2, p. 196

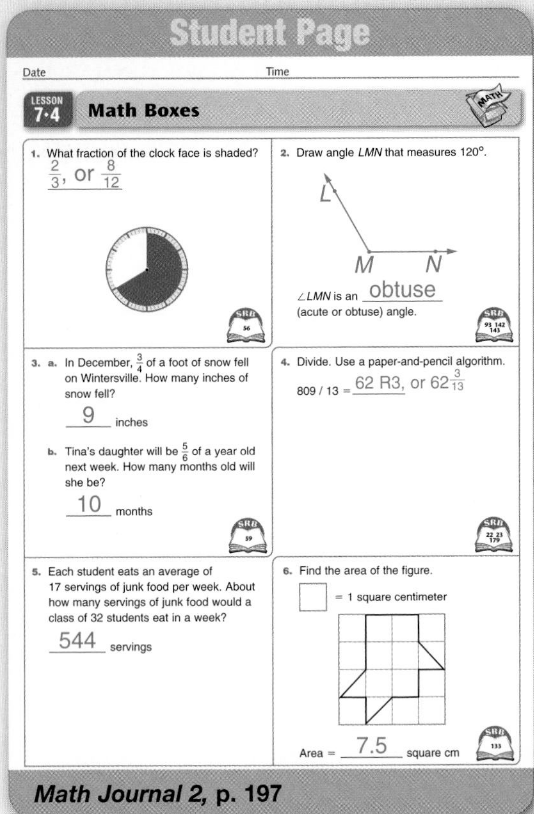
Student Page

Date Time

LESSON 7·4 **Math Boxes**

1. What fraction of the clock face is shaded? $\frac{2}{3}$, or $\frac{8}{12}$

2. Draw angle *LMN* that measures 120°.
∠*LMN* is an obtuse (acute or obtuse) angle.

3. a. In December, $\frac{3}{4}$ of a foot of snow fell on Wintersville. How many inches of snow fell? 9 inches

b. Tina's daughter will be $\frac{5}{6}$ of a year old next week. How many months old will she be? 10 months

4. Divide. Use a paper-and-pencil algorithm.
809 / 13 = 62 R3, or $62\frac{3}{13}$

5. Each student eats an average of 17 servings of junk food per week. About how many servings of junk food would a class of 32 students eat in a week? 544 servings

6. Find the area of the figure.
□ = 1 square centimeter
Area = 7.5 square cm

Math Journal 2, p. 197

Study Link Master

Name Date Time

STUDY LINK 7·4 **Dividing Squares**

Use a straightedge and the dots below to help you divide each of the squares into equal parts.

Example: Squares A, B, C, and D are each divided in half in a different way.

A B C D

1. Square E is divided into fourths. Divide squares F, G, and H into fourths, each in a different way. Sample answers:

E F G H

2. Square I is divided into eighths. Divide squares J, K, and L into eighths, each in a different way. Sample answers:

I J K L

3. Rosa has 15 quarters and 10 nickels. She buys juice from a store for herself and her friends. The juice costs 35 cents per can. She gives the cashier $\frac{2}{3}$ of the quarters and $\frac{3}{5}$ of the nickels. The cashier does not give her any change.

How many cans of juice did she buy? 8 cans

Show your work on the back of this paper.

Practice

4. 0.636 + 0.245 = 0.881
5. 9.845 = 9.085 + 0.76
6. 1.59 = 1.73 − 0.14
7. 0.325 − 0.297 = 0.028

Math Masters, p. 213

▶ Solving Problems about Shape C

(*Math Journal 2,* p. 196; *Math Masters,* p. 212)

Problems 13–16 on journal page 196 are challenging. Because it is not possible to completely cover Shape C with hexagon blocks, students must determine the fractional values of other pattern blocks. For example, because two trapezoids make one hexagon and one trapezoid is $\frac{1}{8}$ of Shape C, a hexagon is $\frac{2}{8}$, or $\frac{1}{4}$, of Shape C.

Ongoing Assessment: Recognizing Student Achievement

Math Log or Exit Slip

Use a **Math Log** or an **Exit Slip** (*Math Masters,* page 388 or 389) to assess students' understanding of the relationship between the whole and its fractional parts. Have students explain why the same pattern blocks take on different fractional values for each of Shapes A, B, and C. Students are making adequate progress if they indicate that the shapes represent different wholes.

Some students may note the relationship between the size of the shapes and how this relationship affects the fractional values of the pattern blocks. For example, the area of Shape B is twice the area of Shape A. Therefore, the fractional value of each pattern block for Shape B is half its fractional value for Shape A. The area of Shape C is four times the area of Shape A. It takes 8 trapezoids to cover Shape C and 2 trapezoids to cover Shape A.

[Number and Numeration Goal 2]

2 Ongoing Learning & Practice

▶ Math Boxes 7·4

INDEPENDENT ACTIVITY

(*Math Journal 2,* p. 197)

Mixed Practice Math Boxes in this lesson are paired with Math Boxes in Lesson 7-2. The skill in Problem 6 previews Unit 8 content.

Writing/Reasoning Have students write a response to the following: *Explain how you determined the number of months in Problem 3b.* Sample answer: There are 12 months in a year. $\frac{1}{6}$ of 12 = 2, so $\frac{5}{6}$ of 12 = 10.

▶ Study Link 7·4

INDEPENDENT ACTIVITY

(*Math Masters,* p. 213)

Home Connection Students divide squares into fourths and eighths in different ways.

3 Differentiation Options

READINESS

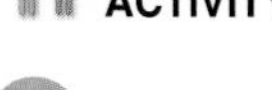
PARTNER ACTIVITY

5–15 Min

Building Rectangles

(*Math Masters,* p. 214)

To explore the relationship of fractional parts to the whole or the ONE, have students use colored squares or tiles to build different rectangles divided into the same fractional parts.

ENRICHMENT

INDEPENDENT ACTIVITY

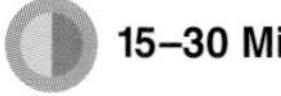
15–30 Min

Exploring Tangrams

(*Math Masters,* pp. 215 and 441)

To further explore the concept of fractional parts of polygonal regions, have students determine the values of tangram pieces.

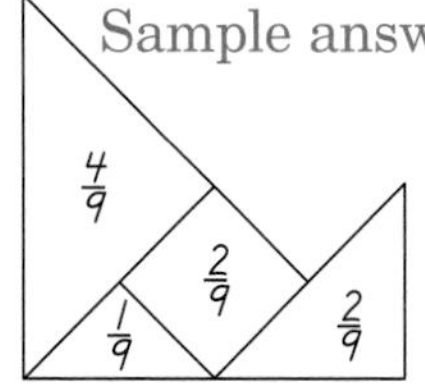

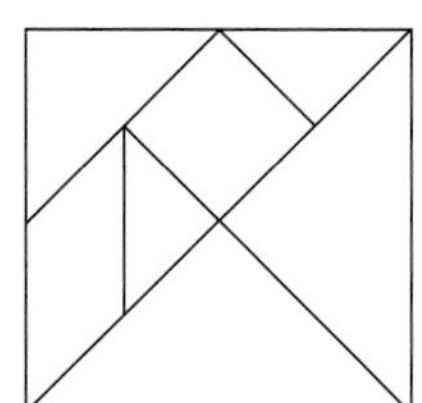

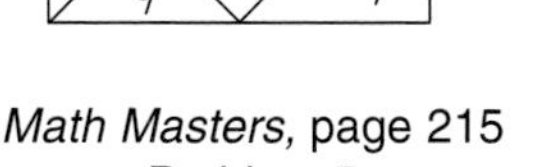
Math Masters, page 215
Problem 5

Completed tangram puzzle

ENRICHMENT

PARTNER ACTIVITY

15–30 Min

Writing Fraction and Mixed-Number Addition Number Stories

To explore decomposing fractions and mixed numbers, have students write addition number stories using the same fraction or mixed number as the sum. For example, students write a number story with the answer $\frac{3}{4}$ that involves adding fractions with the same denominator. Stories might look similar to the following:

- ▷ Abby used $\frac{1}{4}$ cup of flour in one recipe and $\frac{2}{4}$ cup of flour in another. How much flour did she use in all?
- ▷ Supat gave $\frac{1}{4}$ of his baseball cards to his brother, $\frac{1}{4}$ of the cards to his cousin, and $\frac{1}{4}$ of the cards to his friend. What fraction of his baseball cards did Supat give away?

Have students share their stories with a partner and have them record summary number models. Sample answers: $\frac{1}{4} + \frac{2}{4} = \frac{3}{4}$; $\frac{1}{4} + \frac{1}{4} + \frac{1}{4} = \frac{3}{4}$ Encourage partners to write stories that have a different summary number model than the ones that have already been recorded.

Repeat this activity with different fractions and mixed numbers. *Suggestions:*

▷ $\frac{5}{8}$ ▷ $\frac{9}{10}$ ▷ $1\frac{2}{3}$ ▷ $2\frac{1}{4}$

Teaching Master

Name Date Time

LESSON 7•4 **Fractions of Rectangles**

Use red, blue, and green crayons to color the squares at the bottom of the page. Cut out the squares. If your teacher has colored tiles, use those instead.

Use your colored squares to build the following rectangles in at least two *different* ways. Record your work.

Sample answers:

1. $\frac{1}{2}$ red and $\frac{1}{2}$ blue

R	R
B	B

R	R	R	R	R	R
B	B	B	B	B	B

2. $\frac{1}{3}$ red, $\frac{1}{3}$ blue, $\frac{1}{3}$ green

R	B	G

R	B	G
R	B	G
R	B	G

3. $\frac{1}{4}$ red, $\frac{1}{2}$ blue, $\frac{1}{4}$ green

R	B	B	G

R	B	B	G
R	B	B	G

4. Make up a problem of your own.

____ red, ____ blue, ____ green Answers vary.

red	red	red	red	red	red	red	red	red	red
blue	blue	blue	blue	blue	blue	blue	blue	blue	blue
green	green	green	green	green	green	green	green	green	green

Math Masters, p. 214

Teaching Master

Name Date Time

LESSON 7•4 **Exploring Tangrams**

1. Cut out the tangram pieces at the top of *Math Masters,* page 441, and use all 7 pieces to create the large square at the bottom of the page.

2. If the large square is the whole, or the ONE, find the value of each of the tangram pieces.

Small Square	Large Triangle	Medium Triangle	Small Triangle	Parallelogram
$\frac{2}{16}$	$\frac{4}{16}$	$\frac{2}{16}$	$\frac{1}{16}$	$\frac{2}{16}$

3. Describe the strategy you used to find the value of the small triangle.

Sample answer: I figured out how many small triangles it takes to make each of the other shapes. If I were to use just small triangles to make the large square, it would take 16 small triangles. So, a small triangle has a value of $\frac{1}{16}$.

4. Describe how you can prove that you found the correct value of the small triangle.

Sample answer: I could add all the values for each piece needed to make the whole to show that they add up to $\frac{16}{16}$, or 1 $\left(\frac{2}{16} + \frac{4}{16} + \frac{4}{16} + \frac{2}{16} + \frac{1}{16} + \frac{1}{16} + \frac{2}{16}\right)$.

Try This

5. Use several tangram pieces to create a polygon for which the small square is worth $\frac{2}{9}$. Trace the polygon on the back of this page. Give the value of each tangram piece in the polygon.

Math Masters, p. 215

7•5 Fraction and Mixed-Number Addition and Subtraction

Objective To guide students in the use of pattern blocks to add and subtract fractions and mixed numbers.

Technology Resources www.everydaymathonline.com

ePresentations

eToolkit

Algorithms Practice

EM Facts Workshop Game™

Family Letters

Assessment Management

Common Core State Standards

Curriculum Focal Points

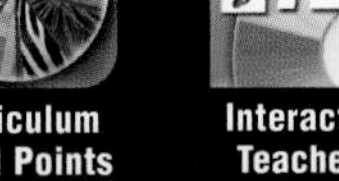

Interactive Teacher's Lesson Guide

1 Teaching the Lesson

Key Concepts and Skills

- Identify the whole or the ONE.
  [Number and Numeration Goal 2]
- Represent fractions and mixed numbers with pattern blocks.
  [Number and Numeration Goal 2]
- Identify equivalent fractions.
  [Number and Numeration Goal 5]
- Model fraction and mixed-number addition and subtraction with pattern blocks.
  [Operations and Computation Goal 5]
- Identify a triangle, hexagon, trapezoid, and rhombus.
  [Geometry Goal 2]

Key Activities

Students model fraction and mixed-number sums and differences with pattern blocks.

Ongoing Assessment: Recognizing Student Achievement
Use journal page 198.
[Operations and Computation Goal 5]

Materials

Math Journal 2, pp. 198–198B
Study Link 7•4
pattern blocks ◆ calculator ◆ slate ◆ overhead pattern blocks (optional) ◆ colored chalk (optional)

2 Ongoing Learning & Practice

Playing *Angle Tangle*
Student Reference Book, p. 230
Math Masters, p. 457
protractor ◆ straightedge
Students practice measuring and estimating the measures of angles.

Math Boxes 7•5
Math Journal 2, p. 199
Students practice and maintain skills through Math Box problems.

Study Link 7•5
Math Masters, p. 216
Students practice and maintain skills through Study Link activities.

3 Differentiation Options

READINESS

Exploring Fractions that Sum to One
Math Masters, p. 217
Students divide cakes into thirds, fourths, sixths, and eighths and write number models.

EXTRA PRACTICE

Solving Frames-and-Arrows Problems
Math Masters, p. 393
Students practice adding and subtracting fractions.

Advance Preparation

For the optional Readiness activity in Part 3, obtain a copy of ***Full House: An Invitation to Fractions*** by Dayle Ann Dodds (Candlewick Press, 2009).

***Teacher's Reference Manual,* Grades 4–6** pp. 29–35, 142, 149, 150

Getting Started

Mental Math and Reflexes

Write fractions and mixed numbers on the board for students to decompose on their slates in at least two different ways. *Suggestions:* Sample answers are given.

●○○ $\frac{5}{11}$ $\frac{5}{11} = \frac{2}{11} + \frac{3}{11}$; $\frac{5}{11} = \frac{1}{11} + \frac{4}{11}$

$\frac{7}{8}$ $\frac{7}{8} = \frac{1}{8} + \frac{6}{8}$; $\frac{7}{8} = \frac{3}{8} + \frac{3}{8} + \frac{1}{8}$

$\frac{3}{5}$ $\frac{3}{5} = \frac{1}{5} + \frac{1}{5} + \frac{1}{5}$; $\frac{3}{5} = \frac{2}{5} + \frac{1}{5}$

●●○ $\frac{8}{15}$ $\frac{8}{15} = \frac{5}{15} + \frac{3}{15}$; $\frac{8}{15} = \frac{4}{15} + \frac{4}{15}$

$\frac{12}{25}$ $\frac{12}{25} = \frac{5}{15} + \frac{5}{15} + \frac{2}{15}$; $\frac{12}{15} = \frac{3}{15} + \frac{9}{15}$

$\frac{7}{10}$ $\frac{7}{10} = \frac{5}{10} + \frac{2}{10}$; $\frac{7}{10} = \frac{1}{10} + \frac{2}{10} + \frac{4}{10}$

●●● $3\frac{2}{3}$ $3\frac{2}{3} = 2 + \frac{3}{3} + \frac{2}{3}$; $3\frac{2}{3} = \frac{6}{3} + \frac{3}{3} + \frac{1}{3} + \frac{1}{3}$

$1\frac{5}{6}$ $1\frac{5}{6} = \frac{6}{6} + \frac{5}{6}$; $1\frac{5}{6} = 1 + \frac{3}{6} + \frac{2}{6}$

$2\frac{4}{9}$ $2\frac{4}{9} = \frac{9}{9} + \frac{9}{9} + \frac{4}{9}$; $2\frac{4}{9} = 1 + \frac{9}{9} + \frac{3}{9} + \frac{1}{9}$

Math Message

If the hexagon pattern block is the whole, what fractions are represented by the trapezoid, the rhombus, and the triangle?

Study Link 7·4 Follow-Up

Ask students to share their solution strategies for Problem 3.

Sample answer: $\frac{2}{3}$ of 15 quarters = 10 quarters, or \$2.50; $\frac{3}{5}$ of 10 nickels = 6 nickels, or 30 cents. Therefore, Rosa spent \$2.50 + \$0.30 = \$2.80. Each can costs 35 cents, so she was able to buy 8 cans with her money.

1 Teaching the Lesson

Math Message Follow-Up

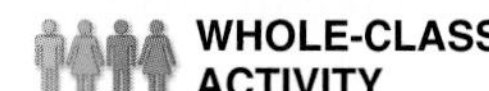

WHOLE-CLASS ACTIVITY

Review answers. The trapezoid represents $\frac{1}{2}$, the rhombus represents $\frac{1}{3}$, and the triangle represents $\frac{1}{6}$.

Ask students to use a trapezoid, a rhombus, and a triangle to form a hexagon. Ask what number model describes what they just did. $\frac{1}{2} + \frac{1}{3} + \frac{1}{6} = 1$

Tell students that in this lesson they will use pattern blocks to model fraction and mixed-number addition and subtraction problems. For all of the activities, the hexagon pattern block represents the whole, or the ONE.

Adjusting the Activity

ELL

Use colored chalk that matches the pattern block colors to write the number model on the board: $\frac{1}{2} + \frac{1}{3} + \frac{1}{6} = 1$.

AUDITORY ◆ KINESTHETIC ◆ TACTILE ◆ VISUAL

Modeling Fraction and Mixed-Number Sums

WHOLE-CLASS ACTIVITY

Use pattern blocks on the overhead to work through fraction and mixed-number addition problems with the class. *Suggestions:*

- $\frac{2}{6} + \frac{1}{6} = \frac{3}{6}$, or $\frac{1}{2}$
- $\frac{1}{6} + \frac{3}{6} = \frac{4}{6}$, or $\frac{2}{3}$
- $\frac{1}{3} + \frac{1}{3} = \frac{2}{3}$
- $\frac{2}{3} + \frac{1}{6} = \frac{5}{6}$
- $\frac{1}{3} + \frac{1}{2} = \frac{5}{6}$
- $\frac{5}{6} + \frac{1}{3} = \frac{7}{6}$, or $1\frac{1}{6}$
- $2\frac{1}{3} + \frac{1}{3} = 2\frac{2}{3}$
- $1\frac{1}{2} + \frac{1}{2} = 1\frac{2}{2}$, or 2
- $2\frac{1}{3} + 3\frac{1}{3} = 5\frac{2}{3}$
- $2\frac{1}{2} + 1\frac{3}{6} = 3\frac{2}{2}$, or 4
- $1\frac{1}{3} + 1\frac{1}{6} = 2\frac{3}{6}$, or $2\frac{1}{2}$
- $2\frac{4}{6} + 1\frac{2}{3} = 4\frac{1}{3}$

Links to the Future

These activities provide exposure to adding and subtracting fractions using manipulatives. Paper-and-pencil addition and subtraction of fractions is a Grade 5 Goal.

Modeling Fraction and Mixed-Number Addition with Like Denominators

Have students use pattern blocks to find the sum of fractions and mixed numbers with like denominators.

Example 1: $\frac{1}{3} + \frac{1}{3} = ?$

Have students take 2 rhombuses and combine them to form $\frac{2}{3}$.

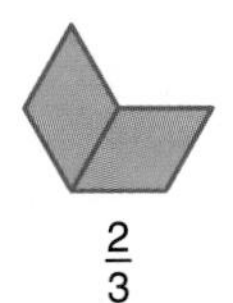

$\frac{2}{3}$

Example 2: $1\frac{1}{6} + \frac{3}{6} = ?$

Have students take 1 hexagon and 1 triangle to represent $1\frac{1}{6}$, and 3 triangles to represent $\frac{3}{6}$. Then have students combine them to form $1\frac{4}{6}$.

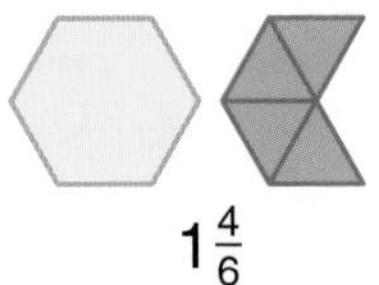

$1\frac{4}{6}$

Modeling Fraction and Mixed-Number Addition with Unlike Denominators

You can either let students devise their own methods or demonstrate the following step-by-step procedure. This process involves an extra step of trading in blocks for one kind of block.

Example 1: $\frac{2}{3} + \frac{1}{6} = ?$

Step 1: Model the fractions to be added.

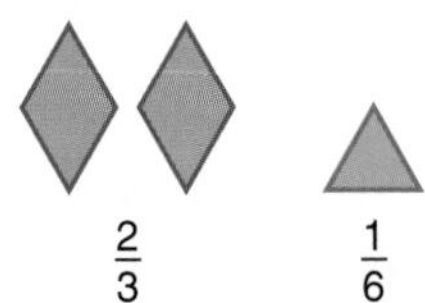

Step 2: Combine the blocks to show the sum.

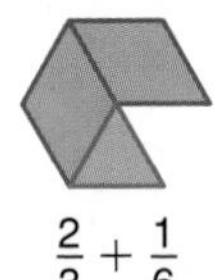

$\frac{2}{3} + \frac{1}{6}$

Step 3: Trade for one kind of block.

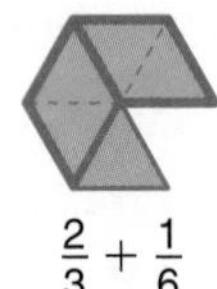

$\frac{2}{3} + \frac{1}{6}$

Step 4: Name the fraction for the sum.

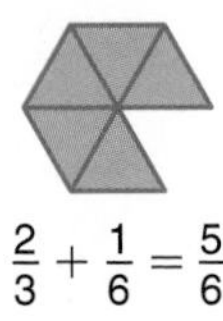

$\frac{2}{3} + \frac{1}{6} = \frac{5}{6}$

Example 2: $1\frac{2}{3} + 1\frac{1}{6} = ?$

Step 1: Model the numbers to be added.

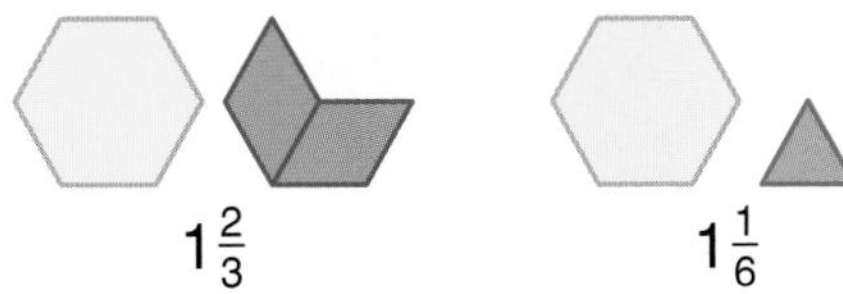

Step 2: Combine the blocks to show the sum.

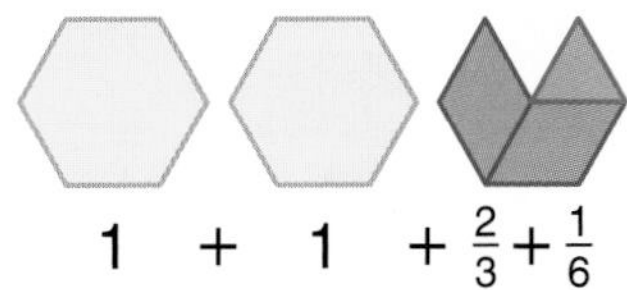

Step 3: Trade for one kind of block.

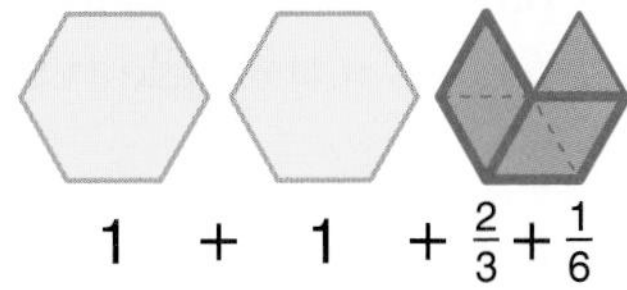

Step 4: Name the mixed number for the sum.

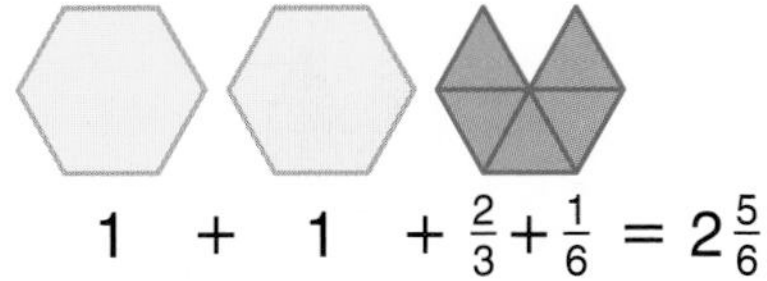

Modeling Fraction and Mixed-Number Differences

Modeling Fraction and Mixed-Number Subtraction with Like Denominators

Now have students use pattern blocks to find differences of fractions and mixed numbers with like denominators.

Example 1: $\frac{2}{3} - \frac{1}{3} = ?$

Have students take 2 rhombuses and then remove or cover 1 rhombus to show the difference is $\frac{1}{3}$.

Example 2: $2\frac{3}{6} - 1\frac{1}{6} = ?$

Have students take 2 hexagons 3 triangles and then remove or cover 1 hexagon and 1 triangle to show the difference is $1\frac{2}{6}$.

Modeling Fraction and Mixed-Number Subtraction with Unlike Denominators

Ask students how they could use pattern blocks to solve $\frac{5}{6} - \frac{2}{3}$. After a few minutes, ask students to share their approaches. Subtraction can be harder to model than addition, so students' methods may be awkward. Below are two approaches.

Cover-Up Method

Model both fractions with pattern blocks. Then put the blocks representing the smaller fraction on top of the blocks representing the larger fraction. The part of the larger fraction that remains uncovered is the difference.

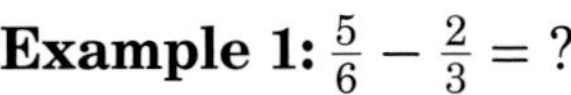

Example 1: $\frac{5}{6} - \frac{2}{3} = ?$

Step 1: Model the fractions with pattern blocks.

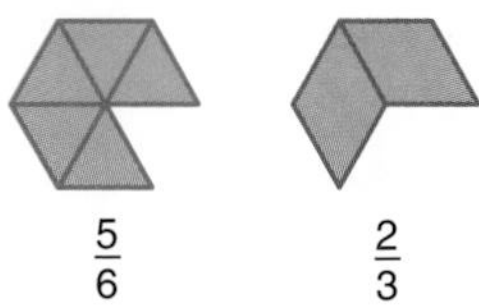

Step 2: Cover up the larger fraction with the smaller fraction.

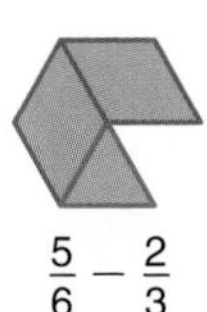

Step 3: The uncovered part of the larger fraction is the difference. The uncovered part is a triangle representing $\frac{1}{6}$. So, $\frac{5}{6} - \frac{2}{3} = \frac{1}{6}$.

Example 2: $2\frac{5}{6} - 1\frac{1}{3} = ?$

Step 1: Model the mixed numbers with pattern blocks.

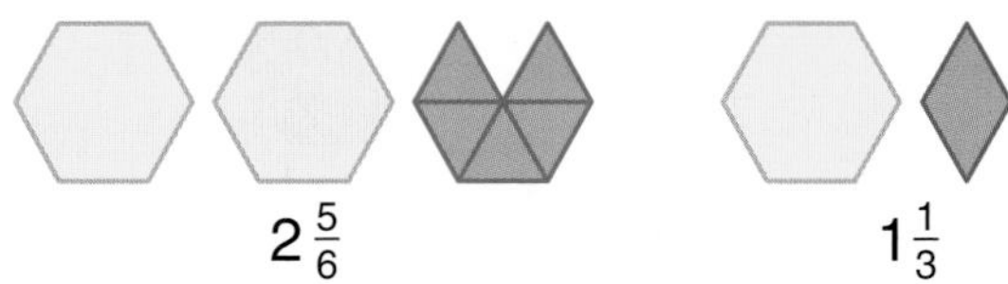

Step 2: Cover up the larger mixed number with the smaller mixed number.

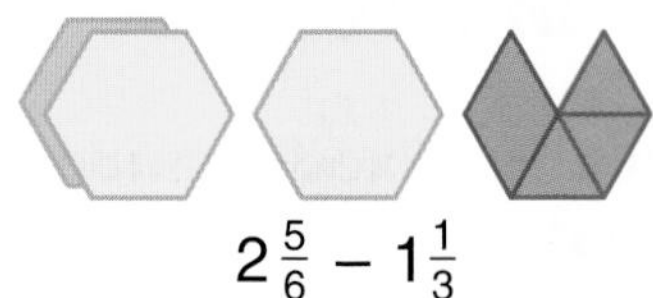

Step 3: The uncovered part of the larger mixed number is the difference. The uncovered part is 1 hexagon and 3 triangles representing $1\frac{3}{6}$. So, $2\frac{5}{6} - 1\frac{1}{3} = 1\frac{3}{6}$, or $1\frac{1}{2}$.

Take-Away Method

Model the larger fraction with pattern blocks. Then take away blocks representing the smaller fraction, trading for blocks of the proper size if necessary. The remaining blocks represent the difference.

Example 1: $\frac{5}{6} - \frac{2}{3} = ?$

Step 1: Model the larger fraction with pattern blocks.

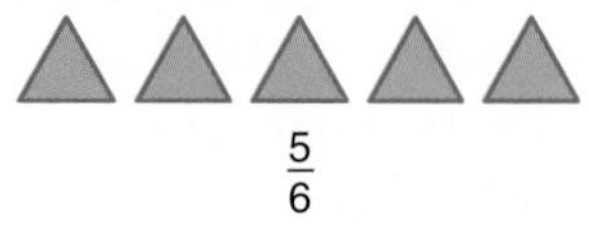

Step 2: Remove blocks representing the smaller fraction. The smaller number, $\frac{2}{3}$, can be represented by 2 rhombuses. Since there are no rhombuses, trade 4 triangles for 2 rhombuses. Then remove 2 rhombuses. (*See margin.*)

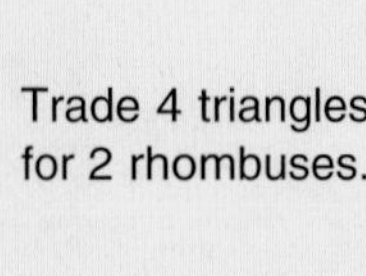

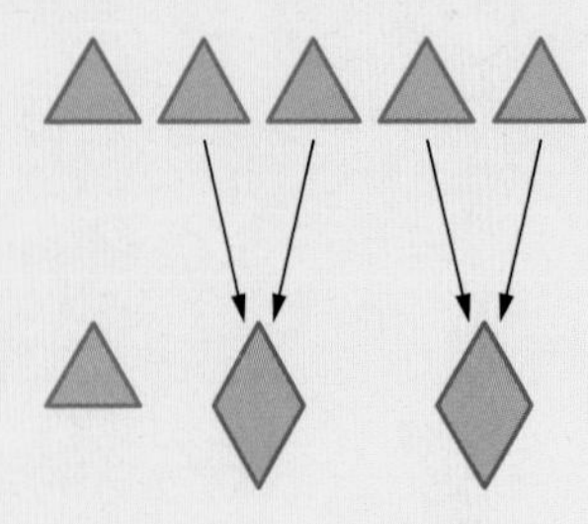

Take away 2 rhombuses.

Step 3: The block(s) that are left represent the difference.

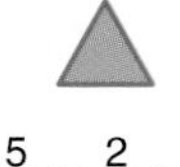

$\frac{5}{6} - \frac{2}{3} = \frac{1}{6}$

Example 2: $1\frac{1}{2} - \frac{1}{6} = ?$

Step 1: Model the larger mixed number with pattern blocks.

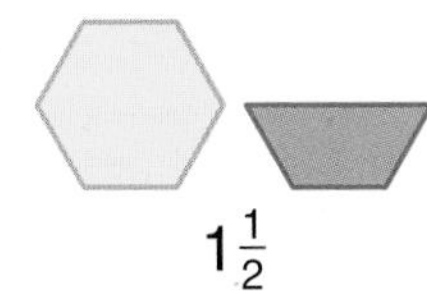

$1\frac{1}{2}$

Step 2: Remove blocks representing the smaller number. The smaller number, $\frac{1}{6}$, can be represented by a triangle. Since there are no triangles, trade 1 trapezoid for 3 triangles. Then remove 1 triangle.

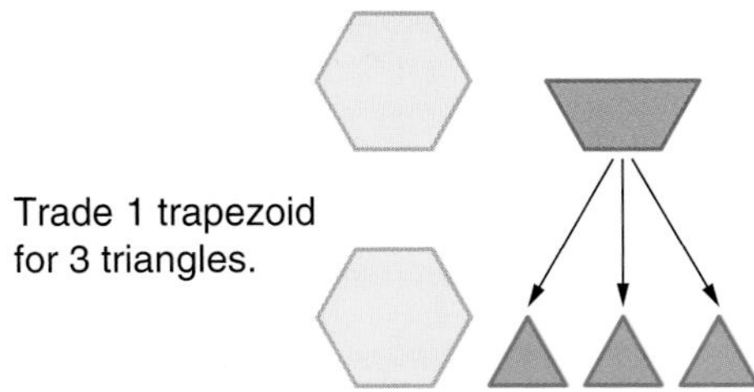
Trade 1 trapezoid
for 3 triangles.

Step 3: The block(s) that are left represent the difference.

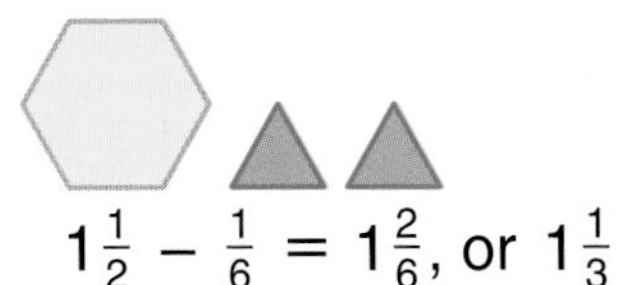

$1\frac{1}{2} - \frac{1}{6} = 1\frac{2}{6}$, or $1\frac{1}{3}$

Pose fraction and mixed number subtraction problems for students to solve with pattern blocks. *Suggestions:*

- $\frac{5}{6} - \frac{2}{6} = \frac{3}{6}$, or $\frac{1}{2}$
- $\frac{2}{3} - \frac{1}{3} = \frac{1}{3}$
- $\frac{2}{3} - \frac{1}{2} = \frac{1}{6}$
- $\frac{1}{2} - \frac{1}{3} = \frac{1}{6}$
- $\frac{2}{3} - \frac{1}{6} = \frac{3}{6}$, or $\frac{1}{2}$
- $1\frac{5}{6} - \frac{4}{6} = 1\frac{1}{6}$
- $2\frac{2}{3} - 2\frac{1}{3} = \frac{1}{3}$
- $1\frac{1}{2} - \frac{2}{2} = \frac{1}{2}$
- $1\frac{1}{2} - \frac{2}{3} = \frac{5}{6}$
- $1\frac{1}{3} - \frac{5}{6} = \frac{3}{6}$, or $\frac{1}{2}$

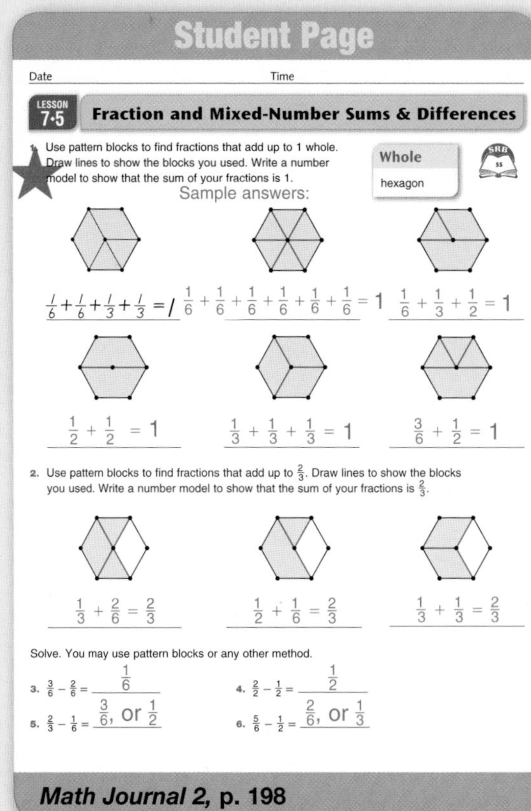

Student Page

Date Time

LESSON 7·5 **Fraction and Mixed-Number Sums & Differences**

1. Use pattern blocks to find fractions that add up to 1 whole. Draw lines to show the blocks you used. Write a number model to show that the sum of your fractions is 1. Sample answers:

Whole: hexagon

$\frac{1}{6} + \frac{1}{6} + \frac{1}{3} + \frac{1}{3} = 1$ | $\frac{1}{6} + \frac{1}{6} + \frac{1}{6} + \frac{1}{6} + \frac{1}{6} + \frac{1}{6} = 1$ | $\frac{1}{6} + \frac{1}{3} + \frac{1}{2} = 1$

$\frac{1}{2} + \frac{1}{2} = 1$ | $\frac{1}{3} + \frac{1}{3} + \frac{1}{3} = 1$ | $\frac{3}{6} + \frac{1}{2} = 1$

2. Use pattern blocks to find fractions that add up to $\frac{2}{3}$. Draw lines to show the blocks you used. Write a number model to show that the sum of your fractions is $\frac{2}{3}$.

$\frac{1}{3} + \frac{2}{6} = \frac{2}{3}$ | $\frac{1}{2} + \frac{1}{6} = \frac{2}{3}$ | $\frac{1}{3} + \frac{1}{3} = \frac{2}{3}$

Solve. You may use pattern blocks or any other method.

3. $\frac{3}{6} - \frac{2}{6} = \frac{1}{6}$
4. $\frac{2}{2} - \frac{1}{2} = \frac{1}{2}$
5. $\frac{2}{3} - \frac{1}{6} = \frac{3}{6}$, or $\frac{1}{2}$
6. $\frac{5}{6} - \frac{1}{2} = \frac{2}{6}$, or $\frac{1}{3}$

Math Journal 2, p. 198

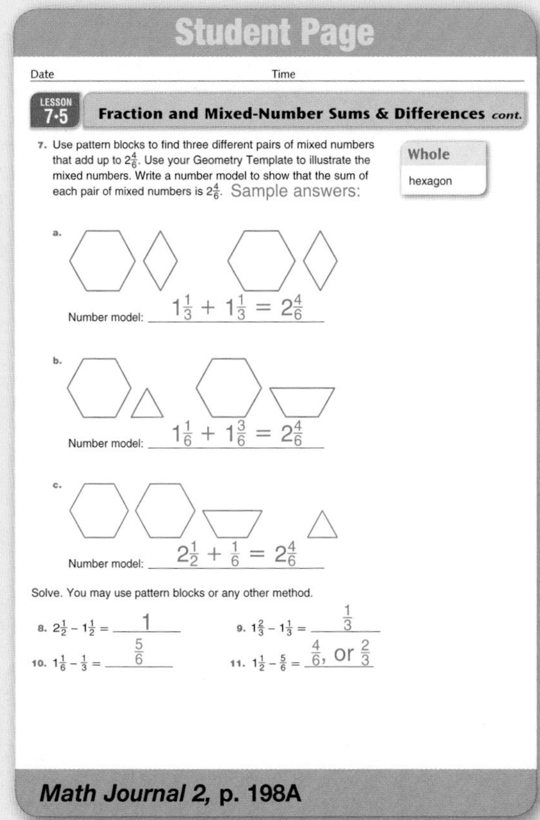

Student Page

Date Time

LESSON 7·5 **Fraction and Mixed-Number Sums & Differences** *cont.*

7. Use pattern blocks to find three different pairs of mixed numbers that add up to $2\frac{4}{6}$. Use your Geometry Template to illustrate the mixed numbers. Write a number model to show that the sum of each pair of mixed numbers is $2\frac{4}{6}$. Sample answers:

Whole: hexagon

a. Number model: $1\frac{1}{3} + 1\frac{1}{3} = 2\frac{4}{6}$

b. Number model: $1\frac{1}{6} + 1\frac{3}{6} = 2\frac{4}{6}$

c. Number model: $2\frac{1}{2} + \frac{1}{6} = 2\frac{4}{6}$

Solve. You may use pattern blocks or any other method.

8. $2\frac{1}{2} - 1\frac{1}{2} = 1$
9. $1\frac{2}{3} - 1\frac{1}{3} = \frac{1}{3}$
10. $1\frac{1}{6} - \frac{1}{3} = \frac{5}{6}$
11. $1\frac{1}{2} - \frac{5}{6} = \frac{4}{6}$, or $\frac{2}{3}$

Math Journal 2, p. 198A

Student Page

Date Time

LESSON 7·5 Solving Fraction Number Stories

1. Rithik ate $\frac{3}{6}$ of a cheese pizza. He then ate $\frac{1}{6}$ of a veggie pizza.
   a. What fraction of a pizza did he eat in all? $\frac{4}{6}$ of a pizza, or $\frac{2}{3}$ of a pizza
      Number model: $\frac{3}{6} + \frac{1}{6} = \frac{4}{6}$ Sample number models are given.
   b. Did he eat more or less than a whole pizza? less How do you know?
      Sample answer: $\frac{6}{6}$ would be 1 whole pizza, and $\frac{4}{6} < \frac{6}{6}$.
2. Karina walked $\frac{1}{4}$ of a mile to school. After school, she walked $\frac{2}{4}$ of a mile to the store, and then $\frac{1}{4}$ of a mile back to her home.
   a. How far did she walk after school? $\frac{3}{4}$ mile
      Number model: $\frac{2}{4} + \frac{1}{4} = \frac{3}{4}$
   b. How far did she walk in all? $\frac{4}{4}$ mile, or 1 mile
      Number model: $\frac{1}{4} + \frac{2}{4} + \frac{1}{4} = \frac{4}{4}$
3. Stephano is making pancakes and waffles for his guests.
   a. He needs $\frac{2}{3}$ cup of milk for the pancakes and $\frac{2}{3}$ cup of milk for the waffles. How much milk does he need in all? $\frac{4}{3}$, or $1\frac{1}{3}$ cups
      Number model: $\frac{2}{3} + \frac{2}{3} = \frac{4}{3}$
   b. Stephano has $1\frac{2}{3}$ cups of milk. Will he have any left over? If so, how much milk will be left? Yes. $\frac{1}{3}$ cup
      Number model: $1\frac{2}{3} - 1\frac{1}{3} = \frac{1}{3}$

Try This

4. Kumba has one dollar. He spent $\frac{1}{2}$ of the dollar on a pencil and $\frac{2}{10}$ of the dollar on an eraser.
   a. What fraction of the dollar did he spend? $\frac{7}{10}$
      Number model: $\frac{1}{2} + \frac{2}{10} = \frac{7}{10}$
   b. What fraction of the dollar does he have left? $\frac{3}{10}$
      Number model: $1 - \frac{7}{10} = \frac{3}{10}$

Math Journal 2, p. 198B

▶ Solving Fraction and Mixed-Number Addition and Subtraction Problems

PARTNER ACTIVITY

(*Math Journal 2,* pp. 198 and 198A)

Students use pattern blocks to solve fraction and mixed-number addition problems. They use pattern blocks or any other method to solve fraction and mixed-number subtraction problems.

Ongoing Assessment: Recognizing Student Achievement

Journal page 198 Problem 1

Use **journal page 198, Problem 1** to assess students' ability to use pattern blocks to solve fraction addition problems. Students are making adequate progress if they are able to show at least one combination of pattern blocks that adds up to 1 and write an appropriate number model. Some students might be able to show multiple solutions to the problem.

[Operations and Computation Goal 5]

▶ Using a Calculator to Add and Subtract Fractions

Have students practice entering fraction addition and subtraction problems on their calculators.

Example 1: $\frac{2}{3} + \frac{1}{6} = \frac{5}{6}$

▷ On a TI-15: 2 [n] 3 [d] + 1 [n] 6 [d] [Enter]

▷ On a Casio *fx*-55: 2 [b/c] 3 + 1 [b/c] 6 [=]

Example 2: $\frac{1}{2} - \frac{1}{3} = \frac{1}{6}$

▷ On a TI-15: 1 [n] 2 [d] − 1 [n] 3 [d] [Enter]

▷ On a Casio *fx*-55: 1 [b/c] 2 − 1 [b/c] 3 [=]

▶ Solving Fraction Number Stories

PARTNER ACTIVITY

(*Math Journal 2,* p. 198B)

Have students solve number stories involving fractions and mixed numbers. They can use pattern blocks or any other method to solve.

Student Page

Date Time

LESSON 7·5 Math Boxes

1. Circle $\frac{1}{5}$ of all the triangles. Mark Xs on $\frac{2}{3}$ of all the triangles.
   Sample answer:
2. Insert parentheses to make these number sentences true.
   a. $8.2 - (5.2 + 2.5) = 0.5$
   b. $13.6 - (5 + 8) = 0.6$
   c. $9.1 = (28.4 - 1.1) \div 3$
   d. $9 * (2.5 + 3.5) = 54$
3. Plot and label each point on the coordinate grid.
   A (5,0)
   B (3,5)
   C (1,4)
   D (1,1)
   E (2,4)
4. Draw and label a 45° angle.
   Sample answer:
   This angle is an acute (acute or obtuse) angle.
5. A bag contains
   6 red blocks,
   4 blue blocks,
   7 green blocks, and
   3 orange blocks.
   You put your hand in the bag and, without looking, pull out a block. About what fraction of the time would you expect to get a blue block?
   $\frac{4}{20}$, or $\frac{1}{5}$
6. If 1 centimeter on a map represents 10 kilometers, then
   a. 6 cm represent 60 km.
   b. 19.5 cm represent 195 km.
   c. 3 cm represent 30 km.
   d. 5.5 cm represent 55 km.
   e. 0.5 cm represent 5 km.

Math Journal 2, p. 199

2 Ongoing Learning & Practice

▶ Playing *Angle Tangle*

(*Student Reference Book,* p. 230; *Math Masters,* p. 457)

Students play *Angle Tangle* to practice measuring and estimating the measures of angles. See Lesson 6-6 for additional information.

Math Boxes 7·5

INDEPENDENT ACTIVITY

(*Math Journal 2,* p. 199)

Mixed Practice Math Boxes in this lesson are paired with Math Boxes in Lesson 7-7. The skill in Problem 6 previews Unit 8 content.

Study Link 7·5

INDEPENDENT ACTIVITY

(*Math Masters,* p. 216)

Home Connection Students solve fraction addition and subtraction problems.

3 Differentiation Options

READINESS

SMALL-GROUP ACTIVITY

Exploring Fractions that Sum to One

5–15 Min

(*Math Masters,* p. 217)

Literature Link To explore the addition of fractions with like denominators, read ***Full House: An Invitation to Fractions*** by Dayle Ann Dodds (Candlewick Press, 2009). Record the number model to show how the cake was divided among the people. Have students divide the cakes and write number models to show how one cake can be evenly divided among different numbers of people.

EXTRA PRACTICE

INDEPENDENT ACTIVITY

Solving Frames-and-Arrows Problems

5–15 Min

(*Math Masters,* p. 393)

To provide practice adding and subtracting fractions, have students solve Frames-and-Arrows problems. Use *Math Masters,* page 393 to create problems to meet the needs of individual students or have students create and solve their own problems.

Planning Ahead

In preparation for Lesson 7-6, direct students to remove Activity Sheets 5 and 6 from the back of the journal and cut the Fraction Cards apart. Have students write their initials on the cards for identification.

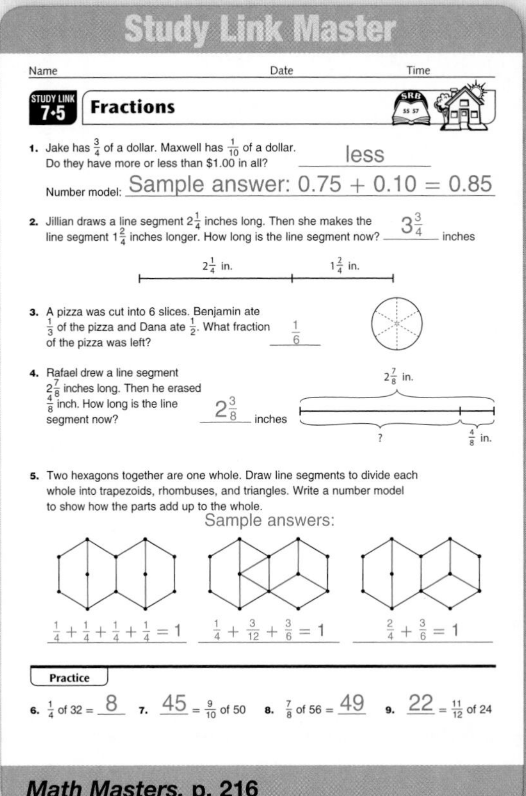

Study Link Master

Name Date Time

STUDY LINK 7·5 **Fractions**

1. Jake has $\frac{3}{4}$ of a dollar. Maxwell has $\frac{1}{10}$ of a dollar. Do they have more or less than \$1.00 in all? less

Number model: Sample answer: $0.75 + 0.10 = 0.85$

2. Jillian draws a line segment $2\frac{1}{4}$ inches long. Then she makes the line segment $1\frac{2}{4}$ inches longer. How long is the line segment now? $3\frac{3}{4}$ inches

$2\frac{1}{4}$ in. $1\frac{2}{4}$ in.

3. A pizza was cut into 6 slices. Benjamin ate $\frac{1}{3}$ of the pizza and Dana ate $\frac{1}{2}$. What fraction of the pizza was left? $\frac{1}{6}$

4. Rafael drew a line segment $2\frac{7}{8}$ inches long. Then he erased $\frac{4}{8}$ inch. How long is the line segment now? $2\frac{3}{8}$ inches

$2\frac{7}{8}$ in. ? $\frac{4}{8}$ in.

5. Two hexagons together are one whole. Draw line segments to divide each whole into trapezoids, rhombuses, and triangles. Write a number model to show how the parts add up to the whole.

Sample answers:

$\frac{1}{4} + \frac{1}{4} + \frac{1}{4} + \frac{1}{4} = 1$ $\frac{1}{4} + \frac{3}{12} + \frac{3}{6} = 1$ $\frac{2}{4} + \frac{3}{6} = 1$

Practice

6. $\frac{1}{4}$ of 32 = 8
7. 45 = $\frac{9}{10}$ of 50
8. $\frac{7}{8}$ of 56 = 49
9. 22 = $\frac{11}{12}$ of 24

Math Masters, p. 216

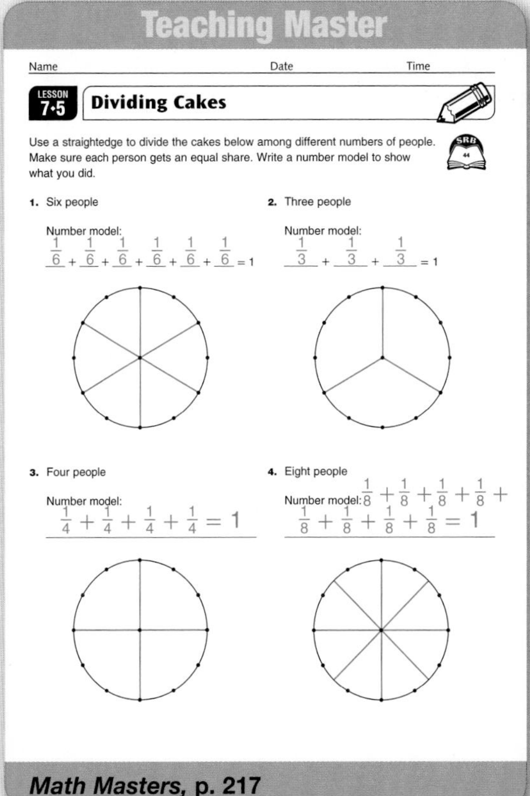

Teaching Master

Name Date Time

LESSON 7·5 **Dividing Cakes**

Use a straightedge to divide the cakes below among different numbers of people. Make sure each person gets an equal share. Write a number model to show what you did.

1. Six people

Number model: $\frac{1}{6} + \frac{1}{6} + \frac{1}{6} + \frac{1}{6} + \frac{1}{6} + \frac{1}{6} = 1$

2. Three people

Number model: $\frac{1}{3} + \frac{1}{3} + \frac{1}{3} = 1$

3. Four people

Number model: $\frac{1}{4} + \frac{1}{4} + \frac{1}{4} + \frac{1}{4} = 1$

4. Eight people

Number model: $\frac{1}{8} + \frac{1}{8} + \frac{1}{8} + \frac{1}{8} + \frac{1}{8} + \frac{1}{8} + \frac{1}{8} + \frac{1}{8} = 1$

Math Masters, p. 217

7•6 Many Names for Fractions

Objective To provide practice identifying equivalent fractions.

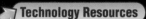

Technology Resources www.everydaymathonline.com

ePresentations

eToolkit

Algorithms Practice

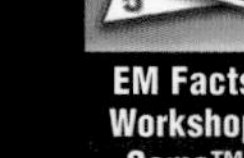
EM Facts Workshop Game™

Family Letters

Assessment Management

Common Core State Standards

Curriculum Focal Points

Interactive Teacher's Lesson Guide

1 Teaching the Lesson

Key Concepts and Skills

- Identify fractional parts of regions. [Number and Numeration Goal 2]
- Name equivalent fractions. [Number and Numeration Goal 5]
- Use patterns in a table to find equivalent fractions. [Patterns, Functions, and Algebra Goal 1]

Key Activities

Students use Fraction Cards to help them start a table of equivalent fractions.

Ongoing Assessment: Informing Instruction See page 599.

Materials

Math Journal 2, pp. 342 and 343
Study Link 7•5
Fraction Cards (*Math Journal 2,* Activity Sheets 5 and 6)

2 Ongoing Learning & Practice

Playing *Grab Bag*
Student Reference Book, p. 249
Math Masters, pp. 483–485
per partnership: 3 six-sided dice
Students practice calculating the probability of an event.

Adding and Subtracting Fractions and Mixed Numbers
Math Journal 2, p. 200A
pattern blocks
Students add and subtract fractions and mixed numbers with like denominators.

Math Boxes 7•6
Math Journal 2, p. 200
Students practice and maintain skills through Math Box problems.

Ongoing Assessment: Recognizing Student Achievement
Use Math Boxes, Problem 4.
[Measurement and Reference Frames Goal 1]

Study Link 7•6
Math Masters, p. 218
Students practice and maintain skills through Study Link activities.

3 Differentiation Options

READINESS

Finding Equivalent Fractions
Math Masters, pp. 219–221
scissors ◆ glue
Students find equivalent fractions by matching fractional parts of circles.

ENRICHMENT

Modeling Fraction Equivalencies
Math Masters, p. 222
Students use a clock face to model equivalencies of fractions with denominators of 2, 3, 4, 5, 6, 10, 12, 15, 20, 30, and 60.

EXTRA PRACTICE

Playing *Fraction Match*
Student Reference Book, p. 243
Math Masters, pp. 389 and 473–476
scissors
Students practice identifying equivalent fractions.

Advance Preparation

If students have not removed Activity Sheets 5 and 6 from the back of the journal and cut the fraction cards apart, have them do so prior to teaching Part 1 of the lesson. Ask students to write their initials on the cards for identification. For the optional Extra Practice activity in Part 3, consider copying *Math Masters,* pages 473–476 on cardstock.

***Teacher's Reference Manual,* Grades 4–6** pp. 141, 142

Getting Started

Mental Math and Reflexes

Pose fraction and mixed-number addition and subtraction problems. Have students estimate whether the answer is greater than or less than 1 and explain their answers. *Suggestions:*

●○○ $\frac{1}{3} + \frac{1}{3}$ less
$\frac{3}{4} + \frac{3}{4}$ greater
$1\frac{2}{4} - \frac{1}{4}$ greater
$\frac{3}{3} - \frac{1}{3}$ less

●●○ $\frac{9}{10} + \frac{7}{8}$ greater
$\frac{6}{8} + \frac{1}{3}$ greater
$\frac{3}{2} - \frac{3}{4}$ less
$1\frac{1}{2} - \frac{1}{16}$ greater

●●● $\frac{2}{3} + \frac{6}{9}$ greater
$\frac{2}{3} + \frac{1}{12}$ less
$\frac{14}{7} - \frac{9}{8}$ less
$1\frac{5}{6} - \frac{1}{12}$ greater

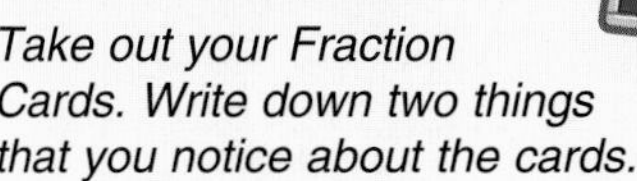

Math Message

Take out your Fraction Cards. Write down two things that you notice about the cards.

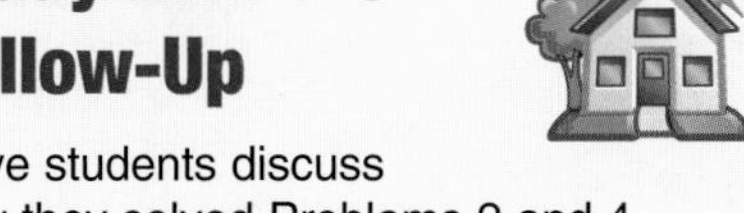

Study Link 7•5 Follow-Up

Have students discuss how they solved Problems 2 and 4.

1 Teaching the Lesson

Math Message Follow-Up

(*Math Journal 2,* Activity Sheets 5 and 6)

Students share observations.

▷ One side of each card is divided into equal parts, and some of the parts are shaded.

▷ A fraction with the numerator or denominator missing appears on the other side of each card.

Ask students to write the missing numerator or denominator in order to name the *fractional part of the card that is shaded.* For example, if the rectangle is divided into 6 equal parts and 2 of them are shaded, the completed fraction on the back should be $\frac{2}{6}$.

Ongoing Assessment: Informing Instruction

Watch for students who make the common error of writing $\frac{2}{4}$ for a Fraction Card such as this:

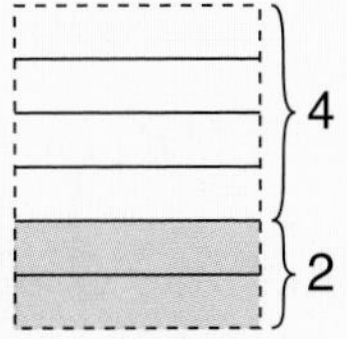

Remind students that the numerator is the counting number. It tells how many parts are shaded (2 parts). The denominator tells what is being counted. There are 6 parts in all, so sixths are being counted.

Tell students that in this lesson they will use the Fraction Cards as a tool to help them name equivalent fractions.

NOTE In the Mental Math and Reflexes activity, you might have students identify the fractions with numerators that are greater than or equal to their denominators. $\frac{3}{3}, \frac{3}{2}, \frac{14}{7}, \frac{9}{8}$ Fractions like these are sometimes called *improper fractions.*

Student Page

Date Time

Equivalent Names for Fractions

Fraction	Equivalent Fractions	Decimal	Percent
$\frac{0}{2}$		0	0%
$\frac{1}{2}$	$\frac{2}{4}$, $\frac{3}{6}$		
$\frac{2}{2}$		1	100%
$\frac{1}{3}$			
$\frac{2}{3}$			
$\frac{1}{4}$			
$\frac{3}{4}$			
$\frac{1}{5}$			
$\frac{2}{5}$			
$\frac{3}{5}$			
$\frac{4}{5}$			
$\frac{1}{6}$			
$\frac{5}{6}$			
$\frac{1}{8}$			
$\frac{3}{8}$			
$\frac{5}{8}$			
$\frac{7}{8}$			

Math Journal 2, p. 342

Links to the Future

Students begin filling in the column for decimals in Lesson 7-8 and the column for percents in Unit 9.

Student Page

Games

Grab Bag

Materials ☐ 1 deck of *Grab Bag* Cards (*Math Masters,* pp. 483–484)
☐ 1 *Grab Bag* Record Sheet for each player or team (*Math Masters,* p. 485)
☐ 3 six-sided dice

Players 2, or two teams of 2

Skill Variable substitution; calculating probabilities of events

Object of the game To score more points by calculating the probabilities of events.

Directions

1. Shuffle the deck of *Grab Bag* cards and place it problem-side down on the table.
2. Players (or teams) take turns. When it is your turn:
   - Draw a card and place it problem-side up on the table. Two quantities are missing from each card. They are shown with the variables x and y.
   - Roll the 3 dice and substitute the numbers rolled for the variables x and y in the following way:
     Replace x with the number shown on 1 of the dice.
     Replace y with the sum of the numbers on the other 2 dice.
   - Solve the problem and give an answer. The opposing player (or team) checks the answer. Your score for the round is calculated as follows:
     10 points: if the event is unlikely (probability is less than $\frac{1}{2}$).
     30 points: if the event is likely (probability is greater than $\frac{1}{2}$).
     50 points: if the event has a 50–50 chance (probability exactly $\frac{1}{2}$).
3. The player (or team) with the higher score after 5 rounds wins.

Note
Use a strategy when replacing x and y by the dice numbers to earn the most points possible for that turn.

Example Paul draws the card shown to the right.

He rolls 6, 1, and 4, and substitutes 1 for x and $6 + 4 = 10$ for y.

Lina's grab bag has 2 red, 2 blue, 1 pink, and 10 green ribbons. The probability of Lina picking a green ribbon is 10 out of 15 or $\frac{10}{15}$ or $\frac{2}{3}$.

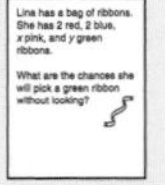

Picking a green ribbon is likely (probability is greater than $\frac{1}{2}$).

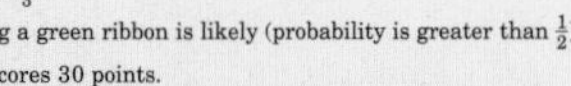

Paul scores 30 points.

Student Reference Book, p. 249

▶ Starting a Collection of Fraction Names

PARTNER ACTIVITY
ELL

(*Math Journal 2,* pp. 342 and 343)

Have one student in each partnership put his or her Fraction Cards away. Model the following procedure:

1. Ask students to find the card with 1 out of 2 parts shaded and the card with 2 out of 4 parts shaded. Point out that the fractions on the back of the cards ($\frac{1}{2}$ and $\frac{2}{4}$) are not the same, but the same amount is shaded on each of these cards. So $\frac{1}{2}$ and $\frac{2}{4}$ are names for the same fraction.
2. Ask students to find all of the other cards that are half-shaded. $\frac{3}{6}, \frac{4}{8}, \frac{5}{10}, \frac{6}{12}$
3. Have students turn to the Equivalent Names for Fractions table on journal page 342. Next to the fraction $\frac{1}{2}$ in the table, have them record all the fractions for the cards that are half-shaded. $\frac{2}{4}, \frac{3}{6}, \frac{4}{8}, \frac{5}{10}, \frac{6}{12}$

To support English language learners, make the connection between the Equivalent Names for Fractions table and the name-collection boxes completed in prior lessons.

▶ Continuing a Collection of Fraction Names

PARTNER ACTIVITY
PROBLEM SOLVING

(*Math Journal 2,* pp. 342 and 343)

Instruct partners to sort the remaining cards into groups that have the same amount shaded. Then have them record the fractions in each of these groups on the appropriate lines in the Equivalent Names for Fractions table.

2 Ongoing Learning & Practice

▶ Playing *Grab Bag*

PARTNER ACTIVITY

(*Student Reference Book,* p. 249; *Math Masters,* pp. 483–485)

Algebraic Thinking Students play *Grab Bag* to practice calculating the probability of an event.

Adjusting the Activity

ELL

Have students draw pictures to model the problems they generate while playing *Grab Bag.*

AUDITORY ◆ KINESTHETIC ◆ TACTILE ◆ VISUAL

Adding and Subtracting Fractions and Mixed Numbers

(*Math Journal 2,* p. 200A)

Students use pattern blocks to add and subtract fractions and mixed numbers with like denominators.

Math Boxes 7·6

INDEPENDENT ACTIVITY

(*Math Journal 2,* p. 200)

Mixed Practice Math Boxes in this lesson are paired with Math Boxes in Lesson 7-8. The skill in Problem 6 previews Unit 8 content.

Ongoing Assessment: Recognizing Student Achievement

Math Boxes Problem 4 

Use **Math Boxes, Problem 4** to assess students' ability to estimate the measure of an angle. Students are making adequate progress if they are able to identify the angle as obtuse. Some students may be able to measure it with a full- or half-circle protractor to within 3 degrees.

[Measurement and Reference Frames Goal 1]

Study Link 7·6

(*Math Masters,* p. 218)

Home Connection Students match fractions with pictures of shaded regions and collections of objects.

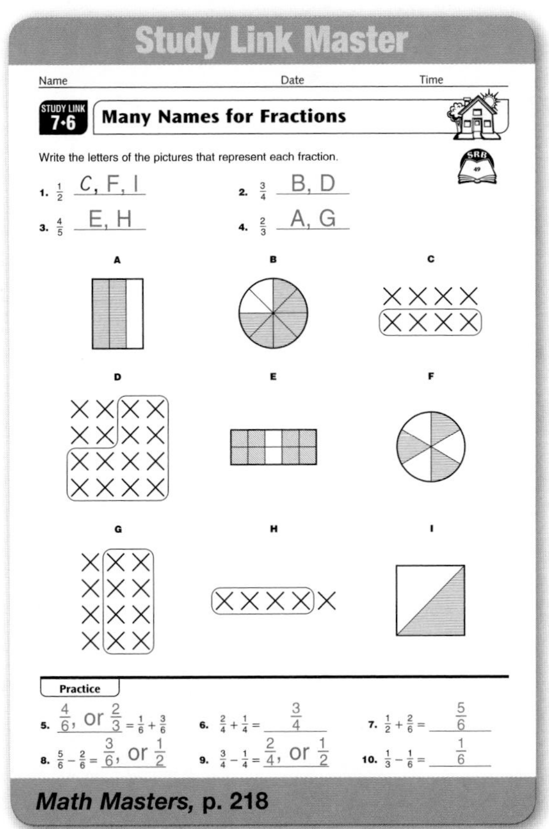

Study Link Master

Name Date Time

STUDY LINK 7·6 **Many Names for Fractions**

Write the letters of the pictures that represent each fraction.

1. $\frac{1}{2}$ C, F, I
2. $\frac{3}{4}$ B, D
3. $\frac{4}{5}$ E, H
4. $\frac{2}{3}$ A, G

Practice

5. $\frac{4}{6}$, or $\frac{2}{3}$ = $\frac{1}{6} + \frac{3}{6}$
6. $\frac{2}{4} + \frac{1}{4} = \frac{3}{4}$
7. $\frac{1}{2} + \frac{2}{6} = \frac{5}{6}$
8. $\frac{5}{6} - \frac{2}{6} = \frac{3}{6}$, or $\frac{1}{2}$
9. $\frac{3}{4} - \frac{1}{4} = \frac{2}{4}$, or $\frac{1}{2}$
10. $\frac{1}{3} - \frac{1}{6} = \frac{1}{6}$

Math Masters, p. 218

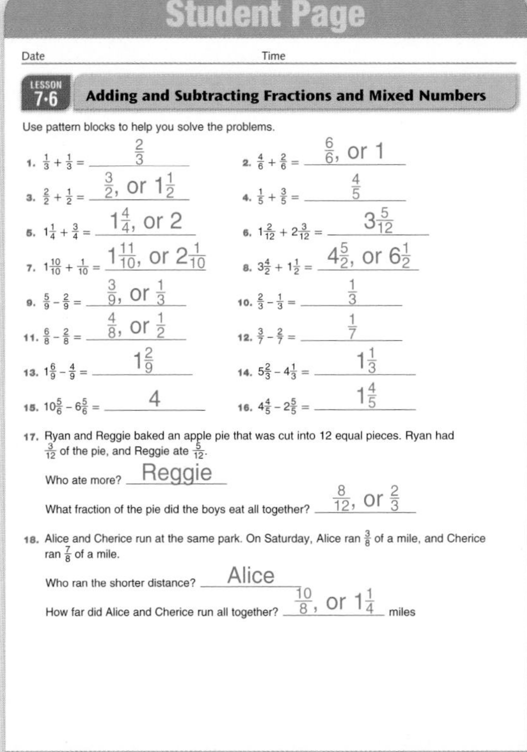

Student Page

Date Time

LESSON 7·6 **Adding and Subtracting Fractions and Mixed Numbers**

Use pattern blocks to help you solve the problems.

1. $\frac{1}{3} + \frac{1}{3} = \frac{2}{3}$
2. $\frac{4}{6} + \frac{2}{6} = \frac{6}{6}$, or 1
3. $\frac{2}{2} + \frac{1}{2} = \frac{3}{2}$, or $1\frac{1}{2}$
4. $\frac{1}{5} + \frac{3}{5} = \frac{4}{5}$
5. $1\frac{1}{4} + \frac{3}{4} = 1\frac{4}{4}$, or 2
6. $1\frac{2}{12} + 2\frac{3}{12} = 3\frac{5}{12}$
7. $1\frac{10}{10} + \frac{1}{10} = 1\frac{11}{10}$, or $2\frac{1}{10}$
8. $3\frac{4}{2} + 1\frac{1}{2} = 4\frac{5}{2}$, or $6\frac{1}{2}$
9. $\frac{5}{9} - \frac{2}{9} = \frac{3}{9}$, or $\frac{1}{3}$
10. $\frac{2}{3} - \frac{1}{3} = \frac{1}{3}$
11. $\frac{6}{8} - \frac{2}{8} = \frac{4}{8}$, or $\frac{1}{2}$
12. $\frac{3}{7} - \frac{2}{7} = \frac{1}{7}$
13. $1\frac{6}{9} - \frac{4}{9} = 1\frac{2}{9}$
14. $5\frac{2}{3} - 4\frac{1}{3} = 1\frac{1}{3}$
15. $10\frac{5}{6} - 6\frac{5}{6} = 4$
16. $4\frac{4}{5} - 2\frac{5}{5} = 1\frac{4}{5}$
17. Ryan and Reggie baked an apple pie that was cut into 12 equal pieces. Ryan had $\frac{3}{12}$ of the pie, and Reggie ate $\frac{5}{12}$.

    Who ate more? Reggie

    What fraction of the pie did the boys eat all together? $\frac{8}{12}$, or $\frac{2}{3}$
18. Alice and Cherice run at the same park. On Saturday, Alice ran $\frac{3}{8}$ of a mile, and Cherice ran $\frac{7}{8}$ of a mile.

    Who ran the shorter distance? Alice

    How far did Alice and Cherice run all together? $\frac{10}{8}$, or $1\frac{1}{4}$ miles

Math Journal 2, p. 200A

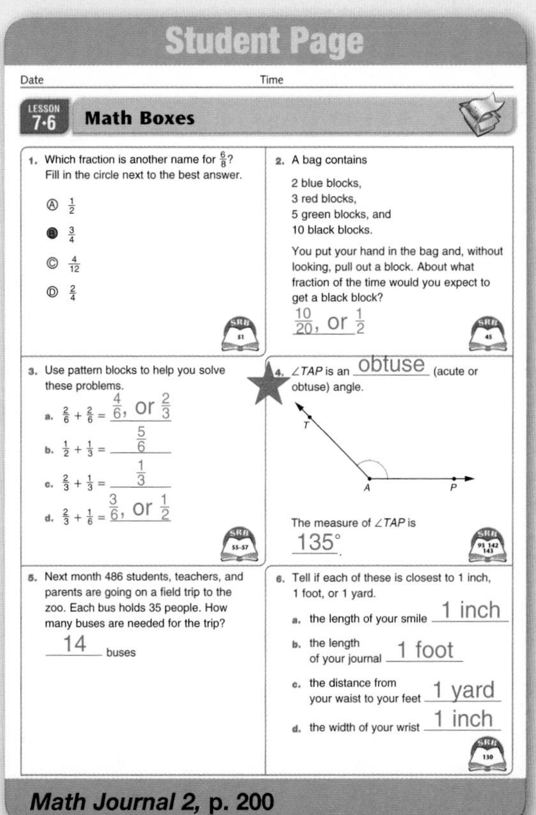

Student Page

Date Time

LESSON 7·6 **Math Boxes**

1. Which fraction is another name for $\frac{6}{8}$? Fill in the circle next to the best answer.

   Ⓐ $\frac{1}{2}$

   Ⓑ $\frac{3}{4}$ (filled in)

   Ⓒ $\frac{4}{12}$

   Ⓓ $\frac{2}{4}$

   SRB 51

2. A bag contains

   2 blue blocks,
   3 red blocks,
   5 green blocks, and
   10 black blocks.

   You put your hand in the bag and, without looking, pull out a block. About what fraction of the time would you expect to get a black block?

   $\frac{10}{20}$, or $\frac{1}{2}$

   SRB 45

3. Use pattern blocks to help you solve these problems.

   a. $\frac{2}{6} + \frac{2}{6} = \frac{4}{6}$, or $\frac{2}{3}$

   b. $\frac{1}{2} + \frac{1}{3} = \frac{5}{6}$

   c. $\frac{2}{3} + \frac{1}{3} = \frac{1}{3}$

   d. $\frac{2}{3} + \frac{1}{6} = \frac{3}{6}$, or $\frac{1}{2}$

   SRB 55-57

4. $\angle TAP$ is an obtuse (acute or obtuse) angle.

   The measure of $\angle TAP$ is 135°.

   SRB 93 142 143

5. Next month 486 students, teachers, and parents are going on a field trip to the zoo. Each bus holds 35 people. How many buses are needed for the trip?

   14 buses

6. Tell if each of these is closest to 1 inch, 1 foot, or 1 yard.

   a. the length of your smile 1 inch

   b. the length of your journal 1 foot

   c. the distance from your waist to your feet 1 yard

   d. the width of your wrist 1 inch

   SRB 130

Math Journal 2, p. 200

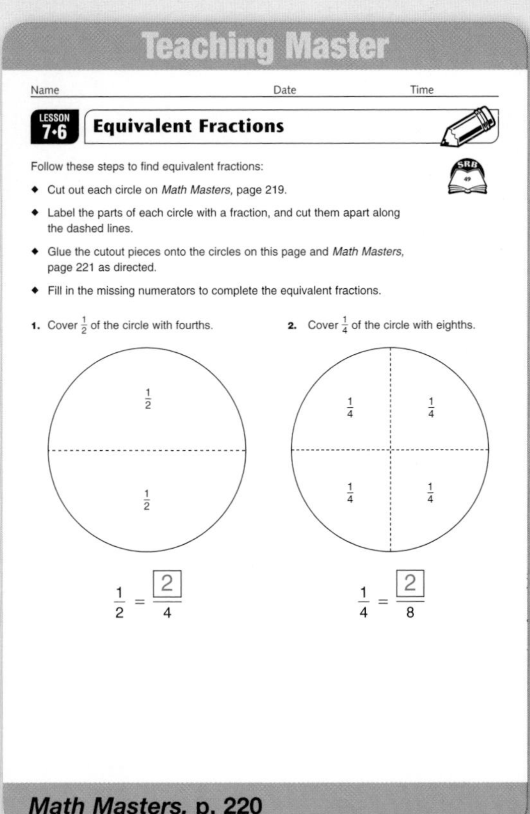
Teaching Master

Name Date Time

LESSON 7·6 **Equivalent Fractions**

Follow these steps to find equivalent fractions:

- Cut out each circle on *Math Masters*, page 219.
- Label the parts of each circle with a fraction, and cut them apart along the dashed lines.
- Glue the cutout pieces onto the circles on this page and *Math Masters*, page 221 as directed.
- Fill in the missing numerators to complete the equivalent fractions.

1. Cover $\frac{1}{2}$ of the circle with fourths.
2. Cover $\frac{1}{4}$ of the circle with eighths.

$\frac{1}{2} = \frac{2}{4}$ $\frac{1}{4} = \frac{2}{8}$

Math Masters, p. 220

3 Differentiation Options

READINESS

PARTNER ACTIVITY

▶ Finding Equivalent Fractions

15–30 Min

(*Math Masters*, pp. 219–221)

To explore equivalent names for fractions, have students find equivalent fractions by matching fractional parts of circles.

ENRICHMENT

INDEPENDENT ACTIVITY

▶ Modeling Fraction Equivalencies

5–15 Min

(*Math Masters,* p. 222)

To further explore equivalent fractions, have students use a clock face to model equivalencies of fractions with denominators that are factors of 60. Have students discuss how the clock faces might be used to help them model fraction addition and subtraction.

EXTRA PRACTICE

SMALL-GROUP ACTIVITY

▶ Playing *Fraction Match*

5–15 Min

(*Student Reference Book,* p. 243; *Math Masters,* pp. 389 and 473–476)

To practice identifying equivalent fractions, have students play *Fraction Match.* Have students describe on an Exit Slip how they know that two of the fractions are equivalent. See Lesson 7-7 for additional information.

Teaching Master

Name Date Time

LESSON 7·6 **Equivalent Fractions** *continued*

3. Cover $\frac{2}{4}$ of the circle with eighths.
4. Cover $\frac{1}{2}$ of the circle with sixths.

$\frac{2}{4} = \frac{4}{8}$ $\frac{1}{2} = \frac{3}{6}$

5. Cover $\frac{1}{3}$ of the circle with sixths.
6. Cover $\frac{2}{3}$ of the circle with sixths.

$\frac{1}{3} = \frac{2}{6}$ $\frac{2}{3} = \frac{4}{6}$

Math Masters, p. 221

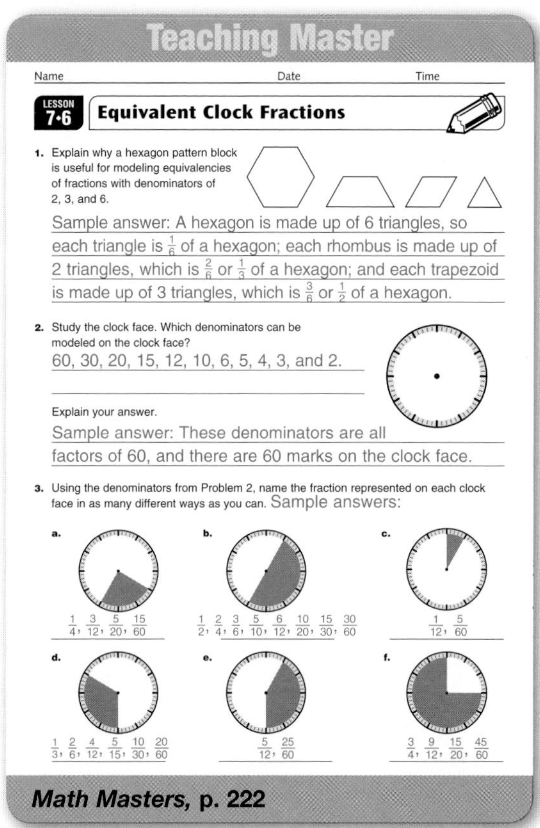
Teaching Master

Name Date Time

LESSON 7·6 **Equivalent Clock Fractions**

1. Explain why a hexagon pattern block is useful for modeling equivalencies of fractions with denominators of 2, 3, and 6.
Sample answer: A hexagon is made up of 6 triangles, so each triangle is $\frac{1}{6}$ of a hexagon; each rhombus is made up of 2 triangles, which is $\frac{2}{6}$ or $\frac{1}{3}$ of a hexagon; and each trapezoid is made up of 3 triangles, which is $\frac{3}{6}$ or $\frac{1}{2}$ of a hexagon.

2. Study the clock face. Which denominators can be modeled on the clock face?
60, 30, 20, 15, 12, 10, 6, 5, 4, 3, and 2.
Explain your answer.
Sample answer: These denominators are all factors of 60, and there are 60 marks on the clock face.

3. Using the denominators from Problem 2, name the fraction represented on each clock face in as many different ways as you can. Sample answers:

a. $\frac{1}{4}, \frac{3}{12}, \frac{5}{20}, \frac{15}{60}$
b. $\frac{1}{2}, \frac{2}{4}, \frac{3}{6}, \frac{5}{10}, \frac{6}{12}, \frac{10}{20}, \frac{15}{30}, \frac{30}{60}$
c. $\frac{1}{12}, \frac{5}{60}$
d. $\frac{1}{3}, \frac{2}{6}, \frac{4}{12}, \frac{5}{15}, \frac{10}{30}, \frac{20}{60}$
e. $\frac{5}{12}, \frac{25}{60}$
f. $\frac{3}{4}, \frac{9}{12}, \frac{15}{20}, \frac{45}{60}$

Math Masters, p. 222

7•7 Equivalent Fractions

Objective To guide the development and use of a rule for generating equivalent fractions.

Technology Resources www.everydaymathonline.com

ePresentations

eToolkit

Algorithms Practice

EM Facts Workshop Game™

Family Letters

Assessment Management

Common Core State Standards

Curriculum Focal Points

Interactive Teacher's Lesson Guide

1 Teaching the Lesson

Key Concepts and Skills

- Identify fractional parts of regions. [Number and Numeration Goal 2]
- Name equivalent fractions. [Number and Numeration Goal 5]
- Use a rule for generating equivalent fractions. [Number and Numeration Goal 5]
- Develop a rule for generating equivalent fractions. [Patterns, Functions, and Algebra Goal 1]

Key Activities

Students use examples of equivalent fractions to develop a rule for finding equivalent fractions.

Ongoing Assessment: Informing Instruction See page 605.

Ongoing Assessment: Recognizing Student Achievement Use *Math Masters,* page 225. [Number and Numeration Goal 5]

Key Vocabulary

equivalent fractions ◆ Equivalent Fractions Rule

Materials

Math Journal 2, pp. 201, 342, and 343
Study Link 7•6
Math Masters, p. 225
calculator ◆ colored chalk ◆ slate

2 Ongoing Learning & Practice

Playing *Fraction Match*
Student Reference Book, p. 243
Math Masters, pp. 389 and 473–476
Students practice identifying equivalent names for fractions.

Fraction and Mixed-Number Addition and Subtraction
Math Journal 2, p. 200B
pattern blocks
Students add and subtract fractions and mixed numbers.

Math Boxes 7•7
Math Journal 2, p. 202
Students practice and maintain skills through Math Box problems.

Study Link 7•7
Math Masters, p. 223
Students practice and maintain skills through Study Link activities.

3 Differentiation Options

READINESS

Identifying Equivalent Fractions on the Fraction Number-Line Poster
Math Masters, p. 388 or 389
per group: Fraction Number-Line Poster (*Math Masters,* pp. 204 and 205), straightedge
Students use a Fraction Number-Line Poster to identify equivalent fractions.

ENRICHMENT

Investigating Egyptian Fractions
Math Masters, p. 224
Students investigate how early Egyptians represented a fraction as the sum of unit fractions.

EXTRA PRACTICE

Completing Name-Collection Boxes
Math Masters, p. 397
Students complete name-collection boxes for fractions.

EXTRA PRACTICE

5-Minute Math
5-Minute Math™, pp. 1, 17, 79, and 165
Students practice finding equivalent fractions.

Advance Preparation

***Teacher's Reference Manual,* Grades 4–6** pp. 141, 142

Getting Started

Mental Math and Reflexes

Have students name all the factor pairs for numbers less than 100.
Suggestions:

●○○ 6 1 and 6; 2 and 3
4 1 and 4; 2 and 2
5 1 and 5

●●○ 12 1 and 12; 2 and 6; 3 and 4
15 1 and 15; 3 and 5
21 1 and 21; 3 and 7

●●● 50 1 and 50; 2 and 25; 5 and 10
52 1 and 52; 2 and 26; 4 and 13
72 1 and 72; 2 and 36; 3 and 24; 4 and 18; 6 and 12; 8 and 9

Math Message

Complete journal page 201.

Study Link 7·6 Follow-Up

Have small groups compare answers. Ask volunteers to draw additional representations of the fractions in Problems 1–4.

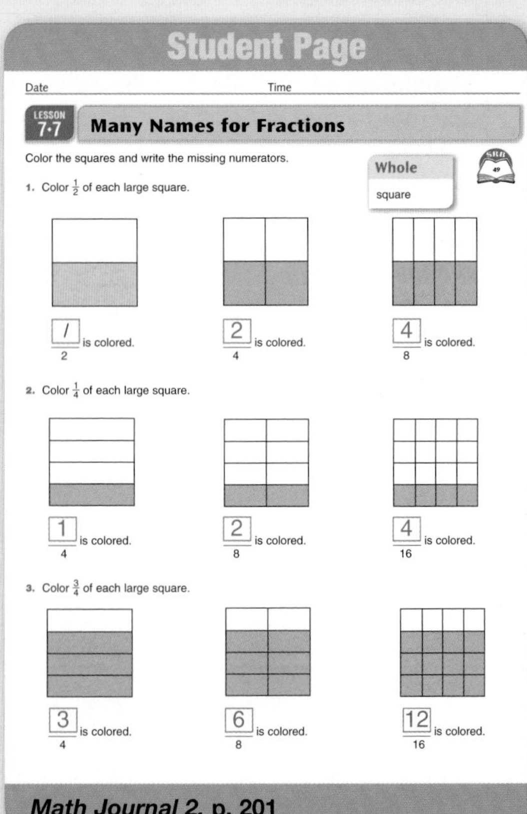

Student Page

Date Time

LESSON 7·7 **Many Names for Fractions**

Color the squares and write the missing numerators.

Whole: square

1. Color $\frac{1}{2}$ of each large square.

$\frac{1}{2}$ is colored. $\frac{2}{4}$ is colored. $\frac{4}{8}$ is colored.

2. Color $\frac{1}{4}$ of each large square.

$\frac{1}{4}$ is colored. $\frac{2}{8}$ is colored. $\frac{4}{16}$ is colored.

3. Color $\frac{3}{4}$ of each large square.

$\frac{3}{4}$ is colored. $\frac{6}{8}$ is colored. $\frac{12}{16}$ is colored.

Math Journal 2, p. 201

1 Teaching the Lesson

▶ Math Message Follow-Up

WHOLE-CLASS DISCUSSION
ELL

(*Math Journal 2,* p. 201)

Ask students to examine the squares they colored on journal page 201. Point out that the three fractions they wrote for each problem all name the same fractional part of the square. Such fractions are called **equivalent fractions.** To support English language learners, have students write *equivalent fractions* next to the examples in the journals.

Students should notice that whenever the total number of equal parts is doubled (or quadrupled), the number of colored parts is also doubled (or quadrupled), but the fractional part represented by the colored parts does not change.

Tell students that in this lesson they will develop a rule for finding equivalent fractions.

▶ Developing a Rule for Finding Equivalent Fractions

WHOLE-CLASS DISCUSSION
ELL

(*Math Journal 2,* p. 201)

In each problem on journal page 201, the numerator and denominator of the first fraction are each multiplied by 2 to obtain the second fraction. They are each multiplied by 4 to obtain the third fraction.

To support English language learners, write the following on the board.

Problem 1:

$\frac{1 * 2}{2 * 2} = \frac{2}{4}$ $\frac{1 * 4}{2 * 4} = \frac{4}{8}$

Problem 2:

$\frac{1 * 2}{4 * 2} = \frac{2}{8}$ $\frac{1 * 4}{4 * 4} = \frac{4}{16}$

Problem 3:

$\frac{3 * \mathbf{2}}{4 * \mathbf{2}} = \frac{6}{8}$ $\qquad$ $\frac{3 * \mathbf{4}}{4 * \mathbf{4}} = \frac{12}{16}$

Write $\frac{2}{2}$ and $\frac{4}{4}$ with colored chalk to emphasize that the numerator and denominator were multiplied by the same number.

The **Equivalent Fractions Rule** can be used to rename any fraction: If the numerator and denominator of a fraction are multiplied by the same nonzero number, the result is a fraction that is equivalent to the original fraction.

Adjusting the Activity

Present a more abstract rationale for this rule:

- ▷ If any number is multiplied by 1, the product is the number you started with.
- ▷ A fraction with the same numerator and denominator, such as $\frac{4}{4}$, is equivalent to 1.
- ▷ Multiplying the numerator and denominator of a fraction by the same number (not 0) is the same as multiplying the fraction by 1. So, the product is equivalent to the original fraction.

AUDITORY ◆ KINESTHETIC ◆ TACTILE ◆ VISUAL

▸ Generating Equivalent Fractions

PARTNER ACTIVITY

(*Math Journal 2,* pp. 342 and 343; *Math Masters,* p. 225)

Have students turn to the Equivalent Names for Fractions table on journal page 342. Ask them to write 10 fractions that are equivalent to $\frac{1}{3}$. Ask students to explain how they know these fractions are all equivalent to $\frac{1}{3}$. Encourage them to use pattern blocks or drawings to support their reasoning.

Have students look for patterns in fractions that are equivalent to $\frac{1}{3}$. Point out how these patterns relate to the Equivalent Fractions Rule.

Ongoing Assessment: Informing Instruction

Watch for students who note that not every pair of equivalent fractions can be found by multiplying (or dividing) by the same *whole* number. *For example:*

$$\frac{3 * 1\frac{1}{3}}{6 * 1\frac{1}{3}} = \frac{4}{8}$$

In this example, the numerator and denominator are both multiplied by the mixed number $1\frac{1}{3}$.

Working in pairs, students use the Equivalent Fractions Rule to find three equivalent fractions for each of the remaining fractions in the table.

Ask students to explain how to use a calculator to find equivalent fractions. Sample answer: Enter a fraction. Multiply it by any fraction whose numerator and denominator are the same.

Student Page

Date Time

Equivalent Names for Fractions

Fraction	Equivalent Fractions	Decimal	Percent
$\frac{0}{2}$		0	0%
$\frac{1}{2}$	$\frac{2}{4}$, $\frac{3}{6}$		
$\frac{2}{2}$		1	100%
$\frac{1}{3}$			
$\frac{2}{3}$			
$\frac{1}{4}$			
$\frac{3}{4}$			
$\frac{1}{5}$			
$\frac{2}{5}$			
$\frac{3}{5}$			
$\frac{4}{5}$			
$\frac{1}{6}$			
$\frac{5}{6}$			
$\frac{1}{8}$			
$\frac{3}{8}$			
$\frac{5}{8}$			
$\frac{7}{8}$			

Math Journal 2, p. 342

Student Page

Date Time

Equivalent Names for Fractions *continued*

Fraction	Equivalent Fractions	Decimal	Percent
$\frac{1}{9}$			
$\frac{2}{9}$			
$\frac{4}{9}$			
$\frac{5}{9}$			
$\frac{7}{9}$			
$\frac{8}{9}$			
$\frac{1}{10}$			
$\frac{3}{10}$			
$\frac{7}{10}$			
$\frac{9}{10}$			
$\frac{1}{12}$			
$\frac{5}{12}$			
$\frac{7}{12}$			
$\frac{11}{12}$			

Math Journal 2, p. 343

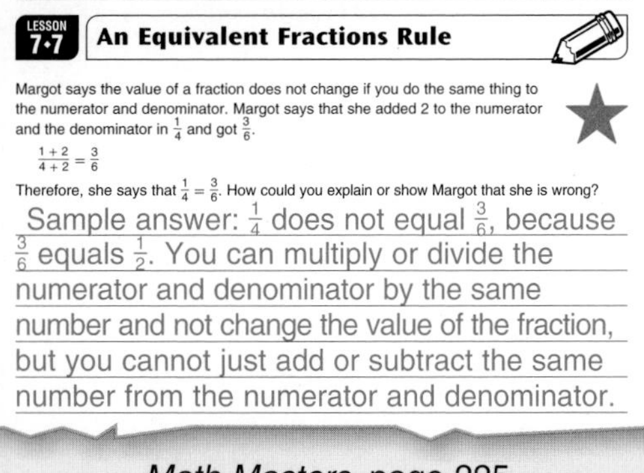

Name Date Time

LESSON 7·7 **An Equivalent Fractions Rule**

Margot says the value of a fraction does not change if you do the same thing to the numerator and denominator. Margot says that she added 2 to the numerator and the denominator in $\frac{1}{4}$ and got $\frac{3}{6}$.

$\frac{1+2}{4+2} = \frac{3}{6}$

Therefore, she says that $\frac{1}{4} = \frac{3}{6}$. How could you explain or show Margot that she is wrong?

Sample answer: $\frac{1}{4}$ does not equal $\frac{3}{6}$, because $\frac{3}{6}$ equals $\frac{1}{2}$. You can multiply or divide the numerator and denominator by the same number and not change the value of the fraction, but you cannot just add or subtract the same number from the numerator and denominator.

Math Masters, page 225

When students complete their work on journal pages 342 and 343, ask them to solve the problem on *Math Masters,* page 225 on their own.

Ongoing Assessment: Recognizing Student Achievement

Math Masters Page 225

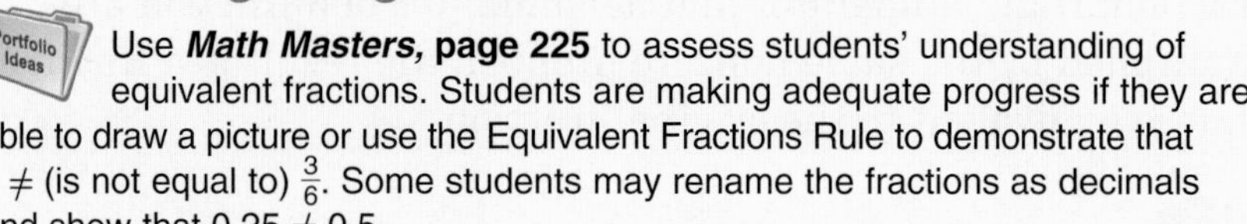

Use ***Math Masters,* page 225** to assess students' understanding of equivalent fractions. Students are making adequate progress if they are able to draw a picture or use the Equivalent Fractions Rule to demonstrate that $\frac{1}{4} \neq$ (is not equal to) $\frac{3}{6}$. Some students may rename the fractions as decimals and show that $0.25 \neq 0.5$.

[Number and Numeration Goal 5]

Adjusting the Activity

Have a table of equivalent fractions available, such as *Math Journal 2,* pages 342 and 343 or *Student Reference Book,* page 51.

AUDITORY ◆ KINESTHETIC ◆ TACTILE ◆ VISUAL

2 Ongoing Learning & Practice

▶ Playing *Fraction Match*

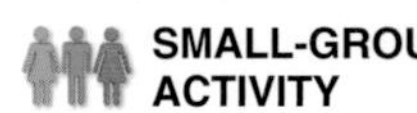

SMALL-GROUP ACTIVITY

(*Student Reference Book,* p. 243; *Math Masters,* pp. 389 and 473–476)

Students play *Fraction Match* to practice naming equivalent fractions. When students have finished playing the game, ask them to select two fractions that match. On an Exit Slip, have them explain how they know the fractions are equivalent.

▶ Fraction and Mixed-Number Addition and Subtraction

INDEPENDENT ACTIVITY

(*Math Journal 2,* p. 200B)

Students add and subtract fractions and mixed numbers. Encourage students to use pattern blocks or a method of their choice to solve the problems.

▶ Math Boxes 7·7

INDEPENDENT ACTIVITY

(*Math Journal 2,* p. 202)

Mixed Practice Math Boxes in this lesson are paired with Math Boxes in Lesson 7-5. The skill in Problem 6 previews Unit 8 content.

Writing/Reasoning Have students write a response to the following: *How did you determine the number of squares you needed to circle in Problem 1?* Sample answer: There are 24 total squares. I divided them into 8 equal groups with 3 squares in each group. Then I circled 3 of the groups.

Student Page

Games

Fraction Match

Materials ☐ 1 deck of *Fraction Match* Cards (*Math Masters,* pp. 473–476)

Players 2 to 4

Skill Recognizing equivalent fractions

Object of the game To match all of your cards and have none left.

Directions

1. Shuffle the deck and deal 7 cards to each player. Place the remaining cards facedown on the table. Turn over the top card and place it beside the deck. This is the *target card.* If a WILD card is drawn, return it to the deck and continue drawing until the first target card is a fraction.
2. Players take turns trying to match the target card with a card from their hand in one of 3 possible ways:
   - a card with an equivalent fraction
   - a card with a like denominator
   - a WILD card.

Example $\frac{2}{3}$ is the target card. It can be matched with:

- an equivalent fraction card such as $\frac{4}{6}$, $\frac{6}{9}$, or $\frac{8}{12}$, or
- a like denominator card such as $\frac{0}{3}$, $\frac{1}{3}$, or $\frac{3}{3}$, or
- a WILD card. The player names any fraction (with a denominator of 2, 3, 4, 5, 6, 8, 9, 10, or 12) that is equivalent to the target card. The player can match $\frac{2}{3}$ by saying $\frac{4}{6}$, $\frac{6}{9}$, or $\frac{8}{12}$. The player may not match $\frac{2}{3}$ by saying $\frac{2}{3}$.

3. If a match is made, the player's matching card is placed on top of the pile and becomes the new target card. It is now the next player's turn. When a WILD card is played, the next player uses the fraction just stated for the new target card.
4. If no match can be made, the player takes 1 card from the deck. If the card drawn matches the target card, it may be played. If not, the player keeps the card and the turn ends.
5. The game is over when one of the players runs out of cards, when there are no cards left in the *Fraction Match* deck, or time runs out. The player with the fewest cards wins.

WILD WILD
WILD
Name an equivalent fraction with a denominator of 2, 3, 4, 5, 6, 8, 9, 10, or 12.

***Student Reference Book,* p. 243**

Study Link 7·7

INDEPENDENT ACTIVITY

(*Math Masters,* p. 223)

Home Connection Students identify the missing numerator or denominator of equivalent fractions to complete name-collection boxes.

3 Differentiation Options

READINESS

SMALL-GROUP ACTIVITY

Identifying Equivalent Fractions on the Fraction Number-Line Poster

5–15 Min

(*Math Masters,* pp. 204, 205, and 388 or 389)

To explore equivalent fractions using a number-line model, have students use a straightedge to vertically line up fractions on the Fraction Number-Line Poster (see the optional Readiness activity in Lesson 7-1) that are equivalent to $\frac{1}{4}$, $\frac{1}{3}$, $\frac{1}{2}$, $\frac{2}{3}$, and so on. Ask students to record the results of their exploration in a Math Log or on an Exit Slip.

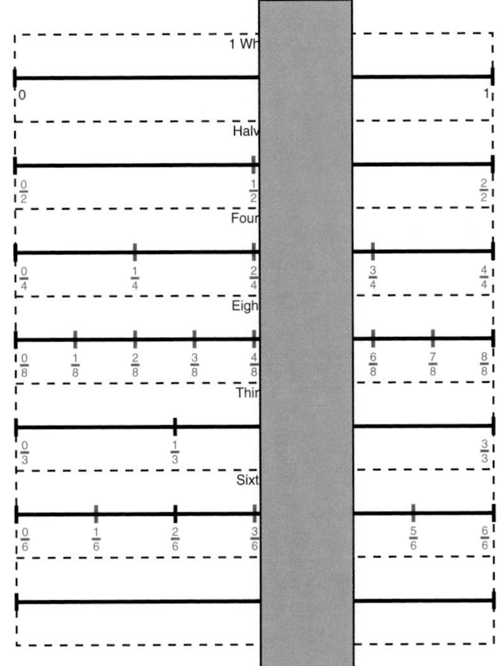

A straightedge highlights equivalent fractions.

Student Page

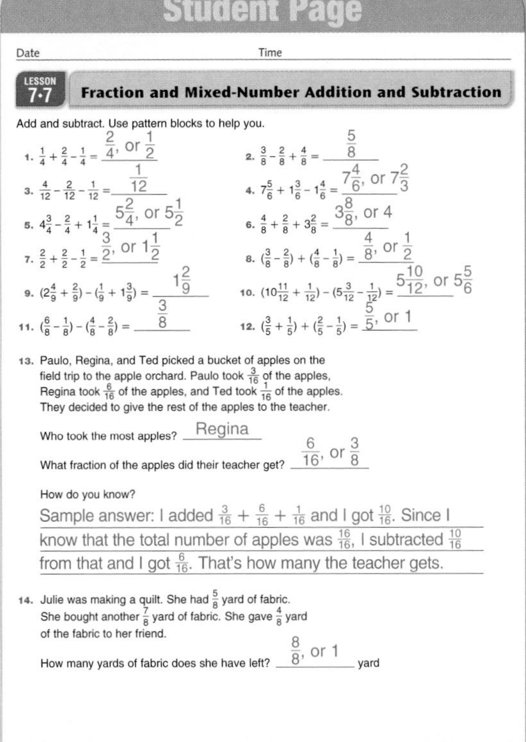

Date ____ Time ____

LESSON 7·7 **Fraction and Mixed-Number Addition and Subtraction**

Add and subtract. Use pattern blocks to help you.

1. $\frac{1}{4}+\frac{2}{4}-\frac{1}{4}=$ $\frac{2}{4}$, or $\frac{1}{2}$
2. $\frac{3}{8}-\frac{2}{8}+\frac{4}{8}=$ $\frac{5}{8}$
3. $\frac{4}{12}-\frac{2}{12}-\frac{1}{12}=$ $\frac{1}{12}$
4. $7\frac{5}{6}+1\frac{3}{6}-1\frac{4}{6}=$ $7\frac{4}{6}$, or $7\frac{2}{3}$
5. $4\frac{3}{4}-\frac{2}{4}+1\frac{1}{4}=$ $5\frac{2}{4}$, or $5\frac{1}{2}$
6. $\frac{4}{8}+\frac{2}{8}+3\frac{2}{8}=$ $3\frac{8}{8}$, or 4
7. $\frac{2}{2}+\frac{2}{2}-\frac{1}{2}=$ $\frac{3}{2}$, or $1\frac{1}{2}$
8. $(\frac{3}{8}-\frac{2}{8})+(\frac{4}{8}-\frac{1}{8})=$ $\frac{4}{8}$, or $\frac{1}{2}$
9. $(2\frac{4}{9}+\frac{2}{9})-(\frac{1}{9}+1\frac{3}{9})=$ $1\frac{2}{9}$
10. $(10\frac{11}{12}+\frac{1}{12})-(5\frac{3}{12}-\frac{1}{12})=$ $5\frac{10}{12}$, or $5\frac{5}{6}$
11. $(\frac{6}{8}-\frac{1}{8})-(\frac{4}{8}-\frac{2}{8})=$ $\frac{3}{8}$
12. $(\frac{3}{5}+\frac{1}{5})+(\frac{2}{5}-\frac{1}{5})=$ $\frac{5}{5}$, or 1

13. Paulo, Regina, and Ted picked a bucket of apples on the field trip to the apple orchard. Paulo took $\frac{3}{16}$ of the apples, Regina took $\frac{6}{16}$ of the apples, and Ted took $\frac{1}{16}$ of the apples. They decided to give the rest of the apples to the teacher.

Who took the most apples? Regina

What fraction of the apples did their teacher get? $\frac{6}{16}$, or $\frac{3}{8}$

How do you know?

Sample answer: I added $\frac{3}{16}+\frac{6}{16}+\frac{1}{16}$ and I got $\frac{10}{16}$. Since I know that the total number of apples was $\frac{16}{16}$, I subtracted $\frac{10}{16}$ from that and I got $\frac{6}{16}$. That's how many the teacher gets.

14. Julie was making a quilt. She had $\frac{5}{8}$ yard of fabric. She bought another $\frac{7}{8}$ yard of fabric. She gave $\frac{4}{8}$ yard of the fabric to her friend.

How many yards of fabric does she have left? $\frac{8}{8}$, or 1 yard

Math Journal 2, p. 200B

Student Page

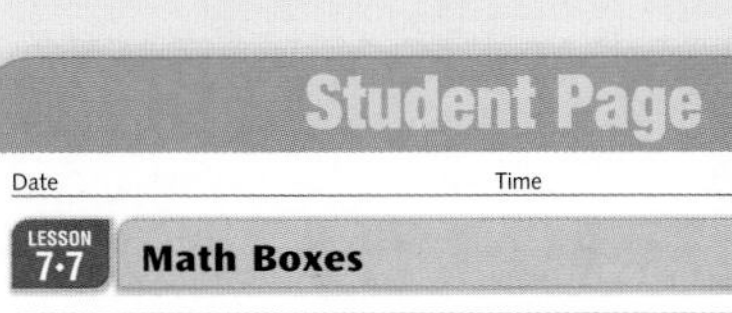

Date ____ Time ____

LESSON 7·7 **Math Boxes**

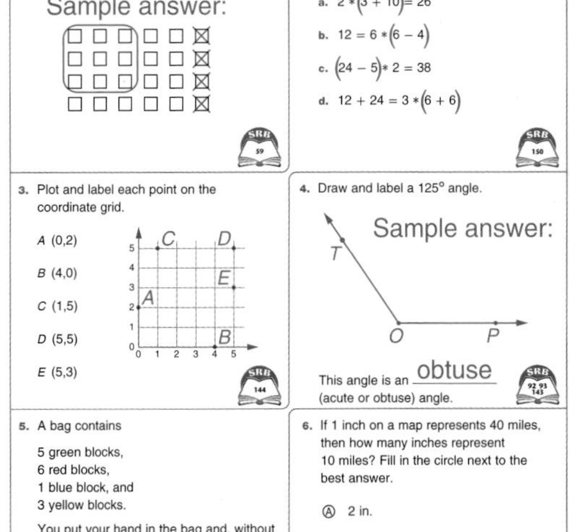

1. Circle $\frac{3}{8}$ of all the squares. Mark Xs on $\frac{1}{6}$ of all the squares.

Sample answer:

2. Insert parentheses to make these number sentences true.

a. 2 ∗ (3 + 10) = 26

b. 12 = 6 ∗ (6 − 4)

c. (24 − 5) ∗ 2 = 38

d. 12 + 24 = 3 ∗ (6 + 6)

3. Plot and label each point on the coordinate grid.

A (0,2)

B (4,0)

C (1,5)

D (5,5)

E (5,3)

4. Draw and label a 125° angle.

Sample answer:

This angle is an obtuse (acute or obtuse) angle.

5. A bag contains

5 green blocks,
6 red blocks,
1 blue block, and
3 yellow blocks.

You put your hand in the bag and, without looking, pull out a block. About what fraction of the time would you expect to get a blue block?

$\frac{1}{15}$

6. If 1 inch on a map represents 40 miles, then how many inches represent 10 miles? Fill in the circle next to the best answer.

Ⓐ 2 in.

● $\frac{1}{4}$ in.

Ⓒ $\frac{1}{2}$ in.

Ⓓ 4 in.

Math Journal 2, p. 202

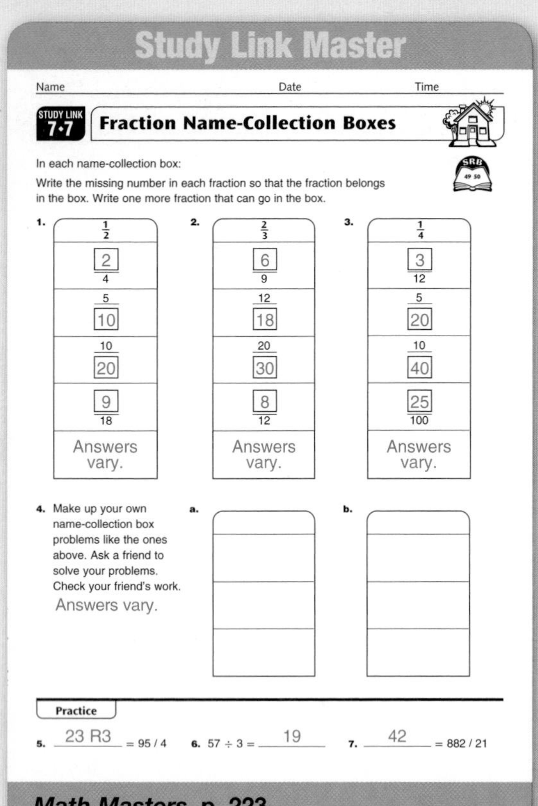

Study Link Master

Name Date Time

STUDY LINK 7·7 **Fraction Name-Collection Boxes**

In each name-collection box:

Write the missing number in each fraction so that the fraction belongs in the box. Write one more fraction that can go in the box.

1. $\frac{1}{2}$	2. $\frac{2}{3}$	3. $\frac{1}{4}$
$\frac{2}{4}$	$\frac{6}{9}$	$\frac{3}{12}$
$\frac{5}{10}$	$\frac{12}{18}$	$\frac{5}{20}$
$\frac{10}{20}$	$\frac{20}{30}$	$\frac{10}{40}$
$\frac{9}{18}$	$\frac{8}{12}$	$\frac{25}{100}$
Answers vary.	Answers vary.	Answers vary.

4. Make up your own name-collection box problems like the ones above. Ask a friend to solve your problems. Check your friend's work.
Answers vary.

a. b.

Practice

5. 23 R3 = 95 / 4
6. 57 ÷ 3 = 19
7. 42 = 882 / 21

Math Masters, p. 223

ENRICHMENT

15–30 Min

▶ Investigating Egyptian Fractions

(*Math Masters,* p. 224)

To apply students' understanding of fraction addition and equivalent fractions, have students investigate how early Egyptians represented a fraction as the sum of unit fractions.

To solve Problems 5 and 6, students need to divide the rectangle into more regions than indicated by the denominator of the fraction.

NOTE Egyptians also used the fraction $\frac{2}{3}$.

EXTRA PRACTICE

INDEPENDENT ACTIVITY

5–15 Min

▶ Completing Name-Collection Boxes

(*Math Masters,* p. 397)

To provide practice generating equivalent names for fractions, have students complete name-collection boxes. Encourage students to complete the boxes with equivalent fractions and mathematical expressions that include fractions.

Use *Math Masters,* page 397 to create problems to meet the needs of individual students or have students create and solve their own problems.

EXTRA PRACTICE

5–15 Min

▶ *5-Minute Math*

To offer students more experience with equivalent fractions, see *5-Minute Math,* pages 1, 17, 79, and 165.

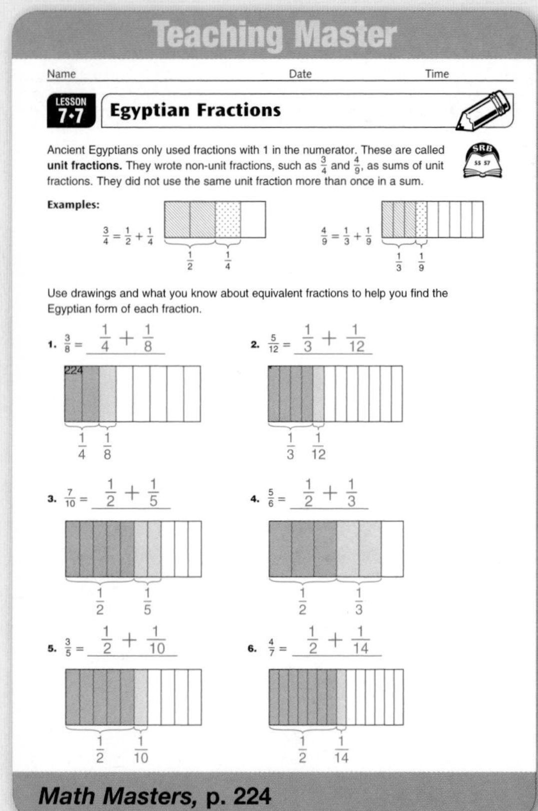

Teaching Master

Name Date Time

LESSON 7·7 **Egyptian Fractions**

Ancient Egyptians only used fractions with 1 in the numerator. These are called **unit fractions.** They wrote non-unit fractions, such as $\frac{3}{4}$ and $\frac{4}{9}$, as sums of unit fractions. They did not use the same unit fraction more than once in a sum.

Examples:

$\frac{3}{4} = \frac{1}{2} + \frac{1}{4}$ $\frac{4}{9} = \frac{1}{3} + \frac{1}{9}$

Use drawings and what you know about equivalent fractions to help you find the Egyptian form of each fraction.

1. $\frac{3}{8} = \frac{1}{4} + \frac{1}{8}$
2. $\frac{5}{12} = \frac{1}{3} + \frac{1}{12}$
3. $\frac{7}{10} = \frac{1}{2} + \frac{1}{5}$
4. $\frac{5}{6} = \frac{1}{2} + \frac{1}{3}$
5. $\frac{3}{5} = \frac{1}{2} + \frac{1}{10}$
6. $\frac{4}{7} = \frac{1}{2} + \frac{1}{14}$

Math Masters, p. 224

7•8 Fractions and Decimals

Objectives To provide experience with renaming fractions as decimals and decimals as fractions; and to develop an understanding of the relationship between fractions and division.

www.everydaymathonline.com

ePresentations

eToolkit

Algorithms Practice

EM Facts Workshop Game™

Family Letters

Assessment Management

Common Core State Standards

Curriculum Focal Points

Interactive Teacher's Lesson Guide

1 Teaching the Lesson

Key Concepts and Skills

- Read and write decimals through hundredths.
  [Number and Numeration Goal 1]
- Represent a shaded region as a fraction and a decimal.
  [Number and Numeration Goal 2]
- Rename fractions with 10 and 100 in the denominator as decimals.
  [Number and Numeration Goal 5]
- Use equal sharing to solve division problems.
  [Operations and Computation Goal 4]

Key Activities

Students rename fractions as decimals and decimals as fractions. They also explore the relationship between fractions and division.

Ongoing Assessment: Recognizing Student Achievement
Use journal page 203.
[Number and Numeration Goal 5]

Materials

Math Journal 2, pp. 203, 342, and 343
Student Reference Book, p. 46
Study Link 7•7
Math Masters, p. 426 (optional)
transparency of *Math Masters,* p. 426 ◆ base-10 blocks ◆ calculator ◆ slate ◆ overhead base-10 blocks (optional)

2 Ongoing Learning & Practice

Math Boxes 7•8
Math Journal 2, p. 204
Students practice and maintain skills through Math Box problems.

Study Link 7•8
Math Masters, p. 226
Students practice and maintain skills through Study Link activities.

3 Differentiation Options

READINESS

Creating Base-10 Block Designs
Math Masters, p. 442
base-10 blocks
Students make a design with base-10 blocks, copy the design on a grid, and write a decimal and a fraction to describe what part of the grid is covered by the blocks.

ENRICHMENT

Finding Fractions, Decimals, and Percents on Grids
Math Masters, p. 227
Students shade a 10-by-10 grid to represent fractions and find the percent and decimal equivalencies.

ENRICHMENT

Designing a Baseball Cap Rack
Math Masters, pp. 227A and 227B
Students use fractions with denominators of 10; 100; or 1,000 to design a baseball cap rack.

EXTRA PRACTICE

Taking a 50-Facts Test
Math Masters, pp. 412 and 414; p. 416 (optional)
pen or colored pencil
Students take a 50-facts test. They use a line graph to record individual and optional class scores.

Advance Preparation

***Teacher's Reference Manual,* Grades 4–6** pp. 62, 63, 153, 154

Getting Started

Mental Math and Reflexes

Write a fraction on the board. Students write an equivalent fraction on their slates. *Suggestions:*

Sample answers:

●○○ $\frac{1}{2}$ $\frac{2}{4}$, $\frac{3}{6}$
$\frac{1}{4}$ $\frac{2}{8}$, $\frac{3}{12}$
$\frac{1}{3}$ $\frac{2}{6}$, $\frac{3}{9}$

●●○ $\frac{1}{5}$ $\frac{2}{10}$, $\frac{3}{15}$
$\frac{50}{100}$ $\frac{5}{10}$, $\frac{25}{50}$
$\frac{3}{4}$ $\frac{6}{8}$, $\frac{9}{12}$

●●● $\frac{6}{9}$ $\frac{2}{3}$, $\frac{12}{18}$
$\frac{5}{8}$ $\frac{10}{16}$, $\frac{50}{80}$
$\frac{3}{5}$ $\frac{6}{10}$, $\frac{9}{15}$

Math Message

Write the following fractions as decimals:

$\frac{1}{10}$ $\frac{32}{100}$ $\frac{7}{10}$ $\frac{9}{100}$

Study Link 7·7 Follow-Up

Have students compare answers and share the name-collection boxes they created.

1 Teaching the Lesson

▶ Math Message Follow-Up

WHOLE-CLASS DISCUSSION

(*Math Masters,* p. 426)

Display a transparency of *Math Masters,* page 426 as you discuss the answers. Remind students that the square is the "whole." You can color the grid sections to show fractional parts or cover them with base-10 blocks.

Color or cover one column of the bottom grid.

- What fractional part of the square is this? $\frac{1}{10}$

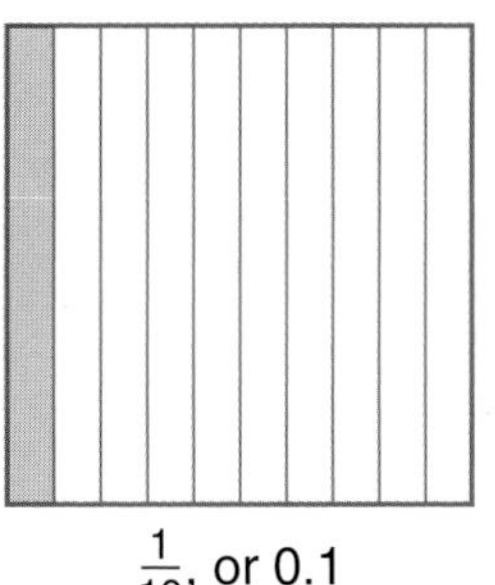

$\frac{1}{10}$, or 0.1

- How would you write $\frac{1}{10}$ as a decimal? 0.1

Repeat with other fractions in tenths, including $\frac{3}{10}$ and $\frac{7}{10}$.

Adjusting the Activity

ELL

Provide students with base-10 blocks and a copy of *Math Masters,* page 426, so they can model the decimal numbers at their desks.

AUDITORY ◆ KINESTHETIC ◆ TACTILE ◆ VISUAL

Teaching Aid Master

Name Date Time

Base-10 Grids

Math Masters, p. 426

Next, color (or cover) one small square of the top grid on the transparency.

- What fractional part of the square is this? $\frac{1}{100}$

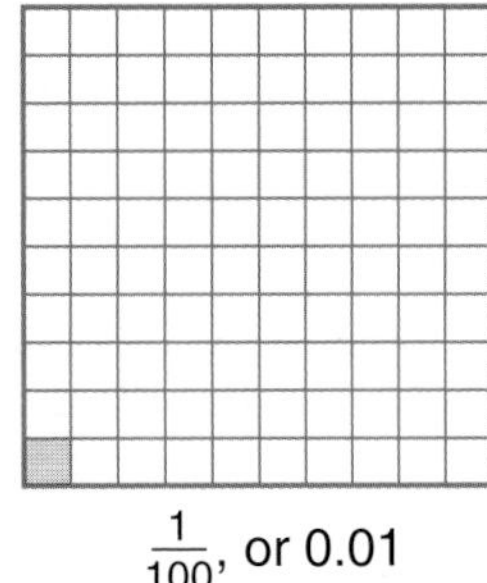

- How would you write $\frac{1}{100}$ as a decimal? 0.01

Repeat with other fractions in hundredths, including $\frac{32}{100}$ and $\frac{9}{100}$. Also, give students practice converting decimals into fractions; for example, 0.3 and 0.25.

Tell students that in this lesson they will use a base-10 grid as a tool to help them rename fractions as decimals.

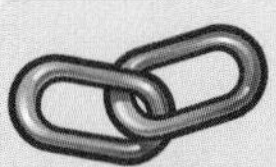

Links to the Future

Do not be concerned with reducing fractions to simplest form when converting between decimals and fractions. At this stage, it is enough for students simply to make the conversions. Naming fractions in simplest form is a Grade 5 Goal.

Renaming Fractions as Decimals and Decimals as Fractions

INDEPENDENT ACTIVITY

(*Math Journal 2,* pp. 203, 342, and 343; *Math Masters,* p. 426)

Students complete journal page 203. Discuss answers, using a transparency of *Math Masters,* page 426. For each problem, ask by which number the numerator and denominator were multiplied to obtain the second fraction.

Ask students to record the decimals in the Equivalent Names for Fractions table on journal pages 342 and 343.

Ongoing Assessment: Recognizing Student Achievement

Journal page 203 Problems 1–4, 7, and 8

Use **journal page 203, Problems 1–4, 7, and 8** to assess students' ability to rename tenths and hundredths as decimals with the assistance of a visual model. Students are making adequate progress if they are able to name the number of tenths or hundredths shaded on the grid as a fraction and rename the fraction as a decimal. Some students may be able to solve Problems 5 and 6 on journal page 203, which do not include a visual prompt.

[Number and Numeration Goal 5]

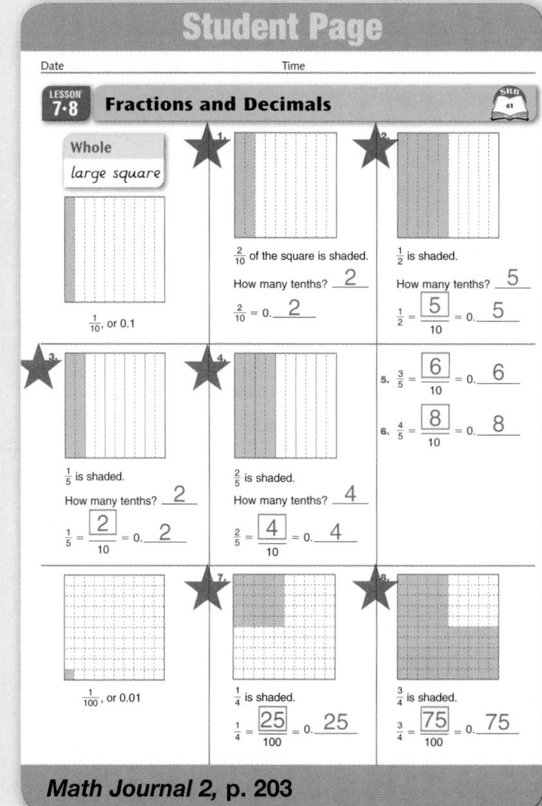

Student Page

Date Time

LESSON 7·8 **Fractions and Decimals**

Whole: large square

$\frac{1}{10}$, or 0.1

1. $\frac{2}{10}$ of the square is shaded. How many tenths? 2. $\frac{2}{10}$ = 0.2

2. $\frac{1}{2}$ is shaded. How many tenths? 5. $\frac{1}{2} = \frac{5}{10}$ = 0.5

3. $\frac{1}{5}$ is shaded. How many tenths? 2. $\frac{1}{5} = \frac{2}{10}$ = 0.2

4. $\frac{2}{5}$ is shaded. How many tenths? 4. $\frac{2}{5} = \frac{4}{10}$ = 0.4

5. $\frac{3}{5} = \frac{6}{10}$ = 0.6

6. $\frac{4}{5} = \frac{8}{10}$ = 0.8

$\frac{1}{100}$, or 0.01

7. $\frac{1}{4}$ is shaded. $\frac{1}{4} = \frac{25}{100}$ = 0.25

8. $\frac{3}{4}$ is shaded. $\frac{3}{4} = \frac{75}{100}$ = 0.75

Math Journal 2, p. 203

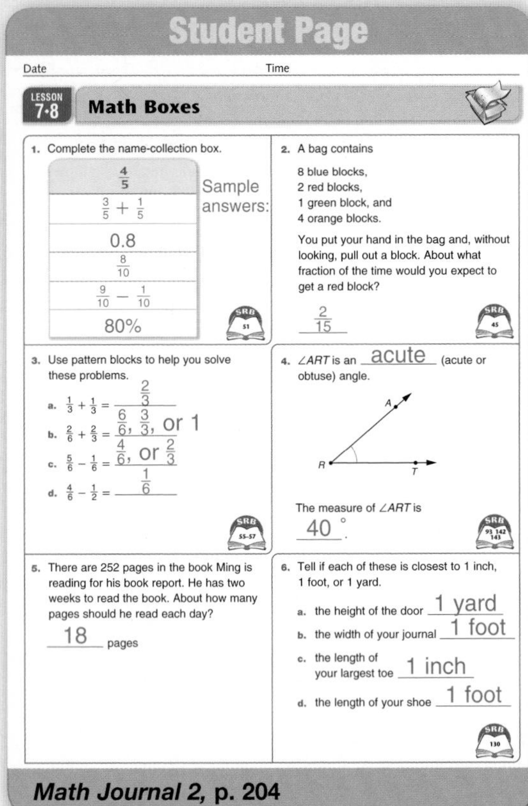

Student Page

Date Time

LESSON 7·8 **Math Boxes**

1. Complete the name-collection box.

$\frac{4}{5}$
$\frac{3}{5} + \frac{1}{5}$
0.8
$\frac{8}{10}$
$\frac{9}{10} - \frac{1}{10}$
80%

Sample answers:

SRB 31

2. A bag contains

8 blue blocks,
2 red blocks,
1 green block, and
4 orange blocks.

You put your hand in the bag and, without looking, pull out a block. About what fraction of the time would you expect to get a red block?

$\frac{2}{15}$

SRB 45

3. Use pattern blocks to help you solve these problems.

a. $\frac{1}{3} + \frac{1}{3} = \frac{2}{3}$

b. $\frac{2}{6} + \frac{2}{3} = \frac{6}{6}, \frac{3}{3}$, or 1

c. $\frac{5}{6} - \frac{1}{6} = \frac{4}{6}$, or $\frac{2}{3}$

d. $\frac{4}{6} - \frac{1}{2} = \frac{1}{6}$

SRB 55-57

4. ∠*ART* is an acute (acute or obtuse) angle.

The measure of ∠*ART* is 40°.

SRB 95 142 143

5. There are 252 pages in the book Ming is reading for his book report. He has two weeks to read the book. About how many pages should he read each day?

18 pages

6. Tell if each of these is closest to 1 inch, 1 foot, or 1 yard.

a. the height of the door 1 yard

b. the width of your journal 1 foot

c. the length of your largest toe 1 inch

d. the length of your shoe 1 foot

SRB 130

Math Journal 2, p. 204

Renaming Fractions as Decimals with a Calculator

WHOLE-CLASS ACTIVITY

(*Math Journal 2*, p. 203)

Use Problem 7 on journal page 203 to model renaming fractions as decimals on a calculator.

For the TI-15:

▷ Enter the fraction $\frac{1}{4}$ (press 1 [n] 4 [d]).

▷ Then press [Enter] [F↔D]. 0.25

For the Casio *fx*-55:

▷ Enter the fraction $\frac{1}{4}$ (press 1 [b/c] 4).

▷ Then press [F↔D]. 0.25

Use Problem 8 to model renaming a decimal as a fraction.

For the TI-15:

▷ Enter the decimal 0.75, then press [Enter] [F↔D]. $\frac{75}{100}$

For the Casio *fx*-55:

▷ Enter the decimal 0.75, then press [F↔D]. $\frac{3}{4}$

Discussing Fractions and Division

WHOLE-CLASS DISCUSSION

(*Student Reference Book*, p. 46)

Read and discuss "Fractions and Division" on page 46 of the *Student Reference Book*. Have students apply their understanding of division to equal-sharing division problems. *For example:*

▷ Nina and her mother baked 4 dozen cookies for the book club meeting. The club has 8 members. How many cookies are there for each member?

Four dozen equals 4 ∗ 12, or 48. The number models 48/8 = 6, 48 ÷ 8 = 6, and $\frac{48}{8} = 6$ fit this problem. The first and second number models suggest "dealing out" the 48 cookies to the 8 club members. Each member would get 6 cookies. The third number model, $\frac{48}{8} = 6$, suggests dividing each cookie into eighths and giving $\frac{1}{8}$ of every cookie to each person. Each person would end up with 48 eighths. If the 48 eighths were reassembled, they would be equivalent to 6 cookies.

NOTE $\frac{48}{8}$ is called an *improper fraction* because the numerator is greater than the denominator. Improper fractions have numerators that are greater than or equal to their denominators.

Also discuss problems in which the divisor is greater than the dividend. *For example:*

▷ Adam ordered 3 pizzas for a party. There will be 5 people at the party. How much pizza is there for each person?

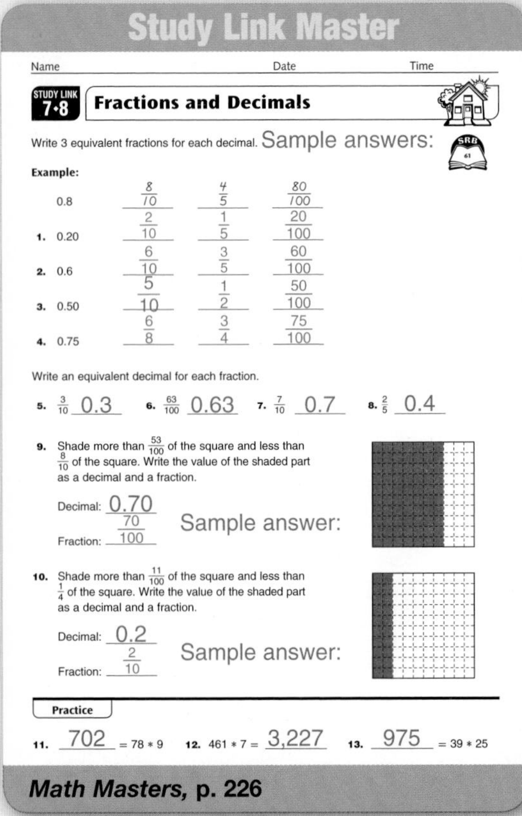

Study Link Master

Name Date Time

STUDY LINK 7·8 **Fractions and Decimals**

Write 3 equivalent fractions for each decimal. Sample answers:

SRB 61

Example: 0.8	$\frac{8}{10}$	$\frac{4}{5}$	$\frac{80}{100}$
1. 0.20	$\frac{2}{10}$	$\frac{1}{5}$	$\frac{20}{100}$
2. 0.6	$\frac{6}{10}$	$\frac{3}{5}$	$\frac{60}{100}$
3. 0.50	$\frac{5}{10}$	$\frac{1}{2}$	$\frac{50}{100}$
4. 0.75	$\frac{6}{8}$	$\frac{3}{4}$	$\frac{75}{100}$

Write an equivalent decimal for each fraction.

5. $\frac{3}{10}$ 0.3 6. $\frac{63}{100}$ 0.63 7. $\frac{7}{10}$ 0.7 8. $\frac{2}{5}$ 0.4

9. Shade more than $\frac{53}{100}$ of the square and less than $\frac{8}{10}$ of the square. Write the value of the shaded part as a decimal and a fraction.

Sample answer:

Decimal: 0.70

Fraction: $\frac{70}{100}$

10. Shade more than $\frac{11}{100}$ of the square and less than $\frac{1}{4}$ of the square. Write the value of the shaded part as a decimal and a fraction.

Sample answer:

Decimal: 0.2

Fraction: $\frac{2}{10}$

Practice

11. 702 = 78 ∗ 9 12. 461 ∗ 7 = 3,227 13. 975 = 39 ∗ 25

Math Masters, p. 226

Point out that this problem and the cookie problem are both about sharing. The main difference is that in this problem, each share is less than one whole pizza. Draw 3 pizzas on the board or on the overhead transparency, and divide each one into fifths for the 5 people. If **A**dam's guests are named **B**ob, **C**harles, **D**arryl, and **E**d, the pizzas could be shared in the following way:

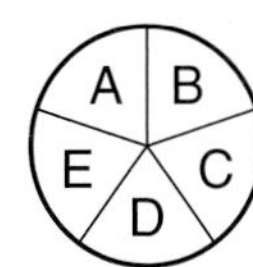

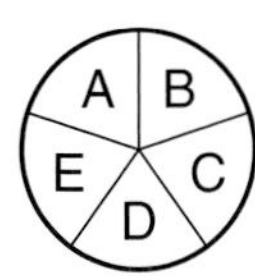

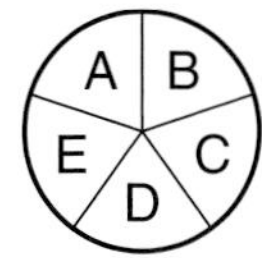

Help students see how the number model $3 / 5 = \frac{3}{5}$ fits this problem. The left side, 3 / 5, suggests dividing 3 pizzas among 5 people. The right side, $\frac{3}{5}$, tells how much each person would get.

Explain that in high school and beyond, the symbol ÷ is almost never used for division. Division is usually shown with a slash (/) or a fraction bar (—).

2 Ongoing Learning & Practice

Math Boxes 7•8

(*Math Journal 2,* p. 204)

Mixed Practice Math Boxes in this lesson are paired with Math Boxes in Lesson 7-6. The skill in Problem 6 previews Unit 8 content.

Writing/Reasoning Have students write a response to the following: *Explain how you solved Problem 2.* Sample answer: There are 15 blocks in the bag, and 2 of them are red. So the chance of getting a red block is $\frac{2}{15}$.

Study Link 7•8

(*Math Masters,* p. 226)

Home Connection Students rename decimals as fractions and fractions as decimals. They color fractional parts of a base-10 grid and write the value of the shaded part as a decimal and a fraction.

Teaching Master

Name Date Time

LESSON 7•8 **Designing a Baseball Cap Rack**

Karen plans to design and construct two identical horizontal racks to display her baseball cap collection. She has 12 different caps to hang on pegs. Karen's sister suggested that she add extra pegs for caps she may get in the future. Karen measured the width of some caps and decided that the pegs need to be 2 decimeters ($\frac{2}{10}$ meter) apart. Also, in order to fit on her wall, each rack cannot be more than 160 centimeters long.

Help Karen design one of the identical racks. Use metric units. Fill in the blanks below as you create the design. Sample answers are given.

1. Each of Karen's racks will have 8 pegs for hats.
2. The total length of the rack will be 160 centimeters.
3. The first peg will be 10 centimeters from the edge of the rack.
4. In the space below, draw a rough sketch of the rack. Include the measurements in your sketch.

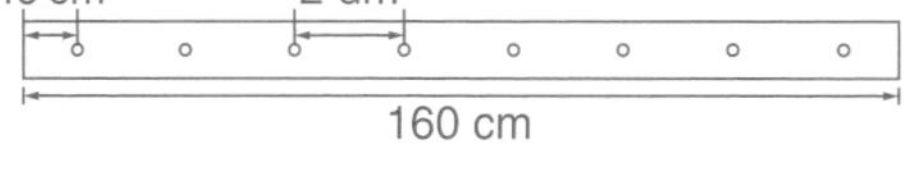

5. Write a fraction addition number sentence to show the total length of the rack.
Sample answer: $\frac{10}{100} + \frac{2}{10} + \frac{2}{10} + \frac{2}{10} + \frac{2}{10} + \frac{2}{10} + \frac{2}{10} + \frac{2}{10} + \frac{10}{100} = \frac{160}{100}$ m, or 160 cm
6. Could there be 9 pegs on the rack? Explain your answer.
No. Nine hats would require about 200 cm, and the rack can only be 160 cm long.

Math Masters, **p. 227A**

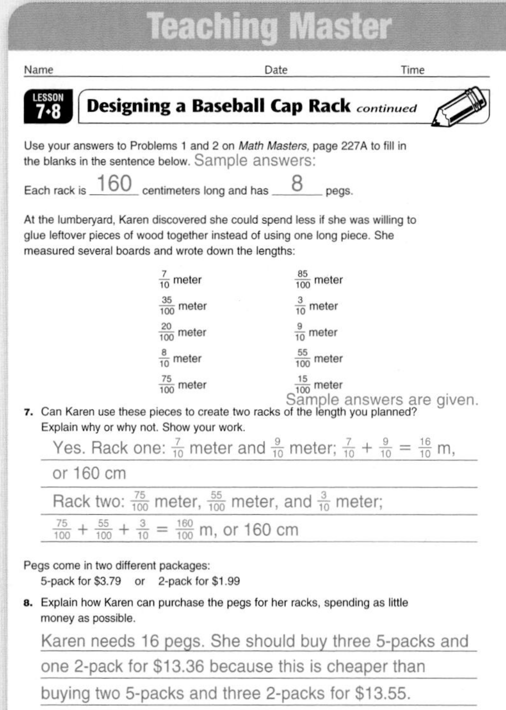

Teaching Master

Name Date Time

LESSON 7•8 **Designing a Baseball Cap Rack** *continued*

Use your answers to Problems 1 and 2 on *Math Masters,* page 227A to fill in the blanks in the sentence below. Sample answers:

Each rack is 160 centimeters long and has 8 pegs.

At the lumberyard, Karen discovered she could spend less if she was willing to glue leftover pieces of wood together instead of using one long piece. She measured several boards and wrote down the lengths:

$\frac{7}{10}$ meter	$\frac{85}{100}$ meter
$\frac{35}{100}$ meter	$\frac{3}{10}$ meter
$\frac{20}{100}$ meter	$\frac{9}{10}$ meter
$\frac{8}{10}$ meter	$\frac{55}{100}$ meter
$\frac{75}{100}$ meter	$\frac{15}{100}$ meter

Sample answers are given.

7. Can Karen use these pieces to create two racks of the length you planned? Explain why or why not. Show your work.
Yes. Rack one: $\frac{7}{10}$ meter and $\frac{9}{10}$ meter; $\frac{7}{10} + \frac{9}{10} = \frac{16}{10}$ m, or 160 cm
Rack two: $\frac{75}{100}$ meter, $\frac{55}{100}$ meter, and $\frac{3}{10}$ meter; $\frac{75}{100} + \frac{55}{100} + \frac{3}{10} = \frac{160}{100}$ m, or 160 cm

Pegs come in two different packages:
5-pack for \$3.79 or 2-pack for \$1.99

8. Explain how Karen can purchase the pegs for her racks, spending as little money as possible.
Karen needs 16 pegs. She should buy three 5-packs and one 2-pack for \$13.36 because this is cheaper than buying two 5-packs and three 2-packs for \$13.55.

Math Masters, **p. 227B**

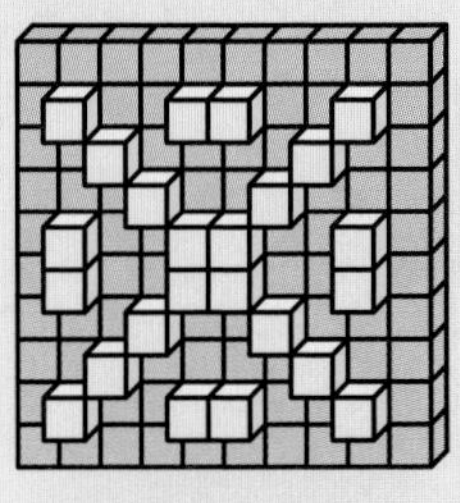

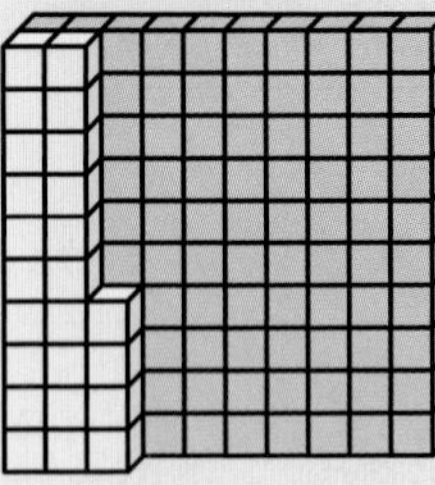

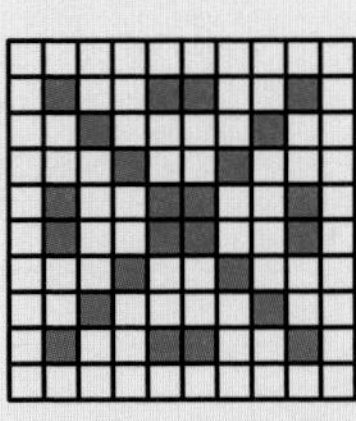

Decimal: 0.24

Fraction: $\frac{24}{100}$

3 Differentiation Options

READINESS

INDEPENDENT ACTIVITY

▶ Creating Base-10 Block Designs

30+ Min

(*Math Masters,* p. 442)

To explore representing fractions and decimals on a base-10 grid, have students make a design on a base-10 block flat with cubes and then copy the design onto one of the grids shown on *Math Masters,* page 442. Students determine how much of the flat is covered by their design and express this number as a decimal and a fraction. (*See margin.*) Students may choose to exchange as many cubes as possible for longs, which would result in a certain number of longs (tenths) and cubes (hundredths).

ENRICHMENT

PARTNER ACTIVITY

▶ Finding Fractions, Decimals, and Percents on Grids

15–30 Min

(*Math Masters,* p. 227)

To further investigate fraction, decimal, and percent equivalencies, have students shade a base-10 grid to show $\frac{1}{8}$, $\frac{1}{3}$, $\frac{1}{6}$, and $\frac{4}{6}$. Encourage students to discuss patterns they see and strategies they used. Ask: *How could you have found the percent equivalent for $\frac{4}{6}$ without shading the grid?* Sample answer: Use the answer for $\frac{1}{6}$ and multiply by 4.

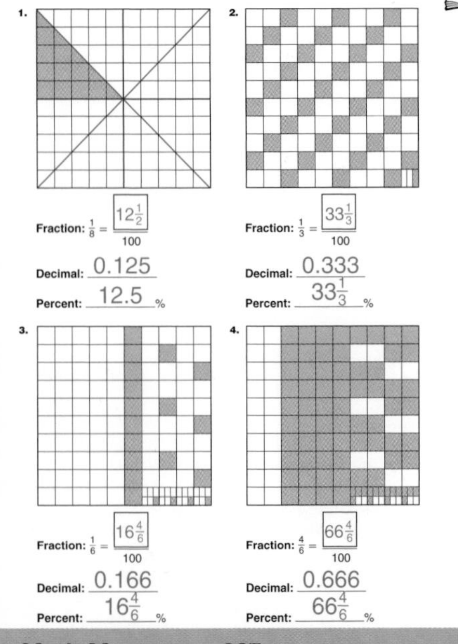

Teaching Master

Name Date Time

LESSON 7·8 **Fraction, Decimal, and Percent Grids**

Fill in the missing numbers. Shade the grids. Sample answers:

1. Fraction: $\frac{1}{8} = \frac{12\frac{1}{2}}{100}$
Decimal: 0.125
Percent: 12.5 %

2. Fraction: $\frac{1}{3} = \frac{33\frac{1}{3}}{100}$
Decimal: 0.333
Percent: $33\frac{1}{3}$ %

3. Fraction: $\frac{1}{6} = \frac{16\frac{4}{6}}{100}$
Decimal: 0.166
Percent: $16\frac{4}{6}$ %

4. Fraction: $\frac{4}{6} = \frac{66\frac{4}{6}}{100}$
Decimal: 0.666
Percent: $66\frac{4}{6}$ %

Math Masters, p. 227

ENRICHMENT

PARTNER ACTIVITY

▶ Designing a Baseball Cap Rack

15–30 Min

(*Math Masters,* pp. 227A and 227B)

To further investigate the relationships among fractions with denominators of 10; 100; or 1,000, have students design two identical racks to display a baseball cap collection. Encourage students to work with a partner to complete the activity.

EXTRA PRACTICE

SMALL-GROUP ACTIVITY

▶ Taking a 50-Facts Test

5–15 Min

(*Math Masters,* pp. 412, 414, and 416)

See Lesson 3-4 for details regarding the administration of the 50-facts test and the recording and graphing of individual and optional class results.

7•9 Comparing Fractions

Objective To provide practice ordering sets of fractions.

Technology Resources www.everydaymathonline.com

ePresentations

eToolkit

Algorithms Practice

EM Facts Workshop Game™

Family Letters

Assessment Management

Common Core State Standards

Curriculum Focal Points

Interactive Teacher's Lesson Guide

1 Teaching the Lesson

Key Concepts and Skills

- Compare fractions.
  [Number and Numeration Goal 6]
- Order fractions.
  [Number and Numeration Goal 6]
- Explain strategies used to compare and order fractions.
  [Number and Numeration Goal 6]
- Use patterns to compare and order fractions.
  [Patterns, Functions, and Algebra Goal 1]

Key Activities

Students use Fraction Cards to determine whether a fraction is greater or less than another fraction and then order sets of Fraction Cards from smallest to largest. They also compare fractions to $\frac{1}{2}$ and write different sets of fractions in order.

Ongoing Assessment: Informing Instruction See page 617.

Ongoing Assessment: Recognizing Student Achievement Use journal page 206.
[Number and Numeration Goal 6]

Materials

Math Journal 2, pp. 205 and 206
Study Link 7•8
Fraction Cards (*Math Journal 2,* Activity Sheets 5 and 6) ◆ slate ◆ calculator (optional) ◆ pattern blocks (optional)

2 Ongoing Learning & Practice

Playing *Over and Up Squares*
Student Reference Book, p. 257
Math Masters, p. 494
per partnership: 2 six-sided dice ◆ colored pencils
Students practice plotting ordered number pairs on a coordinate grid.

Playing *Angle Add-Up*
Math Masters, pp. 507–509
per partnership: 4 of each of number cards 1–8 and 1 of each of number cards 0 and 9 (from the Everything Math Deck, if available) ◆ full-circle protractor (transparency of *Math Masters,* p. 439) ◆ dry-erase markers ◆ straightedge
Students draw angles and then use addition and subtraction to find the measures of unknown angles.

Math Boxes 7•9
Math Journal 2, p. 207
Students practice and maintain skills through Math Box problems.

Study Link 7•9
Math Masters, p. 228
Students practice and maintain skills through Study Link activities.

3 Differentiation Options

READINESS

Sorting Fractions
Math Masters, p. 229
scissors ◆ tape
Students explore relative sizes of fractions.

ENRICHMENT

Using Digits to Create Fractions
Math Masters, p. 230
Students use digits to create specified fractions.

EXTRA PRACTICE

Playing *Fraction Top-It*
Student Reference Book, p. 247
Math Masters, p. 506
Fraction Cards (*Math Journal 2,* Activity Sheets 5 and 6)
Students practice comparing and ordering fractions.

Advance Preparation

***Teacher's Reference Manual,* Grades 4–6** pp. 77–79

Getting Started

Mental Math and Reflexes

Write fraction addition problems involving tenths and hundredths on the board. Students find the value of x. *Suggestions:*

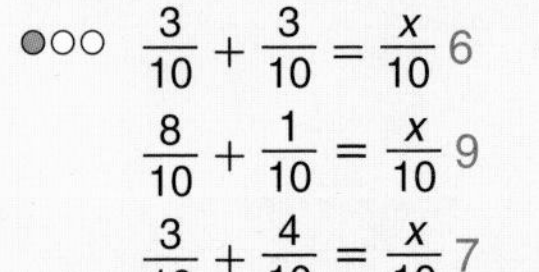

●○○ $\frac{3}{10} + \frac{3}{10} = \frac{x}{10}$ 6

$\frac{8}{10} + \frac{1}{10} = \frac{x}{10}$ 9

$\frac{3}{10} + \frac{4}{10} = \frac{x}{10}$ 7

●●○ $\frac{7}{10} + \frac{2}{10} = \frac{x}{100}$ 90

$\frac{4}{10} + \frac{2}{10} = \frac{x}{100}$ 60

$\frac{5}{10} + \frac{5}{10} = \frac{x}{100}$ 100

●●● $\frac{5}{10} + \frac{34}{100} = \frac{x}{100}$ 84

$\frac{9}{10} + \frac{2}{100} = \frac{x}{100}$ 92

$\frac{6}{10} + \frac{19}{100} = \frac{x}{100}$ 79

Math Message

Work with a partner to solve Problems 1 and 2 on journal page 205.

Study Link 7·8 Follow-Up

Partners compare answers. Ask students to explain how they solved Problems 9 and 10.

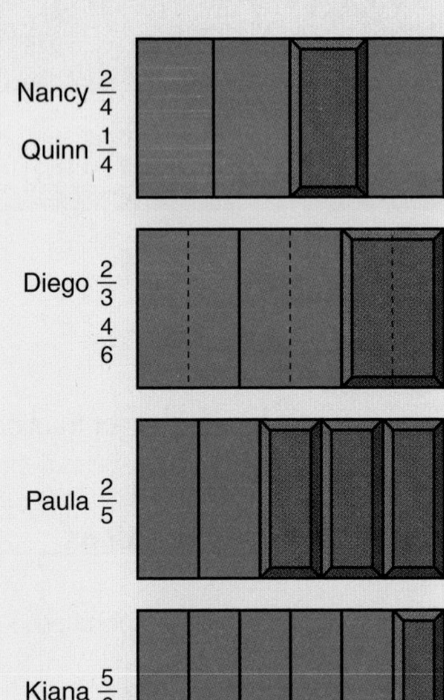

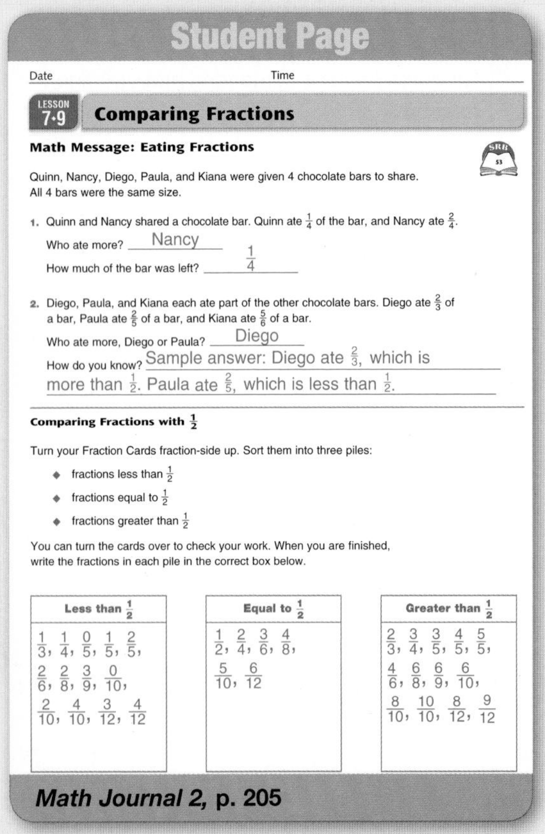

Student Page

Date Time

LESSON 7·9 **Comparing Fractions**

Math Message: Eating Fractions

Quinn, Nancy, Diego, Paula, and Kiana were given 4 chocolate bars to share. All 4 bars were the same size.

1. Quinn and Nancy shared a chocolate bar. Quinn ate $\frac{1}{4}$ of the bar, and Nancy ate $\frac{2}{4}$.
   Who ate more? Nancy
   How much of the bar was left? $\frac{1}{4}$

2. Diego, Paula, and Kiana each ate part of the other chocolate bars. Diego ate $\frac{2}{3}$ of a bar, Paula ate $\frac{2}{5}$ of a bar, and Kiana ate $\frac{5}{6}$ of a bar.
   Who ate more, Diego or Paula? Diego
   How do you know? Sample answer: Diego ate $\frac{2}{3}$, which is more than $\frac{1}{2}$. Paula ate $\frac{2}{5}$, which is less than $\frac{1}{2}$.

Comparing Fractions with $\frac{1}{2}$

Turn your Fraction Cards fraction-side up. Sort them into three piles:

- fractions less than $\frac{1}{2}$
- fractions equal to $\frac{1}{2}$
- fractions greater than $\frac{1}{2}$

You can turn the cards over to check your work. When you are finished, write the fractions in each pile in the correct box below.

Less than $\frac{1}{2}$	Equal to $\frac{1}{2}$	Greater than $\frac{1}{2}$
$\frac{1}{3}, \frac{1}{4}, \frac{0}{5}, \frac{1}{5}, \frac{2}{5}, \frac{2}{6}, \frac{2}{8}, \frac{3}{9}, \frac{0}{10}, \frac{2}{10}, \frac{4}{10}, \frac{3}{12}, \frac{4}{12}$	$\frac{1}{2}, \frac{2}{4}, \frac{3}{6}, \frac{4}{8}, \frac{5}{10}, \frac{6}{12}$	$\frac{2}{3}, \frac{3}{4}, \frac{3}{5}, \frac{4}{5}, \frac{5}{5}, \frac{4}{6}, \frac{6}{8}, \frac{6}{9}, \frac{6}{10}, \frac{8}{10}, \frac{10}{10}, \frac{8}{12}, \frac{9}{12}$

Math Journal 2, p. 205

1 Teaching the Lesson

▶ Math Message Follow-Up

WHOLE-CLASS DISCUSSION

(*Math Journal 2*, p. 205)

Students should have had no trouble concluding that Nancy ate more chocolate than Quinn (Problem 1), but they may have had more difficulty comparing the amounts eaten by Diego and Paula (Problem 2). Ask them to share their solution strategies. Students might have used any of these strategies:

▷ If Diego's chocolate bar were divided into 3 equal pieces and Paula's into 5 equal pieces, Diego's pieces would have been larger than Paula's pieces. There would be more chocolate in two of Diego's pieces than in two of Paula's pieces, so Diego ate more chocolate than Paula did.

▷ Diego ate more than half a bar ($\frac{2}{3}$ is more than half). Paula ate less than half a bar ($\frac{2}{5}$ is less than half). So Diego ate more.

▷ Only $\frac{1}{3}$ of Diego's bar is left, but $\frac{3}{5}$ of Paula's bar is left. Since less of Diego's bar is left, he ate more.

Next, ask students who ate more, Diego or Kiana. Have them explain their answers. Students might have used any of the following strategies:

▷ If Diego's chocolate bar were divided into 6 equal pieces, he would have eaten 4 of the pieces because $\frac{4}{6}$ is equivalent to $\frac{2}{3}$. Diego ate $\frac{4}{6}$ of a bar and Kiana ate $\frac{5}{6}$ of a bar, so Kiana ate more chocolate.

▷ Kiana has only $\frac{1}{6}$ of her bar left, but Diego has $\frac{1}{3}$ left. Because $\frac{1}{6}$ is less than $\frac{1}{3}$, Kiana has less left over, so she must have eaten more.

Finally, have students determine who ate more chocolate, Diego or Nancy, and give their reasoning. Discuss how they know Diego ate more.

Ordering Fractions

WHOLE-CLASS ACTIVITY

(*Math Journal 2,* Activity Sheets 5 and 6)

Tell the class that in this lesson they will use their Fraction Cards (Activity Sheets 5 and 6) as a tool to help them compare and order fractions.

NOTE Fractions with 1 in the numerator are called **unit fractions.**

Like Numerators

Have students take out all the Fraction Cards with 1 in the numerator ($\frac{1}{2}$, $\frac{1}{3}$, $\frac{1}{4}$, and $\frac{1}{5}$) and turn them fraction-side up. Ask them to line up the cards from smallest (at the left) to largest (at the right). They can check by turning the cards over. Ask:

- What pattern do you notice? As the denominator gets larger, the fraction gets smaller.
- What is the reason for this pattern? As the denominator gets larger, the pieces get smaller because the whole is being divided into more pieces.

Ongoing Assessment: Informing Instruction

Watch for students who reason that, for example, 5 is more than 4, so fifths must be larger than fourths. Remind students that the denominator represents the number of pieces the whole is divided into.

Like Denominators

Have students take out all the Fraction Cards with 10 in the denominator ($\frac{0}{10}$, $\frac{2}{10}$, $\frac{4}{10}$, $\frac{5}{10}$, $\frac{6}{10}$, $\frac{8}{10}$, and $\frac{10}{10}$). Ask them to turn the cards fraction-side up and arrange them in a row from smallest fraction to largest fraction.

- What pattern do you see? The larger the numerator is, the bigger the fraction is.
- What is the reason for this pattern? All the pieces are the same size, so more pieces make a bigger fraction.

Different Numerators and Denominators

Have students take out the cards for $\frac{1}{4}$, $\frac{2}{4}$, $\frac{2}{3}$, $\frac{2}{5}$, and $\frac{6}{8}$, and turn them fraction-side up. Have students line up these cards from smallest fraction to largest fraction.

▷ Tell students to place the $\frac{2}{4}$ card in front of them.

▷ Name one of the other cards ($\frac{1}{4}$, $\frac{2}{3}$, $\frac{2}{5}$, or $\frac{6}{8}$), and ask students whether the fraction is more or less than $\frac{2}{4}$ and how they know.

▷ Ask students to place that card in the correct position—to the right or left of the $\frac{2}{4}$ card to indicate if it is smaller or larger than $\frac{2}{4}$.

▷ Name the rest of the cards one by one. Students place the cards in order while you ask for justification for each card's placement.

Adjusting the Activity

Draw a number line from 0 to 1 on the board. Have students estimate the relative size of the fractions and order the fractions by writing them on the number line.

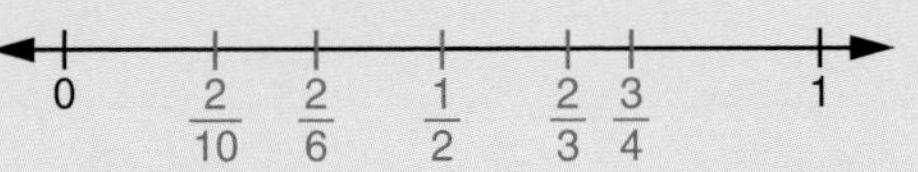

AUDITORY ◆ KINESTHETIC ◆ TACTILE ◆ VISUAL

NOTE On journal page 206, you may want students to identify the relative positions of the fractions in Problems 1–4 on a number line.

Student Page

Date ______ Time ______

LESSON 7·9 Ordering Fractions

Write the fractions in order from smallest to largest.

1. $\frac{4}{10}, \frac{7}{10}, \frac{8}{10}, \frac{2}{10}, \frac{1}{10}$

$\frac{1}{10}$ (smallest), $\frac{2}{10}$, $\frac{4}{10}$, $\frac{7}{10}$, $\frac{8}{10}$ (largest)

2. $\frac{1}{4}, \frac{1}{2}, \frac{1}{9}, \frac{1}{5}, \frac{1}{100}$

$\frac{1}{100}$ (smallest), $\frac{1}{9}$, $\frac{1}{5}$, $\frac{1}{4}$, $\frac{1}{2}$ (largest)

3. $\frac{2}{4}, \frac{2}{2}, \frac{2}{9}, \frac{2}{5}, \frac{2}{100}$

$\frac{2}{100}$ (smallest), $\frac{2}{9}$, $\frac{2}{5}$, $\frac{2}{4}$, $\frac{2}{2}$ (largest)

4. $\frac{4}{25}, \frac{1}{25}, \frac{7}{8}, \frac{6}{12}, \frac{7}{15}$

$\frac{1}{25}$ (smallest), $\frac{4}{25}$, $\frac{7}{15}$, $\frac{6}{12}$, $\frac{7}{8}$ (largest)

5. Choose 5 fractions or mixed numbers. Write them in order from smallest to largest.

Answers vary.

smallest ______ largest

6. Which fraction is larger: $\frac{2}{5}$ or $\frac{2}{7}$? $\frac{2}{5}$ Explain how you know.

Sample answer: $\frac{2}{5}$ has a smaller denominator than $\frac{2}{7}$, so each fifth is bigger than each seventh.

Math Journal 2, p. 206

Have students work with partners to order the following Fraction Cards: $\frac{1}{2}$, $\frac{2}{10}$, $\frac{2}{6}$, $\frac{2}{3}$, and $\frac{3}{4}$. They should begin with the cards fraction-side up. They can check the order by turning the cards over. Discuss strategies.

▶ Comparing Fractions with $\frac{1}{2}$

PARTNER ACTIVITY

(*Math Journal 2,* p. 205)

Have students follow the directions at the bottom of journal page 205 to sort the Fraction Cards into three categories: less than $\frac{1}{2}$, equal to $\frac{1}{2}$, and greater than $\frac{1}{2}$. Ask students to look at the equal-to-$\frac{1}{2}$ pile. Have them explain how they know that the fractions in that pile are equal to $\frac{1}{2}$. Encourage them to draw pictures or use pattern blocks to justify their answers.

Encourage partnerships to compare their sort to that of another group before recording their answers on journal page 205.

Adjusting the Activity

Have students explain how a calculator can help determine whether a fraction is less than $\frac{1}{2}$, equal to $\frac{1}{2}$, or greater than $\frac{1}{2}$. *Possible strategies:*

▷ Subtract the fraction from $\frac{1}{2}$. If the difference is positive, it is less than $\frac{1}{2}$. If the difference is 0, it is equal to $\frac{1}{2}$. If the difference is negative, it is greater than $\frac{1}{2}$.

▷ Add the fraction to $\frac{1}{2}$. If the sum is less than 1, the fraction is less than $\frac{1}{2}$. If the sum is 1, then the fraction equals $\frac{1}{2}$. If the sum is greater than 1, the fraction is greater than $\frac{1}{2}$.

▷ Find the decimal equivalent by dividing the numerator by the denominator, and compare each decimal to 0.5.

AUDITORY ◆ KINESTHETIC ◆ TACTILE ◆ VISUAL

▶ Ordering Fractions

PARTNER ACTIVITY

(*Math Journal 2,* p. 206)

Students write fractions in order from smallest to largest. They choose their own set of fractions or mixed numbers and write them in order.

Ongoing Assessment: Recognizing Student Achievement

Journal page 206 Problem 6 ★

Use **journal page 206, Problem 6** to assess students' ability to compare fractions and explain their strategies. Students are making adequate progress if their explanations include information such as the following:

▷ $\frac{2}{5}$ is larger than $\frac{2}{7}$.

▷ The numerators are the same, so each fraction has the same number of pieces.

▷ The size of the pieces (denominator) needs to be compared. The smaller the denominator is, the bigger the pieces are.

Some students may include pictures to support their answer or use a calculator to rename the fractions as decimals.

[Number and Numeration Goal 6]

2 Ongoing Learning & Practice

Playing *Over and Up Squares*

(*Student Reference Book,* p. 257; *Math Masters,* p. 494)

Students play *Over and Up Squares* to practice plotting ordered number pairs on a coordinate grid. See Lesson 6-9 for additional information.

Playing *Angle Add-Up*

(*Math Masters,* pp. 507–509)

To further explore the idea that angle measures are additive, have students draw angles and then use addition and subtraction to find the measures of unknown angles. Note that Round 1 requires students to use addition to find the unknown angle measure. Rounds 2 and 3 require subtraction. The given measures of 90° and 180° degrees provide practice with complementary and supplementary angles.

Math Boxes 7·9

INDEPENDENT ACTIVITY

(*Math Journal 2,* p. 207)

Mixed Practice Math Boxes in this lesson are paired with Math Boxes in Lessons 7-11 and 7-12a. The skill in Problem 6 previews Unit 8 content.

Writing/Reasoning Have students write a response to the following: *Explain why $\frac{2}{2}$ inch might have been given as a possible answer in Problem 3.* Sample answer: Some students might incorrectly think that to subtract fractions you subtract the numerators and denominators. If this is done, then an incorrect answer is $\frac{3}{4}$ in. $- \frac{1}{2}$ in. $= \frac{2}{2}$ in.

Study Link 7·9

(*Math Masters,* p. 228)

Home Connection Students compare and order fractions.

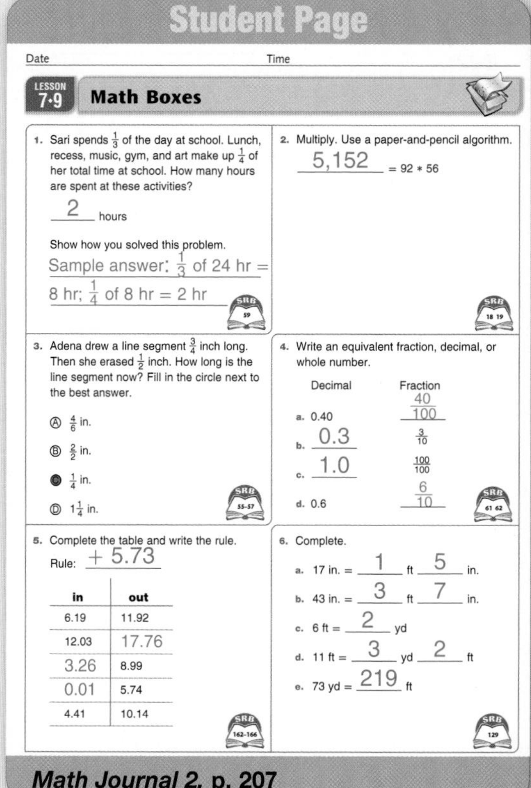

Student Page

Date ______ Time ______

LESSON 7·9 **Math Boxes**

1. Sari spends $\frac{1}{3}$ of the day at school. Lunch, recess, music, gym, and art make up $\frac{1}{4}$ of her total time at school. How many hours are spent at these activities?

   2 hours

   Show how you solved this problem.
   Sample answer: $\frac{1}{3}$ of 24 hr = 8 hr; $\frac{1}{4}$ of 8 hr = 2 hr

   SRB 59

2. Multiply. Use a paper-and-pencil algorithm.

   5,152 = 92 * 56

   SRB 18 19

3. Adena drew a line segment $\frac{3}{4}$ inch long. Then she erased $\frac{1}{2}$ inch. How long is the line segment now? Fill in the circle next to the best answer.

   Ⓐ $\frac{4}{6}$ in.
   Ⓑ $\frac{2}{2}$ in.
   ● $\frac{1}{4}$ in.
   Ⓓ $1\frac{1}{4}$ in.

   SRB 55-57

4. Write an equivalent fraction, decimal, or whole number.

	Decimal	Fraction
a.	0.40	$\frac{40}{100}$
b.	0.3	$\frac{3}{10}$
c.	1.0	$\frac{100}{100}$
d.	0.6	$\frac{6}{10}$

   SRB 61 62

5. Complete the table and write the rule.

   Rule: + 5.73

in	out
6.19	11.92
12.03	17.76
3.26	8.99
0.01	5.74
4.41	10.14

   SRB 162-166

6. Complete.

   a. 17 in. = 1 ft 5 in.
   b. 43 in. = 3 ft 7 in.
   c. 6 ft = 2 yd
   d. 11 ft = 3 yd 2 ft
   e. 73 yd = 219 ft

   SRB 129

Math Journal 2, p. 207

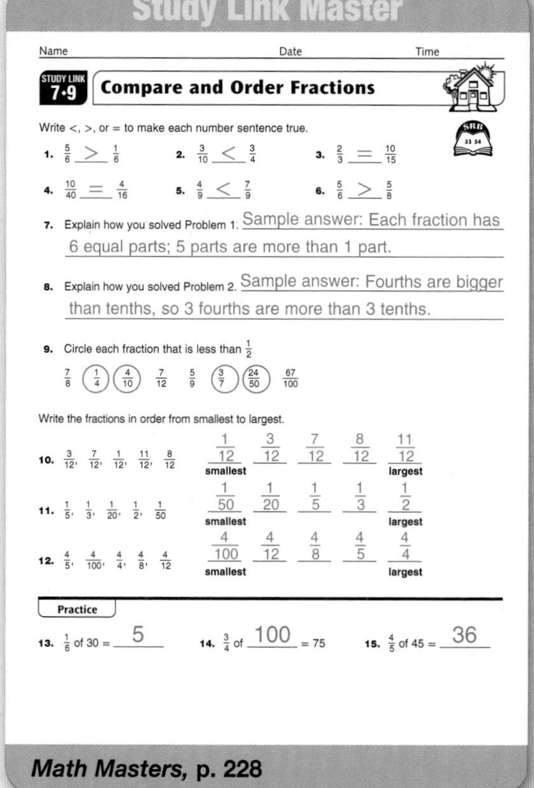

Study Link Master

Name ______ Date ______ Time ______

STUDY LINK 7·9 **Compare and Order Fractions**

Write <, >, or = to make each number sentence true. SRB 53 54

1. $\frac{5}{6} > \frac{1}{6}$
2. $\frac{3}{10} < \frac{3}{4}$
3. $\frac{2}{3} = \frac{10}{15}$
4. $\frac{10}{40} = \frac{4}{16}$
5. $\frac{4}{9} < \frac{7}{9}$
6. $\frac{5}{6} > \frac{5}{8}$
7. Explain how you solved Problem 1. Sample answer: Each fraction has 6 equal parts; 5 parts are more than 1 part.
8. Explain how you solved Problem 2. Sample answer: Fourths are bigger than tenths, so 3 fourths are more than 3 tenths.
9. Circle each fraction that is less than $\frac{1}{2}$

   $\frac{7}{8}$ ($\frac{1}{4}$) ($\frac{4}{10}$) $\frac{7}{12}$ $\frac{5}{9}$ ($\frac{3}{7}$) ($\frac{24}{50}$) $\frac{67}{100}$

Write the fractions in order from smallest to largest.

10. $\frac{3}{12}, \frac{7}{12}, \frac{1}{12}, \frac{11}{12}, \frac{8}{12}$ — $\frac{1}{12}$ (smallest), $\frac{3}{12}$, $\frac{7}{12}$, $\frac{8}{12}$, $\frac{11}{12}$ (largest)
11. $\frac{1}{5}, \frac{1}{3}, \frac{1}{20}, \frac{1}{2}, \frac{1}{50}$ — $\frac{1}{50}$ (smallest), $\frac{1}{20}$, $\frac{1}{5}$, $\frac{1}{3}$, $\frac{1}{2}$ (largest)
12. $\frac{4}{5}, \frac{4}{100}, \frac{4}{4}, \frac{4}{8}, \frac{4}{12}$ — $\frac{4}{100}$ (smallest), $\frac{4}{12}$, $\frac{4}{8}$, $\frac{4}{5}$, $\frac{4}{4}$ (largest)

Practice

13. $\frac{1}{6}$ of 30 = 5
14. $\frac{3}{4}$ of 100 = 75
15. $\frac{4}{5}$ of 45 = 36

Math Masters, p. 228

Name Date Time

LESSON 7·9 **Two-Digit Fractions**

Any fraction can be made from the digits 0–9. A fraction can have two digits like $\frac{3}{4}$ or $\frac{8}{7}$ or many digits like $\frac{347}{983}$. A fraction may not have a denominator of 0.

SRB 53

Use any two digits to make each of the following fractions.

1. The smallest possible fraction greater than 0 $\frac{1}{9}$
2. The largest possible fraction $\frac{9}{1}$
3. The largest fraction less than 1 $\frac{8}{9}$
4. The smallest fraction greater than $\frac{1}{2}$ $\frac{5}{9}$
5. Make up your own problem. Answers vary.

Math Masters, page 230

3 Differentiation Options

READINESS

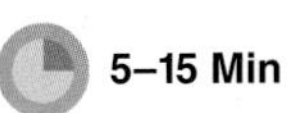

PARTNER ACTIVITY

▶ Sorting Fractions

5–15 Min

(*Math Masters,* p. 229)

To explore comparing fractions, have students sort fractions represented as area and number-line models into groups according to their relative size. When they finish the sort, have students describe how they chose their groups.

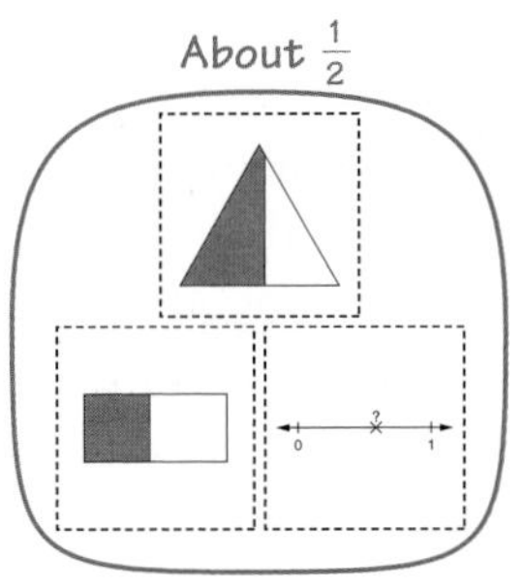

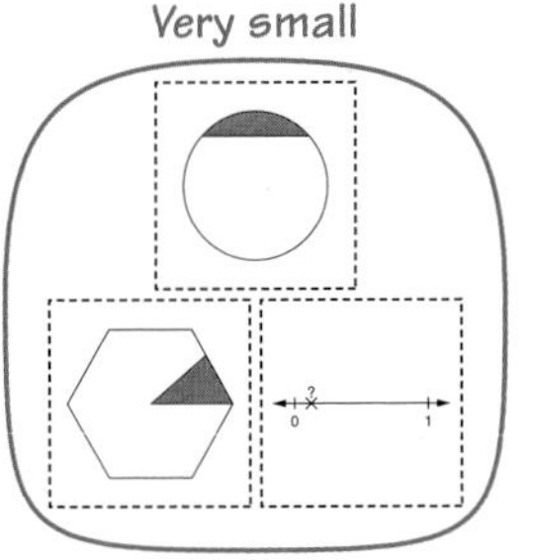

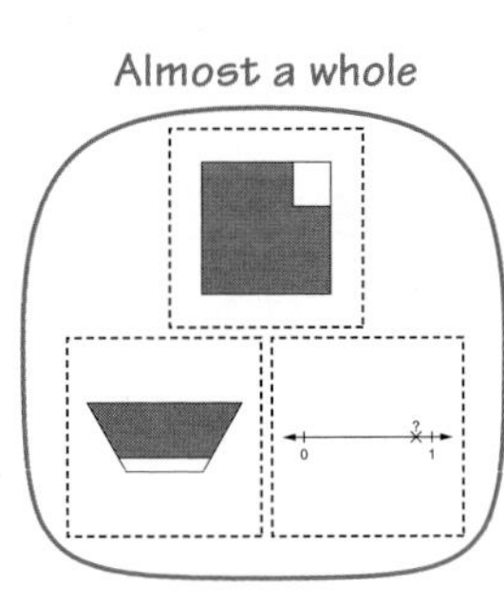

ENRICHMENT

PARTNER ACTIVITY

▶ Using Digits to Create Fractions

5–15 Min

(*Math Masters,* p. 230)

To extend students' ability to compare fractions, have them use digits to create specified fractions. For each problem, have students share their reasoning.

EXTRA PRACTICE

SMALL-GROUP ACTIVITY

▶ Playing *Fraction Top-It*

5–15 Min

(*Student Reference Book,* p. 247; *Math Masters,* p. 506)

To practice comparing and ordering fractions, have students play *Fraction Top-It*. See Lesson 7-10 for additional information.

Student Page

Games

Fraction Top-It

Materials ☐ 1 set of Fraction Cards 1 and 2 (*Math Journal* 2, Activity Sheets 5 and 6)

Players 2 to 4

Skill Comparing fractions

Object of the game To collect the most cards.

Directions

Advance Preparation Before beginning the game, write the fraction for the shaded part on the back of each card.

1. Deal the same number of cards, fraction-side up, to each player:
   - If there are 2 players, 16 cards each.
   - If there are 3 players, 10 cards each.
   - If there are 4 players, 8 cards each.
2. Players spread their cards out, fraction-side up, so that all of the cards may be seen.
3. Starting with the dealer and going in a clockwise direction, each player plays one card. Place the cards fraction-side up on the table.
4. The player with the largest fraction wins the round and takes the cards. Players may check who has the largest fraction by turning over the cards and comparing the amounts shaded.
5. If there is a tie for the largest fraction, each player plays another card. The player with the largest fraction takes all the cards from both plays.
6. The player who takes the cards starts the next round.
7. The game is over when all cards have been played. The player who takes the most cards wins.

Fraction Cards 1

Fraction Cards 2

***Student Reference Book,* p. 247**

7•10 The ONE for Fractions

Objective To guide students as they find the whole, or the ONE, for given fractions.

www.everydaymathonline.com

ePresentations

eToolkit

Algorithms Practice

EM Facts Workshop Game™

Family Letters

Assessment Management

Common Core State Standards

Curriculum Focal Points

Interactive Teacher's Lesson Guide

1 Teaching the Lesson

Key Concepts and Skills

- Given a fractional part of a region, name the ONE.
  [Number and Numeration Goal 2]
- Given a fractional part of a collection, name the ONE.
  [Number and Numeration Goal 2]
- Identify a hexagon, trapezoid, and rhombus.
  [Geometry Goal 2]

Key Activities

Students use pattern blocks and counters to find the ONE for given fractions, and they solve "What is the ONE?" problems.

Materials

Math Journal 2, pp. 208 and 209
Study Link 7•9
pattern blocks ◆ beans, pennies, or other counters ◆ slate ◆ Geometry Template ◆ overhead pattern blocks (optional)

2 Ongoing Learning & Practice

Playing *Fraction Top-It*
Student Reference Book, p. 247
Math Masters, p. 506
Fraction Cards (*Math Journal 2,* Activity Sheets 5 and 6)
Students practice comparing fractions.

Ongoing Assessment: Recognizing Student Achievement
Use *Math Masters,* page 506.
[Number and Numeration Goal 6]

Plotting Insect Data
Math Journal 2, pp. 209A and 209B
Students plot insect lengths on a line plot.

Math Boxes 7•10
Math Journal 2, p. 210
Students practice and maintain skills through Math Box problems.

Study Link 7•10
Math Masters, p. 231
Students practice and maintain skills through Study Link activities.

3 Differentiation Options

ENRICHMENT

Playing *Getting to One*
Student Reference Book, p. 248
calculator
Students apply their proportional reasoning skills and their understanding of the concept of ONE.

ENRICHMENT

Finding the ONE
Math Masters, p. 232
Students determine how a candy bar was divided.

Advance Preparation

***Teacher's Reference Manual,* Grades 4–6** pp. 143–147

Getting Started

Mental Math and Reflexes

Write fractions with denominators of 10 or 100 on the board, and have students write the equivalent decimals on their slates. Then write decimals on the board, and have students write the equivalent fractions or mixed numbers on their slates. Do not insist that the fractions be in simplest form. *Suggestions:*

●○○ $\frac{34}{100}$ 0.34
$\frac{80}{100}$ 0.80, or 0.8
0.6 $\frac{6}{10}$
0.3 $\frac{3}{10}$

●●○ $\frac{5}{100}$ 0.05
$\frac{9}{100}$ 0.09
0.03 $\frac{3}{100}$
0.065 $\frac{65}{1,000}$

●●● $\frac{132}{100}$ 1.32
$\frac{206}{100}$ 2.06
1.99 $\frac{199}{100}$ or $1\frac{99}{100}$
65.79 $\frac{6,579}{100}$, or $65\frac{79}{100}$

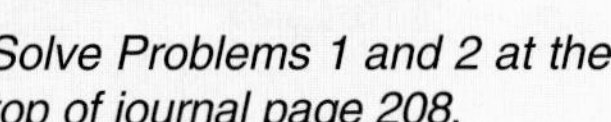

Math Message

Solve Problems 1 and 2 at the top of journal page 208.

Study Link 7·9 Follow-Up

Have students share how they know the fractions in Problems 3 and 4 are equivalent. Encourage students to use a model to explain.

NOTE The blocks that make up the ONE can often be arranged in several ways. Investigating various arrangements is worthwhile, but in this lesson, it does not matter how the blocks in the ONE are arranged.

1 Teaching the Lesson

▶ Math Message Follow-Up

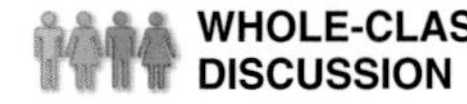

WHOLE-CLASS DISCUSSION

Discuss students' answers. For Problem 2, have volunteers describe or show how they solved the problem.

Tell students that in this lesson they will use pattern blocks and counters as tools to help them find the ONE.

▶ Using Pattern Blocks to Find the ONE

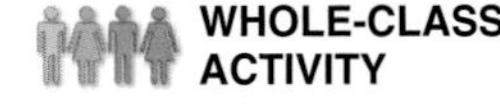

WHOLE-CLASS ACTIVITY

Pose problems like those below in which a part is given and students are to find the whole, or the ONE. Display one or two pattern blocks on the overhead projector, and tell what fraction is represented by this block or pair of blocks. Then direct students to use their pattern blocks to show the ONE. Discuss solutions. *Suggestions:*

- If [triangle] is $\frac{1}{2}$, then what is the ONE? 1 wide rhombus or equivalent
- If [trapezoid] is $\frac{3}{4}$, then what is the ONE? 2 wide rhombuses or equivalent
- If [hexagon] is $\frac{2}{3}$, then what is the ONE? 3 trapezoids or equivalent
- If [two squares] is $\frac{1}{3}$, then what is the ONE? 6 squares
- If [two wide rhombuses] is $\frac{1}{2}$, then what is the ONE? 4 wide rhombuses

Using Counters to Find the ONE

WHOLE-CLASS ACTIVITY

Pose more problems in which part of a collection of objects is given and students are to find the ONE. Display beans, pennies, or other counters on the overhead projector. Tell and write what fraction is represented. Ask students to use their slates to write the number of counters in the ONE. *Suggestions:*

- If ○○○ is $\frac{1}{2}$, then what is the ONE? 6 counters
- If ○○○ is $\frac{1}{3}$, then what is the ONE? 9 counters
- If ○○○○ is $\frac{2}{5}$, then what is the ONE? 10 counters
- If ○○○○ is $\frac{2}{3}$, then what is the ONE? 6 counters
- If ○○ is $\frac{1}{4}$, then what is the ONE? 8 counters

Adjusting the Activity

ELL

Draw boxes around counters to create a visual representation of the problems.

Example 1:

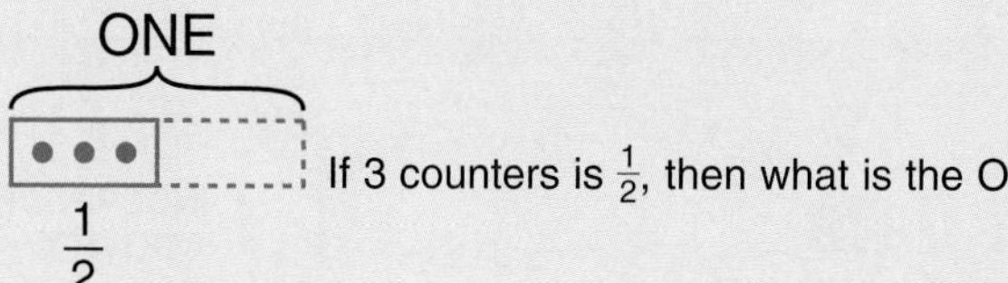

If 3 counters is $\frac{1}{2}$, then what is the ONE?

Example 2:

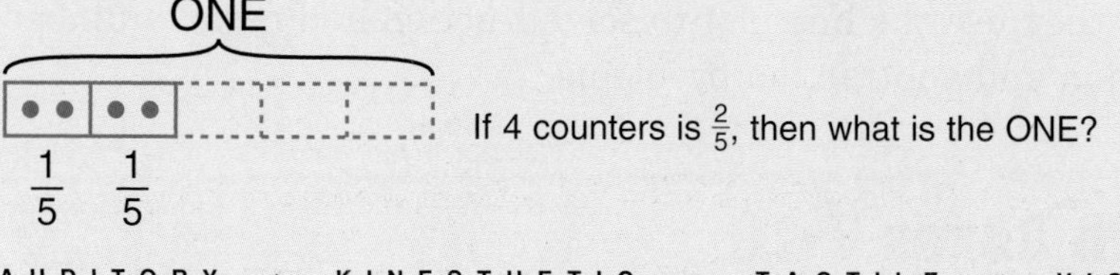

If 4 counters is $\frac{2}{5}$, then what is the ONE?

AUDITORY • KINESTHETIC • TACTILE • VISUAL

Solving "What Is the ONE?" Problems

PARTNER ACTIVITY

PROBLEM SOLVING

(*Math Journal 2,* pp. 208 and 209)

Students solve problems in which a fractional part is given, and students identify the ONE.

Adjusting the Activity

ELL

Have students use pattern blocks and counters to model the problems.

AUDITORY • KINESTHETIC • TACTILE • VISUAL

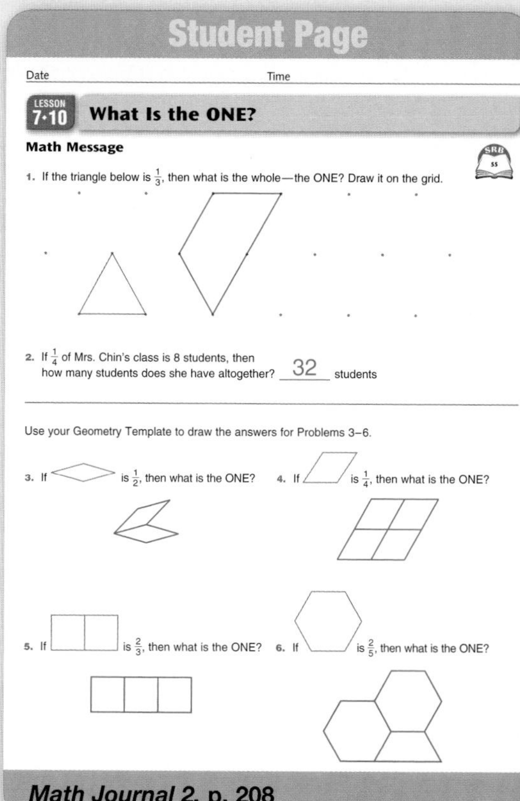

Student Page

Date Time

LESSON 7·10 **What Is the ONE?**

Math Message

1. If the triangle below is $\frac{1}{3}$, then what is the whole—the ONE? Draw it on the grid.

2. If $\frac{1}{4}$ of Mrs. Chin's class is 8 students, then how many students does she have altogether? 32 students

Use your Geometry Template to draw the answers for Problems 3–6.

3. If [shape] is $\frac{1}{2}$, then what is the ONE?

4. If [shape] is $\frac{1}{4}$, then what is the ONE?

5. If [shape] is $\frac{2}{3}$, then what is the ONE?

6. If [shape] is $\frac{2}{5}$, then what is the ONE?

Math Journal 2, p. 208

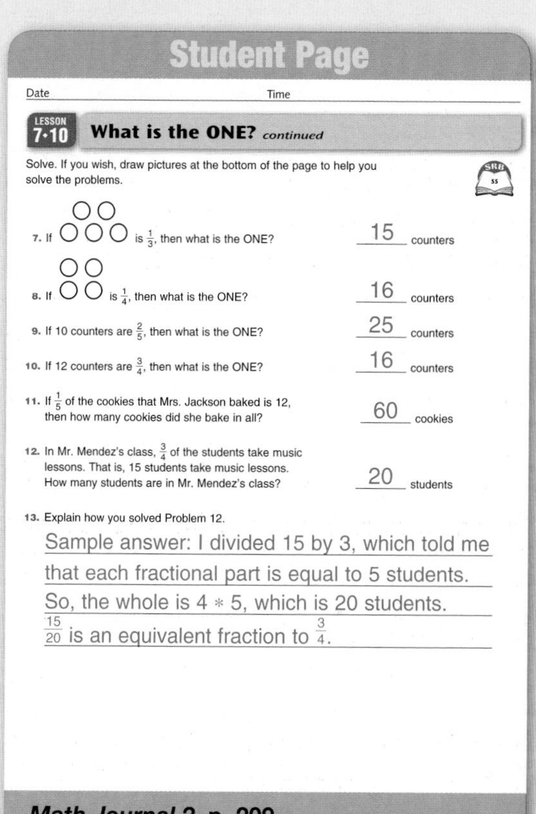

Student Page

Date Time

LESSON 7·10 **What is the ONE?** *continued*

Solve. If you wish, draw pictures at the bottom of the page to help you solve the problems.

7. If ○○○○○ is $\frac{1}{3}$, then what is the ONE? 15 counters

8. If ○○○○ is $\frac{1}{4}$, then what is the ONE? 16 counters

9. If 10 counters are $\frac{2}{5}$, then what is the ONE? 25 counters

10. If 12 counters are $\frac{3}{4}$, then what is the ONE? 16 counters

11. If $\frac{1}{5}$ of the cookies that Mrs. Jackson baked is 12, then how many cookies did she bake in all? 60 cookies

12. In Mr. Mendez's class, $\frac{3}{4}$ of the students take music lessons. That is, 15 students take music lessons. How many students are in Mr. Mendez's class? 20 students

13. Explain how you solved Problem 12.

Sample answer: I divided 15 by 3, which told me that each fractional part is equal to 5 students. So, the whole is 4 * 5, which is 20 students. $\frac{15}{20}$ is an equivalent fraction to $\frac{3}{4}$.

Math Journal 2, p. 209

Student Page

Date ______ Time ______

LESSON 7·10 Insect Data

Veronica collected 15 insects for a science project. She measured the length of each insect to the nearest $\frac{1}{8}$ inch. Her measurements are shown in the table below.

Insect	Length (to the nearest $\frac{1}{8}$ inch)	Insect	Length (to the nearest $\frac{1}{8}$ inch)
Darner dragonfly	$1\frac{1}{2}$	Red legged grasshopper	$1\frac{1}{8}$
Boreal firefly	$\frac{3}{8}$	American cockroach	$1\frac{1}{2}$
Yellow bumblebee	$\frac{3}{4}$	June beetle	$\frac{5}{8}$
Damselfly	$1\frac{1}{4}$	Paper wasp	$\frac{7}{8}$
Ground beetle	$\frac{7}{8}$	Field cricket	$\frac{7}{8}$
Green lacewing	1	Indian meal moth	$\frac{3}{8}$
Lady bug	$\frac{5}{8}$	Katydid	$1\frac{3}{4}$
Carolina mantid	$1\frac{3}{4}$		

Plot the insect lengths on the line plot below. Then use the completed plot to answer the questions on the next page.

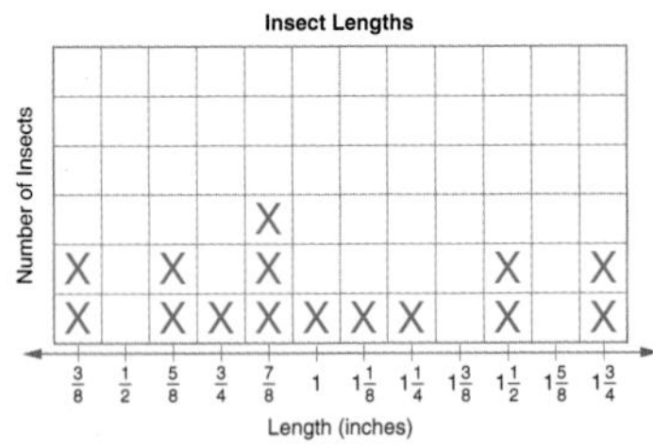

Math Journal 2, p. 209A

Student Page

Date ______ Time ______

LESSON 7·10 Insect Data *continued*

Use the line plot on journal page 209A to answer the questions. Write a number model to summarize each problem. Sample number models are given.

1. a. What is the maximum insect length? $1\frac{3}{4}$ in. The minimum? $\frac{3}{8}$ in.
   b. What is the range of the data set? $1\frac{3}{8}$ in. Number model: $1\frac{3}{4} - \frac{3}{8} = 1\frac{3}{8}$
2. a. What is the median of the data set? $\frac{7}{8}$ in.
   b. How much longer is the median length than the minimum length? $\frac{4}{8}$, or $\frac{1}{2}$ in.
   Number model: $\frac{7}{8} - \frac{3}{8} = \frac{1}{2}$
3. a. What is the mode of the data set? $\frac{7}{8}$ in.
   b. How much longer is the maximum length than the mode length? $\frac{7}{8}$ in.
   Number model: $1\frac{3}{4} - \frac{7}{8} = \frac{7}{8}$
4. Two insects have the maximum length. What is the difference in length between these insects and the next-longest insects? $\frac{1}{4}$ in.
   Number model: $1\frac{3}{4} - 1\frac{1}{2} = \frac{1}{4}$
5. There are three insects in Veronica's collection that are from $\frac{1}{2}$ inch to $\frac{3}{4}$ inch long. If these three insects were placed end to end, how long would the line of insects be?
   $\frac{16}{8}$, or 2 in. Number model: $\frac{5}{8} + \frac{5}{8} + \frac{3}{4} = 2$
6. How long would the line of insects be if all the insects less than $\frac{1}{2}$ inch long were placed end to end? $\frac{6}{8}$, or $\frac{3}{4}$ in.
   Number model: $\frac{3}{8} + \frac{3}{8} = \frac{3}{4}$ in.
7. Make up and solve your own problem about the insect data.
   Answers vary.
   Number model: ______

Math Journal 2, p. 209B

2 Ongoing Learning & Practice

▶ Playing *Fraction Top-It*

(*Student Reference Book,* p. 247; *Math Masters,* p. 506)

Students play *Fraction Top-It* to practice comparing fractions.

Adjusting the Activity

ELL

Have students play with the shaded side of the cards up. Or have students play in groups of four and order the fractions. Players score 4 points for the largest fraction and 2 points for the smallest fraction. The player with the most points at the end of the game is the winner.

AUDITORY ◆ KINESTHETIC ◆ TACTILE ◆ VISUAL

Ongoing Assessment: Recognizing Student Achievement

***Math Masters* Page 506**

Use **Math Masters, page 506** to assess students' ability to compare fractions. Students are making adequate progress if they are able to determine which fraction is larger, with or without referring to the shaded sides of the cards, and write a number model to illustrate the comparison. Some students may be able to compare fractions using only the numerical representations.

[Number and Numeration Goal 6]

▶ Plotting Insect Data

(*Math Journal 2,* pp. 209A and 209B)

Students plot insect lengths in fractions of an inch on a line plot. Then they use the line plot to solve fraction and mixed-number addition and subtraction problems.

▶ Math Boxes 7·10

(*Math Journal 2,* p. 210)

Mixed Practice Math Boxes in this lesson are paired with Math Boxes in Lesson 7-12. The skill in Problem 6 previews Unit 8 content.

Writing/Reasoning Have students write a response to the following: *Describe two different ways to check your answer for Problem 5.* Sample answer: I could divide to check the multiplication. 8,432 / 68 = 124 and 8,432 / 124 = 68. I could also make a ballpark estimate. 70 ∗ 120 = (70 ∗ 100) + (70 ∗ 20) = 7,000 + 1,400 = 8,400. The ballpark estimate 8,400 is close to the product 8,432.

Study Link 7·10

INDEPENDENT ACTIVITY

(*Math Masters,* p. 231)

Home Connection Students solve "What is the ONE?" problems.

3 Differentiation Options

ENRICHMENT

PARTNER ACTIVITY

5–15 Min

Playing *Getting to One*

(*Student Reference Book,* p. 248)

To apply students' proportional reasoning skills and their understanding of the concept of the ONE, have them play *Getting to One.* Ask students to use a "What's My Rule?" table to organize their guesses and explain their thinking. *For example:*

in	out	
55	0.846...	When 55 is divided by the ONE, the result is a decimal close to one. The ONE must be greater than 55.
70	1.076...	When 70 is divided by the ONE, the result is greater than 1. The ONE must be less than 70.
65	1	When 65 is divided by the ONE, the result is 1. The ONE must be 65.

ENRICHMENT

INDEPENDENT ACTIVITY

15–30 Min

Finding the ONE

(*Math Masters,* p. 232)

To apply students' understanding of the concept of the ONE, have them determine how a candy bar was divided.

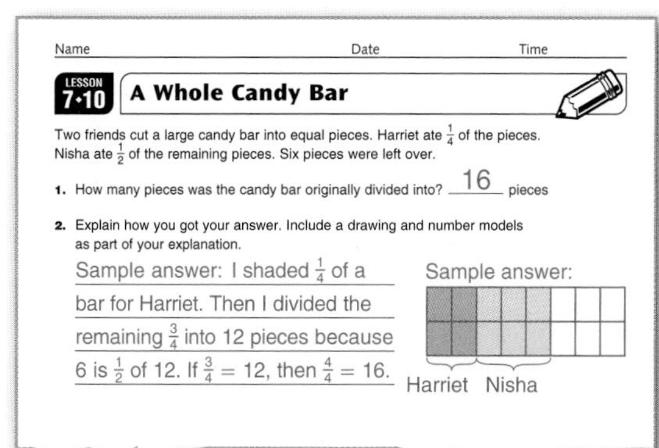

Name Date Time

LESSON 7·10 **A Whole Candy Bar**

Two friends cut a large candy bar into equal pieces. Harriet ate $\frac{1}{4}$ of the pieces. Nisha ate $\frac{1}{2}$ of the remaining pieces. Six pieces were left over.

1. How many pieces was the candy bar originally divided into? 16 pieces
2. Explain how you got your answer. Include a drawing and number models as part of your explanation.
   Sample answer: I shaded $\frac{1}{4}$ of a bar for Harriet. Then I divided the remaining $\frac{3}{4}$ into 12 pieces because 6 is $\frac{1}{2}$ of 12. If $\frac{3}{4}$ = 12, then $\frac{4}{4}$ = 16.
   Sample answer: Harriet Nisha

Math Masters, page 232

Student Page

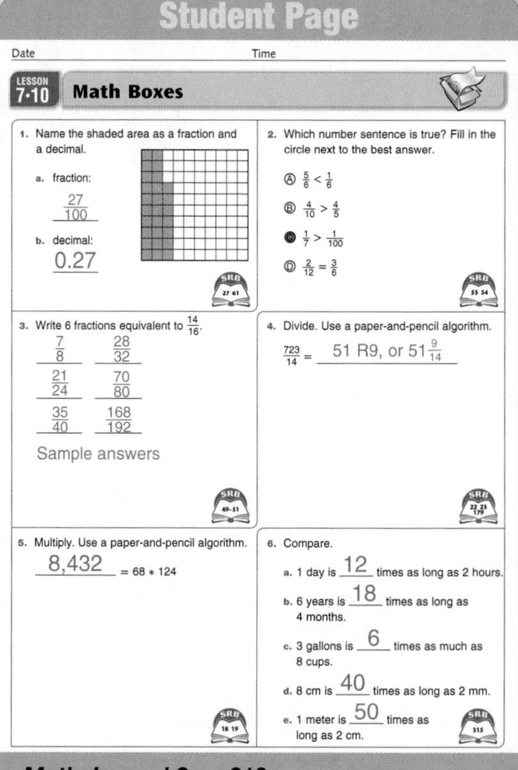

Date Time

LESSON 7·10 **Math Boxes**

1. Name the shaded area as a fraction and a decimal.
   a. fraction: $\frac{27}{100}$
   b. decimal: 0.27
2. Which number sentence is true? Fill in the circle next to the best answer.
   Ⓐ $\frac{5}{6} < \frac{1}{8}$
   Ⓑ $\frac{4}{10} > \frac{4}{5}$
   ● $\frac{1}{7} > \frac{1}{100}$
   Ⓓ $\frac{2}{12} = \frac{3}{6}$
3. Write 6 fractions equivalent to $\frac{14}{16}$.
   $\frac{7}{8}$ $\frac{28}{32}$ $\frac{21}{24}$ $\frac{70}{80}$ $\frac{35}{40}$ $\frac{168}{192}$
   Sample answers
4. Divide. Use a paper-and-pencil algorithm.
   $\frac{723}{14}$ = 51 R9, or $51\frac{9}{14}$
5. Multiply. Use a paper-and-pencil algorithm.
   8,432 = 68 ∗ 124
6. Compare.
   a. 1 day is 12 times as long as 2 hours.
   b. 6 years is 18 times as long as 4 months.
   c. 3 gallons is 6 times as much as 8 cups.
   d. 8 cm is 40 times as long as 2 mm.
   e. 1 meter is 50 times as long as 2 cm.

Math Journal 2, p. 210

Study Link Master

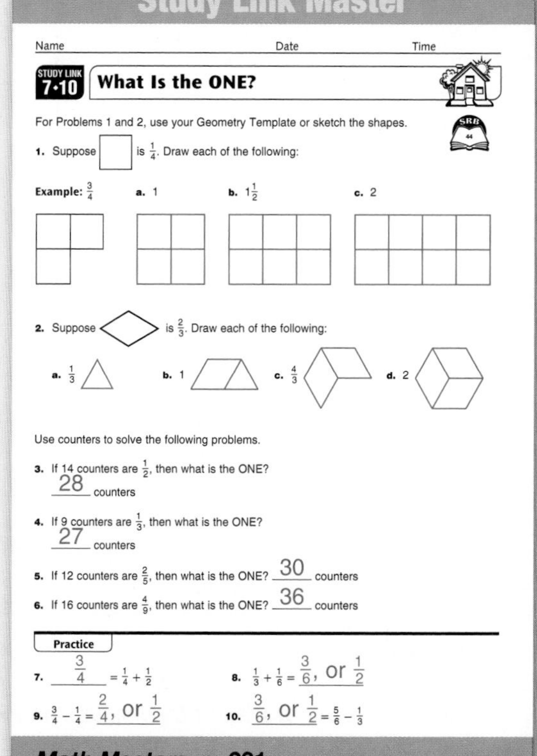

Name Date Time

STUDY LINK 7·10 **What Is the ONE?**

For Problems 1 and 2, use your Geometry Template or sketch the shapes.

1. Suppose □ is $\frac{1}{4}$. Draw each of the following:
   Example: $\frac{3}{4}$ a. 1 b. $1\frac{1}{2}$ c. 2
2. Suppose ◇ is $\frac{2}{3}$. Draw each of the following:
   a. $\frac{1}{3}$ b. 1 c. $\frac{4}{3}$ d. 2

Use counters to solve the following problems.

3. If 14 counters are $\frac{1}{2}$, then what is the ONE? 28 counters
4. If 9 counters are $\frac{1}{3}$, then what is the ONE? 27 counters
5. If 12 counters are $\frac{2}{5}$, then what is the ONE? 30 counters
6. If 16 counters are $\frac{4}{9}$, then what is the ONE? 36 counters

Practice

7. $\frac{3}{4} = \frac{1}{4} + \frac{1}{2}$
8. $\frac{1}{3} + \frac{1}{6} = \frac{3}{6}$, or $\frac{1}{2}$
9. $\frac{3}{4} - \frac{1}{4} = \frac{2}{4}$, or $\frac{1}{2}$
10. $\frac{3}{6}$, or $\frac{1}{2} = \frac{5}{6} - \frac{1}{3}$

Math Masters, p. 231

7•11 Probability, Fractions, and Spinners

Objectives To review basic ideas of probability, including fairness and expected results; and to guide the application of fractions to spinners.

www.everydaymathonline.com

ePresentations

eToolkit

Algorithms Practice

EM Facts Workshop Game™

Family Letters

Assessment Management

Common Core State Standards

Curriculum Focal Points

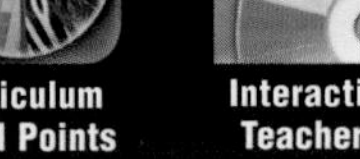

Interactive Teacher's Lesson Guide

1 Teaching the Lesson

Key Concepts and Skills

- Name fractional parts of regions. [Number and Numeration Goal 2]
- Use equivalent fractions to design spinners. [Number and Numeration Goal 5]
- Use probability language to describe the likelihood of events. [Data and Chance Goal 3]
- Conduct experiments and calculate expected probability. [Data and Chance Goal 4]

Key Activities

Students apply basic concepts and vocabulary associated with chance events.

Ongoing Assessment: Informing Instruction See page 630.

Ongoing Assessment: Recognizing Student Achievement Use Mental Math and Reflexes. [Data and Chance Goal 4]

Key Vocabulary

fair (die or spinner) ◆ equal chance ◆ expect ◆ equally (more, less) likely

Materials

Math Journal 2, p. 211
Study Link 7•10
Math Masters, p. 233
crayons, markers, or colored pencils (red, green, blue, and at least 3 other colors) ◆ straightedge ◆ 1 large (2") paper clip and 2 pieces of removable tape per student ◆ slate ◆ data pad or chart paper (optional) ◆ computer with Internet access (optional)

2 Ongoing Learning & Practice

Playing *Chances Are*

Student Reference Book, pp. 236 and 237
Math Masters, pp. 462–466
scissors ◆ crayons (optional)
Students practice using basic probability language to describe the likelihood of an event occurring.

Math Boxes 7•11

Math Journal 2, p. 212
Students practice and maintain skills through Math Box problems.

Study Link 7•11

Math Masters, pp. 234–236
Students practice and maintain skills through Study Link activities.

3 Differentiation Options

READINESS

Dividing Circles into Fractional Parts

Math Masters, p. 237
straightedge ◆ crayons or markers
Students review fractional parts of regions.

ENRICHMENT

Investigating Chance Events

per partnership: 2 six-sided dice (optional)
Students explore probability activities in *Do You Wanna Bet? Your Chance to Find Out About Probability.*

ELL SUPPORT

Building a Math Word Bank

Differentiation Handbook, p. 140
Students add the terms *fair* and *equal chance* to their Math Word Banks.

Advance Preparation

For Part 2, consider copying *Math Masters,* pages 462, 463, 465, and 466 on cardstock. For the optional Enrichment activity in Part 3, obtain the book ***Do You Wanna Bet? Your Chance to Find Out About Probability*** by Jean Cushman (Houghton Mifflin, 2007).

***Teacher's Reference Manual,* Grades 4–6** pp. 156–158, 170–173

Getting Started

Mental Math and Reflexes 

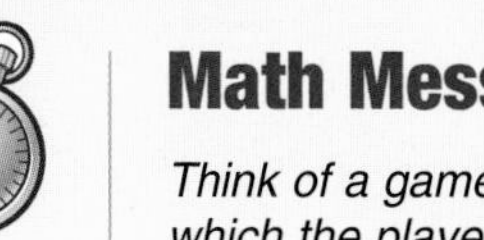

Pose probability questions. Have students write the appropriate fractions and basic probability terms on their slates. *Suggestions:*

●○○ There are 5 red and 5 blue blocks in the bag.

What are the chances of picking a red block? $\frac{5}{10}$, $\frac{1}{2}$, or 50-50 chance

A blue block? $\frac{5}{10}$, $\frac{1}{2}$, 50-50 chance

A green block? $\frac{0}{10}$, impossible

●●○ There are 3 red, 1 blue, and 2 green blocks in the bag.

What are the chances of picking a red block? $\frac{3}{6}$, $\frac{1}{2}$, 50-50 chance

A blue block? $\frac{1}{6}$, unlikely, or very unlikely

A green block? $\frac{2}{6}$, $\frac{1}{3}$, unlikely

●●● There are 25 red, 25 blue, 20 green, and 30 yellow blocks in the bag.

What are the chances of picking a red or a blue block? $\frac{50}{100}$, $\frac{1}{2}$, 50-50 chance

A green block? $\frac{20}{100}$, $\frac{2}{10}$, $\frac{1}{5}$, unlikely

A yellow block? $\frac{30}{100}$, $\frac{3}{10}$, unlikely

Math Message

Think of a game you like in which the players roll dice. Be prepared to explain how dice are used in the game.

Study Link 7·10 Follow-Up

Have students compare answers. Ask volunteers to explain how they solved Problems 5 and 6. Students indicate thumbs-up if they agree with the strategies used.

Ongoing Assessment: Recognizing Student Achievement

Mental Math and Reflexes ★

Use **Mental Math and Reflexes** to assess students' ability to express the probability of an event as a fraction. Students are making adequate progress if they express the expected probability with a fraction. Some students may write the fraction in simplest form, for example, rename $\frac{20}{100}$ as $\frac{1}{5}$.

[Data and Chance Goal 4]

1 Teaching the Lesson

Math Message Follow-Up

WHOLE-CLASS DISCUSSION

ELL

Discuss the use of dice in games. *For example:*

▷ Dice are used to determine how far a player can move.

▷ Dice are used to determine numbers that are used in a game.

▷ You cannot know which number will come up on a die. To support English language learners, discuss the meaning of the word *die* in this mathematical context.

▷ You should have a **fair die**—there must be an **equal chance** for it to land with any one of its faces up.

Ask students what other devices they have used for the same purposes as dice. Sample answers: Spinners, coins, number cards

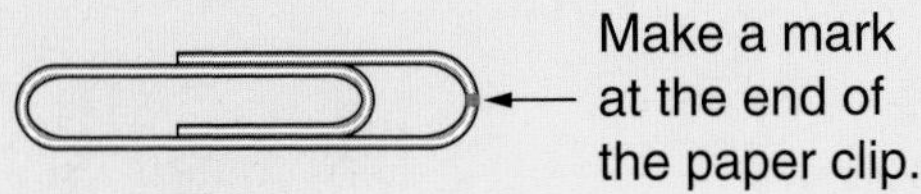

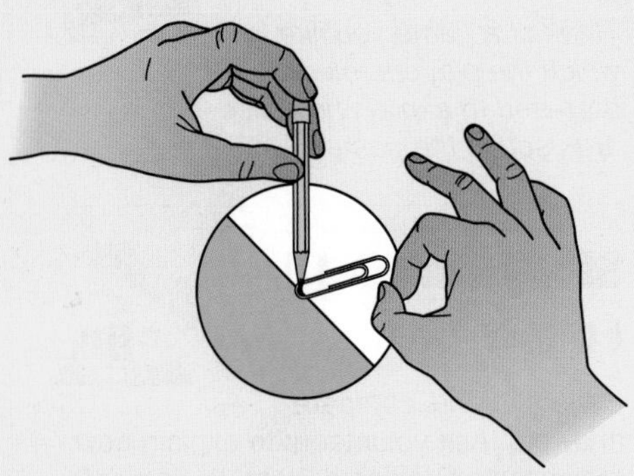

A student uses one hand to hold the pencil and the other hand to flick the paper clip.

▶ Spinning a Spinner

PARTNER ACTIVITY

(*Math Masters,* p. 233)

Tell students that in this lesson they will use spinners to experiment with situations in which they cannot tell for sure what will happen.

Pass out *Math Masters,* page 233 and ask each partnership to tape it to a flat, level surface. Show them how to make and use a paper-clip spinner. *(See margin.)*

Discuss what constitutes a **fair spinner**—one in which the paper clip has an **equal chance** of landing on any part of the circle. For example, placing a spinner on an uneven surface will alter the results of the spins. Therefore, this would not be a fair spinner.

▶ Doing Spinner Experiments

(*Math Masters,* p. 233)

Experiment 1

1. Partners use the first spinner on *Math Masters,* page 233. They spin the paper clip four times and record the results in Problem 1a.
2. Students report their results to you. You tally them on chart paper or on the board.
3. You and the class find the class totals. Students record them in Problem 1b.

Ask students to summarize their results. Encourage language like the following:

▷ "The paper clip has the same chance of landing on the shaded part as on the white part."

▷ "If you spin the paper clip many times, it should land on white 1 out of 2 times."

▷ "Chances are, the paper clip will land on the white part half of the time, because each part is half of the circle."

▷ "The chance of landing on the shaded part is 50% (or $\frac{1}{2}$)."

Experiment 2

Ask partners to color the second spinner on *Math Masters,* page 233 blue and red in such a way that the paper clip is twice as likely to land on blue as on red. Point out that the circle has been divided into 12 equal parts.

Have students share spinner designs. Students should have colored $\frac{2}{3}$ of the circle blue and $\frac{1}{3}$ red. There are many possible designs.

NOTE Have students work in pencil until they are sure they have a correct solution.

Teaching Master

Name Date Time

LESSON 7·11 **Spinner Experiments**

1. Use a paper clip and pencil to make a spinner.

a. Spin the paper clip 4 times. Record the number of times it lands on the shaded part and on the white part.

Answers vary.

shaded	white

b. Record the number of times the paper clip lands on the shaded part and on the white part **for the whole class.**

shaded	white

2. Make another spinner. Color the circle blue and red so that the paper clip is **twice as likely** to land on blue as on red.

Sample answer: red, blue

a. Spin the paper clip 4 times. Record the number of times it lands on blue and on red.

blue	red

b. Record the number of times the paper clip lands on blue and on red **for the whole class.**

blue	red

c. What would you expect after spinning the paper clip 300 times?

blue	red
200	100

Math Masters, p. 233

Repeat the procedure using the blue-and-red spinners:

1. Partners spin four times and record the results in Problem 2a.
2. Students report their results to you. You tally them on chart paper or on the board.
3. You and the class find the class totals. Students record them in Problem 2b.

Ask students to summarize their results. Encourage language like the following:

▷ "The paper clip is more likely to land on blue than on red."

▷ "If you spin many times, blue will come up twice as often."

▷ "It is hard to know for sure, but if you spin a lot of times, blue will come up about 2 out of 3 spins, or $\frac{2}{3}$ of the time."

▷ "There is a $\frac{2}{3}$ chance of landing on blue."

Finally, have students complete Problem 2c and discuss their answers. Make sure they understand the meaning of the word **expect** in this context. One would *expect* the paper clip to land on red *about* 100 times, but this does not mean that it will do so *exactly* 100 times. In fact, it probably will *not* land on red exactly 100 times.

When students describe chance events, encourage them to use a variety of words and phrases, such as *likely, unlikely, 3 out of 4, three-fourths of the time, 75% chance, the chances are,* and *you can expect.*

ELL

As probability terms enter class discussions in the context of solving problems, write them on chart paper or on the board and review their meanings.

AUDITORY ◆ KINESTHETIC ◆ TACTILE ◆ VISUAL

Designing Spinners

PARTNER ACTIVITY

PROBLEM SOLVING

(*Math Journal 2,* p. 211)

Have students complete journal page 211 and then share results and spinner designs.

Technology Link Alternatively, have students visit http://illuminations.nctm.org/ActivityDetail.aspx?id=79 to create their own spinners and compare the expected results for a specified number of spins to the actual results.

For Problem 1, students will probably divide the circle into 6 equal parts. Ask how they decided what size to make each part. $\frac{1}{6}$ of 12 = 2, so the circle can be divided into 6 equal parts by starting at 0 and counting by 2s.

Encourage students to use such phrases as **"equally likely,"** "equal chance," and "1 out of 6 chances of landing on red" when they discuss their spinner designs.

Student Page

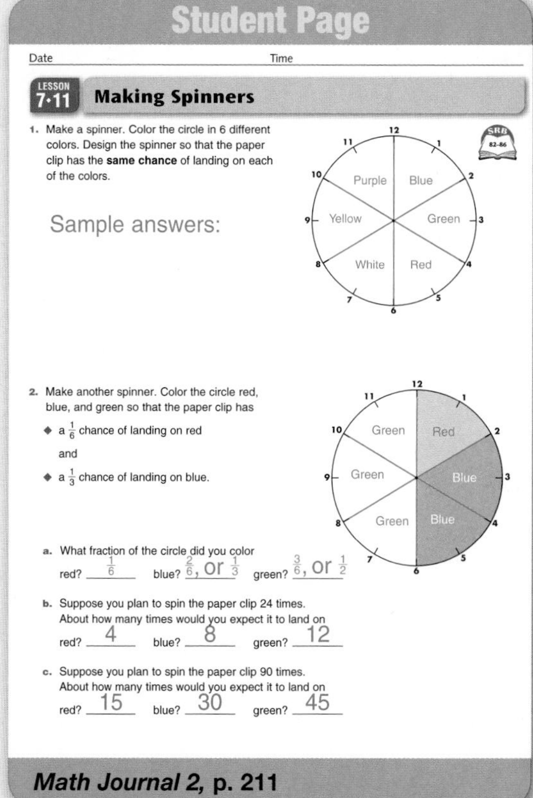
Date Time

LESSON 7·11 **Making Spinners**

1. Make a spinner. Color the circle in 6 different colors. Design the spinner so that the paper clip has the **same chance** of landing on each of the colors.

Sample answers:

2. Make another spinner. Color the circle red, blue, and green so that the paper clip has
   - a $\frac{1}{6}$ chance of landing on red

   and
   - a $\frac{1}{3}$ chance of landing on blue.

a. What fraction of the circle did you color red? $\frac{1}{6}$ blue? $\frac{2}{6}$, or $\frac{1}{3}$ green? $\frac{3}{6}$, or $\frac{1}{2}$

b. Suppose you plan to spin the paper clip 24 times. About how many times would you expect it to land on red? 4 blue? 8 green? 12

c. Suppose you plan to spin the paper clip 90 times. About how many times would you expect it to land on red? 15 blue? 30 green? 45

Math Journal 2, p. 211

In discussing Problems 2b and 2c, give students opportunities to use the language of chance events and to compare the likelihood of the paper clip landing on the various colors. *For example:*

▷ "The paper clip is **more likely** to land on blue than on red, but **less likely** to land on blue than on green."

▷ "The paper clip is 3 times as likely to land on green as on red, and twice as likely to land on blue as on red."

▷ "The chance of landing on red is $\frac{1}{6}$, so $\frac{1}{6}$ of the circle should be red."

▷ "The chance of landing on red is 1 out of 6, or 1 red for every 6 spins. So I would expect 4 reds if I spin 24 times."

Ongoing Assessment: Informing Instruction

Watch for students who may misunderstand the term *expect.* For example, in Problem 2b, the paper clip will not necessarily land on red *exactly* 4 times out of every 24 spins, or *exactly* 8 times on blue.

2 Ongoing Learning & Practice

▶ Playing *Chances Are*

(*Student Reference Book,* pp. 236 and 237; *Math Masters,* pp. 462–466)

Students play *Chances Are* to practice using basic probability terms to describe the likelihood of events.

Adjusting the Activity

ELL

Have students use crayons to color code the balls and blocks on the appropriate Event Cards (*Math Masters,* page 463).

Have students express the probability of the event as a fraction.

AUDITORY ◆ KINESTHETIC ◆ TACTILE ◆ VISUAL

▶ Math Boxes 7•11

(*Math Journal 2,* p. 212)

Mixed Practice Math Boxes in this lesson are paired with Math Boxes in Lessons 7-9 and 7-12a. The skill in Problem 6 previews Unit 8 content.

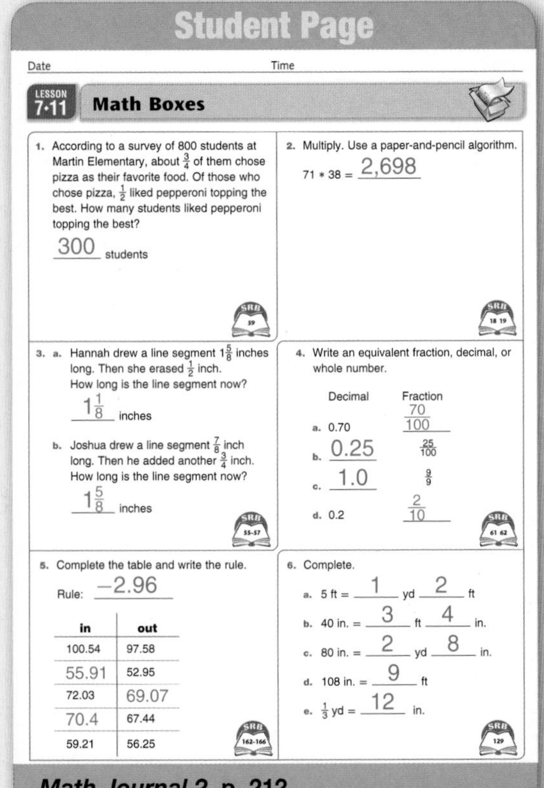

Student Page

Date Time

LESSON 7•11 Math Boxes

1. According to a survey of 800 students at Martin Elementary, about $\frac{3}{4}$ of them chose pizza as their favorite food. Of those who chose pizza, $\frac{1}{2}$ liked pepperoni topping the best. How many students liked pepperoni topping the best?
300 students

2. Multiply. Use a paper-and-pencil algorithm.
71 * 38 = 2,698

3. a. Hannah drew a line segment $1\frac{5}{8}$ inches long. Then she erased $\frac{1}{2}$ inch. How long is the line segment now?
$1\frac{1}{8}$ inches

b. Joshua drew a line segment $\frac{7}{8}$ inch long. Then he added another $\frac{3}{4}$ inch. How long is the line segment now?
$1\frac{5}{8}$ inches

4. Write an equivalent fraction, decimal, or whole number.

	Decimal	Fraction
a.	0.70	$\frac{70}{100}$
b.	0.25	$\frac{25}{100}$
c.	1.0	$\frac{9}{9}$
d.	0.2	$\frac{2}{10}$

5. Complete the table and write the rule.
Rule: −2.96

in	out
100.54	97.58
55.91	52.95
72.03	69.07
70.4	67.44
59.21	56.25

6. Complete.
a. 5 ft = 1 yd 2 ft
b. 40 in. = 3 ft 4 in.
c. 80 in. = 2 yd 8 in.
d. 108 in. = 9 ft
e. $\frac{1}{3}$ yd = 12 in.

Math Journal 2, p. 212

Study Link 7·11

INDEPENDENT ACTIVITY

(*Math Masters,* pp. 234–236)

Home Connection Students design and describe a spinner. Also, in preparation for Lesson 8-1, students are asked to measure the distance between the appliances in their kitchens.

3 Differentiation Options

READINESS

PARTNER ACTIVITY

5–15 Min

Dividing Circles into Fractional Parts

(*Math Masters,* p. 237)

To explore fractional parts of regions, have students divide circles into equal parts and color specified fractions of the regions. Discuss how equivalent fractions can be used to solve the problems.

ENRICHMENT

SMALL-GROUP ACTIVITY

15–30 Min

Investigating Chance Events

Literature Link To apply students' understanding of probability, have them conduct and report results for experiments found in ***Do You Wanna Bet? Your Chance to Find Out About Probability*** by Jean Cushman (Houghton Mifflin, 2007). *Suggestions:*

- ▷ Chapter 7, "Winners and Losers, Roll of the Dice": Students tally each "double" in 100 rolls of two dice and compare expected and actual results.
- ▷ Chapter 5, "Sampling and Statistics, Left Hand or Right": Students survey the fourth grade to see if the established ratio of 1 in 10 applies to class data on left-handed students.

ELL SUPPORT

SMALL-GROUP ACTIVITY

5–15 Min

Building a Math Word Bank

(*Differentiation Handbook*, p. 140)

To provide language support for probability, have students use the Word Bank Template found on *Differentiation Handbook,* page 140. Ask students to write the terms *fair* and *equal chance,* draw pictures related to each term, and write other related words. See the *Differentiation Handbook* for more information.

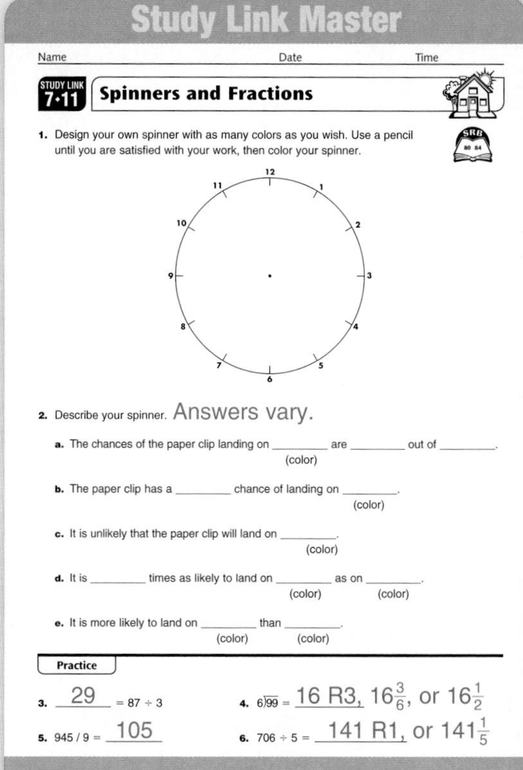

Study Link Master

Name Date Time

STUDY LINK 7·11 Spinners and Fractions

1. Design your own spinner with as many colors as you wish. Use a pencil until you are satisfied with your work, then color your spinner.

2. Describe your spinner. Answers vary.

a. The chances of the paper clip landing on ________ (color) are ________ out of ________.

b. The paper clip has a ________ chance of landing on ________ (color).

c. It is unlikely that the paper clip will land on ________ (color).

d. It is ________ times as likely to land on ________ (color) as on ________ (color).

e. It is more likely to land on ________ (color) than ________ (color).

Practice

3. 29 = 87 ÷ 3

4. 6)99 = 16 R3, $16\frac{3}{6}$, or $16\frac{1}{2}$

5. 945 / 9 = 105

6. 706 ÷ 5 = 141 R1, or $141\frac{1}{5}$

Math Masters, p. 234

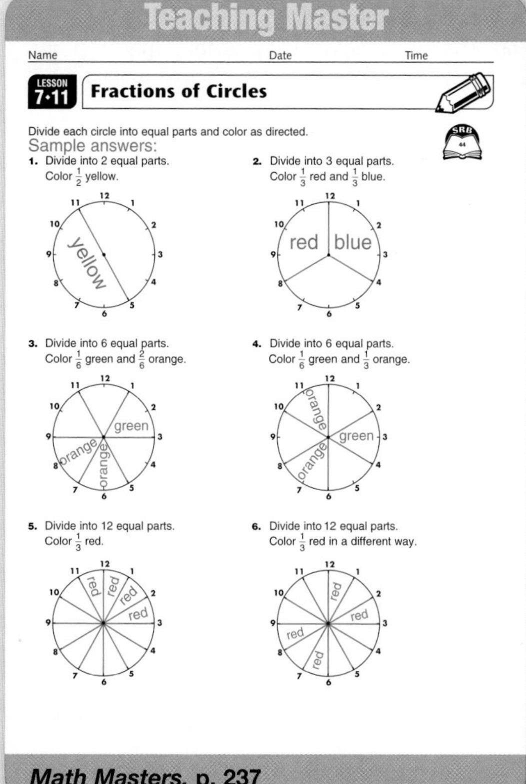

Teaching Master

Name Date Time

LESSON 7·11 Fractions of Circles

Divide each circle into equal parts and color as directed.

Sample answers:

1. Divide into 2 equal parts. Color $\frac{1}{2}$ yellow.

2. Divide into 3 equal parts. Color $\frac{1}{3}$ red and $\frac{1}{3}$ blue.

3. Divide into 6 equal parts. Color $\frac{1}{6}$ green and $\frac{2}{6}$ orange.

4. Divide into 6 equal parts. Color $\frac{1}{6}$ green and $\frac{1}{3}$ orange.

5. Divide into 12 equal parts. Color $\frac{1}{3}$ red.

6. Divide into 12 equal parts. Color $\frac{1}{3}$ red in a different way.

Math Masters, p. 237

7•12 A Cube-Drop Experiment

Objective To guide students in comparing predicted and actual results from an experiment with equally likely outcomes.

Technology Resources www.everydaymathonline.com

ePresentations

eToolkit

Algorithms Practice

EM Facts Workshop Game™

Family Letters

Assessment Management

Common Core State Standards

Curriculum Focal Points

Interactive Teacher's Lesson Guide

1 Teaching the Lesson

Key Concepts and Skills

- Rename fractions as percents. [Number and Numeration Goal 5]
- Use basic probability terms to describe the likelihood of events. [Data and Chance Goal 3]
- Conduct a cube-drop experiment. [Data and Chance Goal 4]
- Use fractions and percents to predict the outcomes of an experiment. [Data and Chance Goal 4]
- Compare predicted outcomes and actual results. [Data and Chance Goal 4]

Key Activities

Students color a 10-by-10 grid. They determine the chance that a centimeter cube, dropped onto the grid, will land on a particular color. They perform the experiment and compare the actual results with their predictions.

Ongoing Assessment: Informing Instruction See page 635.

Ongoing Assessment: Recognizing Student Achievement Use a Math Log or Exit Slip (*Math Masters,* page 388 or 389). [Data and Chance Goal 4]

Materials

Math Journal 2, pp. 213–215
Study Link 7•11
Math Masters, p. 238; p. 388 or 389 (optional)
colored pencils, markers, or crayons (yellow, red, green, blue) ◆ per partnership: 1 cm cube ◆ slate ◆ shoe box or copier-paper box (optional)

2 Ongoing Learning & Practice

Reviewing Place Value in Whole Numbers
Math Journal 2, p. 216
Students solve place-value problems.

Decomposing Fractions
Math Masters, p. 397
Geometry Template (optional) ◆ pattern blocks (optional)
Students decompose fractions into sums of fractions.

Math Boxes 7•12
Math Journal 2, p. 217
Students practice and maintain skills through Math Box problems.

Study Link 7•12
Math Masters, p. 239
Students practice and maintain skills through Study Link activities.

3 Differentiation Options

READINESS
Renaming Fractions as Percents
Math Masters, p. 240
base-10 blocks (1 flat, 10 longs, cubes)
Students use base-10 blocks to model fractions and their percent equivalents.

ENRICHMENT
Comparing Actual and Expected Results of 1,000 Cube Drops
Math Masters, pp. 241, 242, and 388 or 389
Students combine the results of 1,000 actual cube drops and compare them with the expected results.

EXTRA PRACTICE
5-Minute Math
5-Minute Math™, pp. 42–47
Students solve probability problems.

ELL SUPPORT
Building a Math Word Bank
Differentiation Handbook, p. 140
Students add the terms *predicted* and *actual* to their Math Word Banks.

Advance Preparation

For the cube-drop experiment, gather shoe box or copier-paper box bottoms or tops to contain the bouncing cubes during the experiment.

***Teacher's Reference Manual,* Grades 4–6** pp. 157, 158, 160–167

Getting Started

Mental Math and Reflexes

Write fractions with denominators of 10 or 100 on the board, and have students write the equivalent decimals on their slates. Then write decimals on the board and tell students to write the equivalent fractions and mixed numbers. Do not insist that they write fractions in simplest form. *Suggestions:*

●○○ $\frac{2}{10}$ 0.2
$\frac{50}{100}$ 0.50
0.24 $\frac{24}{100}$
0.60 $\frac{60}{100}$

●●○ $\frac{8}{100}$ 0.08
$\frac{72}{1,000}$ 0.072
0.03 $\frac{3}{100}$
0.029 $\frac{29}{1,000}$

●●● $7\frac{6}{1,000}$ 7.006
$32\frac{1}{100}$ 32.01
1.9 $1\frac{9}{10}$
6.5 $6\frac{5}{10}$

Math Message

Complete journal page 213.

Study Link 7•11 Follow-Up

Have students share their spinner designs and descriptions in small groups.

1 Teaching the Lesson

Math Message Follow-Up

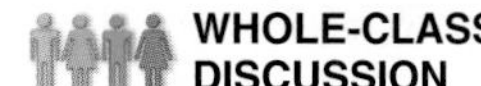

WHOLE-CLASS DISCUSSION

(*Math Journal 2,* p. 213)

Discuss the answers to Problems 1 and 2, and have students explain their reasoning. Ask whether students would be surprised if their predictions were not fulfilled exactly. Discuss why the actual results for 24 spins and 12 rolls might not match the predicted outcomes. The predictions are based on what is likely to happen; the actual outcomes will probably differ from the predictions.

Explain that this lesson involves an experiment in which students will compare their predicted outcomes with actual results.

Predicting the Result of an Experiment

INDEPENDENT ACTIVITY

(*Math Journal 2,* p. 214; *Math Masters,* p. 238)

Direct students to color the grid on *Math Masters,* page 238 according to the directions given.

Students can color the squares using any pattern they choose as long as they end up with the specified number of squares of each color. (Students will actually *color* only 50 of the squares.)

Have students read about the cube-drop experiment on journal page 214. Ask:

- If a cube is dropped onto the 10-by-10 grid, on which color is it most likely to land? White, because there are more white squares than squares of any other color
- On which color is it least likely to land? yellow

Have students complete the page on their own.

Student Page

Date Time

LESSON 7•12 Expected Spinner Results

1. If this spinner is spun 24 times, how many times do you expect it to land on each color?

SRB 82-86

a. Fill in the table.

Color	Expected Number in 24 Spins
red	8
blue	8
yellow	4
green	4
Total	**24**

yellow red red blue blue green

b. Explain how you determined the expected number of times the spinner would land on each color.

Sample answer: Red and blue each cover $\frac{2}{6}$ or $\frac{1}{3}$ of the circle. $\frac{1}{3}$ of 24 spins is 8 spins. Green and yellow each cover $\frac{1}{6}$ of the circle. $\frac{1}{6}$ of 24 spins is 4 spins.

Try This

2. If a six-sided die is rolled 12 times, how many times would you expect to roll
   a. an odd number? 6
   b. a number less than 4? 6
   c. a 6? 2
   d. a square number? 4
   e. a triangular number? 6
   f. a prime number? 6

Math Journal 2, p. 213

Adjusting the Activity

Have students describe how dropping a cube onto a colored grid and spinning a spinner are similar. Look for answers such as the following:

▷ For both the grid and the spinner, the chance of landing on a specific color is the fraction of times you expect to land on that color. For example, if 4 out of every 100 squares on a grid or sections on a spinner are colored red, then the chance of landing on red is $\frac{4}{100}$, or 4 out of 100, or 4%.

AUDITORY ◆ KINESTHETIC ◆ TACTILE ◆ VISUAL

Student Page

Date Time

LESSON 7·12 A Cube-Drop Experiment

Getting Ready

SRB 80–86

1. Follow the directions for coloring the grid on *Math Masters,* page 238. You may color the squares in any way. The colors can even form a pattern or a picture.
2. For this experiment, you are going to place your grid on the floor and hold a centimeter cube about 2 feet above the grid. Without aiming, you will let it drop onto the grid. You will then record the color of the square on which the cube finally lands.
   - ◆ If the cube does not land on the grid, the drop does not count.
   - ◆ If the cube lands on more than one color, record the color that is covered by most of the cube. If you cannot tell, the toss does not count.

Making a Prediction

3. On which color is the cube *most likely* to land? white
4. On which color is it *least likely* to land? yellow
5. Suppose you were to drop the cube 100 times. How many times would you expect it to land on each color? Record your predictions below.

Predicted Results of 100 Cube Drops

Color	Number of Squares	Predicted Results Fraction	Predicted Results Percent
yellow	1	$\frac{1}{100}$	1 %
red	4	$\frac{4}{100}$	4 %
green	10	$\frac{10}{100}$	10 %
blue	35	$\frac{35}{100}$	35 %
white	50	$\frac{50}{100}$	50 %
Total	**100**	**1**	**100%**

Math Journal 2, p. 214

Bring the class together to share predicted outcomes. Encourage statements such as the following:

▷ "Only 1 square out of 100 is yellow, so I should hit yellow about once out of every 100 drops. The chance of the cube landing on yellow is 1 out of 100."

▷ "White is easy. Half of the squares are white, so I would hit white half of the time. If I dropped the cube 100 times, it would hit white 50 times. If I dropped the cube 50 times, it would hit white 25 times."

▷ "For green, it is 10 out of 100. So I expect 10 greens if I toss 100 times. If I toss 500 times, I should get 5 times as many—that's 50 greens."

▶ Performing a Cube-Drop Experiment

PARTNER ACTIVITY

(*Math Journal 2,* p. 215; *Math Masters,* p. 238)

Review the directions on journal page 215. Have partners take turns performing the experiment:

1. One partner drops a cube 50 times onto his or her 10-by-10 grid. The other partner records the results in the first partner's journal.
2. Partners switch roles.
3. Students count the number of drops for each color and complete the "My Results for 50 Cube Drops" table on journal page 215. (*See sample table below.*)

My Results for 50 Cube Drops

Color	Number of Drops	Percent
yellow	1	2%
red	2	4%
green	3	6%
blue	16	32%
white	28	56%
Total	**50**	**100%**

NOTE Have students kneel when dropping the cube, or place something under the grid to cushion the cube drop and reduce the bounce.

Ongoing Assessment: Informing Instruction

Watch for students who note that converting fractions to percents in this activity is similar to calculating percent scores on the multiplication facts tests.

Comparing Actual and Expected Results

WHOLE-CLASS ACTIVITY

(*Math Journal 2,* pp. 214 and 215)

Bring students together to compare their actual results with their predictions. Individual students' results probably show a wide range. For example, some students may have hit a white square as many as 35 out of 50 tosses (70% of the time), while others may have done so only 15 times (30% of the time). Students should notice that although some individual results may be very close to the expected results, others may be far off.

Ongoing Assessment: Recognizing Student Achievement

Math Log or Exit Slip

Use a **Math Log** or an **Exit Slip** (*Math Masters,* page 388 or 389) to assess students' ability to predict the outcomes of an experiment and test the predictions using manipulatives. Have students write about how the predicted outcomes for the cube-drop experiment compare with the actual results. Students are making adequate progress if their responses include the following:

▷ Some predictions are closer than others to the actual results.

▷ Predictions are *expected* results, not exactly what will happen.

Some students may be able to use the results to predict future events. For example, what might happen if the cube were dropped 500 times?

[Data and Chance Goal 4]

Student Page

Date ____ Time ____

LESSON 7·12 **A Cube-Drop Experiment** *continued*

Doing the Experiment

You and your partner will each drop a centimeter cube onto your own colored grid.

6. One partner drops the cube. The other partner records the color in the grid below by writing a letter in one of the squares. Drop the cube a total of 50 times.

Write **y** for yellow, **r** for red, **g** for green, **b** for blue, and **w** for white.

w	w	w	b	w	r	g	b	b	b
y	w	b	w	w	b	r	w	b	w
w	g	w	w	b	w	b	b	b	w
w	b	w	w	w	b	w	b	b	w
w	w	b	g	w	w	w	w	w	w

Sample answer: (grid above)

7. Then trade roles. Do another 50 drops, and record the results in the other partner's journal.

Sample answers:

8. Count the number for each color.

Write it in the "Number of Drops" column.

Check that the total is 50.

My Results for 50 Cube Drops

Color	Number of Drops	Percent
yellow	1	2%
red	2	4%
green	3	6%
blue	16	32%
white	28	56%
Total	**50**	**100%**

9. When you have finished, fill in the percent column in the table.

Example: If your cube landed on blue 15 times out of 50 drops, this is the same as 30 times out of 100 drops, or 30% of the time.

Math Journal 2, **p. 215**

2 Ongoing Learning & Practice

Reviewing Place Value in Whole Numbers

INDEPENDENT ACTIVITY

(*Math Journal 2,* p. 216)

Students solve problems that involve ordering numbers, identifying place value, determining the values of digits, and reading and writing whole numbers.

Decomposing Fractions

PARTNER ACTIVITY

(*Math Masters,* p. 397)

Have students complete name-collection boxes (*Math Masters,* p. 397) for fractions and mixed numbers by decomposing the numbers into sums of fractions with the same denominator. Encourage students to use pattern blocks or draw pictures of pattern blocks using their Geometry Template to justify their work. *Suggestions:*

▷ $\frac{3}{8}$ ▷ $\frac{5}{9}$ ▷ $2\frac{1}{8}$ ▷ $3\frac{2}{3}$

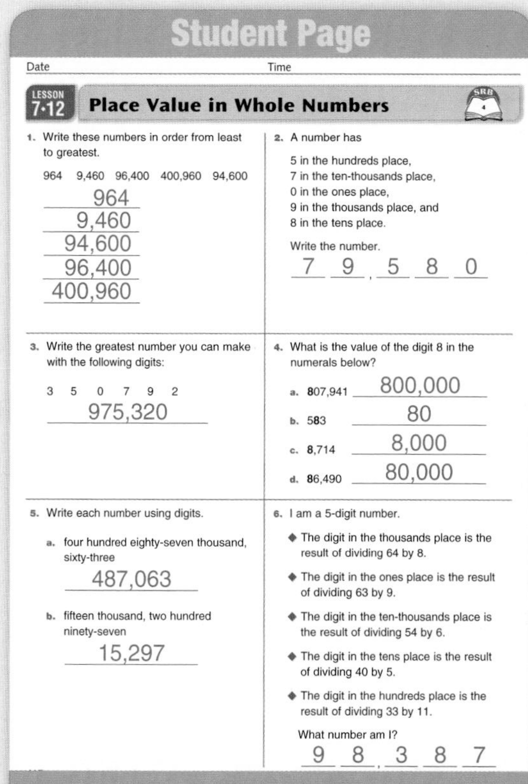

Student Page

Date ____ Time ____

LESSON 7·12 **Place Value in Whole Numbers**

1. Write these numbers in order from least to greatest.

964 9,460 96,400 400,960 94,600

964
9,460
94,600
96,400
400,960

2. A number has

5 in the hundreds place,
7 in the ten-thousands place,
0 in the ones place,
9 in the thousands place, and
8 in the tens place.

Write the number. 7 9 , 5 8 0

3. Write the greatest number you can make with the following digits:

3 5 0 7 9 2

975,320

4. What is the value of the digit 8 in the numerals below?

a. 807,941 800,000
b. 583 80
c. 8,714 8,000
d. 86,490 80,000

5. Write each number using digits.

a. four hundred eighty-seven thousand, sixty-three
487,063

b. fifteen thousand, two hundred ninety-seven
15,297

6. I am a 5-digit number.

◆ The digit in the thousands place is the result of dividing 64 by 8.
◆ The digit in the ones place is the result of dividing 63 by 9.
◆ The digit in the ten-thousands place is the result of dividing 54 by 6.
◆ The digit in the tens place is the result of dividing 40 by 5.
◆ The digit in the hundreds place is the result of dividing 33 by 11.

What number am I?
9 8 , 3 8 7

Math Journal 2, **p. 216**

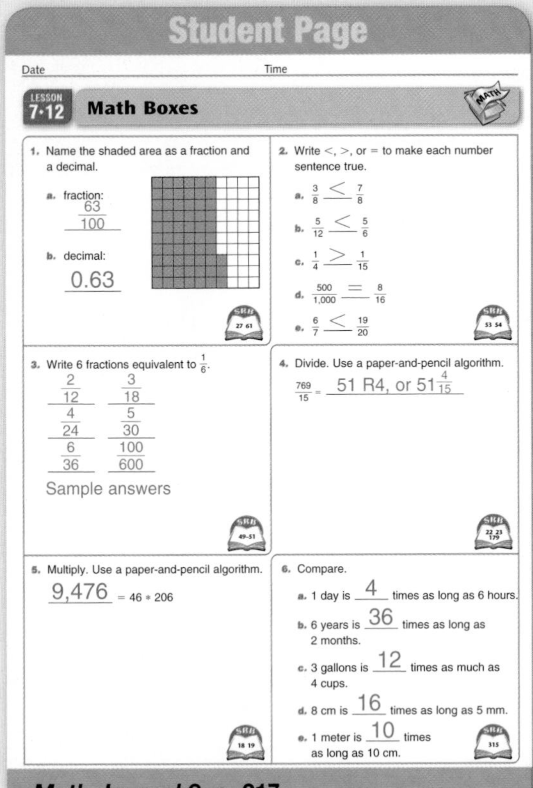

Student Page

Date Time

LESSON 7·12 **Math Boxes**

1. Name the shaded area as a fraction and a decimal.
   a. fraction: $\frac{63}{100}$
   b. decimal: 0.63

2. Write <, >, or = to make each number sentence true.
   a. $\frac{3}{8} < \frac{7}{8}$
   b. $\frac{5}{12} < \frac{5}{6}$
   c. $\frac{1}{4} > \frac{1}{15}$
   d. $\frac{500}{1,000} = \frac{8}{16}$
   e. $\frac{6}{7} < \frac{19}{20}$

3. Write 6 fractions equivalent to $\frac{1}{6}$.
   $\frac{2}{12}$, $\frac{3}{18}$, $\frac{4}{24}$, $\frac{5}{30}$, $\frac{6}{36}$, $\frac{100}{600}$
   Sample answers

4. Divide. Use a paper-and-pencil algorithm.
   $\frac{769}{15}$ = 51 R4, or $51\frac{4}{15}$

5. Multiply. Use a paper-and-pencil algorithm.
   9,476 = 46 ∗ 206

6. Compare.
   a. 1 day is 4 times as long as 6 hours.
   b. 6 years is 36 times as long as 2 months.
   c. 3 gallons is 12 times as much as 4 cups.
   d. 8 cm is 16 times as long as 5 mm.
   e. 1 meter is 10 times as long as 10 cm.

Math Journal 2, p. 217

Study Link Master

Name Date Time

STUDY LINK 7·12 **What Are the Chances?**

1. You are going to toss 2 pennies 20 times. How many times do you expect the 2 pennies will come up as
   a. 2 heads? ______ times
   b. 2 tails? ______ times
   c. 1 head and 1 tail? ______ times
   Answers vary.

2. Now toss 2 pennies together 20 times. Record the results in the table.
   Answers vary.

A Penny Toss	
Results	Number of Times
2 heads	
2 tails	
1 head and 1 tail	

3. What fraction of the tosses came up as Answers vary.
   a. 2 heads? ______ b. 2 tails? ______ c. 1 head and 1 tail? ______

4. Suppose you were to flip the coins 1,000 times. What fraction do you expect would come up as Sample answers:
   a. 2 heads? $\frac{250}{1,000}$, or $\frac{1}{4}$
   b. 2 tails? $\frac{250}{1,000}$, or $\frac{1}{4}$
   c. 1 head and 1 tail? $\frac{500}{1,000}$, or $\frac{1}{2}$

5. Explain how you got your answers for Problem 4. Sample answer: I think it will be the same fraction for 1,000 times as it is for 20 times.

Practice

6. 7 ∗ 48 = 336
7. 874 ∗ 9 = 7,866
8. 3,870 = 45 ∗ 86
9. 4,828 = 34 ∗ 142

Math Masters, p. 239

▶ Math Boxes 7·12

INDEPENDENT ACTIVITY

(*Math Journal 2,* p. 217)

Mixed Practice Math Boxes in this lesson are paired with Math Boxes in Lesson 7-10. The skill in Problem 6 previews Unit 8 content.

Writing/Reasoning Have students write a response to the following: *Explain the strategy you used to decide which fraction was greater in Problem 2e.* Sample answer: $\frac{19}{20}$ is $\frac{1}{20}$ away from 1. $\frac{6}{7}$ is $\frac{1}{7}$ away from 1. $\frac{1}{20}$ is less than $\frac{1}{7}$, so $\frac{19}{20}$ is closer to 1 than $\frac{6}{7}$ is.

▶ Study Link 7·12

INDEPENDENT ACTIVITY

(*Math Masters,* p. 239)

Home Connection Students predict the outcome of a coin toss experiment, check their predictions by performing the experiment, and express the results as fractions.

3 Differentiation Options

READINESS

INDEPENDENT ACTIVITY

▶ Renaming Fractions as Percents

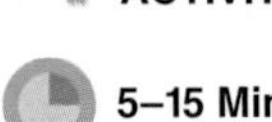

5–15 Min

(*Math Masters,* p. 240)

To explore renaming fractions as percents, have students represent fractions with base-10 blocks and rename them as percents. Ask students to discuss how they solved Problems 5 and 6.

ENRICHMENT

SMALL-GROUP ACTIVITY

▶ Comparing Actual and Expected Results of 1,000 Cube Drops

15–30 Min

(*Math Masters,* pp. 241, 242, and p. 388 or 389)

To further explore the effect of sample size on actual results, have students combine the class results of the cube-drop experiment to generate actual data on how many times a cube landed on each color for 1,000 cube drops.

Randomly select 20 students to report the results of their cube-dropping experiment on a "Results" slip, cut from *Math Masters,* page 241. Students combine the data into a "Class Results" table on *Math Masters,* page 242.

NOTE Select the results for 20 students, because data for 1,000 cube drops (20 ∗ 50) can be easily converted into percents. If your class has fewer than 20 students, select an even number of students; that way, the total number of cube drops (even number ∗ 50) will be a multiple of 100.

In a Math Log or on an Exit Slip, have students compare the results of 1,000 cube drops with the predictions they made on journal page 214. The actual results should be very close to the predicted outcomes. Ask students to explain why they think the actual results are closer to the predicted outcomes when the cubes are dropped 1,000 times. The larger the sample size is, the closer the predicted results will be to the actual results.

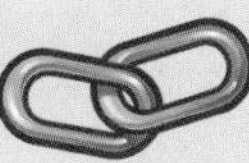

Links to the Future

This activity is an exposure to the concept of sample size. Explaining how sample size affects results is a Grade 6 Goal.

EXTRA PRACTICE

SMALL-GROUP ACTIVITY

5-Minute Math

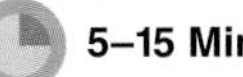

5–15 Min

To offer students more experience with probability, see *5-Minute Math,* pages 42–47.

ELL SUPPORT

SMALL-GROUP ACTIVITY

Building a Math Word Bank

5–15 Min

(*Differentiation Handbook*, p. 140)

To provide language support for probability, have students use the Word Bank Template found on *Differentiation Handbook,* page 140. Ask students to write the terms *predicted* and *actual,* draw pictures relating to each term, and write other related words. See the *Differentiation Handbook* for more information.

Planning Ahead

Remind students to complete Study Link 7-11, *Math Masters,* pages 235 and 236, in time for Lesson 8-1.

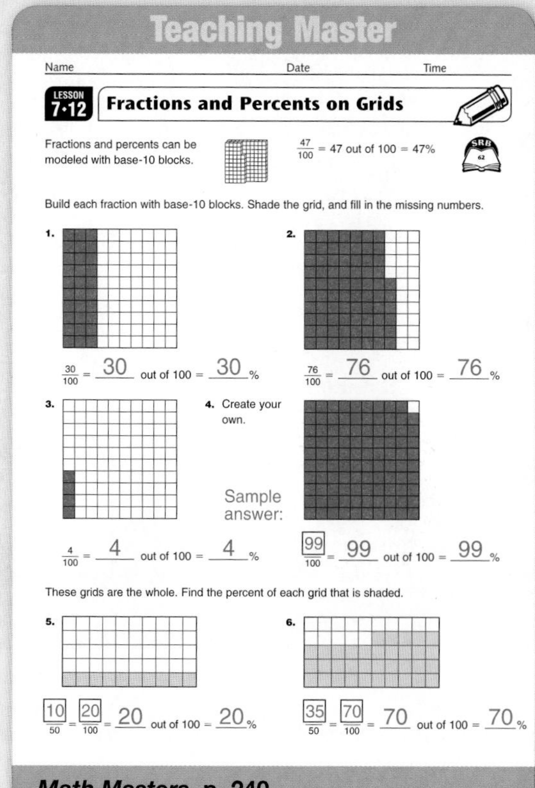

Teaching Master

Name Date Time

LESSON 7·12 **Fractions and Percents on Grids**

Fractions and percents can be modeled with base-10 blocks. $\frac{47}{100}$ = 47 out of 100 = 47%

Build each fraction with base-10 blocks. Shade the grid, and fill in the missing numbers.

1. $\frac{30}{100}$ = 30 out of 100 = 30%

2. $\frac{76}{100}$ = 76 out of 100 = 76%

3. $\frac{4}{100}$ = 4 out of 100 = 4%

4. Create your own. Sample answer: $\frac{99}{100}$ = 99 out of 100 = 99%

These grids are the whole. Find the percent of each grid that is shaded.

5. $\frac{10}{50}$ = $\frac{20}{100}$ = 20 out of 100 = 20%

6. $\frac{35}{50}$ = $\frac{70}{100}$ = 70 out of 100 = 70%

Math Masters, p. 240

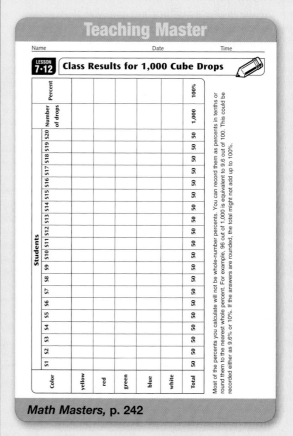

Teaching Master

Name Date Time

LESSON 7·12 **Class Results for 1,000 Cube Drops**

Color	S1	S2	S3	S4	S5	S6	S7	S8	S9	S10	S11	S12	S13	S14	S15	S16	S17	S18	S19	S20	Number of drops	Percent
yellow																						
red																						
green																						
blue																						
white																						
Total	50	50	50	50	50	50	50	50	50	50	50	50	50	50	50	50	50	50	50	50	1,000	100%

(Columns S1–S20: Students)

Most of the percents you calculate will not be whole-number percents. You can record them as percents in tenths or round them to the nearest whole percent. For example, 96 out of 1,000 is equivalent to 9.6 out of 100. This could be recorded either as 9.6% or 10%. If the answers are rounded, the total might not add up to 100%.

Math Masters, p. 242

7•12a Multiplying Fractions by Whole Numbers

Objective To apply and extend previous understandings of multiplication to multiply a fraction by a whole number.

www.everydaymathonline.com

ePresentations

eToolkit

Algorithms Practice

EM Facts Workshop Game™

Family Letters

Assessment Management

Common Core State Standards

Curriculum Focal Points

Interactive Teacher's Lesson Guide

1 Teaching the Lesson

Key Concepts and Skills

- Use a number line to represent a fraction.
  [Number and Numeration Goal 2]
- Understand a fraction $\frac{a}{b}$ as a multiple of $\frac{1}{b}$.
  [Number and Numeration Goal 3]
- Determine between which two whole numbers a fraction lies.
  [Number and Numeration Goal 6]
- Solve number stories involving multiplication of a fraction by a whole number.
  [Operations and Computation Goal 7]
- Write equations to model number stories.
  [Patterns, Functions, and Algebra Goal 2]

Key Activities

Students use a number line as a visual fraction model to represent a fraction $\frac{a}{b}$ multiplied by a whole number n as the product $n * (\frac{a}{b})$ or $\frac{(n * a)}{b}$. They solve number stories involving multiplication of a fraction by a whole number by using visual fraction models and equations to represent the problems.

Ongoing Assessment: Informing Instruction See page 637D.

Key Vocabulary

multiple ◆ equation

Materials

Math Journal 2, pp. 217A–217E
Study Link 7•12
half-sheets of paper ◆ calculator (optional)

2 Ongoing Learning & Practice

Math Boxes 7•12a
Math Journal 2, p. 217F
Students practice and maintain skills through Math Box problems.

Ongoing Assessment: Recognizing Student Achievement
Use Math Boxes, Problem 3.
[Operations and Computation Goal 5]

Study Link 7•12a
Math Masters, p. 242A
Students practice and maintain skills through Study Link activities.

3 Differentiation Options

READINESS

Skip Counting to Show Multiples of Unit Fractions
Math Masters, p. 242B
calculator
Students use calculators to skip count by unit fractions.

ENRICHMENT

Visual Models for Multiplying a Fraction by a Whole Number
Student Reference Book, p. 58
Math Masters, pp. 242C and 242D
Students explore alternative visual fraction models for multiplying a fraction by a whole number.

EXTRA PRACTICE

5-Minute Math
5-Minute Math™, pp. 22 and 23
Students practice multiplying fractions by whole numbers.

Advance Preparation

***Teacher's Reference Manual,* Grades 4–6** pp. 143, 144

Getting Started

Mental Math and Reflexes

Have students name the next three multiples in a sequence. *Suggestions:*

●○○ 8, 16, 24, ... 32, 40, 48
50, 60, 70, ... 80, 90, 100
25, 50, 75, ... 100, 125, 150

●●○ 82, 84, 86, ... 88, 90, 92
56, 60, 64, ... 68, 72, 76
18, 27, 36, ... 45, 54, 63

●●● 70, 140, 210, ... 280, 350, 420
600; 1,200; 1,800; ... 2,400; 3,000; 3,600
125, 250, 375, ... 500, 625, 750

Math Message

Name the next three multiples in each sequence.

$\frac{1}{10}, \frac{2}{10}, \frac{3}{10}, \ldots \frac{4}{10}, \frac{5}{10}, \frac{6}{10}$

$\frac{1}{4}, \frac{2}{4}, \frac{3}{4}, \ldots \frac{4}{4}, \frac{5}{4}, \frac{6}{4}$

Study Link 7•12 Follow-Up

Have small groups compare the results of the penny toss experiment. Ask volunteers to share their answers for Problem 5. Have students indicate thumbs-up if they agree.

1 Teaching the Lesson

Math Message Follow-Up

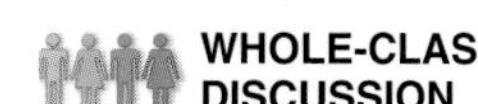

WHOLE-CLASS DISCUSSION

Ask students how they determined the next three **multiples** in each sequence. *Possible strategies:*

▷ Think of the problem as skip counting by $\frac{1}{10}$s. To get the next multiple, add $\frac{1}{10}$ to the previous fraction. For example, $\frac{1}{10} + \frac{1}{10} = \frac{2}{10}$; $\frac{2}{10} + \frac{1}{10} = \frac{3}{10}$; $\frac{3}{10} + \frac{1}{10} = \frac{4}{10}$; and so on.

▷ Think in terms of equal groups. For example, 1 group of $\frac{1}{4}$ is $\frac{1}{4}$; 2 groups of $\frac{1}{4}$ is $\frac{2}{4}$; 3 groups of $\frac{1}{4}$ is $\frac{3}{4}$; 4 groups of $\frac{1}{4}$ is $\frac{4}{4}$; and so on.

Tell students that in this lesson they will use their understanding of multiples to multiply fractions by whole numbers.

Using a Visual Fraction Model to Multiply a Unit Fraction by a Whole Number

PARTNER ACTIVITY

(*Math Journal 2,* pp. 217A)

Draw the number line below on the board or overhead.

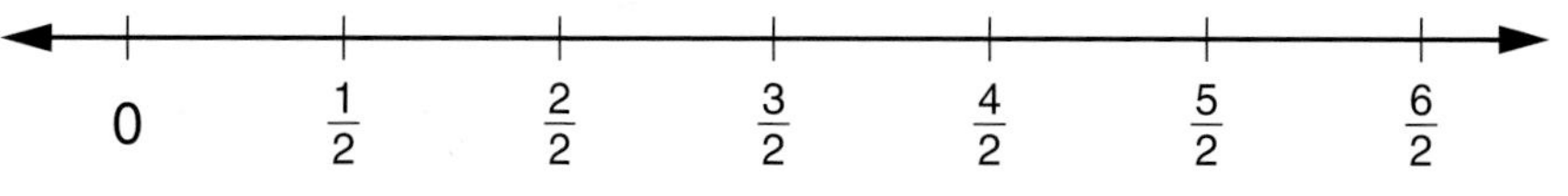

Have volunteers explain how they could use the number line and their understanding of multiples to help them solve the problem $3 * \frac{1}{2}$.

Adjusting the Activity

Provide students with calculators to assist with skip counting. See the Part 3 Readiness activity for additional information.

AUDITORY ◆ KINESTHETIC ◆ TACTILE ◆ VISUAL

NOTE In *Third Grade Everyday Mathematics* children participated in skip-counting activities to help them memorize the multiplication facts. While completing these activities, they were finding multiples. A *multiple* of a number is the product of a counting number and the number itself.

Student Page

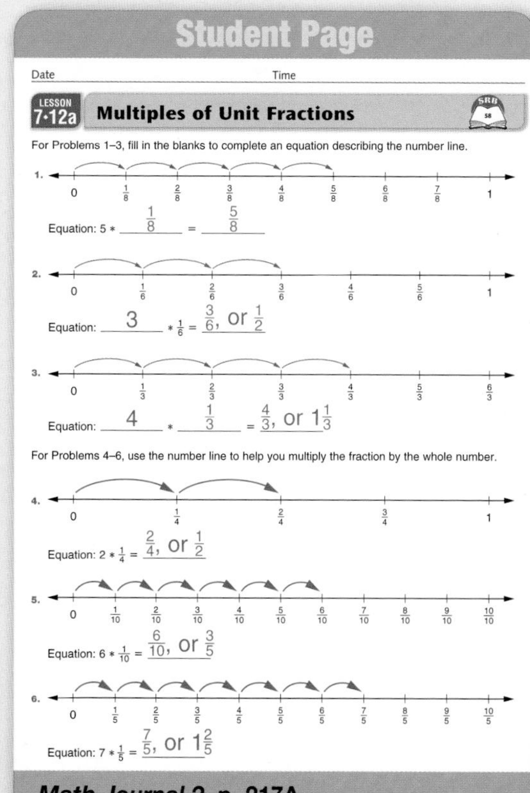

Date Time

LESSON 7•12a **Multiples of Unit Fractions**

For Problems 1–3, fill in the blanks to complete an equation describing the number line.

1. Equation: $5 * \frac{1}{8} = \frac{5}{8}$

2. Equation: $3 * \frac{1}{6} = \frac{3}{6}$, or $\frac{1}{2}$

3. Equation: $4 * \frac{1}{3} = \frac{4}{3}$, or $1\frac{1}{3}$

For Problems 4–6, use the number line to help you multiply the fraction by the whole number.

4. Equation: $2 * \frac{1}{4} = \frac{2}{4}$, or $\frac{1}{2}$

5. Equation: $6 * \frac{1}{10} = \frac{6}{10}$, or $\frac{3}{5}$

6. Equation: $7 * \frac{1}{5} = \frac{7}{5}$, or $1\frac{2}{5}$

Math Journal 2, p. 217A

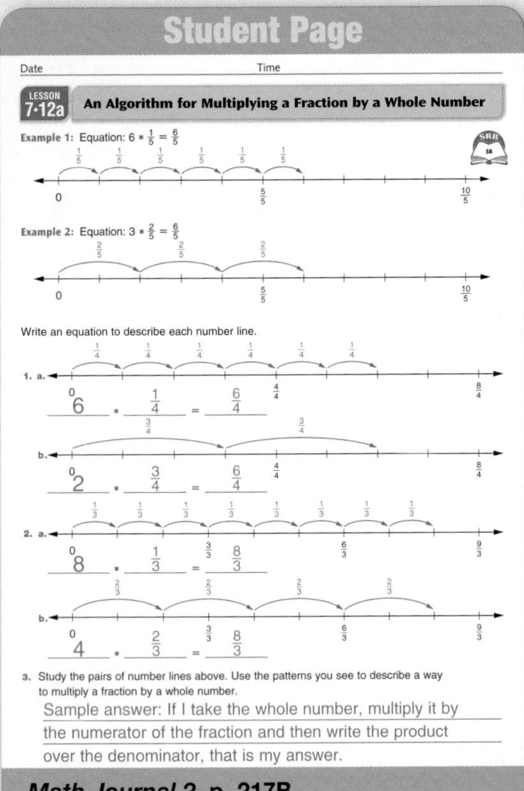

Student Page

Date Time

LESSON 7·12a **An Algorithm for Multiplying a Fraction by a Whole Number**

Example 1: Equation: $6 * \frac{1}{5} = \frac{6}{5}$

Example 2: Equation: $3 * \frac{2}{5} = \frac{6}{5}$

Write an equation to describe each number line.

1. a. $6 * \frac{1}{4} = \frac{6}{4}$

b. $2 * \frac{3}{4} = \frac{6}{4}$

2. a. $8 * \frac{1}{3} = \frac{8}{3}$

b. $4 * \frac{2}{3} = \frac{8}{3}$

3. Study the pairs of number lines above. Use the patterns you see to describe a way to multiply a fraction by a whole number.
Sample answer: If I take the whole number, multiply it by the numerator of the fraction and then write the product over the denominator, that is my answer.

Math Journal 2, p. 217B

Student Page

Date Time

LESSON 7·12a **Multiplying Fractions by Whole Numbers**

Use number lines to help you solve the problems.

1. $5 * \frac{1}{6} = \frac{5}{6}$

2. $6 * \frac{1}{3} = \frac{6}{3}$, or 2

3. $\frac{3}{8} = 3 * \frac{1}{8}$ Sample answer:

4. $2 * \frac{4}{3} = \frac{8}{3}$, or $2\frac{2}{3}$

5. $\frac{12}{8}$, or $1\frac{4}{8}$, or $1\frac{1}{2} = 4 * \frac{3}{8}$

6. $\frac{6}{10}$, or $\frac{3}{5} = 3 * \frac{2}{10}$ Sample answer:

Math Journal 2, p. 217C

One way is to visualize jumps or hops on the number line, starting at 0. The fraction tells the size of the jump; the whole number tells the number of jumps. Thus, $3 * \frac{1}{2}$ is 3 jumps, each $\frac{1}{2}$ unit long. You end up at $\frac{3}{2}$. So, $3 * \frac{1}{2} = \frac{3}{2}$, or $1\frac{1}{2}$.

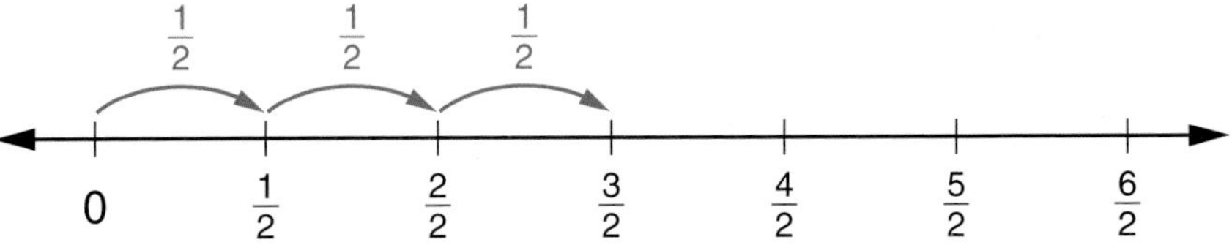

Partners complete journal page 217A. Tell students that an **equation** is a number sentence with an equals sign, such as $3 * \frac{1}{2} = \frac{3}{2}$. As you circulate and assist, pose questions such as the following:

- Which number in the equation tells you the size of the jump? The first fraction
- Which number in the equation tells you the number of jumps? The whole number
- Can you name the products in Problems 3 and 6 as mixed numbers? $\frac{4}{3} = 1\frac{1}{3}$; $\frac{7}{5} = 1\frac{2}{5}$

▶ Using a Visual Fraction Model to Multiply Any Fraction by a Whole Number

(*Math Journal 2,* pp. 217B and 217C)

Have partners study the examples at the top of journal page 217B. On a half-sheet of paper, students should record any similarities and differences they see between the equations modeled on the number lines.

Expect students to share observations such as the following:

▷ Both equations involve multiplication of a fraction by a whole number.

▷ Both equations have the same product.

▷ The factors in the equations are different, but $\frac{2}{5}$ is a multiple of $\frac{1}{5}$ and 6 is a multiple of 3.

▷ It takes more jumps of $\frac{1}{5}$ to get to $\frac{6}{5}$ than it does jumps of $\frac{2}{5}$ because the jumps of $\frac{1}{5}$ are smaller than the jumps of $\frac{2}{5}$.

▷ The whole number factor in $6 * \frac{1}{5} = \frac{6}{5}$ is twice as much as the whole number factor in $3 * \frac{2}{5} = \frac{6}{5}$. The fraction factor in $6 * \frac{1}{5} = \frac{6}{5}$ is half as much as the fraction factor in $3 * \frac{2}{5} = \frac{6}{5}$.

Have partners complete Problems 1 and 2 on journal page 217B by writing a multiplication equation to describe each number line. When students have completed Problem 3, bring the class together to discuss the algorithm for multiplication of a fraction by a whole number. The pattern can be expressed as: $n * \frac{a}{b} = \frac{(n * a)}{b}$.

Have students complete journal page 217C for additional practice multiplying fractions by whole numbers. Encourage students to use the pattern they discovered on journal page 217B to check their answers.

Solving Number Stories

PARTNER ACTIVITY

(*Math Journal 2,* pp. 217D and 217E)

Pose the following number story:

When Carlos goes to the gym, he exercises for $\frac{3}{4}$ of an hour and burns about 200 calories. Last week he went to the gym 5 times. How many hours did Carlos spend at the gym last week?

Ongoing Assessment: Informing Instruction

Watch for students who are distracted by the "extra" 200 in the number story. Encourage them to eliminate irrelevant information by determining exactly what they want to find out, what information they already know, and what they might need to know in order to solve the problem.

On a half-sheet of paper, have students draw a visual fraction model to represent the number story. Expect drawings such as the following:

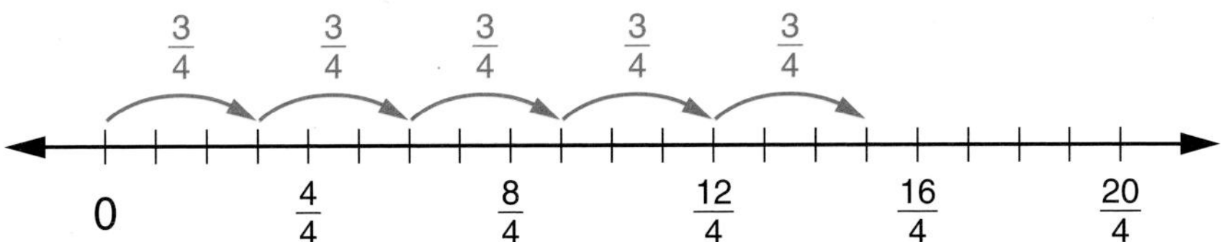

Then have students write a multiplication equation to represent the problem. $5 * \frac{3}{4} = \frac{15}{4}$

Ask students to determine between which two whole numbers of hours the product lies. 3 and 4 hours Have them explain their strategy for finding the answer. *Possible strategies:*

- ▷ Use the number line drawn to represent the number story. Note that the product lies between $\frac{12}{4}$, or 3, and $\frac{16}{4}$, or 4.
- ▷ The fraction $\frac{15}{4}$ can be renamed as the mixed number $3\frac{3}{4}$ by dividing the numerator, 15, by the denominator, 4: 15 / 4 → 3 R3. The quotient, 3, is the whole number part of the mixed number. The remainder, 3, is the numerator of the fraction part of the mixed number. It tells how many fourths are left over after making as many wholes as possible.

Student Page

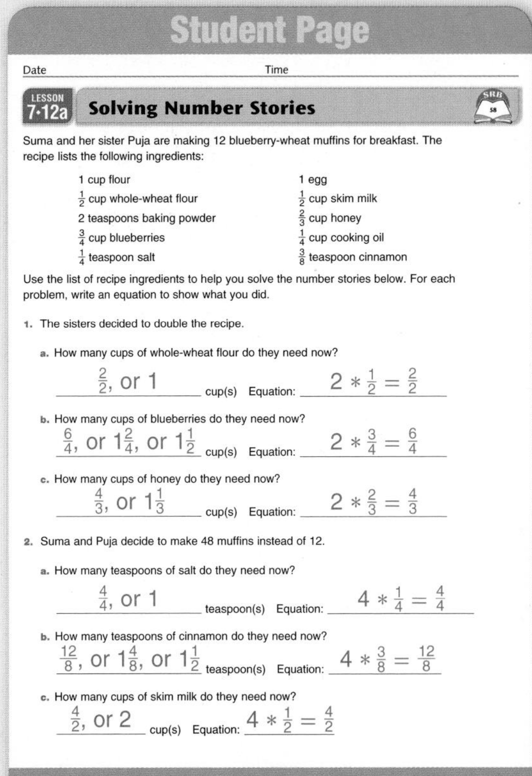

Date Time

LESSON 7•12a **Solving Number Stories**

Suma and her sister Puja are making 12 blueberry-wheat muffins for breakfast. The recipe lists the following ingredients:

1 cup flour	1 egg
$\frac{1}{2}$ cup whole-wheat flour	$\frac{1}{2}$ cup skim milk
2 teaspoons baking powder	$\frac{2}{3}$ cup honey
$\frac{3}{4}$ cup blueberries	$\frac{1}{4}$ cup cooking oil
$\frac{1}{4}$ teaspoon salt	$\frac{3}{8}$ teaspoon cinnamon

Use the list of recipe ingredients to help you solve the number stories below. For each problem, write an equation to show what you did.

1. The sisters decided to double the recipe.
   a. How many cups of whole-wheat flour do they need now? $\frac{2}{2}$, or 1 cup(s) Equation: $2 * \frac{1}{2} = \frac{2}{2}$
   b. How many cups of blueberries do they need now? $\frac{6}{4}$, or $1\frac{2}{4}$, or $1\frac{1}{2}$ cup(s) Equation: $2 * \frac{3}{4} = \frac{6}{4}$
   c. How many cups of honey do they need now? $\frac{4}{3}$, or $1\frac{1}{3}$ cup(s) Equation: $2 * \frac{2}{3} = \frac{4}{3}$
2. Suma and Puja decide to make 48 muffins instead of 12.
   a. How many teaspoons of salt do they need now? $\frac{4}{4}$, or 1 teaspoon(s) Equation: $4 * \frac{1}{4} = \frac{4}{4}$
   b. How many teaspoons of cinnamon do they need now? $\frac{12}{8}$, or $1\frac{4}{8}$, or $1\frac{1}{2}$ teaspoon(s) Equation: $4 * \frac{3}{8} = \frac{12}{8}$
   c. How many cups of skim milk do they need now? $\frac{4}{2}$, or 2 cup(s) Equation: $4 * \frac{1}{2} = \frac{4}{2}$

Math Journal 2, p. 217D

NOTE In Lesson 3-8, students used number models to model number stories. A *number model* is a number sentence or part of a number sentence. A number model can include an equal sign, but it is not required. An *equation* is a number sentence with an equal sign. See Section 10.2 in the *Teacher's Reference Manual* for more information.

Have partners complete journal pages 217D and 217E. Encourage students to use visual fraction models, such as number lines, to help them solve the problems. When reviewing answers, pose questions such as the following:

- Which of the products on journal page 217D can you rename as whole numbers? Problem 1a: $\frac{2}{2} = 1$; Problem 2a: $\frac{4}{4} = 1$; Problem 2c: $\frac{4}{2} = 2$
- Between which two whole numbers does the product in Problem 2b lie? 1 and 2
- In Problem 2, how did you decide which whole number you would multiply the recipe ingredients by? Sample answer: The recipe makes 12 muffins. If the sisters want 48 muffins they will need to quadruple the recipe because $12 * 4 = 48$.
- How did you solve Problem 6? Sample answer: Let the letter a stand for the number of meetings Cole would need to attend and write the equation $a * \frac{5}{2} = \frac{15}{2}$. Use the algorithm for multiplying a fraction by a whole number and think: What number times 5 will give me 15? $3 * 5 = 15$, so $3 * \frac{5}{2} = \frac{15}{2}$. Cole will need to attend 3 meetings.
- In Problem 6, between which two whole-number distances does the distance $\frac{15}{2}$ miles lie? Between 7 and 8 miles

Allow time for students to share and solve the number stories they wrote for Problem 7. For each problem, pose questions such as the following:

- Between which two whole numbers does the answer lie?
- Can you use a visual fraction model or an equation to represent the problem?

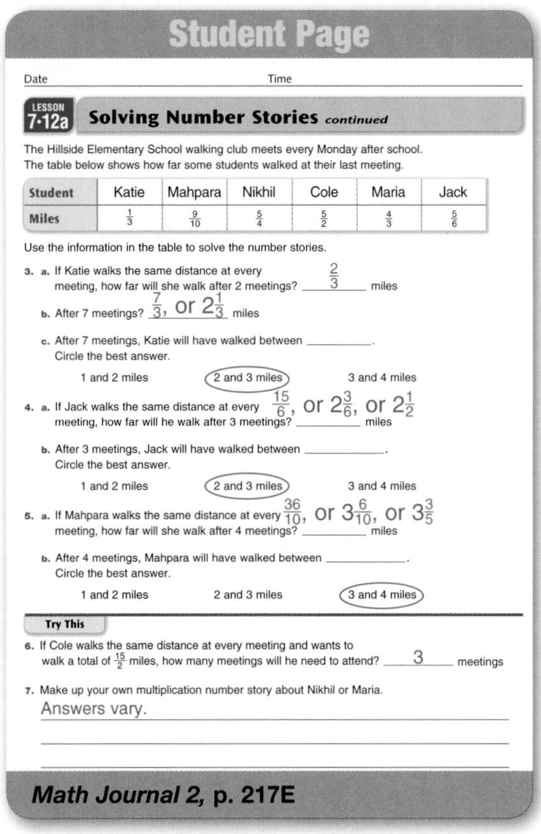

Student Page

Date Time

LESSON 7·12a **Solving Number Stories** *continued*

The Hillside Elementary School walking club meets every Monday after school. The table below shows how far some students walked at their last meeting.

Student	Katie	Mahpara	Nikhil	Cole	Maria	Jack
Miles	$\frac{1}{3}$	$\frac{9}{10}$	$\frac{5}{4}$	$\frac{5}{2}$	$\frac{4}{3}$	$\frac{5}{6}$

Use the information in the table to solve the number stories.

3. a. If Katie walks the same distance at every meeting, how far will she walk after 2 meetings? $\frac{2}{3}$ miles
   b. After 7 meetings? $\frac{7}{3}$, or $2\frac{1}{3}$ miles
   c. After 7 meetings, Katie will have walked between _____. Circle the best answer.
   1 and 2 miles (2 and 3 miles) 3 and 4 miles
4. a. If Jack walks the same distance at every meeting, how far will he walk after 3 meetings? $\frac{15}{6}$, or $2\frac{3}{6}$, or $2\frac{1}{2}$ miles
   b. After 3 meetings, Jack will have walked between _____. Circle the best answer.
   1 and 2 miles (2 and 3 miles) 3 and 4 miles
5. a. If Mahpara walks the same distance at every meeting, how far will she walk after 4 meetings? $\frac{36}{10}$, or $3\frac{6}{10}$, or $3\frac{3}{5}$ miles
   b. After 4 meetings, Mahpara will have walked between _____. Circle the best answer.
   1 and 2 miles 2 and 3 miles (3 and 4 miles)

Try This

6. If Cole walks the same distance at every meeting and wants to walk a total of $\frac{15}{2}$ miles, how many meetings will he need to attend? 3 meetings
7. Make up your own multiplication number story about Nikhil or Maria.
   Answers vary.

Math Journal 2, p. 217E

2 Ongoing Learning & Practice

Math Boxes 7•12a

INDEPENDENT ACTIVITY

(*Math Journal 2,* p. 217F)

Mixed Practice Math Boxes in this lesson are paired with Math Boxes in Lessons 7-9 and 7-11. The skill in Problem 6 previews Unit 8 content.

Ongoing Assessment: Recognizing Student Achievement

Math Boxes Problem 3

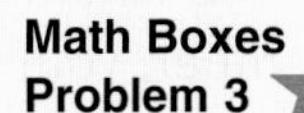

Use **Math Boxes, Problem 3** to assess students' ability to solve mixed-number addition problems. Students are making adequate progress if they are able to solve Problem 3a, which involves mixed numbers with like denominators. Some students may be able to solve Problem 3b, which involves mixed numbers with unlike denominators, by using equivalent mixed numbers with like denominators, using manipulatives, or drawing pictures.

[Operations and Computation Goal 5]

Study Link 7•12a

INDEPENDENT ACTIVITY

(*Math Masters,* p. 242A)

Home Connection Students use number lines to multiply fractions by whole numbers.

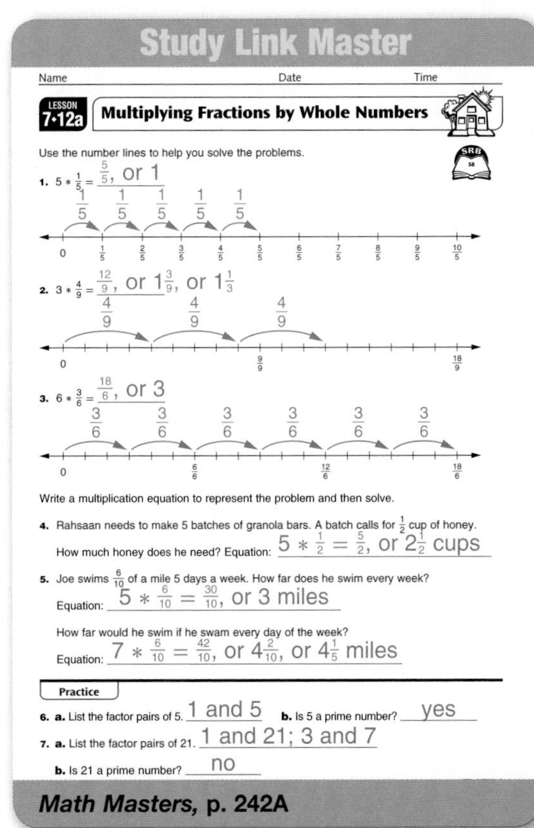

Study Link Master

Name Date Time

LESSON 7•12a **Multiplying Fractions by Whole Numbers**

Use the number lines to help you solve the problems.

1. $5 * \frac{1}{5} = \frac{5}{5}$, or 1

2. $3 * \frac{4}{9} = \frac{12}{9}$, or $1\frac{3}{9}$, or $1\frac{1}{3}$

3. $6 * \frac{3}{6} = \frac{18}{6}$, or 3

Write a multiplication equation to represent the problem and then solve.

4. Rahsaan needs to make 5 batches of granola bars. A batch calls for $\frac{1}{2}$ cup of honey. How much honey does he need? Equation: $5 * \frac{1}{2} = \frac{5}{2}$, or $2\frac{1}{2}$ cups

5. Joe swims $\frac{6}{10}$ of a mile 5 days a week. How far does he swim every week? Equation: $5 * \frac{6}{10} = \frac{30}{10}$, or 3 miles

How far would he swim if he swam every day of the week? Equation: $7 * \frac{6}{10} = \frac{42}{10}$, or $4\frac{2}{10}$, or $4\frac{1}{5}$ miles

Practice

6. a. List the factor pairs of 5. 1 and 5 b. Is 5 a prime number? yes

7. a. List the factor pairs of 21. 1 and 21; 3 and 7

b. Is 21 a prime number? no

Math Masters, p. 242A

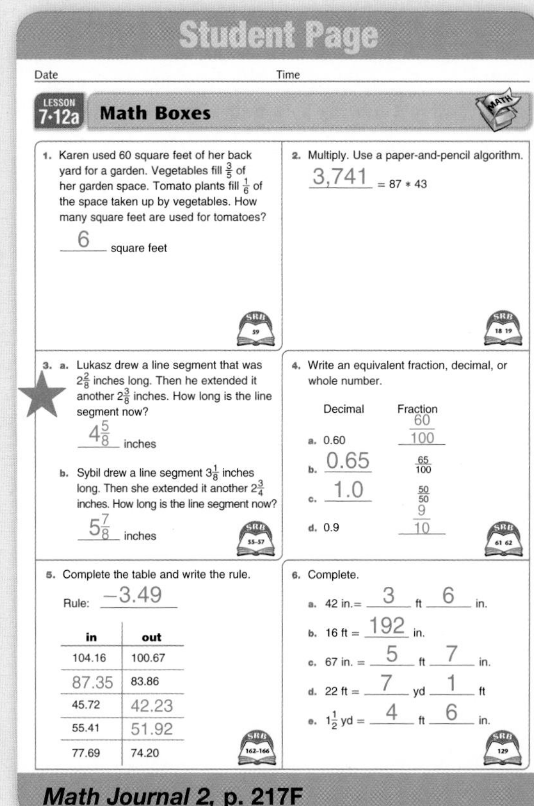

Student Page

Date Time

LESSON 7•12a **Math Boxes**

1. Karen used 60 square feet of her back yard for a garden. Vegetables fill $\frac{3}{5}$ of her garden space. Tomato plants fill $\frac{1}{6}$ of the space taken up by vegetables. How many square feet are used for tomatoes? 6 square feet

2. Multiply. Use a paper-and-pencil algorithm. 3,741 = 87 * 43

3. a. Lukasz drew a line segment that was $2\frac{2}{8}$ inches long. Then he extended it another $2\frac{3}{8}$ inches. How long is the line segment now? $4\frac{5}{8}$ inches

b. Sybil drew a line segment $3\frac{1}{8}$ inches long. Then she extended it another $2\frac{3}{4}$ inches. How long is the line segment now? $5\frac{7}{8}$ inches

4. Write an equivalent fraction, decimal, or whole number.

	Decimal	Fraction
a.	0.60	$\frac{60}{100}$
b.	0.65	$\frac{65}{100}$
c.	1.0	$\frac{50}{50}$
d.	0.9	$\frac{9}{10}$

5. Complete the table and write the rule.

Rule: −3.49

in	out
104.16	100.67
87.35	83.86
45.72	42.23
55.41	51.92
77.69	74.20

6. Complete.

a. 42 in. = 3 ft 6 in.

b. 16 ft = 192 in.

c. 67 in. = 5 ft 7 in.

d. 22 ft = 7 yd 1 ft

e. $1\frac{1}{2}$ yd = 4 ft 6 in.

Math Journal 2, p. 217F

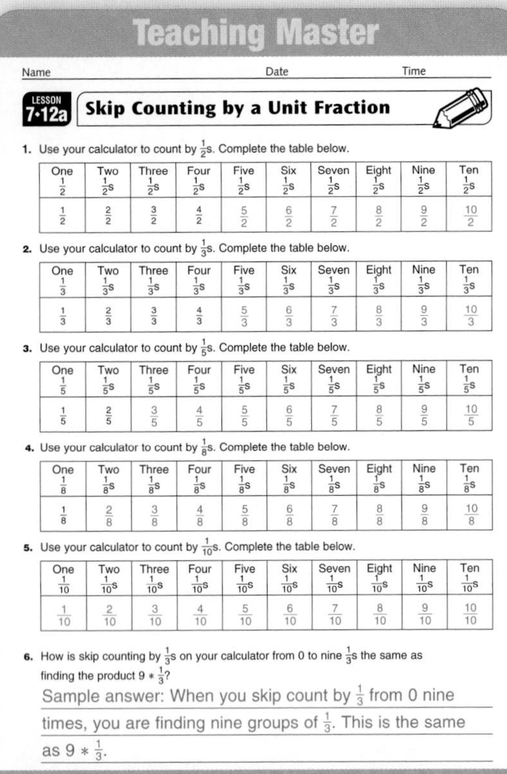
Teaching Master

Name Date Time

LESSON 7•12a **Skip Counting by a Unit Fraction**

1. Use your calculator to count by $\frac{1}{2}$s. Complete the table below.

One $\frac{1}{2}$	Two $\frac{1}{2}$s	Three $\frac{1}{2}$s	Four $\frac{1}{2}$s	Five $\frac{1}{2}$s	Six $\frac{1}{2}$s	Seven $\frac{1}{2}$s	Eight $\frac{1}{2}$s	Nine $\frac{1}{2}$s	Ten $\frac{1}{2}$s
$\frac{1}{2}$	$\frac{2}{2}$	$\frac{3}{2}$	$\frac{4}{2}$	$\frac{5}{2}$	$\frac{6}{2}$	$\frac{7}{2}$	$\frac{8}{2}$	$\frac{9}{2}$	$\frac{10}{2}$

2. Use your calculator to count by $\frac{1}{3}$s. Complete the table below.

One $\frac{1}{3}$	Two $\frac{1}{3}$s	Three $\frac{1}{3}$s	Four $\frac{1}{3}$s	Five $\frac{1}{3}$s	Six $\frac{1}{3}$s	Seven $\frac{1}{3}$s	Eight $\frac{1}{3}$s	Nine $\frac{1}{3}$s	Ten $\frac{1}{3}$s
$\frac{1}{3}$	$\frac{2}{3}$	$\frac{3}{3}$	$\frac{4}{3}$	$\frac{5}{3}$	$\frac{6}{3}$	$\frac{7}{3}$	$\frac{8}{3}$	$\frac{9}{3}$	$\frac{10}{3}$

3. Use your calculator to count by $\frac{1}{5}$s. Complete the table below.

One $\frac{1}{5}$	Two $\frac{1}{5}$s	Three $\frac{1}{5}$s	Four $\frac{1}{5}$s	Five $\frac{1}{5}$s	Six $\frac{1}{5}$s	Seven $\frac{1}{5}$s	Eight $\frac{1}{5}$s	Nine $\frac{1}{5}$s	Ten $\frac{1}{5}$s
$\frac{1}{5}$	$\frac{2}{5}$	$\frac{3}{5}$	$\frac{4}{5}$	$\frac{5}{5}$	$\frac{6}{5}$	$\frac{7}{5}$	$\frac{8}{5}$	$\frac{9}{5}$	$\frac{10}{5}$

4. Use your calculator to count by $\frac{1}{8}$s. Complete the table below.

One $\frac{1}{8}$	Two $\frac{1}{8}$s	Three $\frac{1}{8}$s	Four $\frac{1}{8}$s	Five $\frac{1}{8}$s	Six $\frac{1}{8}$s	Seven $\frac{1}{8}$s	Eight $\frac{1}{8}$s	Nine $\frac{1}{8}$s	Ten $\frac{1}{8}$s
$\frac{1}{8}$	$\frac{2}{8}$	$\frac{3}{8}$	$\frac{4}{8}$	$\frac{5}{8}$	$\frac{6}{8}$	$\frac{7}{8}$	$\frac{8}{8}$	$\frac{9}{8}$	$\frac{10}{8}$

5. Use your calculator to count by $\frac{1}{10}$s. Complete the table below.

One $\frac{1}{10}$	Two $\frac{1}{10}$s	Three $\frac{1}{10}$s	Four $\frac{1}{10}$s	Five $\frac{1}{10}$s	Six $\frac{1}{10}$s	Seven $\frac{1}{10}$s	Eight $\frac{1}{10}$s	Nine $\frac{1}{10}$s	Ten $\frac{1}{10}$s
$\frac{1}{10}$	$\frac{2}{10}$	$\frac{3}{10}$	$\frac{4}{10}$	$\frac{5}{10}$	$\frac{6}{10}$	$\frac{7}{10}$	$\frac{8}{10}$	$\frac{9}{10}$	$\frac{10}{10}$

6. How is skip counting by $\frac{1}{3}$s on your calculator from 0 to nine $\frac{1}{3}$s the same as finding the product $9 * \frac{1}{3}$?

Sample answer: When you skip count by $\frac{1}{3}$ from 0 nine times, you are finding nine groups of $\frac{1}{3}$. This is the same as $9 * \frac{1}{3}$.

Math Masters, **p. 242B**

3 Differentiation Options

READINESS

SMALL-GROUP ACTIVITY

15–30 Min

▶ Skip Counting to Show Multiples of Unit Fractions

(*Math Masters,* p. 242B)

To explore multiples of unit fractions, have students skip count on the calculator. Remind students that when you skip count by a number, your counts are the multiples of that number.

Review the steps for counting by 5s on the calculator. Students can program their calculator using the following steps:

TI-15:

1. Press (On/Off) and (Clear) simultaneously. This clears your calculator display and memory.
2. Press (Op1) + 5 (Op1). This tells the calculator to count up by 5s.
3. Press 0. This is the starting number.

Casio *fx*-55:

1. Press (AC). This clears your calculator display and memory.
2. Press 5. This tells the calculator to count by 5s.
3. Press (+) (+). This tells the calculator to count up.
4. Press 0. This is the starting number.

Now the calculator is ready to count by 5s. Without clearing their calculators, have students press the (Op1) key or the (=) key. Press the (Op1) key or the (=) key repeatedly as the students count together by 5s.

Next have students skip count by the unit fraction $\frac{1}{4}$. You may first need to remind students of the steps to enter a fraction on their calculators.

To enter $\frac{1}{4}$:

▷ On a TI-15: 1 (n) 4 (d).

▷ On a Casio *fx*-55: 1 (b/c) 4.

Have students skip count by unit fractions to complete the tables on *Math Masters,* page 242B. Afterward, discuss how Problem 6 highlights the concept that a fraction such as $\frac{9}{3}$ means the same thing as $9 * (\frac{1}{3})$. In general, $\frac{a}{b} = a * (\frac{1}{b})$.

ENRICHMENT

Visual Models for Multiplying a Fraction by a Whole Number

15–30 Min

(*Student Reference Book,* p. 58; *Math Masters,* pp. 242C and 242D)

To extend students' understanding of fraction multiplication, have them explore two different models: addition and area. Begin by having students read *Student Reference Book,* page 58. Discuss the example provided for each model as a group.

Have students complete *Math Masters,* pages 242C and 242D. For page 242C, encourage the groups to discuss how each number in the problem was represented in the model. The whole number is the number of rectangles drawn. The denominator of the fraction is the number of equal parts each rectangle is divided into. The numerator of the fraction is the number of parts of each rectangle that are shaded.

EXTRA PRACTICE

SMALL-GROUP ACTIVITY

5-Minute Math

5–15 Min

To offer students more experience with multiplying fractions by whole numbers, see *5-Minute Math,* pages 22 and 23.

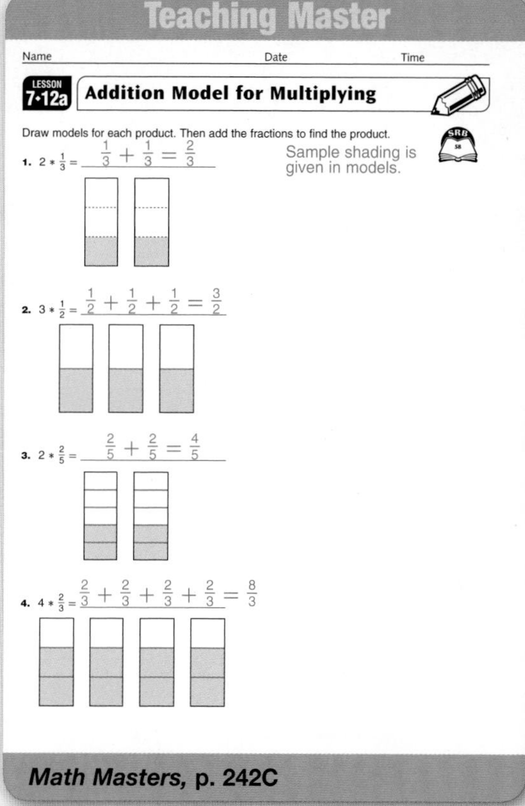

Teaching Master

Name Date Time

LESSON 7•12a **Addition Model for Multiplying**

Draw models for each product. Then add the fractions to find the product.

Sample shading is given in models.

1. $2 * \frac{1}{3} = \frac{1}{3} + \frac{1}{3} = \frac{2}{3}$

2. $3 * \frac{1}{2} = \frac{1}{2} + \frac{1}{2} + \frac{1}{2} = \frac{3}{2}$

3. $2 * \frac{2}{5} = \frac{2}{5} + \frac{2}{5} = \frac{4}{5}$

4. $4 * \frac{2}{3} = \frac{2}{3} + \frac{2}{3} + \frac{2}{3} + \frac{2}{3} = \frac{8}{3}$

Math Masters, p. 242C

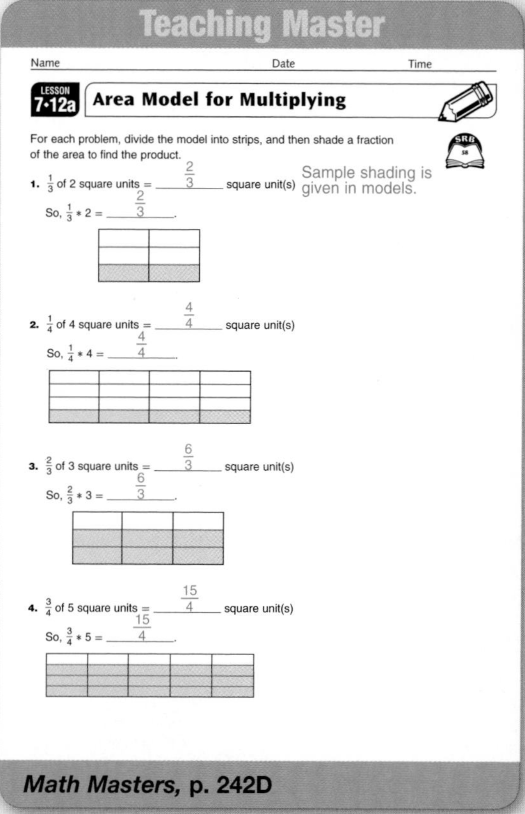

Teaching Master

Name Date Time

LESSON 7•12a **Area Model for Multiplying**

For each problem, divide the model into strips, and then shade a fraction of the area to find the product.

Sample shading is given in models.

1. $\frac{1}{3}$ of 2 square units = $\frac{2}{3}$ square unit(s)
So, $\frac{1}{3} * 2 = \frac{2}{3}$.

2. $\frac{1}{4}$ of 4 square units = $\frac{4}{4}$ square unit(s)
So, $\frac{1}{4} * 4 = \frac{4}{4}$.

3. $\frac{2}{3}$ of 3 square units = $\frac{6}{3}$ square unit(s)
So, $\frac{2}{3} * 3 = \frac{6}{3}$.

4. $\frac{3}{4}$ of 5 square units = $\frac{15}{4}$ square unit(s)
So, $\frac{3}{4} * 5 = \frac{15}{4}$.

Math Masters, p. 242D

7•13 Progress Check 7

Objective To assess students' progress on mathematical content through the end of Unit 7.

1 Looking Back: Cumulative Assessment

Input student data from Progress Check 7 into the **Assessment Management Spreadsheets**.

Materials

- Study Link 7•12a
- *Assessment Handbook,* pp. 102–109, 184–188, 222, and 270–273
- slate; straightedge; pattern blocks; colored pencils (optional)

CONTENT ASSESSED	LESSON(S)	ASSESSMENT ITEMS: SELF	ORAL/SLATE	WRITTEN: PART A	WRITTEN: PART B	OPEN RESPONSE
Solve problems involving fractional parts of regions and collections; identify the ONE. [Number and Numeration Goal 2]	7•1–7•5, 7•7, 7•9–7•12	1	4	9–11	24	✓
Rename tenths and hundredths as decimals. [Number and Numeration Goal 5]	7•8–7•12		3			
Find equivalent fractions. [Number and Numeration Goal 5]	7•6–7•10, 7•12	2		1–3, 6		
Compare and order fractions. [Number and Numeration Goal 6]	7•8–7•10, 7•12	3	1	4–8	18	
Solve multidigit multiplication and division problems. [Operations and Computation Goal 4]	7•1–7•4, 7•6, 7•8–7•12	4		14–17		
Add and subtract fractions and mixed numbers. [Operations and Computation Goal 5]	7•3–7•6, 7•8, 7•9, 7•11	5			20–24	✓
Use ordered number pairs on a coordinate grid. [Measurement and Reference Frames Goal 4]	7•1, 7•3, 7•5, 7•7, 7•9			13		
Use basic probability terms. [Data and Chance Goal 3]	7•3, 7•6, 7•11, 7•12		2			
Calculate expected probability. [Data and Chance Goal 4]	7•3, 7•5–7•8, 7•11, 7•12	6		12	19	

2 Looking Ahead: Preparing for Unit 8

Math Boxes 7•13

Study Link 7•13: Unit 8 Family Letter

Materials

- *Math Journal 2,* p. 218
- *Math Masters,* pp. 243–246

Getting Started

Math Message • Self Assessment

Complete the Self Assessment (Assessment Handbook, *page 184*).

Study Link 7·12a Follow-Up

Have partners compare answers.

1 Looking Back: Cumulative Assessment

Math Message Follow-Up

(Self Assessment, *Assessment Handbook,* p. 184)

The Self Assessment offers students the opportunity to reflect upon their progress.

Oral and Slate Assessments

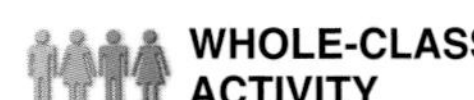

Problems 2 and 3 provide summative information and can be used for grading purposes. Problems 1 and 4 provide formative information that can be useful in planning future instruction.

Oral Assessment

1. Write pairs of fractions on the board. Have students identify the greater fraction and explain how they know it is greater. *Suggestions:*
   - $\frac{2}{5}$ and $\frac{2}{20}$ $\frac{2}{5}$; The fractions have like numerators. The smaller the denominator is, the larger the fraction is.
   - $\frac{4}{12}$ and $\frac{9}{12}$ $\frac{9}{12}$; The fractions have like denominators. The larger the numerator is, the larger the fraction is.
   - $\frac{5}{12}$ and $\frac{9}{16}$ $\frac{9}{16}$; $\frac{5}{12}$ is less than $\frac{1}{2}$, and $\frac{9}{16}$ is greater than $\frac{1}{2}$.
2. Ask students to use probability language to describe the likelihood of the event. *Suggestions:*
   - I will flip a coin, and it will land on heads. 50-50 chance
   - I will flip a coin, and it will land on heads or tails. certain
   - I will roll a six-sided die, and it will land on a number less than 6. very likely
   - I will roll a six-sided die, and it will land on 23. impossible
   - I will roll a six-sided die, and it will land on a number less than 2. unlikely

Assessment Master

Name Date Time

LESSON 7·13 **Self Assessment** Progress Check 7

Think about each skill listed below. Assess your own progress by checking the most appropriate box.

Skills	I can do this on my own and explain how to do it.	I can do this on my own.	I can do this if I get help or look at an example.
1. Solve "fraction-of" problems like these: $\frac{1}{4}$ of 8, $\frac{4}{5}$ of 30			
2. Find equivalent fractions.			
3. Compare fractions like these: $\frac{1}{4}$ and $\frac{1}{10}$, $\frac{2}{5}$ and $\frac{2}{9}$			
4. Divide multidigit numbers like these: 492 / 7, 684 / 5			
5. Add fractions like these: $\frac{1}{6}+\frac{2}{6}$, $\frac{1}{3}+\frac{1}{6}$, $\frac{1}{2}+\frac{1}{3}$			
6. Use a fraction to describe the probability of an event.			

Assessment Handbook, **p. 184**

Assessment Master

Name Date Time

LESSON 7·13 **Written Assessment** Progress Check 7

Part A

For each fraction, write two equivalent fractions. Sample answers:

1. $\frac{1}{2}$ $\frac{2}{4}$, $\frac{3}{6}$ 2. $\frac{1}{3}$ $\frac{2}{6}$, $\frac{5}{15}$ 3. $\frac{6}{8}$ $\frac{3}{4}$, $\frac{75}{100}$

Write >, <, or = to make each number sentence true.

4. $\frac{1}{6}$ > $\frac{1}{8}$ 5. $\frac{11}{12}$ > $\frac{5}{12}$ 6. $\frac{2}{3}$ = $\frac{8}{12}$

Write each set of fractions in order from smallest to largest.

7. $\frac{2}{10}$, $\frac{9}{10}$, $\frac{7}{10}$, $\frac{1}{10}$, $\frac{5}{10}$ $\frac{1}{10}$ (smallest), $\frac{2}{10}$, $\frac{5}{10}$, $\frac{7}{10}$, $\frac{9}{10}$ (largest)

8. $\frac{1}{7}$, $\frac{1}{2}$, $\frac{1}{5}$, $\frac{1}{10}$, $\frac{1}{3}$ $\frac{1}{10}$ (smallest), $\frac{1}{7}$, $\frac{1}{5}$, $\frac{1}{3}$, $\frac{1}{2}$ (largest)

Use pattern blocks to help solve Problems 9 and 10.

9. If the red trapezoid is the whole, what fraction of the whole is
   a. 1 green triangle? $\frac{1}{3}$ b. 1 blue rhombus? $\frac{2}{3}$

10. Suppose the green triangle is $\frac{1}{2}$ of the whole. Which pattern block is
    a. 1 whole? rhombus b. $1\frac{1}{2}$ wholes? trapezoid

11. Liam had 9 quarters. He spent $\frac{1}{3}$ of them on video games.
    a. How many quarters did he spend? 3 quarters
    b. How many quarters does he have left? 6 quarters
    c. How much money does he have left? $1.50

Assessment Handbook, **p. 185**

Assessment Master

Name ______ Date ______ Time ______

LESSON 7•13 **Written Assessment** *continued*

12. A bag contains

 2 blue blocks,
 3 purple blocks,
 4 green blocks, and
 1 yellow block.

 You put your hand in the bag and pull out a block. About what fraction of the time would you expect to get a yellow block? $\frac{1}{10}$

13. Plot and label each point on the coordinate grid.

 A (4,1)
 B (3,4)
 C (1,5)
 D (2,2)
 E (2,5)

Multiply and divide. Use paper-and-pencil algorithms of your choice.

14. $47 * 23 =$ 1,081
15. 3,007 $= 97 * 31$
16. $93 \div 4 =$ 23 R1, or $23\frac{1}{4}$
17. $7\overline{)542} =$ 77 R3, or $77\frac{3}{7}$

Assessment Handbook, p. 186

Use the checklists on pages 271 and 273 of the *Assessment Handbook* to record results. Then input the data into the **Assessment Management Spreadsheets** to keep an ongoing record of students' progress toward Grade-Level Goals.

Assessment Master

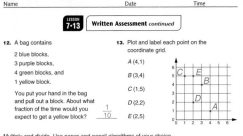

Name ______ Date ______ Time ______

LESSON 7•13 **Written Assessment** *continued*

Part B

18. Which fraction is larger: $\frac{6}{7}$ or $\frac{9}{10}$? $\frac{9}{10}$ Explain how you know.
 Sample answer: $\frac{9}{10}$ is only $\frac{1}{10}$ away from 1, and $\frac{6}{7}$ is $\frac{1}{7}$ away from 1. $\frac{1}{10}$ is a smaller fraction than $\frac{1}{7}$, so $\frac{9}{10}$ is closer to 1 than $\frac{6}{7}$ is. Also, $\frac{6}{7}$ is about 0.86 as a decimal, and $\frac{9}{10}$ is 0.9. 0.9 is greater than 0.86, so $\frac{9}{10}$ is greater than $\frac{6}{7}$.

19. Make a spinner. Sample answer:
 a. Color it so that the paper clip will land on red about $\frac{1}{2}$ of the time and on blue about $\frac{1}{3}$ of the time. Color the rest yellow.
 b. About what fraction of the time should you expect the paper clip to land on yellow? $\frac{1}{6}$

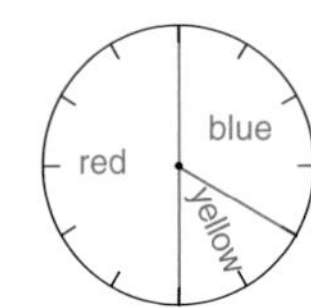

Add or subtract. Use pattern blocks to help you.

20. $\frac{1}{6} + \frac{4}{6} =$ $\frac{5}{6}$
21. $2\frac{1}{6} + 1\frac{1}{3} =$ $3\frac{3}{6}$, or $3\frac{1}{2}$
22. $2\frac{5}{6} - \frac{3}{6} =$ $2\frac{2}{6}$, or $2\frac{1}{3}$
23. $\frac{2}{3} - \frac{1}{6} =$ $\frac{3}{6}$, or $\frac{1}{2}$

24. It took Denise $\frac{3}{4}$ of an hour to drive from Zion to Platt and $\frac{1}{2}$ hour to drive from Platt to Rome. To figure out her total driving time, Denise wrote the following number model: $\frac{3}{4} + \frac{1}{2} = \frac{4}{6}$.

 Do you agree that it took her about $\frac{4}{6}$ of an hour? no Explain.
 Sample answer: She added the denominators, which is not correct. She should have changed $\frac{1}{2}$ to $\frac{2}{4}$, and then added the numerators. The correct answer is $\frac{3}{4} + \frac{2}{4} = \frac{5}{4}$, or $1\frac{1}{4}$ hours. She should have noticed that her answer should be greater than 1 hour since she drove $\frac{1}{2}$ hour plus more than $\frac{1}{2}$ hour ($\frac{3}{4}$ hour).

Assessment Handbook, p. 187

Slate Assessment

3. Write fractions with denominators of 10 or 100 on the board, and have students write the equivalent decimals. Then write decimals on the board, and ask students to write an equivalent fraction for each. Do not insist that they write fractions in simplest form. *Suggestions:*
 - $\frac{8}{10}$ 0.8
 - $\frac{30}{100}$ 0.30
 - $\frac{46}{100}$ 0.46
 - 0.98 $\frac{98}{100}$
 - 0.7 $\frac{7}{10}$
 - 0.20 $\frac{20}{100}$
4. Pose "fraction-of" problems. *Suggestions:*
 - What is $\frac{1}{4}$ of 8? 2 $\frac{3}{4}$ of 8? 6
 - What is $\frac{1}{5}$ of 30? 6 $\frac{4}{5}$ of 30? 24
 - What is $\frac{1}{3}$ of 18? 6 $\frac{2}{3}$ of 18? 12
 - What is $\frac{1}{6}$ of 12? 2 $\frac{5}{6}$ of 12? 10

▶ Written Assessment

INDEPENDENT ACTIVITY

(*Assessment Handbook,* pp. 185–187)

Part A Recognizing Student Achievement

Problems 1–17 provide summative information and may be used for grading purposes.

Problem(s)	Description
1–3	Write equivalent fractions.
4–6	Compare fractions.
7, 8	Order fractions.
9–11	Name fractions of regions or collections; find the ONE.
12	Calculate expected probability of an event.
13	Plot coordinates on a grid.
14, 15	Multiply multidigit numbers.
16, 17	Divide multidigit numbers by one-digit divisors.

Part B Informing Instruction

Problems 18–24 provide formative information that can be used in planning future instruction.

Problem(s)	Description
18	Explain a strategy to compare fractions.
19	Create a spinner, and predict the probability of an event.
20–23	Add and subtract fractions and mixed numbers.
24	Solve a fraction number story.

Open Response

INDEPENDENT ACTIVITY

(*Assessment Handbook,* p. 188)

Queen Arlene's Dilemma

The open-response item requires students to apply concepts and skills from Unit 7 to solve a multistep problem. See *Assessment Handbook,* pages 105–109 for rubrics and students' work samples for this problem.

2 Looking Ahead: Preparing for Unit 8

Math Boxes 7•13

INDEPENDENT ACTIVITY

(*Math Journal 2,* p. 218)

Mixed Practice This Math Boxes page previews Unit 8 content.

Study Link 7•13: Unit 8 Family Letter

INDEPENDENT ACTIVITY

(*Math Masters,* pp. 243–246)

Home Connection The Unit 8 Family Letter provides parents and guardians with information and activities related to Unit 8 topics.

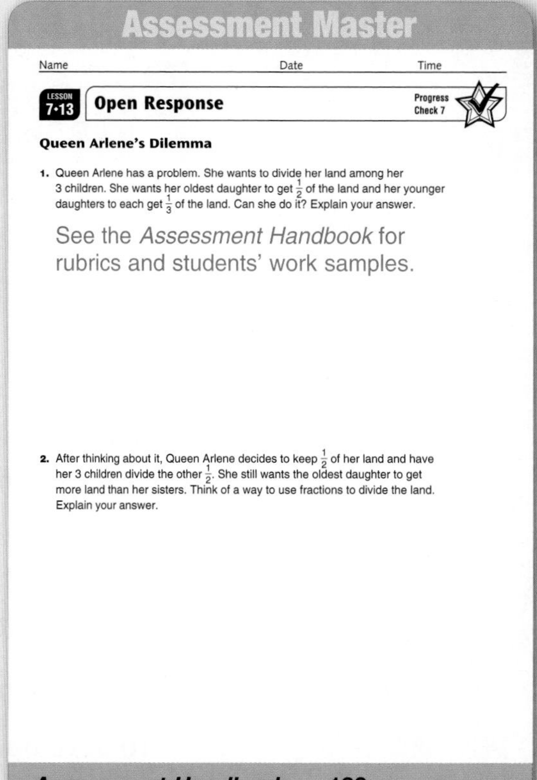

Assessment Master

Name Date Time

LESSON 7•13 **Open Response** Progress Check 7

Queen Arlene's Dilemma

1. Queen Arlene has a problem. She wants to divide her land among her 3 children. She wants her oldest daughter to get $\frac{1}{2}$ of the land and her younger daughters to each get $\frac{1}{3}$ of the land. Can she do it? Explain your answer.

See the *Assessment Handbook* for rubrics and students' work samples.

2. After thinking about it, Queen Arlene decides to keep $\frac{1}{2}$ of her land and have her 3 children divide the other $\frac{1}{2}$. She still wants the oldest daughter to get more land than her sisters. Think of a way to use fractions to divide the land. Explain your answer.

***Assessment Handbook,* p. 188**

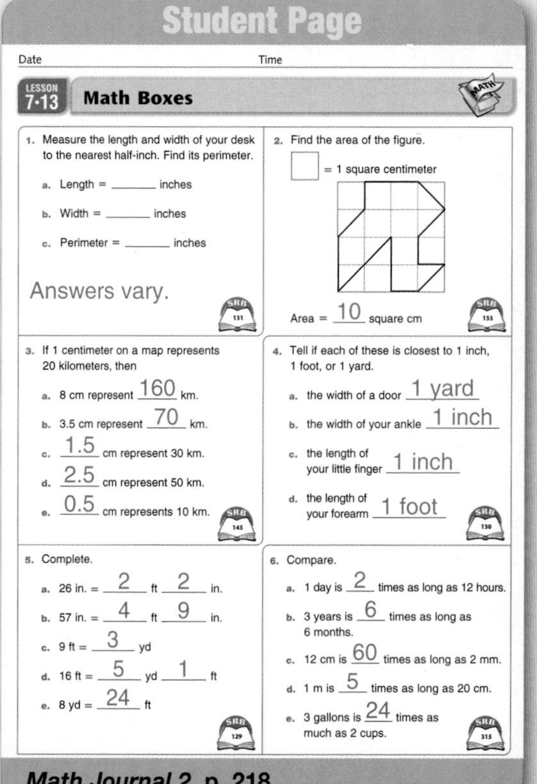

Student Page

Date Time

LESSON 7•13 **Math Boxes**

1. Measure the length and width of your desk to the nearest half-inch. Find its perimeter.
   a. Length = ______ inches
   b. Width = ______ inches
   c. Perimeter = ______ inches

   Answers vary.

2. Find the area of the figure.
   □ = 1 square centimeter

   Area = 10 square cm

3. If 1 centimeter on a map represents 20 kilometers, then
   a. 8 cm represent 160 km.
   b. 3.5 cm represent 70 km.
   c. 1.5 cm represent 30 km.
   d. 2.5 cm represent 50 km.
   e. 0.5 cm represents 10 km.

4. Tell if each of these is closest to 1 inch, 1 foot, or 1 yard.
   a. the width of a door 1 yard
   b. the width of your ankle 1 inch
   c. the length of your little finger 1 inch
   d. the length of your forearm 1 foot

5. Complete.
   a. 26 in. = 2 ft 2 in.
   b. 57 in. = 4 ft 9 in.
   c. 9 ft = 3 yd
   d. 16 ft = 5 yd 1 ft
   e. 8 yd = 24 ft

6. Compare.
   a. 1 day is 2 times as long as 12 hours.
   b. 3 years is 6 times as long as 6 months.
   c. 12 cm is 60 times as long as 2 mm.
   d. 1 m is 5 times as long as 20 cm.
   e. 3 gallons is 24 times as much as 2 cups.

***Math Journal 2,* p. 218**

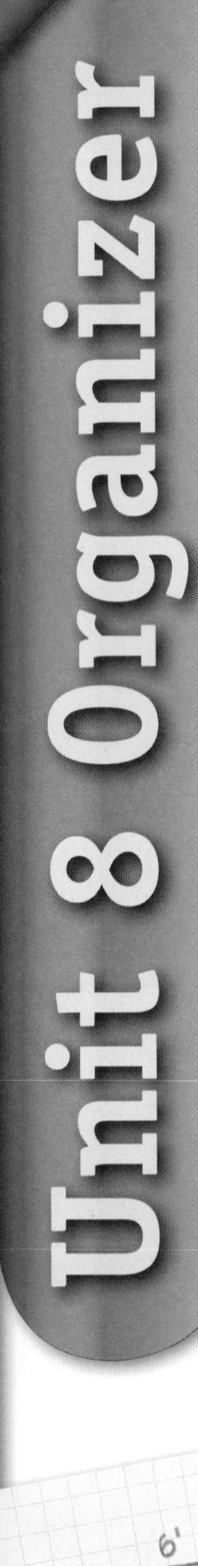

Perimeter and Area

Overview

Unit 8 revolves around perimeter, area, and scale drawings. It begins with a review of perimeter and area concepts previously introduced in *Everyday Mathematics,* and extends knowledge by developing formulas as mathematical models for the areas of rectangles, parallelograms, and triangles. Unit 8 also explores applications of area with the help of scale drawings. Unit 8 has three main areas of focus:

- To review perimeter and area concepts,
- To develop formulas as mathematical models for the areas of rectangles, parallelograms, and triangles, and
- To explore applications of area with scale drawings.

CCSS Linking to the Common Core State Standards

The content of Unit 8 addresses the Common Core State Standards for Mathematics in *Measurement and Data.* The correlation of the Common Core State Standards to the *Everyday Mathematics* Grade 4 lessons begins on page CS1.

Contents

Learning In Perspective

	Lesson Objectives	Links to the Past	Links to the Future
8·1	To provide experience measuring and adding distances; finding the median and other landmarks of a set of measurements; and finding the perimeters of triangles.	Grades 1 and 2: Define and calculate minimum, maximum, middle value (median), and mode by listing or tallying data. Grade 3: Define and calculate mean (average) and range. Use lists, tally charts, line plots, and graphs to determine landmarks.	Grades 5 and 6: Applications and maintenance.
8·2	To provide practice measuring distance to the nearest foot; and to provide experience creating a scale drawing on a grid using measurements and a given scale.	Grade 4: Use a map scale to estimate distances. Grade 3: Use a map scale to estimate the direct distance between two places.	Grade 5: Use a map scale to estimate actual distances. Grade 6: Use a scale to calculate actual size from a scale drawing.
8·3	To review basic area concepts; to provide practice estimating the area of a polygon by counting unit squares and using a scale drawing to find area.	Grade 2: Tile surfaces. Estimate areas using centimeter and inch grids; find areas of geoboard rectangles. Grade 3: Estimate areas of surfaces and measure with 1-foot or 1-yard squares. Find areas of rectangles by counting squares.	Grade 5: Find areas of rectangles on grids. Use a rectangle method for finding areas of triangles and parallelograms.
8·4	To demonstrate how to estimate the area of a surface having a curved boundary; and to provide practice converting from one square unit to another.	Grade 3: Refer to tables of equivalent units of measure.	Grades 5 and 6: Applications and maintenance.
8·5	To guide the development and use of a formula for the area of a rectangle.	Grade 2: Explore area and area units. Grade 3: Tile rectangles with pattern blocks; review the meaning of area and square units using models of square feet and square yards; discuss how to find the area of a room to be carpeted; use a geoboard to act out calculating areas of rectangles.	Grade 4: Use formulas to find volumes (Units 11 and 12). Grade 5: Develop and apply formulas for areas of triangles and parallelograms. Identify personal references for metric and customary units of area. Grade 6: Use formulas to find perimeter, circumference, and area.
8·6	To review the properties of parallelograms; and to guide the development and use of a formula for the area of a parallelogram.	Grade 2: Explore area and area units. Grade 3: Tile rectangles with pattern blocks; review the meaning of area and square units using models of square feet and square yards; discuss how to find the area of a room to be carpeted; use a geoboard to act out calculating areas of rectangles.	Grade 4: Use formulas to find volumes (Units 11 and 12). Grade 5: Develop and apply formulas for areas of triangles and parallelograms. Identify personal references for metric and customary units of area. Grade 6: Use formulas to find perimeter, circumference, and area.
8·7	To guide the development and use of a formula for the area of a triangle.	Grade 2: Explore area and area units. Grade 3: Tile rectangles with pattern blocks; review the meaning of area and square units using models of square feet and square yards; discuss how to find the area of a room to be carpeted; use a geoboard to act out calculating areas of rectangles.	Grade 4: Use formulas to find volumes (Units 11 and 12). Grade 5: Develop and apply formulas for areas of triangles and parallelograms. Identify personal references for metric and customary units of area. Grade 6: Use formulas to find perimeter, circumference, and area.
8·8	To discuss how geographical areas are measured; and to provide practice using division to compare two quantities with like units.	Grade 3: Discuss tools used to measure distances; explore division as equal sharing. Solve division problems by direct modeling, arrays, and other methods.	Grades 5 and 6: Applications and maintenance.

	Key Concepts and Skills	Grade 4 Goals*
8•1	Create a tally chart.	Data and Chance Goal 1
	Find the minimum, maximum, mode, and median of a data set; use landmarks to draw conclusions.	Data and Chance Goal 2
	Measure distances in feet and inches.	Measurement and Reference Frames Goal 1
	Calculate the perimeter of a triangle.	Measurement and Reference Frames Goal 2
	Add mixed units; convert between feet and inches.	Measurement and Reference Frames Goal 3
8•2	Find the median of a data set.	Data and Chance Goal 2
	Make a rough floor plan of the classroom.	Operations and Computation Goal 7; Measurement and Reference Frames Goal 1
	Make a scale drawing of the classroom.	Operations and Computation Goal 7; Measurement and Reference Frames Goal 1
	Measure to the nearest foot.	Measurement and Reference Frames Goal 1
8•3	Use a scale drawing to estimate the area of the classroom.	Operations and Computation Goal 7; Measurement and Reference Frames Goal 2
	Find the areas of polygons by counting squares and partial squares.	Measurement and Reference Frames Goal 2
	Identify polygons.	Geometry Goal 2
8•4	Use the terms *estimate* and *guess.*	Operations and Computation Goal 6
	Use an estimate to judge the reasonableness of a solution.	Operations and Computation Goal 6
	Count squares and partial squares or use a formula to estimate area.	Measurement and Reference Frames Goal 2
	Convert between square inches and square feet.	Measurement and Reference Frames Goal 3
8•5	Rename fractions as decimals.	Number and Numeration Goal 5
	Count unit squares or use a formula to find the area of a rectangle.	Measurement and Reference Frames Goal 2
	Use patterns in a table to develop a formula for the area of a rectangle.	Patterns, Functions, and Algebra Goal 1
	Apply the Distributive Property of Multiplication over Addition.	Patterns, Functions, and Algebra Goal 4
8•6	Find the area of a rectangle.	Measurement and Reference Frames Goal 2
	Develop a formula for calculating the area of a parallelogram.	Measurement and Reference Frames Goal 2
	Calculate perimeter.	Measurement and Reference Frames Goal 2
	Identify perpendicular line segments and right angles.	Geometry Goal 1
	Describe properties of parallelograms.	Geometry Goal 2
8•7	Find the areas of rectangles and parallelograms.	Measurement and Reference Frames Goal 2
	Develop a formula for calculating the area of a triangle.	Measurement and Reference Frames Goal 2
	Identify perpendicular line segments and right angles.	Geometry Goal 1
	Describe properties of and types of triangles.	Geometry Goal 2
	Evaluate numeric expressions containing parentheses.	Patterns, Functions, and Algebra Goal 3
8•8	Use division to compare two quantities with like units.	Operations and Computation Goal 4
	Use "times as many" language to compare area measurements.	Operations and Computation Goal 4
	Estimate and compare area measurements.	Measurement and Reference Frames Goal 2

*See the Appendix for a complete list of Grade 4 Goals.

A Balanced Curriculum

Ongoing Practice

Everyday Mathematics provides numerous opportunities for ongoing practice. These activities are embedded throughout the lessons:

Mental Math and Reflexes activities promote speed and accuracy in mental computation.

Math Boxes offer mixed practice and are paired across lessons as shown in the brackets below. This makes them useful as assessment tools. The last one or two boxes on each page preview the next unit's content.

Mixed practice	[8•1, 8•3], [8•2, 8•4], [8•5, 8•7], [8•6, 8•8]
Mixed practice with multiple choice	8•1, 8•2, 8•4, 8•7
Mixed practice with writing/reasoning opportunity	8•1, 8•3, 8•4, 8•7, 8•8

Study Links are daily homework assignments that review the content of the lesson and often contain ongoing facts practice or computation practice.

5-Minute Math problems are offered for additional practice in Lesson 8•1.

EM Facts Workshop Game provides online practice of basic facts and computation.

EXTRA PRACTICE **Extra Practice** activities are included in Lessons 8•1, 8•2, 8•3, 8•4, and 8•7.

Practice through Games

Games are an essential component of practice in the *Everyday Mathematics* program. Games offer skills practice and promote strategic thinking. See the *Differentiation Handbook* for ways to adapt games to meet students' needs.

Lesson	Game	Skill Practiced
8•1	*Fraction Match*	Naming equivalent fractions [NN Goal 5]
8•3	*Fraction Top-It*	Comparing and ordering fractions [NN Goal 6]
8•6	*Fraction Of*	Finding fractions of collections [NN Goal 2]
8•6	*Angle Add-Up*	Solving addition and subtraction problems to find the measures of unknown angles [OC Goal 2]
8•7	*Rugs and Fences*	Calculating the area and perimeter of a polygon [MRF Goal 2]
8•8	*Grab Bag*	Calculating the probabilities of events [DC Goal 4]

[NN] Number and Numeration
[MRF] Measurement and Reference Frames
[OC] Operations and Computation
[GEO] Geometry
[DC] Data and Chance
[PFA] Patterns, Functions, and Algebra

Problem Solving 

Experts at problem solving and mathematical modeling generally do these things:

- Identify the problem.
- Decide what information is needed to solve the problem.
- Play with and study the data to find patterns and meaning.
- Identify and use mathematical procedures to solve the problem.
- Decide whether the solution makes sense and whether it can be applied to other problems.

The table below lists some of the opportunities in this unit for students to practice these strategies.

Lessons that teach *through* problem solving, not just *about* problem solving

Lesson	Activity
8•1	Analyze and rate the efficiency of a kitchen.
8•2	Make a classroom floor plan.
8•3	Estimate areas of polygons by counting squares.
8•4	Estimate the area of your skin.
8•5–8•7	Develop formulas for area.
8•8	Compare country areas.

See Chapter 18: Problem Solving in the *Teacher's Reference Manual* for more information.

The Language of Mathematics

Everyday Mathematics provides lesson-specific suggestions to help all students acquire, process, and express mathematical ideas. Throughout Unit 8, there are lesson-specific language development notes that address the needs of English language learners, indicated by ELL.

ELL SUPPORT Activities to support English language learners are in Part 3 of Lessons 8•2, 8•3, and 8•5.

The *English Learners Handbook* and the *Differentiation Handbook* have suggestions for promoting language development and acquisition of mathematics vocabulary. See Unit 8 in each handbook.

Unit 8 Vocabulary

area
base
equilateral triangle
formula
height
isosceles triangle
length
perimeter
perpendicular
right triangle
rough floor plan
scale
scale drawing
scalene triangle
square units
time-and-motion study
variable
width
work triangle

Literacy Connection

Actual Size, by Steve Jenkins, Houghton Mifflin, 2004

Castle, by David Macaulay, Houghton Mifflin, 1982

For more literacy connections, see the *Home Connection Handbook,* Grades 4–6.

Cross-Curricular Links 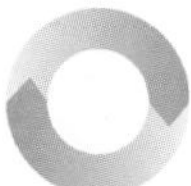

Industrial Arts
Lesson 8•1 Students learn about kitchen work triangles.

Science
Lesson 8•8 Students determine the gravitational pull of each planet relative to Earth.

Social Studies
Lesson 8•4 Students visit a second country in South America on the World Tour.

Lesson 8•8 Students compare areas of countries in South America to Brazil's area.

Balanced Assessment

Daily Assessments

- **Recognizing Student Achievement** – A daily assessment that is included in every lesson to evaluate students' progress toward the Grade 4 Grade-Level Goals.
- **Informing Instruction** – Notes that appear throughout the unit to help anticipate students' common errors and suggest appropriate problem-solving strategies.

Lesson	Recognizing Student Achievement	Informing Instruction
8•1	Rename fractions with denominators of 10 and 100 as decimals and percents. [NN Goal 5]	
8•2	Find the perimeter of a figure. [MRF Goal 2]	Use equal floor lengths in making a rough classroom floor plan.
8•3	Count whole squares and half squares to find the area of a polygon. [MRF Goal 2]	Use strategies to find area.
8•4	Count unit squares and fractions of unit squares to estimate the area of an irregular figure. [MRF Goal 2]	
8•5	Calculate the perimeter of a figure when the length of one side is missing. [MRF Goal 2]	Use different multiplication strategies for finding the area of a triangle.
8•6	Solve fraction addition and subtraction problems. [OC Goal 5]	Understand the difference between parallelogram and rectangle perimeter measurement.
8•7	Describe a strategy for finding and comparing the areas of a square and a polygon. [MRF Goal 2]	
8•8	Calculate and express the probability of an event as a fraction. [DC Goal 4]	

[NN] Number and Numeration
[MRF] Measurement and Reference Frames
[OC] Operations and Computation
[GEO] Geometry
[DC] Data and Chance
[PFA] Patterns, Functions, and Algebra

Portfolio Opportunities

The following lessons provide opportunities to gather samples of students' mathematical writings, drawings, and creations to add balance to the assessment process: Lessons 8•1, 8•2, 8•3, 8•6, 8•7, and 8•9.

See pages 16 and 17 in the *Assessment Handbook* for more information about portfolios and how to use them.

Unit Assessment

Progress Check 8 – A cumulative assessment of concepts and skills taught in Unit 8 and in previous units, providing information for evaluating students' progress and planning for future instruction. These assessments include oral/slate, written, and open-response activities, as shown below in the sample Progress Check lesson opener.

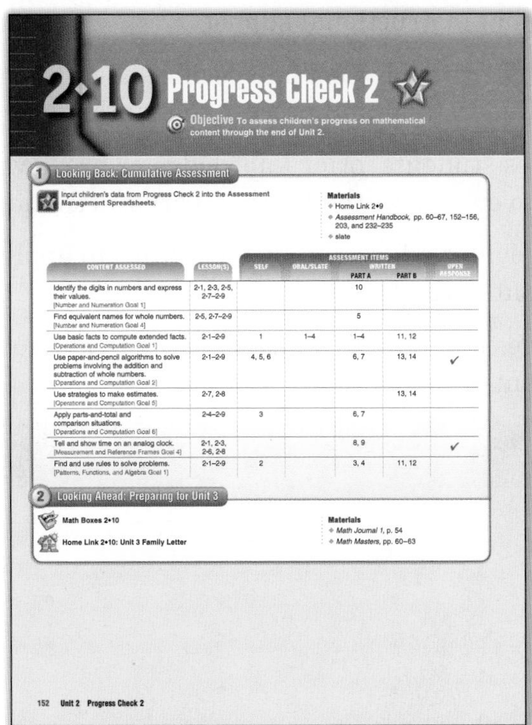

2·10 Progress Check 2

Objective To assess children's progress on mathematical content through the end of Unit 2.

1 Looking Back: Cumulative Assessment

Input children's data from Progress Check 2 into the Assessment Management Spreadsheets.

Materials
- Home Link 2•9
- *Assessment Handbook,* pp. 60–67, 152–156, 203, and 232–235
- slate

Content Assessed	Lesson(s)	Assessment Items: Self	Oral/Slate	Written: Part A	Written: Part B	Open Response
Identify the digits in numbers and express their values. [Number and Numeration Goal 1]	2·1, 2·3, 2·5, 2·7–2·9			10		
Find equivalent names for whole numbers. [Number and Numeration Goal 4]	2·5, 2·7–2·9			5		
Use basic facts to compute extended facts. [Operations and Computation Goal 1]	2·1–2·9	1	1–4	1–4	11, 12	
Use paper-and-pencil algorithms to solve problems involving the addition and subtraction of whole numbers. [Operations and Computation Goal 2]	2·1–2·9	4, 5, 6		6, 7	13, 14	✓
Use strategies to make estimates. [Operations and Computation Goal 5]	2·7, 2·8				13, 14	
Apply parts-and-total and comparison situations. [Operations and Computation Goal 6]	2·4–2·9	3		6, 7		
Tell and show time on an analog clock. [Measurement and Reference Frames Goal 4]	2·1, 2·3, 2·6, 2·8			8, 9		✓
Find and use rules to solve problems. [Patterns, Functions, and Algebra Goal 1]	2·1–2·9	2		3, 4	11, 12	

2 Looking Ahead: Preparing for Unit 3

Math Boxes 2•10

Home Link 2•10: Unit 3 Family Letter

Materials
- *Math Journal 1,* p. 54
- *Math Masters,* pp. 60–63

152 Unit 2 Progress Check 2

Core Assessment Resources

Assessment Handbook

- **Unit 8 Assessment Overview,** pages 110–117
- **Unit 8 Assessment Masters,** pages 189–194
- **Unit 8 Individual Profiles of Progress,** pages 274, 275, and 302
- **Unit 8 Class Checklists,** pages 276, 277, and 303
- **Math Logs,** pages 306–308
- **Exit Slip,** page 311
- **Other Student Assessment Forms,** pages 304, 305, 309, and 310

Assessment Management Spreadsheets

The Assessment Management Spreadsheets consist of the Digital Class Checklists and Individual Profile of Progress Checklists. Use them to monitor, record, and report student progress.

Addressing All Needs

Differentiated Instruction

Adjusting the Activity – suggests adaptations that target advanced learners, English language learners, or learners who need additional instructional support.

ELL SUPPORT / ELL – provides lesson-specific suggestions to help English language learners understand and process the mathematical content.

READINESS – accesses students' prior knowledge or previews content that prepares students to engage in the lesson's Part 1 activities.

EXTRA PRACTICE – provides additional opportunities to apply the mathematical content of the lesson.

ENRICHMENT – enables students to apply or further explore the mathematical content of the lesson.

Lesson	Adjusting the Activity	ELL Support/ ELL	Readiness	Extra Practice	Enrichment
8•1	•		•	•	•
8•2		•	•	•	•
8•3	•	•	•	•	•
8•4	•	•	•	•	
8•5	•	•	•		•
8•6					•
8•7	•	•		•	•
8•8	•		•		•

Additional Resources

Differentiation Handbook
Provides ideas and strategies for differentiating instruction.
Pages 97–103

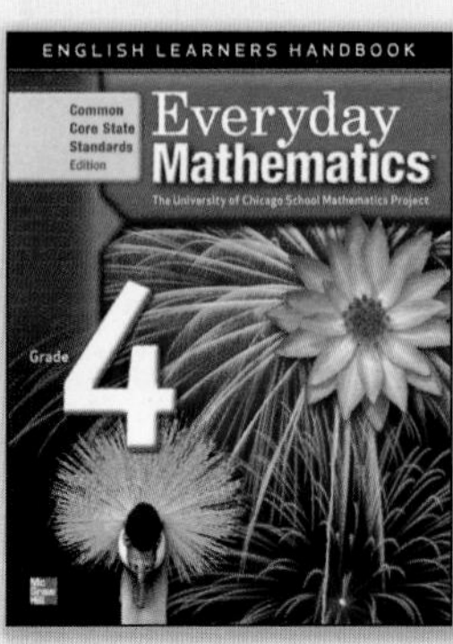

English Learners Handbook
Contains lesson-specific comprehension strategies.
Pages 72–79

Multilingual Handbook
Previews concepts and vocabulary. It is written in six languages.
Pages 143–158

Planning Tips

Multiage Classroom

Companion Lessons from Grades 3 and 5 can help you meet instructional needs of a multiage classroom. The full Scope and Sequence can be found in the Appendix.

Grade 3	3•4		3•6, 3•7		3•6–3•8			3•7
Grade 4	**8•1**	**8•2**	**8•3**	**8•4**	**8•5**	**8•6**	**8•7**	**8•8**
Grade 5			9•4–9•6	9•5	9•4	9•6	9•6	9•7

Pacing for Success

Pacing depends on a number of factors, such as students' individual needs and how long your school has been using *Everyday Mathematics*. At the beginning of Unit 8, you may want to use tools available at www.everydaymathonline.com to help you set your pace.

Home Support

Unit 8 Family Letter (English/Spanish) provides families with an overview, Do-Anytime Activities, Building Skills through Games, a list of vocabulary, and answers to the daily homework (Study Links). Family Letters in English, Spanish, and seven other languages are also available online.

Study Links are the daily homework assignments. They consist of active projects and ongoing review problems.

Home Support Resources

Home Connection Handbook
Offers ideas and reproducible masters for communicating with families. See Table of Contents for unit information.

Student Reference Book
Provides a resource for students and parents.
Pages 114, 117, 118, 133, 243–245, 247, 249, 260, 261, 276, 277, 280, 286, 287, 295, 297, 302–305

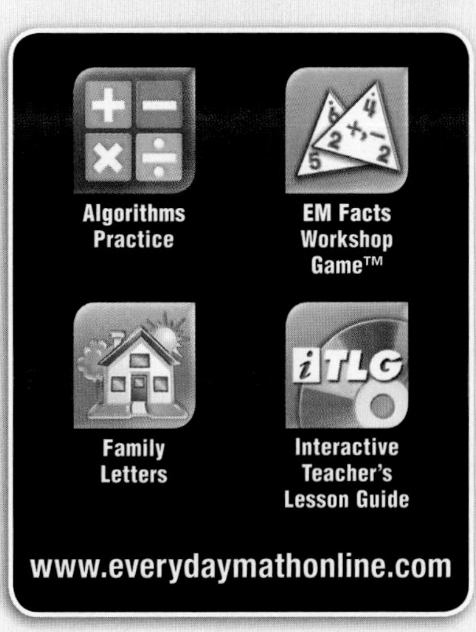

Materials

Technology Resources www.everydaymathonline.com

ePresentations

eToolkit

Algorithms Practice

EM Facts Workshop Game™

Family Letters

Assessment Management

Common Core State Standards

Curriculum Focal Points

Interactive Teacher's Lesson Guide

Lesson	Masters	Manipulative Kit	Other Items
8•1	Study Link 7•11 Study Link Master, p. 247 Teaching Masters, pp. 248 and 249 Game Masters, pp. 473–476 Teaching Aid Masters, pp. 389 and 437	geoboard; rubber bands; pattern blocks; slate	scissors; tape; straightedge; yardstick*; ruler; Geometry Template
8•2	Teaching Aid Masters, pp. 388 or 389, 413, 414, 416*, and 443* Transparency of *Math Masters,* p. 443* Study Link Master, p. 250 Teaching Masters, pp. 251–253	per partnership: 1 tape measure; slate	straightedge; tape; ruler; scissors; pen or colored pencil
8•3	Study Link Master, p. 254 Game Master, p. 506 Teaching Aid Master, p. 437 *Differentiation Handbook,* p. 140	geoboard; rubber bands; slate	unit squares; scissors; tape; straightedge; 1 deck of 32 Fraction Cards
8•4	Teaching Aid Masters, pp. 388 or 389, 419*, 420*, and 444 Study Link Master, p. 255	slate	scissors; tape; objects with flat irregular surfaces; masking tape; square stick-on notes; calculator*
8•5	Study Link Master, p. 256 Teaching Masters, pp. 257–259 Teaching Aid Master, p. 444 *Differentiation Handbook,* p. 140	1 six-sided die; 36 square pattern blocks; slate	24-inch string loop; tape; calculator*
8•6	Teaching Masters, pp. 260, 263, and 264 Transparency of *Math Masters,* p. 439 Study Link Masters, pp. 261 and 262 Game Masters, pp. 477–480 and 507–509 Teaching Aid Master, p. 437	straws and twist-ties; compass; slate; per partnership: 4 each of number cards 1–8 and 1 each of number cards 0 and 9	scissors; tape; index card or other square-corner object; straightedge; centimeter ruler; dry-erase markers
8•7	Teaching Masters, pp. 265, 267, and 268 Transparency of *Math Masters,* p. 403* Study Link Master, p. 266 Game Masters, pp. 498–502 Teaching Aid Master, p. 454A	slate	scissors; tape; index card or other square-corner object; centimeter ruler
8•8	Study Link Master, p. 269 Game Masters, pp. 483–485 Teaching Masters, pp. 270–273	3 six-sided dice; slate	world map or globe; scissors; calculator; centimeter ruler
8•9	Assessment Masters, pp. 189–194 Study Link Masters, pp. 274–277	slate	scissors; centimeter ruler

*Denotes optional materials

Mathematical Background

The discussion below highlights the major content ideas presented in Unit 8 and helps establish instructional priorities.

Perimeter and Area

(Lesson 8◆1 and following)

Unit 8 begins with a review of perimeter (Lesson 8-1). Students use the measurements they made for Study Link 7◆11 (*Math Masters,* pages 235 and 236) to evaluate the arrangement of appliances in their home kitchens. Then, in Lesson 8-2, they make scale drawings of their classroom. This activity serves several purposes:

- It provides practice in measuring lengths and in using a scale to make a scale drawing. Students use this skill again to make scale drawings of their bedrooms and their bedroom furniture in an optional activity in Lesson 8-2. They use their scale drawings to evaluate various arrangements of their bedroom furniture.
- Students use their scale drawings of the classroom floor to find the area of the floor in Lesson 8-3.

Length and *perimeter* (or *circumference*) are measures of distance along a linear path. Area is a measure of a finite amount of surface. This surface may be "flat" (for example, the interior of a rectangle), or it may be "curved" (for example, the surface of a cylinder or cone).

It is important to note that, like other measures, area always includes both a number and a unit. Units of area are typically *square units* based on linear units, such as a square yard, a square meter, and a square mile. Note that there are several units of area in which the word *square* does not appear; for example, an *acre* of land (now $\frac{1}{640}$ of a square mile) is said to have been based, a long time ago, on the amount of land a farmer could plow in one day. In the metric system, the *hectare* is used to measure land areas.

Unit 8 Organizer

Use tiling to demonstrate area.
(discrete model)

In most schoolbooks, the definition of area is based on the idea of "tiling," or covering a surface with identical unit squares, without gaps or overlaps, and then counting those units.

If the surface is bounded by a rectangle, it is natural to arrange the tiles in an array, and to multiply the number of tiles per row by the number of rows. The usual formulas, $A = l * w$ or $A = b * h$, are then easily linked to array multiplication: area is equal to the number of square unit tiles in one row (equal to the length of the base in some linear unit) times the number of rows (equal to the width, or height, in that same linear unit). For other surfaces, defined by regular or irregular boundaries, tiling with square units can be thought of as (or actually done by) laying a grid of appropriate square units on the region and counting, estimating, or calculating how many squares it takes to cover that region.

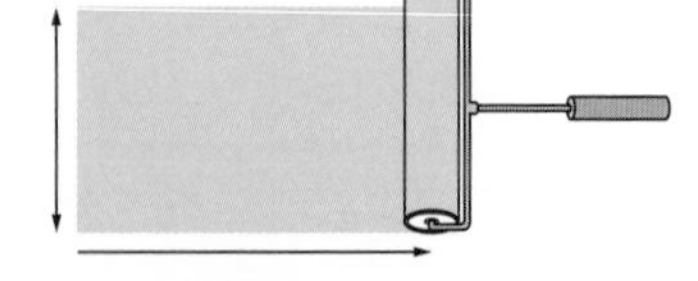

Use painting to demonstrate area.
(continuous model)

Another, more dynamic conception of area has proven to be useful in some applications and in more advanced mathematics courses. Imagine running a one-foot-wide paint roller on the floor of a rectangular room along one wall. For every foot the roller travels, 1 square foot of the floor is painted. Now suppose the room is 20 feet wide and the roller is the width of the room (a 20-foot-wide roller). Then, for every foot the roller travels along the length of the floor, 20 square feet of floor are painted. When the roller reaches the other side of the floor, the entire floor will have been painted. If you think of the floor as the interior of a rectangle, then the area of the rectangle is obtained not by counting squares (a *discrete* conception), but by sweeping the width of the rectangle across the interior of the rectangle, parallel to its base (a *continuous* conception). The area is simply the product of the length of the base and the width of the rectangle. In the classroom, this can be shown by rubbing the long part of a piece of chalk on the board to mark a rectangular surface—the farther you sweep it along, the bigger the rectangle and the greater the area.

For most purposes, you will probably choose the traditional conception of area—counting or computing the number of square units required to cover a surface. However, the authors recommend that you also introduce the continuous conception, for it is easily extended to conceptions of *volume.* For example, students can think of the volume of a prism in terms of a prism that is gradually filled with water: The surface of the water is shaped like the base of the prism; the higher the level of the water, the more space it occupies and the greater the volume. This leads to the formula for the volume of a prism and a cylinder as the area of the base multiplied by the height. This formula for volume works no matter what the shape of the base.

Students often confuse perimeter with area, perhaps because they are not clear about the meaning of formulas they have been taught by rote. Perimeter is a measure of length, or distance; area is a measure of surface. Perimeter can be illustrated with a trundle wheel that rolls along the boundary of a surface; the word *perimeter* contains the word *rim.* Area can be illustrated with the sweep of a paint roller across a surface or a piece of chalk across the board. Perimeter is measured in units of length. Area is measured in square units—the number of unit squares needed to cover a surface. Occasionally remind your students of these basic differences.

Use the trundle wheel to demonstrate perimeter.

For additional information regarding perimeter and area, see Sections 14.3 and 14.4 of the *Teacher's Reference Manual.*

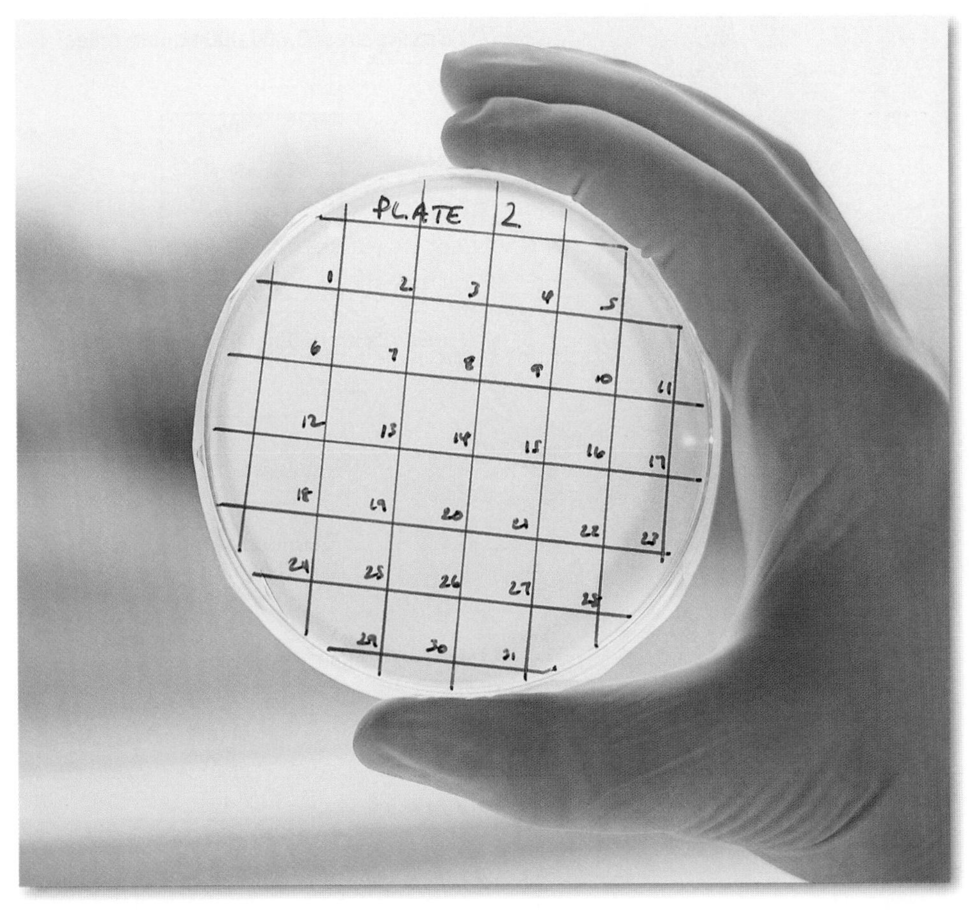

Developing and Using Formulas

(Lessons 8◆4–8◆8)

In Lessons 8-5, 8-6, and 8-7 students develop and use formulas for finding the area of rectangles, parallelograms, and triangles.

Lessons 8-4 and 8-8 deal with areas that are not calculated from formulas. In Lesson 8-4, students estimate the area of one side of their hands by tracing them onto a grid and counting squares and fractions of squares. Students then use these estimates to compute the area of the skin on their entire bodies by applying a rule of thumb (area of skin is about 100 times the area of one side your hand). In Lesson 8-8, students learn about area measurements of some of the geographical features they have encountered on the World Tour. They use division and a calculator to compare areas of South American countries.

Brazil's area: 3,300,000 square miles

Peru's area: 500,000 square miles

Ecuador's area:
110,000 square miles

In this unit, the formula for the area of a rectangle (area = length of base times width, or height) is assumed as a basic "axiom." The formula for the area of a parallelogram is developed by cutting apart a parallelogram and rearranging the parts into a rectangular shape. Similarly, the formula for the area of a triangle is developed by cutting triangles and reassembling them to form parallelograms. Similar cut-and-paste methods will be used later in *Everyday Mathematics* to develop formulas for the areas of other two-dimensional shapes—always with the idea of transforming a given shape into another shape of the same area, for which a formula is already known.

Once students learn a formula, they tend to use it without much thought as to its origin. It is important to remind students occasionally of why formulas make sense. Such derivations have the advantage of demonstrating an important mathematical process—one fact is taken as an "axiom" on which there is agreement, and other rules or relationships are developed from the axiom.

Most schoolbooks (and many standardized tests) express the formula for the area of a rectangle as the product of the *length* times the *width* ($A = l * w$). The formulas for the area of a parallelogram ($A = b * h$) and a triangle ($A = \frac{1}{2} * b * h$) are expressed in terms of the length of the *base* and the *height*. Students who have been taught only the formula $A = l * w$ will often mistakenly multiply the lengths of two adjacent sides when calculating the area of a parallelogram. Similar errors are made in finding the areas of triangles. While students should be familiar with the formula $A = l * w$, point out that since a rectangle is a special kind of parallelogram, it makes sense to use the formula $A = b * h$ for the area of rectangle.

An added advantage to using the base-times-height formula is that it is consistent with the formulas used to find the volumes of many three-dimensional figures. For example, no matter what the shape of the base, the volume of a prism is always equal to the area of a base multiplied by its height.

In most math textbooks, nearly every illustration in connection with the area of a polygon shows the base as a horizontal segment on which the figure "sits." But the base can be any side, and the height can be measured on a perpendicular to whichever side is designated as the base.

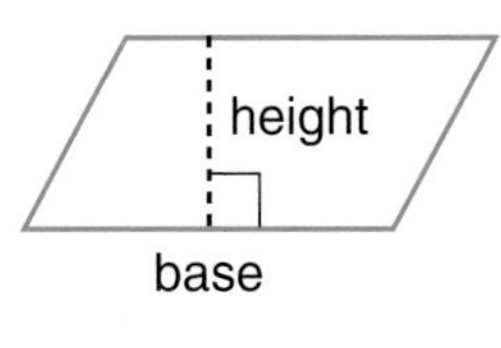

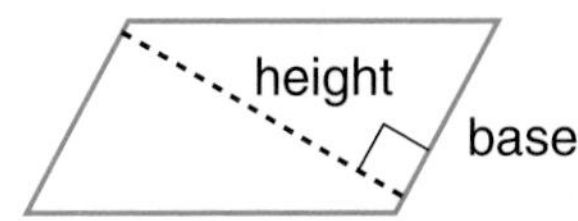

Two ways of designating the base and height of a parallelogram

To learn more about developing and using formulas, see Section 14.4.2 in the *Teacher's Reference Manual.*

8•1 Kitchen Layouts and Perimeter

Objectives To provide experience measuring and adding distances; finding the median and other landmarks of a set of measurements; and finding the perimeters of triangles.

www.everydaymathonline.com

ePresentations

eToolkit

Algorithms Practice

EM Facts Workshop Game™

Family Letters

Assessment Management

Common Core State Standards

Curriculum Focal Points

Interactive Teacher's Lesson Guide

1 Teaching the Lesson

Key Concepts and Skills

- Create a tally chart.
  [Data and Chance Goal 1]
- Find the minimum, maximum, mode, and median of a data set; use landmarks to draw conclusions.
  [Data and Chance Goal 2]
- Measure distances in feet and inches.
  [Measurement and Reference Frames Goal 1]
- Calculate the perimeter of a triangle.
  [Measurement and Reference Frames Goal 2]
- Add mixed units; convert between feet and inches.
  [Measurement and Reference Frames Goal 3]

Key Activities

Students sketch arrangements of their kitchen appliances. They calculate the perimeter of the work triangle and compare individual and class results with recommended distances.

Students find landmarks of the perimeter data collected.

Ongoing Assessment: Recognizing Student Achievement
Use Mental Math and Reflexes.
[Number and Numeration Goal 5]

Key Vocabulary

time-and-motion study ◆ work triangle ◆ perimeter

Materials

Math Journal 2, pp. 219–222
Study Link 7•11 (*Math Masters,* pp. 235 and 236)
slate ◆ scissors ◆ tape ◆ straightedge ◆ yardstick (optional)

2 Ongoing Learning & Practice

Playing *Fraction Match*
Student Reference Book, p. 243
Fraction Match Cards (*Math Masters,* pp. 473–476)
Math Masters, p. 389
Students practice naming equivalent fractions.

Math Boxes 8•1
Math Journal 2, p. 223
Students practice and maintain skills through Math Box problems.

Study Link 8•1
Math Masters, p. 247
ruler
Students practice and maintain skills through Study Link activities.

3 Differentiation Options

READINESS

Investigating Perimeters on a Geoboard
Math Masters, pp. 248 and 437
geoboard ◆ rubber bands
Students construct rectangles and squares of a given perimeter on a geoboard.

ENRICHMENT

Investigating Pattern-Block Perimeters
Math Masters, p. 249
Geometry Template ◆ pattern blocks
Students use pattern blocks to make polygons with different perimeters.

EXTRA PRACTICE

5-Minute Math
5-Minute Math™, p. 50
Students solve problems involving perimeter.

Advance Preparation

***Teacher's Reference Manual,* Grades 4–6** pp. 218, 219, 233, 234

Getting Started

Mental Math and Reflexes ★

Ask students to give the decimal and percent equivalents for fractions with denominators of 100, 10, 5, and 4. *Suggestions:*

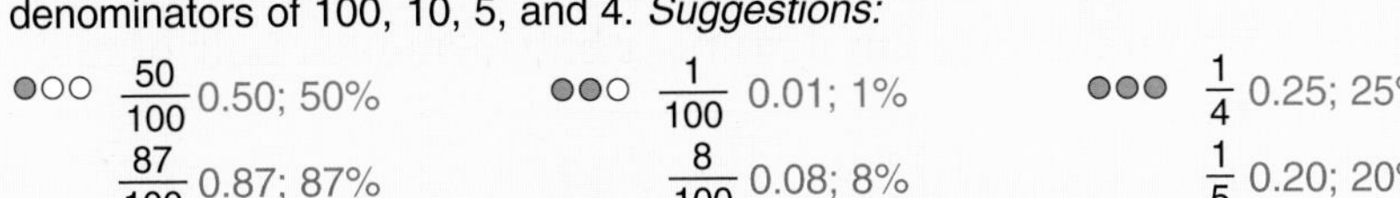

●○○ $\frac{50}{100}$ 0.50; 50%
$\frac{87}{100}$ 0.87; 87%
$\frac{23}{100}$ 0.23; 23%
$\frac{42}{100}$ 0.42; 42%

●●○ $\frac{1}{100}$ 0.01; 1%
$\frac{8}{100}$ 0.08; 8%
$\frac{7}{10}$ 0.7; 70%
$\frac{5}{10}$ 0.5; 50%

●●● $\frac{1}{4}$ 0.25; 25%
$\frac{1}{5}$ 0.20; 20%
$\frac{4}{5}$ 0.80; 80%
$\frac{3}{4}$ 0.75; 75%

Math Message

Complete Problems 1 and 2 on journal page 220.

Ongoing Assessment: Recognizing Student Achievement

Mental Math and Reflexes ★

Use **Mental Math and Reflexes** to assess students' ability to rename fractions as decimals and percents. Students are making adequate progress if they are able to solve the ●○○ and ●●○ problems involving fractions with denominators of 10 and 100. Some students may be able to solve the ●●● problems involving fractions with denominators of 4 and 5.

[Number and Numeration Goal 5]

1 Teaching the Lesson

▶ Math Message Follow-Up

WHOLE-CLASS ACTIVITY

(*Math Journal 2,* pp. 219 and 220; *Math Masters,* pp. 235 and 236)

Ask small groups of students to compare the layout of the stove, sink, and refrigerator in their kitchens.

Read journal page 219 as a class. Discuss the layouts shown. Have students circle the layout they have in their homes.

Survey the number of students who have a one-wall kitchen, an L-shaped kitchen, a U-shaped kitchen, or a Pullman or galley kitchen. Ask:

- Do any of you have "islands" in your kitchens? Some kitchens have island work areas that include a sink or stove. Share any sketches that show kitchen islands with the class.
- Why might a one-wall kitchen be less efficient than the other types? A person may have to walk longer distances from one appliance to another.

Tell students that in this lesson they will review perimeter by analyzing the placement of the appliances in their kitchens.

Interactive whiteboard-ready ePresentations are available at www.everydaymathonline.com to help you teach the lesson.

Student Page

Date Time

LESSON 8•1 **Kitchen Layouts and Kitchen Efficiency**

Here are four common ways to arrange the appliances in a kitchen:

One wall
L-shaped
U-shaped
Pullman or galley

Pullman kitchens are usually found on passenger trains. **Galleys** are the kitchens on boats and airplanes. The kitchen areas on trains, boats, and airplanes are small. The cooking area is usually lined up against a single wall (a one-wall kitchen) or against two walls with a corridor between them (a Pullman or galley kitchen).

◆ What kind of kitchen layout do you have in your home? Circle one. Answers vary.

One wall L-shaped U-shaped Pullman or galley

Kitchen efficiency experts are people who study the ways we use our kitchens. They carry out **time-and-motion** studies to find how long it takes to do some kitchen tasks and how much a person has to move about in order to do them. They want to find the best ways to arrange the stove, the sink, and the refrigerator. In an efficient kitchen, a person should have to do very little walking to move from one appliance to another. However, the appliances should not be too close to each other, because the person would feel cramped.

A bird's-eye sketch is often drawn to see how well the appliances in a kitchen are arranged. The stove, the sink, and the refrigerator are connected with line segments as shown below. These segments form a triangle called a **work triangle.** The work triangle shows the distance between pairs of appliances.

Work Triangle

6' 4'3" 6'10"

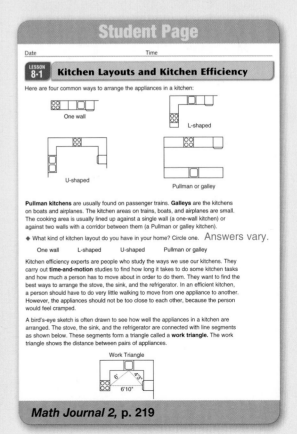

Math Journal 2, p. 219

Student Page

Date ______ Time ______

LESSON 8·1 **Layout of My Kitchen**

1. Copy the distances between your appliances from *Math Masters,* page 235.

Between stove and refrigerator: About ______ feet ______ inches

Between refrigerator and sink: About ______ feet ______ inches

Between sink and stove: About ______ feet ______ inches

2. Cut out the sketch of your kitchen from *Math Masters,* page 236 and tape it in the space below.

***Math Journal 2,* p. 220**

Work Triangle

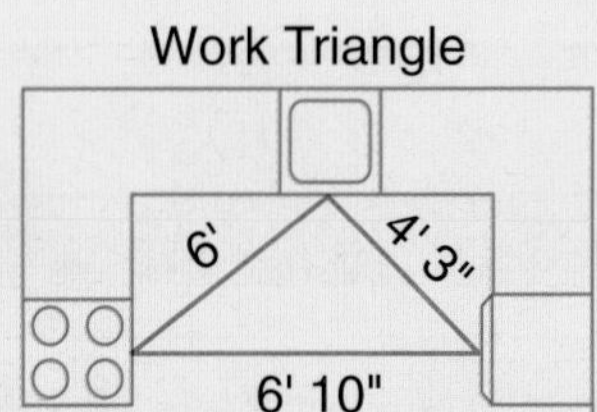

Perimeter	Number of Triangles
Less than 11 ft	/
11 ft	/
12 ft	///
13 ft	/

Tallying perimeters of work triangles

▶ Rating the Efficiency of a Kitchen

Industrial Arts Link As a result of **time-and-motion studies,** kitchen efficiency experts have recommended minimum and maximum distances between each pair of major appliances.

Range of Distances between:
Stove and refrigerator: 4 to 9 feet
Refrigerator and sink: 4 to 7 feet
Sink and stove: 4 to 6 feet

Write these recommendations on the board. Then sketch a stove, sink, and refrigerator and connect them with line segments. The resulting triangle, called a **work triangle,** can be used to show distances between pairs of appliances.

Remind students that the distance around a polygon is called its **perimeter.** Ask questions about the perimeter of a work triangle.

- What is the smallest perimeter of a work triangle that meets the experts' recommendations? $4 + 4 + 4 = 12$ feet
- What is the largest perimeter? $9 + 7 + 6 = 22$ feet
- What is the middle value for the range of recommended perimeters? The number halfway between 12 and 22 feet is 17 feet.

▶ Analyzing Kitchen Arrangements

WHOLE-CLASS ACTIVITY

PROBLEM SOLVING

(*Math Journal 2,* pp. 220 and 221)

1. Ask students to use straightedges to connect the three appliances in their sketches on journal page 220 and write the distances between appliances on the sides of their triangles. Then have them find the perimeters of their work triangles.

Adjusting the Activity

Suggest that students think in terms of the partial-sums algorithm when adding mixed units—add feet, add inches, and then convert inches to feet, if necessary. For example, 6' + 4' 3" + 6' 10" = 16' 13" = 17' 1".

Encourage students to use a yardstick to help them visualize and rename mixed feet-and-inches measurements in simpler form.

AUDITORY • KINESTHETIC • TACTILE • VISUAL

2. Have students report the perimeters of their own work triangles. You or a student tallies these perimeters on the board. To simplify the record-keeping, ignore the inches in the perimeter or round each perimeter to the nearest foot.

3. Have students find the minimum, maximum, mode, and median of the class perimeters and record them in Problem 4 on journal page 221. Ask:

- Is the class median close to 17 feet—the median of the recommended perimeters?
- Does anyone have a work triangle with a perimeter outside the recommended range (less than 12 feet or greater than 22 feet)? If so, share your sketches with the class.
- Does anyone have a work triangle in which the distance between two appliances is *outside* the recommended range but whose *perimeter* is within the recommended range? (For example, the distance between stove and sink is 3 feet, but the perimeter is 14 feet.)

Sketching Work Triangles of Given Perimeters

PARTNER ACTIVITY

(*Math Journal 2,* p. 222)

Have students sketch work triangles that meet the conditions specified on journal page 222 and share solution strategies.

One possible approach might be to establish the distance from sink to stove as 4, 5, or 6 feet.

▷ If the distance between sink and stove is 4 feet, then the sum of the other two distances must be 17 feet (4 + 17 = 21). But this sum may not exceed 16 feet (9 + 7). Therefore, the distance between sink and stove cannot be 4 feet.

▷ If the distance between sink and stove is 5 feet, then the sum of the other two distances must be 16 feet (5 + 16 = 21). So the distance between stove and refrigerator would be 9 feet, and the distance between refrigerator and sink would be 7 feet.

▷ If the distance between sink and stove is 6 feet, then the sum of the other two distances must be 15 feet (6 + 15 = 21). Therefore, the other two distances would be either 8 feet and 7 feet, or 9 feet and 6 feet.

2 Ongoing Learning & Practice

Playing *Fraction Match*

SMALL-GROUP ACTIVITY

(*Student Reference Book,* p. 243; *Math Masters,* pp. 389 and 473–476)

Students play *Fraction Match* to practice naming equivalent fractions. Have students describe on an Exit Slip how they know that two of the fractions are equivalent. See Lesson 7-7 for additional information.

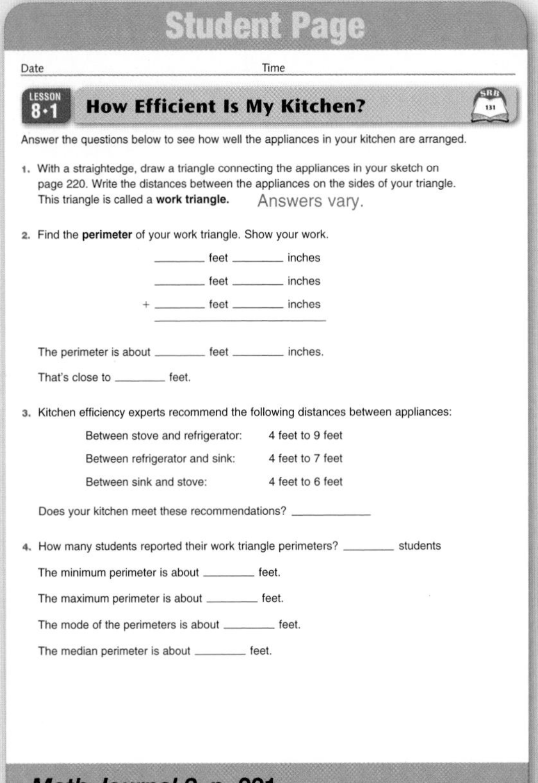

Student Page

Date Time

LESSON 8•1 **How Efficient Is My Kitchen?**

Answer the questions below to see how well the appliances in your kitchen are arranged.

1. With a straightedge, draw a triangle connecting the appliances in your sketch on page 220. Write the distances between the appliances on the sides of your triangle. This triangle is called a **work triangle.** Answers vary.

2. Find the **perimeter** of your work triangle. Show your work.

_____ feet _____ inches
_____ feet _____ inches
+ _____ feet _____ inches

The perimeter is about _____ feet _____ inches.

That's close to _____ feet.

3. Kitchen efficiency experts recommend the following distances between appliances:

Between stove and refrigerator:	4 feet to 9 feet
Between refrigerator and sink:	4 feet to 7 feet
Between sink and stove:	4 feet to 6 feet

Does your kitchen meet these recommendations? _____

4. How many students reported their work triangle perimeters? _____ students

The minimum perimeter is about _____ feet.

The maximum perimeter is about _____ feet.

The mode of the perimeters is about _____ feet.

The median perimeter is about _____ feet.

Math Journal 2, p. 221

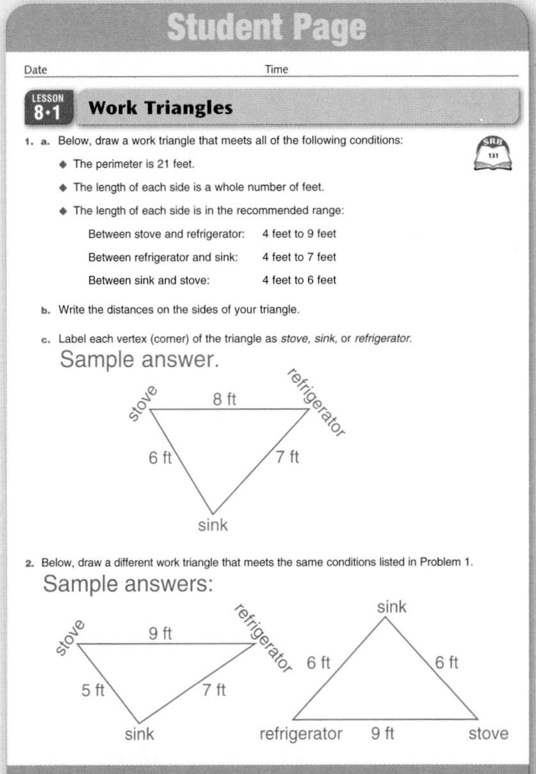

Student Page

Date Time

LESSON 8•1 **Work Triangles**

1. a. Below, draw a work triangle that meets all of the following conditions:
   - The perimeter is 21 feet.
   - The length of each side is a whole number of feet.
   - The length of each side is in the recommended range:

Between stove and refrigerator:	4 feet to 9 feet
Between refrigerator and sink:	4 feet to 7 feet
Between sink and stove:	4 feet to 6 feet

   b. Write the distances on the sides of your triangle.

   c. Label each vertex (corner) of the triangle as *stove, sink,* or *refrigerator.*

2. Below, draw a different work triangle that meets the same conditions listed in Problem 1.

Math Journal 2, p. 222

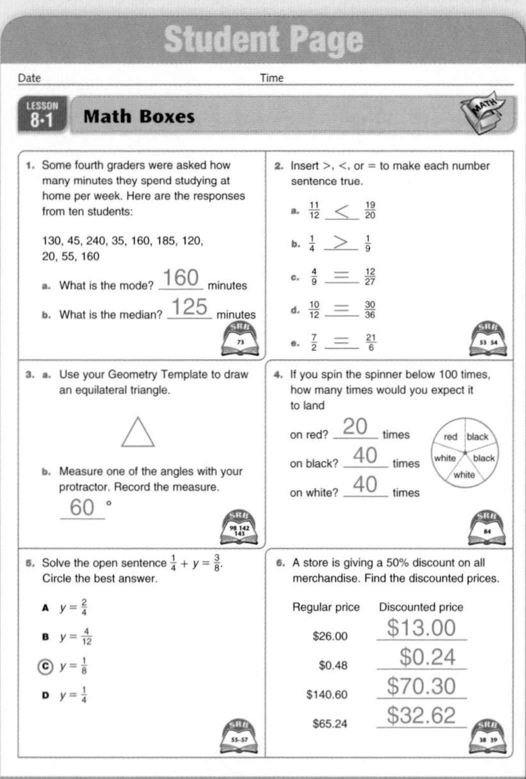
Student Page

Date Time

LESSON 8·1 **Math Boxes**

1. Some fourth graders were asked how many minutes they spend studying at home per week. Here are the responses from ten students:

   130, 45, 240, 35, 160, 185, 120, 20, 55, 160

   a. What is the mode? 160 minutes

   b. What is the median? 125 minutes

2. Insert >, <, or = to make each number sentence true.

   a. $\frac{11}{12} < \frac{19}{20}$

   b. $\frac{1}{4} > \frac{1}{9}$

   c. $\frac{4}{9} = \frac{12}{27}$

   d. $\frac{10}{12} = \frac{30}{36}$

   e. $\frac{7}{2} = \frac{21}{6}$

3. a. Use your Geometry Template to draw an equilateral triangle.

   b. Measure one of the angles with your protractor. Record the measure. 60 °

4. If you spin the spinner below 100 times, how many times would you expect it to land

   on red? 20 times

   on black? 40 times

   on white? 40 times

5. Solve the open sentence $\frac{1}{4} + y = \frac{3}{8}$. Circle the best answer.

   A $y = \frac{2}{4}$

   B $y = \frac{4}{12}$

   (C) $y = \frac{1}{8}$

   D $y = \frac{1}{4}$

6. A store is giving a 50% discount on all merchandise. Find the discounted prices.

Regular price	Discounted price
$26.00	$13.00
$0.48	$0.24
$140.60	$70.30
$65.24	$32.62

Math Journal 2, p. 223

Math Boxes 8·1

INDEPENDEN ACTIVITY

(*Math Journal 2*, p. 223)

Mixed Practice Math Boxes in this lesson are paired with Math Boxes in Lesson 8-3. The skill in Problem 6 previews Unit 9 content.

Writing/Reasoning Have students write a response to the following: *Explain how you solved Problem 4.* Sampl answer: $\frac{1}{5}$ of the spinner is red, $\frac{2}{5}$ of the spinner is black, and $\frac{2}{5}$ of the spinner is white. Since $\frac{1}{5}$ of 100 is 20, I expect the spinner to land on red 20 times. $\frac{2}{5}$ of 100 is 40, so I expect the spinner to land on black 40 times and on white 40 times.

Study Link 8·1

INDEPENDEN ACTIVITY

(*Math Masters*, p. 247)

Home Connection Students measure figures to the nearest centimeter and nearest $\frac{1}{4}$ inch and calculate the perimeter of each. They draw rectangles of a given perimeter.

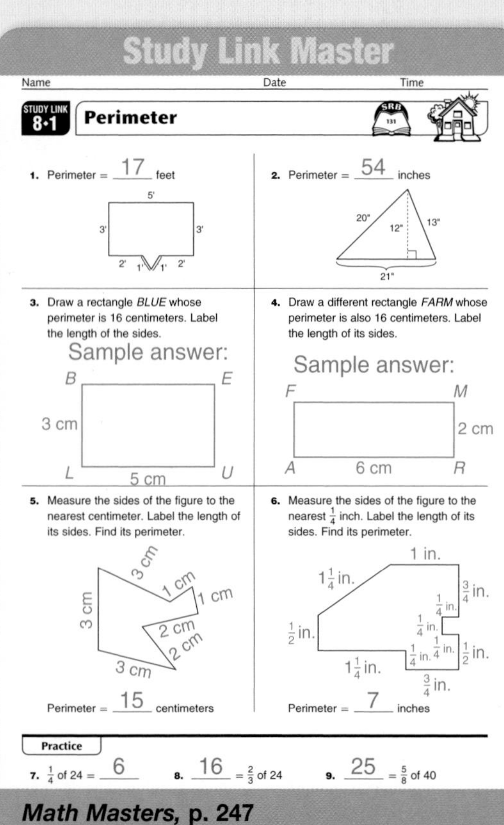
Study Link Master

Name Date Time

STUDY LINK 8·1 **Perimeter**

1. Perimeter = 17 feet

2. Perimeter = 54 inches

3. Draw a rectangle *BLUE* whose perimeter is 16 centimeters. Label the length of the sides.

   Sample answer:

4. Draw a different rectangle *FARM* whose perimeter is also 16 centimeters. Label the length of its sides.

   Sample answer:

5. Measure the sides of the figure to the nearest centimeter. Label the length of its sides. Find its perimeter.

   Perimeter = 15 centimeters

6. Measure the sides of the figure to the nearest $\frac{1}{4}$ inch. Label the length of its sides. Find its perimeter.

   Perimeter = 7 inches

Practice

7. $\frac{1}{4}$ of 24 = 6

8. 16 = $\frac{2}{3}$ of 24

9. 25 = $\frac{5}{8}$ of 40

Math Masters, p. 247

3 Differentiation Options

READINESS

PARTNE ACTIVIT

15–30 Mi

Investigating Perimeters on a Geoboard

(*Math Masters*, pp. 248 and 437)

To explore the concept of perimeter using a concrete model, have students construct rectangles and squares of a given perimeter on a geoboard and record the lengths of the sides on *Math Masters*, page 248. Consider having students use a straightedge to sketch their rectangles and squares on *Math Masters*, page 437.

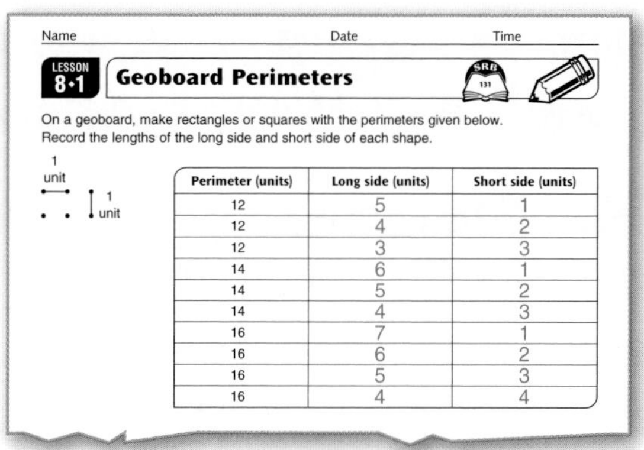
Name Date Time

LESSON 8·1 **Geoboard Perimeters**

On a geoboard, make rectangles or squares with the perimeters given below. Record the lengths of the long side and short side of each shape.

Perimeter (units)	Long side (units)	Short side (units)
12	5	1
12	4	2
12	3	3
14	6	1
14	5	2
14	4	3
16	7	1
16	6	2
16	5	3
16	4	4

Math Masters, page 248

ENRICHMENT

PARTNER ACTIVITY

15–30 Min

Investigating Pattern-Block Perimeters

(*Math Masters,* p. 249)

Portfolio Ideas

To apply students' understanding of perimeter, have them use a given set of pattern blocks (1 hexagon, 3 trapezoids, 3 blue rhombi, and 3 triangles) to create polygons with as many different perimeters as possible. Acknowledge that many different polygons can be made with the *same* perimeter, but encourage students to look for polygons with different perimeters. Have students discuss and compare their strategies. *Sample answers:*

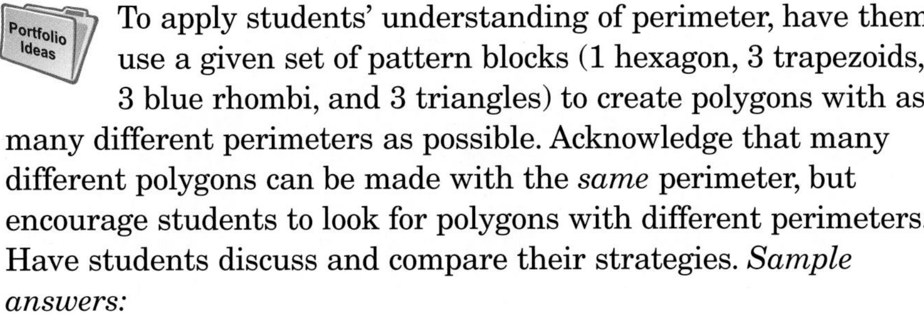
24 units 22 units 20 units 18 units

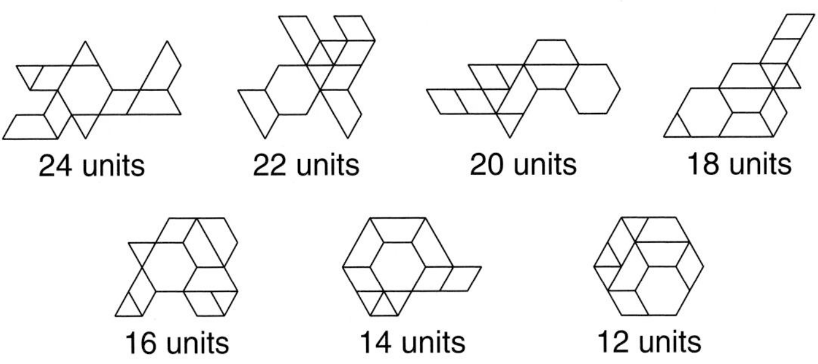
16 units 14 units 12 units

EXTRA PRACTICE

SMALL-GROUP ACTIVITY

5–15 Min

5-Minute Math

To offer students more experience with perimeter, see *5-Minute Math,* page 50.

Planning Ahead

Starting in Lesson 8-3, students will study area. Make and display unit squares with sides measuring 1 inch, 1 foot, 1 yard, 1 centimeter, 1 decimeter, and 1 meter. Use any kind of paper. Label each square in two ways, such as *1 square inch* and *1 in^2*.

Teaching Master

Name Date Time

LESSON 8•1 **Pattern-Block Perimeters**

1. Use the following pattern blocks to create shapes with as many *different* perimeters as you can: 1 hexagon, 3 trapezoids, 3 blue rhombi, and 3 triangles.
   - Every shape must include all 10 pattern blocks.
   - Each side of a pattern block measures 1 unit. The long side of a trapezoid pattern block measures 2 units.
   - At least one side of every pattern block must *line up exactly* with a side of another pattern block. See figures.

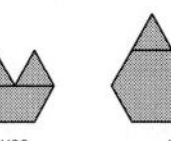
yes

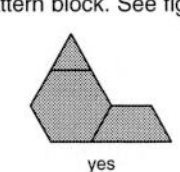
yes

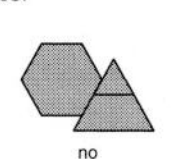
no

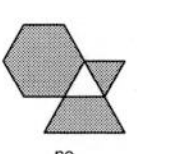
no

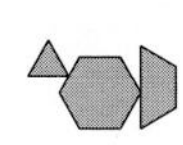
no

2. Use your Geometry Template to record your shapes on a separate sheet of paper. The polygons should all have different perimeters. Write the perimeter next to each shape.

Sample answers:

3. What was the smallest perimeter you were able to make? 14 units
   Describe the strategy you used to find this perimeter.
   The tighter the blocks are packed together, the smaller the distance around the outside will be.

4. What was the largest perimeter you were able to make? 24 units
   Describe the strategy you used to find this perimeter.
   If the blocks are spread out, then the distance around the outside will be greater.

Math Masters, p. 249

8•2 Scale Drawings

Objectives To provide practice measuring distance to the nearest foot; and to provide experience creating a scale drawing on a grid using measurements and a given scale.

Technology Resources www.everydaymathonline.com

ePresentations

eToolkit

Algorithms Practice

EM Facts Workshop Game™

Family Letters

Assessment Management

Common Core State Standards

Curriculum Focal Points

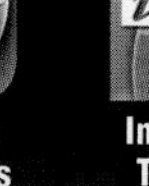

Interactive Teacher's Lesson Guide

1 Teaching the Lesson

Key Concepts and Skills

- Find the median of a data set. [Data and Chance Goal 2]
- Make a rough floor plan of the classroom. [Operations and Computation Goal 7; Measurement and Reference Frames Goal 1]
- Make a scale drawing of the classroom. [Operations and Computation Goal 7; Measurement and Reference Frames Goal 1]
- Measure to the nearest foot. [Measurement and Reference Frames Goal 1]

Key Activities

Students make a rough floor plan of the classroom. They use the rough floor plan to create a scale drawing of the classroom on grid paper.

Ongoing Assessment: Informing Instruction See page 666.

Key Vocabulary

rough floor plan ◆ scale drawing ◆ scale

Materials

Math Journal 2, pp. 224 and 225
Study Link 8•1
Math Masters, p. 443 (optional)
transparency of *Math Masters,* p. 443 (optional) ◆ straightedge ◆ per partnership: 1 tape measure ◆ slate

2 Ongoing Learning & Practice

Multiplying a Fraction by a Whole Number

Math Journal 2, pp. 226A and 226B
Students practice multiplying fractions by whole numbers.

Math Boxes 8•2

Math Journal 2, p. 226
Students practice and maintain skills through Math Box problems.

Ongoing Assessment: Recognizing Student Achievement
Use Math Boxes, Problem 1.
[Measurement and Reference Frames Goal 2]

Study Link 8•2

Math Masters, p. 250
ruler
Students practice and maintain skills through Study Link activities.

3 Differentiation Options

READINESS

Measuring to the Nearest Foot

Math Masters, p. 251 and p. 388 or 389
scissors
Students use a "foot-long foot" to measure objects to the nearest foot.

ENRICHMENT

Making a Scale Drawing of Your Bedroom

Math Masters, pp. 252 and 253
straightedge ◆ tape measure ◆ scissors ◆ tape
Students make scale drawings of their bedrooms and bedroom furniture.

EXTRA PRACTICE

Taking a 50-Facts Test

Math Masters, pp. 413 and 414; p. 416 (optional)
pen or colored pencil
Students take a 50-facts test. They use a line graph to record individual and optional class scores.

ELL SUPPORT

Building Background for Mathematics Words

Students list possible ways of using the word *scale*.

Advance Preparation

The grid on journal page 225 accommodates a classroom up to 25 feet by 30 feet. If a larger grid is needed, make a copy of *Math Masters,* page 443 for each student to cut out and tape next to the grid on the journal page. Or, let $\frac{1}{4}$ inch represent 2 feet on the journal grid (although this scale is harder to use). The scale drawing will also be used in Lesson 8•3.

***Teacher's Reference Manual,* Grades 4–6** p. 252

Getting Started

Mental Math and Reflexes

Pose multiplication facts and extended facts.
Suggestions:

●○○ 6 * 7 = 42
8 * 3 = 24
7 * 4 = 28

●●○ 80 * 7 = 560
90 * 80 = 7,200
500 * 80 = 40,000

●●● 400 * 500 = 200,000
5,000 * 60 = 300,000
70 * 300 = 21,000

Math Message

Work with a partner and estimate:

The long side of our classroom is about _____ feet long.
The short side is about _____ feet long.

Write your estimates in the table on the board.

Dimensions of Classroom

Longer Side (feet)	Shorter Side (feet)

Study Link 8·1 Follow-Up

Have students compare answers and share the rectangle dimensions they chose for Problems 3 and 4.

1 Teaching the Lesson

▸ Math Message Follow-Up

Ask students to find the median of the estimates for the longer and shorter sides. Record them on the board. After students measure the classroom, compare the median estimates with their actual measurements.

▸ Making a Rough Floor Plan of the Classroom

(*Math Journal 2,* p. 224)

Tell students that they are going to make a **rough floor plan** of the classroom. They will then use the rough plan to make a very accurate drawing of the classroom called a **scale drawing.**

Links to the Future

This is an introduction to scale drawing. Students will do additional work with scales in *Fifth* and *Sixth Grade Everyday Mathematics.*

Ask students to look at the two drawings on journal page 224.

▷ The first drawing is a rough floor plan of a room. It is not carefully drawn, but it does include all of the information needed to make an accurate drawing.

▷ The second drawing is a scale drawing for the same room. It is drawn on a grid and is very accurate.

Student Page

Date Time

LESSON 8·2 **A Floor Plan of My Classroom**

When architects design a room or house, they usually make two drawings. The first drawing is called a **rough floor plan.** It is not carefully drawn. But the rough floor plan includes all of the information that is needed to make an accurate drawing. The second drawing is called a **scale drawing.** It is drawn on a grid and is very accurate.

Rough floor plan for a bedroom

Scale drawing for a bedroom (1 grid length represents 1 foot.)

1. What information do you need to draw a rough floor plan?
Sample answer: You need the dimensions of the walls, windows, and doors. You also need to know the shape of the room.

Architects use these symbols to show windows and doors: window, door opening to left, door opening to right

2. Make a rough floor plan of your classroom in the space below.
Answers vary.

Math Journal 2, p. 224

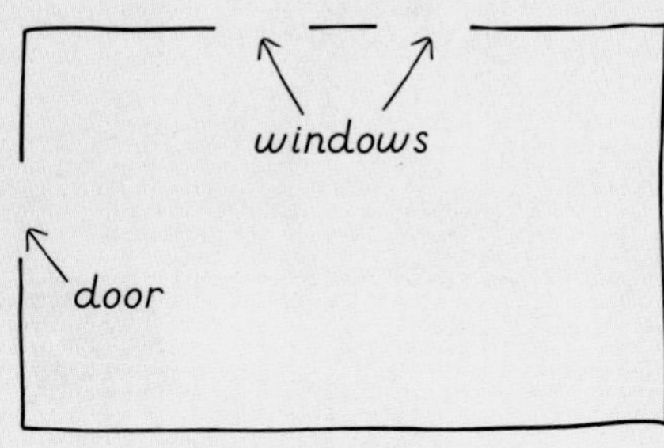

Figure 1

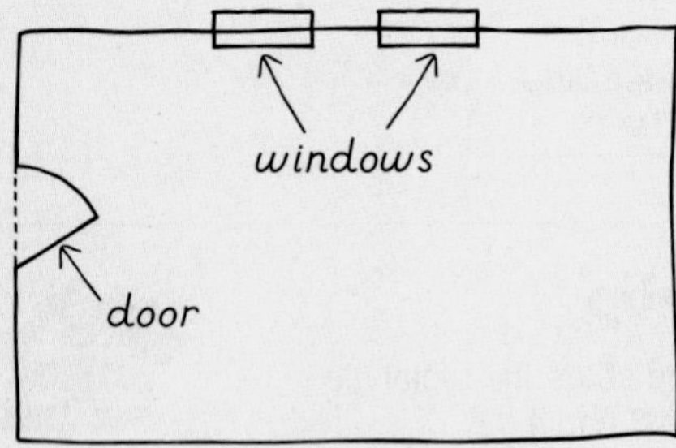

Figure 2

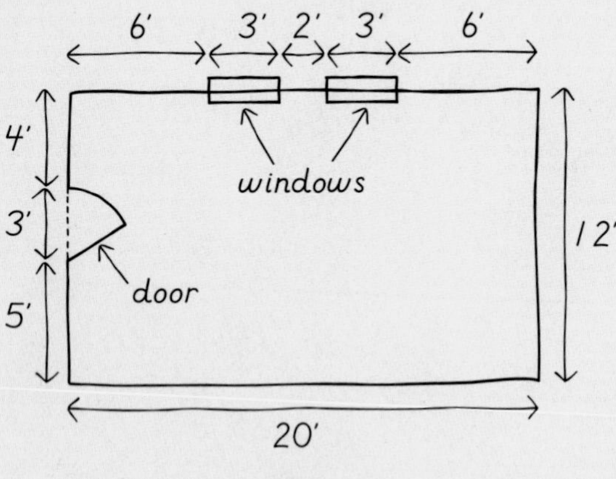

Figure 3

Student Page

Date Time

LESSON 8·2 **A Floor Plan of My Classroom** *continued*

3. Make a scale drawing of your classroom. Scale: $\frac{1}{4}$ inch represents 1 foot.
Each side of a small square in the grid below is $\frac{1}{4}$ inch long. Answers vary.

For use in Lesson 8-3: The area of my classroom is about ______ square feet.

Math Journal 2, p. 225

Have students discuss with their partners the information needed to make a rough floor plan of the classroom. They list this information in Problem 1 on journal page 224 and then sketch a rough outline of the classroom in Problem 2.

With students' help, draw a simple, rough floor plan of the classroom on the board. Students should add refinements to their own sketches as you add them to yours.

1. Draw the walls and show the doors and windows. (*See Figure 1.*)
2. Show the symbols commonly used to represent doors and windows and add them to the sketch. (*See Figure 2.*)

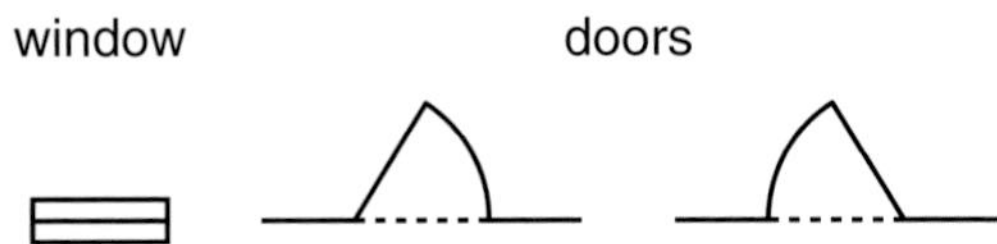

3. Give a measurement assignment to each partnership. For example, one pair of students measures the total length of a wall; another, the width of a window or door opening; another, the distance from a corner to a door or window; and so on. Ask students to make their measurements accurate to the nearest foot and to record them on the board sketch using two-headed arrows. (*See Figure 3.*)
4. With the class, check the reported measurements:
   - ▷ The sum of the lengths of wall sections, windows, and door openings along each wall should be close to the total length of that wall.
   - ▷ Opposite walls should have nearly equal lengths (assuming the floor is rectangular).

Ongoing Assessment: Informing Instruction

Watch for students who note that the opposite walls of their rectangular classroom do not have the same length due to rounding to the nearest foot. Have students revise one of the measurements so that they have equal lengths.

▶ Making the Scale Drawing

(*Math Journal 2,* pp. 224 and 225; *Math Masters,* p. 443)

Have students examine the grid on journal page 225. Explain that accurate floor plans are often drawn on this kind of grid. Ask:

- What is the length of the side of a small square? $\frac{1}{4}$ inch How many small square sides make up 1 inch? 4

Write "Scale: $\frac{1}{4}$ inch represents 1 foot" on the board, and ask students to copy this onto the journal page. Tell them that this is the **scale** they will use in their scale drawings. Ask:

- How many small square sides are needed to represent a 6-foot wall? 6 A $2\frac{1}{2}$-foot door opening? $2\frac{1}{2}$
- On the scale drawing, what would be the length of a 14-foot wall? 14 small square sides, or $3\frac{1}{2}$ inches

The class now has all the information needed to make the scale drawing. If you wish, use a transparency of a $\frac{1}{4}$-inch grid (*Math Masters,* page 443) to make the scale drawing of the classroom as students follow your lead on journal page 225. Remind students that the length of 1 grid square ($\frac{1}{4}$ inch) represents 1 foot of actual length.

After students have completed both the rough floor plan and the scale drawing of the classroom, ask the following questions:

- When would someone want to make just a rough floor plan of a room? Sample answer: shopping for furniture
- When would someone need to make a more accurate scale drawing? Sample answer: remodeling a room

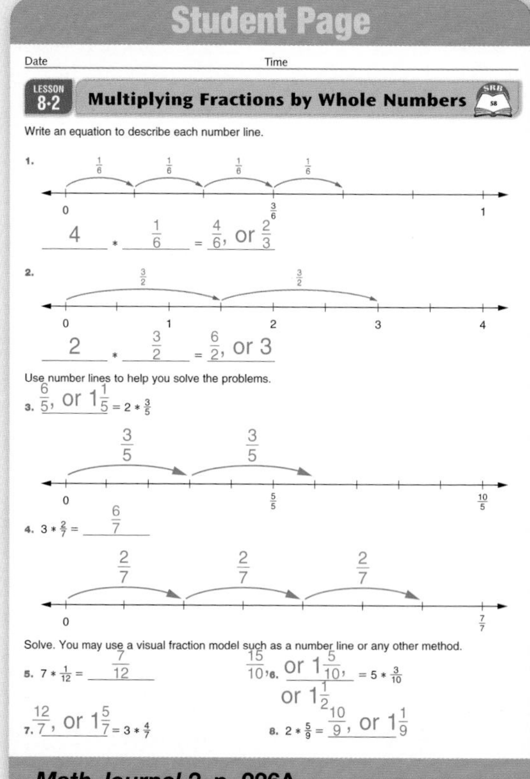

Student Page

Date Time

LESSON 8·2 **Multiplying Fractions by Whole Numbers**

Write an equation to describe each number line.

1. $4 * \frac{1}{6} = \frac{4}{6}$, or $\frac{2}{3}$

2. $2 * \frac{3}{2} = \frac{6}{2}$, or 3

Use number lines to help you solve the problems.

3. $\frac{6}{5}$, or $1\frac{1}{5} = 2 * \frac{3}{5}$

4. $3 * \frac{2}{7} = \frac{6}{7}$

Solve. You may use a visual fraction model such as a number line or any other method.

5. $7 * \frac{1}{12} = \frac{7}{12}$

6. $\frac{15}{10}$, or $1\frac{5}{10}$, or $1\frac{1}{2} = 5 * \frac{3}{10}$

7. $\frac{12}{7}$, or $1\frac{5}{7} = 3 * \frac{4}{7}$

8. $2 * \frac{5}{9} = \frac{10}{9}$, or $1\frac{1}{9}$

Math Journal 2, p. 226A

2 Ongoing Learning & Practice

Multiplying a Fraction by a Whole Number

PARTNER ACTIVITY

(*Math Journal 2,* pp. 226A and 226B)

Students practice multiplying fractions by whole numbers.

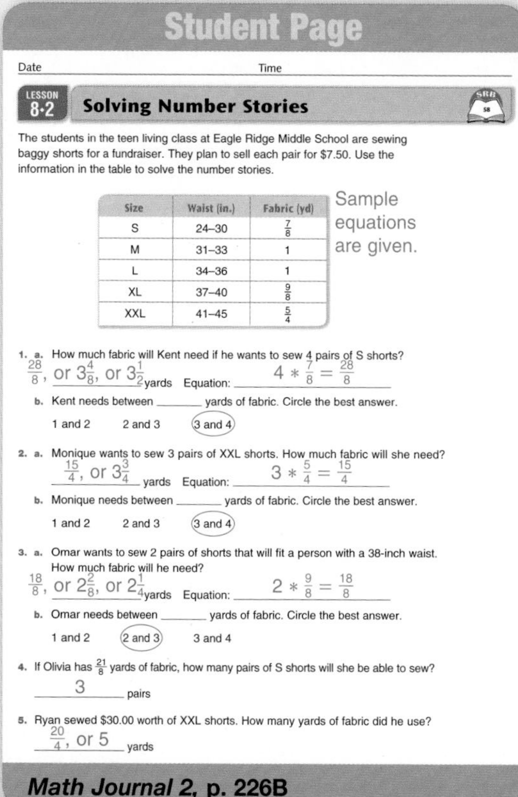

Student Page

Date Time

LESSON 8·2 **Solving Number Stories**

The students in the teen living class at Eagle Ridge Middle School are sewing baggy shorts for a fundraiser. They plan to sell each pair for $7.50. Use the information in the table to solve the number stories.

Size	Waist (in.)	Fabric (yd)
S	24–30	$\frac{7}{8}$
M	31–33	1
L	34–36	1
XL	37–40	$\frac{9}{8}$
XXL	41–45	$\frac{5}{4}$

Sample equations are given.

1. a. How much fabric will Kent need if he wants to sew 4 pairs of S shorts? $\frac{28}{8}$, or $3\frac{4}{8}$, or $3\frac{1}{2}$ yards Equation: $4 * \frac{7}{8} = \frac{28}{8}$
   b. Kent needs between ______ yards of fabric. Circle the best answer. 1 and 2 2 and 3 (3 and 4)
2. a. Monique wants to sew 3 pairs of XXL shorts. How much fabric will she need? $\frac{15}{4}$, or $3\frac{3}{4}$ yards Equation: $3 * \frac{5}{4} = \frac{15}{4}$
   b. Monique needs between ______ yards of fabric. Circle the best answer. 1 and 2 2 and 3 (3 and 4)
3. a. Omar wants to sew 2 pairs of shorts that will fit a person with a 38-inch waist. How much fabric will he need? $\frac{18}{8}$, or $2\frac{2}{8}$, or $2\frac{1}{4}$ yards Equation: $2 * \frac{9}{8} = \frac{18}{8}$
   b. Omar needs between ______ yards of fabric. Circle the best answer. 1 and 2 (2 and 3) 3 and 4
4. If Olivia has $\frac{21}{8}$ yards of fabric, how many pairs of S shorts will she be able to sew? 3 pairs
5. Ryan sewed $30.00 worth of XXL shorts. How many yards of fabric did he use? $\frac{20}{4}$, or 5 yards

Math Journal 2, p. 226B

Math Boxes 8·2

INDEPENDENT ACTIVITY

(*Math Journal 2,* p. 226)

Mixed Practice Math Boxes in this lesson are paired with Math Boxes in Lesson 8-4. The skill in Problem 6 previews Unit 9 content.

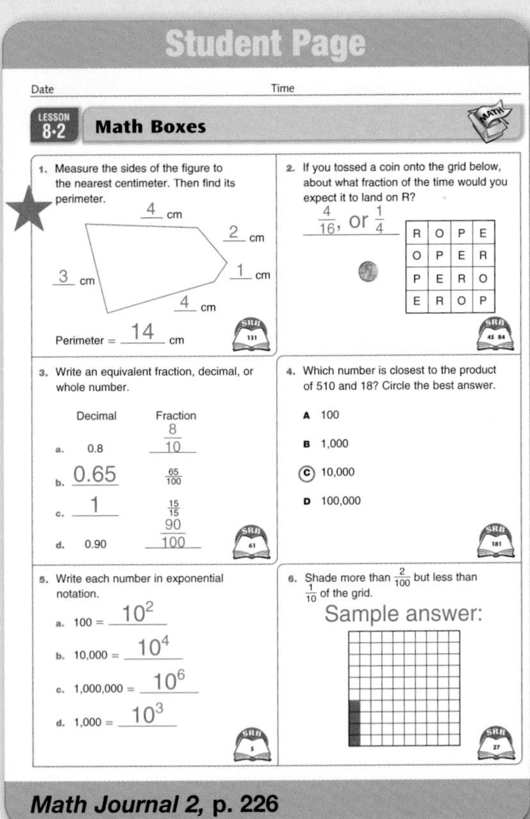

Student Page

Date Time

LESSON 8·2 **Math Boxes**

1. Measure the sides of the figure to the nearest centimeter. Then find its perimeter.

4 cm, 2 cm, 1 cm, 4 cm, 3 cm

Perimeter = 14 cm

2. If you tossed a coin onto the grid below, about what fraction of the time would you expect it to land on R?

$\frac{4}{16}$, or $\frac{1}{4}$

R	O	P	E
O	P	E	R
P	E	R	O
E	R	O	P

3. Write an equivalent fraction, decimal, or whole number.

	Decimal	Fraction
a.	0.8	$\frac{8}{10}$
b.	0.65	$\frac{65}{100}$
c.	1	$\frac{15}{15}$
d.	0.90	$\frac{90}{100}$

4. Which number is closest to the product of 510 and 18? Circle the best answer.

A 100

B 1,000

(C) 10,000

D 100,000

5. Write each number in exponential notation.

a. 100 = 10^2

b. 10,000 = 10^4

c. 1,000,000 = 10^6

d. 1,000 = 10^3

6. Shade more than $\frac{2}{100}$ but less than $\frac{1}{10}$ of the grid.

Sample answer:

Math Journal 2, p. 226

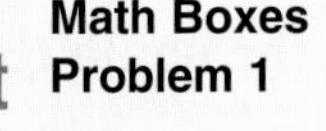

Ongoing Assessment: Recognizing Student Achievement

Use **Math Boxes, Problem 1** to assess students' ability to find the perimeter of a figure. Students are making adequate progress if they are able to find the lengths of the sides and add the measurements to find the perimeter. Some students may be able to write a number model that includes parentheses. $(2 * 4) + 3 + 2 + 1 = 14$ cm

[Measurement and Reference Frames Goal 2]

▶ Study Link 8·2

(*Math Masters,* p. 250)

Home Connection Students solve problems involving scale. They need a ruler to complete the page.

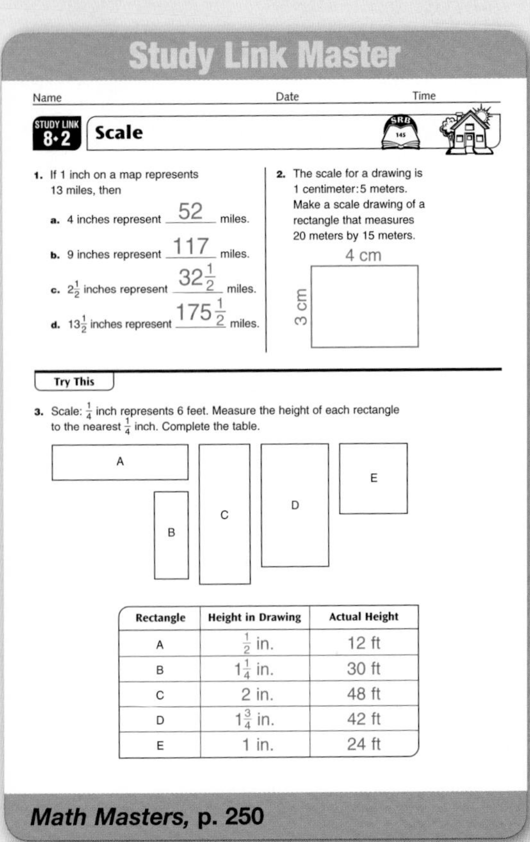

Study Link Master

Name Date Time

STUDY LINK 8·2 **Scale**

1. If 1 inch on a map represents 13 miles, then

a. 4 inches represent 52 miles.

b. 9 inches represent 117 miles.

c. $2\frac{1}{2}$ inches represent $32\frac{1}{2}$ miles.

d. $13\frac{1}{2}$ inches represent $175\frac{1}{2}$ miles.

2. The scale for a drawing is 1 centimeter:5 meters. Make a scale drawing of a rectangle that measures 20 meters by 15 meters.

4 cm, 3 cm

Try This

3. Scale: $\frac{1}{4}$ inch represents 6 feet. Measure the height of each rectangle to the nearest $\frac{1}{4}$ inch. Complete the table.

A B C D E

Rectangle	Height in Drawing	Actual Height
A	$\frac{1}{2}$ in.	12 ft
B	$1\frac{1}{4}$ in.	30 ft
C	2 in.	48 ft
D	$1\frac{3}{4}$ in.	42 ft
E	1 in.	24 ft

Math Masters, p. 250

3 Differentiation Options

READINESS

▶ Measuring to the Nearest Foot

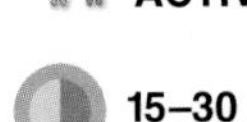

(*Math Masters,* p. 251 and p. 388 or 389)

To explore measuring to the nearest foot, have students cut out the "foot-long foot" on *Math Masters,* page 251 and use it to measure objects or distances. Have students record their work in a Math Log or on an Exit Slip.

Discuss why it is important to avoid overlaps or gaps while measuring and how having the $\frac{1}{2}$-foot marking helps to determine the nearest foot.

ENRICHMENT

▶ Making a Scale Drawing of Your Bedroom

30+ Min

(*Math Masters,* pp. 252 and 253)

Portfolio Ideas

To apply students' understanding of scale drawings, have them make scale drawings of their bedrooms on *Math Masters,* page 252. Students then make a scale drawing of the bird's-eye view of each piece of bedroom furniture on *Math Masters,* page 253. Then they cut out the drawings of the furniture and tape them in place on the scale drawings of their bedrooms.

Encourage students to think about ways to improve the layouts of their bedrooms.

- Would taking out or adding a piece of furniture make the room more comfortable?
- Would rearranging the furniture help?
- Are there ways to make better use of outside light? Of indoor light?

Students can experiment with various furniture arrangements on their scale drawings.

EXTRA PRACTICE

Taking a 50-Facts Test

5–15 Min

(*Math Masters,* pp. 413, 414, and 416)

See Lesson 3-4 for details regarding the administration of the 50-facts test and the recording and graphing of individual and optional class results.

ELL SUPPORT

Building Background for Mathematics Words

5–15 Min

To provide language support for scale, have students list possible ways of using the word *scale.* Then have them highlight and discuss the mathematical meanings. *For example:*

▷ The map *scale* shows that 1 inch represents 50 miles.

▷ Julie's dollhouse is a *scale* model of her actual house.

▷ My thermometer has two *scales* (Fahrenheit and Celsius).

▷ My ruler also has two *scales* (U.S. customary and metric).

▷ Every morning, my dad weighs himself on the bathroom *scale*. Today he weighs 182 pounds.

▷ The adventurers decided to *scale* the mountain. They think it will take about 4 days to get to the top.

▷ The body of a fish is covered with *scales*. The body of a human is covered with skin.

▷ Chris *scaled* the fish and then placed it on the grill to cook it.

▷ The trumpet players warmed up for the concert by playing *scales*.

▷ The class did very poorly on the test, so the teacher decided to *scale* it.

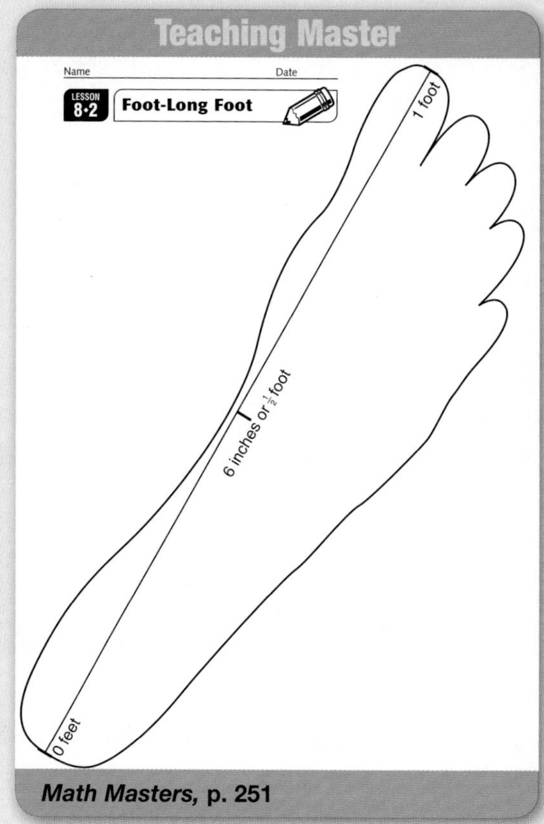

Math Masters, p. 251

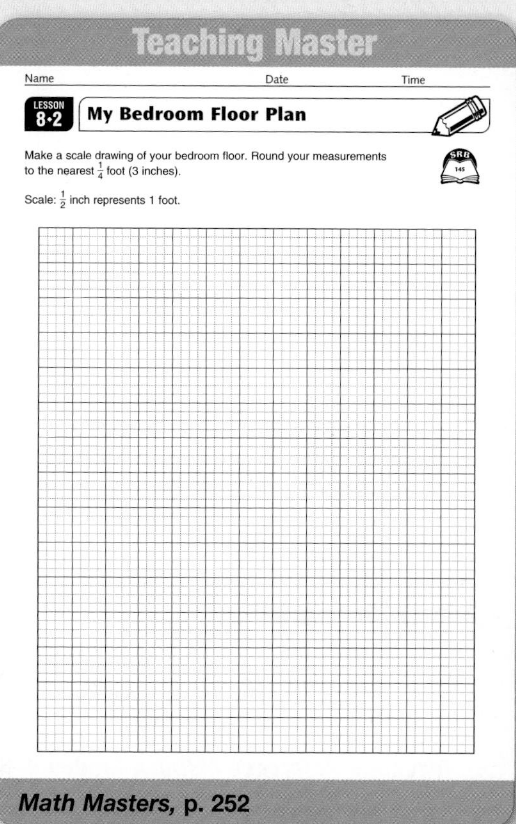

Teaching Master
Name
Date
Time
LESSON 8·2
My Bedroom Floor Plan
Make a scale drawing of your bedroom floor. Round your measurements to the nearest $\frac{1}{4}$ foot (3 inches).
SRB 145
Scale: $\frac{1}{2}$ inch represents 1 foot.

Math Masters, p. 252

8•3 Area

Objectives To review basic area concepts; to provide practice estimating the area of a polygon by counting unit squares and using a scale drawing to find area.

Technology Resources www.everydaymathonline.com

ePresentations

eToolkit

Algorithms Practice

EM Facts Workshop Game™

Family Letters

Assessment Management

Common Core State Standards

Curriculum Focal Points

Interactive Teacher's Lesson Guide

1 Teaching the Lesson

Key Concepts and Skills

- Use a scale drawing to estimate the area of the classroom. [Operations and Computation Goal 7; Measurement and Reference Frames Goal 2]
- Find the areas of polygons by counting squares and partial squares. [Measurement and Reference Frames Goal 2]
- Identify polygons. [Geometry Goal 2]

Key Activities

Students review the meaning of area as a measure of a surface in square units and estimate polygon areas in square centimeters by counting unit squares. They use the scale drawing made in Lesson 8•2 to find the area of the classroom floor.

Ongoing Assessment: Recognizing Student Achievement Use journal page 227. [Measurement and Reference Frames Goal 2]

Ongoing Assessment: Informing Instruction See page 672.

Key Vocabulary

area ◆ square units

Materials

Math Journal 2, pp. 225 and 227
Student Reference Book, p. 133
Study Link 8•2
unit squares ◆ slate

2 Ongoing Learning & Practice

Playing *Fraction Top-It*
Student Reference Book, p. 247
Math Masters, p. 506
1 deck of 32 Fraction Cards (*Math Journal 2,* Activity Sheets 5 and 6)
Students practice comparing and ordering fractions.

Math Boxes 8•3
Math Journal 2, p. 228
Students practice and maintain skills through Math Box problems.

Study Link 8•3
Math Masters, p. 254
scissors ◆ tape
Students practice and maintain skills through Study Link activities.

3 Differentiation Options

READINESS

Searching for Squares on a Geoboard
Math Masters, p. 437
geoboard ◆ rubber bands ◆ straightedge
Students identify and find the area of squares on a geoboard.

ENRICHMENT

Exploring Different Polygons with the Same Area
Math Masters, p. 437
geoboard ◆ rubber bands ◆ scissors ◆ straightedge
Students use geoboards to find polygons with an area of four square units.

EXTRA PRACTICE

Investigating Geoboard Areas
geoboard ◆ rubber bands
Students form polygons on their geoboards and find their areas.

ELL SUPPORT

Building a Math Word Bank
Differentiation Handbook, p. 140
Students add the terms *area* and *square* to their Math Word Banks.

Advance Preparation

For Part 1, display unit squares on a wall or bulletin board (see Planning Ahead in Lesson 8•1). Put them in order of increasing size with the metric unit squares in one row and the U.S. customary unit squares in another row.

***Teacher's Reference Manual,* Grades 4–6** pp. 220, 221

Getting Started

Mental Math and Reflexes

COMPUTATION PRACTICE

Pose mental addition problems. *Suggestions:*

●○○	●●○	●●●
20 + 30 = 50	126 + 40 = 166	72 + 45 = 117
60 + 40 = 100	363 + 30 = 393	56 + 56 = 112
25 + 75 = 100	642 + 60 = 702	159 + 159 = 318
55 + 35 = 90	70 + 586 = 656	315 + 682 = 997

Math Message

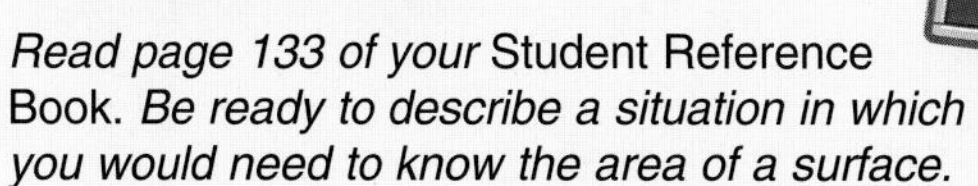

Read page 133 of your Student Reference Book. *Be ready to describe a situation in which you would need to know the area of a surface.*

Study Link 8·2 Follow-Up

Have small groups compare answers and discuss how they drew the rectangle to scale in Problem 2.

1 Teaching the Lesson

▶ Math Message Follow-Up

WHOLE-CLASS DISCUSSION

(*Student Reference Book,* p. 133)

Use page 133 of the *Student Reference Book* to review basic area concepts. As part of the discussion, remind the class that **area** is a measure of the surface inside a shape. Area is commonly measured in **square units.**

▷ The area of a surface is the number of unit squares and fractions of unit squares needed to cover the surface without overlaps and/or gaps.

Call students' attention to the classroom display of unit squares and to alternative ways of writing the units: *square inch* or in^2, *square meter* or m^2, and so on.

Tell students that in this lesson they will review a counting-squares strategy to find area and then use their scale drawings from the previous lesson to find the area of the classroom.

Links to the Future

In Lesson 8-4, students estimate the areas of figures whose boundaries are not made of line segments. In Lessons 8-5 through 8-7, students explore formulas for calculating the areas of rectangles, parallelograms, and triangles.

Student Page

Measurement

Area

Sometimes you want to know the amount of **surface inside** a shape. The amount of surface inside a shape is called its **area.** You can find the area of a shape by counting the number of squares of a certain size that cover the inside of the shape. The squares must cover the entire inside of the shape and must not overlap, have any gaps, or cover any surface outside of the shape. Sometimes a shape cannot be covered by an exact number of squares. If this is so, count the number of whole squares and the fractions of squares that cover the shape.

Example What is the area of the rectangle?

The rectangle at the right is covered by squares that are 1 centimeter on each side. Each square is called a **square centimeter (cm^2).**

Six of the squares cover the rectangle.
The area of the rectangle is 6 square centimeters.
This is written as 6 sq. cm, or 6 cm^2.

3 cm
2 cm

1 cm
1 cm
1 square centimeter (actual size)

Reminder: Be careful not to confuse the **area** of a shape with its **perimeter.** The **area** is the amount of surface *inside* the shape. The **perimeter** is the distance *around* the shape. Area is measured in units such as square inches, square feet, square centimeters, square meters, and square miles. Perimeter is measured in units such as inches, feet, centimeters, meters, and miles.

1 in.
1 in.
1 square inch (actual size)
Area = 1 $in.^2$
Perimeter = 4 in.

There are many situations where it is important to know the area.

- You may want to install carpeting in your living room. You will need to find the area of the floor to figure out how much carpeting to buy. For units, you would use **square yards (yd^2)** in the United States and **square meters (m^2)** in the rest of the world.
- You may want to paint the walls and ceilings of the rooms in your home. You will need to find the total area of all the surfaces to be painted to figure out how many gallons of paint to buy. Labels on cans of paint usually tell about how many **square feet (ft^2)** of surface can be painted with the paint in that can.
- In the "World Tour" section of this book, the area of each country you visit is given in **square miles.** This information is important when comparing the sizes of different countries.

Did You Know?

The Pacific Ocean covers an area of about 64,200,000 square miles.

***Student Reference Book,* p. 133**

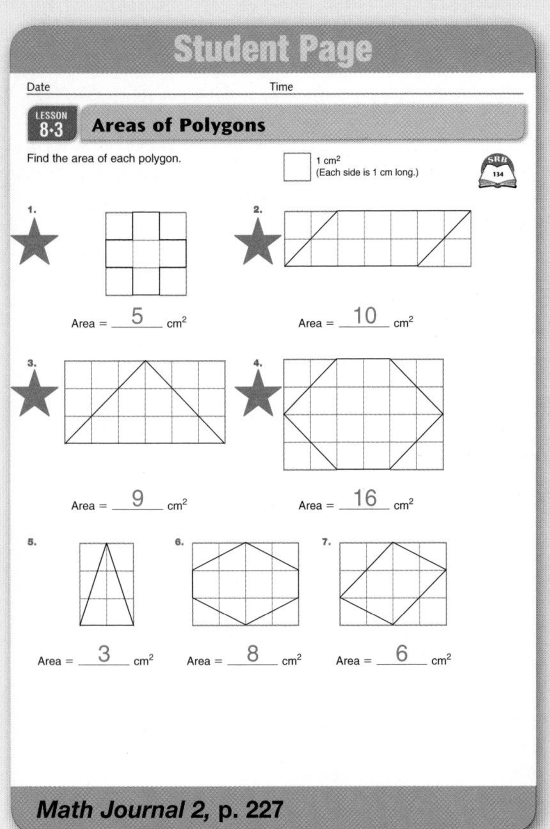

Student Page
Date
Time
LESSON 8·3
Areas of Polygons
Find the area of each polygon.
1 cm²
(Each side is 1 cm long.)
Area = 5 cm²
Area = 10 cm²
Area = 9 cm²
Area = 16 cm²
Area = 3 cm²
Area = 8 cm²
Area = 6 cm²

Math Journal 2, p. 227

Estimating Areas of Polygons by Counting Squares

INDEPENDENT ACTIVITY

PROBLEM SOLVING

(*Math Journal 2,* p. 227)

Have students complete Problems 1–4 independently. They can complete Problems 5–7 with a partner.

Ongoing Assessment: Recognizing Student Achievement

Journal page 227 Problems 1–4

Use **journal page 227, Problems 1–4** to assess students' ability to find the area of a polygon. Students are making adequate progress if they are able to count whole squares and half squares to find the total area of each polygon. Some students may be able to solve Problems 5–7 in which they count whole squares first and then combine partial squares to form whole squares.

[Measurement and Reference Frames Goal 2]

Estimating the Area of the Classroom Floor

PARTNER ACTIVITY

(*Math Journal 2,* p. 225)

Have students turn to their scale drawings of the classroom on journal page 225. Students work in pairs to find the area of the classroom from their scale drawings. Make sure they understand that each grid square in their scale drawing represents 1 square foot of classroom floor.

Ongoing Assessment: Informing Instruction

Watch for strategies that students use to find the area.

- Did they count the squares in their scale drawing?
- Did they use a more efficient method, such as multiplying the number of rows by the number of the squares in each row?

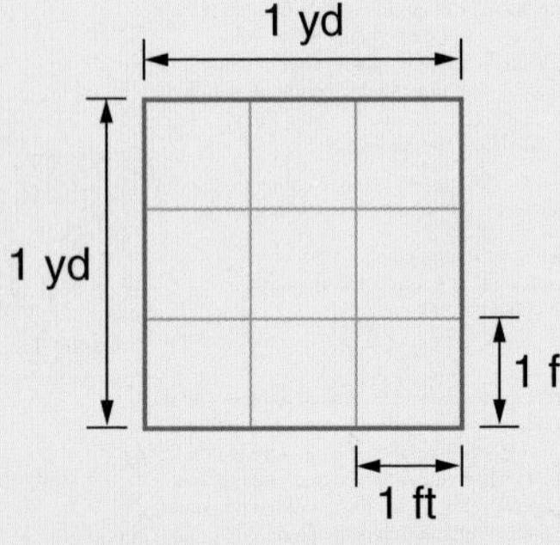

1 square yard = 9 square feet

$1\ yd^2 = 9\ ft^2$

Adjusting the Activity

Draw a grid on the board like the one shown in the margin. Ask students to think of a way to estimate the area of the classroom floor in *square yards. Possible strategies:*

- Since there are 3 feet in 1 yard, divide the scale drawing into larger 3-by-3 squares. Each 3-by-3 square represents 1 square yard. Count these larger squares and parts of squares.
- Since 1 square yard = 9 square feet, convert square feet to square yards by dividing the number of square feet by 9.

AUDITORY ◆ KINESTHETIC ◆ TACTILE ◆ VISUAL

2 Ongoing Learning & Practice

Playing *Fraction Top-It*

SMALL-GROUP ACTIVITY

(*Student Reference Book,* p. 247; *Math Masters,* p. 506; *Math Journal 2,* Activity Sheets 5 and 6)

Students play *Fraction Top-It* to practice comparing and ordering fractions. See Lesson 7-10 for additional information.

Math Boxes 8◆3

INDEPENDENT ACTIVITY

(*Math Journal 2,* p. 228)

Mixed Practice Math Boxes in this lesson are paired with Math Boxes in Lesson 8-1. The skill in Problem 6 previews Unit 9 content.

Writing/Reasoning Have students write a response to the following: *Describe the strategy you used in Problem 2c to decide which fraction, $\frac{4}{8}$ or $\frac{7}{15}$, is greater.* Sample answer: $\frac{4}{8}$ is equivalent to $\frac{1}{2}$. Since $\frac{1}{2}$ of 15 is $7\frac{1}{2}$, $\frac{7}{15}$ is less than $\frac{1}{2}$. Therefore, $\frac{7}{15}$ is less than $\frac{4}{8}$.

Study Link 8◆3

(*Math Masters,* p. 254)

Home Connection Students cut a rectangle into pieces and then rearrange the pieces to make a new shape. They compare the area of the original rectangle with the area of the new shape.

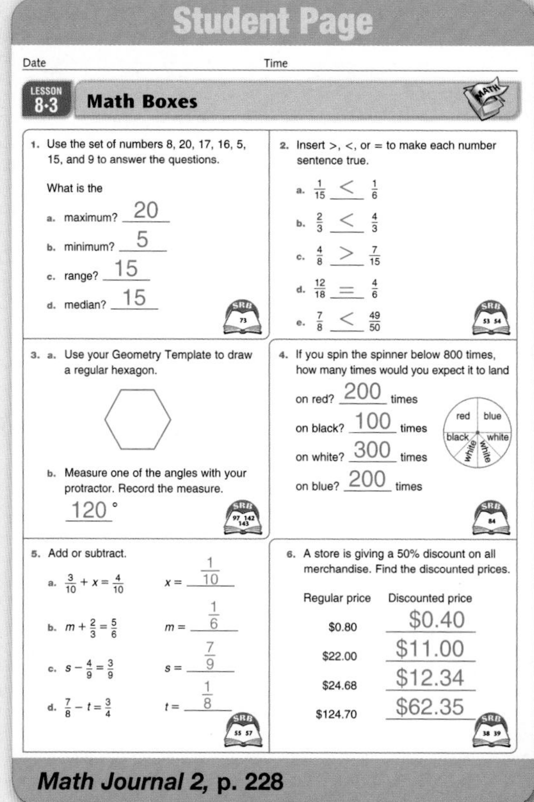

Student Page

Date Time

LESSON 8◆3 **Math Boxes**

1. Use the set of numbers 8, 20, 17, 16, 5, 15, and 9 to answer the questions.
What is the
a. maximum? 20
b. minimum? 5
c. range? 15
d. median? 15

2. Insert >, <, or = to make each number sentence true.
a. $\frac{1}{15} < \frac{1}{6}$
b. $\frac{2}{3} < \frac{4}{3}$
c. $\frac{4}{8} > \frac{7}{15}$
d. $\frac{12}{18} = \frac{4}{6}$
e. $\frac{7}{8} < \frac{49}{50}$

3. a. Use your Geometry Template to draw a regular hexagon.
b. Measure one of the angles with your protractor. Record the measure.
120°

4. If you spin the spinner below 800 times, how many times would you expect it to land
on red? 200 times
on black? 100 times
on white? 300 times
on blue? 200 times

5. Add or subtract.
a. $\frac{3}{10} + x = \frac{4}{10}$ $x = \frac{1}{10}$
b. $m + \frac{2}{3} = \frac{5}{6}$ $m = \frac{1}{6}$
c. $s - \frac{4}{9} = \frac{3}{9}$ $s = \frac{7}{9}$
d. $\frac{7}{8} - t = \frac{3}{4}$ $t = \frac{1}{8}$

6. A store is giving a 50% discount on all merchandise. Find the discounted prices.

Regular price	Discounted price
\$0.80	\$0.40
\$22.00	\$11.00
\$24.68	\$12.34
\$124.70	\$62.35

Math Journal 2, p. 228

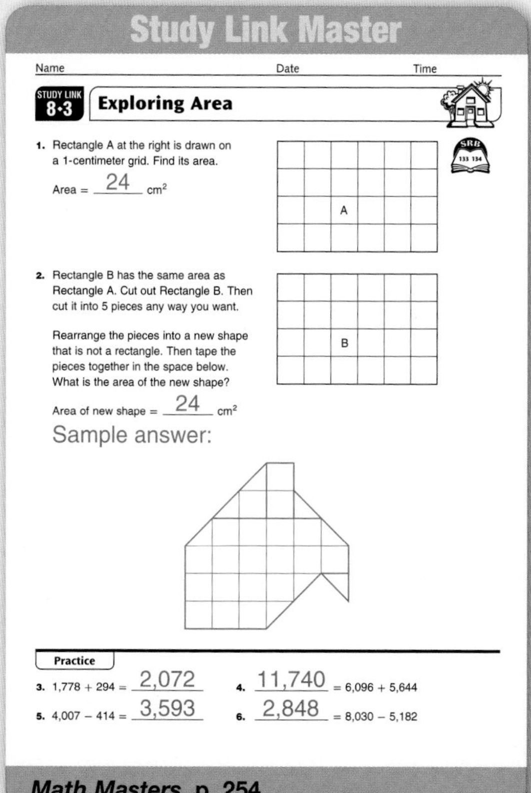

Study Link Master

Name Date Time

STUDY LINK 8◆3 **Exploring Area**

1. Rectangle A at the right is drawn on a 1-centimeter grid. Find its area.
Area = 24 cm²

2. Rectangle B has the same area as Rectangle A. Cut out Rectangle B. Then cut it into 5 pieces any way you want.
Rearrange the pieces into a new shape that is not a rectangle. Then tape the pieces together in the space below. What is the area of the new shape?
Area of new shape = 24 cm²
Sample answer:

Practice

3. 1,778 + 294 = 2,072
4. 11,740 = 6,096 + 5,644
5. 4,007 − 414 = 3,593
6. 2,848 = 8,030 − 5,182

Math Masters, p. 254

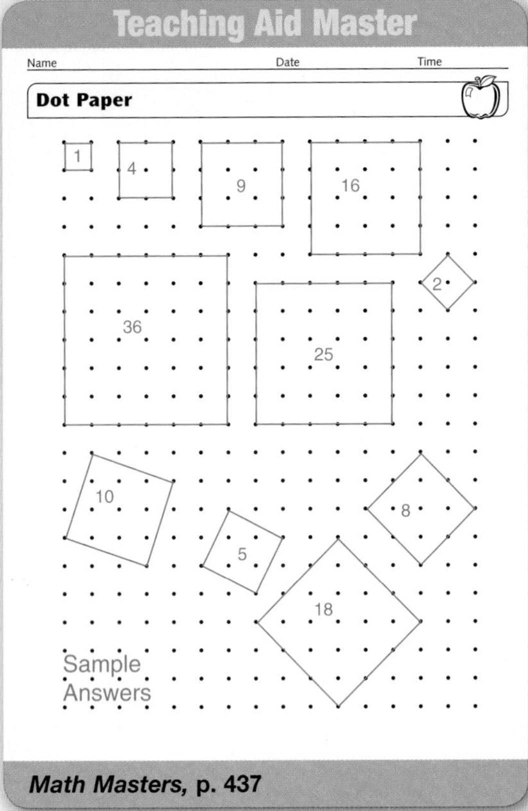

Sample answers for **Readiness** activity

Sample answers for **Enrichment** activity

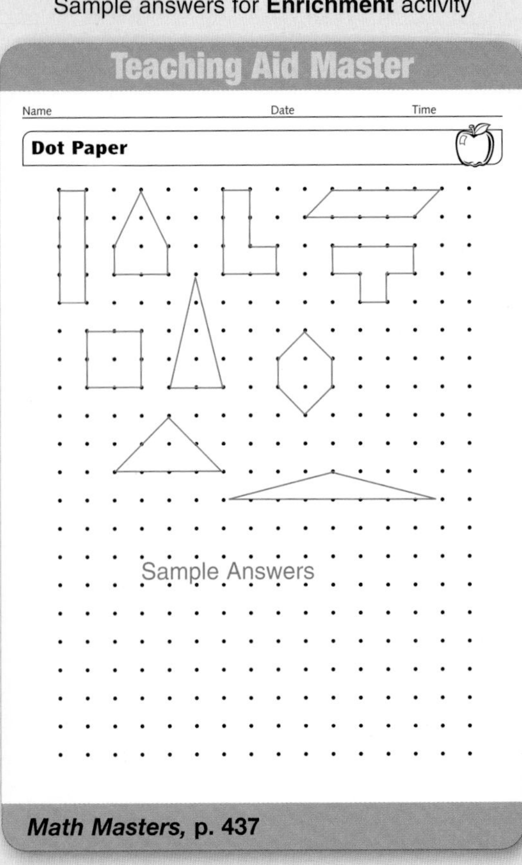

3 Differentiation Options

READINESS

PARTN
ACTIVIT

5–15 Mi

▶ Searching for Squares on a Geoboard

(*Math Masters,* p. 437)

To explore finding the area of a polygon using a concrete model, have students search for squares that can be made on a 7-by-7 geoboard and draw them on *Math Masters,* page 437. Ask students to record the area of each square and tell how they found it.

ENRICHMENT

PARTN
ACTIVIT

5–15 Mi

▶ Exploring Different Polygons with the Same Area

(*Math Masters,* p. 437)

To apply students' understanding of area, have them use geoboards to find polygons with an area of four square units and record them on *Math Masters,* page 437.

Ask students to cut out the polygons and sort them into groups. Remind students that if a polygon can be flipped or turned to fit exactly on top of another polygon, then the polygons are *congruer* and they are not different polygons. Have students record what the polygons in each group have in common.

EXTRA PRACTICE

PARTN
ACTIVIT

5–15 Mi

▶ Investigating Geoboard Areas

To provide practice finding the areas of polygons, have students use rubber bands to form polygons on their geoboards and count whole squares and partial squares to find the area. Have partners trade geoboards, find the areas of their partner's polygons, and compare answers.

ELL SUPPORT

5–15 Min

▶ Building a Math Word Bank

(*Differentiation Handbook,* p. 140)

To provide language support for area, have students use the Word Bank Template found on *Differentiation Handbook,* page 140. Ask students to write the terms *area* and *square unit,* draw pictures relating to each term, and write other related words. See the *Differentiation Handbook* for more information.

8·4 What is the Area of My Skin?

Objectives To demonstrate how to estimate the area of a surface having a curved boundary; and to provide practice converting from one square unit to another.

Technology Resources www.everydaymathonline.com

ePresentations

eToolkit

Algorithms Practice

EM Facts Workshop Game™

Family Letters

Assessment Management

Common Core State Standards

Curriculum Focal Points

Interactive Teacher's Lesson Guide

1 Teaching the Lesson

Key Concepts and Skills

- Use the terms *estimate* and *guess*. [Operations and Computation Goal 6]
- Use an estimate to judge the reasonableness of a solution. [Operations and Computation Goal 6]
- Count squares and partial squares or use a formula to estimate area. [Measurement and Reference Frames Goal 2]
- Convert between square inches and square feet. [Measurement and Reference Frames Goal 3]

Key Activities

Students estimate the area of the front of their hand by tracing it on a 1-inch grid and counting squares. Then they use a rule of thumb to estimate their total skin area. Students convert measurements from square inches to square feet and from square feet to square yards.

Ongoing Assessment: Recognizing Student Achievement Use a Math Log or Exit Slip (*Math Masters,* page 388 or 389). [Measurement and Reference Frames Goal 2]

Materials

Math Journal 2, pp. 230 and 231
Study Link 8•3
Math Masters, p. 388 or 389 (optional); p. 444
calculator (optional) ◆ scissors ◆ tape ◆ slate

2 Ongoing Learning & Practice

World Tour Option: Visiting South America

Math Journal 2, p. 329 (optional); pp. 330, 331, 334, and 335
Student Reference Book, pp. 276, 277, 280, 286, 287, 297, and 302–305
Math Masters, pp. 419 and 420 (optional)
Students resume the World Tour in South America.

Math Boxes 8•4

Math Journal 2, p. 229
Students practice and maintain skills through Math Box problems.

Study Link 8•4

Math Masters, p. 255
Students practice and maintain skills through Study Link activities.

3 Differentiation Options

READINESS

Counting Squares to Find Area

Math Masters, p. 388 or 389
square stick-on notes ◆ masking tape
Students use square stick-on notes to determine the area of an irregular region.

EXTRA PRACTICE

Estimating Areas of Irregular Regions

Math Masters, p. 444
objects with flat irregular surfaces
Students place objects on a grid, trace their outlines, and count grid squares to estimate their areas.

Advance Preparation

For Part 1, make 3 copies of 1-inch grid paper (*Math Masters,* page 444) for each student. Place copies near the Math Message.

***Teacher's Reference Manual,* Grades 4–6** pp. 220, 221

Getting Started

Mental Math and Reflexes

COMPUTATION PRACTICE

Pose mental subtraction problems. *Suggestions:*

●○○	●●○	●●●
80 − 50 = 30	86 − 41 = 45	64 − 45 = 19
120 − 30 = 90	149 − 42 = 107	203 − 150 = 53
250 − 60 = 190	278 − 73 = 205	671 − 80 = 591
370 − 90 = 280	357 − 122 = 235	417 − 60 = 357

Math Message

Take 3 sheets of grid paper. Cut and tape the grids to make a square with sides that measure 1 foot (12 inches). How many square inches are there in 1 square foot?

Study Link 8·3 Follow-Up

Have students share their conclusions about the area of their new shapes. Confirm with the class that shapes that look different can have the same area.

1 Teaching the Lesson

▶ Math Message Follow-Up

(*Math Journal 2,* p. 230)

Each student should have made a square consisting of 12 rows with 12 one-inch squares in each row.

▷ Since 12 ∗ 12 = 144, there are 144 square inches in 1 square foot.

Students record this equivalency in Problem 1 on journal page 230. Tell students that in this lesson they will use the 1-foot square to estimate the area of their skin.

▶ Estimating the Area of Your Skin

PARTNER ACTIVITY

(*Math Journal 2,* pp. 230 and 231)

Ask students to guess the total area of their skin in square feet and record it in Problem 2 on journal page 230. Have them refer to their 1-foot square to help them with their guess.

Tell them to use the following to check their guess.

Rule of Thumb: The total area of your skin is about 100 times the area of the outline of your hand.

Then have partners follow these steps:

1. Trace the outline of your partner's hand on the grid on your partner's journal page 231.
2. Estimate the area of your own hand by counting grid squares (square inches) inside the tracing of your hand.
3. Use the rule of thumb to estimate the total area of your skin (area of skin = 100 ∗ area of hand).

Students record the results in Problems 3 and 4.

Student Page

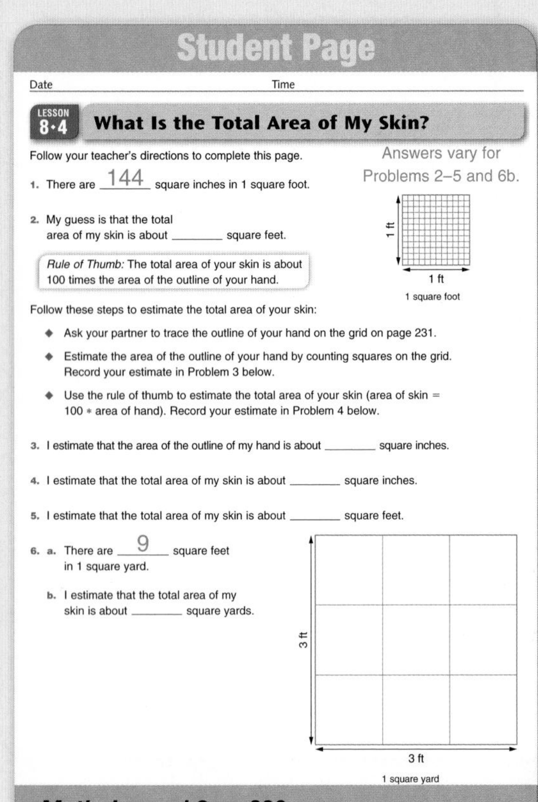

Date Time

LESSON 8·4 **What Is the Total Area of My Skin?**

Follow your teacher's directions to complete this page.

Answers vary for Problems 2–5 and 6b.

1. There are 144 square inches in 1 square foot.
2. My guess is that the total area of my skin is about ________ square feet.

Rule of Thumb: The total area of your skin is about 100 times the area of the outline of your hand.

1 ft, 1 ft, 1 square foot

Follow these steps to estimate the total area of your skin:

- Ask your partner to trace the outline of your hand on the grid on page 231.
- Estimate the area of the outline of your hand by counting squares on the grid. Record your estimate in Problem 3 below.
- Use the rule of thumb to estimate the total area of your skin (area of skin = 100 ∗ area of hand). Record your estimate in Problem 4 below.

3. I estimate that the area of the outline of my hand is about ________ square inches.
4. I estimate that the total area of my skin is about ________ square inches.
5. I estimate that the total area of my skin is about ________ square feet.
6. a. There are 9 square feet in 1 square yard.

   b. I estimate that the total area of my skin is about ________ square yards.

3 ft, 3 ft, 1 square yard

Math Journal 2, p. 230

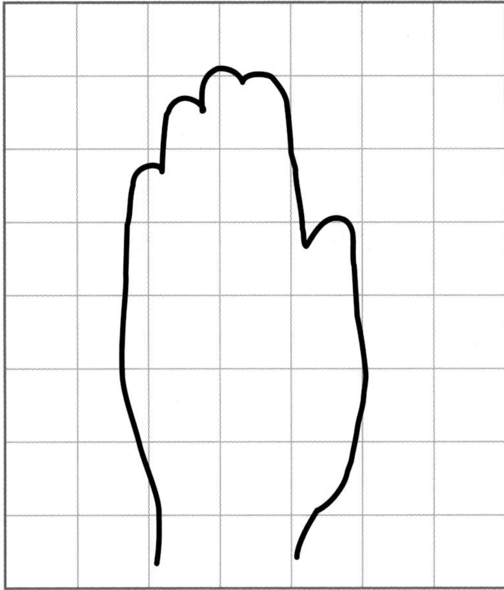

A student's fingers should be *closed* when his or her partner traces the hand outline on journal page 231.

Ongoing Assessment: Recognizing Student Achievement

Math Log or Exit Slip

Use a **Math Log** or an **Exit Slip** (*Math Masters,* page 388 or 389) to assess students' ability to count unit squares and fractions of unit squares to estimate the area of an irregular figure. Have students explain how they found the area of their hands. Students are making adequate progress if their strategy includes counting whole squares and combining partial squares to approximate whole squares. Some students may describe a strategy in which they find the area of a rectangular region within the hand tracing by multiplying its length and width.

[Measurement and Reference Frames Goal 2]

Sharing the Results of the Experiment

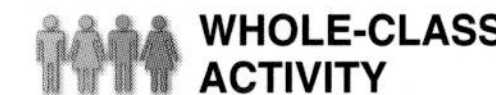

WHOLE-CLASS ACTIVITY

(*Math Journal 2,* pp. 230 and 231)

Review the information students have obtained so far.

▷ In Problem 2, they *guessed* the total area of their skin in *square feet.*

▷ In Problem 4, they *estimated* the total area of their skin in *square inches.*

Remind students about the difference between a guess and an estimate—an estimate is more systematic and usually more accurate than a guess.

Ask students to compare how close the guesses they made in Problem 2 are to their estimates in Problem 4.

▷ The guess and the estimate cannot be immediately compared because the guess is in square feet and the estimate is in square inches.

▷ Help students convert their square-inch estimates to square feet. Have them record the square-foot estimates in Problem 5.

Example: Guess is 15 square feet. Estimate is 1,512 square inches. Convert 1,512 square inches to square feet. Use the fact that 144 square inches equals 1 square foot. You want to know how many 144s there are in 1,512. Since $1{,}512 \div 144 = 10.5$, it follows that 1,512 square inches equals 10.5 square feet.

Adjusting the Activity

ELL

Have students use their 1-foot squares to model the conversion of a volunteer's skin estimate in square inches to square feet. Ask students to come to the board, one at a time, with 1-foot squares and tape them onto the board. Have a student with a calculator add 144 each time a 1-foot square is added.

Students should tape the first nine 1-foot squares in three rows with three squares in each row. Call attention to the fact that 9 square feet is equal to 1 square yard.

Have students tape 1-foot squares until the total is equal to or greater than the estimated area. Discuss how to use the taped squares to find the approximate area in square feet. For example, 1,500 square inches is between 10 square feet ($10 * 144 = 1{,}440$) and 11 square feet ($11 * 144 = 1{,}584$).

AUDITORY ♦ KINESTHETIC ♦ TACTILE ♦ VISUAL

Now ask students to convert their estimates to an approximate number of square yards (probably between 1 and 2) and record it in Problem 6. To convert to square yards, students divide the number of square feet by 9.

2 Ongoing Learning & Practice

▶ World Tour Option: Visiting South America

(*Math Journal 2,* pp. 329–331, 334, and 335; *Student Reference Book,* pp. 276, 277, 280, 286, 287, 297, and 302–305; *Math Masters,* pp. 419 and 420)

Social Studies Link If you have chosen to extend the scope of the World Tour for your class, have small groups visit a second country in South America. You may let them choose which countries to visit, or you may assign a country to each group. Remind students to update their Route Log (if they are keeping one) and Route Map and to complete Country Notes for the country they visit.

Adjusting the Activity

Have students determine the latitude and longitude of the capital city of the country they visit.

AUDITORY ♦ KINESTHETIC ♦ TACTILE ♦ VISUAL

Math Boxes 8•4

INDEPENDENT ACTIVITY

(*Math Journal 2,* p. 229)

Mixed Practice Math Boxes in this lesson are paired with Math Boxes in Lesson 8-2. The skill in Problem 6 previews Unit 9 content.

Writing/Reasoning Have students write a response to the following: *Describe the strategy you used to estimate the product in Problem 4.* Sample answer: I used 200 instead of 192, and 50 instead of 49, because they are "close-but-easier" numbers. $200 * 50 = 10{,}000$

Study Link 8•4

INDEPENDENT ACTIVITY

(*Math Masters,* p. 255)

Home Connection Students estimate the area of São Paulo State and Rio de Janeiro State in Brazil.

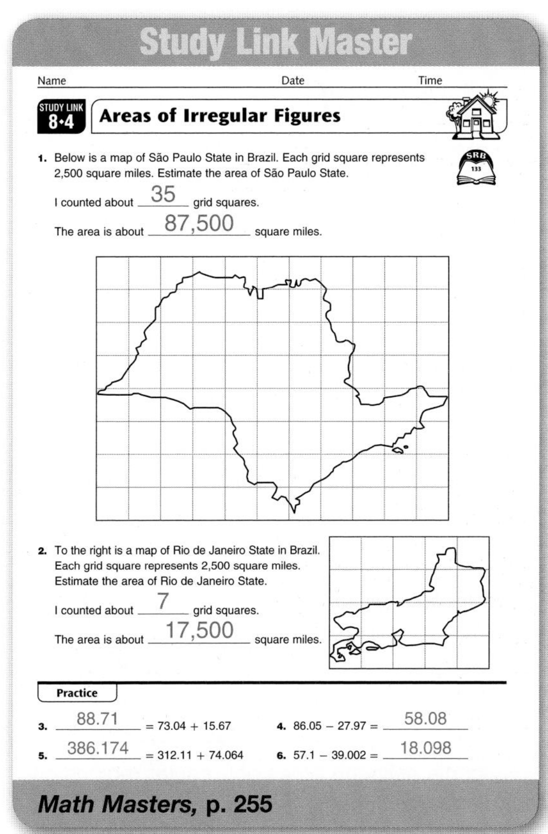

Study Link Master

Name Date Time

STUDY LINK 8•4 **Areas of Irregular Figures**

1. Below is a map of São Paulo State in Brazil. Each grid square represents 2,500 square miles. Estimate the area of São Paulo State.

I counted about 35 grid squares.

The area is about 87,500 square miles.

2. To the right is a map of Rio de Janeiro State in Brazil. Each grid square represents 2,500 square miles. Estimate the area of Rio de Janeiro State.

I counted about 7 grid squares.

The area is about 17,500 square miles.

Practice

3. 88.71 = 73.04 + 15.67

4. 86.05 − 27.97 = 58.08

5. 386.174 = 312.11 + 74.064

6. 57.1 − 39.002 = 18.098

Math Masters, p. 255

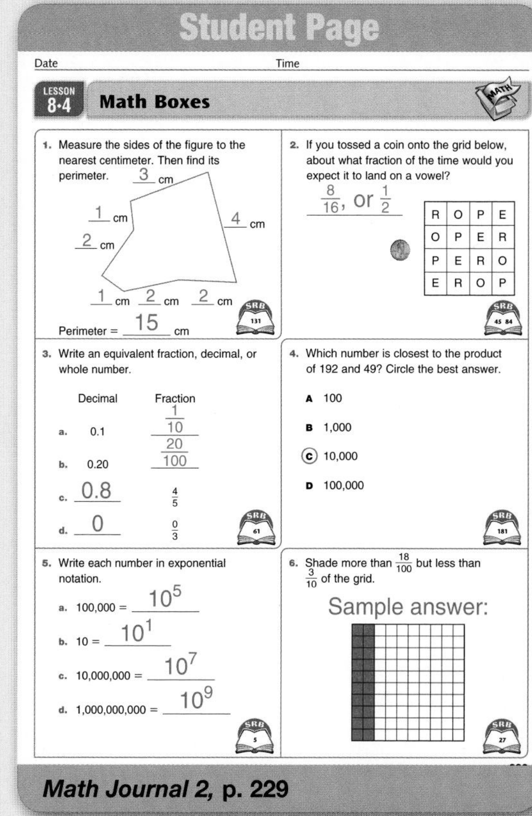

Student Page

Date Time

LESSON 8•4 **Math Boxes**

1. Measure the sides of the figure to the nearest centimeter. Then find its perimeter.

3 cm, 1 cm, 2 cm, 4 cm, 1 cm, 2 cm, 2 cm

Perimeter = 15 cm

2. If you tossed a coin onto the grid below, about what fraction of the time would you expect it to land on a vowel?

$\frac{8}{16}$, or $\frac{1}{2}$

R	O	P	E
O	P	E	R
P	E	R	O
E	R	O	P

3. Write an equivalent fraction, decimal, or whole number.

	Decimal	Fraction
a.	0.1	$\frac{1}{10}$
b.	0.20	$\frac{20}{100}$
c.	0.8	$\frac{4}{5}$
d.	0	$\frac{0}{3}$

4. Which number is closest to the product of 192 and 49? Circle the best answer.

A 100

B 1,000

(C) 10,000

D 100,000

5. Write each number in exponential notation.

a. 100,000 = 10^5

b. 10 = 10^1

c. 10,000,000 = 10^7

d. 1,000,000,000 = 10^9

6. Shade more than $\frac{18}{100}$ but less than $\frac{3}{10}$ of the grid.

Sample answer:

Math Journal 2, p. 229

3 Differentiation Options

READINESS

PARTNER ACTIVITY

5–15 Min

▶ Counting Squares to Find Area

(*Math Masters,* p. 388 or 389)

To explore the concept of area as the number of unit squares and fractions of unit squares needed to cover a surface without gaps or overlaps, have students use square stick-on notes to cover an irregular region.

Using masking tape, create (or have students create) a large figure on the floor. Students first estimate the area and then cover the figure with stick-on notes. They count stick-on notes and partial areas not covered by stick-on notes to refine their estimates.

In a Math Log or on an Exit Slip, have students describe how they determined the area of the irregular region.

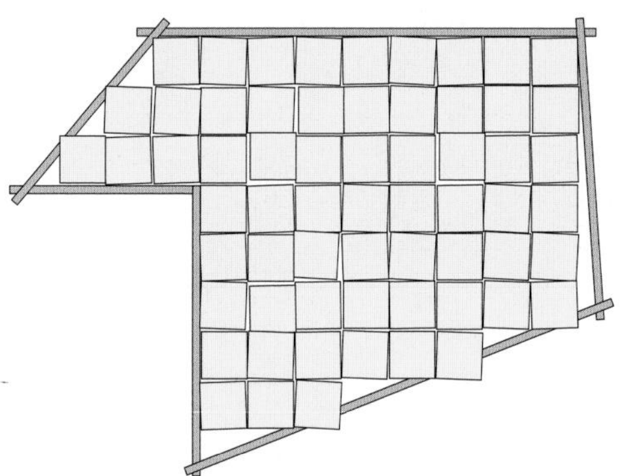

Students use square stick-on notes to estimate the area of an irregular region.

EXTRA PRACTICE

INDEPENDENT ACTIVITY

5–15 Min

▶ Estimating Areas of Irregular Regions

(*Math Masters,* p. 444)

To practice finding the area of irregular regions, have students place objects that have flat, irregular surfaces on a grid and trace their outlines. Then have students count grid squares and partial grid squares to estimate the areas.

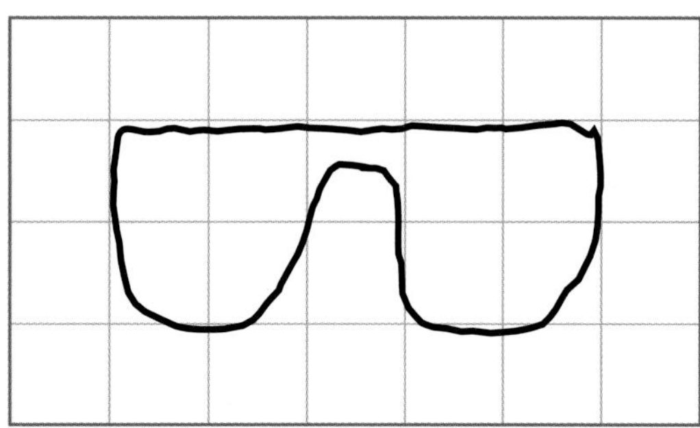

Students estimate areas of irregular regions on *Math Masters,* page 444.

8•5 Formula for the Area of a Rectangle

Objective To guide the development and use of a formula for the area of a rectangle.

www.everydaymathonline.com

ePresentations

eToolkit

Algorithms Practice

EM Facts Workshop Game™

Family Letters

Assessment Management

Common Core State Standards

Curriculum Focal Points

Interactive Teacher's Lesson Guide

1 Teaching the Lesson

Key Concepts and Skills

- Rename fractions as decimals.
  [Number and Numeration Goal 5]
- Count unit squares or use a formula to find the area of a rectangle.
  [Measurement and Reference Frames Goal 2]
- Use patterns in a table to develop a formula for the area of a rectangle.
  [Patterns, Functions, and Algebra Goal 1]
- Apply the Distributive Property of Multiplication over Addition.
  [Patterns, Functions, and Algebra Goal 4]

Key Activities

Students count squares to find the areas of rectangles and then develop a formula for the area of a rectangle. They use the formula to find the area of a rectangle whose length and/or width is not a whole number of units.

Ongoing Assessment: Informing Instruction See page 684.

Key Vocabulary

length ◆ base ◆ width ◆ height ◆ area ◆ formula ◆ variable

Materials

Math Journal 2, pp. 232 and 233
Study Link 8•4
calculator (optional) ◆ slate

2 Ongoing Learning & Practice

Using a Coordinate Grid
Math Journal 2, p. 234
Students plot and name points on a coordinate grid.

Math Boxes 8•5
Math Journal 2, p. 235
Students practice and maintain skills through Math Box problems.

Ongoing Assessment: Recognizing Student Achievement
Use Math Boxes, Problem 2.
[Measurement and Reference Frames Goal 2]

Study Link 8•5
Math Masters, p. 256
Students practice and maintain skills through Study Link activities.

3 Differentiation Options

READINESS

Finding Areas of Rectangles
Math Masters, p. 257
1 six-sided die ◆ 36 square pattern blocks
Students roll a die to determine the dimensions of a rectangle. They build the rectangle and find its area.

ENRICHMENT

Finding the Area of a Tennis Court
Math Masters, p. 258
Students find the areas of rectangles using the dimensions of a tennis court.

ENRICHMENT

Exploring the Relationship between the Perimeter and Area of a Rectangle
Math Masters, pp. 259 and 444
24-inch string loop ◆ tape
Students use a string loop to find rectangles with various areas that all have a perimeter of 24 inches.

ELL SUPPORT

Building a Math Word Bank
Differentiation Handbook, p. 140
Students add the terms *length, width, base,* and *height* to their Math Word Banks.

Advance Preparation

For Part 1, draw the table shown at the right on the board.

Rectangle	Length of Base	Width (height)	Area
A			
B			
C			

***Teacher's Reference Manual,* Grades 4–6** pp. 180–185, 221, 222

Getting Started

Mental Math and Reflexes

Pose multiplication facts and problems.
Suggestions:

●○○ 6 ∗ 7 = 42	●●○ 70 ∗ 50 = 3,500	●●● 62 ∗ 5 = 310
4 ∗ 8 = 32	40 ∗ 60 = 2,400	58 ∗ 6 = 348
7 ∗ 9 = 63	80 ∗ 60 = 4,800	49 ∗ 8 = 392
8 ∗ 6 = 48	90 ∗ 300 = 27,000	6 ∗ 123 = 738
9 ∗ 4 = 36	700 ∗ 80 = 56,000	4 ∗ 217 = 868

Math Message

Complete Problem 1 on journal page 232.

Study Link 8·4 Follow-Up

Students share estimation strategies. One approach is to combine areas of partial squares. Some students may describe a strategy in which they found the area of large rectangular regions within São Paulo State by multiplying length by width.

Ask students to share the number models they used to determine the area in square miles.

1 Teaching the Lesson

▶ Math Message Follow-Up

(*Math Journal 2,* p. 232)

Most students will simply count the number of squares in Rectangles A and B. For Rectangle C, some students may count the number of squares in one row 5, count the number of rows 6, and multiply. $6 * 5 = 30$, so the area equals 30 cm^2.

Remind students how to write a number model for the area of Rectangle A: There are 2 rows with 4 squares in each row, for a total of 8 squares. Two rows of 4 squares each is equivalent to $2 * 4 = 8$ squares. Have students record this information in the table in Problem 2 on journal page 232. They can complete the table for Rectangles B and C on their own.

Tell students that in this lesson they will develop a formula for the area of any rectangle.

▶ Developing a Formula for the Area of a Rectangle

WHOLE-CLASS ACTIVITY

ELL

PROBLEM SOLVING

(*Math Journal 2,* p. 232)

Algebraic Thinking Draw a rectangle on the board. Choose one of the sides (for example, the side on which the rectangle "sits") and label it the base. (Any side can be designated as the base.) The *length of the base* of a rectangle is called either **length** or **base,** for short.

Explain that the shortest distance between the base and the side opposite the base is called either the **width** or **height** of the rectangle. Label it on the drawing. In a rectangle, the width is the length of a side adjacent to the base.

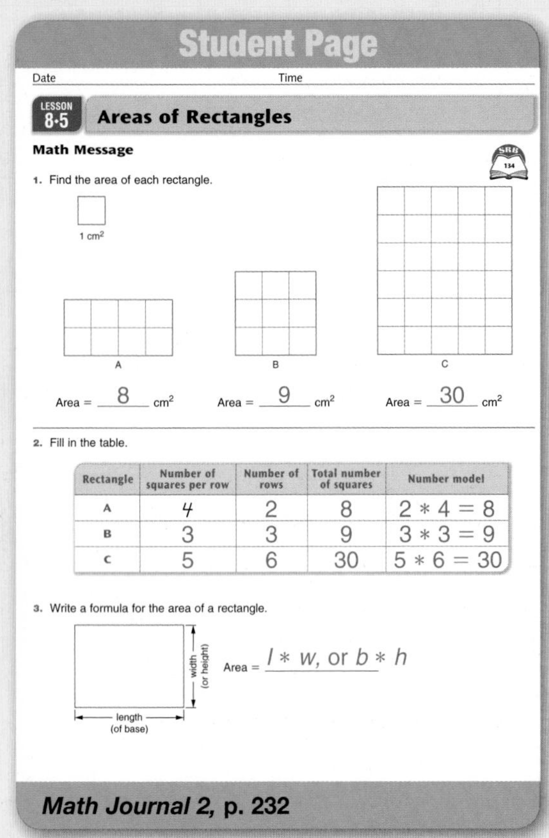

Student Page

Date Time

LESSON 8·5 **Areas of Rectangles**

Math Message

1. Find the area of each rectangle.

1 cm²

A Area = 8 cm² B Area = 9 cm² C Area = 30 cm²

2. Fill in the table.

Rectangle	Number of squares per row	Number of rows	Total number of squares	Number model
A	4	2	8	2 ∗ 4 = 8
B	3	3	9	3 ∗ 3 = 9
C	5	6	30	5 ∗ 6 = 30

3. Write a formula for the area of a rectangle.

width (or height) length (of base)

Area = *l ∗ w, or b ∗ h*

Math Journal 2, p. 232

Ask students to help you fill out the following table.

Rectangle	Length of Base	Width (height)	Area
A	4 cm	2 cm	8 cm^2
B	3 cm	3 cm	9 cm^2
C	5 cm	6 cm	30 cm^2

width, or height

length of base

Have small groups of students look at the patterns in the table and generate a rule that could be used to find the area of any rectangle. Ask students to share their rules.

Summary: If the length of the base and the width of a rectangle are known, the area can be found by multiplying.

Area of a rectangle = length of the base ∗ width of the rectangle

Such a rule is called a **formula.** It can be abbreviated as

$$A = l * w$$

In the formula, the letter A stands for *area of a rectangle,* the letter l for *length of the base,* and the letter w for *width of the rectangle*. Another way of writing this formula is

$$A = b * h$$

Here the letter b stands for *length of the base* and the letter h for *height of the rectangle*.

Have students record a formula for the area of a rectangle in Problem 3 on journal page 232. Remind the class that the letters in a formula are called **variables.** They can take on any value; that is, their values can *vary.* To support English language learners, write the word *variable* on the board and provide some examples.

NOTE Since a rectangle is a special kind of parallelogram, and the usual formula for the area of a parallelogram is $A = b * h$, the authors will most often use this form for the area of a rectangle. However, in certain contexts, the formula $A = l * w$ is preferable.

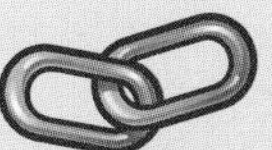

Links to the Future

The use of a formula to calculate the area of a rectangle is a Grade 5 Goal.

▶ Using a Formula for the Area of a Rectangle

(*Math Journal 2,* p. 233)

Algebraic Thinking Ask partners to count squares to find the areas of the rectangles in Problem 4 on journal page 233 and to record the results in the second column in the table.

Adjusting the Activity

ELL

Have students label the base (b) and the height (h) of each rectangle before working on the journal page.

AUDITORY ◆ KINESTHETIC ◆ TACTILE ◆ VISUAL

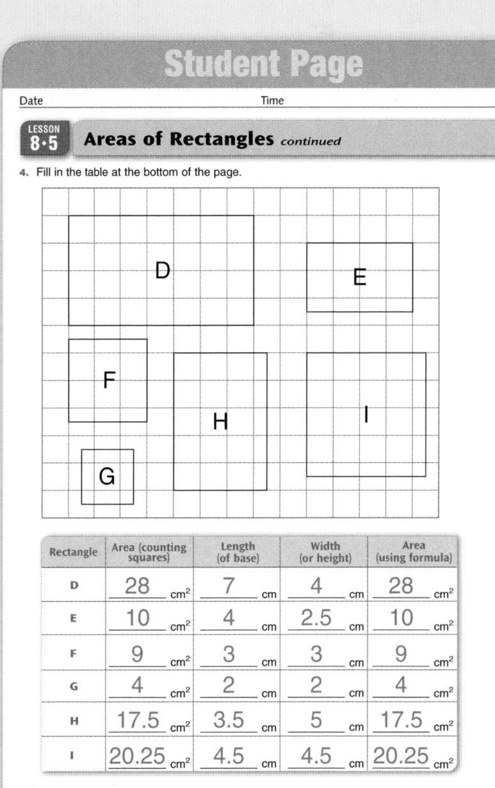

Student Page

Date Time

LESSON 8·5 **Areas of Rectangles** *continued*

4. Fill in the table at the bottom of the page.

Rectangle	Area (counting squares)	Length (of base)	Width (or height)	Area (using formula)
D	28 cm^2	7 cm	4 cm	28 cm^2
E	10 cm^2	4 cm	2.5 cm	10 cm^2
F	9 cm^2	3 cm	3 cm	9 cm^2
G	4 cm^2	2 cm	2 cm	4 cm^2
H	17.5 cm^2	3.5 cm	5 cm	17.5 cm^2
I	20.25 cm^2	4.5 cm	4.5 cm	20.25 cm^2

Math Journal 2, p. 233

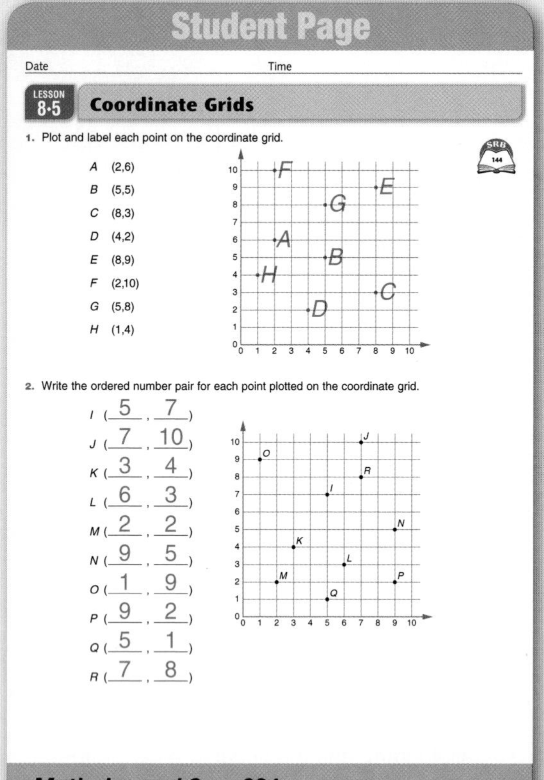
Student Page

Date Time

LESSON 8•5 **Coordinate Grids**

1. Plot and label each point on the coordinate grid.

A (2,6)
B (5,5)
C (8,3)
D (4,2)
E (8,9)
F (2,10)
G (5,8)
H (1,4)

2. Write the ordered number pair for each point plotted on the coordinate grid.

I (5, 7)
J (7, 10)
K (3, 4)
L (6, 3)
M (2, 2)
N (9, 5)
O (1, 9)
P (9, 2)
Q (5, 1)
R (7, 8)

Math Journal 2, p. 234

Have students share their results. Students should note that all rectangles except D contain half-squares, and that Rectangles G and I contain quarter-squares. Make sure that students understand how to count the partial squares. *For example:*

- Rectangle G—2 half-squares are the same as 1 square, and 4 quarter-squares are the same as 1 square.
- Rectangle H—5 half-squares are the same as $2\frac{1}{2}$ squares.

Next, have students record the length of the base and the height of each rectangle. Then have them use the formula to find the area of a rectangle by multiplying the base times the height.

Ongoing Assessment: Informing Instruction

Watch for different multiplication strategies. For example, the length of the base of Rectangle E is 4 centimeters and the height is $2\frac{1}{2}$ centimeters.

- Students use the fraction keys to enter $2\frac{1}{2}$ into their calculator or enter 2.5 as the decimal equivalent. $2\frac{1}{2} * 4 = 10$ or $2.5 * 4 = 10$
- Students use the Distributive Property of Multiplication over Addition to set up the problem. $4 * 2\frac{1}{2} = 4 * (2 + \frac{1}{2}) = (4 * 2) + (4 * \frac{1}{2})$ Then they use repeated addition to multiply the fraction $\frac{1}{2}$ by the whole number 4. $8 + \frac{1}{2} + \frac{1}{2} + \frac{1}{2} + \frac{1}{2} = 10$

2 Ongoing Learning & Practice

Using a Coordinate Grid

INDEPENDENT ACTIVITY

(*Math Journal 2,* p. 234)

Students plot and label points on a coordinate grid. They write the ordered number pair for each point on another grid.

Math Boxes 8•5

INDEPENDENT ACTIVITY

(*Math Journal 2,* p. 235)

Mixed Practice Math Boxes in this lesson are paired with Math Boxes in Lesson 8-7. The skill in Problem 6 previews Unit 9 content.

Ongoing Assessment: Recognizing Student Achievement

Math Boxes Problem 2 

Use **Math Boxes, Problem 2** to assess students' ability to find the perimeter of a figure. Students are making adequate progress if they are able to find the length of the missing side and add the measurements to find the perimeter. Some students may be able to write a number model that includes parentheses. $(3 * 4) + (4 * 1) + 6 = 22$

[Measurement and Reference Frames Goal 2]

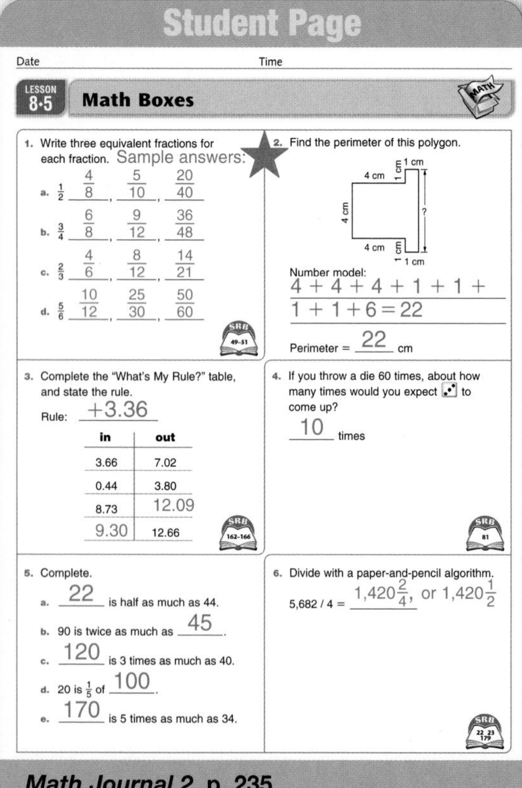
Student Page

Date Time

LESSON 8•5 **Math Boxes**

1. Write three equivalent fractions for each fraction. Sample answers:
   a. $\frac{1}{2}$ $\frac{4}{8}$, $\frac{5}{10}$, $\frac{20}{40}$
   b. $\frac{3}{4}$ $\frac{6}{8}$, $\frac{9}{12}$, $\frac{36}{48}$
   c. $\frac{2}{3}$ $\frac{4}{6}$, $\frac{8}{12}$, $\frac{14}{21}$
   d. $\frac{5}{6}$ $\frac{10}{12}$, $\frac{25}{30}$, $\frac{50}{60}$

2. Find the perimeter of this polygon.
   Number model: 4 + 4 + 4 + 1 + 1 + 1 + 1 + 6 = 22
   Perimeter = 22 cm

3. Complete the "What's My Rule?" table, and state the rule.
   Rule: +3.36

in	out
3.66	7.02
0.44	3.80
8.73	12.09
9.30	12.66

4. If you throw a die 60 times, about how many times would you expect ⚄ to come up?
   10 times

5. Complete.
   a. 22 is half as much as 44.
   b. 90 is twice as much as 45.
   c. 120 is 3 times as much as 40.
   d. 20 is $\frac{1}{5}$ of 100.
   e. 170 is 5 times as much as 34.

6. Divide with a paper-and-pencil algorithm.
   5,682 / 4 = $1{,}420\frac{2}{4}$, or $1{,}420\frac{1}{2}$

Math Journal 2, p. 235

Study Link 8•5

INDEPENDENT ACTIVITY

(*Math Masters,* p. 256)

Home Connection Students use a formula to calculate areas of rectangles.

3 Differentiation Options

READINESS

PARTNER ACTIVITY

Finding Areas of Rectangles

5–15 Min

(*Math Masters,* p. 257)

To provide experience finding the area of a rectangle using a concrete model, have students build rectangles with square pattern blocks. Ask students to discuss the pattern they see in the table they created on *Math Masters,* page 257.

NOTE Square pattern blocks are prisms, not 2-dimensional polygons as the name implies. For this activity, have students consider only the square face of the pattern block.

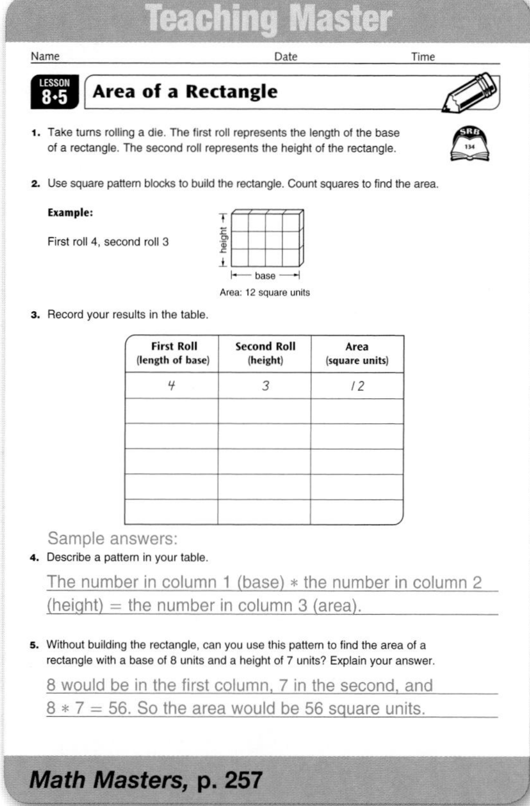

Teaching Master

Name Date Time

LESSON 8•5 **Area of a Rectangle**

1. Take turns rolling a die. The first roll represents the length of the base of a rectangle. The second roll represents the height of the rectangle.
2. Use square pattern blocks to build the rectangle. Count squares to find the area.

Example:

First roll 4, second roll 3

Area: 12 square units

3. Record your results in the table.

First Roll (length of base)	Second Roll (height)	Area (square units)
4	3	12

Sample answers:

4. Describe a pattern in your table.

The number in column 1 (base) $*$ the number in column 2 (height) = the number in column 3 (area).

5. Without building the rectangle, can you use this pattern to find the area of a rectangle with a base of 8 units and a height of 7 units? Explain your answer.

8 would be in the first column, 7 in the second, and $8 * 7 = 56$. So the area would be 56 square units.

Math Masters, **p. 257**

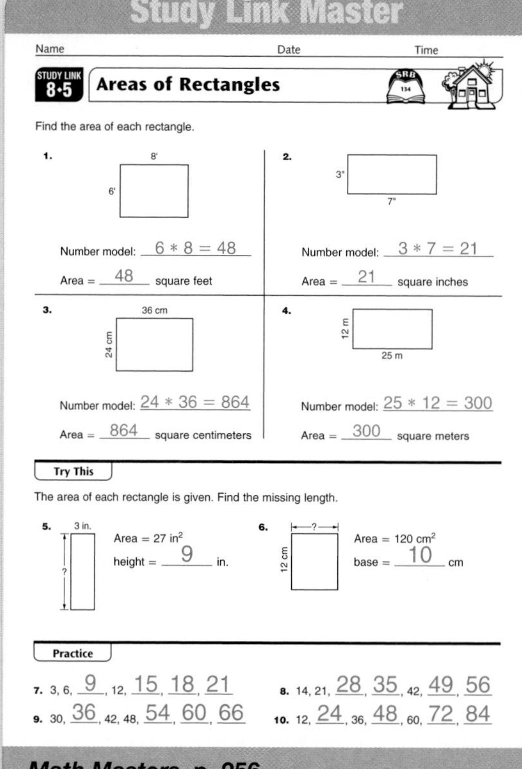

Study Link Master

Name Date Time

STUDY LINK 8•5 **Areas of Rectangles**

Find the area of each rectangle.

1. (8', 6')
Number model: $6 * 8 = 48$
Area = 48 square feet

2. (3", 7")
Number model: $3 * 7 = 21$
Area = 21 square inches

3. (36 cm, 24 cm)
Number model: $24 * 36 = 864$
Area = 864 square centimeters

4. (12 m, 25 m)
Number model: $25 * 12 = 300$
Area = 300 square meters

Try This

The area of each rectangle is given. Find the missing length.

5. (3 in., ?) Area = 27 in^2 height = 9 in.

6. (?, 12 cm) Area = 120 cm^2 base = 10 cm

Practice

7. 3, 6, 9, 12, 15, 18, 21
8. 14, 21, 28, 35, 42, 49, 56
9. 30, 36, 42, 48, 54, 60, 66
10. 12, 24, 36, 48, 60, 72, 84

Math Masters, **p. 256**

ENRICHMENT

INDEPENDENT ACTIVITY

5–15 Min

▶ Finding the Area of a Tennis Court

(*Math Masters,* p. 258)

To apply students' understanding of the formula for the area of a rectangle, have them solve problems involving the dimensions of a tennis court.

ENRICHMENT

PARTNER ACTIVITY

15–30 Min

▶ Exploring the Relationship between the Perimeter and Area of a Rectangle

(*Math Masters,* pp. 259 and 444)

To apply students' understanding of perimeter and area, have them use a 24-inch string loop and 1-inch grid paper to investigate the relationship between the perimeter and area of a rectangle.

ELL SUPPORT

SMALL-GROUP ACTIVITY

5–15 Min

▶ Building a Math Word Bank

(*Differentiation Handbook,* p. 140)

To provide language support for area, have students use the Word Bank Template found on *Differentiation Handbook,* page 140. Ask students to write the terms *length, width, base,* and *height,* draw pictures relating to each term, and write other related words. See the *Differentiation Handbook* for more information.

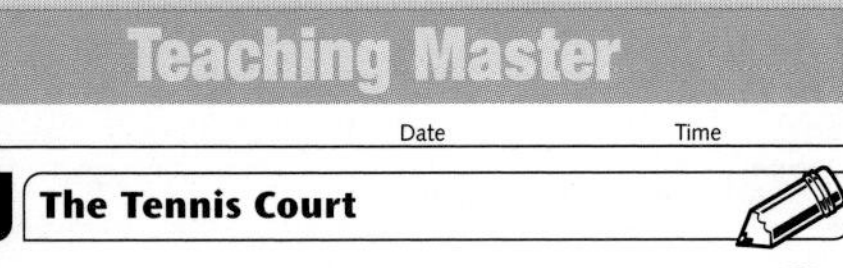

Teaching Master

Name Date Time

LESSON 8·5 **The Tennis Court**

Area of rectangle = length ∗ width

Tennis can be played either by 2 people or by 4 people. When 2 people play, it is called a game of singles. When 4 people play, it is called a game of doubles.

Here is a diagram of a tennis court. The net divides the court in half.

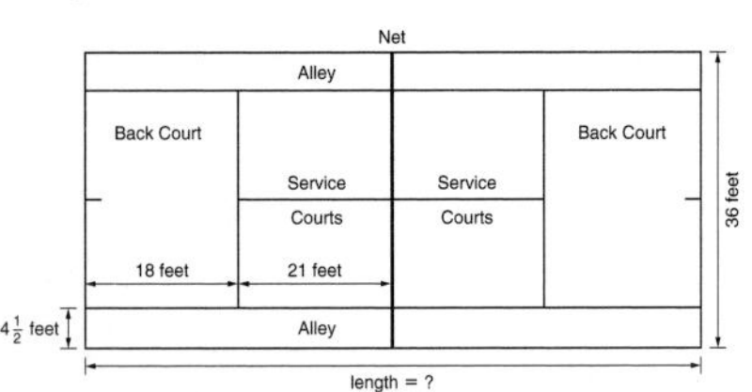

The two *alleys* are used only in doubles. They are never used in singles.

1. What is the total length of a tennis court? 78 ft
2. The court used in a game of doubles is 36 feet wide. Each alley is $4\frac{1}{2}$ feet wide. What is the width of the court used in a game of singles? 27 ft
3. What is the **area** of a singles court? 2,106 ft^2
4. What is the **area** of a doubles court? 2,808 ft^2
5. Do you think a player needs to cover more court in a game of singles or in a game of doubles? Explain.
   Sample answer: Singles game; in a singles game, each player covers $\frac{1}{2}$ of 2,106 sq ft, or 1,053 sq ft. In a doubles game, each player covers $\frac{1}{4}$ of 2,808 sq ft, or 702 sq ft.

***Math Masters,* p. 258**

Teaching Master

Name Date Time

LESSON 8·5 **Perimeter and Area**

1. Tape together two copies of 1-inch grid paper (*Math Masters,* page 444).
2. Use a 24-inch string loop to find as many different rectangles as possible that have a perimeter of 24 inches.

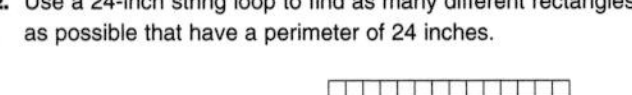

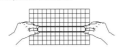

3. Record your results in the table.

Length of Base (in.)	Height (in.)	Perimeter (in.)	Area (in^2)
11	1	24	11
10	2	24	20
9	3	24	27
8	4	24	32
7	5	24	35
6	6	24	36
$10\frac{1}{2}$	$1\frac{1}{2}$	24	$15\frac{3}{4}$
$7\frac{1}{2}$	$4\frac{1}{2}$	24	$33\frac{3}{4}$

4. Use your results to describe a relationship between the lengths of sides and areas of rectangles that have the same perimeter.
   The closer the sides are in length, the larger the area.
5. What is another name for the rectangle with the largest area? square

***Math Masters,* p. 259**

8·6 Formula for the Area of a Parallelogram

Objectives To review the properties of parallelograms; and to guide the development and use of a formula for the area of a parallelogram.

Technology Resources www.everydaymathonline.com

 ePresentations
 eToolkit
 Algorithms Practice
 EM Facts Workshop Game™
 Family Letters
 Assessment Management
 Common Core State Standards
 Curriculum Focal Points
 Interactive Teacher's Lesson Guide

1 Teaching the Lesson

Key Concepts and Skills

- Find the area of a rectangle. [Measurement and Reference Frames Goal 2]
- Develop a formula for calculating the area of a parallelogram. [Measurement and Reference Frames Goal 2]
- Calculate perimeter. [Measurement and Reference Frames Goal 2]
- Identify perpendicular line segments and right angles. [Geometry Goal 1]
- Describe properties of parallelograms. [Geometry Goal 2]

Key Activities

Students construct models of parallelograms and use them to review properties of parallelograms.

Students cut apart and rearrange parallelogram shapes; they develop and use a formula for the area of a parallelogram.

Ongoing Assessment: Informing Instruction See page 690.

Key Vocabulary

base ◆ height ◆ perpendicular

Materials

Math Journal 2, pp. 236–238
Study Link 8•5
Math Masters, p. 260
centimeter ruler ◆ straws and twist-ties ◆ scissors ◆ tape ◆ index card or other square-corner object ◆ slate

2 Ongoing Learning & Practice

Playing *Fraction Of*
Student Reference Book, pp. 244 and 245
Fraction Of Cards (*Math Masters,* pp. 477, 478, and 480)
Math Masters, p. 479
Students practice finding fractions of collections.

Playing *Angle Add-Up*
Math Masters pp. 507–509
per partnership: 4 of each of number cards 1–8 and 1 of each of number cards 0 and 9 (from the Everything Math Deck, if available) ◆ full-circle protractor (transparency of *Math Masters,* p. 439) ◆ dry-erase markers ◆ straightedge
Students draw angles and then use addition and subtraction to find the measures of unknown angles.

Math Boxes 8•6
Math Journal 2, p. 239
Students practice and maintain skills through Math Box problems.

Ongoing Assessment: Recognizing Student Achievement
Use Math Boxes, Problem 4.
[Operations and Computation Goal 5]

Study Link 8•6
Math Masters, pp. 261 and 262
Students practice and maintain skills through Study Link activities.

3 Differentiation Options

ENRICHMENT
Constructing Figures with a Compass and Straightedge
Student Reference Book, pp. 114, 117, and 118
compass ◆ straightedge
Students construct figures with a compass and straightedge.

ENRICHMENT
Solving Area and Perimeter Problems
Math Masters, pp. 263, 264, and 437
scissors ◆ tape
Students explore ways of combining various two-dimensional shapes to form new shapes.

Advance Preparation

For Part 1, each student needs 2 short straws, 2 long straws, and 4 twist-ties. Pairs of straws should be the same length. Place them near the Math Message.

***Teacher's Reference Manual,* Grades 4–6** pp. 180–185, 221, 222

Getting Started

Mental Math and Reflexes

Pose multiplication facts and problems.
Suggestions:

●○○	●●○	●●●
3 * 7 = 21	90 * 8 = 720	8 * 52 = 416
4 * 9 = 36	10 * 90 = 900	4 * 63 = 252
8 * 5 = 40	60 * 70 = 4,200	9 * 76 = 684
9 * 6 = 54	80 * 30 = 2,400	88 * 5 = 440

Math Message

Take 2 short straws, 2 long straws, and 4 twist-ties. Use them to construct a parallelogram.

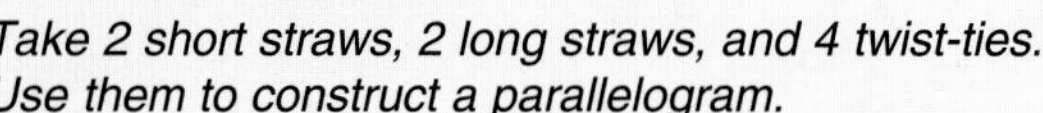

Study Link 8•5 Follow-Up

Have partners compare answers and discuss how they found the missing side measure in Problems 5 and 6.

1 Teaching the Lesson

▶ Math Message Follow-Up

Ask students to tell what they know about parallelograms, using their straw constructions as models, while you list the properties they name on the board. The list should include:

▷ A parallelogram is a four-sided polygon called a quadrangle or quadrilateral.

▷ Opposite sides of a parallelogram are parallel.

▷ Opposite sides of a parallelogram are the same length.

▷ Rectangles and squares are special kinds of parallelograms.

Have students form a rectangle with their straw constructions, and then ask them to pull gently on the opposite corners. They should get a parallelogram that is not a rectangle. Ask the following questions:

- Does the perimeter remain the same? yes
- Does the area remain the same? No, because although the length of the base stays the same, the height decreases, so the area decreases.

Draw a parallelogram on the board. Choose one of the sides, for example, the side on which the parallelogram "sits," and label it the **base.** Explain that *base* is also used to mean the *length of the base.*

The shortest distance between the base and the side opposite the base is called the **height** of the parallelogram. Draw and label a dashed line to show the height. Include a right-angle symbol. Point out that the dashed line can be drawn anywhere between the two sides as long as it is **perpendicular** to (forms a right angle with) the base.

Remind students that rectangles are parallelograms whose sides form right angles. If you think of one side of a rectangle as its *base,* then the length of an adjacent side is its *height.*

NOTE Height is the distance perpendicular to the base of a figure. Any side of a parallelogram can be the base. The choice of the base determines the height.

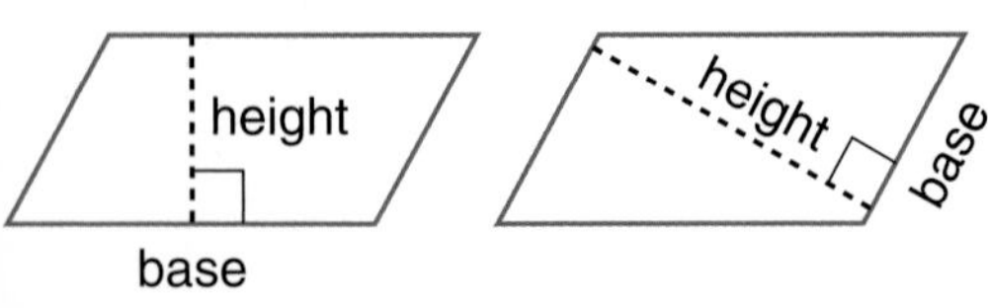

Tell students that in this lesson they will use the formula for the area of a rectangle to develop a formula for the area of a parallelogram.

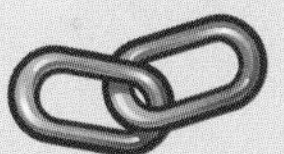

Links to the Future

The use of a formula to calculate the area of a parallelogram is a Grade 5 Goal.

Developing a Formula for the Area of a Parallelogram

(*Math Journal 2,* pp. 236 and 237; *Math Masters,* p. 260)

Point out that Parallelogram A on journal page 236 is the same as Parallelogram A on *Math Masters,* page 260.

Guide students through the following activity:

1. Cut out Parallelogram A from the master.
2. Cut the parallelogram into two pieces along one of the vertical grid lines.
3. Tape the pieces together to form a rectangle.

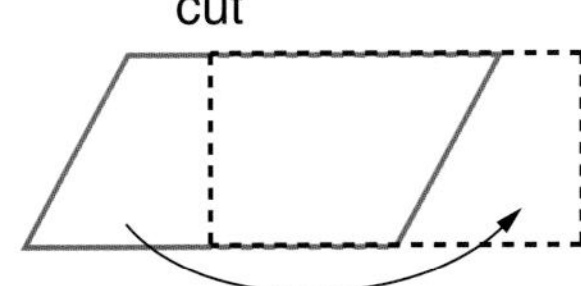

4. Tape this rectangle in the space next to the parallelogram in the journal.

   Discuss the relationship between the parallelogram and the rectangle formed from the parallelogram.

   - Why must the parallelogram and the rectangle both have the same area? The rectangle was constructed from the parallelogram. Nothing was lost or added.

5. Record the dimensions and area of the parallelogram and the rectangle. Length of base of parallelogram and length of base of rectangle = 6 cm; height of parallelogram and width (height) of rectangle = 2 cm; area of each figure = 12 cm^2

Have students repeat these steps with Parallelograms B, C, and D, working on their own or with a partner.

Bring students together to develop a formula for the area of a parallelogram. These are three possible lines of reasoning:

▷ The area of each parallelogram is the same as the area of the rectangle that was made from it.

▷ The area of the rectangle is equal to the length of its base times its width (also called the height).

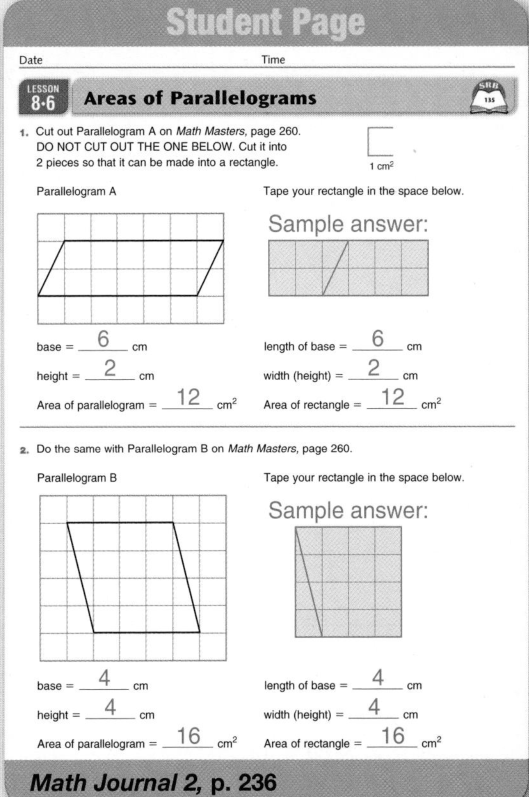

Student Page

Date Time

LESSON 8•6 **Areas of Parallelograms**

1. Cut out Parallelogram A on *Math Masters,* page 260. DO NOT CUT OUT THE ONE BELOW. Cut it into 2 pieces so that it can be made into a rectangle. 1 cm^2

Parallelogram A — Tape your rectangle in the space below. Sample answer:

base = 6 cm — length of base = 6 cm
height = 2 cm — width (height) = 2 cm
Area of parallelogram = 12 cm^2 — Area of rectangle = 12 cm^2

2. Do the same with Parallelogram B on *Math Masters,* page 260.

Parallelogram B — Tape your rectangle in the space below. Sample answer:

base = 4 cm — length of base = 4 cm
height = 4 cm — width (height) = 4 cm
Area of parallelogram = 16 cm^2 — Area of rectangle = 16 cm^2

Math Journal 2, p. 236

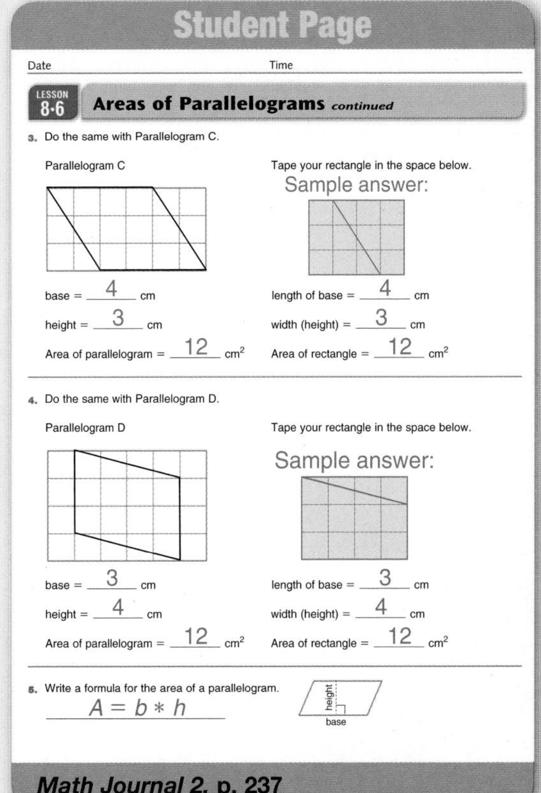

Student Page

Date Time

LESSON 8•6 **Areas of Parallelograms** *continued*

3. Do the same with Parallelogram C.

Parallelogram C — Tape your rectangle in the space below. Sample answer:

base = 4 cm — length of base = 4 cm
height = 3 cm — width (height) = 3 cm
Area of parallelogram = 12 cm^2 — Area of rectangle = 12 cm^2

4. Do the same with Parallelogram D.

Parallelogram D — Tape your rectangle in the space below. Sample answer:

base = 3 cm — length of base = 3 cm
height = 4 cm — width (height) = 4 cm
Area of parallelogram = 12 cm^2 — Area of rectangle = 12 cm^2

5. Write a formula for the area of a parallelogram. $A = b * h$ (height, base)

Math Journal 2, p. 237

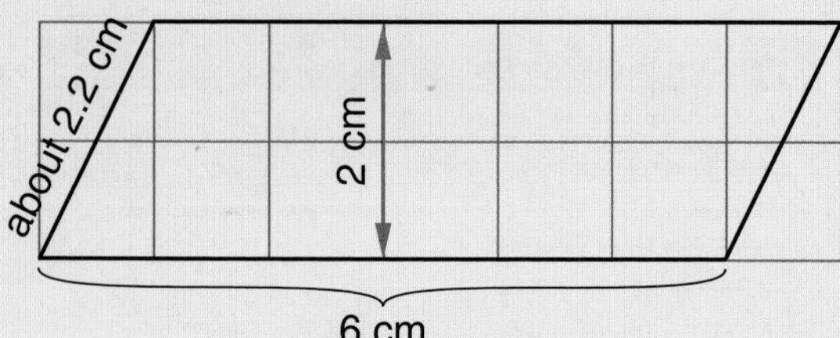

Perimeter = about 16.4 cm

Area = 12 cm^2

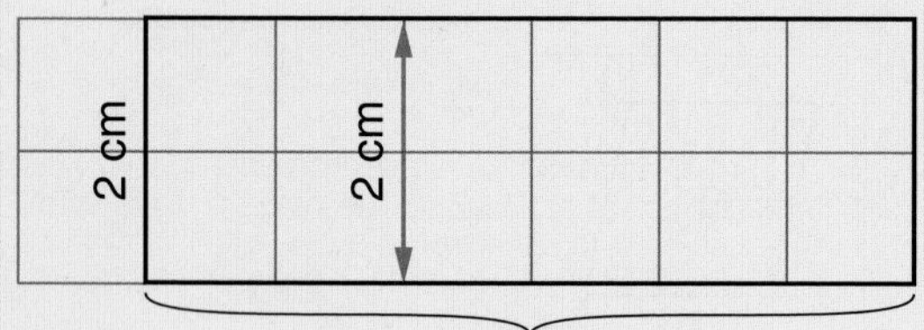

Perimeter = 16 cm

Area = 12 cm^2

Student Page

Date Time

LESSON 8•6 **Areas of Parallelograms** *continued*

6. Draw a line segment to show the height of Parallelogram *DORA*.
Use your ruler to measure the base and height.
Then find the area.
base = 5 cm
height = 4 cm
Area = 20 cm^2

7. Draw the following shapes on the grid below:
   a. A rectangle whose area is 12 square centimeters
   b. A parallelogram, not a rectangle, whose area is 12 square centimeters
   c. A different parallelogram whose area is also 12 square centimeters

Sample answers: a. b. c.

8. What is the area of:
   a. Parallelogram *ABCD?* 24 cm^2
   b. Trapezoid *EBCD?* 18 cm^2
   c. Triangle *ABE?* 6 cm^2

Math Journal 2, p. 238

▷ The length of the base of the parallelogram is equal to the length of the base of the rectangle. The height of that parallelogram is equal to the width (height) of that rectangle. Therefore, the area of the parallelogram is equal to the length of its base times its height. Using variables:

$$A = b * h$$

where b is the length of the base and h is the height.

Have students record the formula at the bottom of journal page 237.

Ongoing Assessment: Informing Instruction

Watch for students who think that the perimeter of each parallelogram and rectangle pair is also the same. Point out that although the height and base are the same measure, the height of a parallelogram is only used in computing its perimeter when the parallelogram is a rectangle or square. (*See margin.*)

▶ Solving Area Problems

(*Math Journal 2,* p. 238)

Algebraic Thinking Work with the whole class on Problem 6, journal page 238. Students can place an index card (or other square-corner object) on top of the shape, align the bottom edge of the card with the base, and then use the edge of the card to draw a line for the height. They will need a centimeter ruler to measure the length of the base and the height.

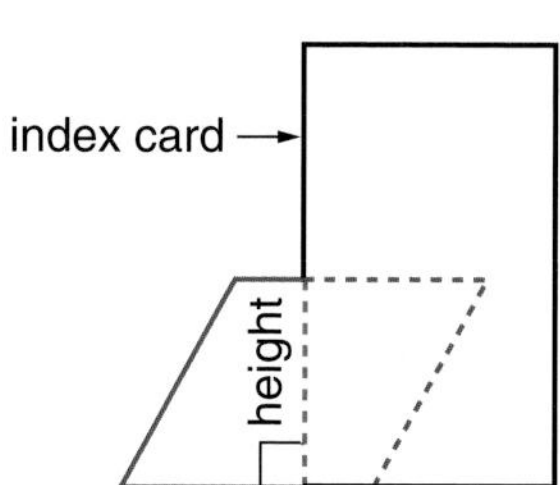

Drawing the height of a parallelogram

Have partnerships complete Problems 7 and 8.

▷ Problem 7 illustrates the fact that shapes that do not look the same can have the same area.

▷ Problem 8b lends itself to a variety of solution strategies. Some students may have partitioned the trapezoid into a rectangle flanked by two triangles. The rectangle covers 12 grid squares. If one triangle were cut apart and placed next to the other triangle to form a rectangle, the pair would cover 6 squares. The rectangle and two triangles cover $12 + 6 = 18$ cm^2.

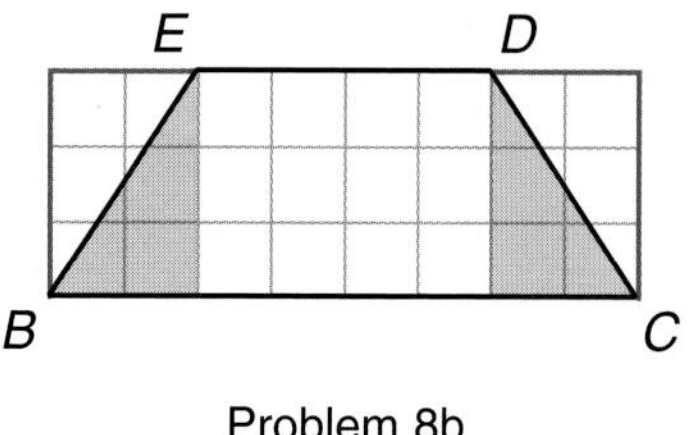

Problem 8b

▷ Problem 8c can be solved without using a formula for the area of a triangle. The parallelogram area minus the trapezoid area is the triangle area. $24 - 18 = 6 \text{ cm}^2$

2 Ongoing Learning & Practice

Playing *Fraction Of*

PARTNER ACTIVITY

(*Student Reference Book,* pp. 244 and 245; *Math Masters,* pp. 477–480)

Students play *Fraction Of* to practice finding fractions of collections. See Lesson 7-3 for additional information.

Playing *Angle Add-Up*

PARTNER ACTIVITY

(*Math Masters*, pp. 439 and 507–509)

To further explore the idea that angle measures are additive, have students play *Angle Add-Up*. See Lesson 7-9 for more information.

Math Boxes 8•6

INDEPENDENT ACTIVITY

(*Math Journal 2,* p. 239)

Mixed Practice Math Boxes in this lesson are paired with Math Boxes in Lesson 8-8. The skill in Problem 5 previews Unit 9 content.

Ongoing Assessment: Recognizing Student Achievement

Math Boxes Problem 4

Use **Math Boxes, Problem 4** to assess students' ability to solve fraction addition and subtraction problems. Students are making adequate progress if they are able to solve Problems 4a and 4c, which involve fractions with like denominators. Some students may be able to solve Problems 4b and 4d by using equivalent fractions with like denominators, using manipulatives, or drawing pictures.

[Operations and Computation Goal 5]

Study Link 8•6

INDEPENDENT ACTIVITY

(*Math Masters,* pp. 261 and 262)

Home Connection Students calculate the areas of parallelograms on *Math Masters,* page 261.

NOTE *Math Masters,* page 262 should be completed before Lesson 9-1, in which students share and discuss examples of percents they have collected.

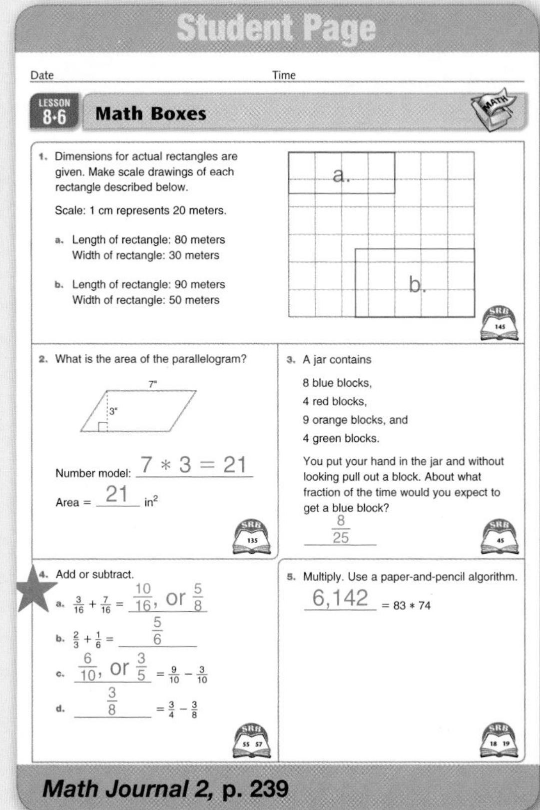

Student Page

Date Time

LESSON 8•6 **Math Boxes**

1. Dimensions for actual rectangles are given. Make scale drawings of each rectangle described below.

Scale: 1 cm represents 20 meters.

a. Length of rectangle: 80 meters
Width of rectangle: 30 meters

b. Length of rectangle: 90 meters
Width of rectangle: 50 meters

2. What is the area of the parallelogram?

Number model: $7 * 3 = 21$

Area = 21 in²

3. A jar contains

8 blue blocks,
4 red blocks,
9 orange blocks, and
4 green blocks.

You put your hand in the jar and without looking pull out a block. About what fraction of the time would you expect to get a blue block? $\frac{8}{25}$

4. Add or subtract.

a. $\frac{3}{16} + \frac{7}{16} = \frac{10}{16}$, or $\frac{5}{8}$

b. $\frac{2}{3} + \frac{1}{6} = \frac{5}{6}$

c. $\frac{6}{10}$, or $\frac{3}{5}$ $= \frac{9}{10} - \frac{3}{10}$

d. $\frac{3}{8} = \frac{3}{4} - \frac{3}{8}$

5. Multiply. Use a paper-and-pencil algorithm.

$6{,}142 = 83 * 74$

Math Journal 2, p. 239

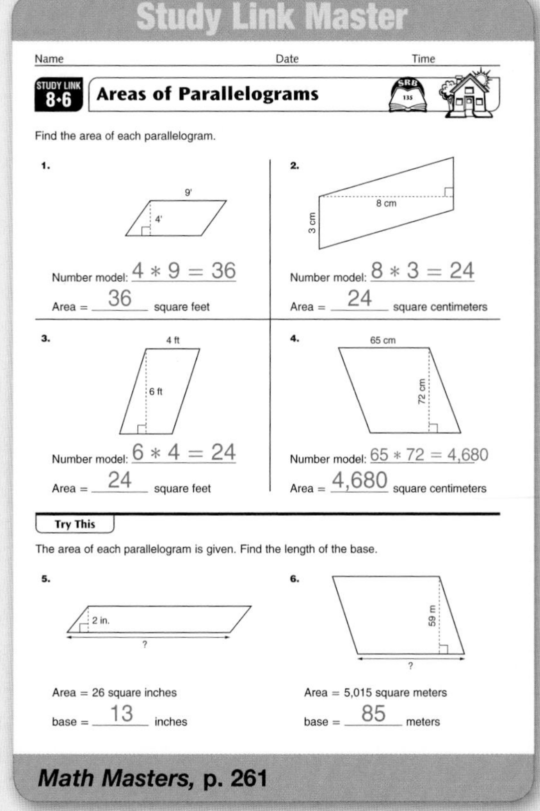

Study Link Master

Name Date Time

STUDY LINK 8•6 **Areas of Parallelograms**

Find the area of each parallelogram.

1. Number model: $4 * 9 = 36$
Area = 36 square feet

2. Number model: $8 * 3 = 24$
Area = 24 square centimeters

3. Number model: $6 * 4 = 24$
Area = 24 square feet

4. Number model: $65 * 72 = 4{,}680$
Area = 4,680 square centimeters

Try This

The area of each parallelogram is given. Find the length of the base.

5. Area = 26 square inches
base = 13 inches

6. Area = 5,015 square meters
base = 85 meters

Math Masters, p. 261

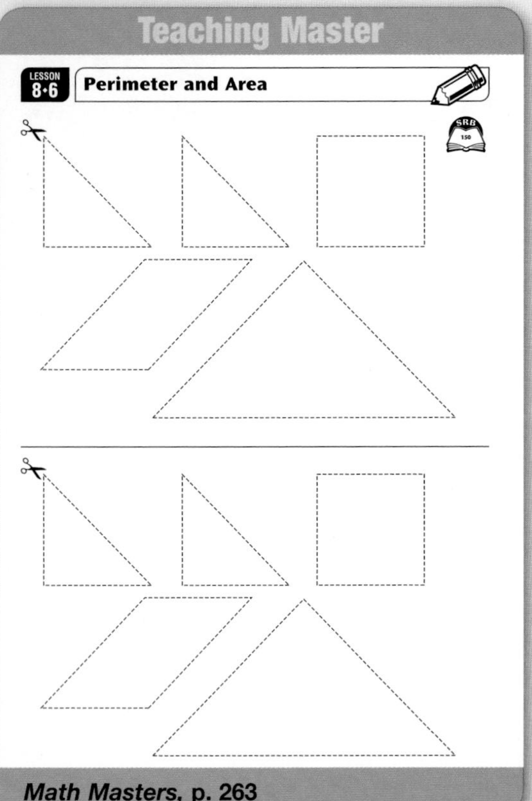
Teaching Master

LESSON 8·6 **Perimeter and Area**

Math Masters, p. 263

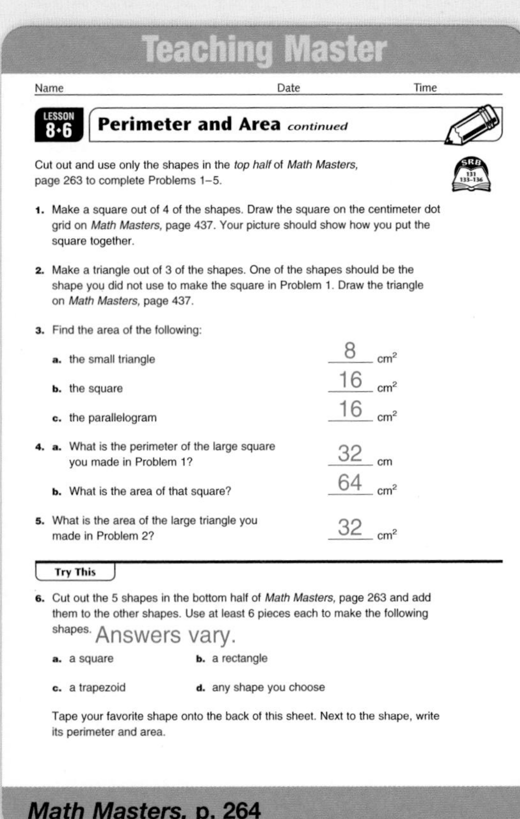
Teaching Master

Name Date Time

LESSON 8·6 **Perimeter and Area** *continued*

Cut out and use only the shapes in the *top half* of *Math Masters,* page 263 to complete Problems 1–5.

1. Make a square out of 4 of the shapes. Draw the square on the centimeter dot grid on *Math Masters,* page 437. Your picture should show how you put the square together.
2. Make a triangle out of 3 of the shapes. One of the shapes should be the shape you did not use to make the square in Problem 1. Draw the triangle on *Math Masters,* page 437.
3. Find the area of the following:
   a. the small triangle 8 cm^2
   b. the square 16 cm^2
   c. the parallelogram 16 cm^2
4. a. What is the perimeter of the large square you made in Problem 1? 32 cm
   b. What is the area of that square? 64 cm^2
5. What is the area of the large triangle you made in Problem 2? 32 cm^2

Try This

6. Cut out the 5 shapes in the bottom half of *Math Masters,* page 263 and add them to the other shapes. Use at least 6 pieces each to make the following shapes. Answers vary.
   a. a square
   b. a rectangle
   c. a trapezoid
   d. any shape you choose

Tape your favorite shape onto the back of this sheet. Next to the shape, write its perimeter and area.

Math Masters, p. 264

3 Differentiation Options

ENRICHMENT

INDEPENDENT ACTIVITY

30+ Min

Constructing Figures with a Compass and Straightedge

(*Student Reference Book,* pp. 114, 117, and 118)

To apply students' understanding of the properties of parallelograms, have them construct parallelograms and perpendicular line segments as described on pages 114, 117, and 118 of the *Student Reference Book.*

ENRICHMENT

PARTNER ACTIVITY

30+ Min

Solving Area and Perimeter Problems

(*Math Masters,* pp. 263, 264, and 437)

To apply students' understanding of area and perimeter, have them explore different ways of combining various 2-dimensional shapes to form new shapes.

Possible solutions to Problem 6:

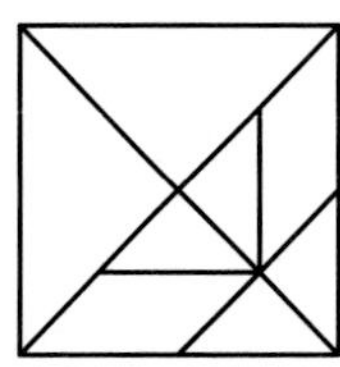

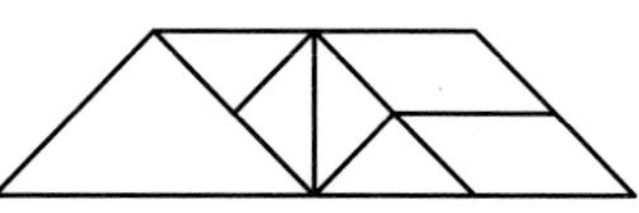

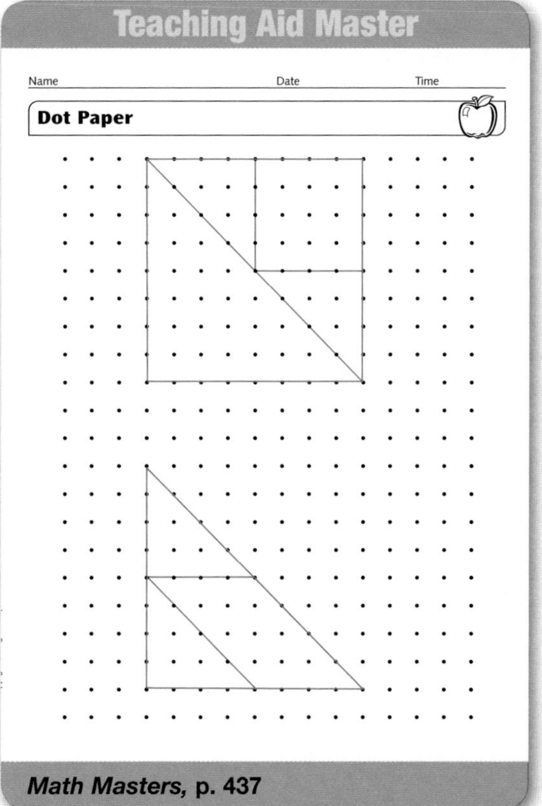
Teaching Aid Master

Name Date Time

Dot Paper

Math Masters, p. 437

8•7 Formula for the Area of a Triangle

Objective To guide the development and use of a formula for the area of a triangle.

Technology Resources www.everydaymathonline.com

ePresentations

eToolkit

Algorithms Practice

EM Facts Workshop Game™

Family Letters

Assessment Management

Common Core State Standards

Curriculum Focal Points

Interactive Teacher's Lesson Guide

1 Teaching the Lesson

Key Concepts and Skills

- Find the areas of rectangles and parallelograms. [Measurement and Reference Frames Goal 2]
- Develop a formula for calculating the area of a triangle. [Measurement and Reference Frames Goal 2]
- Identify perpendicular line segments and right angles. [Geometry Goal 1]
- Describe properties of and types of triangles. [Geometry Goal 2]
- Evaluate numeric expressions containing parentheses. [Patterns, Functions, and Algebra Goal 3]

Key Activities

Students arrange triangles to form parallelograms. They develop and use a formula for finding the area of a triangle.

Ongoing Assessment: Recognizing Student Achievement Use journal page 242. [Measurement and Reference Frames Goal 2]

Key Vocabulary

equilateral triangle ◆ isosceles triangle ◆ scalene triangle ◆ right triangle ◆ base ◆ height

Materials

Math Journal 2, pp. 240–242
Study Link 8•6
Math Masters, pp. 265 and 454A
transparency of *Math Masters,* p. 403 (optional) ◆ slate ◆ centimeter ruler ◆ scissors ◆ tape ◆ index card or other square-corner object

2 Ongoing Learning & Practice

Solving Fraction Problems

Math Journal 2, p. 243
Students identify fractional parts of number lines, collections of objects, and regions.

Math Boxes 8•7

Math Journal 2, p. 244
Students practice and maintain skills through Math Box problems.

Study Link 8•7

Math Masters, p. 266
Students practice and maintain skills through Study Link activities.

3 Differentiation Options

ENRICHMENT

Comparing Areas

Math Masters, p. 267
scissors
Students cut apart a regular hexagon and use the pieces to make area comparisons.

ENRICHMENT

Finding the Area and Perimeter of a Hexagon

Math Masters, p. 268
centimeter ruler
Students use a combination of different area formulas to find the area of a nonregular hexagon.

EXTRA PRACTICE

Playing *Rugs and Fences*

Math Masters, pp. 498–502
Student Reference Book, pp. 260 and 261
Students practice finding the perimeter and area of polygons.

Advance Preparation

For the optional Extra Practice activity in Part 3, consider copying the *Rugs and Fences* Cards on *Math Masters,* pages 498–501 on cardstock.

***Teacher's Reference Manual,* Grades 4–6** pp. 180–185, 221, 222

Getting Started

Mental Math and Reflexes

Dictate large numbers for students to write on their slates. *Suggestions:*

●○○	●●○	●●●
367,891	1,234,895	3,020,300,004
500,602	60,020,597	6,000,000,500
695,003	365,798,421	90,086,351,007

For each number, ask questions such as the following:

- Which digit is in the millions place?
- What is the value of the digit *x?*
- How many hundred millions are there?

Math Message

Make a list of everything that you know about triangles.

Study Link 8·6 Follow-Up

Have small groups compare answers and explain their strategies for finding the length of the base when the height and the area are given.

NOTE Because isosceles triangles are defined as having *at least* two sides of equal length, all equilateral triangles are isosceles. So, some students may include the equilateral triangles in the isosceles pile. If this occurs, you may want to have the class decide on a definition of isosceles triangle that would exclude the equilateral triangles. Sample answer: An isosceles triangle has *exactly* two sides that are the same length.

Student Page

Date Time

LESSON 8·7 **Areas of Triangles** SRB 136

1. Cut out Triangles A and B from *Math Masters,* page 265. DO NOT CUT OUT THE ONE BELOW. Tape the two triangles together to form a parallelogram. 1 cm²

Triangle A — Tape your parallelogram in the space below.

base = 6 cm — base = 6 cm

height = 4 cm — height = 4 cm

Area of triangle = 12 cm² — Area of parallelogram = 24 cm²

2. Do the same with Triangles C and D on *Math Masters,* page 265.

Triangle C — Tape your parallelogram in the space below.

base = 4 cm — base = 4 cm

height = 4 cm — height = 4 cm

Area of triangle = 8 cm² — Area of parallelogram = 16 cm²

Math Journal 2, p. 240

1 Teaching the Lesson

▶ Math Message Follow-Up

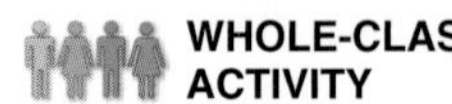

WHOLE-CLASS ACTIVITY

As students share their responses, write them on the board. The list might include:

- ▷ A triangle is a three-sided polygon.
- ▷ The sum of the measures of the angles in a triangle is 180°.
- ▷ A triangle has three vertices.
- ▷ A triangle is a convex polygon.
- ▷ An **equilateral triangle** is a triangle in which all three sides have the same measure, and all three angles have the same measure. An equilateral triangle is a regular polygon.
- ▷ An **isosceles triangle** is a triangle that has at least two sides with the same length and at least two angles with the same measure.
- ▷ A **scalene triangle** is a triangle in which there are no sides of equal length and no angles of equal measure.
- ▷ A **right triangle** is a triangle with one 90° angle.

▶ Exploring Triangle Properties

WHOLE-CLASS ACTIVITY

(*Math Masters,* p. 454A)

Have students cut out the cards on *Math Masters,* page 454A. Ask students to sort the triangles into three categories: equilateral, isosceles, and scalene. equilateral: C, F; isosceles: E, G, H, N, P; scalene: A, B, D, I, J, K, L, M, O.

Discuss the angle properties of each type of triangle: equilateral triangles have three angles of equal measure, isosceles triangles have two angles of equal measure, and scalene triangles have no angles of equal measure.

Draw a right triangle on the board:

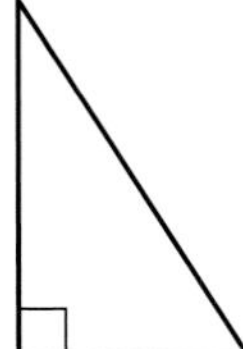

Ask students to tell you the definition of a right triangle. A *right triangle* is a triangle with one 90° angle.

Ask: *Do you see any right triangles in any of the piles?* Yes. Triangles A, H, I, and P are right triangles. *Can an equilateral triangle be a right triangle? Explain.* No. All the angles in an equilateral triangle have the same measure. *Can an isosceles triangle be a right triangle? Explain.* Yes. Triangles H and P are isosceles and right. *Can a scalene triangle be a right triangle? Explain.* Yes. Triangles A and I are scalene and right.

Draw the chart shown in the margin on the board. Ask students to help you fill in the chart with "yes" and "no" to show which types of triangles can be right triangles.

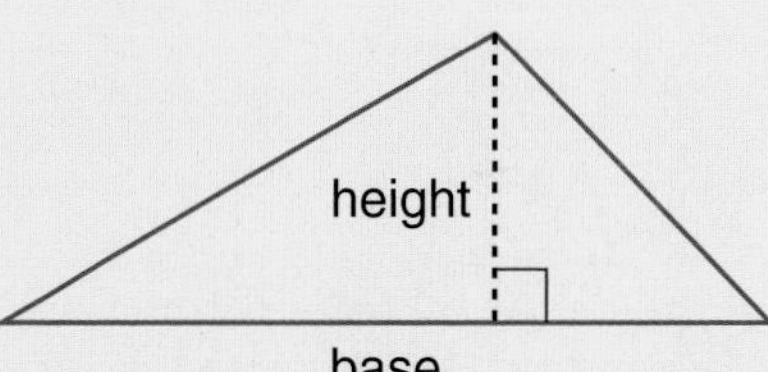

	Right
Equilateral	no
Isosceles	yes
Scalene	yes

Tell students that in this lesson they will develop a formula for the area of a triangle using the formula for the area of a parallelogram.

Links to the Future

The use of a formula to calculate the area of a triangle is a Grade 5 Goal.

Developing a Formula for the Area of a Triangle

(*Math Journal 2,* pp. 240 and 241; *Math Masters,* p. 265)

Draw a triangle on the board. Choose one of the sides—the side on which the triangle "sits," for example—and call it the **base.** Label the base in your drawing. Explain that *base* is also used to mean the *length of the base*.

The shortest distance from the vertex above the base to the base is called the **height** of the triangle. Draw a dashed line to show the height and label it. Include a right-angle symbol. (*See margin.*)

height

base

The height of a triangle is measured along a line segment perpendicular to the base. As with parallelograms, any side of a triangle can be the base. The choice of the base determines the height.

Ask the class to turn to journal page 240 while you distribute copies of *Math Masters,* page 265. Point out that Triangles A and B on the master are the same as Triangle A on the journal page. Guide students through the following activity:

1. Cut out Triangles A and B from the master. Make sure students realize that the triangles have the same area and are congruent.
2. Tape the triangles together at the shaded corners to form a parallelogram.
3. Tape the parallelogram in the space next to Triangle A in the journal.

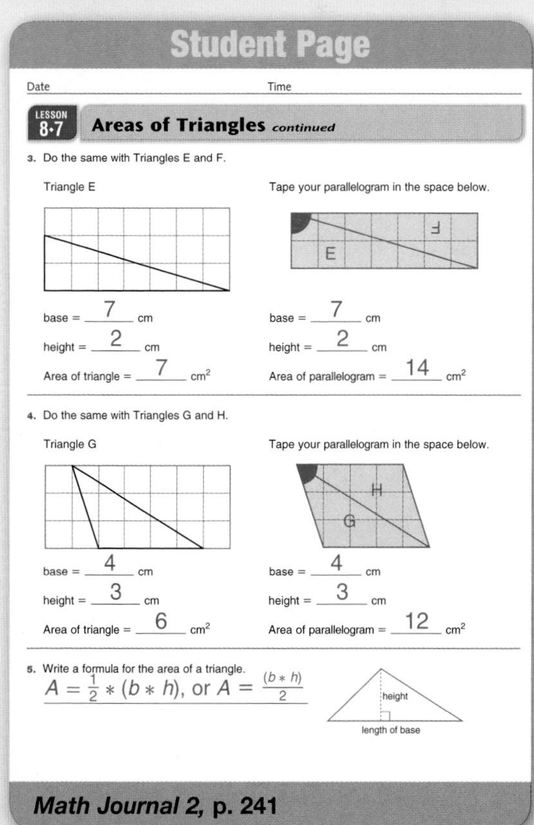

Student Page

Date Time

LESSON 8·7 **Areas of Triangles** *continued*

3. Do the same with Triangles E and F.

Triangle E — Tape your parallelogram in the space below.

base = 7 cm — base = 7 cm
height = 2 cm — height = 2 cm
Area of triangle = 7 cm^2 — Area of parallelogram = 14 cm^2

4. Do the same with Triangles G and H.

Triangle G — Tape your parallelogram in the space below.

base = 4 cm — base = 4 cm
height = 3 cm — height = 3 cm
Area of triangle = 6 cm^2 — Area of parallelogram = 12 cm^2

5. Write a formula for the area of a triangle.
$A = \frac{1}{2} * (b * h)$, or $A = \frac{(b * h)}{2}$

Math Journal 2, p. 241

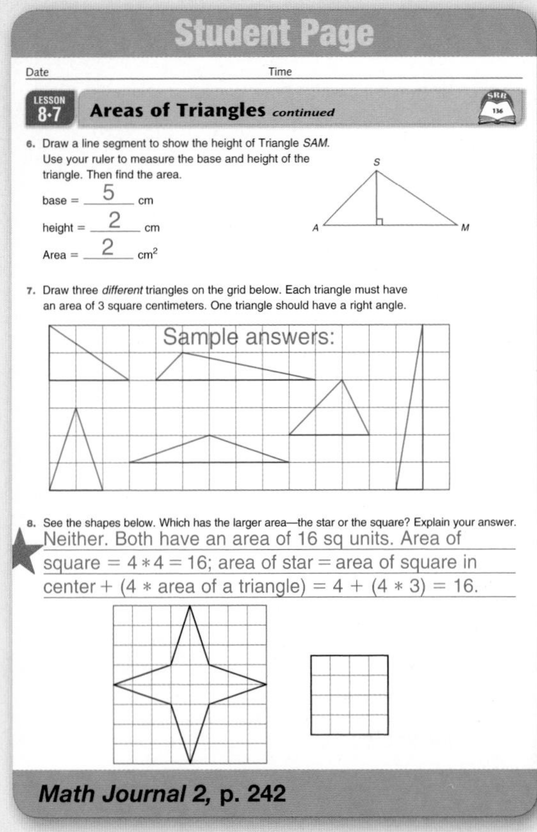
Student Page

Date Time

LESSON 8·7 **Areas of Triangles** *continued*

6. Draw a line segment to show the height of Triangle *SAM*. Use your ruler to measure the base and height of the triangle. Then find the area.

base = 5 cm

height = 2 cm

Area = 2 cm²

7. Draw three *different* triangles on the grid below. Each triangle must have an area of 3 square centimeters. One triangle should have a right angle.

Sample answers:

8. See the shapes below. Which has the larger area—the star or the square? Explain your answer.

Neither. Both have an area of 16 sq units. Area of square = 4 ∗ 4 = 16; area of star = area of square in center + (4 ∗ area of a triangle) = 4 + (4 ∗ 3) = 16.

Math Journal 2, p. 242

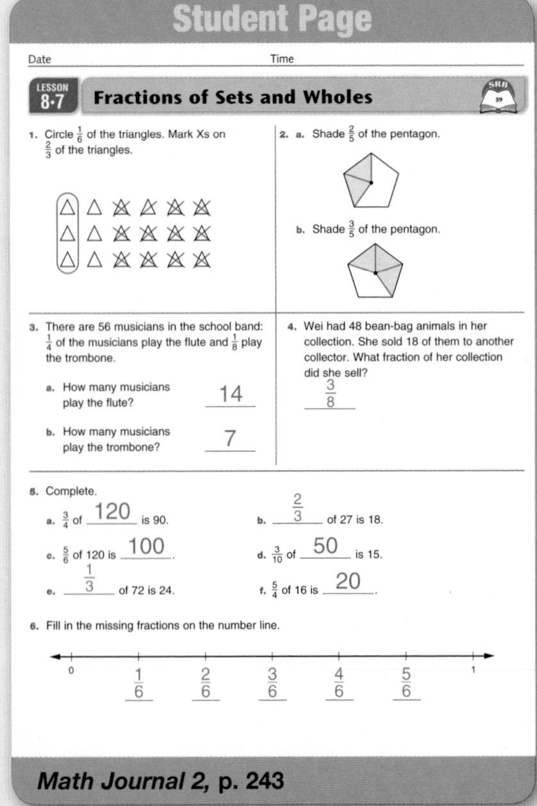
Student Page

Date Time

LESSON 8·7 **Fractions of Sets and Wholes**

1. Circle $\frac{1}{6}$ of the triangles. Mark Xs on $\frac{2}{3}$ of the triangles.

2. a. Shade $\frac{2}{5}$ of the pentagon.

b. Shade $\frac{3}{5}$ of the pentagon.

3. There are 56 musicians in the school band: $\frac{1}{4}$ of the musicians play the flute and $\frac{1}{8}$ play the trombone.

a. How many musicians play the flute? 14

b. How many musicians play the trombone? 7

4. Wei had 48 bean-bag animals in her collection. She sold 18 of them to another collector. What fraction of her collection did she sell? $\frac{3}{8}$

5. Complete.

a. $\frac{3}{4}$ of 120 is 90.

b. $\frac{2}{3}$ of 27 is 18.

c. $\frac{5}{6}$ of 120 is 100.

d. $\frac{3}{10}$ of 50 is 15.

e. $\frac{1}{3}$ of 72 is 24.

f. $\frac{5}{4}$ of 16 is 20.

6. Fill in the missing fractions on the number line.

0, $\frac{1}{6}$, $\frac{2}{6}$, $\frac{3}{6}$, $\frac{4}{6}$, $\frac{5}{6}$, 1

Math Journal 2, p. 243

Discuss the relationship between the area of the triangle and the area of the parallelogram. Triangles A and B have the same area. Therefore, the area of either triangle is half the area of the parallelogram.

4. Record the dimensions and areas of the triangle and the parallelogram. Base of triangle and parallelogram = 6 cm; height of triangle and parallelogram = 4 cm; area of parallelogram = 24 cm^2; area of triangle = $\frac{1}{2}$ the area of parallelogram = 12 cm^2.

Have students repeat these steps with Triangles C and D, E and F, and G and H. Then bring the class together to state a rule and write a formula for the area of a triangle.

Since the base and the height of a triangle are the same as the base and the height of the corresponding parallelogram, then:

Area of the triangle = $\frac{1}{2}$ the Area of the parallelogram, or

Area of the triangle = $\frac{1}{2}$ of (base ∗ height)

Using variables:

$A = \frac{1}{2}$ of $(b * h)$, or $A = \frac{1}{2} * (b * h)$

where b is the length of the base and h is the height.

Have students record the formula at the bottom of journal page 241.

Solving Area Problems

(*Math Journal 2,* p. 242; *Math Masters,* p. 403)

Algebraic Thinking Work with the class on Problem 6. Students can place an index card (or other square-corner object) on top of the triangle, align the bottom edge of the card with the base (making sure that one edge of the card passes through point S), and then draw a line for the height. Students will need a centimeter ruler to measure the base and the height.

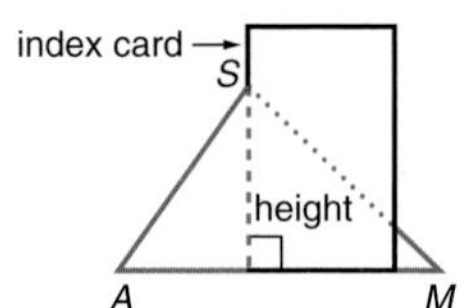

Adjusting the Activity

ELL

On the board, draw a triangle that has an obtuse angle as one of its base angles. Have students draw the height of the triangle. Demonstrate by extending the base along the side of the obtuse angle and drawing a perpendicular line from the opposite vertex to the extended base. *For example:*

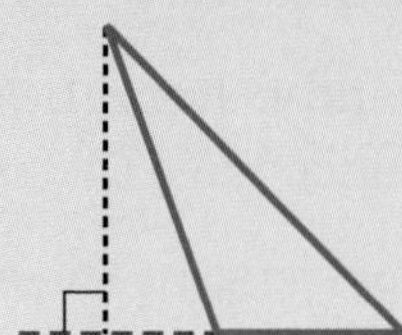

AUDITORY ◆ KINESTHETIC ◆ TACTILE ◆ VISUAL

Have students complete Problems 7 and 8.

- ▷ There are many possibilities for Problem 7. You can use a transparency of a 1-cm grid (*Math Masters,* page 403) on the overhead projector to display a number of them.
- ▷ It may surprise some students that the star and the square in Problem 8 have the same area. One way to find the area of the star is to think of it as a square with a triangle attached to each of its sides. (*See margin.*)

Ongoing Assessment: Recognizing Student Achievement

Journal page 242 Problem 8 ★

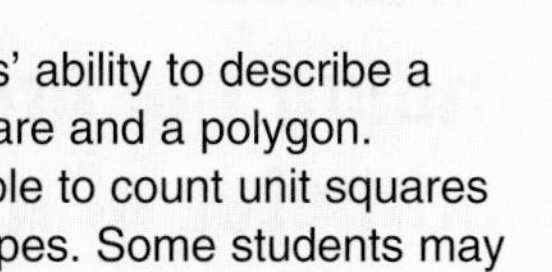

Use **journal page 242, Problem 8** to assess students' ability to describe a strategy for finding and comparing the areas of a square and a polygon. Students are making adequate progress if they are able to count unit squares and partial squares to find the areas of these two shapes. Some students may describe the use of a formula to calculate the areas of the triangles.

[Measurement and Reference Frames Goal 2]

2 Ongoing Learning & Practice

▸ Solving Fraction Problems

INDEPENDENT ACTIVITY

(*Math Journal 2,* p. 243)

Students identify fractional parts of number lines, collections of objects, and regions.

▸ Math Boxes 8·7

INDEPENDENT ACTIVITY

(*Math Journal 2,* p. 244)

Mixed Practice Math Boxes in this lesson are paired with Math Boxes in Lesson 8-5. The skill in Problem 6 previews Unit 9 content.

Writing/Reasoning Have students write a response to the following: *For Problem 4, write two probability questions for which the correct answer would be D—210 times.* Sample answers: If you throw a die 420 times, about how many times would you expect an even number to come up? If you throw a die 1,260 times, how many times would you expect a 6 to come up?

▸ Study Link 8·7

INDEPENDENT ACTIVITY

(*Math Masters,* p. 266)

Home Connection Students calculate the areas of triangles. They continue to work on *Math Masters,* page 262, which should be completed before Lesson 9-1.

Student Page

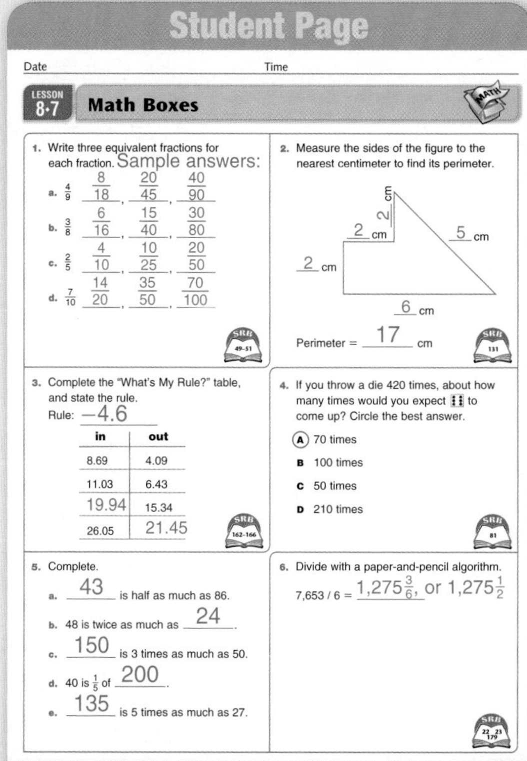

Date Time

LESSON 8·7 **Math Boxes**

1. Write three equivalent fractions for each fraction. Sample answers:
   a. $\frac{4}{9}$ $\frac{8}{18}$, $\frac{20}{45}$, $\frac{40}{90}$
   b. $\frac{3}{8}$ $\frac{6}{16}$, $\frac{15}{40}$, $\frac{30}{80}$
   c. $\frac{2}{5}$ $\frac{4}{10}$, $\frac{10}{25}$, $\frac{20}{50}$
   d. $\frac{7}{10}$ $\frac{14}{20}$, $\frac{35}{50}$, $\frac{70}{100}$
2. Measure the sides of the figure to the nearest centimeter to find its perimeter. (2 cm, 2 cm, 5 cm, 2 cm, 6 cm) Perimeter = 17 cm
3. Complete the "What's My Rule?" table, and state the rule. Rule: −4.6

in	out
8.69	4.09
11.03	6.43
19.94	15.34
26.05	21.45

4. If you throw a die 420 times, about how many times would you expect ⚃ to come up? Circle the best answer.
   (A) 70 times
   B 100 times
   C 50 times
   D 210 times
5. Complete.
   a. 43 is half as much as 86.
   b. 48 is twice as much as 24.
   c. 150 is 3 times as much as 50.
   d. 40 is $\frac{1}{5}$ of 200.
   e. 135 is 5 times as much as 27.
6. Divide with a paper-and-pencil algorithm. 7,653 / 6 = $1,275\frac{3}{6}$, or $1,275\frac{1}{2}$

Math Journal 2, p. 244

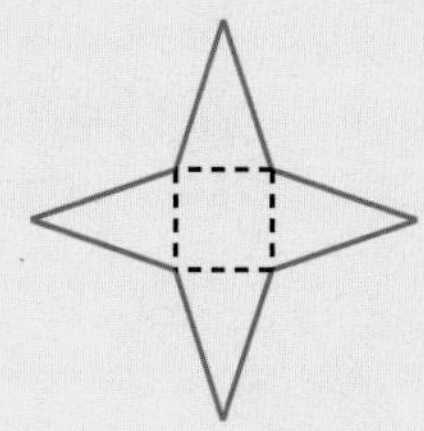

Study Link Master

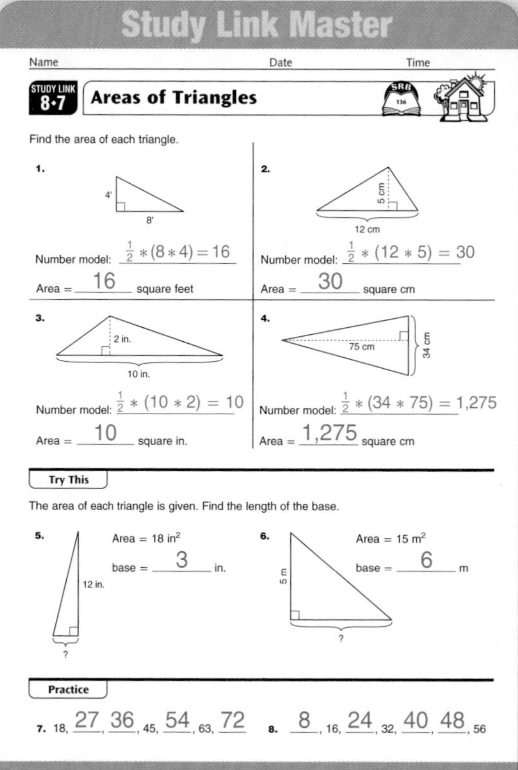

Name Date Time

STUDY LINK 8·7 **Areas of Triangles**

Find the area of each triangle.

1. Number model: $\frac{1}{2} * (8 * 4) = 16$ Area = 16 square feet
2. Number model: $\frac{1}{2} * (12 * 5) = 30$ Area = 30 square cm
3. Number model: $\frac{1}{2} * (10 * 2) = 10$ Area = 10 square in.
4. Number model: $\frac{1}{2} * (34 * 75) = 1,275$ Area = 1,275 square cm

Try This

The area of each triangle is given. Find the length of the base.

5. Area = 18 in² base = 3 in.
6. Area = 15 m² base = 6 m

Practice

7. 18, 27, 36, 45, 54, 63, 72
8. 8, 16, 24, 32, 40, 48, 56

Math Masters, p. 266

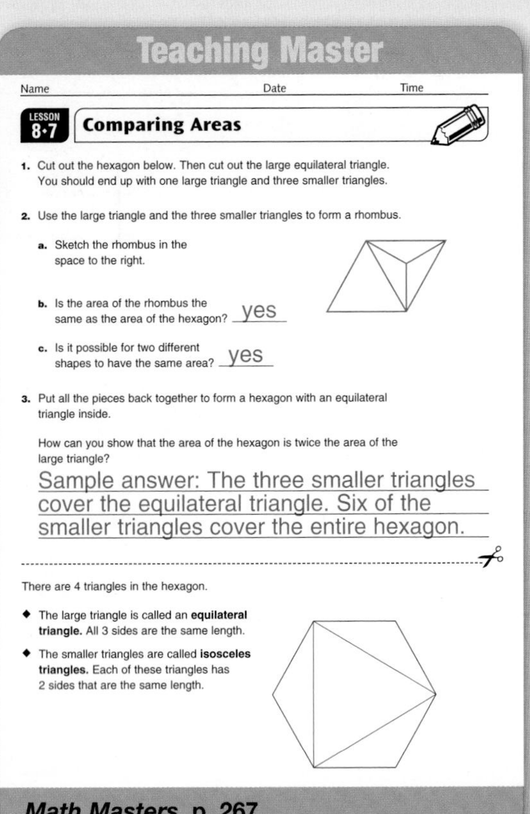
Teaching Master

Name Date Time

LESSON 8·7 **Comparing Areas**

1. Cut out the hexagon below. Then cut out the large equilateral triangle. You should end up with one large triangle and three smaller triangles.
2. Use the large triangle and the three smaller triangles to form a rhombus.
   a. Sketch the rhombus in the space to the right.
   b. Is the area of the rhombus the same as the area of the hexagon? yes
   c. Is it possible for two different shapes to have the same area? yes
3. Put all the pieces back together to form a hexagon with an equilateral triangle inside.

   How can you show that the area of the hexagon is twice the area of the large triangle?

   Sample answer: The three smaller triangles cover the equilateral triangle. Six of the smaller triangles cover the entire hexagon.

There are 4 triangles in the hexagon.

- The large triangle is called an **equilateral triangle.** All 3 sides are the same length.
- The smaller triangles are called **isosceles triangles.** Each of these triangles has 2 sides that are the same length.

Math Masters, p. 267

Teaching Master

Name Date Time

LESSON 8·7 **Area and Perimeter**

1. Find the area of the hexagon below *without* counting squares. *Hint:* Divide the hexagon into figures for which you can calculate the areas: rectangles, parallelograms, and triangles. Use a formula to find the area of each of the figures. Record your work.

   Total area of hexagon = 126 cm^2

2. Find the perimeter of the hexagon. Use a centimeter ruler.

   Perimeter = 48 cm

Sample answer: 10 cm, 24 cm^2, 12 cm, 5 cm, 6 cm^2, 48 cm^2, 8 cm, 24 cm^2, 24 cm^2, 10 cm, 1 cm, 3 cm

Math Masters, p. 268

3 Differentiation Options

ENRICHMENT

PARTNER ACTIVITY

▶ Comparing Areas

5–15 Min

(*Math Masters,* p. 267)

To apply students' understanding of area, have them compare the areas of a rhombus and a hexagon.

ENRICHMENT

INDEPENDENT ACTIVITY

▶ Finding the Area and Perimeter of a Hexagon

5–15 Min

(*Math Masters,* p. 268)

Portfolio Ideas

To apply students' understanding of area formulas, have them find the area and perimeter of a nonregular hexagon. Counting squares to find the area is not permitted; students are encouraged to divide the hexagon into figures and then use a formula to calculate the area of each figure.

One strategy is to partition the polygon as shown below. Another strategy can be found on the reduction of *Math Masters,* page 268.

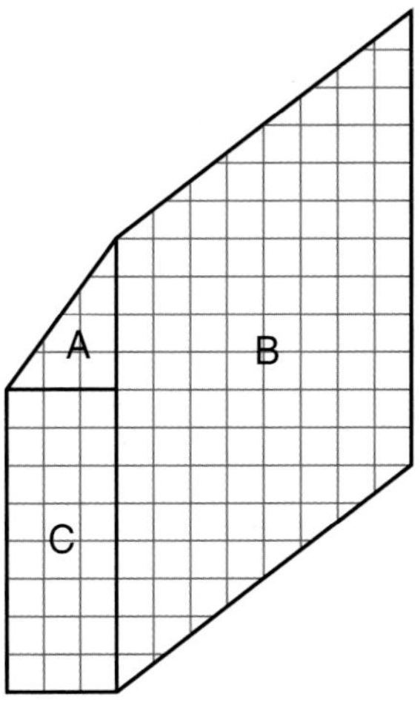

EXTRA PRACTICE

PARTNER ACTIVITY

▶ Playing *Rugs and Fences*

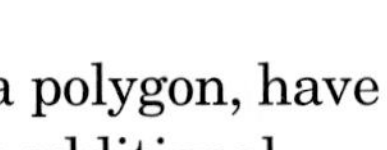
15–30 Min

(*Math Masters,* pp. 498–502; *Student Reference Book,* pp. 260 and 261)

To practice calculating the area and perimeter of a polygon, have students play *Rugs and Fences.* See Lesson 9-2 for additional information.

8•8 Geographical Area Measurements

Objectives To discuss how geographical areas are measured; and to provide practice using division to compare two quantities with like units.

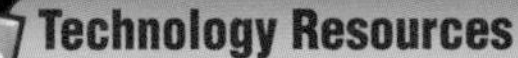

www.everydaymathonline.com

ePresentations

eToolkit

Algorithms Practice

EM Facts Workshop Game™

Family Letters

Assessment Management

Common Core State Standards

Curriculum Focal Points

Interactive Teacher's Lesson Guide

1 Teaching the Lesson

Key Concepts and Skills

- Use division to compare two quantities with like units.
  [Operations and Computation Goal 4]
- Use "times as many" language to compare area measurements.
  [Operations and Computation Goal 4]
- Estimate and compare area measurements.
  [Measurement and Reference Frames Goal 2]

Key Activities

Students examine how geographical areas are measured and the difficulties involved in making accurate measurements. They compare the areas of different countries by guessing and then using division to calculate the ratio of areas.

Materials

Math Journal 2, p. 245
Student Reference Book, pp. 286, 287, and 295
Study Link 8•7
world map or globe ◆ calculator ◆ slate

2 Ongoing Learning & Practice

Playing *Grab Bag*
Student Reference Book, p. 249
Grab Bag Cards (*Math Masters,* pp. 483 and 484)
Math Masters, p. 485
3 six-sided dice
Students practice calculating the probability of an event.

Ongoing Assessment: Recognizing Student Achievement
Use *Math Masters,* page 485.
[Data and Chance Goal 4]

Math Boxes 8•8
Math Journal 2, p. 246
Students practice and maintain skills through Math Box problems.

Study Link 8•8
Math Masters, p. 269
Students practice and maintain skills through Study Link activities.

3 Differentiation Options

READINESS

Comparing Areas
Math Masters, p. 270
scissors
Students explore area comparison using a concrete model.

ENRICHMENT

Calculating Gravitational Pull
Math Masters, p. 271
calculator
Students use patterns in a table of weights to determine the gravitational pull of each planet relative to Earth.

ENRICHMENT

Exploring Similar Figures
Math Masters, pp. 272 and 273
centimeter ruler
Students explore the relationships between the dimensions and areas of similar figures.

Advance Preparation

***Teacher's Reference Manual,* Grades 4–6** pp. 231, 232

Getting Started

Mental Math and Reflexes

Write numbers on the board for students to round to various places. *Suggestions:*

●○○ Round 440,762 to the nearest
- 100 440,800
- 10,000 440,000
- 100,000 400,000

●●○ Round 1,005,518 to the nearest
- 10,000 1,010,000
- 100,000 1,000,000
- 1,000,000 1,000,000

●●● Round 293,571,551 to the nearest
- 100,000 293,600,000
- 1,000,000 294,000,000
- 100,000,000 300,000,000

Math Message

Read page 295 of the Student Reference Book.

Be prepared to give several reasons why it is hard to measure the areas of countries, oceans, and deserts.

Study Link 8·7 Follow-Up

Have small groups compare answers and discuss how they solved Problems 5 and 6. Sample answer: Multiply the area by 2. Then divide that number by the height to find the length of the base.

1 Teaching the Lesson

▶ Math Message Follow-up

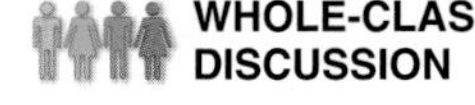

WHOLE-CLASS DISCUSSION

(*Student Reference Book,* p. 295)

Listed below are some ideas that should emerge from a discussion of *Student Reference Book,* page 295.

▷ It is often difficult to make accurate area measurements of land forms.

▷ People do not always agree on where the borders of a country are located, or even on the definition of a land form.

▷ Boundaries may change due to cultivation of the land, political events, or changes in climate.

Students may be surprised to learn that places where the water is always frozen, called tundras, are actually considered deserts.

Tell students that in this lesson they will use division to compare areas of countries to determine relative size.

Links to the Future

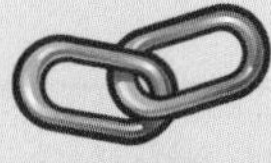

Students used division to solve equal-sharing and equal-grouping problems in Unit 6. This lesson introduces a third use of division: to compare two quantities that are measured with the same unit. In Unit 9, students will have additional experiences with ratio comparisons.

Student Page

World Tour

Geographical Area Measurements

The heights of mountains and the depths of oceans are obtained *directly*. We find heights and depths by measuring the Earth itself.

The areas of countries and the areas of oceans are found *indirectly*. We measure very accurate maps or satellite pictures. The countries and oceans themselves are not measured.

Countries, oceans, and deserts have irregular boundaries. One way that scientists measure areas is to count grid squares. They place a transparent grid of squares on a map. Then they count the squares and parts of squares that cover the region being measured. The squares are drawn to the same scale as the map.

The shoreline of a body of water may shift greatly during different seasons of the year and over the years.

There are several reasons that it is hard to measure the following regions accurately:

Area of a country. Sometimes people disagree about the exact boundary of a country. So the area may depend on which boundary is being used.

Area of a lake, sea, or ocean. Some bodies of water have shorelines that shift greatly depending on the level of the water. So it is very hard to measure accurately the area that is covered by water.

The world's oceans are not separated from one another by shorelines. Sometimes people disagree on the boundaries between the oceans. This makes it difficult to measure the areas of oceans.

Area of a desert. Measuring desert areas is very hard. Desert boundaries may change because the climate changes. When land is cultivated, a desert boundary shifts. Also, scientists do not agree on what a desert actually is. Some define a desert as land that cannot be used for raising crops. Others define it as land that cannot be used for either crops or grazing. There are deserts that are hot and dry only part of the year. Some deserts are dry all year because it is very hot. Other deserts are dry all year because it is very cold and the water is always frozen. Very cold deserts are known as *tundras*.

Desert boundaries often change because of climate changes.

***Student Reference Book,* p. 295**

Comparing Country Areas

WHOLE-CLASS ACTIVITY

(*Math Journal 2,* p. 245; *Student Reference Book,* pp. 286 and 287)

Social Studies Link Ask students to turn to the map of South America on pages 286 and 287 of the *Student Reference Book*. The country in South America with the largest area is Brazil. Use the classroom world map or a globe to compare Brazil and the United States and mention that they have nearly the same area. (The United States is about 10% larger.)

Tell students that they will be comparing the areas of other countries in South America to Brazil's area. Since Brazil and the United States have nearly the same area, these comparisons will be nearly the same as if they had compared the areas of other South American countries to the area of the United States.

Have students find Ecuador on the map. Use the following routine to compare the areas of Ecuador and Brazil. Students fill in the first line of the table on journal page 245 as you work through the steps.

▷ *Guess how many times larger Brazil is than Ecuador.* Ask students to imagine that they have many paper cutouts that are the size and shape of Ecuador. About how many cutouts would it take to cover Brazil? Said another way, how many Ecuadors would fill up Brazil? Expect answers that range from 20 to 50.

▷ *Round the areas of Brazil and Ecuador to the nearest 10,000 square miles.* The area of Ecuador is given in column (2) on the journal page as 109,500 square miles. The rounded area is 110,000 square miles. Brazil's area is reported (at the top of the journal page) as 3,300,000 square miles, which is already rounded to the nearest 10,000 square miles.

▷ *Estimate how many times larger Brazil is than Ecuador.* Point out that students need to figure out how many 110,000s there are in 3,300,000. Write 3,300,000 / 110,000 = ? on the board, and have students use their calculators to divide. Brazil is about 30 times the size of Ecuador. About 30 cutouts or copies of Ecuador would fit inside the boundary of Brazil.

Have partnerships complete journal page 245. Make sure they understand that the different country areas are always compared with Brazil's area. You might want to point out to students that when they complete journal page 245, they are using division to solve real-world multiplicative comparison problems.

In most cases, the division of Brazil's area by the area of another country will lead to a decimal answer. For example, Brazil's area divided by Peru's is 3,300,000 mi^2 / 500,000 mi^2 = 6.6.

Student Page

Date Time

LESSON 8·8 **Comparing Country Areas**

Brazil is the largest country in South America. Brazil's area is about 3,300,000 square miles. The area of the United States is about 3,500,000 square miles. So Brazil is nearly the same size as the United States.

Fill in the table below. This will help you to compare the areas of other countries in South America to Brazil's area. Round quotients in Part 4 to the nearest tenth.

Country	(1) Guess the number of times it would fit in the area of Brazil.	(2) Area	(3) Area (rounded to the nearest 10,000)	(4) Divide the rounded areas. (Brazil area ÷ country area)
Ecuador	Answers vary.	109,500 mi^2	110,000 mi^2	3,300,000 ÷ 110,000 = 30
Argentina		1,068,300 mi^2	1,070,000 mi^2	3,300,000 ÷ 1,070,000 = 3.1
Paraguay		157,000 mi^2	160,000 mi^2	3,300,000 ÷ 160,000 = 20.6
Peru		496,200 mi^2	500,000 mi^2	3,300,000 ÷ 500,000 = 6.6
Uruguay		68,000 mi^2	70,000 mi^2	3,300,000 ÷ 70,000 = 47.1
Chile		292,300 mi^2	290,000 mi^2	3,300,000 ÷ 290,000 = 11.4

Math Journal 2, p. 245

Adjusting the Activity

Have students explore the use of the constant feature on their calculators to do the repeated divisions in which the dividend is 3,300,000.

AUDITORY ◆ KINESTHETIC ◆ TACTILE ◆ VISUAL

Student Page

Date Time

LESSON 8•8 Math Boxes

1. Make scale drawings of each rectangle described below.
   Scale: 1 cm represents 1.5 meters.
   a. Length of rectangle: 6 meters
   Width of rectangle: 3 meters
   b. Length of rectangle: 10.5 meters
   Width of rectangle: 4.5 meters

   a. b.

2. What is the area of the parallelogram?
   8"
   1"
   Number model: $1 * 8 = 8$
   Area = 8 in²

3. A jar contains
   27 blue blocks,
   18 red blocks,
   12 orange blocks, and
   43 green blocks.
   You put your hand in the jar and without looking pull out a block. About what fraction of the time would you expect to get a red block?
   $\frac{18}{100}$, or $\frac{9}{50}$

4. Add or subtract.
   a. $\frac{1}{12} + \frac{11}{12} = \frac{12}{12}$, or 1
   b. $\frac{1}{6} + \frac{2}{3} = \frac{5}{6}$
   c. $\frac{2}{8}$, or $\frac{1}{4}$ $= \frac{7}{8} - \frac{5}{8}$
   d. $\frac{3}{16} = \frac{5}{16} - \frac{1}{8}$

5. Multiply. Use a paper-and-pencil algorithm.
   $91 * 48 =$ 4,368

Math Journal 2, p. 246

Study Link Master

Name Date Time

STUDY LINK 8•8 Turtle Weights

Turtle	Weight (pounds)
Pacific leatherback	1,552
Atlantic leatherback	1,018
Green sea	783
Loggerhead	568
Alligator snapping	220
Flatback sea	171
Hawksbill sea	138
Kemps Ridley	133
Olive Ridley	110
Common snapping	85

Source: The Top 10 of Everything 2004

1. The Atlantic leatherback is about 10 times heavier than the Olive Ridley turtle.
2. The loggerhead is about 7 times the weight of the common snapping turtle.
3. Which turtle weighs about 3 times as much as the loggerhead? Pacific leatherback
4. The flatback sea turtle and the alligator snapping turtle together weigh about half as much as the Green sea turtle.
5. About how many common snapping turtles would equal the weight of two alligator snapping turtles? 5
6. The Atlantic leatherback is about $\frac{2}{3}$ the weight of the Pacific leatherback.

Practice

Name the factors.

7. 50 1, 2, 5, 10, 25, 50
8. 63 1, 3, 7, 9, 21, 63
9. 90 1, 2, 3, 5, 6, 9, 10, 15, 18, 30, 45, 90

Math Masters, p. 269

2 Ongoing Learning & Practice

▶ Playing *Grab Bag*

(*Student Reference Book,* p. 249; *Math Masters,* pp. 483–485)

Algebraic Thinking Students play *Grab Bag* to practice calculating probabilities of events. See Lesson 7-6 for additional information.

Ongoing Assessment: Recognizing Student Achievement

***Math Masters* Page 485**

Use ***Math Masters,* page 485** to assess students' ability to calculate the probability of an event. Students are making adequate progress if they are able to calculate the total number of items in the bag and express the probability of an event as a fraction. Some students may use a strategy when replacing x and y to earn the most possible points for each turn.

[Data and Chance Goal 4]

▶ Math Boxes 8•8

(*Math Journal 2,* p. 246)

Mixed Practice Math Boxes in this lesson are paired with Math Boxes in Lesson 8-6. The skill in Problem 5 previews Unit 9 content.

Writing/Reasoning Have students write a response to the following: *Explain the strategy you used to solve Problem 4d.* Sample answer: $\frac{1}{8}$ is equivalent to $\frac{2}{16}$. I renamed $\frac{1}{8}$ as $\frac{2}{16}$ so that I would have two fractions with the same denominator. $\frac{5}{16} - \frac{2}{16} = \frac{3}{16}$

▶ Study Link 8•8

(*Math Masters,* p. 269)

Home Connection Students compare the weight of the 10 heaviest turtles. They use data in a table to estimate answers to given questions.

3 Differentiation Options

READINESS

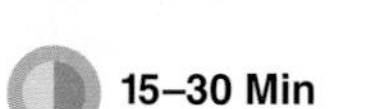

SMALL-GROUP ACTIVITY

15–30 Min

Comparing Areas

(*Math Masters,* p. 270)

To explore area comparisons using a concrete model, have students cut out the shapes on *Math Masters,* page 270 and describe relationships among them.

ENRICHMENT

INDEPENDENT ACTIVITY

5–15 Min

Calculating Gravitational Pull

(*Math Masters,* p. 271)

Science Link To apply students' understanding of comparison strategies, have them use patterns in a table of weights to determine the gravitational pull of each planet relative to Earth.

Teaching Master

Name Date Time

LESSON 8•8 **Weight on Different Planets**

Mercury has about $\frac{1}{3}$ the gravitational pull on your body mass as does Earth—about 0.37 to be more precise. You would weigh about $\frac{1}{3}$ as much on Mercury as you do on Earth.

The table below shows how much Rich, his brother Jean-Claude, and his sister Gayle would weigh on each planet.

1. Use your calculator to find each planet's gravitational pull relative to Earth's.

		Weight in Pounds			
Planet	Gravitational Pull Relative to Earth's	Rich	Jean-Claude	Gayle	Me
Earth	1	86	75	50	
Mercury	0.37	31.82	27.75	18.5	
Venus	0.90	77.4	67.5	45	
Mars	0.37	31.82	27.75	18.5	
Jupiter	2.35	202.1	176.25	117.5	
Saturn	0.91	78.26	68.25	45.5	
Uranus	0.88	75.68	66	44	
Neptune	1.12	96.32	84	56	

Source: Nasa Kids

2. Explain the strategy you used to determine the gravitational pulls.

Sample answer: I divided Rich's weight on each planet by his weight on Earth.

Try This

3. Use the information in the table to calculate your own weight on each planet and record it in the "Me" column in the table above.

Answers vary.

Math Masters, p. 271

ENRICHMENT

INDEPENDENT ACTIVITY

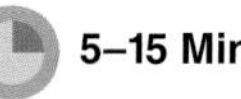

5–15 Min

Exploring Similar Figures

(*Math Masters,* pp. 272 and 273)

To apply students' understanding of area comparisons, have them explore perimeters and areas of similar figures.

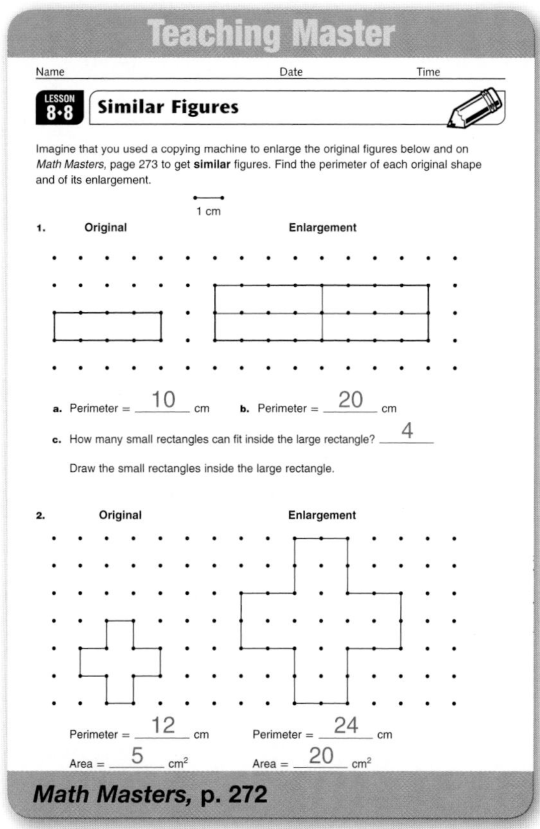

Teaching Master

Name Date Time

LESSON 8•8 **Similar Figures**

Imagine that you used a copying machine to enlarge the original figures below and on *Math Masters,* page 273 to get **similar** figures. Find the perimeter of each original shape and of its enlargement.

1 cm

1. Original Enlargement

a. Perimeter = 10 cm b. Perimeter = 20 cm

c. How many small rectangles can fit inside the large rectangle? 4

Draw the small rectangles inside the large rectangle.

2. Original Enlargement

Perimeter = 12 cm Perimeter = 24 cm

Area = 5 cm² Area = 20 cm²

Math Masters, p. 272

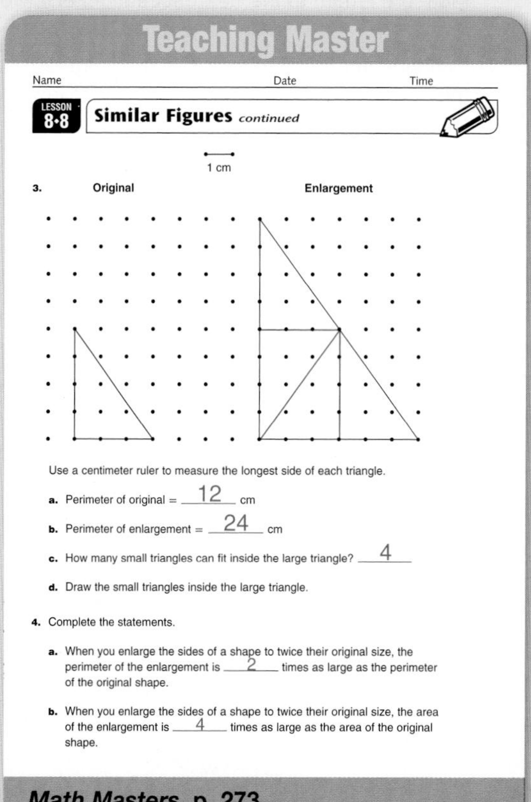

Teaching Master

Name Date Time

LESSON 8•8 **Similar Figures** *continued*

1 cm

3. Original Enlargement

Use a centimeter ruler to measure the longest side of each triangle.

a. Perimeter of original = 12 cm

b. Perimeter of enlargement = 24 cm

c. How many small triangles can fit inside the large triangle? 4

d. Draw the small triangles inside the large triangle.

4. Complete the statements.

a. When you enlarge the sides of a shape to twice their original size, the perimeter of the enlargement is 2 times as large as the perimeter of the original shape.

b. When you enlarge the sides of a shape to twice their original size, the area of the enlargement is 4 times as large as the area of the original shape.

Math Masters, p. 273

8•9 Progress Check 8

Objective To assess students' progress on mathematical content through the end of Unit 8.

1 Looking Back: Cumulative Assessment

Input student data from Progress Check 8 into the **Assessment Management Spreadsheets**.

Materials

- Study Link 8•8
- *Assessment Handbook,* pp. 110–117, 189–194, 223, and 274–277
- slate; centimeter ruler; scissors

CONTENT ASSESSED	LESSON(S)	ASSESSMENT ITEMS				
		SELF	ORAL/SLATE	WRITTEN PART A	WRITTEN PART B	OPEN RESPONSE
Rename tenths and hundredths as decimals. [Number and Numeration Goal 5]	8•1, 8•2, 8•4		4			
Order fractions. [Number and Numeration Goal 6]	8•1–8•4		2			
Use manipulatives, mental arithmetic, and calculators to add and subtract fractions. [Operations and Computation Goal 5]	8•1, 8•3, 8•6, 8•8	1		8–11		
Use scaling to model multiplication and division. [Operations and Computation Goal 7]	8•4, 8•5, 8•7, 8•8	2	3		17, 18	
Predict the outcomes of experiments; express the probability of an event as a fraction. [Data and Chance Goal 4]	8•1–8•8	3		12, 13		
Measure length to the nearest centimeter. [Measurement and Reference Frames Goal 1]	8•1, 8•2, 8•4, 8•6, 8•7				14–18	
Describe and use strategies to measure the perimeters of polygons. [Measurement and Reference Frames Goal 2]	8•1, 8•2, 8•4, 8•5, 8•7	4	1	1, 2, 5	14–16	
Describe and use strategies to find the areas of polygons. [Measurement and Reference Frames Goal 2]	8•3–8•8	5, 6	1	3–7	14–16	✓
Describe and compare plane figures using appropriate geometric terms. [Geometry Goal 2]	8•3, 8•6, 8•7					✓

2 Looking Ahead: Preparing for Unit 9

Math Boxes 8•9

Study Link 8•9: Unit 9 Family Letter

Materials

- *Math Journal 2,* p. 247
- *Math Masters,* pp. 274–277

Getting Started

Math Message • Self Assessment

Complete the Self Assessment (Assessment Handbook, *page 189*).

Study Link 8·9 Follow-Up

Have small groups compare answers. Ask volunteers to make additional comparison statements.

1 Looking Back: Cumulative Assessment

Math Message Follow-Up

INDEPENDENT ACTIVITY

(Self Assessment, *Assessment Handbook,* p. 189)

The Self Assessment offers students the opportunity to reflect upon their progress.

Oral and Slate Assessments

WHOLE-CLASS ACTIVITY

Problems 1 and 4 provide summative information and can be used for grading purposes. Problems 2 and 3 provide formative information that can be useful in planning future instruction.

Oral Assessment

1. Have students explain the differences between *area* and *perimeter*.
2. Write groups of fractions on the board. Have students order the fractions and explain how they did so. *Suggestions:*
   - $\frac{1}{4}, \frac{3}{4}, \frac{5}{8}, \frac{1}{16}, \frac{1}{8}$ $\frac{1}{16}, \frac{1}{8}, \frac{1}{4}, \frac{5}{8}, \frac{3}{4}$
   - $\frac{1}{2}, \frac{15}{16}, \frac{2}{3}, \frac{2}{9}, \frac{1}{3}$ $\frac{2}{9}, \frac{1}{3}, \frac{1}{2}, \frac{2}{3}, \frac{15}{16}$

Slate Assessment

3. Pose problems that require students to interpret a scale. *Suggestions:* If $\frac{1}{2}$ inch on a map represents 30 miles, then
   - 1 inch represents 60 miles.
   - $\frac{1}{4}$ inch represents 15 miles.
   - 2 inches represent 120 miles.
   - $1\frac{3}{4}$ inches represent 105 miles.
4. Write fractions with denominators of 10 or 100 on the board and have students write the equivalent decimals. Then write decimals on the board and ask students to write a fraction equivalent for each. Do not insist that fractions be in simplest form. *Suggestions:*
   - $\frac{6}{10}$ 0.6
   - 0.3 $\frac{3}{10}$
   - 0.86 $\frac{86}{100}$
   - $\frac{53}{100}$ 0.53
   - $\frac{40}{100}$ 0.40
   - 0.50 $\frac{50}{100}$

Assessment Master

Name Date Time

LESSON 8·9 **Self Assessment** Progress Check 8

Think about each skill listed below. Assess your own progress by checking the most appropriate box.

Skills	I can do this on my own and explain how to do it.	I can do this on my own.	I can do this if I get help or look at an example.
1. Add and subtract fractions.			
2. Make a scale drawing.			
3. Determine the probability of an event.			
4. Find the perimeter of a polygon.			
5. Count squares and fractions of squares to find the area of a polygon.			
6. Use a formula to find the area of a rectangle, parallelogram, and triangle.			

Assessment Handbook, p. 189

Assessment Master

Name Date Time

LESSON 8·9 **Written Assessment** Progress Check 8

Part A

Find the perimeter of each polygon.

1. 10 m, 6 m
   Number model: 6 + 6 + 10 + 10 = 32
   Perimeter = 32 m
2. 4 m, 3 m, 3 m, 8 m, ?, ?
   Number model: 8 + 4 + 3 + 3 + 5 + 7 = 30
   Perimeter = 30 m

Find the area of each polygon.

3. 1 cm
   Area = 10 square centimeters
4. 1 cm
   Area = 12 square centimeters
5. Draw a rectangle with an area of 12 square centimeters and a perimeter of 16 centimeters.
   1 cm

Assessment Handbook, p. 190

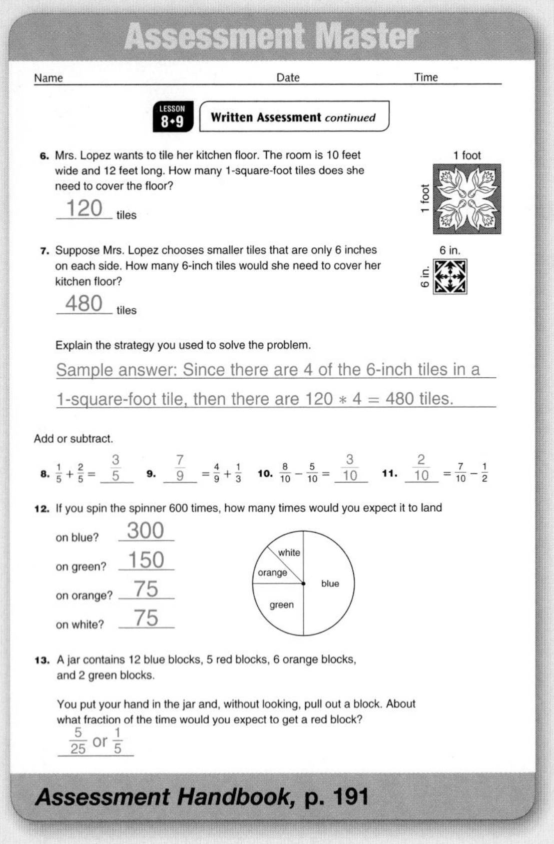

Assessment Master

Name Date Time

LESSON 8•9 **Written Assessment** *continued*

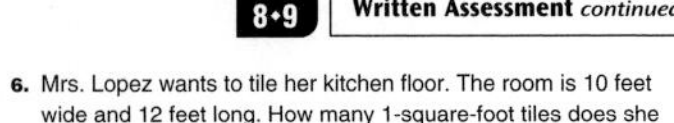

6. Mrs. Lopez wants to tile her kitchen floor. The room is 10 feet wide and 12 feet long. How many 1-square-foot tiles does she need to cover the floor?

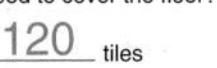

120 tiles

(1 foot × 1 foot tile)

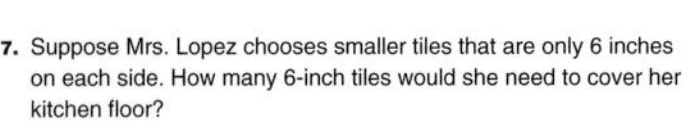

7. Suppose Mrs. Lopez chooses smaller tiles that are only 6 inches on each side. How many 6-inch tiles would she need to cover her kitchen floor?

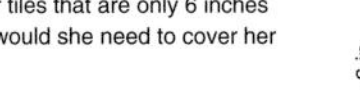

480 tiles

(6 in. × 6 in. tile)

Explain the strategy you used to solve the problem.

Sample answer: Since there are 4 of the 6-inch tiles in a 1-square-foot tile, then there are 120 ∗ 4 = 480 tiles.

Add or subtract.

8. $\frac{1}{5} + \frac{2}{5} = \frac{3}{5}$ 9. $\frac{7}{9} = \frac{4}{9} + \frac{1}{3}$ 10. $\frac{8}{10} - \frac{5}{10} = \frac{3}{10}$ 11. $\frac{2}{10} = \frac{7}{10} - \frac{1}{2}$

12. If you spin the spinner 600 times, how many times would you expect it to land

on blue? 300

on green? 150

on orange? 75

on white? 75

(spinner: white, orange, green, blue)

13. A jar contains 12 blue blocks, 5 red blocks, 6 orange blocks, and 2 green blocks.

You put your hand in the jar and, without looking, pull out a block. About what fraction of the time would you expect to get a red block?

$\frac{5}{25}$ or $\frac{1}{5}$

Assessment Handbook, p. 191

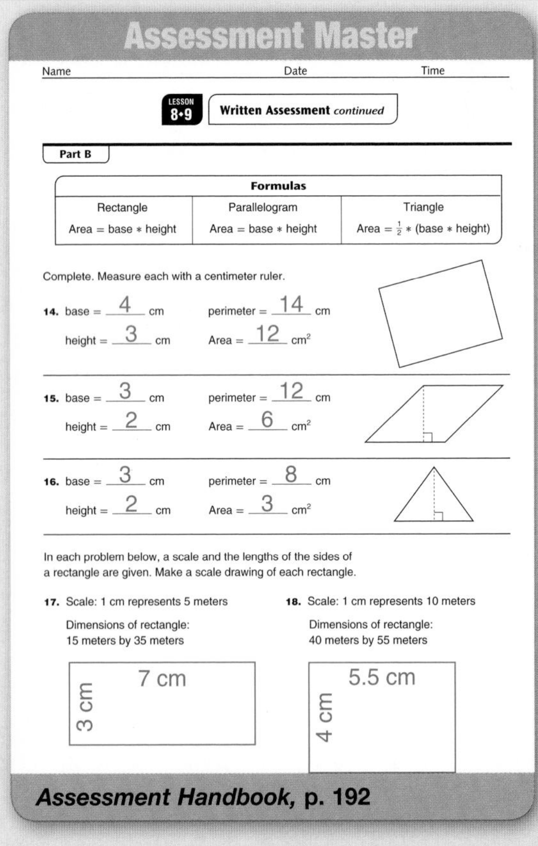

Assessment Master

Name Date Time

LESSON 8•9 **Written Assessment** *continued*

Part B

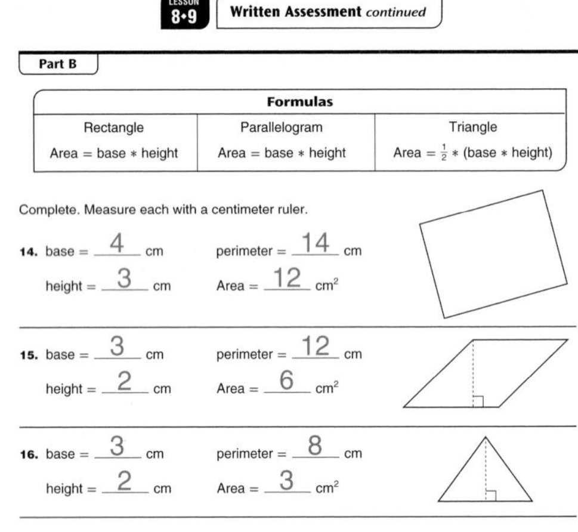

Formulas		
Rectangle	Parallelogram	Triangle
Area = base ∗ height	Area = base ∗ height	Area = $\frac{1}{2}$ ∗ (base ∗ height)

Complete. Measure each with a centimeter ruler.

14. base = 4 cm perimeter = 14 cm
height = 3 cm Area = 12 cm²

15. base = 3 cm perimeter = 12 cm
height = 2 cm Area = 6 cm²

16. base = 3 cm perimeter = 8 cm
height = 2 cm Area = 3 cm²

In each problem below, a scale and the lengths of the sides of a rectangle are given. Make a scale drawing of each rectangle.

17. Scale: 1 cm represents 5 meters
Dimensions of rectangle: 15 meters by 35 meters

18. Scale: 1 cm represents 10 meters
Dimensions of rectangle: 40 meters by 55 meters

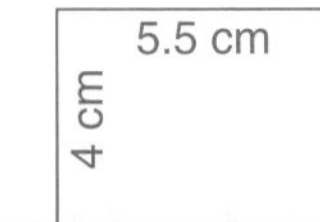

Assessment Handbook, p. 192

▶ Written Assessment

(*Assessment Handbook,* pp. 190–192)

Part A Recognizing Student Achievement

Problems 1–13 provide summative information and may be used for grading purposes.

Problem(s)	Description
1, 2	Find the perimeter of a polygon.
3, 4	Find the area of a polygon drawn on a grid.
5	Draw a rectangle with a given area and perimeter.
6, 7	Solve number stories involving area.
8–11	Add and subtract fractions.
12	Predict the outcomes of a spinner experiment.
13	Express the probability of a block-drawing event as a fraction.

Part B Informing Instruction

Problems 14–18 provide formative information that can be useful in planning future instruction.

Problem(s)	Description
14–16	Use formulas to find the area of a rectangle, parallelogram, and triangle.
17, 18	Use a scale to draw rectangles with given dimensions.

Use the checklists on pages 275 and 277 of the *Assessment Handbook* to record results. Then input the data into the **Assessment Management Spreadsheets** to keep an ongoing record of students' progress toward Grade-Level Goals.

▶ Open Response

(*Assessment Handbook,* pp. 193 and 194)

Comparing Areas

The open-response item requires students to apply concepts and skills from Unit 8 to solve a multistep problem. See *Assessment Handbook,* pages 113–117 for rubrics and students' work samples for this problem.

2 Looking Ahead: Preparing for Unit 9

▸ Math Boxes 8◆9

INDEPENDENT ACTIVITY

(*Math Journal 2,* p. 247)

Mixed Practice This Math Boxes page previews Unit 9 content.

▸ Study Link 8◆9: Unit 9 Family Letter

INDEPENDENT ACTIVITY

(*Math Masters,* pp. 274–277)

Home Connection The Unit 9 Family Letter provides parents and guardians with information and activities related to Unit 9 topics.

Assessment Master

Name Date Time

LESSON 8◆9 **Open Response** *continued* Progress Check 8

Comparing Areas

1. Arrange shapes A–D in order of their area. (You may not measure with a ruler.) List the letters of the shapes from largest to smallest. If some shapes have the same area, write the letters next to each other and circle them.

2. Explain the steps you followed to figure out the order of each of the shapes. You may draw pictures to illustrate your steps.

See the *Assessment Handbook* for rubrics and students' work samples.

Try This

3. Compare shapes A and E. Tell which has the larger area. Explain how you compared the shapes.

***Assessment Handbook,* p. 194**

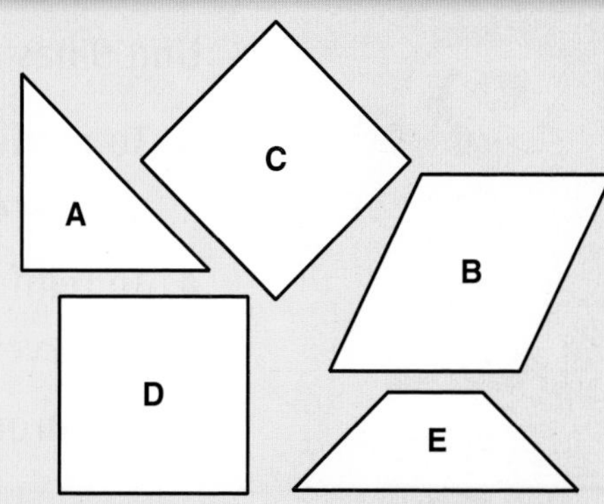

Shapes A–E from *Assessment Handbook,* page 193

Study Link Masters

Name Date Time

STUDY LINK 8◆9 **Unit 9: Family Letter**

Fractions, Decimals, and Percents

In Unit 9, we will be studying percents and their uses in everyday situations. Your child should begin finding examples of percents in newspapers and magazines, on food packages, on clothing labels, and so on, and bring them to class. They will be used to illustrate a variety of percent applications.

As we study percents, your child will learn equivalent values for percents, fractions, and decimals. For example, 50% is equivalent to the fraction $\frac{1}{2}$ and to the decimal 0.5. The class will develop the understanding that **percent** always refers to a **part out of 100.**

Converting "easy" fractions, such as $\frac{1}{2}$, $\frac{1}{3}$, $\frac{1}{10}$, and $\frac{3}{4}$, to decimal and percent equivalents should become automatic for your child. Such fractions are common in percent situations and are helpful with more difficult fractions, decimals, and percents. To help memorize the "easy" fraction/percent equivalencies, your child will play *Fraction/Percent Concentration.*

"Easy" Fractions	Decimals	Percents
$\frac{1}{2}$	0.50	50%
$\frac{1}{4}$	0.25	25%
$\frac{3}{4}$	0.75	75%
$\frac{2}{5}$	0.40	40%
$\frac{7}{10}$	0.70	70%
$\frac{2}{2}$	1.00	100%

Throughout the unit, your child will use a calculator to convert fractions to percents and will learn how to use the percent key (%) to calculate discounts, sale prices, and percents of discount.

As part of the World Tour, your child will explore population data, such as literacy rates and percents of people who live in rural and urban areas.

Finally, the class will begin to apply the multiplication and division algorithms to problems that contain decimals. The approach used in *Everyday Mathematics* is straightforward: Students solve the problems as if the numbers were whole numbers. Then they estimate the answers to help them locate the decimal point in the exact answer. In this unit, we begin with fairly simple problems. Your child will solve more difficult problems in *Fifth* and *Sixth Grade Everyday Mathematics.*

Please keep this Family Letter for reference as your child works through Unit 9.

***Math Masters,* pp. 274–277**

Student Page

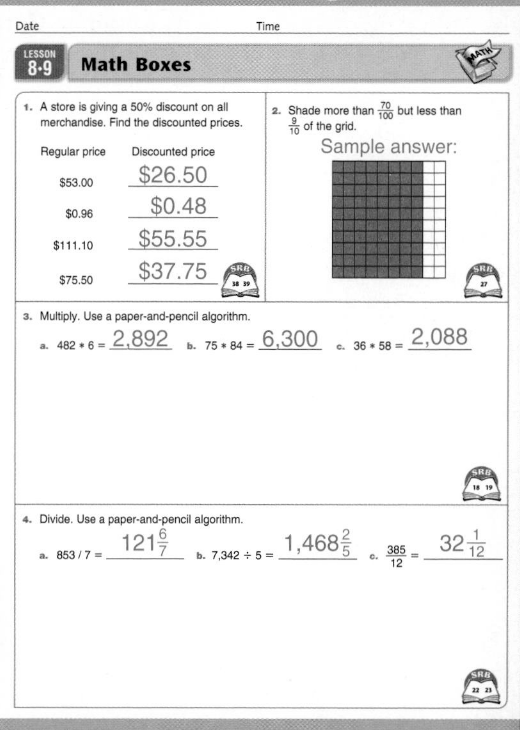

Date Time

LESSON 8◆9 **Math Boxes**

1. A store is giving a 50% discount on all merchandise. Find the discounted prices.

Regular price	Discounted price
\$53.00	\$26.50
\$0.96	\$0.48
\$111.10	\$55.55
\$75.50	\$37.75

2. Shade more than $\frac{70}{100}$ but less than $\frac{9}{10}$ of the grid.

Sample answer:

3. Multiply. Use a paper-and-pencil algorithm.

a. 482 ∗ 6 = 2,892 b. 75 ∗ 84 = 6,300 c. 36 ∗ 58 = 2,088

4. Divide. Use a paper-and-pencil algorithm.

a. 853 / 7 = $121\frac{6}{7}$ b. 7,342 ÷ 5 = $1,468\frac{2}{5}$ c. $\frac{385}{12}$ = $32\frac{1}{12}$

***Math Journal 2,* p. 247**

Unit 9 Organizer

Fractions, Decimals, and Percents

Overview

Unit 9 focuses on the links among fraction, decimal, and percent names for numbers, with a special emphasis on percents. Unit 9 begins with practice converting among fractions, decimals, and percents. Students then use grid pictures, the multiplication rule for renaming fractions, memorization of simple conversions, and a calculator for more complex conversions. Finally, students begin to apply whole-number multiplication and division algorithms to multiplication and division with decimals in the last two lessons of Unit 9. Unit 9 has three main areas of focus:

- To reinforce naming equivalencies among fractions, decimals, and percents,
- To reinforce the use of a data table, guide the organization and tabulation of survey data, and rank and compare data reported as percents, and
- To introduce multiplication and division of decimals by whole numbers.

Linking to the Common Core State Standards

The content of Unit 9 addresses the Common Core State Standards for Mathematics in *Number and Operations–Fractions.* The correlation of the Common Core State Standards to the *Everyday Mathematics* Grade 4 lessons begins on page CS1.

Contents

Learning In Perspective

	Lesson Objectives	Links to the Past	Links to the Future
9·1	To guide the use of percents in describing real-life situations; and to reinforce naming equivalencies among fractions, decimals, and percents.	Grade 4: Find equivalent names for decimals (Units 4 and 5). Grade 3: Find fraction/decimal equivalents.	Grades 5 and 6: Applications and extensions, including games to promote reflex recognition of fraction/decimal/percent equivalents, and practice with equivalent rates and ratios.
9·2	To reinforce renaming fourths, fifths, and tenths as decimals and percents; and to introduce solving percent problems by using equivalent fractions.	Grade 3: Find equivalent fractions using Fraction Cards; identify fractions on a fraction number line. Find fraction/decimal equivalents.	Grade 5: Develop reflex recognition of "easy" fraction-decimal equivalents. Grade 6: Applications and maintenance.
9·3	To introduce renaming any fraction as a decimal by using a calculator; and to reinforce fraction/percent equivalencies for fourths, fifths, and tenths.	Grade 3: Read and display numbers on a calculator. Perform operations on a calculator. Play *Beat the Calculator.*	Grade 5: Use a calculator to find decimal equivalents. Grade 6: Use a calculator to rename fractions as decimals and percents.
9·4	To reinforce renaming fractions as percents using a calculator; and to introduce solving number stories involving discounts expressed as percents.	Grade 3: Read and display numbers on a calculator. Perform operations on a calculator. Play *Beat the Calculator.* Name fractional parts of regions and sets of objects. Fold rectangles to find fractions of fractions.	Grade 5: Use a calculator to find decimal equivalents. Grades 5 and 6: Solve percent-of problems. Find the whole, given a percent of the whole. Grade 6: Use a calculator to rename fractions as decimals and percents.
9·5	To reinforce the use of a data table; and to reinforce renaming fractions as percents using a calculator and renaming decimals as percents.	Grades 2 and 3: Collect, organize, interpret, and display data.	Grade 5: Applications and maintenance.
9·6	To guide the organization and tabulation of survey data; and to introduce the use of percents to compare quantities expressed as fractions with unlike denominators.	Grades 2 and 3: Collect, organize, interpret, and display data.	Grade 5: Use a percent circle to read a circle graph.
9·7	To provide practice ranking and comparing data that are reported as percents and displaying ranked data by coloring maps.	Grades 2 and 3: Collect, organize, interpret, and display data.	Grades 5 and 6: Solve percent-of problems. Find the whole, given a percent of the whole.
9·8	To introduce multiplication of decimals by whole numbers; and to reinforce the partial-products and lattice methods for multiplication.	Grade 4: Estimate the magnitude of a product of multidigit numbers (Unit 5). Grade 3: Model and solve multiplication number stories using arrays, diagrams, and number models. Extend decimal notation to tenths and hundredths.	Grade 5: Make magnitude estimates to place decimal points in products. Extend the partial-products algorithm and lattice method to decimals. Grade 6: Multiply decimals.
9·9	To introduce division of decimals by whole numbers; and to reinforce the partial-quotients division algorithm.	Grade 3: Model and solve division number stories using arrays, diagrams, and number models. Review division as equal sharing and equal grouping. Extend decimal notation to tenths and hundredths using money and base-10 blocks.	Grade 5: Make magnitude estimates for quotients of whole numbers and decimals divided by whole numbers. Grade 6: Extend the partial-quotients algorithm to decimal divisors.

	Key Concepts and Skills	Grade 4 Goals*
9·1	Name the "whole" or the ONE.	Number and Numeration Goal 2
	Solve "percent-of" problems.	Number and Numeration Goal 2
	Rename fractions with denominators of 100 as decimals.	Number and Numeration Goal 5
	Find equivalent names for percents.	Number and Numeration Goal 5
9·2	Find the fraction and percent of a collection and a region.	Number and Numeration Goal 2
	Solve "percent-of" problems.	Number and Numeration Goal 2
	Rename fractions with denominators of 100 as decimals.	Number and Numeration Goal 5
	Find equivalent names for percents.	Number and Numeration Goal 5
9·3	Explore terminating and repeating decimals.	Number and Numeration Goal 5
	Use a calculator to rename fractions as decimals.	Number and Numeration Goal 5
	Describe patterns in terminating and repeating decimals.	Patterns, Functions, and Algebra Goal 1
9·4	Solve number stories involving discounts.	Number and Numeration Goal 2
	Name the whole, or the ONE.	Number and Numeration Goal 2
	Use a calculator to rename fractions as percents.	Number and Numeration Goal 5
	Rename any decimal as a percent.	Number and Numeration Goal 5
9·5	Read and use large numbers.	Number and Numeration Goal 1
	Explore repeating and terminating decimals.	Number and Numeration Goal 5
	Use a calculator to rename fractions as percents; rename decimals as percents by multiplying by 100.	Number and Numeration Goal 5
	Compare two quantities with like units using division.	Operations and Computation Goal 4
	Round to the nearest whole-number percent.	Operations and Computation Goal 6
	Use a data table.	Data and Chance Goal 2
9·6	Use a calculator to convert fractions to percents.	Number and Numeration Goal 5
	Compare fractions with unlike denominators.	Number and Numeration Goal 6
	Create a table and tally chart.	Data and Chance Goal 1
	Analyze survey results and make predictions based on collected data.	Data and Chance Goal 2
9·7	Interpret "percent-of" data.	Number and Numeration Goal 2
	Order data reported as percents.	Number and Numeration Goal 6
	Create a table, chart, and map to display data.	Data and Chance Goal 1
	Interpret data displayed on a map.	Data and Chance Goal 2
9·8	Identify place value in decimals through hundredths.	Number and Numeration Goal 1
	Multiply decimals by whole numbers.	Operations and Computation Goal 4
	Round decimals and estimate products.	Operations and Computation Goal 6
	Use repeated addition to model multiplication.	Operations and Computation Goal 7
	Use a formula to calculate the area of a rectangle.	Measurement and Reference Frames Goal 2
	Use conventional notation to write number sentences.	Patterns, Functions, and Algebra Goal 2
9·9	Identify place value in decimals through hundredths.	Number and Numeration Goal 1
	Divide decimals by whole numbers.	Operations and Computation Goal 4
	Round decimals and estimate quotients.	Operations and Computation Goal 6
	Use conventional notation to write number sentences.	Patterns, Functions, and Algebra Goal 2

*See the Appendix for a complete list of Grade 4 Goals.

A Balanced Curriculum

Ongoing Practice

Everyday Mathematics provides numerous opportunities for ongoing practice. These activities are embedded throughout the lessons:

Mental Math and Reflexes activities promote speed and accuracy in mental computation.

Math Boxes offer mixed practice and are paired across lessons as shown in the brackets below. This makes them useful as assessment tools. The last one or two boxes on each page preview the next unit's content.

Mixed practice	[9•1, 9•3], [9•2, 9•4], [9•5, 9•7, 9•9], [9•6, 9•8]
Mixed practice with multiple choice	9•1, 9•2, 9•4, 9•6, 9•8
Mixed practice with writing/reasoning opportunity	9•1, 9•2, 9•3, 9•4, 9•7, 9•8, 9•9

Study Links are daily homework assignments that review the content of the lesson and often contain ongoing facts practice or computation practice.

5-Minute Math problems are offered for additional practice in Lessons 9•4 and 9•5.

EM Facts Workshop Game provides online practice of basic facts and computation.

EXTRA PRACTICE **Extra Practice** activities are included in Lessons 9•2, 9•3, 9•4, 9•5, and 9•6.

Practice through Games

Games are an essential component of practice in the *Everyday Mathematics* program. Games offer skills practice and promote strategic thinking. See the *Differentiation Handbook* for ways to adapt games to meet students' needs.

Lesson	Game	Skill Practiced
9•1	*Fraction Match*	**Naming equivalent fractions** [NN Goal 5]
9•2	*Rugs and Fences*	**Finding the area and perimeter of a polygon** [MRF Goal 2]
9•3	*Fraction/Percent Concentration*	**Developing automaticity with "easy" fraction/percent equivalencies** [NN Goal 5]
9•8	*Over and Up Squares*	**Locating and plotting points on a coordinate grid** [MRF Goal 4]
9•9	*Polygon Pair-Up*	**Identifying properties of polygons** [GEO Goal 2]

[NN] Number and Numeration
[MRF] Measurement and Reference Frames
[OC] Operations and Computation
[GEO] Geometry
[DC] Data and Chance
[PFA] Patterns, Functions, and Algebra

Problem Solving 

Experts at problem solving and mathematical modeling generally do these things:

- Identify the problem.
- Decide what information is needed to solve the problem.
- Play with and study the data to find patterns and meaning.
- Identify and use mathematical procedures to solve the problem.
- Decide whether the solution makes sense and whether it can be applied to other problems.

The table below lists some of the opportunities in this unit for students to practice these strategies.

Lessons that teach *through* problem solving, not just *about* problem solving

Lesson	Activity
9•1	Write equivalent names for percents.
9•4	Solve number stories involving percents.
9•5	Rename fractions as percents.
9•6	Tabulate survey results for the whole class.
9•7	Rank and display countries according to population data.
9•8	Estimate products of decimals.
9•9	Estimate quotients of decimals.

See Chapter 18: Problem Solving in the *Teacher's Reference Manual* for more information.

The Language of Mathematics

Everyday Mathematics provides lesson-specific suggestions to help all students acquire, process, and express mathematical ideas. Throughout Unit 9, there are lesson-specific language development notes that address the needs of English language learners, indicated by ELL.

ELL SUPPORT Activities to support English language learners are in Part 3 of Lessons 9•1, 9•4, and 9•7.

The *English Learners Handbook* and the *Differentiation Handbook* have suggestions for promoting language development and acquisition of mathematics vocabulary. See Unit 9 in each handbook.

Unit 9 Vocabulary

100% box
discount
discounted price
fraction of discount
life expectancy
list price
percent
percent of discount
rank
regular price
repeating decimal
rural
sale price
terminating decimal
urban

Literacy Connection

Count Your Way through China, by Jim Haskins, Lerner Publishing Group, 1988

Piece = Part = Portion: Fractions = Decimals = Percents, by Scott Gifford, Tricycle Press, 2008

For more literacy connections, see the *Home Connection Handbook,* Grades 4–6.

Cross-Curricular Links 

Language Arts – Lesson 9•1
Consumer – Lesson 9•4
Social Studies – Lessons 9•5, 9•7

Balanced Assessment

Daily Assessments

- **Recognizing Student Achievement** – A daily assessment that is included in every lesson to evaluate students' progress toward the Grade 4 Grade-Level Goals.
- **Informing Instruction** – Notes that appear throughout the unit to help anticipate students' common errors and suggest appropriate problem-solving strategies.

Lesson	Recognizing Student Achievement	Informing Instruction
9•1	Find equivalent fractions. [NN Goal 5]	Understand percents as "per 100."
9•2	Rename fourths, fifths, tenths, and hundredths as decimals and percents. [NN Goal 5]	
9•3	Rename fourths, fifths, tenths, and hundredths as decimals and percents. [NN Goal 5]	
9•4	Solve "fraction-of" problems. [NN Goal 2]	Explain why decimals move when multiplying by 100.
9•5	Divide a multidigit whole number by a 1-digit divisor. [OC Goal 4]	Use a different division strategy for large numbers.
9•6	Interpret a map scale. [OC Goal 7]	
9•7	Draw conclusions from a data representation. [DC Goal 2]	Understand fractional parts of a spinner.
9•8	Estimate the product of a whole number and a decimal. [OC Goal 6]	
9•9	Estimate the quotient of a decimal divided by a whole number. [OC Goal 6]	

[NN] Number and Numeration
[MRF] Measurement and Reference Frames
[OC] Operations and Computation
[GEO] Geometry
[DC] Data and Chance
[PFA] Patterns, Functions, and Algebra

Portfolio Opportunities

The following lessons provide opportunities to gather samples of students' mathematical writings, drawings, and creations to add balance to the assessment process: Lessons 9•2, 9•3, 9•4, 9•6, 9•7, 9•9, and 9•10.

See pages 16 and 17 in the *Assessment Handbook* for more information about portfolios and how to use them.

Unit Assessment

Progress Check 9 – A cumulative assessment of concepts and skills taught in Unit 9 and in previous units, providing information for evaluating students' progress and planning for future instruction. These assessments include oral/slate, written, and open-response activities, as shown below in the sample Progress Check lesson opener.

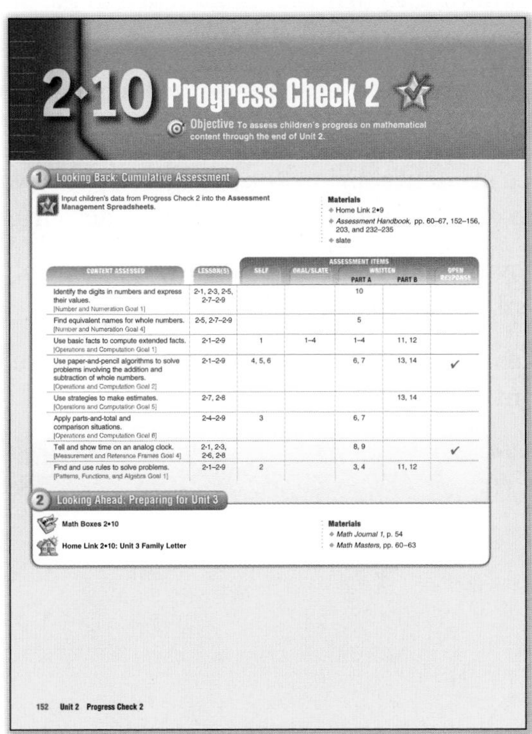

2•10 Progress Check 2

Objective To assess children's progress on mathematical content through the end of Unit 2.

1 Looking Back: Cumulative Assessment

Input children's data from Progress Check 2 into the **Assessment Management Spreadsheets.**

Materials
- Home Link 2•9
- *Assessment Handbook,* pp. 60–67, 152–156, 203, and 232–235
- slate

CONTENT ASSESSED	LESSON(S)	ASSESSMENT ITEMS				
		SELF	ORAL/SLATE	WRITTEN PART A	WRITTEN PART B	OPEN RESPONSE
Identify the digits in numbers and express their values. [Number and Numeration Goal 1]	2•1, 2•3, 2•5, 2•7–2•9			10		
Find equivalent names for whole numbers. [Number and Numeration Goal 4]	2•5, 2•7–2•9			5		
Use basic facts to compute extended facts. [Operations and Computation Goal 1]	2•1–2•9	1	1–4	1–4	11, 12	
Use paper-and-pencil algorithms to solve problems involving the addition and subtraction of whole numbers. [Operations and Computation Goal 2]	2•1–2•9	4, 5, 6		6, 7	13, 14	✓
Use strategies to make estimates. [Operations and Computation Goal 5]	2•7, 2•8				13, 14	
Apply parts-and-total and comparison situations. [Operations and Computation Goal 6]	2•4–2•9	3		6, 7		
Tell and show time on an analog clock. [Measurement and Reference Frames Goal 4]	2•1, 2•3, 2•6, 2•8			8, 9		✓
Find and use rules to solve problems. [Patterns, Functions, and Algebra Goal 1]	2•1–2•9	2		3, 4	11, 12	

2 Looking Ahead: Preparing for Unit 3

Math Boxes 2•10

Home Link 2•10: Unit 3 Family Letter

Materials
- *Math Journal 1,* p. 54
- *Math Masters,* pp. 60–63

152 Unit 2 Progress Check 2

Core Assessment Resources

Assessment Handbook

- **Unit 9 Assessment Overview,** pages 118–125
- **Unit 9 Assessment Masters,** pages 195–199
- **Unit 9 Individual Profiles of Progress,** pages 278, 279, and 302
- **Unit 9 Class Checklists,** pages 280, 281, and 303
- **Quarterly Checklist: Quarter 3,** pages 298 and 299
- **Math Logs,** pages 306–308
- **Exit Slip,** page 311
- **Other Student Assessment Forms,** pages 304, 305, 309, and 310

Assessment Management Spreadsheets

The Assessment Management Spreadsheets consist of the Digital Class Checklists and Individual Profile of Progress Checklists. Use them to monitor, record, and report student progress.

Addressing All Needs

Differentiated Instruction

Adjusting the Activity – suggests adaptations that target advanced learners, English language learners, or learners who need additional instructional support.

ELL SUPPORT / ELL – provides lesson-specific suggestions to help English language learners understand and process the mathematical content.

READINESS – accesses students' prior knowledge or previews content that prepares students to engage in the lesson's Part 1 activities.

EXTRA PRACTICE – provides additional opportunities to apply the mathematical content of the lesson.

ENRICHMENT – enables students to apply or further explore the mathematical content of the lesson.

Lesson	Adjusting the Activity	ELL Support/ ELL	Readiness	Extra Practice	Enrichment
9•1	•	•	•		
9•2	•	•	•	•	•
9•3	•			•	•
9•4	•	•	•	•	•
9•5	•	•	•	•	
9•6	•		•	•	•
9•7	•	•			•
9•8	•		•		•
9•9	•		•		•

Additional Resources

Differentiation Handbook
Provides ideas and strategies for differentiating instruction.
Pages 104–110

English Learners Handbook
Contains lesson-specific comprehension strategies.
Pages 80–88

Multilingual Handbook
Previews concepts and vocabulary. It is written in six languages.
Pages 159–176

Planning Tips

Multiage Classroom

Companion Lessons from Grades 3 and 5 can help you meet instructional needs of a multiage classroom. The full Scope and Sequence can be found in the Appendix.

Grade 3	8•5, 8•6	8•5, 8•6	8•5, 8•6			11•5			
Grade 4	**9•1**	**9•2**	**9•3**	**9•4**	**9•5**	**9•6**	**9•7**	**9•8**	**9•9**
Grade 5	6•8	6•8, 8•8		5•8	5•8, 6•8		3•2	2•8	4•5

Pacing for Success

Pacing depends on a number of factors, such as students' individual needs and how long your school has been using *Everyday Mathematics*. At the beginning of Unit 9, you may want to use tools available at www.everydaymathonline.com to help you set your pace.

Home Support

Unit 9 Family Letter (English/Spanish) provides families with an overview, Do-Anytime Activities, Building Skills through Games, a list of vocabulary, and answers to the daily homework (Study Links). Family Letters in English, Spanish, and seven other languages are also available online.

Study Links are the daily homework assignments. They consist of active projects and ongoing review problems.

Home Support Resources

Home Connection Handbook
Offers ideas and reproducible masters for communicating with families. See Table of Contents for unit information.

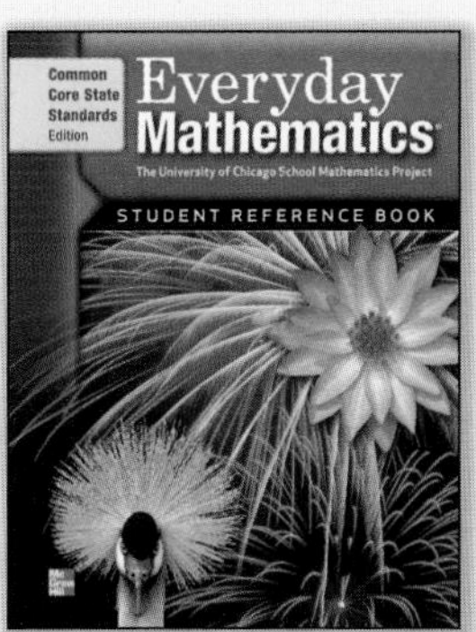

Student Reference Book
Provides a resource for students and parents.

Pages 243, 246, 257, 258, 260, 261, 271, 276, 277, 281, 288, 289, 297, 299–305

Technology Resources

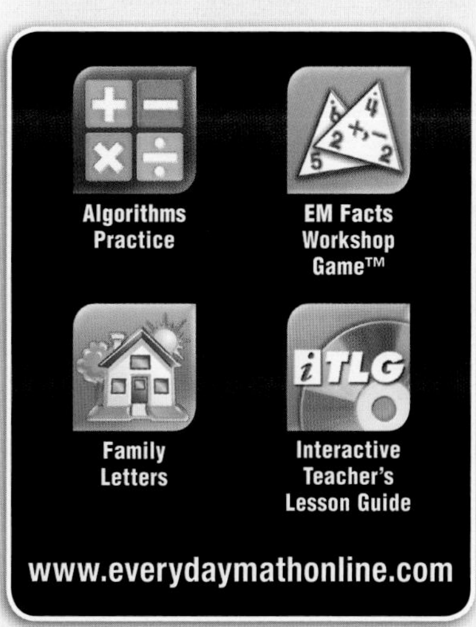

Materials

Technology Resources www.everydaymathonline.com

ePresentations

eToolkit

Algorithms Practice

EM Facts Workshop Game™

Family Letters

Assessment Management

Common Core State Standards

Curriculum Focal Points

Interactive Teacher's Lesson Guide

Lesson	Masters	Manipulative Kit	Other Items
9•1	Study Link Masters, pp. 279 and 280 Game Masters, pp. 473–476 Teaching Masters, pp. 262, 278, and 281	slate	
9•2	Study Link Master, p. 282 Game Masters, pp. 498–502 Teaching Masters, pp. 283, 283A, and 283B Teaching Aid Masters, pp. 426* and 445	slate; base-10 blocks*	
9•3	Teaching Aid Masters, pp. 388 or 389 and 446 Study Link Master, p. 284 Game Masters, pp. 481 and 482	slate	scissors; calculator
9•4	Study Link Master, p. 285 Teaching Masters, pp. 286 and 287	slate; counters	overheard calculator*; store catalogs or advertisements; calculator
9•5	Study Link Master, p. 288 Teaching Aid Masters, pp. 419* and 420* Teaching Master, p. 289	slate	classroom world map; calculator
9•6	Transparency of *Math Masters,* p. 290* Study Link Master, p. 291 Teaching Aid Masters, pp. 403, 410, 414, and 416* Teaching Master, p. 292	slate; pattern blocks	pen or colored pencil; large, clear container; calculator; markers or colored pencils
9•7	Teaching Masters, pp. 293 and 295 Teaching Aid Master, p. 426* Study Link Master, p. 294	slate	red, green, and blue pencils, crayons, or markers; index card*; old magazines; chart paper; scissors
9•8	Teaching Aid Masters, pp. 388 or 389, 404, 428, and 434 Study Link Master, p. 296 Game Master, p. 494 Teaching Masters, pp. 114 and 297	slate; per partnership: 2 six-sided dice; coins	colored pencil
9•9	Teaching Aid Masters, pp. 404* and 428 Study Link Master, p. 298 Game Masters, pp. 496 and 497 Teaching Masters, pp. 114 and 299	slate; coins	
9•10	Assessment Masters, pp. 195–199 Study Link Masters, pp. 300–303		markers or crayons; calculator

*Denotes optional materials

Mathematical Background

The discussion below highlights the major content ideas presented in Unit 9 and helps establish instructional priorities.

Conversions among Fractions, Decimals, and Percents (Lessons 9•1–9•5)

Students begin their work with fraction/decimal/percent names for numbers by exploring pictorial representations of such numbers on a 10-by-10 grid. They use these representations to restate percent situations as fractions and decimals. In particular, they find and memorize equivalencies for "easy" fractions (halves, fourths, fifths, and tenths).

One way to convert a fraction to a percent is to first rename it as a fraction with a denominator of 100. This can be done for "easy" fractions by using the multiplication rule for equivalent fractions.

Example $\frac{3}{5} = \frac{3 * 20}{5 * 20} = \frac{60}{100}$

$\frac{60}{100} = 0.60 = 60\%$

More complicated fractions, which do not lend themselves to conversions by the multiplication rule, can be renamed as decimals by dividing the numerator by the denominator with the help of a calculator.

Example $\frac{3}{7} = 3 \div 7 = 0.428571...$

Note

Terminating and repeating decimals will be covered formally in *Sixth Grade Everyday Mathematics.*

To convert the decimal to a percent, multiply it by 100 and attach the percent symbol to the result.

$0.428571 = (0.428571 * 100)\% = 42.8571\%$, or 43%, rounded to the nearest percent

The percent key on a calculator is really not needed, since the percent equivalent of any ratio or fraction can be calculated by using the division key and multiplying by 100. The authors include a discussion of the percent key mainly to take one more "mystery" off the keypad.

For further information on conversions among fractions, decimals, and percents, refer to Section 9.3 of the *Teacher's Reference Manual.*

Solving Problems Involving Percents (Lessons 9◆4–9◆7)

Nutrition Facts
Serving Size 1 Cookie (26g/0.9 oz)
Servings Per Container 10
Amount Per Serving
Calories 130 Calories from Fat 50
% Daily Value*
Total Fat 6g 9%
Saturated Fat 2.5g 13%
Trans Fat 1g
Polyunsaturated Fat 0g
Monounsaturated Fat 2.5g
Cholesterol 10mg 3%
Sodium 35mg 1%
Total Carbohydrate 16g 5%
Dietary Fiber 2g 8%
Sugars 9g
Protein 1g

As was mentioned in the Overview, solving percent problems often involves conversions among fractions, decimals, and percents. In Lessons 9-4 through 9-7, students use their conversion skills to solve a variety of problems.

▷ In Lesson 9-4, students solve problems that involve percents of discounts. These problems are simple enough so that students can do the conversions without the use of a calculator.

▷ In Lesson 9-5, students use World Tour data to answer questions, such as the following:

- What percent of the world's population lives in China?
- What percent of the world's land area belongs to Russia?

▷ For Study Link 9-1, students conduct a survey. They analyze the results of the survey in Lesson 9-6. In order to compare the results, they need to convert various ratios to percents.

▷ In Lesson 9-7, students create color-coded maps to organize and represent certain population data.

Section 9.3.5 of the *Teacher's Reference Manual* contains more information about solving problems involving percents.

Multiplication and Division with Decimals (Lessons 9◆8 and 9◆9)

Project Note

To teach U.S. traditional multiplication and division with decimals, see Algorithm Projects 6 and 8.

The approach to multiplication and division of decimals used in *Everyday Mathematics* is based on two assumptions:

- The same multiplication and division algorithms may be used for whole numbers and decimals.
- The placement of the decimal point in the answer can be determined by making a rough estimate of the answer.

Example $42 * 23.8 = ?$

Step 1: Estimate the product: $40 * 20 = 800$, or $50 * 20 = 1{,}000$; so $42 * 23.8$ will be about 800 or 1,000.

Step 2: Multiply the numbers, leaving out the decimal point.

$$\begin{array}{r} 238 \\ * \ 42 \\ \hline 9996 \end{array}$$

Step 3: Insert the decimal point in the answer. Since the estimated product is close to 1,000, the exact product must be 999.6.

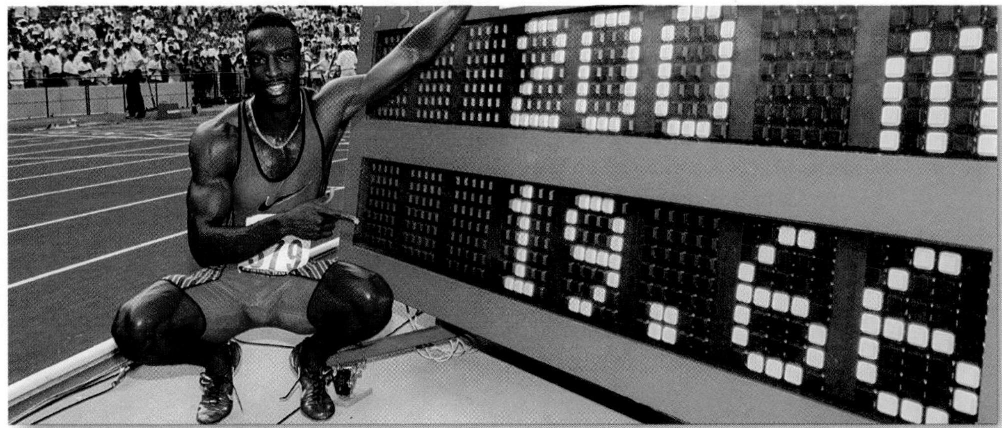

Example $259.2 / 8 = ?$

Step 1: Estimate the quotient: 259.2 is close to 260, and $260 / 8$ is between 30 and 40.

Step 2: Divide the numbers, leaving out the decimal point.

$$2592 / 8 = 324$$

Step 3: Insert the decimal point in the answer. Since the estimated quotient is between 30 and 40, the exact quotient must be 32.4.

Consult Sections 11.2.3 and 11.2.4 of the *Teacher's Reference Manual* for more information about multiplication and division with decimals.

9•1 Fractions, Decimals, and Percents

Objectives To guide the use of percents in describing real-life situations; and to reinforce naming equivalencies among fractions, decimals, and percents.

Technology Resources www.everydaymathonline.com

ePresentations

eToolkit

Algorithms Practice

EM Facts Workshop Game™

Family Letters

Assessment Management

Common Core State Standards

Curriculum Focal Points

Interactive Teacher's Lesson Guide

1 Teaching the Lesson

Key Concepts and Skills

- Name the "whole" or the ONE. [Number and Numeration Goal 2]
- Solve "percent-of" problems. [Number and Numeration Goal 2]
- Rename fractions with denominators of 100 as decimals. [Number and Numeration Goal 5]
- Find equivalent names for percents. [Number and Numeration Goal 5]

Key Activities

Students discuss uses of percents in everyday life. They represent various percent situations by shading 10-by-10 grid squares, and they restate each percent situation using a fraction name and a decimal name.

Ongoing Assessment: Informing Instruction See page 724.

Key Vocabulary

percent ◆ 100% box

Materials

Math Journal 2, pp. 248–250
Study Link 8•6
slate

2 Ongoing Learning & Practice

Playing *Fraction Match*
Student Reference Book, p. 243
Math Masters, p. 278
Fraction Match Cards (*Math Masters,* pp. 473–476)
Students practice naming equivalent fractions.

Ongoing Assessment: Recognizing Student Achievement
Use *Math Masters,* page 278.
[Number and Numeration Goal 5]

Math Boxes 9•1
Math Journal 2, p. 251
Students practice and maintain skills through Math Box problems.

Study Link 9•1
Math Masters, pp. 279 and 280
Students practice and maintain skills through Study Link activities.

3 Differentiation Options

READINESS

Finding 50% of a Square
Math Masters, p. 281
Students shade 50% of a square in different ways.

ELL SUPPORT

Creating a Percents All Around Museum
Math Masters, p. 262
Students collect examples of percents and display them in a Percents All Around Museum.

Advance Preparation

***Teacher's Reference Manual,* Grades 4–6** pp. 62, 63, 69–71

Getting Started

Mental Math and Reflexes

Write fractions on the board. For each fraction, students write the equivalent decimal and percent on their slates. *Suggestions:*

●○○ $\frac{15}{100}$ 0.15, 15%	●●○ $\frac{3}{100}$ 0.03, 3%	●●● $\frac{2}{2}$ 1, 100%
$\frac{55}{100}$ 0.55, 55%	$\frac{1}{10}$ 0.1, 10%	$\frac{1}{5}$ 0.20, 20%
$\frac{29}{100}$ 0.29, 29%	$\frac{7}{10}$ 0.7, 70%	$\frac{3}{4}$ 0.75, 75%

Math Message

Be ready to discuss the examples of percents you collected for Study Link 8-6.

1 Teaching the Lesson

Math Message Follow-Up

WHOLE-CLASS DISCUSSION

(*Math Masters,* p. 262)

Have students share the examples they collected of uses of **percents.** Encourage students to restate each percent situation in a variety of ways.

Example:

Candidate Reed got 50% of the votes.

This can be restated as

▷ "For every 100 votes cast, Reed got 50 votes."

▷ "If 100 people voted, then Reed got 50 votes."

▷ "Reed got 50 out of every 100 votes cast."

▷ "Reed got $\frac{50}{100}$ of the votes cast."

Emphasize that "50 out of 100" *does not mean that exactly 100 votes were cast* but that Reed got 50 votes for every 100 votes that were cast. (Since $\frac{50}{100}$ equals $\frac{1}{2}$, Reed got half the votes cast.) If it were a club election with only 60 votes cast, then Reed would have gotten 50% of 60 votes, or 30 votes. If it were an election for mayor with 30,000 votes cast, then Reed would have gotten 50% of 30,000 votes, or 15,000 votes.

Interactive whiteboard-ready **ePresentations** are available at www.everydaymathonline.com to help you teach the lesson.

Study Link Master

Name Date Time

STUDY LINK 8•6 **Percents in My World**

Percent means "per hundred" or "out of a hundred." *1 percent* means $\frac{1}{100}$ or 0.01.

"48 percent of the students in our school are boys" means that out of every 100 students in the school, 48 are boys.

Percents are written in two ways: with the word *percent,* as in the sentence above, and with the symbol %.

Collect examples of percents. Look in newspapers, magazines, books, almanacs, and encyclopedias. Ask people at home to help. Write the examples below. Also tell where you found them. If an adult says you may, cut out examples and bring them to school.

Encyclopedia: 91% of the area of New Jersey is land, and 9% is covered by water.

Newspaper: 76 percent of the seniors in Southport High School say they plan to attend college next year.

Answers vary.

***Math Masters,* p. 262**

Remind students that, just as with fractions, a percent always represents a *percent of something.* The "something" is the whole 100%, which is the entire object, or the entire collection of objects, or the entire quantity being considered. In the example, the whole, or the ONE, is the total number of votes cast. The total number of votes cast is 100 percent of the votes. The **100% box** serves the same purpose for percents as the *whole box* does for fractions: It helps focus students' attention on the whole, or 100%.

Language Arts Link The word *percent* comes from the Latin *per centum: Per* means "for," and *centum* means "one hundred." Ask students if they can think of other words that begin with *cent-*. Sample answers: Cent ($\frac{1}{100}$ of a dollar), century (100 years), centennial (100th anniversary), centipede (looks like it has 100 legs), centimeter ($\frac{1}{100}$ of a meter)

▶ Making Up Equivalent Names for Percents

WHOLE-CLASS ACTIVITY

(*Math Journal 2,* p. 248)

Tell students that in this lesson they will represent percents on a 10-by-10 square grid. Discuss the example on journal page 248: "Last season, Duncan made 62 percent of his basketball shots."

- ▷ The 10-by-10 grid represents the whole (100%)—in this case, all of the shots Duncan attempted.
- ▷ The 10-by-10 grid is made up of 100 small squares. Each small square is $\frac{1}{100}$, or 1%, of the whole. A decimal name for $\frac{1}{100}$ is 0.01.
- ▷ Sixty-two small squares are shaded. These shaded squares represent the number of shots Duncan made out of every 100 shots he took.
- ▷ Had Duncan taken 100 shots, he would have made 62 shots. This can also be stated as a fraction, $\frac{62}{100}$ of his shots, or as a decimal, 0.62 of his shots.

Ongoing Assessment: Informing Instruction

Watch for students who mistakenly think Duncan took exactly 100 shots and made exactly 62 of them. Explain, for example, that he might have taken only 50 shots and made 31 of them or taken 200 shots and made 124 of them.

Now select two of the examples of percents that students collected and discussed during the Math Message Follow-Up. Work as a class to complete Problems 1 and 2 on journal page 248. Have students write a brief description for each percent example. Then fill in the 100% box, shade the grid to show the percent, and write the fraction and decimal names for the percent.

Student Page

Date Time

LESSON 9·1 **Many Names for Percents**

Your teacher will tell you how to fill in the percent examples. Answers vary.

Fill in the "100% box" for each example. Show the percent by shading the 10-by-10 grid. Then write other names for the percent next to the grid.

Example: Last season, Duncan made 62 percent of his basketball shots.

100% — all of Duncan's shots

That is 62 out of every 100.

Fraction name: $\frac{62}{100}$

Decimal name: 0.62

1. Percent Example: ______

100%

That is ______ out of every 100.

Fraction name: $\frac{\square}{100}$

Decimal name: ______

2. Percent Example: ______

100%

That is ______ out of every 100.

Fraction name: $\frac{\square}{100}$

Decimal name: ______

Math Journal 2, p. 248

Adjusting the Activity

Journal pages 248–250 prompt students to provide an equivalent hundredths-fraction for the percent example. Students may wonder why they need to write a fraction such as $\frac{25}{100}$ when it can be written in simplest form as $\frac{1}{4}$. Encourage students to write both forms whenever possible to emphasize the connection between percents and fractions with 100 in the denominator.

AUDITORY ◆ KINESTHETIC ◆ TACTILE ◆ VISUAL

▸ Finding Equivalent Names for Percents

PARTNER ACTIVITY

(*Math Journal 2,* pp. 249 and 250)

Students complete journal pages 249 and 250.

For Problems 3–5, ask: *Which percent is the largest?* 80% *Did you look at the grid, the fraction, the decimal, or the percent to decide?* For Problems 5–7, students may have difficulty deciding what the "whole" is and how to fill in the 100% box.

▷ Problem 5: The example does not mention a specific time period. The whole (100%) could logically be "1 day" or any longer period (week, month, year). Any period shorter than 1 day could pose a problem. For example, cats are much more likely to be active at night and to sleep a lot during the day.

▷ Problem 6: 40% will be deducted from the original price of any item sold, so the whole (100%) is the "original price."

▷ Problem 7: The buyer must pay 20% of the cost of the carpet at the time of purchase, so the whole (100%) is the "cost of carpet."

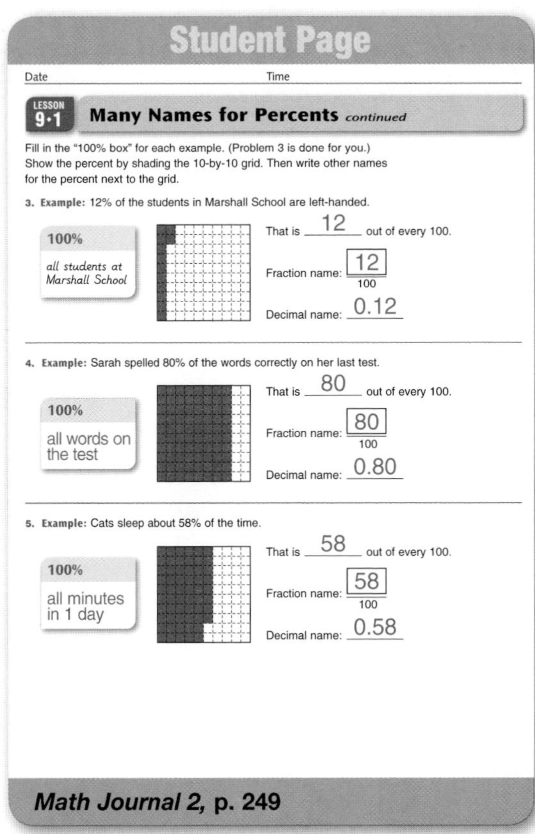

Student Page

Date Time

LESSON 9•1 **Many Names for Percents** *continued*

Fill in the "100% box" for each example. (Problem 3 is done for you.) Show the percent by shading the 10-by-10 grid. Then write other names for the percent next to the grid.

3. **Example:** 12% of the students in Marshall School are left-handed.

100%: all students at Marshall School

That is 12 out of every 100.

Fraction name: $\frac{12}{100}$

Decimal name: 0.12

4. **Example:** Sarah spelled 80% of the words correctly on her last test.

100%: all words on the test

That is 80 out of every 100.

Fraction name: $\frac{80}{100}$

Decimal name: 0.80

5. **Example:** Cats sleep about 58% of the time.

100%: all minutes in 1 day

That is 58 out of every 100.

Fraction name: $\frac{58}{100}$

Decimal name: 0.58

Math Journal 2, p. 249

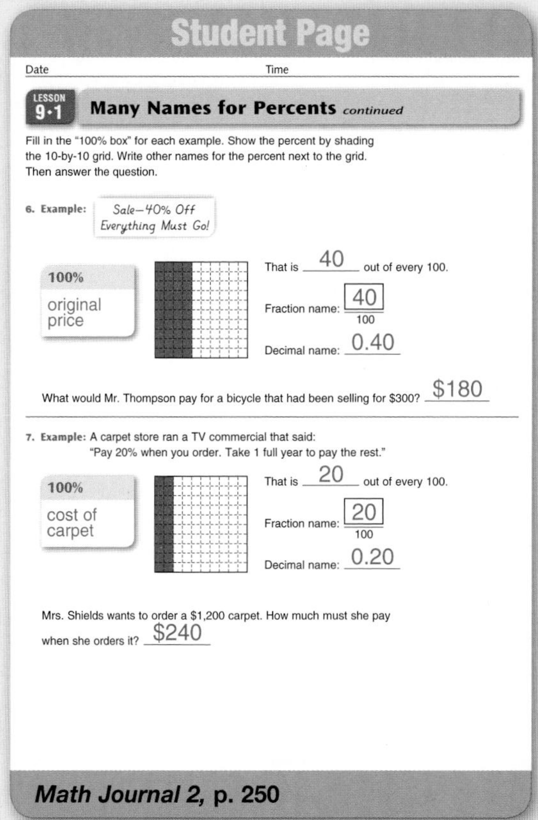

Student Page

Date Time

LESSON 9•1 **Many Names for Percents** *continued*

Fill in the "100% box" for each example. Show the percent by shading the 10-by-10 grid. Write other names for the percent next to the grid. Then answer the question.

6. **Example:** Sale—40% Off Everything Must Go!

100%: original price

That is 40 out of every 100.

Fraction name: $\frac{40}{100}$

Decimal name: 0.40

What would Mr. Thompson pay for a bicycle that had been selling for $300? $180

7. **Example:** A carpet store ran a TV commercial that said: "Pay 20% when you order. Take 1 full year to pay the rest."

100%: cost of carpet

That is 20 out of every 100.

Fraction name: $\frac{20}{100}$

Decimal name: 0.20

Mrs. Shields wants to order a $1,200 carpet. How much must she pay when she orders it? $240

Math Journal 2, p. 250

2 Ongoing Learning & Practice

▶ Playing *Fraction Match*

(*Student Reference Book,* p. 243; *Math Masters,* pp. 278 and 473–476)

Students play *Fraction Match* to practice naming equivalent fractions. See Lesson 7-7 for additional information.

After students have had a chance to play several rounds, ask them to complete *Math Masters,* page 278.

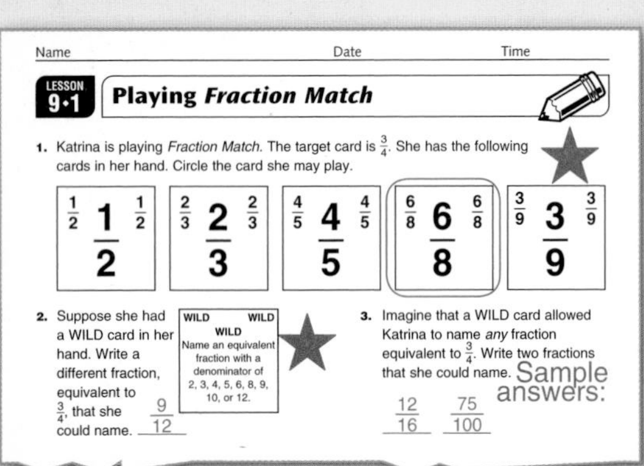

Name Date Time

LESSON 9•1 **Playing *Fraction Match***

1. Katrina is playing *Fraction Match.* The target card is $\frac{3}{4}$. She has the following cards in her hand. Circle the card she may play.

$\frac{1}{2}$	$\frac{2}{3}$	$\frac{4}{5}$	$\frac{6}{8}$ (circled)	$\frac{3}{9}$

2. Suppose she had a WILD card in her hand. Write a different fraction, equivalent to $\frac{3}{4}$, that she could name. $\frac{9}{12}$

WILD — Name an equivalent fraction with a denominator of 2, 3, 4, 5, 6, 8, 9, 10, or 12.

3. Imagine that a WILD card allowed Katrina to name *any* fraction equivalent to $\frac{3}{4}$. Write two fractions that she could name. Sample answers: $\frac{12}{16}$ $\frac{75}{100}$

Math Masters, page 278

Ongoing Assessment: Recognizing Student Achievement

Math Masters **Page 278 Problems 1 and 2**

Use ***Math Masters,* page 278, Problems 1 and 2** to assess students' ability to find equivalent fractions. Students are making adequate progress if they indicate that $\frac{6}{8}$ and $\frac{9}{12}$ are equivalent to $\frac{3}{4}$. Some students may be able to name additional fractions that are equivalent to $\frac{3}{4}$ in Problem 3.

[Number and Numeration Goal 5]

▶ Math Boxes 9•1

(*Math Journal 2,* p. 251)

Mixed Practice Math Boxes in this lesson are paired with Math Boxes in Lesson 9-3. The skill in Problem 6 previews Unit 10 content.

Writing/Reasoning Have students write a response to the following: *In Problem 5, suppose you extended line* ST *to the left and placed a point* Q *on the line to the left of point* S. *What would be the measure of angle* QSR? *Explain.* Sample answer: The two angles together measure 180°. Angle *RST* measures 127°. 180° − 127° = 53°. So, angle *QSR* would measure 53°.

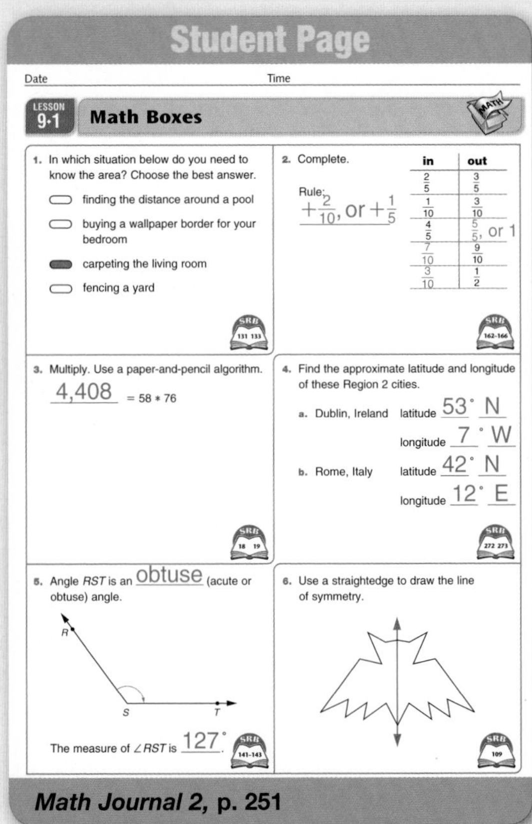

Student Page

Date Time

LESSON 9•1 **Math Boxes**

1. In which situation below do you need to know the area? Choose the best answer.
   - finding the distance around a pool
   - buying a wallpaper border for your bedroom
   - ● carpeting the living room
   - fencing a yard

2. Complete.

Rule: $+\frac{2}{10}$, or $+\frac{1}{5}$

in	out
$\frac{2}{5}$	$\frac{3}{5}$
$\frac{1}{10}$	$\frac{3}{10}$
$\frac{4}{5}$	$\frac{5}{5}$, or 1
$\frac{7}{10}$	$\frac{9}{10}$
$\frac{3}{10}$	$\frac{1}{2}$

3. Multiply. Use a paper-and-pencil algorithm. 4,408 = 58 ∗ 76

4. Find the approximate latitude and longitude of these Region 2 cities.
   a. Dublin, Ireland latitude 53° N longitude 7° W
   b. Rome, Italy latitude 42° N longitude 12° E

5. Angle *RST* is an obtuse (acute or obtuse) angle.
   The measure of ∠*RST* is 127°.

6. Use a straightedge to draw the line of symmetry.

Math Journal 2, p. 251

▶ Study Link 9•1

(*Math Masters,* pp. 279 and 280)

Home Connection Students name equivalent fractions, decimals, and percents and shade grids to represent them. Students complete the survey on the second page of the Study Link to collect data for an activity in Lesson 9-6.

3 Differentiation Options

READINESS

PARTNER ACTIVITY

Finding 50% of a Square

5–15 Min

(*Math Masters,* p. 281)

To explore equivalent names for percents, have students shade 50% of grids in different ways and explain how they know the shaded portions represent 50%.

ELL SUPPORT

SMALL-GROUP ACTIVITY

Creating a Percents All Around Museum

15–30 Min

(*Math Masters,* p. 262)

To provide language support for percents, have students display the examples of percents collected for Study Link 8-6 in a Percents All Around Museum. Ask students to describe the numbers they see in the museum. If several English language learners speak the same language, have them discuss the museum in their own language first and then share what they can in English.

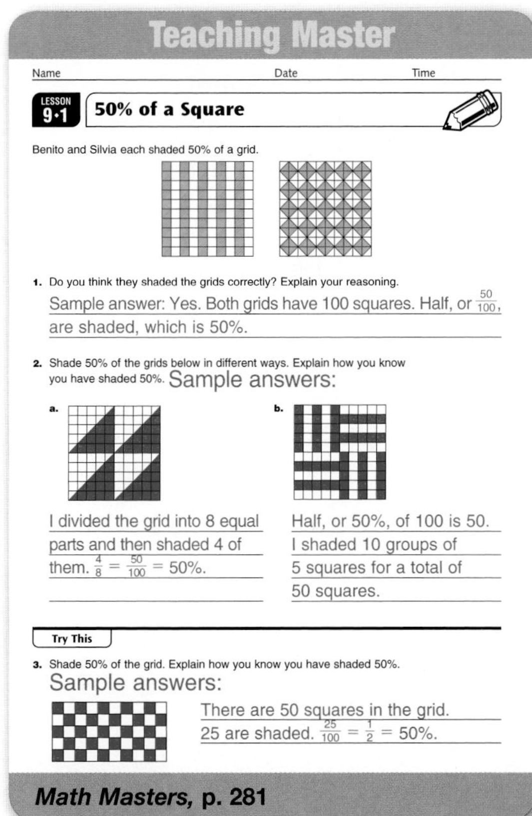
Teaching Master

Name Date Time

LESSON 9·1 **50% of a Square**

Benito and Silvia each shaded 50% of a grid.

1. Do you think they shaded the grids correctly? Explain your reasoning.
Sample answer: Yes. Both grids have 100 squares. Half, or $\frac{50}{100}$, are shaded, which is 50%.

2. Shade 50% of the grids below in different ways. Explain how you know you have shaded 50%. Sample answers:

a. I divided the grid into 8 equal parts and then shaded 4 of them. $\frac{4}{8} = \frac{50}{100} = 50\%$.

b. Half, or 50%, of 100 is 50. I shaded 10 groups of 5 squares for a total of 50 squares.

Try This

3. Shade 50% of the grid. Explain how you know you have shaded 50%.
Sample answers:
There are 50 squares in the grid. 25 are shaded. $\frac{25}{100} = \frac{1}{2} = 50\%$.

Math Masters, p. 281

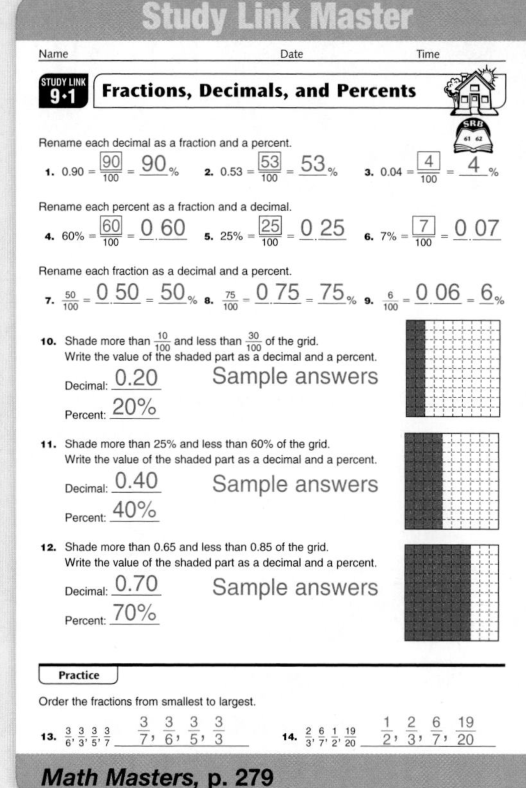
Study Link Master

Name Date Time

STUDY LINK 9·1 **Fractions, Decimals, and Percents**

Rename each decimal as a fraction and a percent.

1. $0.90 = \frac{90}{100} = 90\%$
2. $0.53 = \frac{53}{100} = 53\%$
3. $0.04 = \frac{4}{100} = 4\%$

Rename each percent as a fraction and a decimal.

4. $60\% = \frac{60}{100} = 0.60$
5. $25\% = \frac{25}{100} = 0.25$
6. $7\% = \frac{7}{100} = 0.07$

Rename each fraction as a decimal and a percent.

7. $\frac{50}{100} = 0.50 = 50\%$
8. $\frac{75}{100} = 0.75 = 75\%$
9. $\frac{6}{100} = 0.06 = 6\%$

10. Shade more than $\frac{10}{100}$ and less than $\frac{30}{100}$ of the grid. Write the value of the shaded part as a decimal and a percent.
Decimal: 0.20 Sample answers
Percent: 20%

11. Shade more than 25% and less than 60% of the grid. Write the value of the shaded part as a decimal and a percent.
Decimal: 0.40 Sample answers
Percent: 40%

12. Shade more than 0.65 and less than 0.85 of the grid. Write the value of the shaded part as a decimal and a percent.
Decimal: 0.70 Sample answers
Percent: 70%

Practice

Order the fractions from smallest to largest.

13. $\frac{3}{6}, \frac{3}{3}, \frac{3}{5}, \frac{3}{7}$ — $\frac{3}{7}, \frac{3}{6}, \frac{3}{5}, \frac{3}{3}$
14. $\frac{2}{3}, \frac{6}{7}, \frac{1}{2}, \frac{19}{20}$ — $\frac{1}{2}, \frac{2}{3}, \frac{6}{7}, \frac{19}{20}$

Math Masters, p. 279

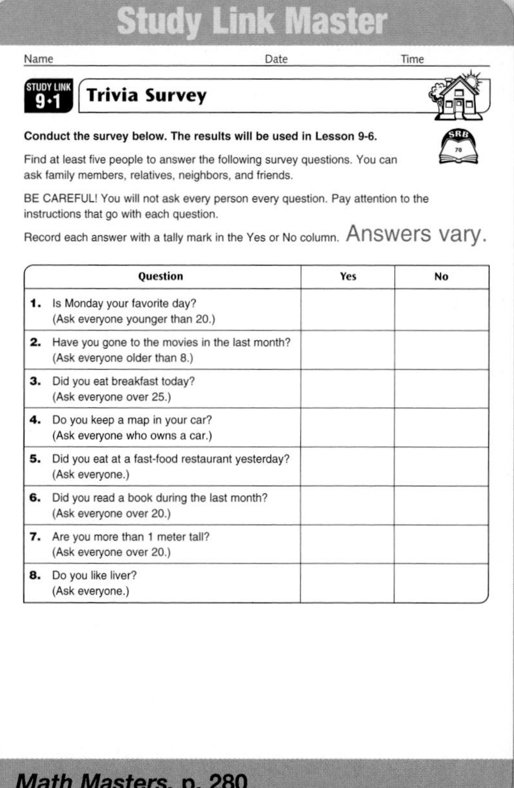
Study Link Master

Name Date Time

STUDY LINK 9·1 **Trivia Survey**

Conduct the survey below. The results will be used in Lesson 9-6.

Find at least five people to answer the following survey questions. You can ask family members, relatives, neighbors, and friends.

BE CAREFUL! You will not ask every person every question. Pay attention to the instructions that go with each question.

Record each answer with a tally mark in the Yes or No column. Answers vary.

Question	Yes	No
1. Is Monday your favorite day? (Ask everyone younger than 20.)		
2. Have you gone to the movies in the last month? (Ask everyone older than 8.)		
3. Did you eat breakfast today? (Ask everyone over 25.)		
4. Do you keep a map in your car? (Ask everyone who owns a car.)		
5. Did you eat at a fast-food restaurant yesterday? (Ask everyone.)		
6. Did you read a book during the last month? (Ask everyone over 20.)		
7. Are you more than 1 meter tall? (Ask everyone over 20.)		
8. Do you like liver? (Ask everyone.)		

Math Masters, p. 280

9•2 Converting "Easy" Fractions to Decimals and Percents

Objectives To reinforce renaming fourths, fifths, and tenths as decimals and percents; and to introduce solving percent problems by using equivalent fractions.

www.everydaymathonline.com

ePresentations

eToolkit

Algorithms Practice

EM Facts Workshop Game™

Family Letters

Assessment Management

Common Core State Standards

Curriculum Focal Points

Interactive Teacher's Lesson Guide

1 Teaching the Lesson

Key Concepts and Skills

- Find the fraction and percent of a collection and a region. [Number and Numeration Goal 2]
- Solve "percent-of" problems. [Number and Numeration Goal 2]
- Rename fractions with denominators of 100 as decimals. [Number and Numeration Goal 5]
- Find equivalent names for percents. [Number and Numeration Goal 5]

Key Activities

Students name shaded parts of 10-by-10 grids as fractions, decimals, and percents. The shaded parts are all "easy" fractions: fourths, fifths, and tenths.

Students solve percent problems by substituting "easy" equivalent fractions for percents.

Ongoing Assessment: Recognizing Student Achievement
Use journal page 253.
[Number and Numeration Goal 5]

Materials

Math Journal 2, pp. 252, 253, 342, and 343
Study Link 9•1
slate

2 Ongoing Learning & Practice

Playing *Rugs and Fences*
Student Reference Book, pp. 260 and 261
Math Masters, p. 502
Rugs and Fences Cards (*Math Masters,* pp. 498–501)
Students practice finding the areas and perimeters of polygons.

Math Boxes 9•2
Math Journal 2, p. 254
Students practice and maintain skills through Math Box problems.

Study Link 9•2
Math Masters, p. 282
Students practice and maintain skills through Study Link activities.

3 Differentiation Options

READINESS

Exploring Percent Patterns
Math Masters, p. 283
Students identify and use patterns to solve percent problems.

ENRICHMENT

Writing and Solving "Percent-of" Number Stories
Students write and solve "percent-of" number stories.

EXTRA PRACTICE

Adding Tenths and Hundredths
Math Masters, pp. 283A and 283B; p. 426 (optional)
base-10 blocks (optional)
Students add fractions with 10 and 100 in the denominator.

EXTRA PRACTICE

Finding Equivalent Names for Fractions
Math Masters, p. 445
Students name a fraction and a percent for the shaded part of a 10-by-10 grid.

Advance Preparation

***Teacher's Reference Manual,* Grades 4–6** pp. 62, 63, 153, 154

Getting Started

Mental Math and Reflexes

Write fractions on the board. For each fraction, students write the equivalent decimal and percent on their slates. Have students explain their strategies for the ●●● problems.
Suggestions:

●○○ $\frac{36}{100}$ 0.36, 36%	●●○ $\frac{3}{10}$ 0.3, 30%	●●● $\frac{7}{20}$ 0.35, 35%
$\frac{87}{100}$ 0.87, 87%	$\frac{1}{2}$ 0.5, 50%	$\frac{3}{25}$ 0.12, 12%
$\frac{19}{100}$ 0.19, 19%	$\frac{4}{5}$ 0.8, 80%	$\frac{14}{2}$ 7.0, 700%

Math Message

Complete Problem 1 on journal page 252.

Study Link 9·1 Follow-Up

Have partners compare answers. Ask volunteers to share different solutions for Problems 10–12.

For Problems 13 and 14, you might have students draw number lines and identify the positions of the fractions.

1 Teaching the Lesson

Math Message Follow-Up

WHOLE-CLASS DISCUSSION

(*Math Journal 2,* p. 252)

Remind students that it is easy to rename a fraction as a percent when the denominator is 100. For example, another name for $\frac{32}{100}$ is 32%.

There are other fractions, such as $\frac{1}{2}$, $\frac{1}{4}$, $\frac{1}{5}$, and $\frac{1}{10}$, that can be renamed as percents fairly easily. Knowing such equivalencies often makes percent problems easier to solve. In Problem 1, Alfred missed 50% of 20 problems. To find how many problems he missed, students may think of 50% as $\frac{1}{2}$ and ask themselves, "What is $\frac{1}{2}$ of 20?"

Some students may reason: $\frac{1}{2}$ of the 10-by-10 grid is shaded. That is 50 small squares, or $\frac{50}{100}$, or 0.50, or 50% of the 10-by-10 grid. 50% of 20 is the same as $\frac{1}{2}$ of 20, or 10.

Use the shaded 10-by-10 grid in Problem 1 to help you illustrate equivalent fraction, decimal, and percent names. Point out the following:

▷ The whole is the 20-problem test—100% of the test.

▷ The whole test is represented by the 10-by-10 grid.

▷ The 10-by-10 grid can be divided into 20 equal parts (rectangles), each representing 1 problem on the test.

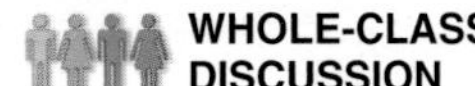

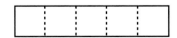

Each rectangle, consisting of 5 small squares, represents 1 problem on the test.

▷ The 10-by-10 grid is also divided into 100 small squares; each small square is $\frac{1}{100}$, or 1%, of the 10-by-10 grid.

Have students solve Problems 2–4 with a partner.

Student Page

Date Time

LESSON 9·2 **"Percent-of" Number Stories**

Alfred, Nadine, Kyla, and Jackson each took the same math test. There were 20 problems on the test.

100%
20-problem test

1. Alfred missed $\frac{1}{2}$ of the problems. He missed 0.50 of the problems. That is 50% of the problems.
How many problems did he miss? 10 problems
$\frac{1}{2}$ of 20 = 10
50% of 20 = 10
$\frac{1}{2}$, or 50% is shaded.

2. Nadine missed $\frac{1}{4}$ of the problems. She missed 0.25 of the problems. That is 25% of the problems.
How many problems did she miss? 5 problems
$\frac{1}{4}$ of 20 = 5
25% of 20 = 5
$\frac{1}{4}$, or 25% is shaded.

3. Kyla missed $\frac{1}{10}$ of the problems. She missed 0.10 of the problems. That is 10% of the problems.
How many problems did she miss? 2 problems
$\frac{1}{10}$ of 20 = 2
10% of 20 = 2
$\frac{1}{10}$, or 10% is shaded.

4. Jackson missed $\frac{1}{5}$ of the problems. He missed 0.20 of the problems. That is 20% of the problems.
How many problems did he miss? 4 problems
$\frac{1}{5}$ of 20 = 4
20% of 20 = 4
$\frac{1}{5}$, or 20% is shaded.

Math Journal 2, p. 252

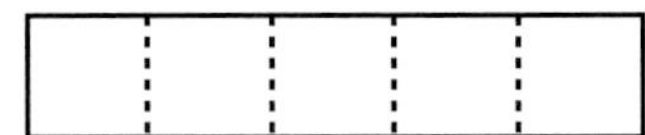

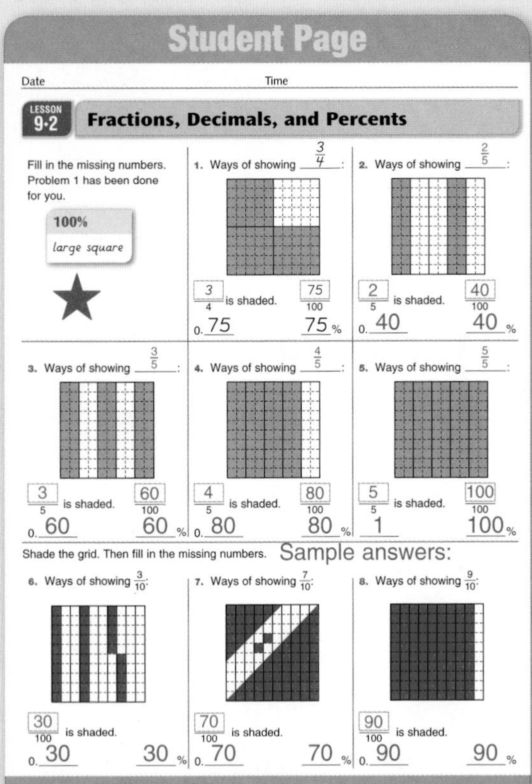

"Easy" Fractions	Decimals	Percents
$\frac{1}{2}$	0.50	50%
$\frac{1}{4}$	0.25	25%
$\frac{3}{4}$	0.75	75%
$\frac{1}{5}$	0.20	20%
$\frac{2}{5}$	0.40	40%
$\frac{3}{5}$	0.60	60%
$\frac{4}{5}$	0.80	80%
$\frac{1}{10}$	0.10	10%
$\frac{3}{10}$	0.30	30%
$\frac{7}{10}$	0.70	70%
$\frac{9}{10}$	0.90	90%

Links to the Future

The ability to use fractions and percents interchangeably will prove useful in later grades when students learn to estimate with percents that are not equivalent to "easy" fractions. For example, by the end of sixth grade, most students should be able to apply the following kind of reasoning: The population of Colombia is about 40 million. About 23% of the population lives in rural areas. Because 23% is equivalent to a little less than $\frac{1}{4}$, and $\frac{1}{4}$ of 40 million is 10 million, about 10 million Colombians live in rural areas.

▶ Finding Equivalent Names for Other "Easy" Fractions

INDEPENDENT ACTIVITY

(*Math Journal 2,* p. 253)

Students find equivalent names for several more "easy" fractions on journal page 253.

Ongoing Assessment: Recognizing Student Achievement

Journal page 253

Use **journal page 253** to assess students' ability to rename fourths, fifths, tenths, and hundredths as decimals and percents. Students are making adequate progress if they are able to fill in the missing numbers and shade the grids. Some students may use shading that involves full and partial squares.

[Number and Numeration Goal 5]

▶ Completing the Table of Equivalent Names for Fractions

INDEPENDENT ACTIVITY

(*Math Journal 2,* pp. 252, 253, 342, and 343)

Ask students to copy the decimal and percent names for the fractions on journal pages 252 and 253 to the table of Equivalent Names for Fractions on journal pages 342 and 343. Students may want to check their answers against the chart on the inside front cover of their journals.

When students have completed this activity, they should have recorded the equivalencies shown in the chart in the margin.

2 Ongoing Learning & Practice

Playing *Rugs and Fences*

PARTNER ACTIVITY

(*Student Reference Book,* pp. 260 and 261; *Math Masters,* pp. 498–502)

Students play *Rugs and Fences* to practice finding the area and perimeter of a polygon. Note that area is reported in square units and perimeter in units. When using Polygon Deck C, students should assume that sides that appear to be the same length are the same length and angles that appear to be right angles are right angles.

Polygon Deck A			Polygon Deck B			Polygon Deck C		
Card	**A**	**P**	**Card**	**A**	**P**	**Card**	**A**	**P**
1	48	28	**17**	35	24	**33**	48	28
2	40	26	**18**	36	26	**34**	22	20
3	20	24	**19**	14	18	**35**	48	36
4	16	20	**20**	60	32	**36**	17	20
5	27	24	**21**	64	32	**37**	28	28
6	49	28	**22**	8	18	**38**	40	36
7	56	30	**23**	36	24	**39**	28	32
8	9	20	**24**	54	30	**40**	24	24
9	24	20	**25**	48	32	**41**	23	26
10	72	34	**26**	6	12	**42**	28	32
11	42	26	**27**	54	36	**43**	86	54
12	63	32	**28**	192	64	**44**	48	32
13	25	20	**29**	32	26	**45**	22	30
14	16	16	**30**	64	36	**46**	48	52
15	28	22	**31**	20	25	**47**	60	32
16	18	18	**32**	216	66	**48**	160	70

Adjusting the Activity

Have students use the following:

- ▷ *Polygon Deck A* to practice counting unit squares and sides of squares to find the area and perimeter of rectangles.
- ▷ *Polygon Deck B* to practice using formulas to find the area and perimeter of rectangles, triangles, and parallelograms.
- ▷ *Polygon Deck C* to practice using combinations of formulas to find the area and perimeter of irregular shapes.

AUDITORY • KINESTHETIC • TACTILE • VISUAL

Student Page

Rugs and Fences

Materials
- ☐ 1 *Rugs and Fences* Polygon Deck A, B, or C (*Math Masters,* page 499, 500, or 501)
- ☐ 1 *Rugs and Fences* Area and Perimeter Deck (*Math Masters,* page 498)
- ☐ 1 *Rugs and Fences* Record Sheet for each player (*Math Masters,* page 502)

Players 2

Skill Calculating area and perimeter

Object of the game To score more points by finding the perimeters and areas of polygons.

Directions

1. Select one of the Polygon Decks—A, B, or C. Shuffle the deck and place it picture-side down on the table. (Variation: Combine 2 or 3 Polygon decks.)
2. Shuffle the deck of Area and Perimeter cards and place it word-side down next to the Polygon Deck.
3. Players take turns. At each turn, a player draws 1 card from each deck and places them faceup on the table. The player finds the area (A) *or* the perimeter (P) of the polygon, as directed by the Area and Perimeter card.
   - ♦ If a "Player's Choice" card is drawn, the *player* may choose to find either the area or the perimeter of the polygon.
   - ♦ If an "Opponent's Choice" card is drawn, the *opposing player* chooses whether the area or the perimeter of the polygon will be found.
4. A player records a turn on his or her Record Sheet. The player records the polygon card number, circles A (area) or P (perimeter), and writes a number model used to calculate the area or perimeter. The solution is the player's score for the round.
5. The player with the higher total score at the end of 8 rounds is the winner.

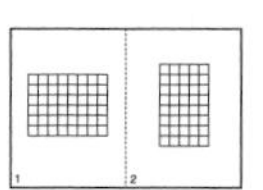

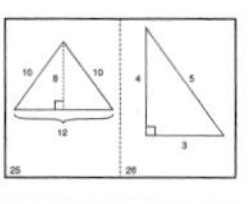

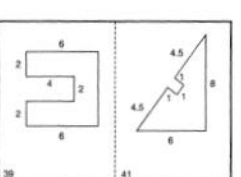

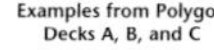
Examples from Polygon Decks A, B, and C

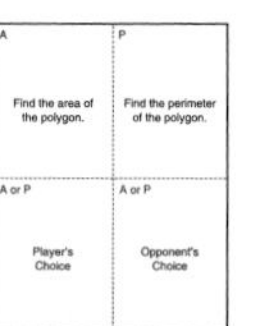

A
Find the area of the polygon.
P
Find the perimeter of the polygon.
A or P
Player's Choice
A or P
Opponent's Choice

There are 4 kinds of Area and Perimeter cards.

***Student Reference Book,* p. 260**

Student Page

Date Time

LESSON 9·2 **Math Boxes**

1. Complete the table with equivalent names.

Fraction	Decimal	Percent
$\frac{1}{5}$	0.20	20%
$\frac{4}{5}$	0.80	80%
$\frac{3}{10}$	0.30	30%
$\frac{9}{10}$	0.90	90%

SRB 61 62

2. About 4.02% of the words on the Internet are *the,* and about 1.68% of the words are *and.* About what percent of all words on the Internet are either *the* or *and?* Choose the best answer.
   - ◯ 5.71%
   - ⬬ 5.7%
   - ◯ 570%
   - ◯ 57%

SRB 34-37

3. Complete.
   - a. 3 yd 2 ft = 11 ft
   - b. 6 yd 1 ft = 19 ft
   - c. 72 in. = 2 yd
   - d. 17 ft = 5 yd 2 ft
   - e. 25 ft = 8 yd 1 ft
   - f. 2 ft 6 in. = 30 in.

SRB 129

4. Zena earned \$12. She spent \$8.
   - a. What fraction of her earnings did she spend? $\frac{8}{12}$, or $\frac{2}{3}$
   - b. What fraction did she have left? $\frac{4}{12}$, or $\frac{1}{3}$
   - c. The amount she spent is how many times as much as the amount she saved? 2 times

SRB 44

5. Find the area and perimeter of the rectangle. Include the correct units.

   7"
   4"

   Area = 28 in^2

   Perimeter = 22 in.

SRB 131 133

6. What temperature is it? −10 °F

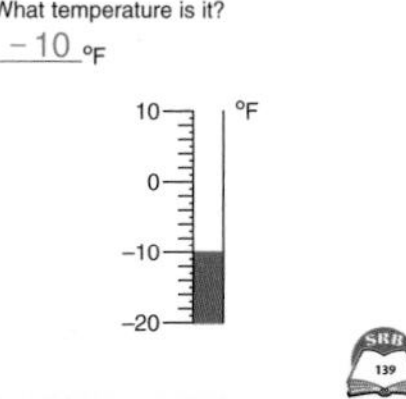

SRB 139

***Math Journal 2,* p. 254**

Study Link Master

Name Date Time

STUDY LINK 9·2 **Coins as Percents of $1**

1. How many pennies in $1? 100 What fraction of $1 is 1 penny? $\frac{1}{100}$
   Write the decimal that shows what part of $1 is 1 penny. 0.01
   What percent of $1 is 1 penny? 1 %
2. How many nickels in $1? 20 What fraction of $1 is 1 nickel? $\frac{1}{20}$, or $\frac{5}{100}$
   Write the decimal that shows what part of $1 is 1 nickel. 0.05
   What percent of $1 is 1 nickel? 5 %
3. How many dimes in $1? 10 What fraction of $1 is 1 dime? $\frac{1}{10}$, or $\frac{10}{100}$
   Write the decimal that shows what part of $1 is 1 dime. 0.10
   What percent of $1 is 1 dime? 10 %
4. How many quarters in $1? 4 What fraction of $1 is 1 quarter? $\frac{1}{4}$, or $\frac{25}{100}$
   Write the decimal that shows what part of $1 is 1 quarter. 0.25
   What percent of $1 is 1 quarter? 25 %
5. How many half-dollars in $1? 2 What fraction of $1 is 1 half-dollar? $\frac{1}{2}$, or $\frac{50}{100}$
   Write the decimal that shows what part of $1 is 1 half-dollar. 0.50
   What percent of $1 is 1 half-dollar? 50 %
6. Three quarters (75¢) is $\frac{3}{4}$ of $1.
   Write the decimal. 0.75
   What percent of $1 is 3 quarters? 75 %
7. Two dimes (20¢) is $\frac{2}{10}$ of $1.
   Write the decimal. 0.20
   What percent of $1 is 2 dimes? 20 %

Practice

8. 4,488 = 748 ∗ 6
9. 51 ∗ 90 = 4,590
10. 25,284 = 28 ∗ 903

Math Masters, p. 282

▶ Math Boxes 9·2

(*Math Journal 2,* p. 254)

Mixed Practice Math Boxes in this lesson are paired with Math Boxes in Lesson 9-4. The skill in Problem 6 previews Unit 10 content.

Writing/Reasoning Have students write a response to the following: *Suppose you tripled the lengths of the sides of the rectangle in Problem 5. What would happen to the area of the rectangle?* Sample answer: The area of the new rectangle would be 252 in^2. It would be 9 times as large as the area of the original rectangle.

▶ Study Link 9·2

(*Math Masters,* p. 282)

Home Connection For each of several coins, students identify what fraction of $1, decimal part of $1, and percent of $1 that coin represents.

3 Differentiation Options

READINESS

▶ Exploring Percent Patterns

(*Math Masters,* p. 283)

To explore the relationship between fractions and percents, have students identify and use patterns to solve percent problems. Ask students to describe how they used the patterns. *For example:*

If there are 20 per 100, then there are

- ▷ 2 per 10. 10 is $\frac{1}{10}$ of 100. $\frac{1}{10}$ of 20 is 2, so 20 per 100 is the same as 2 per 10.
- ▷ 200 per 1,000. 1,000 is 10 times as much as 100. 10 times 20 is 200, so 20 per 100 is the same as 200 per 1,000.
- ▷ 4 per 20. $\frac{2}{10}, \frac{20}{100}, \frac{200}{1,000}$ are all names for $\frac{1}{5}$. 4 is $\frac{1}{5}$ of 20, so 4 per 20 is the same as 20 per 100.
- ▷ 40 per 200. $\frac{40}{200} = \frac{1}{5}$

Teaching Master

Name Date Time

LESSON 9·2 **Percent Patterns**

Complete each set of statements. Use grids or base-10 blocks, or draw pictures to help you. Look for patterns in your answers.

Example:

50% is the same as 50 per 100.
If there are 50 per 100, then there are
5 per 10. 500 per 1,000.
10 per 20. 100 per 200.

1. 20% is the same as 20 per 100.
   If there are 20 per 100, then there are
   2 per 10. 200 per 1,000.
   4 per 20. 40 per 200.
2. 30% is the same as 30 per 100.
   If there are 30 per 100, then there are
   3 per 10. 300 per 1,000.
   6 per 20. 60 per 200.
3. 80% is the same as 80 per 100.
   If there are 80 per 100, then there are
   8 per 10. 800 per 1,000.
   16 per 20. 160 per 200.
4. 60% is the same as 60 per 100.
   If there are 60 per 100, then there are
   6 per 10. 600 per 1,000.
   12 per 20. 120 per 200.

Try This

5. 75% is the same as 75 per 100.
   If there are 75 per 100, then there are
   7.5 per 10. 750 per 1,000.
   15 per 20. 150 per 200.
6. 120% is the same as 120 per 100.
   If there are 120 per 100, then there are
   12 per 10. 1,200 per 1,000.
   24 per 20. 240 per 200.

Math Masters, p. 283

ENRICHMENT

PARTNER ACTIVITY

Writing and Solving "Percent-of" Number Stories

15–30 Min

ELL

To apply students' understanding of fraction and percent equivalencies, have them write, illustrate, and solve "percent-of" number stories. Ask students to exchange stories with a partner, revise if necessary, and solve.

To support English language learners, provide an opportunity for students to share and revise their writing. *For example:*

▷ Read problems aloud or have students read their own problems aloud.

▷ Have students read and comment on each other's drafts.

EXTRA PRACTICE

PARTNER ACTIVITY

Adding Tenths and Hundredths

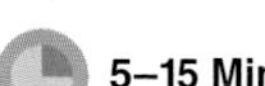
5–15 Min

(*Math Masters,* pp. 283A, 283B, and 426)

To practice adding fractions with 10 and 100 in the denominator, have students shade grids or use base-10 blocks to find the sums. Students may want to use longs and cubes to model the problem.

EXTRA PRACTICE

INDEPENDENT ACTIVITY

Finding Equivalent Names for Fractions

5–15 Min

(*Math Masters,* p. 445)

To practice finding equivalent decimals and percents for fractions, have students shade grids and fill in the missing numbers. Use *Math Masters,* page 445 to create problems to meet the needs of individual students, or have students create and solve their own problems.

Teaching Master

Name ______ Date ______ Time ______

LESSON 9•2 **Adding Tenths and Hundredths**

You can use base-10 blocks to model adding fractions with 10 and 100 in the denominator.

Use a long | to represent $\frac{1}{10}$.

Use a cube ▪ to represent $\frac{1}{100}$.

Example: $\frac{3}{10} + \frac{23}{100} = \frac{53}{100}$

||| + ||▪▪▪

Model the problems with longs and cubes. Record your answer.

1. $\frac{5}{10} + \frac{16}{100} = \frac{66}{100}$

||||| + | • • • • • •

2. $\frac{2}{100} + \frac{8}{10} = \frac{82}{100}$

• • + ||||||||

3. Write your own problem. Have your partner solve it and record the answer.

Solve. You may use base-10 blocks or any other method.

4. $\frac{34}{100} + \frac{17}{100} = \frac{51}{100}$
5. $\frac{55}{100} + \frac{25}{100} = \frac{80}{100}$
6. $\frac{33}{100} + \frac{4}{10} = \frac{73}{100}$
7. $\frac{9}{100} + \frac{7}{10} = \frac{79}{100}$

Math Masters, p. 283A

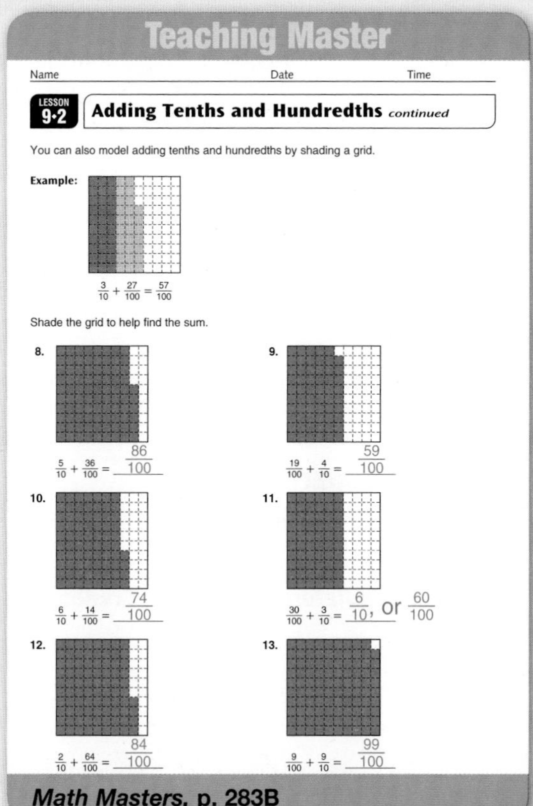
Teaching Master

Name ______ Date ______ Time ______

LESSON 9•2 **Adding Tenths and Hundredths** *continued*

You can also model adding tenths and hundredths by shading a grid.

Example: $\frac{3}{10} + \frac{27}{100} = \frac{57}{100}$

Shade the grid to help find the sum.

8. $\frac{5}{10} + \frac{36}{100} = \frac{86}{100}$
9. $\frac{19}{100} + \frac{4}{10} = \frac{59}{100}$
10. $\frac{6}{10} + \frac{14}{100} = \frac{74}{100}$
11. $\frac{30}{100} + \frac{3}{10} = \frac{6}{10}$, or $\frac{60}{100}$
12. $\frac{2}{10} + \frac{64}{100} = \frac{84}{100}$
13. $\frac{9}{100} + \frac{9}{10} = \frac{99}{100}$

Math Masters, p. 283B

9•3 Using a Calculator to Convert Fractions to Decimals

Objectives To introduce renaming any fraction as a decimal by using a calculator; and to reinforce fraction/percent equivalencies for fourths, fifths, and tenths.

Technology Resources www.everydaymathonline.com

ePresentations

eToolkit

Algorithms Practice

EM Facts Workshop Game™

Family Letters

Assessment Management

Common Core State Standards

Curriculum Focal Points

Interactive Teacher's Lesson Guide

1 Teaching the Lesson

Key Concepts and Skills

- Explore terminating and repeating decimals. [Number and Numeration Goal 5]
- Use a calculator to rename fractions as decimals. [Number and Numeration Goal 5]
- Describe patterns in terminating and repeating decimals. [Patterns, Functions, and Algebra Goal 1]

Key Activities

Students rename fractions as decimals by dividing on their calculators. Students observe that the decimal equivalent to a fraction is either a terminating decimal or a repeating decimal.

Ongoing Assessment: Recognizing Student Achievement Use Mental Math and Reflexes. [Number and Numeration Goal 5]

Key Vocabulary

terminating decimal ◆ repeating decimal

Materials

Math Journal 2, pp. 342 and 343
Study Link 9•2
Math Masters, p. 388 or 389
calculator ◆ slate

2 Ongoing Learning & Practice

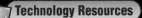

Playing *Fraction/Percent Concentration*
Student Reference Book, p. 246
Math Masters, pp. 481 and 482
calculator ◆ scissors
Students practice "easy" fraction/percent equivalencies.

Math Boxes 9•3
Math Journal 2, p. 255
Students practice and maintain skills through Math Box problems.

Study Link 9•3
Math Masters, p. 284
Students practice and maintain skills through Study Link activities.

3 Differentiation Options

ENRICHMENT
Finding Decimals Close to "Easy" Fractions
Math Masters, p. 388 or 389
Students name "easy" fractions and mixed numbers that are close but not equivalent to given decimals.

EXTRA PRACTICE
Memorizing Equivalent Names for "Easy" Fractions
Math Masters, p. 446
scissors
Students use flash cards to help each other memorize equivalent names for fractions, decimals, and percents.

Advance Preparation

For Part 2, consider copying the *Fraction/Percent Concentration* Cards (*Math Masters,* pages 481 and 482) on cardstock.

***Teacher's Reference Manual,* Grades 4–6** pp. 29–35, 62, 63, 149, 150, 153, 154

Getting Started

Mental Math and Reflexes ★

Write fractions on the board. For each fraction, students write the equivalent decimal and percent on their slates. Have students explain their strategies for the ●●● problems.

Suggestions:

●○○ $\frac{41}{100}$ 0.41, 41%
$\frac{93}{100}$ 0.93, 93%
$\frac{9}{10}$ 0.9, 90%
$\frac{6}{100}$ 0.06, 6%

●●○ $\frac{1}{4}$ 0.25, 25%
$\frac{3}{4}$ 0.75, 75%
$\frac{1}{5}$ 0.20, 20%
$\frac{4}{5}$ 0.80, 80%

●●● $\frac{4}{2}$ 2, 200%
$\frac{1}{20}$ 0.05, 5%
$\frac{11}{20}$ 0.55, 55%
$\frac{9}{25}$ 0.36, 36%

Math Message

Use your calculator to divide the numerators of the following fractions by the denominators: $\frac{1}{2}$, $\frac{3}{4}$, $\frac{4}{5}$, and $\frac{6}{10}$. What do you notice?

Study Link 9·2 Follow-Up

Have students compare answers and discuss the fractions they chose. For example, a nickel could be represented by $\frac{5}{100}$ or $\frac{1}{20}$. Have them consider which form they might find more helpful to figure decimals and percents.

Ongoing Assessment: Recognizing Student Achievement

Mental Math and Reflexes ★

Use **Mental Math and Reflexes** to assess students' ability to rename fourths, fifths, tenths, and hundredths as decimals and percents. Students are making adequate progress if they are able to answer the ●○○ and ●●○ problems correctly. Some students may be able to solve the ●●● problems.

[Number and Numeration Goal 5]

1 Teaching the Lesson

▶ Math Message Follow-Up

WHOLE-CLASS ACTIVITY

(*Math Journal 2,* pp. 342 and 343)

Have volunteers share their observations. One possible answer is:

▷ The number on the calculator display is the decimal name for the fraction. For example, 1 divided by 2 = 0.5. This is the decimal name for $\frac{1}{2}$.

Have students turn to journal pages 342 and 343 to verify that these are the correct decimal names for the fractions.

Help students summarize: One way to rename a fraction as a decimal is to divide its numerator by its denominator.

Tell students that in this lesson they will practice using a calculator to rename any fraction as a decimal.

Student Page

Games

Fraction/Percent Concentration

Materials □ 1 set of Fraction/Percent Tiles (*Math Masters,* pp. 481 and 482)
□ 1 calculator

Players 2 or 3

Skill Recognizing fractions and percents that are equivalent

Object of the game To collect the most tiles by matching equivalent fraction and percent tiles.

Directions

Advance Preparation Before beginning the game, write the letter "F" on the back of each fraction tile. And write the letter "P" on the back of each percent tile.

1. Spread the tiles out number-side down on the table. Create 2 separate piles—a fraction pile and a percent pile. Mix up the tiles in each pile. The 12 fraction tiles should have the letter "F" showing. The 12 percent tiles should have the letter "P" showing.
2. Players take turns. At each turn, a player turns over both a fraction tile and a percent tile. If the fraction and the percent are equivalent, the player keeps the tiles. If the fraction and the percent are not equivalent, the player turns the tiles number-side down.
3. Players may use a calculator to check each other's matches.
4. The game ends when all tiles have been taken. The player with the most tiles wins.

Variations Write the letter "D" on the back of each decimal tile. Play the game using only the "F" and "D" tiles. Or, play the game using only the "P" and "D" tiles.

10%	20%	25%	30%
40%	50%	60%	70%
75%	80%	90%	100%
$\frac{1}{2}$	$\frac{1}{4}$	$\frac{3}{4}$	$\frac{1}{5}$
$\frac{2}{5}$	$\frac{3}{5}$	$\frac{4}{5}$	$\frac{1}{10}$
$\frac{3}{10}$	$\frac{7}{10}$	$\frac{9}{10}$	$\frac{2}{2}$

Fraction/Percent Tiles (number-side up)

Student Reference Book, p. 246

Game Master

Name Date Time

Fraction/Percent Concentration

10%	20%	25%	30%
40%	50%	60%	70%
75%	80%	90%	100%
$\frac{1}{2}$	$\frac{1}{4}$	$\frac{3}{4}$	$\frac{1}{5}$
$\frac{2}{5}$	$\frac{3}{5}$	$\frac{4}{5}$	$\frac{1}{10}$
$\frac{3}{10}$	$\frac{7}{10}$	$\frac{9}{10}$	$\frac{2}{2}$

Math Masters, p. 481

▶ Using a Calculator to Rename Any Fraction as a Decimal

INDEPENDENT ACTIVITY

(*Math Journal 2,* pp. 342 and 343; *Math Masters,* p. 388 or 389)

Ask students to rename each fraction on journal pages 342 and 343 as a decimal by using division. Tell them to write each digit shown in the calculator display, up to 6 digits following the decimal point.

When they have finished, ask students to look for patterns in the results and write about them in a Math Log or on an Exit Slip. *For example:*

- Some of the fractions have short decimal names with 1, 2, or 3 digits after the decimal point and no other digits beyond that. What do these fractions with short decimal names have in common? They are fractions whose denominators are 2, 4, 5, 8, and 10.
- The other fractions have long decimal names that look like they could go on forever if the calculator display could show an endless number of digits. Do you see any patterns in these longer decimal names? If you read the digits from left to right, you come to a digit that seems to repeat forever. For example, $\frac{7}{12}$ has the decimal name 0.5833333333; if you could see more decimal places, they would all be 3s.

Links to the Future

When a fraction is renamed as a decimal, it will be either a **terminating decimal** or a **repeating decimal.** A repeating decimal is one in which a digit or group of digits is repeated endlessly. It is not necessary to use this vocabulary with students. The topic of terminating and repeating decimals will be discussed in later grades. The activity here should be viewed as an exploration of a topic that will be treated formally later.

2 Ongoing Learning & Practice

▶ Playing *Fraction/Percent Concentration*

PARTNER ACTIVITY

(*Student Reference Book,* p. 246; *Math Masters,* pp. 481 and 482)

Students play *Fraction/Percent Concentration* to develop automaticity with the "easy" fraction/percent equivalencies. Have students write P on the back of each percent tile, F on the back of each fraction tile, and D on the back of each decimal tile.

Adjusting the Activity

Have students play with fewer fraction/percent pairs or play with the cards faceup.

Have students play the game using only the Fraction Tiles and the Decimal Tiles (*Math Masters,* page 482).

AUDITORY ◆ KINESTHETIC ◆ TACTILE ◆ VISUAL

Math Boxes 9◆3

INDEPENDENT ACTIVITY

(*Math Journal 2,* p. 255)

Mixed Practice Math Boxes in this lesson are paired with Math Boxes in Lesson 9-1. The skill in Problem 6 previews Unit 10 content.

Portfolio Ideas

Writing/Reasoning Have students write a response to the following: *Mario said, "Without using a protractor, I estimated that the measure of ∠RLA in Problem 5 was about 45°." Explain how Mario might have estimated the measure.* Sample answer: A right angle measures 90°. Angle *RLA* looks like it is about $\frac{1}{2}$ the size of a right angle, and $\frac{1}{2}$ of 90° is 45°.

Study Link 9◆3

INDEPENDENT ACTIVITY

(*Math Masters,* p. 284)

Home Connection Students use a calculator to convert fractions to decimals and make up some conversion problems of their own.

Study Link Master

Name Date Time

STUDY LINK 9◆3 **Calculator Decimals** SRB 206 207

1. Use your calculator to rename each fraction below as a decimal.

Fraction	Decimal	Fraction	Decimal
$\frac{1}{2}$	0.5	$\frac{1}{14}$	0.071428
$\frac{1}{3}$	0.333333	$\frac{1}{15}$	0.066666
$\frac{1}{4}$	0.25	$\frac{1}{16}$	0.0625
$\frac{1}{5}$	0.2	$\frac{1}{17}$	0.058823
$\frac{1}{6}$	0.166666	$\frac{1}{18}$	0.055555
$\frac{1}{7}$	0.142857	$\frac{1}{19}$	0.052631
$\frac{1}{8}$	0.125	$\frac{1}{20}$	0.05
$\frac{1}{9}$	0.111111	$\frac{1}{21}$	0.047619
$\frac{1}{10}$	0.1	$\frac{1}{22}$	0.045454
$\frac{1}{11}$	0.090909	$\frac{1}{23}$	0.043478
$\frac{1}{12}$	0.083333	$\frac{1}{24}$	0.041666
$\frac{1}{13}$	0.076923	$\frac{1}{25}$	0.04

2. Make up some of your own. Answers vary.

Fraction	Decimal	Fraction	Decimal
$\frac{1}{73}$	0.013698	$\frac{1}{}$	
$\frac{1}{}$		$\frac{1}{}$	
$\frac{1}{}$		$\frac{1}{}$	

Practice

3. 6)96 = 16

4. 91 / 5 = 18 R1, or $18\frac{1}{5}$

5. 108 = 864 ÷ 8

6. 575 ÷ 7 = 82 R1, or $82\frac{1}{7}$

Math Masters, p. 284

Game Master

Name Date Time

Fraction/Percent Concentration continued SRB 246

0.10	0.20	0.25	0.30
0.40	0.50	0.60	0.70
0.80	0.75	0.90	1

0.10	0.20	0.25	0.30
0.40	0.50	0.60	0.70
0.80	0.75	0.90	1

Math Masters, p. 482

Math Masters, page 482 provides two sets of decimal cards. Each student needs only one set.

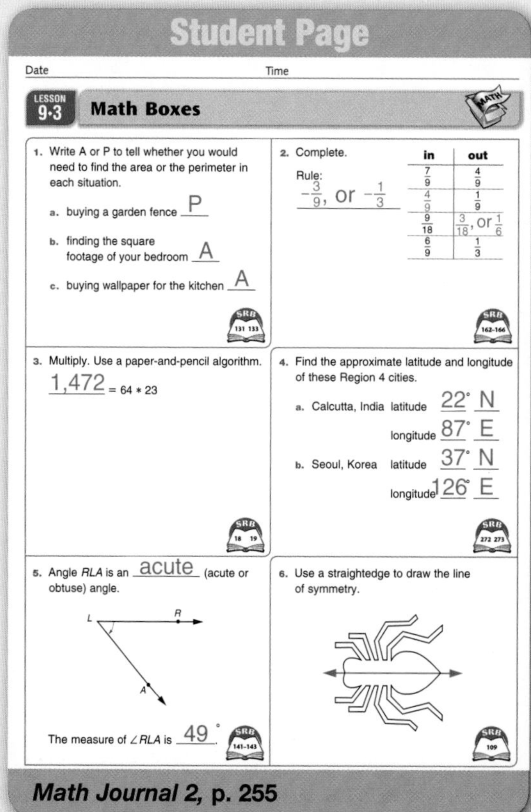

Student Page

Date Time

LESSON 9◆3 **Math Boxes**

1. Write A or P to tell whether you would need to find the area or the perimeter in each situation.
   a. buying a garden fence P
   b. finding the square footage of your bedroom A
   c. buying wallpaper for the kitchen A

SRB 131 133

2. Complete.

Rule: $-\frac{3}{9}$, or $-\frac{1}{3}$

in	out
$\frac{7}{9}$	$\frac{4}{9}$
$\frac{4}{9}$	$\frac{1}{9}$
$\frac{9}{18}$	$\frac{3}{18}$, or $\frac{1}{6}$
$\frac{6}{9}$	$\frac{1}{3}$

SRB 162-164

3. Multiply. Use a paper-and-pencil algorithm.
1,472 = 64 * 23

SRB 18 19

4. Find the approximate latitude and longitude of these Region 4 cities.
   a. Calcutta, India latitude 22° N longitude 87° E
   b. Seoul, Korea latitude 37° N longitude 126° E

SRB 272 273

5. Angle *RLA* is an acute (acute or obtuse) angle.

The measure of ∠*RLA* is 49 °

SRB 141-143

6. Use a straightedge to draw the line of symmetry.

SRB 109

Math Journal 2, p. 255

3 Differentiation Options

ENRICHMENT

▶ Finding Decimals Close to "Easy" Fractions

(*Math Masters,* p. 388 or 389)

To apply students' understanding of decimal/fraction equivalencies, have them name "easy" fractions that are close but not equivalent to given decimals.

Write decimals on the board. In a Math Log or on an Exit Slip, have students write a decimal number that is close to the given decimal and has an "easy" fraction equivalent. Ask students to explain their choice. Students may choose different close decimals. Ask them to decide which is closer. *Suggestions:*

Sample answers:

- 1.77 1.75, $1\frac{3}{4}$
- 0.836 0.8, $\frac{8}{10}$
- 2.59 2.5, $2\frac{1}{2}$
- 0.098 0.1, $\frac{1}{10}$
- 4.287 4.25, $4\frac{1}{4}$
- 0.617 0.6, $\frac{6}{10}$, or $\frac{3}{5}$

EXTRA PRACTICE

▶ Memorizing Equivalent Names for "Easy" Fractions

5–15 Min

(*Math Masters,* p. 446)

To practice "easy" fraction, decimal, and percent equivalencies, have students cut out and use the cards on *Math Masters,* page 446.

Instruct students to place the cards facedown in a pile between them. Partners take turns. One student picks up a card and covers one of the equivalent names with a thumb. The other student must identify the hidden number.

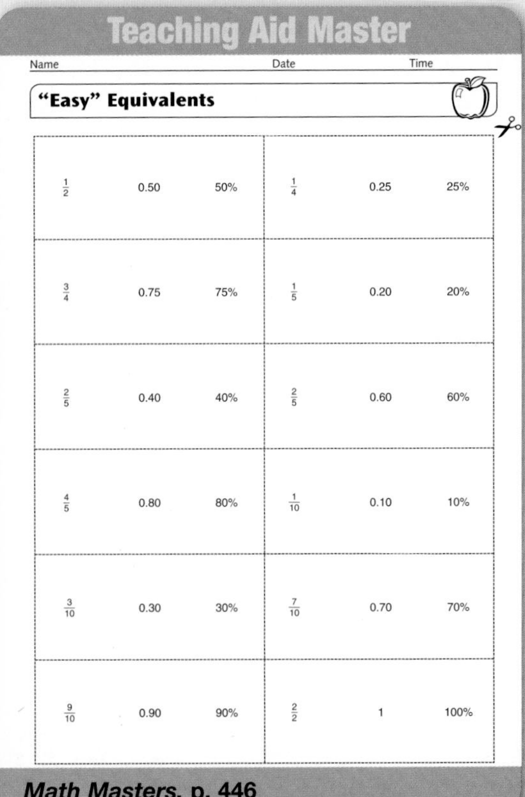

Teaching Aid Master

Name Date Time

"Easy" Equivalents

$\frac{1}{2}$	0.50	50%	$\frac{1}{4}$	0.25	25%
$\frac{3}{4}$	0.75	75%	$\frac{1}{5}$	0.20	20%
$\frac{2}{5}$	0.40	40%	$\frac{2}{5}$	0.60	60%
$\frac{4}{5}$	0.80	80%	$\frac{1}{10}$	0.10	10%
$\frac{3}{10}$	0.30	30%	$\frac{7}{10}$	0.70	70%
$\frac{9}{10}$	0.90	90%	$\frac{2}{2}$	1	100%

Math Masters, p. 446

9•4 Using a Calculator to Rename Fractions as Percents

Objectives To reinforce renaming fractions as percents using a calculator; and to introduce solving number stories involving discounts expressed as percents.

Technology Resources www.everydaymathonline.com

ePresentations

eToolkit

Algorithms Practice

EM Facts Workshop Game™

Family Letters

Assessment Management

Common Core State Standards

Curriculum Focal Points

Interactive Teacher's Lesson Guide

1 Teaching the Lesson

Key Concepts and Skills

- Solve number stories involving discounts. [Number and Numeration Goal 2]
- Name the whole, or the ONE. [Number and Numeration Goal 2]
- Use a calculator to rename fractions as percents. [Number and Numeration Goal 5]
- Rename any decimal as a percent. [Number and Numeration Goal 5]

Key Activities

Students use the percent key on a calculator to rename fractions as percents. They rename fractions as decimals by dividing, and they are shown that a decimal can be easily renamed as a percent by multiplying it by 100. Students solve number stories involving discounts expressed as percents.

Ongoing Assessment: Informing Instruction See page 740.

Key Vocabulary

regular price ◆ list price ◆ discount ◆ percent of discount ◆ fraction of discount ◆ sale price ◆ discounted price

Materials

Math Journal 2, pp. 256 and 257
Study Link 9•3
calculator ◆ overhead calculator (optional) ◆ slate

2 Ongoing Learning & Practice

Creating a Bar Graph

Math Journal 2, p. 258
Student Reference Book, p. 302
Students create a bar graph using cellular-telephone-use data.

Math Boxes 9•4

Math Journal 2, p. 259
Students practice and maintain skills through Math Box problems.

Ongoing Assessment: Recognizing Student Achievement
Use Math Boxes, Problem 4.
[Number and Numeration Goal 2]

Study Link 9•4

Math Masters, p. 285
Students practice and maintain skills through Study Link activities.

3 Differentiation Options

READINESS

Solving "Percent-of" Problems

Math Masters, p. 286
counters
Students use counters to solve "percent-of" problems.

ENRICHMENT

Solving Discount Number Stories

Math Masters, p. 287
Students solve number stories in which they compare discounts for two items.

EXTRA PRACTICE

5-Minute Math

5-Minute Math™, pp. 103, 179, 187, and 196
Students practice solving problems involving percents.

ELL SUPPORT

Building Background for Mathematics Words

store catalogs or advertisements
Students discuss vocabulary used in discount number stories.

Advance Preparation

***Teacher's Reference Manual,* Grades 4–6** pp. 29–35, 69–71, 149, 150, 153, 154

Getting Started

Mental Math and Reflexes

Pose "percent-of" problems. Have students explain their strategies. *Suggestions:*

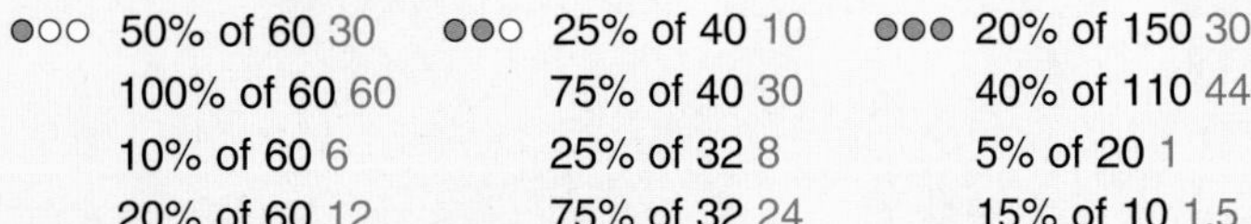

●○○	●●○	●●●
50% of 60 30	25% of 40 10	20% of 150 30
100% of 60 60	75% of 40 30	40% of 110 44
10% of 60 6	25% of 32 8	5% of 20 1
20% of 60 12	75% of 32 24	15% of 10 1.5

Math Message

Experiment with the percent key on your calculator. Find a way to rename $\frac{1}{4}$ as a percent. Write your method on a half sheet of paper.

Study Link 9·3 Follow-Up

Have students compare answers. Ask volunteers to share some of the problems they made up.

Student Page

Date Time

LESSON 9·4 **Discount Number Stories**

1. A store is offering a **discount** of 10% on all items. This means that you save $\frac{1}{10}$ of the **regular price.** Find the sale price of each item below. The **sale price** is the amount you pay after subtracting the discount from the regular price.

Item	Regular Price	Discount (10% of regular price)	Sale Price (Subtract: regular price – discount)
CD player	$140	$14	$126
Giant screen TV	$1,200	$120	$1,080
Radio	$80	$8	$72
DVD player	$30	$3	$27

2. Use a drawing and number models to explain how you found the discount and sale price for the radio.
Sample answer: 10% is $\frac{1}{10}$. Cut $80 into 10 parts. 10% of $80 is $8. $\frac{9}{10}$ is left. 9 * $8 = $72.

Sample picture:
$80
90% 10%

3. An airline offers a 25% discount on the regular airfare for tickets purchased at least 1 month in advance. Find the sale price of each ticket below.

Regular Airfare	Discount (25% of regular airfare)	Sale Price (Subtract: regular airfare – discount)
$400	$100	$300
$240	$60	$180
$300	$75	$225

4. Use a drawing and number models to explain how you found the regular airfare when you knew $75 was 25% of the regular airfare.
Sample answer: 25% = $\frac{1}{4}$. If $\frac{1}{4}$ = $75, then $\frac{4}{4}$ = 4 * $75, or $300.

Sample picture:

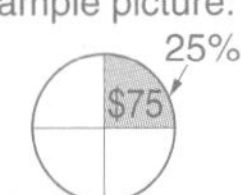

Math Journal 2, p. 256

1 Teaching the Lesson

▶ Math Message Follow-Up

Use an overhead calculator (if available) to demonstrate how to use the percent key to rename fractions as percents. Write the keystrokes on the board to support English language learners. Then have students practice with a few "easy" fractions.

TI-15: 1 (÷) 4 (%) (Enter) Display: 25

Casio *fx*-55: 1 (÷) 4 (%) Display: 25

The percent key does NOT have to be used to rename fractions as percents. Remind students that they can convert any fraction to a decimal by dividing the numerator by the denominator. Once they have the decimal name, it is easy to write the percent name.

▷ To rename $\frac{1}{4}$ as a percent, divide 1 by 4 to get 0.25. This is $\frac{25}{100}$, or 25%.

▷ To rename $\frac{33}{75}$ as a percent, divide 33 by 75 to get 0.44. This is $\frac{44}{100}$, or 44%.

You can use this rule to rename any decimal as a percent: To convert a decimal to a percent, multiply the decimal by 100.

Decimal	100 * decimal	Percent
0.67	67	67%
0.375	37.5	37.5%
0.1666	16.66	16.66%

Ongoing Assessment: Informing Instruction

Watch for students who notice a pattern when multiplying a decimal by 100. Ask them to explain why the decimal moves two places to the right.

Solving Number Stories Involving Discounts

PARTNER ACTIVITY

(*Math Journal 2,* pp. 256 and 257)

Consumer Link Tell students that in this lesson they will use their calculators and mental arithmetic to solve discount number stories. Have students work in partnerships to complete journal pages 256 and 257.

Adjusting the Activity

Rephrase or illustrate the last rows in the tables in Problems 1 and 2 as follows:

Problem 1: If \$3 is $\frac{1}{10}$ of the whole, what is the whole? The whole is $\frac{10}{10}$, which is 10 times as much as $\frac{1}{10}$. So 10 ∗ \$3 = \$30.

Problem 2: If \$75 is 25%, or $\frac{1}{4}$ of the whole, what is the whole? The whole is $\frac{4}{4}$, which is 4 times as much as $\frac{1}{4}$. So 4 ∗ \$75 = \$300.

AUDITORY ◆ KINESTHETIC ◆ TACTILE ◆ VISUAL

When students have completed journal pages 256 and 257, use Problem 5 to demonstrate how to use the percent key to find the discount and the sale price.

TI-15:

Discount: 400 [×] 30 [%] [Enter] Display: 120

Sale price: 400 [−] 400 [×] 30 [%] [Enter] Display: 280

Casio *fx*-55:

Discount: 400 [×] 30 [%] Display: 120

Sale price: 400 [×] 30 [%] [−] Display: 280

Links to the Future

Solving problems involving percents and discounts is a Grade 5 Goal.

2 Ongoing Learning & Practice

Creating a Bar Graph

INDEPENDENT ACTIVITY

(*Math Journal 2,* p. 258; *Student Reference Book,* p. 302)

Students create a bar graph to display cellular-telephone-use data.

Student Page

Date Time

LESSON 9•4 **Discount Number Stories** *continued*

5. The regular price of a swing set is \$400. Mrs. Lefevre received a 30% discount because she ordered it during the Big Spring Sale.

a. How much did she save? \$120

b. How much did she pay? \$280

c. Explain how you solved the problem. Sample answer: If the discount is 10%, then 10%, or $\frac{1}{10}$, of \$400 is \$40. A 30% discount is 3 times as much as a 10% discount, so 3 ∗ \$40 = \$120. Then I subtracted \$120 from \$400 and got \$280.

Try This

6. You can pay for a refrigerator by making 12 payments of \$50 each. Or you can save 25% if you pay for it all at once.

a. How much will the refrigerator cost if you pay for it all at once? \$450

b. Explain how you solved the problem. Sample answer: If I make payments, it will cost 12 ∗ \$50, which is \$600. Paying for it all at once, I'll get a 25% discount. 25% is $\frac{1}{4}$ of \$600, or \$150. Then I subtracted \$150 from \$600 and got \$450.

7. Write your own discount number story. Ask a partner to solve it.

Answers vary.

Math Journal 2, p. 257

Student Page

Date Time

LESSON 9•4 **Cellular Telephone Use**

1. Use the "Subscriptions per 100 People" data in the Cellular Telephone Use table at the bottom of *Student Reference Book,* page 302 to complete the bar graph. Round each decimal to the nearest whole number.

Cellular Telephone Use

Subscriptions per 100 People: 90, 92, 94, 96, 98, 100, 102, 104, 106, 108, 110, 112

Countries: Taiwan, Luxembourg, Italy, Iceland, Israel, Spain

2. Write a question that can be answered by looking at the data displayed in the bar graph. Answer the question.

Answers vary.

Math Journal 2, p. 258

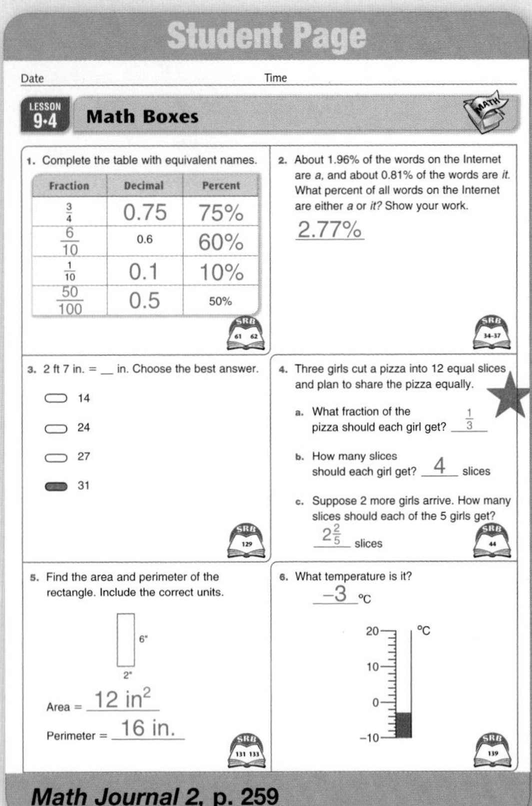

Student Page

Date Time

LESSON 9·4 **Math Boxes**

1. Complete the table with equivalent names.

Fraction	Decimal	Percent
$\frac{3}{4}$	0.75	75%
$\frac{6}{10}$	0.6	60%
$\frac{1}{10}$	0.1	10%
$\frac{50}{100}$	0.5	50%

2. About 1.96% of the words on the Internet are *a*, and about 0.81% of the words are *it*. What percent of all words on the Internet are either *a* or *it*? Show your work.
2.77%

3. 2 ft 7 in. = __ in. Choose the best answer.
- 14
- 24
- 27
- 31

4. Three girls cut a pizza into 12 equal slices and plan to share the pizza equally.
a. What fraction of the pizza should each girl get? $\frac{1}{3}$
b. How many slices should each girl get? 4 slices
c. Suppose 2 more girls arrive. How many slices should each of the 5 girls get? $2\frac{2}{5}$ slices

5. Find the area and perimeter of the rectangle. Include the correct units.
6"
2"
Area = 12 in^2
Perimeter = 16 in.

6. What temperature is it?
−3 °C
20 10 0 −10 °C

Math Journal 2, p. 259

▶ Math Boxes 9·4

INDEPENDENT ACTIVITY

(*Math Journal 2,* p. 259)

Mixed Practice Math Boxes in this lesson are paired with Math Boxes in Lesson 9-2. The skill in Problem 6 previews Unit 10 content.

Writing/Reasoning Have students write a response to the following: *Explain how you found the number of inches in Problem 3.* Sample answer: I know there are 12 inches in a foot, so 2 feet = 24 inches. Then I added 24 to the 7 inches. 24 + 7 = 31

Ongoing Assessment: Recognizing Student Achievement

Math Boxes Problem 4

Use **Math Boxes, Problem 4** to assess students' ability to solve "fraction-of" problems. Students are making adequate progress if they are able to identify the fraction of the pizza each girl gets and the number of slices. Some students may be able to determine the number of slices each girl would get if two more girls arrived and explain how they got their answers.

[Number and Numeration Goal 2]

▶ Study Link 9·4

INDEPENDENT ACTIVITY

(*Math Masters,* p. 285)

Home Connection Students rename fractions as percents with and without a calculator. Note that in Problems 9, 12, and 17, students will have to write the percent using a decimal.

NOTE For Problems 18–20, you might have students draw number lines and identify the positions of the fractions.

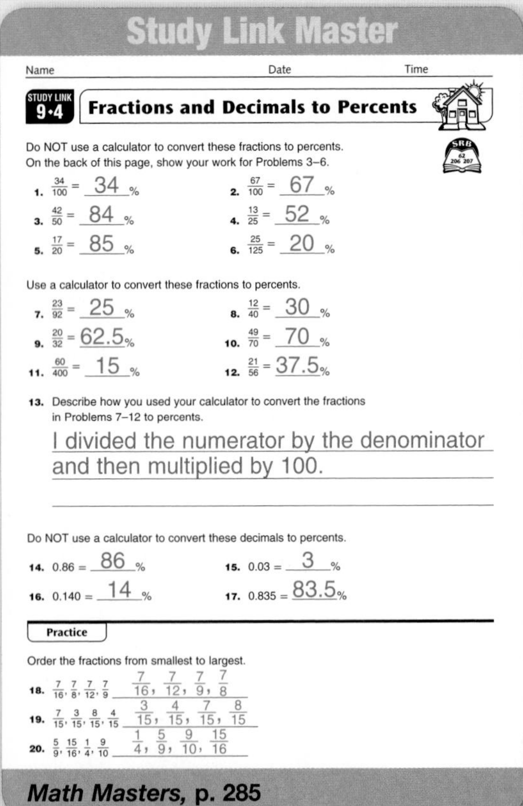

Study Link Master

Name Date Time

STUDY LINK 9·4 **Fractions and Decimals to Percents**

Do NOT use a calculator to convert these fractions to percents. On the back of this page, show your work for Problems 3–6.

1. $\frac{34}{100}$ = 34 %
2. $\frac{67}{100}$ = 67 %
3. $\frac{42}{50}$ = 84 %
4. $\frac{13}{25}$ = 52 %
5. $\frac{17}{20}$ = 85 %
6. $\frac{25}{125}$ = 20 %

Use a calculator to convert these fractions to percents.

7. $\frac{23}{92}$ = 25 %
8. $\frac{12}{40}$ = 30 %
9. $\frac{20}{32}$ = 62.5 %
10. $\frac{49}{70}$ = 70 %
11. $\frac{60}{400}$ = 15 %
12. $\frac{21}{56}$ = 37.5 %

13. Describe how you used your calculator to convert the fractions in Problems 7–12 to percents.
I divided the numerator by the denominator and then multiplied by 100.

Do NOT use a calculator to convert these decimals to percents.

14. 0.86 = 86 %
15. 0.03 = 3 %
16. 0.140 = 14 %
17. 0.835 = 83.5 %

Practice

Order the fractions from smallest to largest.

18. $\frac{7}{16}, \frac{7}{8}, \frac{7}{12}, \frac{7}{9}$ — $\frac{7}{16}, \frac{7}{12}, \frac{7}{9}, \frac{7}{8}$
19. $\frac{7}{15}, \frac{3}{15}, \frac{8}{15}, \frac{4}{15}$ — $\frac{3}{15}, \frac{4}{15}, \frac{7}{15}, \frac{8}{15}$
20. $\frac{5}{9}, \frac{15}{16}, \frac{1}{4}, \frac{9}{10}$ — $\frac{1}{4}, \frac{5}{9}, \frac{9}{10}, \frac{15}{16}$

Math Masters, p. 285

3 Differentiation Options

READINESS

PARTNER ACTIVITY

▶ Solving "Percent-of" Problems

5–15 Min

(*Math Masters,* p. 286)

To explore "percent-of" situations using a concrete model, have students use counters to solve problems. Encourage students to rename the percents as fractions and solve the problems as "fraction-of" problems.

ENRICHMENT

PARTNER ACTIVITY

Solving Discount Number Stories

5–15 Min

(*Math Masters,* p. 287)

To apply students' understanding of "percent-of" situations, have them solve number stories for which they compare the discounts of two items. In one story, students compare the percents of discount; in a second story, they compare the actual discounts.

EXTRA PRACTICE

SMALL-GROUP ACTIVITY

5-Minute Math

5–15 Min

To offer students more experience with percents, see *5-Minute Math,* pages 103, 179, 187, and 196.

ELL SUPPORT

SMALL-GROUP ACTIVITY

Building Background for Mathematics Words

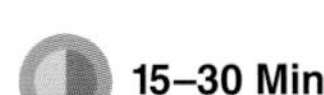

15–30 Min

To provide language support for percents, have students look at store catalogs or advertisements and discuss the following:

- ▷ The **regular price** (sometimes called the **list price**) of an item is the price without a discount.
- ▷ The **discount** is the amount you save. It is given in dollars and cents.
- ▷ The **percent of discount** or the **fraction of discount** is a percent or fraction that tells what part of the regular price you save.
- ▷ The **sale price** (or **discounted price**) is the amount you pay after subtracting the discount from the regular price.

Example:

The regular price of a bird feeder is \$15. It is on sale at a 20% discount. What is the sale price?

The *percent of discount* is 20% of the *regular price*. 20% is $\frac{20}{100}$, or $\frac{1}{5}$. One-fifth of \$15 is \$3, so you save \$3. This is the *discount*. To find the *sale price*, subtract \$3 from \$15. The sale price is \$12.

Teaching Master

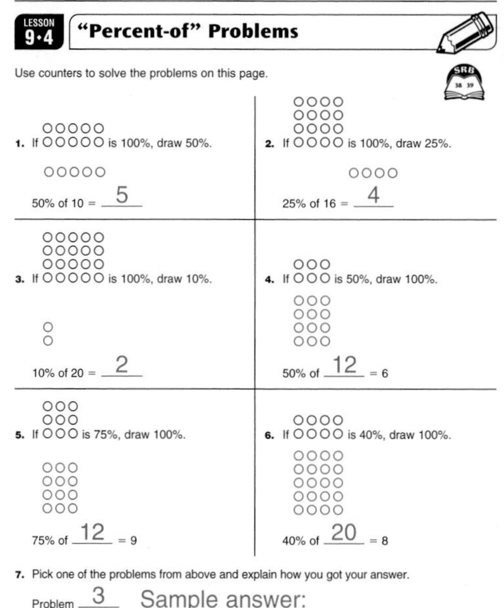

Name Date Time

LESSON 9•4 "Percent-of" Problems

Use counters to solve the problems on this page.

1. If ○○○○○ ○○○○○ is 100%, draw 50%. ○○○○○ 50% of 10 = 5
2. If ○○○○ ○○○○ ○○○○ ○○○○ is 100%, draw 25%. ○○○○ 25% of 16 = 4
3. If ○○○○○ ○○○○○ ○○○○○ ○○○○○ is 100%, draw 10%. ○ ○ 10% of 20 = 2
4. If ○○○ ○○○ is 50%, draw 100%. ○○○ ○○○ ○○○ ○○○ 50% of 12 = 6
5. If ○○○ ○○○ ○○○ is 75%, draw 100%. ○○○ ○○○ ○○○ ○○○ 75% of 12 = 9
6. If ○○○○ ○○○○ is 40%, draw 100%. ○○○○ ○○○○ ○○○○ ○○○○ ○○○○ 40% of 20 = 8
7. Pick one of the problems from above and explain how you got your answer.

Problem 3 Sample answer:
I know that 10% is another name for $\frac{1}{10}$. $\frac{1}{10}$ of 20 is 2, so 10% of 20 is 2.

Math Masters, p. 286

Teaching Master

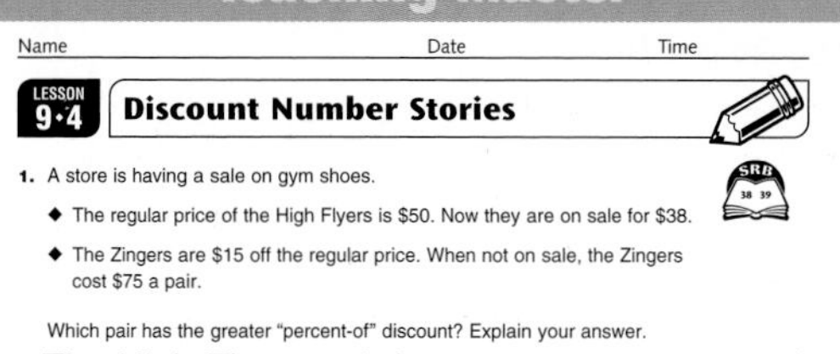

Name Date Time

LESSON 9•4 Discount Number Stories

1. A store is having a sale on gym shoes.
   - The regular price of the High Flyers is \$50. Now they are on sale for \$38.
   - The Zingers are \$15 off the regular price. When not on sale, the Zingers cost \$75 a pair.

   Which pair has the greater "percent-of" discount? Explain your answer.

   The High Flyers pair has a greater percent-of discount. \$50–\$38 = \$12. $\frac{12}{50} = \frac{24}{100}$, so the discount is 24%. The Zingers' discount is $\frac{15}{75} = \frac{1}{5} = \frac{20}{100}$, or 20%.

2. The same store is also having a sale on tennis rackets.
   - The regular price of the Smasher is \$54.00. It is on sale for 25% off the regular price.
   - The regular price of the Fast Flight is \$75.00. It is on sale for 20% off the regular price.

   For which tennis racket are you getting more money taken off the regular price? Explain your answer.

   The Fast Flight has a greater percent-of discount. 20% off \$75.00 = $\frac{\$75}{5}$ = \$15.00. The Smasher's discount is 25% off \$54.00 = $\frac{\$54}{4}$ = \$13.50.

Math Masters, p. 287

9•5 Conversions among Fractions, Decimals, and Percents

Objectives To reinforce the use of a data table; and to reinforce renaming fractions as percents using a calculator and renaming decimals as percents.

Technology Resources www.everydaymathonline.com

ePresentations

eToolkit

Algorithms Practice

EM Facts Workshop Game™

Family Letters

Assessment Management

Common Core State Standards

Curriculum Focal Points

Interactive Teacher's Lesson Guide

1 Teaching the Lesson

Key Concepts and Skills

- Read and use large numbers. [Number and Numeration Goal 1]
- Explore repeating and terminating decimals. [Number and Numeration Goal 5]
- Use a calculator to rename fractions as percents; rename decimals as percents by multiplying by 100. [Number and Numeration Goal 5]
- Compare two quantities with like units using division. [Operations and Computation Goal 4]
- Round to the nearest whole-number percent. [Operations and Computation Goal 6]
- Use a data table. [Data and Chance Goal 2]

Key Activities

Students look up country population and land area data and convert these to percents of the world population and land area. Students complete the percent column of the Equivalent Names for Fractions table on journal pages 342 and 343.

Ongoing Assessment: Informing Instruction See page 746.

Materials

Math Journal 2, pp. 342 and 343
Student Reference Book, pp. 271 and 281
Study Link 9•4
calculator ◆ classroom world map ◆ slate

2 Ongoing Learning & Practice

Updating the World Tour

Math Journal 2, pp. 329–331, 336, and 337
Student Reference Book, pp. 276, 277, 281, 288, 289, 297, and 302–305
Math Masters, pp. 419 and 420 (optional)
Students continue the World Tour.

Angle Addition and Subtraction

Math Journal 2, pp. 260A and 260B
Students practice finding unknown angle measures.

Math Boxes 9•5

Math Journal 2, p. 260
Students practice and maintain skills through Math Box problems.

Ongoing Assessment: Recognizing Student Achievement
Use Math Boxes, Problem 4.
[Operations and Computation Goal 4]

Study Link 9•5

Math Masters, p. 288
Students practice and maintain skills through Study Link activities.

3 Differentiation Options

READINESS

Rounding Percents

Math Masters, p. 289
Students use a curved number-line model to round percents.

EXTRA PRACTICE

5-Minute Math

5-Minute Math™, pp. 93 and 181
calculator
Students practice conversions among fractions, decimals, and percents.

Advance Preparation

***Teacher's Reference Manual,* Grades 4–6** pp. 62, 63, 153, 154

Getting Started

Mental Math and Reflexes

Write fractions on the board. For each fraction, students write the equivalent decimal and percent on their slates. Have students explain their strategies for the ●●● problems. *Suggestions:*

●○○ $\frac{55}{100}$ 0.55, 55%
$\frac{71}{100}$ 0.71, 71%
$\frac{67}{100}$ 0.67, 67%

●●○ $\frac{5}{100}$ 0.05, 5%
$\frac{5}{10}$ 0.5, 50%
$\frac{1}{4}$ 0.25, 25%

●●● $\frac{2}{20}$ 0.10, 10%
$\frac{12}{25}$ 0.48, 48%
$\frac{15}{3}$ 5, 500%

Math Message

Use your calculator to rename these fractions as percents: $\frac{1}{8}$, $\frac{3}{8}$, $\frac{5}{8}$, $\frac{7}{8}$.

Study Link 9·4 Follow-Up

Review answers. Have students share the strategies they used to solve Problems 3–6. *For example:*

▷ Problem 3: $\frac{42}{50} = \frac{84}{100}$ (multiply numerator and denominator by 2); $\frac{84}{100} = 84\%$

▷ Problem 6: $\frac{25}{125} = \frac{1}{5}$ (divide numerator and denominator by 25); $\frac{1}{5} = 20\%$

Ask if any student can describe a solution strategy to solve Problems 7 and 8 without a calculator. *For example:*

▷ Problem 7: $\frac{23}{92} = \frac{1}{4}$ (divide numerator and denominator by 23); $\frac{1}{4} = 25\%$

▷ Problem 8: $\frac{12}{40} = \frac{3}{10}$ (divide numerator and denominator by 4); $\frac{3}{10} = 30\%$

1 Teaching the Lesson

▶ Math Message Follow-Up

Go over the answers: $\frac{1}{8} = 12.5\%$; $\frac{3}{8} = 37.5\%$; $\frac{5}{8} = 62.5\%$; $\frac{7}{8} = 87.5\%$. Students may have renamed the fractions as percents in one of two ways.

▷ Use the percent key. For example, to rename $\frac{3}{8}$ as a percent,

TI-15: 3 [÷] 8 [%] [Enter] Display: 37.5

Casio *fx*-55: 3 [÷] 8 [%] Display: 37.5

▷ Divide numerator by denominator, and multiply by 100. For example, divide 3 by 8 (= 0.375) and multiply by 100 (= 37.5). Remind students that multiplying a decimal by 100 can be done by moving the decimal point two digits to the right.

Students may use either method, but they should be able to use both.

Adjusting the Activity

Ask students to explain how $\frac{1}{8}$, $\frac{3}{8}$, $\frac{5}{8}$, and $\frac{7}{8}$ could be renamed as percents without using a calculator. Record the steps on the board.

▷ $\frac{1}{8}$ is half of $\frac{1}{4}$. Because $\frac{1}{4} = 25\%$ and half of 25% is 12.5%, $\frac{1}{8} = 12.5\%$.

▷ $\frac{3}{8}$ equals $\frac{1}{4} + \frac{1}{8}$, which is 25% + 12.5%, or 37.5%.

▷ $\frac{5}{8}$ and $\frac{7}{8}$ are renamed in the same way.

AUDITORY • KINESTHETIC • TACTILE • VISUAL

Renaming Fractions as Percents

(*Student Reference Book,* pp. 271 and 281)

Social Studies Link Use the classroom world map to identify Russia and China. Russia has the largest land area of any country in the world. China has the largest population of any country in the world. Tell students that in this lesson they will investigate population and land area data and use their calculators to convert these to percents of the world population and land area.

Ask students to use the *Student Reference Book* to find the population of China and the total world population.

Write these populations on the board. Point out that the world population has been rounded to the nearest million.

- ▷ Ask students to round China's population to the nearest million. Record this estimate on the board.
- ▷ Ask students what fraction of the world's population lives in China. Write this fraction on the board.

	Population	Population Rounded	Fraction
China	1,298,848,000	1,299,000,000	$\frac{1,299,000,000}{6,378,000,000}$
World	6,378,000,000	6,378,000,000	

Have students use their calculators to rename this fraction as a percent. They should use both methods and get the same answer:

- ▷ Use the percent key.

  TI-15: 1299000000 ÷ 6378000000 % Enter Display will show 20.36688617.

  Casio *fx*-55: 1299 ÷ 6378 % Display will show 20.366886.

- ▷ Divide numerator by denominator, and multiply by 100.

  1299000000 ÷ 6378000000 Enter Display will show 0.2036688617.

  0.2036688617 × 100 Enter Display will show 20.36688617.

Ongoing Assessment: Informing Instruction

Watch for students who notice that, because both numbers are in millions, it is sufficient to divide 1,299 by 6,378. If students' calculators, such as the Casio *fx*-55, cannot display these large numbers, encourage them to use this strategy.

Help students summarize. Round percent answers to the nearest whole-number percent. In 20.366886179, the digit in the tenths place is less than 5, so the number is rounded down to 20%. About 20 of every 100 people in the world live in China. Because 20% equals $\frac{1}{5}$, about 1 of every 5 people in the world live in China.

Student Page

World Tour

Facts About the World

Continents are large land masses. There are seven continents on the Earth, although Europe and Asia are sometimes thought of as one continent. Most continents contain many countries, but there are no countries at all in Antarctica.

A **country** is a territory and the people who live there under one government. The number of countries in the world often changes as countries split apart or join with other countries. At this time, there are about 200 countries in the world.

Population is the number of people who live in a certain region. Population growth is the change in the population every year after all births and deaths are accounted for. The **population growth rate** is the increase (or decrease) in population per year, written as a percent.

Dimensions of the Earth

Equatorial circumference*: about 24,900 miles (40,000 kilometers)

Equatorial diameter:** about 7,930 miles (12,760 kilometers)

Volume: 2.6×10^{11} cubic miles (1.1×10^{12} cubic kilometers)

Weight (mass): 6.6×10^{21} tons (6.0×10^{21} metric tons)

Total world water area: about 139,433,000 square miles (361,129,000 square kilometers)

*Circumference is the distance around a circle or sphere.

**Diameter is the distance measured by a straight line passing from one side of a circle or sphere, through the center, to the other side.

The world's population is now increasing by about 200,000 people per day, or about 75 million people per year. Over the last 40 years, the world's population has about doubled. It reached the 6 billion mark in 1999. World population is expected to reach about 9 billion people by the year 2050.

The Continents

Continent	Population*	Percent of World Population	Area (sq miles)	Percent of Land Area
North America	509,000,000	8.0%	8,300,000	14.8%
South America	367,000,000	5.8	6,800,000	12.1
Europe	799,000,000	12.5	4,100,000	7.3
Asia	3,797,000,000	59.5	16,700,000	29.8
Africa	874,000,000	13.7	11,500,000	20.5
Australia	32,000,000	0.5	3,300,000	5.9
Antarctica	0	0.0	5,400,000	9.6
World Totals	**6,378,000,000 (about 6.4 billion)**	**100.0%**	**56,100,000**	**100.0%**

*Data are for the year 2004. World population growth rate for the year 2004: about 1.2% per year

***Student Reference Book,* p. 271**

Student Page

World Tour

REGION 4 Asia and Australia

Australia
Area: 2,967,900 sq mi
Population: 19,913,000
Capital: Canberra (**Pop.** 373,000)
Languages: English, aboriginal languages
Monetary unit: Australian Dollar

Bangladesh
Area: 55,600 sq mi
Population: 141,340,000
Capital: Dhaka (**Pop.** 11,560,000)
Languages: Bangla, English
Monetary unit: Taka

China
Area: 3,705,400 sq mi
Population: 1,298,848,000
Capital: Beijing (**Pop.** 10,848,000)
Languages: Mandarin, Gan, Wu, Haka, Yue, Minbei, Xiang, Minnan
Monetary unit: Renminbi (Yuan)

India
Area: 1,269,300 sq mi
Population: 1,065,071,000
Capital: New Delhi (**Pop.** 12,441,000)
Languages: Hindi, English, 14 regional languages
Monetary unit: Rupee

Iran
Area: 636,000 sq mi
Population: 67,503,000
Capital: Tehran (**Pop.** 7,190,000)
Languages: Farsi, Kurdish, Turkic, Luri
Monetary unit: Rial

Japan
Area: 145,900 sq mi
Population: 127,333,000
Capital: Tokyo (**Pop.** 34,997,000)
Language: Japanese
Monetary unit: Yen

Russia
Area: 6,592,800 sq mi
Population: 143,782,000
Capital: Moscow (**Pop.** 6,468,000)
Languages: Russian, many others
Monetary unit: Ruble

Thailand
Area: 198,500 sq mi
Population: 64,866,000
Capital: Bangkok (**Pop.** 6,486,000)
Languages: Thai, English
Monetary unit: Baht

Turkey
Area: 301,400 sq mi
Population: 68,894,000
Capital: Ankara (**Pop.** 3,428,000)
Languages: Turkish, Arabic, Kurdish
Monetary unit: Lira

Vietnam
Area: 127,200 sq mi
Population: 82,690,000
Capital: Hanoi (**Pop.** 3,977,000)
Languages: Vietnamese, Chinese, French, English
Monetary unit: Dong

REGION 5 North America

Canada
Area: 3,851,800 sq mi
Population: 32,508,000
Capital: Ottawa (**Pop.** 1,093,000)
Languages: English, French
Monetary unit: Dollar

Costa Rica
Area: 19,700 sq mi
Population: 3,957,000
Capital: San José (**Pop.** 1,085,000)
Language: Spanish
Monetary unit: Colon

Cuba
Area: 42,800 sq mi
Population: 11,309,000
Capital: Havana (**Pop.** 2,189,000)
Language: Spanish
Monetary unit: Peso

El Salvador
Area: 8,100 sq mi
Population: 6,588,000
Capital: San Salvador (**Pop.** 1,424,000)
Language: Spanish
Monetary unit: Colon

Guatemala
Area: 42,000 sq mi
Population: 14,281,000
Capital: Guatemala City (**Pop.** 951,000)
Languages: Spanish, Mayan languages
Monetary unit: Quetzal

Haiti
Area: 10,700 sq mi
Population: 7,656,000
Capital: Port-au-Prince (**Pop.** 1,961,000)
Languages: French, Haitian Creole
Monetary unit: Gourde

Jamaica
Area: 4,200 sq mi
Population: 2,713,000
Capital: Kingston (**Pop.** 575,000)
Languages: English, Jamaican Creole
Monetary unit: Jamaican Dollar

Mexico
Area: 761,600 sq mi
Population: 104,960,000
Capital: Mexico City (**Pop.** 18,660,000)
Languages: Spanish, Mayan dialects
Monetary unit: New Peso

Panama
Area: 30,200 sq mi
Population: 3,000,000
Capital: Panama City (**Pop.** 930,000)
Languages: Spanish, English
Monetary unit: Balboa

United States of America
Area: 3,717,800 sq mi
Population: 293,028,000
Capital: Washington, D.C. (**Pop.** 563,000)
Languages: English, Spanish
Monetary unit: Dollar

***Student Reference Book,* p. 281**

Repeat this last routine to calculate the percent of the world's land area that is in Russia. Russia's area is about 6,592,800 square miles. The world's land area is about 57,900,000 square miles. The fraction of the world's area that belongs to Russia is about 6,593,000 ÷ 57,900,000 = 0.1138687392. Multiply 0.11 ∗ 100 = 11%. So about 11% of the world's area belongs to Russia.

Completing the Equivalent Names for Fraction Table

INDEPENDENT ACTIVITY

(*Math Journal 2,* pp. 342 and 343)

Students should already have filled in the equivalent fractions and decimals columns of the table on journal pages 342 and 343. Now they will fill in the percents column.

- ▷ On the first page of the table, students find the percents by using the percent key. If the calculator display shows an answer with more than 3 digits, they record only the first 3 digits. For example, for the fraction $\frac{5}{6}$, the percent answer will be displayed on the calculator as 83.33333333, but only 83.3 should be recorded in the table.
- ▷ On the second page of the table, students can find the percents without using a calculator and without making any actual computations. The decimal names are already recorded in the table. Students need only multiply the decimal by 100 (move the decimal point two digits to the right) to rename the decimal as a percent. As before, ask students to record only the first 3 digits for any percent name.

Student Page

Date Time

Equivalent Names for Fractions

Fraction	Equivalent Fractions	Decimal	Percent
$\frac{0}{2}$		0	0%
$\frac{1}{2}$	$\frac{2}{4}$, $\frac{3}{6}$		
$\frac{2}{2}$		1	100%
$\frac{1}{3}$			
$\frac{2}{3}$			
$\frac{1}{4}$			
$\frac{3}{4}$			
$\frac{1}{5}$			
$\frac{2}{5}$			
$\frac{3}{5}$			
$\frac{4}{5}$			
$\frac{1}{6}$			
$\frac{5}{6}$			
$\frac{1}{8}$			
$\frac{3}{8}$			
$\frac{5}{8}$			
$\frac{7}{8}$			

Math Journal 2, **p. 342**

Student Page

Date Time

Equivalent Names for Fractions *continued*

Fraction	Equivalent Fractions	Decimal	Percent
$\frac{1}{9}$			
$\frac{2}{9}$			
$\frac{4}{9}$			
$\frac{5}{9}$			
$\frac{7}{9}$			
$\frac{8}{9}$			
$\frac{1}{10}$			
$\frac{3}{10}$			
$\frac{7}{10}$			
$\frac{9}{10}$			
$\frac{1}{12}$			
$\frac{5}{12}$			
$\frac{7}{12}$			
$\frac{11}{12}$			

Math Journal 2, **p. 343**

Student Page

Date Time

LESSON 9•5 **Finding Unknown Angle Measures**

Without using a protractor, find the measure of the unknown angle. Write an equation to show how you solved the problem. Use a variable to represent the unknown angle measure.
Sample equations are given.

1. 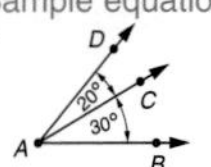

Measure of $\angle DAB$ = 50°
Equation: $20 + 30 = x$

2. 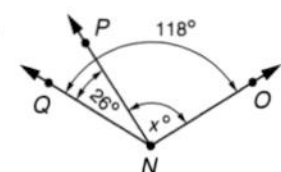

Measure of $\angle HEF$ = 116°
Equation: $57 + 59 = x$

3. 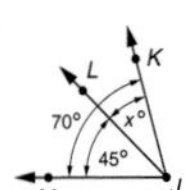

Measure of $\angle KJL$ = 25°
Equation: $70 - 45 = x$

4. Measure of $\angle PNO$ = 92°
Equation: $26 + x = 118$

5. 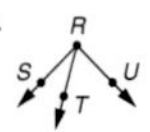

$\angle SRU$ is a right angle.
Measure of $\angle TRU = 60°$
Measure of $\angle TRS$ = 30°
Equation: $90 - 60 = x$

6. 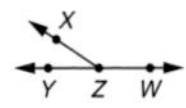

$\angle YZW$ is a straight angle.
Measure of $\angle XZY = 33°$
Measure of $\angle XZW$ = 147°
Equation: $180 = 33 + x$

Math Journal 2, p. 260A

Student Page

Date Time

LESSON 9•5 **Finding Unknown Angle Measures** *continued*

Find the value of *x*. Write an open sentence to show how you solved the problem.
Sample equations are given.

7. 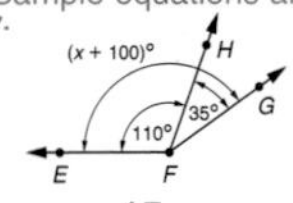

x = 45
Equation: $110 + 35 = x + 100$
Measure of $\angle EFG$ = 145°

8. 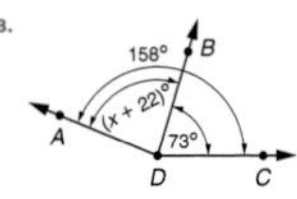

x = 63
Equation: $(x + 22) + 73 = 158$
Measure of $\angle ADB$ = 85°

Try This

9. Angela used her protractor to measure $\angle KJL$ and $\angle NJM$. She found the two angles had the same measure. Angela said, "Without measuring, I also know $\angle KJM$ has the same measure as $\angle NJL$."

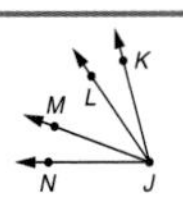

Explain how Angela knows her statement is true.
Sample answer: There is only one angle in between $\angle NJM$ and $\angle KJL$. So, the measure of $\angle NJM$ + the measure of $\angle MJL$ is the same as the measure of $\angle KJL$ + the measure of $\angle LJM$.

Math Journal 2, p. 260B

2 Ongoing Learning & Practice

Updating the World Tour

(*Math Journal 2,* pp. 329–331, 336, and 337; *Student Reference Book,* pp. 276, 277, 281, 288, 289, 297, and 302–305; *Math Masters,* pp. 419 and 420)

Social Studies Link Students follow the established World Tour routine.

- They update the Route Map by drawing a line segment to connect Brasília, Brazil, and Beijing, China.
- They use the World Tour section of the *Student Reference Book* to locate facts about China and Beijing, and they fill in the Country Notes pages for this country and capital.
- Students who are also keeping a Route Log update that as well.

Angle Addition and Subtraction

(*Math Journal 2,* pp. 260A and 260B)

Students practice using addition and subtraction to find unknown angle measures.

Math Boxes 9•5

(*Math Journal 2,* p. 260)

Mixed Practice Math Boxes in this lesson are linked with Math Boxes in Lessons 9-7 and 9-9. The skill in Problem 6 previews Unit 10 content.

Ongoing Assessment: Recognizing Student Achievement

Math Boxes Problem 4 

Use **Math Boxes, Problem 4** to assess students' ability to divide a multidigit whole number by a 1-digit divisor. Students are making adequate progress if they express the quotient as a whole number with a whole-number remainder. Some students may be able to express the remainder as a fraction.

[Operations and Computation Goal 4]

Study Link 9•5

(*Math Masters,* p. 288)

Home Connection Students use a table of data to calculate the approximate percentage of marriages that occurred each month in 2001.

3 Differentiation Options

READINESS

PARTNER ACTIVITY

5–15 Min

Rounding Percents

(*Math Masters,* p. 289)

To explore rounding percents to the nearest whole number, have students plot numbers on a curved number line to see which way the percent will "slide." Ask students to describe how they rounded their numbers. Encourage vocabulary such as *top, bottom, endpoint, middle, closer,* and *farther*.

EXTRA PRACTICE

SMALL-GROUP ACTIVITY

5–15 Min

5-Minute Math

To offer students more experience with conversions among fractions, decimals, and percents, see *5-Minute Math,* pages 93 and 181.

Planning Ahead

Remind students to bring to school the second page of Study Link 9-1 (Trivia Survey). Their survey results will be used in Lesson 9-6.

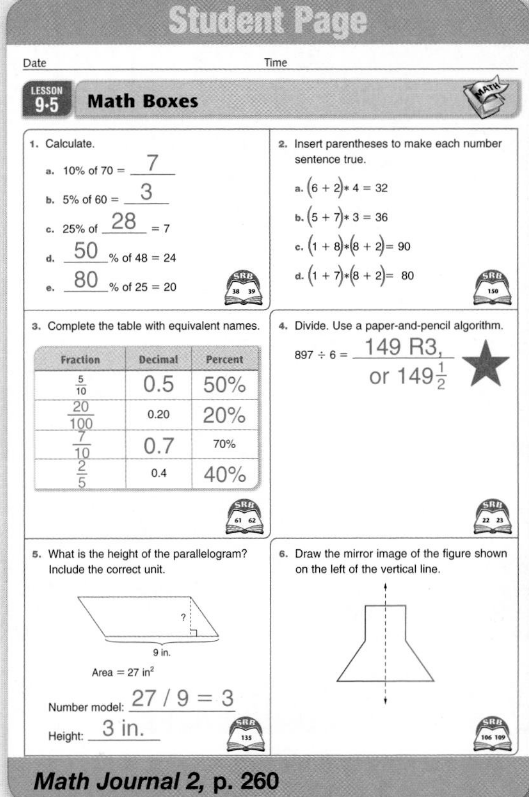

Student Page

Date Time

LESSON 9·5 **Math Boxes**

1. Calculate.
   a. 10% of 70 = 7
   b. 5% of 60 = 3
   c. 25% of 28 = 7
   d. 50 % of 48 = 24
   e. 80 % of 25 = 20

2. Insert parentheses to make each number sentence true.
   a. (6 + 2) ∗ 4 = 32
   b. (5 + 7) ∗ 3 = 36
   c. (1 + 8) ∗ (8 + 2) = 90
   d. (1 + 7) ∗ (8 + 2) = 80

3. Complete the table with equivalent names.

Fraction	Decimal	Percent
$\frac{5}{10}$	0.5	50%
$\frac{20}{100}$	0.20	20%
$\frac{7}{10}$	0.7	70%
$\frac{2}{5}$	0.4	40%

4. Divide. Use a paper-and-pencil algorithm.
   897 ÷ 6 = 149 R3, or $149\frac{1}{2}$

5. What is the height of the parallelogram? Include the correct unit.
   9 in.
   Area = 27 in²
   Number model: 27 / 9 = 3
   Height: 3 in.

6. Draw the mirror image of the figure shown on the left of the vertical line.

Math Journal 2, p. 260

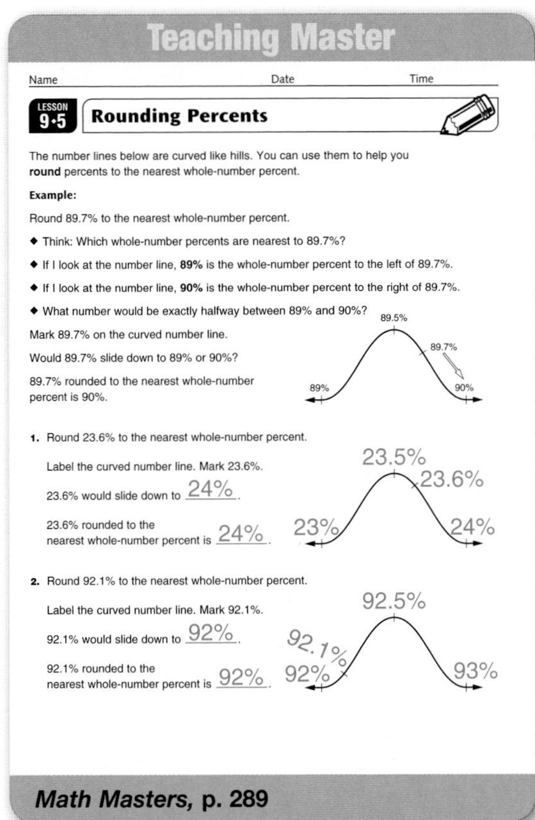

Teaching Master

Name Date Time

LESSON 9·5 **Rounding Percents**

The number lines below are curved like hills. You can use them to help you **round** percents to the nearest whole-number percent.

Example:

Round 89.7% to the nearest whole-number percent.

- Think: Which whole-number percents are nearest to 89.7%?
- If I look at the number line, **89%** is the whole-number percent to the left of 89.7%.
- If I look at the number line, **90%** is the whole-number percent to the right of 89.7%.
- What number would be exactly halfway between 89% and 90%?

Mark 89.7% on the curved number line.

Would 89.7% slide down to 89% or 90%?

89.7% rounded to the nearest whole-number percent is 90%.

1. Round 23.6% to the nearest whole-number percent.
   Label the curved number line. Mark 23.6%.
   23.6% would slide down to 24%.
   23.6% rounded to the nearest whole-number percent is 24%.

2. Round 92.1% to the nearest whole-number percent.
   Label the curved number line. Mark 92.1%.
   92.1% would slide down to 92%.
   92.1% rounded to the nearest whole-number percent is 92%.

Math Masters, p. 289

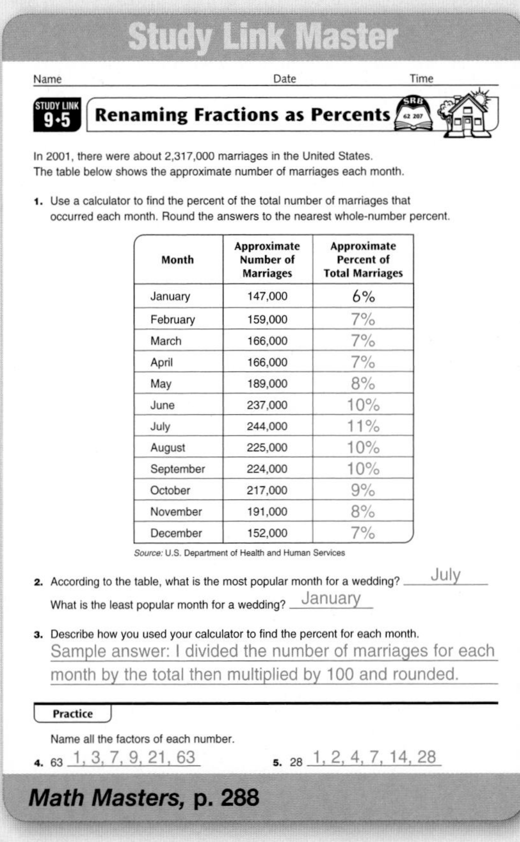

Study Link Master

Name Date Time

STUDY LINK 9·5 **Renaming Fractions as Percents**

In 2001, there were about 2,317,000 marriages in the United States. The table below shows the approximate number of marriages each month.

1. Use a calculator to find the percent of the total number of marriages that occurred each month. Round the answers to the nearest whole-number percent.

Month	Approximate Number of Marriages	Approximate Percent of Total Marriages
January	147,000	6%
February	159,000	7%
March	166,000	7%
April	166,000	7%
May	189,000	8%
June	237,000	10%
July	244,000	11%
August	225,000	10%
September	224,000	10%
October	217,000	9%
November	191,000	8%
December	152,000	7%

Source: U.S. Department of Health and Human Services

2. According to the table, what is the most popular month for a wedding? July
   What is the least popular month for a wedding? January

3. Describe how you used your calculator to find the percent for each month.
   Sample answer: I divided the number of marriages for each month by the total then multiplied by 100 and rounded.

Practice

Name all the factors of each number.

4. 63 1, 3, 7, 9, 21, 63
5. 28 1, 2, 4, 7, 14, 28

Math Masters, p. 288

9·6 Comparing the Results of a Survey

Objectives To guide the organization and tabulation of survey data; and to introduce the use of percents to compare quantities expressed as fractions with unlike denominators.

www.everydaymathonline.com

ePresentations

eToolkit

Algorithms Practice

EM Facts Workshop Game™

Family Letters

Assessment Management

Common Core State Standards

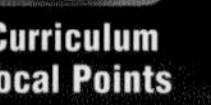
Curriculum Focal Points

Interactive Teacher's Lesson Guide

1 Teaching the Lesson

Key Concepts and Skills

- Use a calculator to convert fractions to percents.
  [Number and Numeration Goal 5]
- Compare fractions with unlike denominators.
  [Number and Numeration Goal 6]
- Create a table and tally chart.
  [Data and Chance Goal 1]
- Analyze survey results and make predictions based on collected data.
  [Data and Chance Goal 2]

Key Activities

Students tabulate the results from the trivia survey distributed in Lesson 9•1. For each survey question, they write a fraction to express the number of Yes answers as a part of the total number of answers. Then they convert each fraction to a percent.

Materials

Math Journal 2, p. 261
Study Links 9•1 (*Math Masters,* p. 280) and 9•5
transparency of *Math Masters,* p. 290 (optional) ◆ calculator ◆ slate

2 Ongoing Learning & Practice

Solving Number Stories with Multiplication and Division
Math Journal 2, pp. 261A and 261B
Students solve multiplication and division number stories about gardening.

Math Boxes 9·6
Math Journal 2, p. 262
Students practice and maintain skills through Math Box problems.

Ongoing Assessment: Recognizing Student Achievement
Use Math Boxes, Problem 4.
[Operations and Computation Goal 7]

Study Link 9·6
Math Masters, p. 291
Students practice and maintain skills through Study Link activities.

3 Differentiation Options

READINESS

Comparing Estimates for the "Fraction-of" a Collection
Math Masters, p. 292
pattern blocks ◆ large, clear container
Students estimate the number of trapezoids in a collection of pattern blocks and compare estimates.

ENRICHMENT

Graphing Survey Results
Math Journal 2, p. 261
Math Masters, p. 403
markers or colored pencils
Students make a side-by-side (double) bar graph of the class survey results.

EXTRA PRACTICE

Taking a 50-Facts Test
Math Masters, pp. 410 and 414; p. 416 (optional)
pen or colored pencil
Students take a 50-facts test. They use a line graph to record individual and optional class scores.

Advance Preparation

For the optional Readiness activity in Part 3, gather a large collection of pattern blocks and place them in a clear container.

***Teacher's Reference Manual,* Grades 4–6** pp. 69–71, 160–169

Getting Started

Mental Math and Reflexes

Write fraction addition problems on the board where tenths are added to tenths, hundredths to hundredths, and tenths to hundredths. Ask students to share their strategies for solving the ●●● problems. *Suggestions:*

●○○ $\frac{6}{10} + \frac{3}{10} = \frac{9}{10}$

$\frac{2}{10} + \frac{5}{10} = \frac{7}{10}$

$\frac{7}{10} + \frac{1}{10} = \frac{8}{10}$

$\frac{4}{10} + \frac{5}{10} = \frac{9}{10}$

●●○ $\frac{40}{100} + \frac{50}{100} = \frac{90}{100}$

$\frac{32}{100} + \frac{20}{100} = \frac{52}{100}$

$\frac{25}{100} + \frac{25}{100} = \frac{50}{100}$

$\frac{15}{100} + \frac{75}{100} = \frac{90}{100}$

●●● $\frac{6}{10} + \frac{20}{100} = \frac{80}{100}$, or $\frac{8}{10}$

$\frac{10}{100} + \frac{8}{10} = \frac{90}{100}$, or $\frac{9}{10}$

$\frac{9}{100} + \frac{9}{10} = \frac{99}{100}$

$\frac{5}{100} + \frac{5}{10} = \frac{55}{100}$

Math Message

Use your calculator to rename the following fractions as percents to the nearest whole percent:

$\frac{18}{63}, \frac{57}{78}, \frac{42}{59}, \frac{2}{47}$

Study Link 9·5 Follow-Up

Have partners compare answers. Ask if the percents in the table add up to 100%. yes Students should note that sometimes because of rounding, percents might not add up to 100%.

1 Teaching the Lesson

Math Message Follow-Up

WHOLE-CLASS DISCUSSION

Go over the answers. 29%, 73%, 71%, 4% Ask volunteers to show what they did to rename the fractions as percents. Make sure that both methods are presented:

▷ Using the percent key on a calculator

▷ Dividing the numerator by the denominator and multiplying by 100

Tell students that in this lesson they will rename the fractions from the Trivia Survey as percents.

Making a Prediction Based on Individual Survey Data

WHOLE-CLASS DISCUSSION

(*Math Masters,* p. 280)

Have students make some rough guesses about people's behavior based on their survey results. Ask: Do you think it is more likely that a person will

- read a book or go to a movie?
- eat breakfast or eat at a fast-food restaurant?
- like liver or like Mondays?

Take a vote and record the results on the board.

Study Link Master

Name Date Time

STUDY LINK 9·1 **Trivia Survey**

Conduct the survey below. The results will be used in Lesson 9-6.

Find at least five people to answer the following survey questions. You can ask family members, relatives, neighbors, and friends.

BE CAREFUL! You will not ask every person every question. Pay attention to the instructions that go with each question.

Record each answer with a tally mark in the Yes or No column. Answers vary.

Question	Yes	No
1. Is Monday your favorite day? (Ask everyone younger than 20.)		
2. Have you gone to the movies in the last month? (Ask everyone older than 8.)		
3. Did you eat breakfast today? (Ask everyone over 25.)		
4. Do you keep a map in your car? (Ask everyone who owns a car.)		
5. Did you eat at a fast-food restaurant yesterday? (Ask everyone.)		
6. Did you read a book during the last month? (Ask everyone over 20.)		
7. Are you more than 1 meter tall? (Ask everyone over 20.)		
8. Do you like liver? (Ask everyone.)		

Math Masters, p. 280

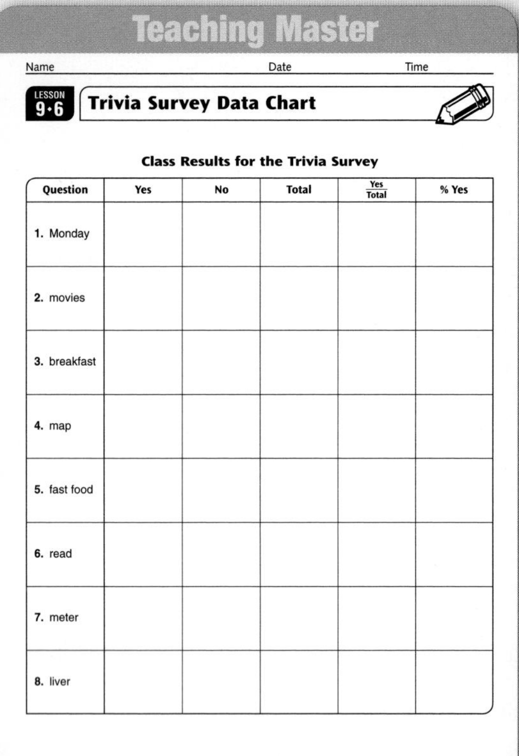

Teaching Master

Name Date Time

LESSON 9·6 **Trivia Survey Data Chart**

Class Results for the Trivia Survey

Question	Yes	No	Total	$\frac{\text{Yes}}{\text{Total}}$	% Yes
1. Monday					
2. movies					
3. breakfast					
4. map					
5. fast food					
6. read					
7. meter					
8. liver					

Math Masters, p. 290

Student Page

Date Time

LESSON 9·6 **Trivia Survey Results**

1. The chart below will show the results of the trivia survey for the whole class. Wait for your teacher to explain how to fill in the chart.

Class Results for the Trivia Survey

Question	Yes	No	Total	$\frac{\text{Yes}}{\text{Total}}$	% Yes
1. Is Monday your favorite day?					
2. Have you gone to the movies in the last month?					
3. Did you eat breakfast today?					
4. Do you keep a map in your car?					
5. Did you eat at a fast-food restaurant yesterday?					
6. Did you read a book during the last month?					
7. Are you more than 1 meter tall?					
8. Do you like liver?					

2. On the basis of the survey results, is it more likely that a person will
   a. read a book or go to a movie? Answers vary.
   b. eat breakfast or eat at a fast-food restaurant?
   c. like liver or like Mondays?

Math Journal 2, p. 261

▶ Tabulating Survey Results for the Whole Class

WHOLE-CLASS ACTIVITY

PROBLEM SOLVING

(*Math Journal 2,* p. 261; *Math Masters,* pp. 280 and 290)

Tell students that they will use the results of all the surveys to check their guesses. The first step is to combine the results from all the surveys. The goal is to create a chart that shows the total number of Yes and No answers to each question for the whole class.

Ask for suggestions on how to do this most efficiently. One possibility is to divide the class into small groups of four or five. For each question on the survey, have the students in each group find the total number of Yes answers and the total number of No answers for their group. Each group can then report its totals. You or a student volunteer can add these as they are reported. Finally, record the total number of Yes and the total number of No answers to each question on the transparency of *Math Masters,* page 290.

Students copy the results in the Yes and No columns on page 261 in their journals. They add the Yes and No results and record the sums in the Total column. These are the total numbers of people who answered the survey questions.

Next, students record the Yes answers as a fraction of the total number of answers in the $\frac{\text{Yes}}{\text{Total}}$ column. If necessary, help them complete the $\frac{\text{Yes}}{\text{Total}}$ column for the first two rows of the chart. At this point, the classroom chart might look as follows:

Question	Yes	No	Total	$\frac{\text{Yes}}{\text{Total}}$	% Yes
1. Monday	18	45	63	$\frac{18}{63}$	
2. movies	57	21	78	$\frac{57}{78}$	

▶ Analyzing the Survey Results

WHOLE-CLASS ACTIVITY

(*Math Journal 2,* p. 261)

Have students analyze the survey results so far.
Ask: Do you think it is more likely that a person will

- read a book or go to a movie?
- eat breakfast or eat at a fast-food restaurant?
- like liver or like Mondays?

Some students might argue that you need to simply compare the Yes answers.

Example:

Suppose that 45 out of 50 people interviewed read a book and that 57 out of 78 people saw a movie last month.

- Is it correct to conclude that because more people saw a movie than read a book, people are more likely to go to the movies than to read a book?
- Does the total number of people interviewed need to be taken into account?

This discussion is *crucial* to understanding why percents are useful. Students should see that it is difficult to compare quantities that are expressed as fractions with unlike denominators. Explain that this is why we rename fractions with unlike denominators as fractions that have the same denominator. The denominator 100—used in percents—is especially useful, because in our base-ten system, it is easy to rename such fractions as decimals and percents.

Once students understand why it is helpful to rename the fraction of Yes answers as percents, have them use their calculators to fill in the % Yes column. Ask them to round the answers to the nearest whole percent. Students' completed charts should resemble your classroom chart, which might look like this:

Question	Yes	No	Total	$\frac{\text{Yes}}{\text{Total}}$	% Yes
1. Monday	18	45	63	$\frac{18}{63}$	29%
2. movies	57	21	78	$\frac{57}{78}$	73%

Have partners use their completed table to answer Problem 2 at the bottom of journal page 261.

Adjusting the Activity

Have students combine the trivia survey data from all of the fourth-grade classes in the school. Discuss why % Yes estimates based on the combined data are more reliable than estimates based on the data collected by any single classroom.

AUDITORY ◆ KINESTHETIC ◆ TACTILE ◆ VISUAL

Student Page

Date Time

LESSON 9·6 Planting a Vegetable Garden

Kim and Carl decide to plant a vegetable garden. Solve the following problems about their garden. Sample number models are given.

1. Kim and Carl plan to make their garden in the shape of a rectangle that is 8 feet long. They have 36 feet of fencing. How wide should their garden be if they want to use all the fencing?

   (36 / 2) − 8 = w (number model(s) with unknown) Answer: 10 feet wide

   (36 / 2) − 8 = 10 (summary number model(s))

2. Pepper plants are on sale. The original price for 6 plants was $14.95. The sale price for 6 plants is $9.72. If they purchase 12 plants on sale, how much will they spend?

   $9.72 * 2 = c (number model(s) with unknown) Answer: $19.44

   $9.72 * 2 = $19.44 (summary number model(s))

3. Some small vegetable seeds come attached to a 15-foot tape instead of in a seed packet. Kim purchased lettuce, carrot, and radish seed tapes, each costing $4.95. What is the cost per foot for a seed tape?

   $4.95 / 15 = f (number model(s) with unknown) Answer: 33 cents

   $4.95 / 15 = $0.33 (summary number model(s))

4. Carl told Kim that a radish takes about 600 hours to grow after the seed is planted. About how long, in weeks and days, does Kim have to wait to eat a radish after she plants the seeds?

   (600 / 24) / 7 = w (number model(s) with unknown)

   Answer: 3 weeks 4 days

   (600 / 24) / 7 → 3 R4 (summary number model(s))

Math Journal 2, **p. 261A**

Student Page

Date Time

LESSON 9·6 Planting a Vegetable Garden *continued*

5. The tomatoes take about 77 days to grow. The leaf lettuce takes 45 days to grow. How many hours longer does it take the tomatoes to grow than the leaf lettuce?

   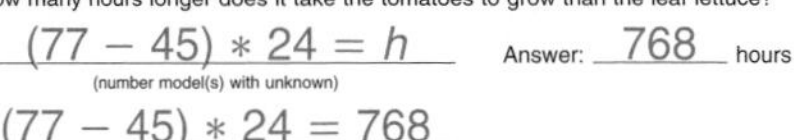

   (77 − 45) * 24 = h (number model(s) with unknown) Answer: 768 hours

   (77 − 45) * 24 = 768 (summary number model(s))

6. Carl and Kim's garden was a great success. Kim and Carl picked 132 tomatoes from their garden. They put aside a third of the tomatoes to make spaghetti sauce. If each batch of spaghetti sauce uses 10 tomatoes, how many full batches of sauce will they be able to make?

   (132 / 3) / 10 = b (number model(s) with unknown) Answer: 4 batches

   (132 / 3) / 10 → 4 R4 (summary number model(s))

7. They sold most of the carrots at farmer's markets. They tied the carrots into bundles of 6. Then they placed 8 bundles into each basket. If they sold 15 baskets of carrots during the season, how many carrots did they sell in all?

   6 * 8 * 15 = c (number model(s) with unknown) Answer: 720 carrots

   6 * 8 * 15 = 720 (summary number model(s))

Try This

8. They picked about 23 pounds of green beans over the summer. The family ate about 12 pounds of green beans. Their mother froze the rest in plastic bags weighing about 22 ounces each. About how many bags of green beans did their mother freeze? (*Hint:* There are 16 ounces in a pound.)

   (23 − 12) * 16 = 176; 176 / 22 = b (number model(s) with unknown)

   Answer: 8 bags

   (23 − 12) * 16 = 176; 176 / 22 = 8 (summary number model(s))

Math Journal 2, **p. 261B**

Student Page

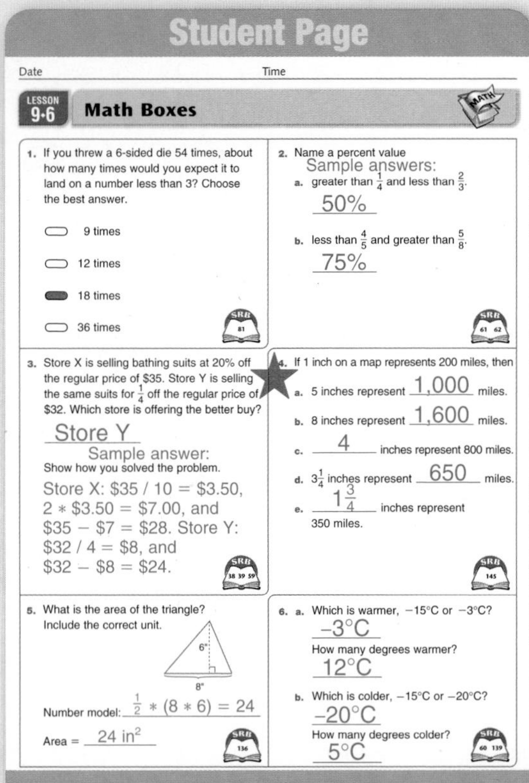

Date Time

LESSON 9·6 **Math Boxes**

1. If you threw a 6-sided die 54 times, about how many times would you expect it to land on a number less than 3? Choose the best answer.
   - ○ 9 times
   - ○ 12 times
   - ● 18 times
   - ○ 36 times

2. Name a percent value
   Sample answers:
   a. greater than $\frac{1}{4}$ and less than $\frac{2}{3}$. 50%
   b. less than $\frac{4}{5}$ and greater than $\frac{5}{8}$. 75%

3. Store X is selling bathing suits at 20% off the regular price of $35. Store Y is selling the same suits for $\frac{1}{4}$ off the regular price of $32. Which store is offering the better buy?
   Store Y
   Sample answer:
   Show how you solved the problem.
   Store X: $35 / 10 = $3.50, 2 * $3.50 = $7.00, and $35 − $7 = $28. Store Y: $32 / 4 = $8, and $32 − $8 = $24.

4. If 1 inch on a map represents 200 miles, then
   a. 5 inches represent 1,000 miles.
   b. 8 inches represent 1,600 miles.
   c. 4 inches represent 800 miles.
   d. $3\frac{1}{4}$ inches represent 650 miles.
   e. $1\frac{3}{4}$ inches represent 350 miles.

5. What is the area of the triangle? Include the correct unit.
   6" 8"
   Number model: $\frac{1}{2} * (8 * 6) = 24$
   Area = 24 in²

6. a. Which is warmer, −15°C or −3°C? −3°C
   How many degrees warmer? 12°C
   b. Which is colder, −15°C or −20°C? −20°C
   How many degrees colder? 5°C

Math Journal 2, p. 262

Study Link Master

Name Date Time

STUDY LINK 9·6 **Use Percents to Compare Fractions**

1. The girls' varsity basketball team won 8 of the 10 games it played. The junior varsity team won 6 of 8 games. Which team has the better record? Explain your reasoning.
   The varsity team. They won $\frac{8}{10}$ = 80% of their games.
   The junior varsity team won $\frac{6}{8} = \frac{3}{4}$ = 75% of their games.

2. Complete the table of shots taken (not including free throws) during a game. Calculate the percent of shots made to the nearest whole percent.

Player	Shots Made	Shots Missed	Total Shots	Shots Made / Total Shots	% of Shots Made
1	5	12	17	$\frac{5}{17}$	29%
2	5	6	11	$\frac{5}{11}$	45%
3	3	0	3	$\frac{3}{3}$	100%
4	9	2	11	$\frac{9}{11}$	82%
5	4	3	7	$\frac{4}{7}$	57%
6	11	5	16	$\frac{11}{16}$	69%
7	6	4	10	$\frac{6}{10}$	60%
8	1	1	2	$\frac{1}{2}$	50%

3. The basketball game is tied. Your team has the ball. There is only enough time for one more shot. Based only on the information in the table, which player would you choose to take the shot? Why?
   Sample answer: I would choose Player 4, who has taken 11 shots and made 82% of her shots. Player 3 has a higher percent of shots made (100%), but she has only taken 3 shots.

Practice

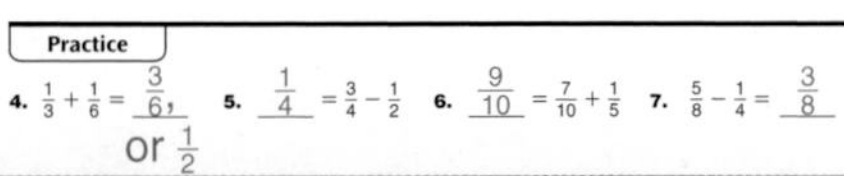

4. $\frac{1}{3} + \frac{1}{6} = \frac{3}{6}$, or $\frac{1}{2}$ 5. $\frac{1}{4} = \frac{3}{4} - \frac{1}{2}$ 6. $\frac{9}{10} = \frac{7}{10} + \frac{1}{5}$ 7. $\frac{5}{8} - \frac{1}{4} = \frac{3}{8}$

Math Masters, p. 291

2 Ongoing Learning & Practice

▶ Solving Number Stories with Multiplication and Division

(*Math Journal* 2, pp. 261A and 261B)

Students solve multiplication and division number stories about gardening. Some problems involve multistep calculations and interpreting remainders. Students write a number model with an unknown, solve the problem, and then write a summary number model.

▶ Math Boxes 9·6

(*Math Journal 2,* p. 262)

Mixed Practice Math Boxes in this lesson are paired with Math Boxes in Lesson 9-8. The skill in Problem 6 previews Unit 10 content.

Ongoing Assessment: Recognizing Student Achievement

Math Boxes Problem 4

Use **Math Boxes, Problem 4** to assess students' ability to interpret a map scale. Students are making adequate progress if they are able to solve Problems 4a–4c. Some students may be able to solve Problems 4d and 4e, which involve fractions of inches.

[Operations and Computation Goal 7]

▶ Study Link 9·6

(*Math Masters,* p. 291)

Home Connection Students use percents to compare quantities expressed as fractions with unlike denominators.

3 Differentiation Options

READINESS

Comparing Estimates for the "Fraction-of" a Collection

(*Math Masters,* p. 292)

To explore the comparison of quantities expressed as fractions with unlike denominators using a concrete model, have students compare estimates for the number of red trapezoids in a collection of pattern blocks.

Have students share their strategies for making comparisons. Discuss how finding nearby "easy" fractions or converting to decimals could help them compare their estimates. Ask why estimates with different denominators cannot be compared directly.

ENRICHMENT

Graphing Survey Results

(*Math Journal 2,* p. 261; *Math Masters,* p. 403)

To apply students' ability to represent data, have them graph the results of the class survey on centimeter grid paper (*Math Masters,* page 403). You might suggest that students use a side-by-side (double) bar graph. *For example:*

Survey Questions

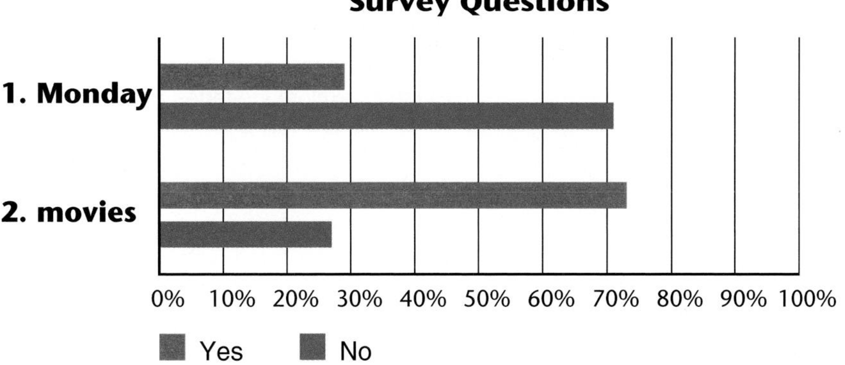

EXTRA PRACTICE

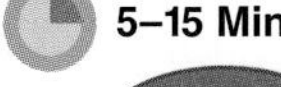

Taking a 50-Facts Test

(*Math Masters,* pp. 410, 414, and 416)

See Lesson 3-4 for details regarding the administration of a 50-facts test and the recording and graphing of individual and optional class results.

Teaching Master

Name ______ Date ______ Time ______

LESSON 9·6 **"Fraction-of" a Collection**

Part One Answers vary.

1. Estimate the total number of pattern blocks in the jar given to you by your teacher. ______ pattern blocks
2. Estimate the total number of red trapezoids in the jar. ______ red trapezoids
3. Write your estimates as a fraction. $\frac{\text{total number of red trapezoids}}{\text{total number of pattern blocks}} = \frac{\square}{\square}$
4. Record the estimates made by the members of your group. ______ ______ ______ ______

Part Two

5. Count the number of pattern blocks in the jar. ______ pattern blocks
6. Count the number of red trapezoids in the jar. ______ red trapezoids
7. Record the counts as a fraction. $\frac{\text{total number of red trapezoids}}{\text{total number of pattern blocks}} = \frac{\square}{\square}$

Part Three

8. Which of your group members' estimates do you think was closest to the actual fraction of trapezoids in the jar? ______

Explain why you think so.

______

Math Masters, p. 292

9•7 Comparing Population Data

Objective To provide practice ranking and comparing data that are reported as percents and displaying ranked data by coloring maps.

Technology Resources www.everydaymathonline.com

ePresentations | eToolkit | Algorithms Practice | EM Facts Workshop Game™ | Family Letters | Assessment Management | Common Core State Standards | Curriculum Focal Points | Interactive Teacher's Lesson Guide

1 Teaching the Lesson

Key Concepts and Skills

- Interpret "percent-of" data.
  [Number and Numeration Goal 2]
- Order data reported as percents.
  [Number and Numeration Goal 6]
- Create a table, chart, and map to display data.
  [Data and Chance Goal 1]
- Interpret data displayed on a map.
  [Data and Chance Goal 2]

Key Activities

Students rank the countries in Region 4 (Asia and Australia) according to the percent of the population that is rural and the percent of the population that is 14 years old or younger.

Students color maps to display the ranked data and interpret the maps.

Ongoing Assessment: Recognizing Student Achievement Use journal page 265.
[Data and Chance Goal 2]

Key Vocabulary

urban ◆ rural ◆ life expectancy ◆ rank

Materials

Math Journal 2, pp. 264 and 265
Student Reference Book, pp. 300 and 301
Study Link 9•6
Math Masters, p. 293; p. 426 (optional)
red, green, and blue pencils, crayons, or markers ◆ slate ◆ index card (optional)

2 Ongoing Learning & Practice

Solving Probability Problems
Math Journal 2, p. 266
Students solve problems involving spinners, dice, and coins.

Ongoing Assessment: Informing Instruction See page 760.

Math Boxes 9•7
Math Journal 2, p. 263
Students practice and maintain skills through Math Box problems.

Study Link 9•7
Math Masters, p. 294
Students practice and maintain skills through Study Link activities.

3 Differentiation Options

ENRICHMENT

Displaying Literacy Data
Math Journal 2, p. 264
Student Reference Book, p. 299
Math Masters, pp. 293 and 295
red, green, and blue pencils, crayons, or markers
Students draw conclusions about the relationships among percent of population ages 0–14, percent of rural population, and percent of population that is literate.

ELL SUPPORT

Building Background for Mathematics Words
old magazines ◆ chart paper ◆ scissors
Students explore the terms *rural* and *urban.*

Advance Preparation

For Part 1, make two copies of *Math Masters,* page 293 for each student. For the optional ELL Support activity in Part 3, gather old magazines for students to cut apart.

***Teacher's Reference Manual,* Grades 4–6** pp. 69–71, 160–169

Getting Started

Mental Math and Reflexes

Write two fractions on the board. Have students write the greater fraction on their slates and explain their strategy for comparing them. *Suggestions:*

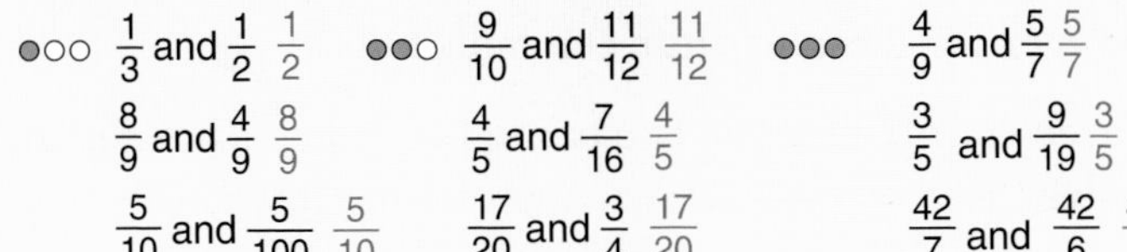

●○○ $\frac{1}{3}$ and $\frac{1}{2}$ $\frac{1}{2}$

$\frac{8}{9}$ and $\frac{4}{9}$ $\frac{8}{9}$

$\frac{5}{10}$ and $\frac{5}{100}$ $\frac{5}{10}$

●●○ $\frac{9}{10}$ and $\frac{11}{12}$ $\frac{11}{12}$

$\frac{4}{5}$ and $\frac{7}{16}$ $\frac{4}{5}$

$\frac{17}{20}$ and $\frac{3}{4}$ $\frac{17}{20}$

●●● $\frac{4}{9}$ and $\frac{5}{7}$ $\frac{5}{7}$

$\frac{3}{5}$ and $\frac{9}{19}$ $\frac{3}{5}$

$\frac{42}{7}$ and $\frac{42}{6}$ $\frac{42}{6}$

Math Message

Look at the table of data on Student Reference Book, *page 301. Be ready to talk about what kind of information is in the table.*

Study Link 9·6 Follow-Up

Review answers. Note that for Problem 3, there is more than one correct answer. Some students may choose Player 3 because she hit 100% of her shots. Some students may choose Player 4 because she hit a high percentage of her shots. Because Player 4 took more shots than Player 3, she may be more capable of taking a shot in a pressure situation. Acknowledge students who mention that in making a decision such as this, a coach would need to consider many different variables.

1 Teaching the Lesson

▸ Math Message Follow-Up

WHOLE-CLASS DISCUSSION

(*Student Reference Book,* pp. 300 and 301)

Social Studies Link Discuss the kinds of information shown in the table.

- According to the table, 21% of the population in the United States is 14 years old or younger. What does this mean? 21 out of 100 people in the United States are 14 or younger.
- Which countries have the largest and the smallest numbers in the Percent of Population Ages 0–14 column, and what do the numbers mean? The largest is 47 for Ethiopia: 47%, or 47 out of 100 Ethiopians, are 14 or younger. The smallest is 14 for Italy: 14%, or 14 out of 100 Italians, are 14 or younger.

Adjusting the Activity

Have students use an index card to highlight a specific row of data.

AUDITORY ◆ KINESTHETIC ◆ TACTILE ◆ VISUAL

Review the meanings of the words **urban** and **rural** as they refer to a town or city and a country area.

▷ According to the last two columns of the table, 80% of the U.S. population lives in towns or cities, and 20% of the U.S. population lives in the country. These two percents add up to 100% because the urban and rural groups together include everyone.

Student Page

World Tour

Population Data

The table on the opposite page lists population information for each country.

Life expectancy is the average number of years a person can expect to live. It is listed separately for males and females because women usually live longer than men.

Examples In the United States, women live an average of 80 years, and men live an average of 75 years. In Russia, women live an average of 13 years longer than men. Zimbabwe is the only country where men on average live longer than women.

Farming couple in Siberia

The **percent of people ages 0–14** is the number of people out of every 100 who are very young.

Examples In Liberia, 43% of the people are 14 or younger. That's nearly 50%, or one-half, of the people who are very young. In Italy, only 14% of the people are very young. Italy's fraction of very young people is much smaller than Liberia's fraction.

Percent urban is the number of people out of 100 who live in towns or cities. **Percent rural** is the number of people out of 100 who live in the country. These two percents add up to 100%.

Examples In the United States, 80 of 100 people live in towns or cities, while 20 out of 100 people live in the country. 80% + 20% = 100%

U.S. farmer feeding cattle

The population in most countries grows larger each year. The **percent population growth** is one way to measure how fast the population is growing.

Examples The population in Haiti increases by 2% each year.

For every 100 Haitians at the beginning of the year, there are 102 Haitians at the end of the year.

Student Reference Book, p. 300

Student Page

World Tour

Population Data

Region	Country	Percent of Population Ages 0–14	Life Expectancy: Males	Life Expectancy: Females	Percent Population Growth in 1 Year	Percent Urban	Percent Rural
Region 1	Algeria	34	71	74	1.3	59	41
	Egypt	34	68	73	1.9	42	58
	Ethiopia	47	40	42	1.9	16	84
	Ghana	40	55	57	1.4	45	55
	Kenya	41	45	45	1.2	39	61
	Liberia	43	47	49	2.7	47	53
	Morocco	34	68	73	1.7	58	42
	Senegal	44	55	58	2.5	50	50
	South Africa	32	44	44	–0.2	57	43
	Zimbabwe	38	39	37	0.7	35	65
Region 2	France	19	76	83	0.3	76	24
	Greece	15	76	82	0.0	61	39
	Hungary	16	68	77	–0.3	65	35
	Iceland	23	78	82	0.7	93	7
	Italy	14	77	83	–0.1	92	8
	Netherlands	18	76	81	0.3	66	34
	Norway	20	77	82	0.2	79	21
	Poland	18	70	79	0.1	62	38
	Spain	15	76	83	0.1	77	23
	United Kingdom	19	76	81	0.1	89	11
Region 3	Argentina	26	72	80	1.0	90	10
	Bolivia	38	63	68	1.7	63	37
	Brazil	28	68	76	1.1	83	17
	Chile	27	73	80	1.0	87	13
	Colombia	32	68	75	1.6	77	23
	Ecuador	35	73	79	1.9	62	38
	Paraguay	39	72	77	2.5	57	43
	Peru	34	68	71	1.5	74	26
	Uruguay	24	73	79	0.5	93	7
	Venezuela	32	71	77	1.4	88	12
Region 4	Australia	20	77	83	0.5	92	8
	Bangladesh	34	62	62	2.2	24	76
	China	24	70	74	0.6	39	61
	India	33	63	65	1.4	28	72
	Iran	32	68	71	1.2	67	33
	Japan	15	78	85	0.1	79	21
	Russia	17	60	73	–0.6	73	27
	Thailand	23	70	74	0.9	32	68
	Turkey	28	70	75	1.1	66	34
	Vietnam	33	68	73	1.3	26	74
Region 5	Canada	19	77	84	0.3	80	20
	Costa Rica	31	74	79	1.5	61	39
	Cuba	21	75	79	0.5	76	24
	El Salvador	37	67	75	2.2	60	40
	Guatemala	42	64	66	2.8	46	54
	Haiti	40	51	53	2.0	38	62
	Jamaica	29	74	78	1.2	67	33
	Mexico	33	72	78	1.7	76	24
	Panama	30	70	75	1.4	69	31
	U.S.	21	75	80	0.6	80	20

Student Reference Book, p. 301

Math Masters, p. 293

- Which countries have the greatest and least percents of their populations living in the country? 84% of Ethiopia's population is rural. 7% of both Iceland's and Uruguay's populations are rural.

The table includes **life expectancy** data, the average number of years a person can expect to live. Data for males and females are given separately. Highlight that in most countries the average lifetime is longer for females than for males. Ask:

- Which three countries have the same life expectancy for males and females? Kenya, South Africa, and Bangladesh
- In which country do males live longer than females? Zimbabwe 39 years for males and 37 years for females

The table includes population growth data expressed as percent growth for 1 year. Explain this column by giving examples:

▷ Haiti's growth is 2.0% in one year. For every 100 people in Haiti at the beginning of the year, there will be 100 + 2, or 102, people at the end of the year.

▷ Italy's growth is –0.1% in one year. A negative percent growth means the population is getting smaller. For every 100 people in Italy at the beginning of the year, there will be $100 - \frac{1}{10}$, or 99.9, people at the end of the year. That is, for every 1,000 people at the beginning of the year, there will be 999 people at the end of the year.

Adjusting the Activity

Have students add to or shade the hundreds grid at the top of *Math Masters,* page 426 to represent population growth for the countries in Region 4. See *Student Reference Book,* page 300 for a model.

AUDITORY ◆ KINESTHETIC ◆ TACTILE ◆ VISUAL

▶ Tallying Predictions

WHOLE-CLASS ACTIVITY

Tell students that in this activity they will focus on the percent of population ages 0–14 and the percent of population that lives in rural areas for Region 4—Asia and Australia. Ask:

- Do you think there is a connection between the percent of young people who live in a particular country and the percent of people who live in rural areas?

Make a tally of students' predictions on the board. Ask volunteers to explain the reasoning for their predictions.

Ranking Countries and Coloring Maps to Display Population Data

(*Math Journal 2,* p. 264; *Student Reference Book,* p. 301; *Math Masters,* p. 293)

Have partners use the top part of journal page 264 to **rank** and display the countries in Region 4 according to the data of the Population Data table (percent of population ages 0–14). They use the bottom part of journal page 264 to rank and display the countries according to the percent rural data.

Show students how to rank the countries in Region 4 according to the percent of population ages 0–14. Make a list numbered from 1 to 10 on the board.

- ▷ Ask which country in Region 4 has the smallest percent in the ages 0–14 column. Japan, 15% Write *Japan* as the first country on your list.
- ▷ Ask which country has the next-smallest percent in that column. Russia, 17% Write *Russia* as the second country on your list.
- ▷ Continue in the same way until all 10 countries in Region 4 have been listed. Note that Vietnam and India have the same percent.

We rank data when we list it in order from least to greatest or from greatest to least. The list students create ranks Region 4 countries from least to greatest percent of population ages 0–14 years.

Have students work with a partner to rank the Region 4 countries from least to greatest percent of population that is rural. Students record their lists at the bottom of journal page 264.

Tell students to title each copy of the map on *Math Masters,* page 293. Explain how to color the maps using the color code shown on journal page 264. For example, because Japan is ranked first on the chart for percent of population ages 0–14 and the color code for line 1 is blue, Japan should be colored blue on the map for that subject. On this same map, Turkey should be colored green, and India should be colored red.

When finished, each student will have two tables of country rankings and two colored maps—for percent of population ages 0–14 and for percent rural.

NOTE Suggest that students compare their rankings of the countries with those of other students and come to an agreement before coloring the maps.

Student Page

Date Time

LESSON 9•7 Color-Coded Population Maps

1. List the countries in Region 4 from *least to greatest* according to the **percent of population, ages 0–14.** Take one copy of *Math Masters,* page 293 and write a title for your first map. Color these countries using the color code shown below.

Rank	Country	Percent of Population Ages 0–14	Color Code
1	Japan	15%	blue
2	Russia	17%	blue
3	Australia	20%	blue
4	Thailand	23%	green
5	China	24%	green
6	Turkey	28%	green
7	Iran	32%	green
8	Vietnam	33%	red
9	India	33%	red
10	Bangladesh	34%	red

2. List the countries in Region 4 from *least to greatest* according to the **percent of population that is rural.** Take another copy of *Math Masters,* page 293 and write a title for your second map. Color these countries using the color code shown below.

Rank	Country	Percent of Rural Population	Color Code
1	Australia	8%	blue
2	Japan	21%	blue
3	Russia	27%	blue
4	Iran	33%	green
5	Turkey	34%	green
6	China	61%	green
7	Thailand	68%	green
8	India	72%	red
9	Vietnam	74%	red
10	Bangladesh	76%	red

Math Journal 2, p. 264

Student Page

Date Time

LESSON 9•7 Color-Coded Population Maps *continued*

3. What do the map colors mean?
   a. blue Lowest percent of population
   b. green Middle percent of population
   c. red Highest percent of population

4. a. Which countries are colored blue on both maps? Japan, Russia, Australia
   b. What does this tell you about these countries? They do not have many children under age 14, and most of the people live in urban areas, not rural areas.

5. a. Which countries are colored red on both maps? Bangladesh, India, and Vietnam
   b. What does this tell you about these countries? They have many children under age 14, and most of the people live in rural areas.

6. a. Based on the data tables and maps, do you think there is a connection between the percent of young people who live in a particular country and the percent of people who live in rural areas? yes
   Explain your answer. Sample answer: The 3 countries that have the lowest percentages of people under 14 also have the lowest percentages of people living in rural areas. The 3 countries with the highest percentages of children under 14 also have the highest percentages of people living in rural areas. ★
   b. How does your conclusion compare with the prediction that you made at the beginning of the lesson? Answers vary.

Math Journal 2, p. 265

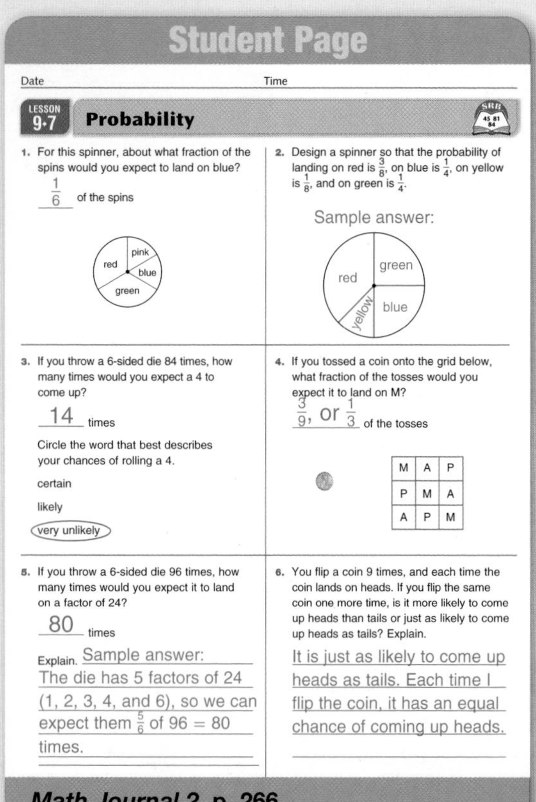

Student Page

Date Time

LESSON 9·7 **Probability**

1. For this spinner, about what fraction of the spins would you expect to land on blue? $\frac{1}{6}$ of the spins

2. Design a spinner so that the probability of landing on red is $\frac{3}{8}$, on blue is $\frac{1}{4}$, on yellow is $\frac{1}{8}$, and on green is $\frac{1}{4}$.
Sample answer:

3. If you throw a 6-sided die 84 times, how many times would you expect a 4 to come up? 14 times
Circle the word that best describes your chances of rolling a 4.
certain
likely
very unlikely (circled)

4. If you tossed a coin onto the grid below, what fraction of the tosses would you expect it to land on M? $\frac{3}{9}$, or $\frac{1}{3}$ of the tosses

M	A	P
P	M	A
A	P	M

5. If you throw a 6-sided die 96 times, how many times would you expect it to land on a factor of 24? 80 times
Explain. Sample answer: The die has 5 factors of 24 (1, 2, 3, 4, and 6), so we can expect them $\frac{5}{6}$ of 96 = 80 times.

6. You flip a coin 9 times, and each time the coin lands on heads. If you flip the same coin one more time, is it more likely to come up heads than tails or just as likely to come up heads as tails? Explain.
It is just as likely to come up heads as tails. Each time I flip the coin, it has an equal chance of coming up heads.

Math Journal 2, p. 266

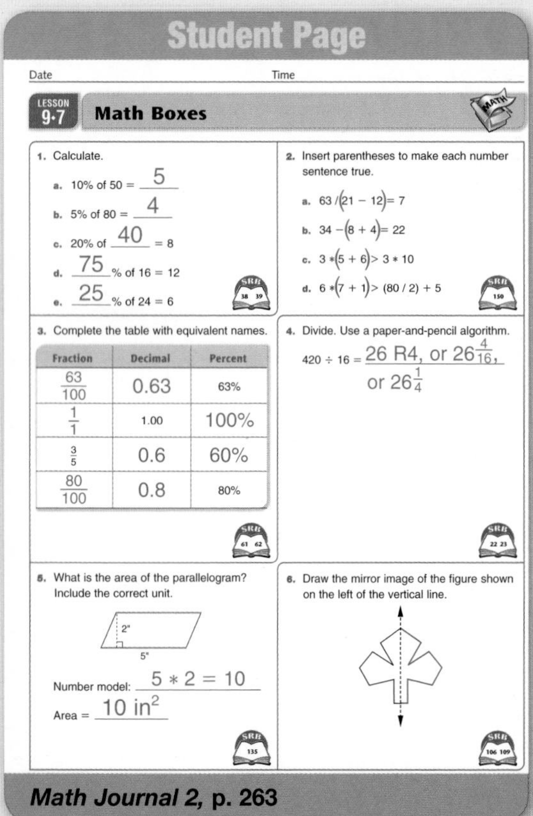

Student Page

Date Time

LESSON 9·7 **Math Boxes**

1. Calculate.
a. 10% of 50 = 5
b. 5% of 80 = 4
c. 20% of 40 = 8
d. 75 % of 16 = 12
e. 25 % of 24 = 6

2. Insert parentheses to make each number sentence true.
a. 63 / (21 − 12) = 7
b. 34 − (8 + 4) = 22
c. 3 ∗ (5 + 6) > 3 ∗ 10
d. 6 ∗ (7 + 1) > (80 / 2) + 5

3. Complete the table with equivalent names.

Fraction	Decimal	Percent
$\frac{63}{100}$	0.63	63%
$\frac{1}{1}$	1.00	100%
$\frac{3}{5}$	0.6	60%
$\frac{80}{100}$	0.8	80%

4. Divide. Use a paper-and-pencil algorithm.
420 ÷ 16 = 26 R4, or $26\frac{4}{16}$, or $26\frac{1}{4}$

5. What is the area of the parallelogram? Include the correct unit.
Number model: 5 ∗ 2 = 10
Area = 10 in^2

6. Draw the mirror image of the figure shown on the left of the vertical line.

Math Journal 2, p. 263

Interpreting the Maps

(*Math Journal 2,* p. 265; *Math Masters,* p. 293)

Have small groups use their maps to answer Problems 3–5 on journal page 265. Ask students to answer Problem 6 independently.

Ongoing Assessment: Recognizing Student Achievement

Journal page 265 Problem 6

Use **journal page 265, Problem 6** to assess students' ability to draw conclusions from a data representation. Students are making adequate progress if they state that there seems to be a connection between the percent of young people and the percent of people who live in a rural area. Some students may note that there are countries that have the same color coding, but whose percentages differ greatly, while other countries have a different color coding but have similar percentages.

[Data and Chance Goal 2]

When most groups have completed the journal page, ask: *What are some advantages and disadvantages of displaying data by coloring maps?* This discussion should include the following points:

- It is easier to compare data about countries and groups of countries at a glance. However, the map does not give you as accurate of a picture as a data table would.
- For example, Turkey and Thailand have the same color on the percentage-rural map, meaning that both countries are in the middle group for this measure. But we know from the table that Thailand has double the percent of population living in rural areas (68%) that Turkey does (34%).

2 Ongoing Learning & Practice

Solving Probability Problems

(*Math Journal 2,* p. 266)

Students solve problems involving spinners, dice, and coins.

Ongoing Assessment: Informing Instruction

Watch for students who expect the spinner to land on blue $\frac{1}{4}$ of the time in Problem 1. Point out that the spinner is divided into 4 parts, but the 4 parts are not equal. Blue is $\frac{1}{6}$ of the region.

Math Boxes 9·7

INDEPENDENT ACTIVITY

(*Math Journal 2,* p. 263)

Mixed Practice Math Boxes in this lesson are linked with Math Boxes in Lessons 9-5 and 9-9. The skill in Problem 6 previews Unit 10 content.

Writing/Reasoning Have students write a response to the following: *Use a drawing and number models to explain how you found the percent for Problem 1e.* Sample answer: 24 is the ONE, or the whole. 6 is $\frac{1}{4}$ of 24, and $\frac{1}{4}$ is equivalent to 25%, so 25% of 24 is 6.

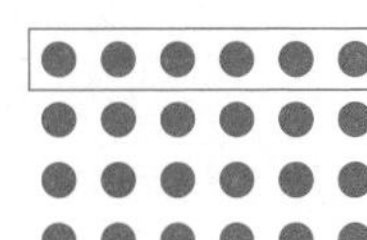

$\frac{6}{24} = \frac{1}{4} = 25\%$

Study Link 9·7

(*Math Masters,* p. 294)

Home Connection Students use population data from the 10 least-populated countries in the world to solve problems.

3 Differentiation Options

ENRICHMENT

Displaying Literacy Data

(*Math Journal 2,* p. 264, *Student Reference Book,* p. 299; *Math Masters,* pp. 293 and 295)

To apply students' ability to display and interpret data, have them rank countries and color a map to show literacy data. Then have them use this information to draw conclusions about the relationships among percent of population ages 0–14 years, percent of rural population, and percent of population literacy.

ELL SUPPORT

Building Background for Mathematics Words

To provide language support for population data, have students create a poster with visual references, which might include magazine photos, for the terms *rural* and *urban*. Point out map examples of U.S. rural and urban areas. Ask students whether they live in a rural or an urban area and tell why they think so.

Study Link Master

Name Date Time

STUDY LINK 9·7 **Least-Populated Countries**

The table below shows the approximate population for the 10 least-populated countries in the world. Use the data to estimate answers to the problems.

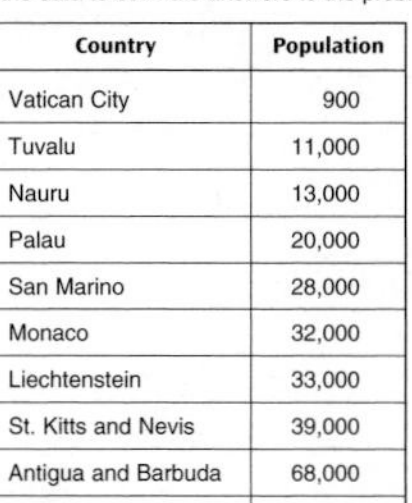

Country	Population
Vatican City	900
Tuvalu	11,000
Nauru	13,000
Palau	20,000
San Marino	28,000
Monaco	32,000
Liechtenstein	33,000
St. Kitts and Nevis	39,000
Antigua and Barbuda	68,000
Dominica	69,000

Source: Top Ten of Everything 2004

1. The population of Liechtenstein is about 50 % of the population of Dominica.
2. What country's population is about 33% of Liechtenstein's population? Tuvalu
3. The population of Vatican City is about 5 % of the population of Palau.
4. The population of the 10 countries listed is 314,900. What 3 country populations together equal about 50% of that total? Sample answer: Dominica, Antigua and Barbuda, and Palau
5. The population of St. Kitts and Nevis is about 300 % of Nauru's population.

Practice

6. 27 * 4 = 108
7. 4,064 = 508 * 8
8. 5,418 = 63 * 86
9. 849 * 52 = 44,148

Math Masters, p. 294

Teaching Master

Name Date Time

LESSON 9·7 **Color-Coded Map for Percent of Literacy**

A **literate** person is a person who can read and write. People who cannot read and write are said to be **illiterate.**

Percent of literacy is the fraction of the total population that is literate—the number of people out of 100 who are literate. Young children are not counted until they reach an age at which they are expected to read and write.

1. Make a prediction: Do you think there is a relationship among population statistics on literacy, age, and rural or urban living? Answers vary.
2. In the table below, list the countries in Region 4 from *greatest* to *least* according to the percent of the population that is literate. (See *Student Reference Book,* page 299.)

Rank	Country	Percent of Literacy	Color Code
1	Australia	100%	blue
2	Japan	100%	blue
3	Russia	100%	blue
4	Thailand	96%	green
5	Vietnam	94%	green
6	Turkey	87%	green
7	China	86%	green
8	Iran	79%	red
9	India	60%	red
10	Bangladesh	43%	red

3. Color these countries on the map on *Math Masters,* page 293 according to the color code in the table.
4. Compare this map with the population ages 0–14 and percent rural maps. Do the data support the prediction you made in Problem 1? ________

Explain your answer on the back of this page. Include reasons why you think a country might be colored red or blue on all three maps.

Math Masters, p. 295

9•8 Multiplication of Decimals

Objectives To introduce multiplication of decimals by whole numbers; and to reinforce the partial-products and lattice methods for multiplication.

www.everydaymathonline.com

ePresentations

eToolkit

Algorithms Practice

EM Facts Workshop Game™

Family Letters

Assessment Management

Common Core State Standards

Curriculum Focal Points

Interactive Teacher's Lesson Guide

1 Teaching the Lesson

Key Concepts and Skills

- Identify place value in decimals through hundredths.
  [Number and Numeration Goal 1]
- Multiply decimals by whole numbers.
  [Operations and Computation Goal 4]
- Round decimals and estimate products.
  [Operations and Computation Goal 6]
- Use repeated addition to model multiplication.
  [Operations and Computation Goal 7]
- Use a formula to calculate the area of a rectangle.
  [Measurement and Reference Frames Goal 2]
- Use conventional notation to write number sentences.
  [Patterns, Functions, and Algebra Goal 2]

Key Activities

Students use an estimation strategy for multiplying decimals. They solve a set of decimal multiplication problems that offers review and practice of the partial-products and lattice algorithms.

Ongoing Assessment: Recognizing Student Achievement
Use journal page 268.
[Operations and Computation Goal 6]

Materials

Math Journal 2, pp. 268 and 269
Study Link 9•7
Math Masters, pp. 404 and 434
slate

2 Ongoing Learning & Practice

Playing *Over and Up Squares*
Student Reference Book, p. 257
Math Masters, p. 494
per partnership: 2 six-sided dice, colored pencils
Students practice locating and plotting points on a coordinate grid.

Math Boxes 9•8
Math Journal 2, p. 267
Students practice and maintain skills through Math Box problems.

Study Link 9•8
Math Masters, p. 296
Students practice and maintain skills through Study Link activities.

3 Differentiation Options

READINESS

Multiplying Whole Numbers and Estimating Products
Math Masters, p. 297
Students multiply whole numbers and estimate products.

READINESS

Solving Number Stories
Math Masters, pp. 114 and 428
coins
Students use bills and coins to model multiplication number stories involving whole numbers and decimals.

ENRICHMENT

Comparing Products
Math Masters, p. 388 or 389
Students estimate and compare the product of two decimal numbers with the product of two mixed numbers.

Advance Preparation

***Teacher's Reference Manual,* Grades 4–6** pp. 126–132

Getting Started

Mental Math and Reflexes

Pose multiplication problems. Have students estimate the product and write a number model to show how they estimated. Discuss the strategies used. *Suggestions:*

Sample answers:

●○○		●●○		●●●	
9 ∗ 18	9 ∗ 20 = 180	28 ∗ 49	30 ∗ 50 = 1,500	81 ∗ 119	80 ∗ 100 = 8,000
11 ∗ 42	10 ∗ 40 = 400	53 ∗ 78	50 ∗ 80 = 4,000	45 ∗ 188	50 ∗ 200 = 10,000
22 ∗ 76	20 ∗ 75 = 1,500	63 ∗ 63	60 ∗ 60 = 3,600	72 ∗ 414	70 ∗ 400 = 28,000
87 ∗ 15	90 ∗ 20 = 1,800	98 ∗ 59	100 ∗ 59 = 5,900	609 ∗ 684	600 ∗ 700 = 420,000

Math Message

Solve the problem at the top of journal page 268.

Study Link 9·7 Follow-Up

Have students share their answers and solution strategies. Some students may note that when working with populations rounded to the nearest ten thousand, they only have to consider the first two digits.

1 Teaching the Lesson

Math Message Follow-Up

WHOLE-CLASS DISCUSSION

(*Math Journal 2,* p. 268)

Have students share their solution strategies.

▷ Use repeated addition: 1.2 + 1.2 + . . . + 1.2 = 9.6.

▷ Multiply 8 and 1 and then add up 0.2 eight times.

▷ Others may approach it as a multiplication problem. Have those students explain how they decided where to place the decimal point. Ask: *Why are 96 and 0.96 not reasonable answers?* Because 1.2 is less than 2, the answer must be less than 16, so 96 is not a reasonable answer. Because 1.2 is greater than 0.96, 0.96 is too small, so the answer must be 9.6.

Links to the Future

Use of mental arithmetic, paper-and-pencil algorithms, and calculators to solve problems involving the multiplication of decimals is a Grade 5 Goal.

Estimating Products of Decimals

WHOLE-CLASS ACTIVITY

Tell students that in this lesson they will learn to find the product of decimals by multiplying the numbers as if they were whole numbers and then using estimation to place the decimal point in the answer.

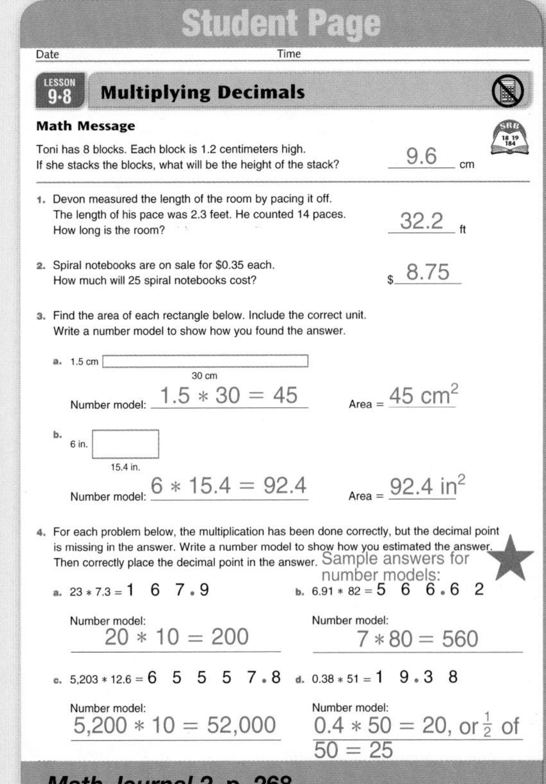

Student Page
Date
Time
LESSON 9·8
Multiplying Decimals
Math Message
Toni has 8 blocks. Each block is 1.2 centimeters high.
If she stacks the blocks, what will be the height of the stack?
9.6 cm
1. Devon measured the length of the room by pacing it off.
The length of his pace was 2.3 feet. He counted 14 paces.
How long is the room?
32.2 ft
2. Spiral notebooks are on sale for $0.35 each.
How much will 25 spiral notebooks cost?
$ 8.75
3. Find the area of each rectangle below. Include the correct unit.
Write a number model to show how you found the answer.
a. 1.5 cm
30 cm
Number model: 1.5 ∗ 30 = 45
Area = 45 cm²
b. 6 in.
15.4 in.
Number model: 6 ∗ 15.4 = 92.4
Area = 92.4 in²
4. For each problem below, the multiplication has been done correctly, but the decimal point is missing in the answer. Write a number model to show how you estimated the answer. Then correctly place the decimal point in the answer.
Sample answers for number models:
a. 23 ∗ 7.3 = 1 6 7.9
Number model: 20 ∗ 10 = 200
b. 6.91 ∗ 82 = 5 6 6.6 2
Number model: 7 ∗ 80 = 560
c. 5,203 ∗ 12.6 = 6 5 5 5 7.8
Number model: 5,200 ∗ 10 = 52,000
d. 0.38 ∗ 51 = 1 9.3 8
Number model: 0.4 ∗ 50 = 20, or ½ of 50 = 25

Math Journal 2, p. 268

To practice estimating products, write the following problems on the board:

11 ∗ 2.8 110 ∗ 2.8 11 ∗ 0.28

Ask students to estimate each product. Write some of their responses next to the problems, and discuss their estimates. For example, some students may round 11 ∗ 2.8 to 11 ∗ 3 and estimate 33. Others may multiply 10 ∗ 3 = 30 or 10 ∗ 2 = 20. The purpose of this estimate is to help them place the decimal point, so any of these estimates is satisfactory. Ask:

- Which problem is most likely to have the answer 30.8? 11 ∗ 2.8
- How do you know? The estimates made for this problem were about 20 or 30. The estimates for the other problems were much larger or smaller.

Write the number 308 next to the problem 110 ∗ 2.8. Ask:

- Where would you place the decimal point? After the 8
- How do you know? Sample answer: The answer must be larger than 110 ∗ 1.

Write the number 308 next to the problem 11 ∗ 0.28. Ask:

- Where would you place the decimal point? Between the 3 and 0
- How do you know? Sample answer: The answer is less than 11 ∗ 1 = 11; so 308 and 30.8 are too large. The answer is much larger than 1 ∗ 0.28; so 0.308 is too small. That leaves 3.08 as the answer.

Now write the following problem on the board:

Calculators are on sale for $9.29 each. How much will 5 of them cost?

Ask students to estimate the cost of 5 calculators.

5 ∗ $9 = $45 and 5 ∗ $10 = $50, so they will cost between 45 and 50 dollars.

Have volunteers come to the board and multiply 5 ∗ 929 (9.29 without the decimal point). Ask some students to use the partial-products method and others to use the lattice method. (*See margin.*)

Finally, have students use their initial estimates of the total cost to place the decimal. 5 ∗ 929 = 4,645 and the estimate was about $50. So place the decimal point after the 6; the total cost is $46.45.

```
   929
 ∗   5
 4,500
   100
+   45
 4,645
```

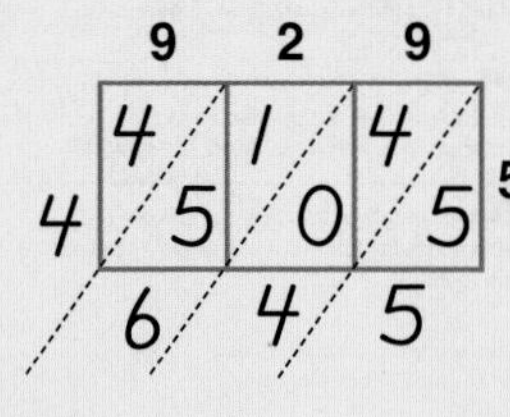

Help students summarize the use of estimation to place the decimal point in the answer when multiplying decimals.

Example: $6 * 3.7 = ?$

1. Estimate the product.

   $6 * 3.7$ is about $6 * 4$, or 24.

2. Multiply the factors as though they were whole numbers.

   $6 * 37 = 222$

3. Use the estimate to place the decimal point in the answer.

   22.2 is close to the estimate of 24.

Multiplying Decimals

(*Math Journal 2,* pp. 268 and 269; *Math Masters,* pp. 404 and 434)

Ask students to complete journal pages 268 and 269 and compare answers.

Adjusting the Activity

Have students use lattice multiplication adapted for decimals. Show them how to find the intersection of the decimal points along the horizontal and vertical lines; then slide down the diagonal. Encourage students to still make estimates in order to check their work.

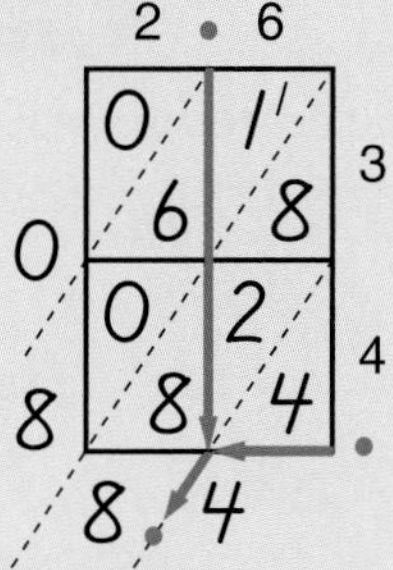

Decimal multiplied by whole number

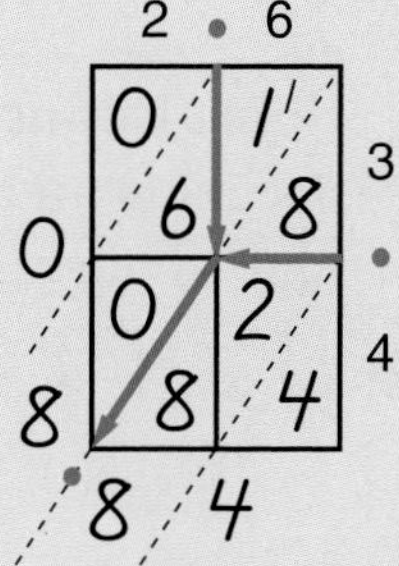

Decimal multiplied by decimal

AUDITORY ◆ KINESTHETIC ◆ TACTILE ◆ VISUAL

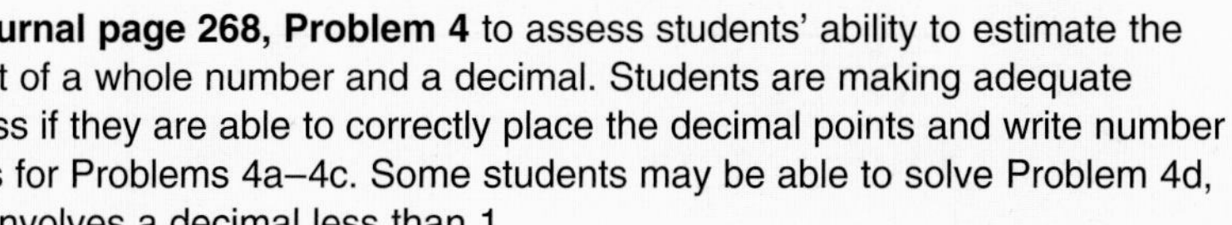

Ongoing Assessment: Recognizing Student Achievement

Journal page 268 Problem 4

Use **journal page 268, Problem 4** to assess students' ability to estimate the product of a whole number and a decimal. Students are making adequate progress if they are able to correctly place the decimal points and write number models for Problems 4a–4c. Some students may be able to solve Problem 4d, which involves a decimal less than 1.

[Operations and Computation Goal 6]

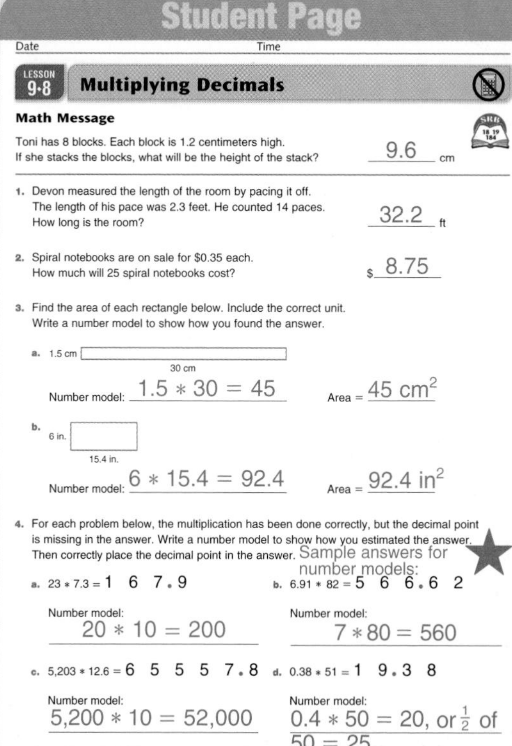

Student Page

Date Time

LESSON 9•8 **Multiplying Decimals**

Math Message

Toni has 8 blocks. Each block is 1.2 centimeters high. If she stacks the blocks, what will be the height of the stack? 9.6 cm

1. Devon measured the length of the room by pacing it off. The length of his pace was 2.3 feet. He counted 14 paces. How long is the room? 32.2 ft

2. Spiral notebooks are on sale for $0.35 each. How much will 25 spiral notebooks cost? $8.75

3. Find the area of each rectangle below. Include the correct unit. Write a number model to show how you found the answer.

   a. 1.5 cm, 30 cm — Number model: $1.5 * 30 = 45$ Area = 45 cm^2

   b. 6 in., 15.4 in. — Number model: $6 * 15.4 = 92.4$ Area = 92.4 in^2

4. For each problem below, the multiplication has been done correctly, but the decimal point is missing in the answer. Write a number model to show how you estimated the answer. Then correctly place the decimal point in the answer. Sample answers for number models:

   a. $23 * 7.3 =$ 1 6 7 . 9 — Number model: $20 * 10 = 200$

   b. $6.91 * 82 =$ 5 6 6 . 6 2 — Number model: $7 * 80 = 560$

   c. $5{,}203 * 12.6 =$ 6 5 5 5 7 . 8 — Number model: $5{,}200 * 10 = 52{,}000$

   d. $0.38 * 51 =$ 1 9 . 3 8 — Number model: $0.4 * 50 = 20$, or $\frac{1}{2}$ of $50 = 25$

Math Journal 2, p. 268

Algorithm Project In this lesson, students use partial products and lattice multiplication to solve decimal multiplication problems. To teach U.S. traditional multiplication with decimals, see Algorithm Project 6 on page A26.

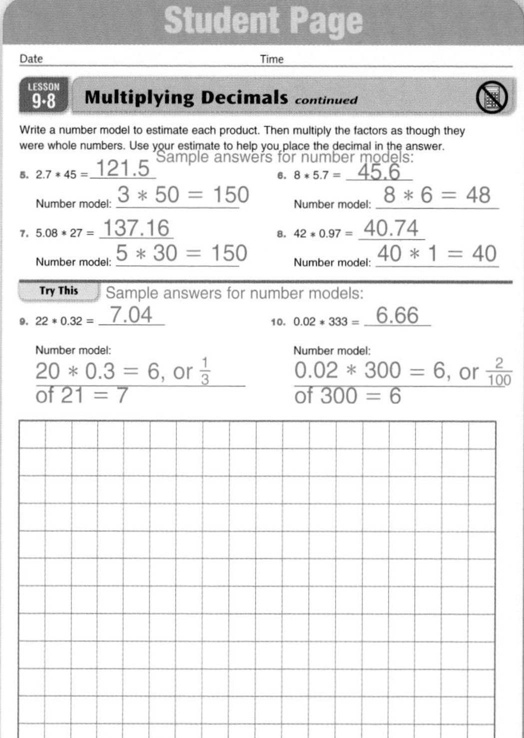

Student Page

Date Time

LESSON 9•8 **Multiplying Decimals** *continued*

Write a number model to estimate each product. Then multiply the factors as though they were whole numbers. Use your estimate to help you place the decimal in the answer. Sample answers for number models:

5. $2.7 * 45 =$ 121.5 — Number model: $3 * 50 = 150$

6. $8 * 5.7 =$ 45.6 — Number model: $8 * 6 = 48$

7. $5.08 * 27 =$ 137.16 — Number model: $5 * 30 = 150$

8. $42 * 0.97 =$ 40.74 — Number model: $40 * 1 = 40$

Try This Sample answers for number models:

9. $22 * 0.32 =$ 7.04 — Number model: $20 * 0.3 = 6$, or $\frac{1}{3}$ of $21 = 7$

10. $0.02 * 333 =$ 6.66 — Number model: $0.02 * 300 = 6$, or $\frac{2}{100}$ of $300 = 6$

Math Journal 2, p. 269

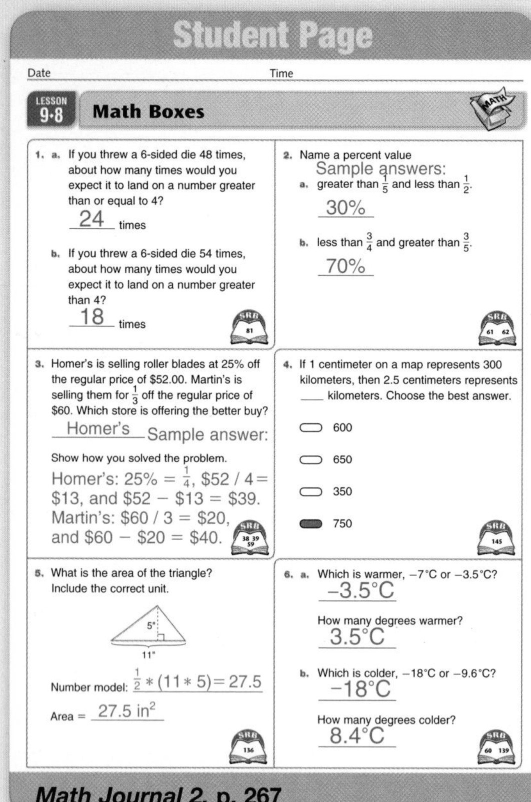
Student Page

Date Time

LESSON 9·8 **Math Boxes**

1. a. If you threw a 6-sided die 48 times, about how many times would you expect it to land on a number greater than or equal to 4? 24 times

b. If you threw a 6-sided die 54 times, about how many times would you expect it to land on a number greater than 4? 18 times

2. Name a percent value Sample answers:

a. greater than $\frac{1}{5}$ and less than $\frac{1}{2}$. 30%

b. less than $\frac{3}{4}$ and greater than $\frac{3}{5}$. 70%

3. Homer's is selling roller blades at 25% off the regular price of \$52.00. Martin's is selling them for $\frac{1}{3}$ off the regular price of \$60. Which store is offering the better buy? Homer's Sample answer:

Show how you solved the problem.

Homer's: $25\% = \frac{1}{4}$, \$52 / 4 = \$13, and \$52 − \$13 = \$39. Martin's: \$60 / 3 = \$20, and \$60 − \$20 = \$40.

4. If 1 centimeter on a map represents 300 kilometers, then 2.5 centimeters represents ____ kilometers. Choose the best answer.

- 600
- 650
- 350
- 750 (filled in)

5. What is the area of the triangle? Include the correct unit.

Number model: $\frac{1}{2} * (11 * 5) = 27.5$

Area = 27.5 in^2

6. a. Which is warmer, −7°C or −3.5°C? −3.5°C

How many degrees warmer? 3.5°C

b. Which is colder, −18°C or −9.6°C? −18°C

How many degrees colder? 8.4°C

Math Journal 2, p. 267

NOTE In Math Boxes, Problem 6, students compare Celsius temperatures. For a monthlong activity recording, graphing, and comparing temperatures using Celsius and Fahrenheit, see www.everydaymathonline.com.

2 Ongoing Learning & Practice

▶ Playing *Over and Up Squares*

PARTNER ACTIVITY

(*Student Reference Book,* p. 257; *Math Masters,* p. 494)

Students play *Over and Up Squares* to practice locating and plotting points on a coordinate grid. See Lesson 6-9 for additional information.

▶ Math Boxes 9·8

INDEPENDENT ACTIVITY

(*Math Journal 2,* p. 267)

Mixed Practice Math Boxes in this lesson are paired with Math Boxes in Lesson 9-6. The skill in Problem 6 previews Unit 10 content.

Writing/Reasoning Have students write a response to the following: *Explain how you solved Problem 2b.* Sample answer: $\frac{3}{4}$ is equivalent to 75%. $\frac{3}{5}$ is equivalent to 60%. I named a percent value between 60% and 75%.

▶ Study Link 9·8

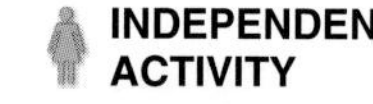
INDEPENDENT ACTIVITY

(*Math Masters,* p. 296)

Home Connection Students estimate products of decimals and whole numbers. They multiply decimals and whole numbers.

Study Link Master

Name Date Time

STUDY LINK 9·8 **Multiplying Decimals**

For each problem below, the multiplication has been done correctly, but the decimal point is missing in the answer. Correctly place the decimal point in the answer.

1. 6 ∗ 4.3 = 2 5.8
2. 72 ∗ 6.8 = 4 8 9.6
3. 0.96 ∗ 47 = 4 5.1 2
4. 5.12 ∗ 22 = 1 1 2.6 4
5. 8,457 ∗ 9.8 = 8 2 8 7 8.6
6. 0.04 ∗ 140 = 5.6

7. Explain how you decided where to place the decimal point in Problem 4. Sample answer: I rounded the numbers to 5 and 20 and then multiplied to get 100. So, the product should be close to 100, and 112.64 is.

Try This

Multiply. Show your work.

8. 5.9 ∗ 36 = 212.4
9. 0.46 ∗ 84 = 38.64
10. 382.13 = 7.21 ∗ 53

Practice

11. 16 = 96 ÷ 6
12. 4)67 = 16 R3, or $16\frac{3}{4}$
13. 137 = 411 / 3
14. 9)903 = 100 R3, or $100\frac{3}{9}$

Math Masters, p. 296

3 Differentiation Options

READINESS

Multiplying Whole Numbers and Estimating Products

COMPUTATION PRACTICE

(*Math Masters,* p. 297)

To provide experience with whole-number multiplication and estimating products, have students complete *Math Masters,* page 297.

READINESS

Solving Number Stories

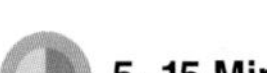

(*Math Masters,* pp. 114 and 428)

To explore multiplication of whole numbers by decimals using a money context, have students use the items on *Math Masters,* page 114 and dollars and cents to model, write, and solve multiplication number stories. *For example:*

Max bought 5 packs of light bulbs.

About how much money did he spend?

$5 * \$1.09 = \$5.45$

ENRICHMENT

Comparing Products

(*Math Masters,* p. 388 or 389)

To apply students' understanding of decimal multiplication and decimal/fraction equivalencies, have students estimate and compare the product of two mixed numbers and the product of two decimals. Ask students to record their responses to the following in a Math Log or on an Exit Slip:

Think about these two multiplication problems:

$5\frac{1}{2} * 2\frac{1}{3}$ $\quad$ $2.36 * 5.206$

Without using a paper-and-pencil algorithm or a calculator, which product do you think is greater? Explain. Sample answer: $5\frac{1}{2} * 2\frac{1}{3}$; $5\frac{1}{2} = 5.5$ and $5.5 > 5.206$. $2\frac{1}{3} = 2.3\overline{3}$, which is only a bit less than 2.36. So the first product is greater.

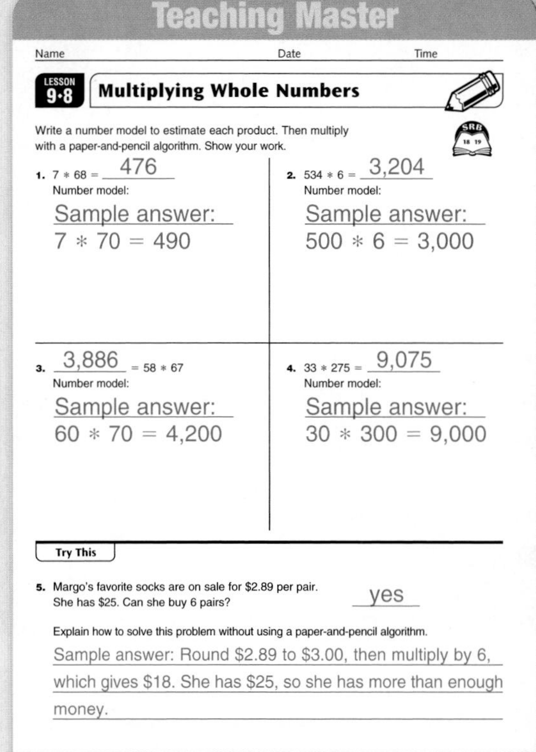

Teaching Master

Name Date Time

LESSON 9·8 **Multiplying Whole Numbers**

Write a number model to estimate each product. Then multiply with a paper-and-pencil algorithm. Show your work.

1. $7 * 68 =$ 476
Number model: Sample answer: $7 * 70 = 490$

2. $534 * 6 =$ 3,204
Number model: Sample answer: $500 * 6 = 3,000$

3. 3,886 $= 58 * 67$
Number model: Sample answer: $60 * 70 = 4,200$

4. $33 * 275 =$ 9,075
Number model: Sample answer: $30 * 300 = 9,000$

Try This

5. Margo's favorite socks are on sale for \$2.89 per pair. She has \$25. Can she buy 6 pairs? yes

Explain how to solve this problem without using a paper-and-pencil algorithm.
Sample answer: Round \$2.89 to \$3.00, then multiply by 6, which gives \$18. She has \$25, so she has more than enough money.

Math Masters, p. 297

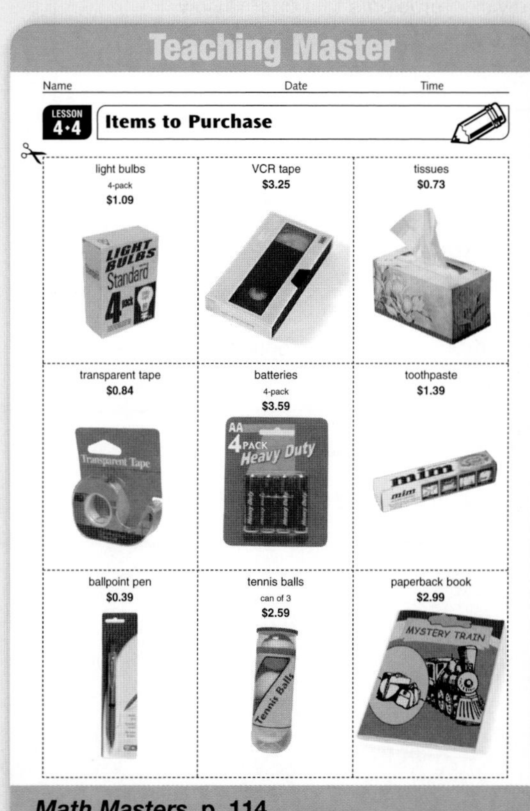

Teaching Master

Name Date Time

LESSON 4·4 **Items to Purchase**

light bulbs 4-pack \$1.09	VCR tape \$3.25	tissues \$0.73
transparent tape \$0.84	batteries 4-pack \$3.59	toothpaste \$1.39
ballpoint pen \$0.39	tennis balls can of 3 \$2.59	paperback book \$2.99

Math Masters, p. 114

9•9 Division of Decimals

Objectives To introduce division of decimals by whole numbers; and to reinforce the partial-quotients division algorithm.

www.everydaymathonline.com

ePresentations

eToolkit

Algorithms Practice

EM Facts Workshop Game™

Family Letters

Assessment Management

Common Core State Standards

Curriculum Focal Points

Interactive Teacher's Lesson Guide

1 Teaching the Lesson

Key Concepts and Skills

- Identify place value in decimals through hundredths. [Number and Numeration Goal 1]
- Divide decimals by whole numbers. [Operations and Computation Goal 4]
- Round decimals and estimate quotients. [Operations and Computation Goal 6]
- Use conventional notation to write number sentences. [Patterns, Functions, and Algebra Goal 2]

Key Activities

Students use an estimation strategy for dividing decimals. They solve decimal division problems that offer review and practice of the partial-quotients division algorithm.

Ongoing Assessment: Recognizing Student Achievement Use journal page 270. [Operations and Computation Goal 6]

Materials

Math Journal 2, pp. 270 and 271
Study Link 9•8
Math Masters, p. 404 (optional)
slate

2 Ongoing Learning & Practice

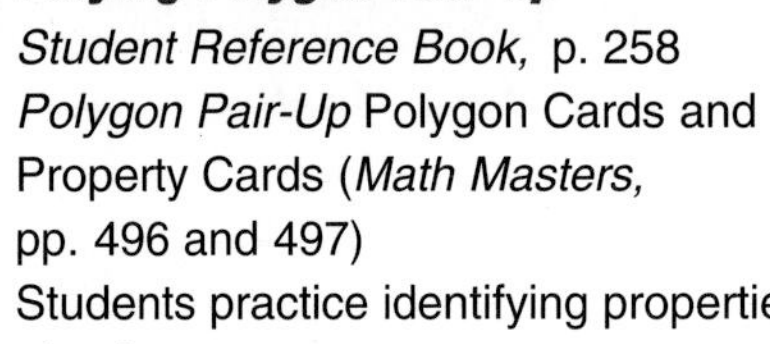

Playing *Polygon Pair-Up*
Student Reference Book, p. 258
Polygon Pair-Up Polygon Cards and Property Cards (*Math Masters,* pp. 496 and 497)
Students practice identifying properties of polygons.

Math Boxes 9•9
Math Journal 2, p. 272
Students practice and maintain skills through Math Box problems.

Study Link 9•9
Math Masters, p. 298
Students practice and maintain skills through Study Link activities.

3 Differentiation Options

READINESS

Dividing Whole Numbers and Estimating Quotients
Math Masters, p. 299
Students divide whole numbers by whole numbers and estimate quotients.

READINESS

Solving Division Number Stories Involving Money
Math Masters, pp. 114 and 428
coins
Students use bills and coins to model division number stories involving decimals and whole numbers.

ENRICHMENT

Writing and Solving Division Number Stories with Decimals
Students write and solve number stories involving division of decimals.

Advance Preparation

***Teacher's Reference Manual,* Grades 4–6** pp. 132–140

Getting Started

Mental Math and Reflexes

Pose division problems. Have students estimate the quotient and write a number model to show how they estimated. Discuss the strategies used. *Suggestions:*

Sample answers:

●○○		●●○		●●●	
61 / 3	60 / 3 = 20	135 / 7	140 / 7 = 20	731 / 99	700 / 100 = 7
37 / 2	40 / 2 = 20	344 / 5	350 / 5 = 70	419 / 51	400 / 50 = 8
59 / 5	60 / 5 = 12	641 / 8	640 / 8 = 80	555 / 62	540 / 60 = 9
86 / 3	90 / 3 = 30	459 / 9	450 / 9 = 50	1,946 / 204	2,000 / 200 = 10

Math Message

Think of a number story that could be solved by dividing 4.2 by 7. Be prepared to discuss your answer.

Study Link 9·8 Follow-Up

Have small groups compare answers. Ask volunteers to share the strategies they used to determine where to place the decimal point in each product. Students indicate thumbs-up if they used a similar strategy.

1 Teaching the Lesson

Math Message Follow-Up

WHOLE-CLASS DISCUSSION

Discuss students' answers. The goal of the Math Message and follow-up activity is to increase students' awareness of how decimal division problems are based on real-life problems.

Suggest examples like the following, which illustrate different uses for division:

▷ **Partitioning into equal parts:** A ribbon is 4.2 meters long. It must be cut into 7 pieces of the same length. 0.6 meters or 60 cm each

▷ **Money and equal sharing:** Think of 4.2 as \$4.20, which is to be shared equally among 7 students. \$0.60 or 60¢ each

▷ **Calculating an average:** Tom watched TV for a total of 4.2 hours in one week. His average viewing time per day was $4.2 \div 7$ hours. 0.6 hours or 36 minutes

▷ **Calculating a fraction or a percent:** Alice and Dave took a 7-hour trip, and Alice drove for 4.2 hours. So $\frac{4.2}{7}$ is the fraction of time that Alice drove, and $(4.2 \div 7) * 100$ equals the percent of the time that she drove. $0.6 * 100 = 60$ percent

Links to the Future

Use of mental arithmetic, paper-and-pencil algorithms, and calculators to solve problems involving the division of decimals by whole numbers is a Grade 5 Goal.

▶ Estimating Quotients of Decimals

As they did with multiplication of decimals, students will use estimation to place decimal points in the answers to problems involving division of decimals.

Write the following problems on the board. Write the 4-digit quotient shown for each problem, but do not include any decimal point.

$$\begin{array}{r}1350\\3\overline{)40.5}\end{array}\qquad\begin{array}{r}3772\\4\overline{)150.88}\end{array}\qquad\begin{array}{r}4200\\6\overline{)2.52}\end{array}\qquad\begin{array}{r}2200\\7\overline{)1.54}\end{array}$$

Tell students that each problem shows the solution, but the decimal point is missing in the quotient. Ask students to decide where each decimal point should go by estimating the quotient. Discuss students' estimates and answers. Possible responses:

$$\begin{array}{r}13.50\\3\overline{)40.5}\end{array}$$

10 threes equals 30; this is a bit less than 40.5, so the quotient is somewhat larger than 10. The number 135.0 is too large, so the answer that is close to 10 is 13.50.

$$\begin{array}{r}37.72\\4\overline{)150.88}\end{array}$$

There are at least 30 fours in 150 ($30 * 4 = 120$). There are not 40 fours in 150 ($40 * 4 = 160$). The quotient must be between 30 and 40. So 37.72 is the answer.

$$\begin{array}{r}.4200\\6\overline{)2.52}\end{array}$$

$2.52 \div 6$ is about $3 \div 6$, which is $\frac{1}{2}$, or 0.5. So the only possible quotient is 0.4200. The other possible answers are all greater than 1.

$$\begin{array}{r}.2200\\7\overline{)1.54}\end{array}$$

There are many ways to round the numbers to create easy estimates: $2 \div 10$, $1 \div 10$, $2 \div 5$, and $1 \div 5$. All of these have answers from 0.1 to 0.4. Or, think of sharing \$1.54 among 7 people: Each share will be less than \$1.00 but more than \$0.10. All estimates are between 0.1 and 1.0, so the answer must be 0.2200. Because the purpose of this estimate is to help students place the decimal point, any of these estimates is satisfactory.

Now write the following problem on the board:

▷ Bill paid \$5.52 for 8 ballpoint pens. How much did 1 pen cost?

Ask students to estimate the cost of 1 pen. Round \$5.52 to \$5 or to \$6, and round 8 to 10. $\$5 \div 10 = \$0.50$, or $\$6 \div 10 = \$0.60$; so the cost of 1 pen is about 50 or 60 cents.

Have volunteers come to the board and divide 552 by 8 (ignoring the decimal point). Remind students about the division algorithm they have used before. If students are having difficulty getting started, remind them that either of the estimates they just made (50 or 60) would be a good starting point.

```
 8)552   |               8)552   |
- 400    | 50           - 480    | 60
  152    |                 72    |
 - 80    | 10            - 72    |  9
   72    |                  0    | 69
 - 72    |  9
    0    | 69
```

Finally, have students use their initial estimates of the total cost to place the decimal point in the answer. $552 \div 8 = 69$; the estimate was about \$0.50 or \$0.60, so place the decimal point before the 6. The cost for 1 pen is \$0.69.

Adjusting the Activity

Have students rename quotients involving amounts in dollars and cents as cents. Use the amount in cents to estimate and then rename the estimate as a dollars-and-cents amount. For example, in the problem above, think of \$5.52 as 552 cents. Then 1 pen costs between 50 cents and 60 cents, or between \$0.50 and \$0.60.

AUDITORY ◆ KINESTHETIC ◆ TACTILE ◆ VISUAL

Help students summarize the use of estimation to place the decimal point when dividing decimals.

Example:

$3.66 \div 6 = ?$

1. Estimate the quotient. $3.66 \div 6$ is about $3 \div 6$, or 0.5.
2. Divide the numbers as though they were whole numbers. $366 \div 6 = 61$
3. Use the estimate to place the decimal point. 0.61 is close to the estimate of 0.5.

▸ Dividing Decimals

(*Math Journal 2,* pp. 270 and 271; *Math Masters,* p. 404)

Students complete journal pages 270 and 271. Encourage them to explain the strategies they used to place the decimal points in the quotients.

Ongoing Assessment: Recognizing Student Achievement

Journal page 270 Problems 5–7 ★

Use **journal page 270, Problems 5–7** to assess students' ability to estimate the quotient of a decimal divided by a whole number. Students are making adequate progress if they are able to correctly place the decimal points and write number models for Problems 5–7. Some students may be able to solve Problem 8, which involves a quotient less than 1.

[Operations and Computation Goal 6]

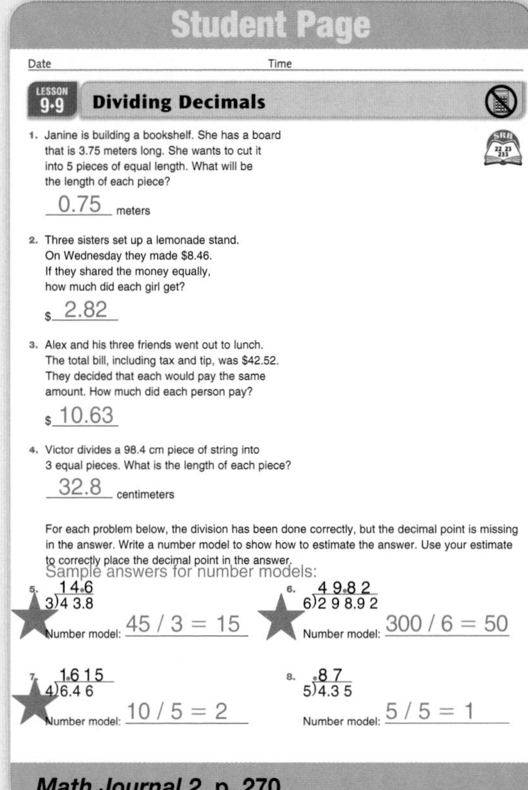

Student Page

Date Time

LESSON 9·9 **Dividing Decimals**

1. Janine is building a bookshelf. She has a board that is 3.75 meters long. She wants to cut it into 5 pieces of equal length. What will be the length of each piece?
   0.75 meters
2. Three sisters set up a lemonade stand. On Wednesday they made \$8.46. If they shared the money equally, how much did each girl get?
   \$ 2.82
3. Alex and his three friends went out to lunch. The total bill, including tax and tip, was \$42.52. They decided that each would pay the same amount. How much did each person pay?
   \$ 10.63
4. Victor divides a 98.4 cm piece of string into 3 equal pieces. What is the length of each piece?
   32.8 centimeters

For each problem below, the division has been done correctly, but the decimal point is missing in the answer. Write a number model to show how to estimate the answer. Use your estimate to correctly place the decimal point in the answer.
Sample answers for number models:

5. 3)43.8 = 14.6 — Number model: 45 / 3 = 15
6. 6)298.92 = 49.82 — Number model: 300 / 6 = 50
7. 4)6.46 = 1.615 — Number model: 10 / 5 = 2
8. 5)4.35 = .87 — Number model: 5 / 5 = 1

Math Journal 2, p. 270

Algorithm Project In this lesson, students use partial quotients to solve decimal division problems. To teach U.S. traditional division with decimals, see Algorithm Project 8 on page A37.

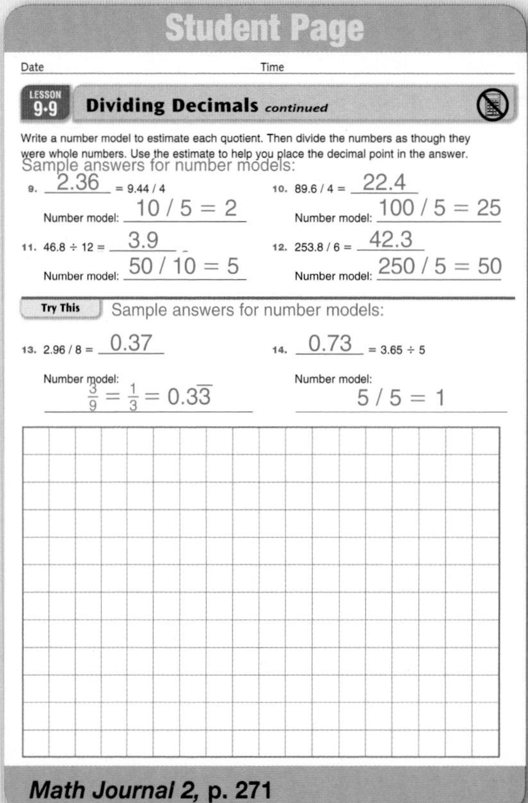

Student Page

Date Time

LESSON 9·9 **Dividing Decimals** *continued*

Write a number model to estimate each quotient. Then divide the numbers as though they were whole numbers. Use the estimate to help you place the decimal point in the answer.
Sample answers for number models:

9. 2.36 = 9.44 / 4 — Number model: 10 / 5 = 2
10. 89.6 / 4 = 22.4 — Number model: 100 / 5 = 25
11. 46.8 ÷ 12 = 3.9 — Number model: 50 / 10 = 5
12. 253.8 / 6 = 42.3 — Number model: 250 / 5 = 50

Try This Sample answers for number models:

13. 2.96 / 8 = 0.37 — Number model: $\frac{3}{9} = \frac{1}{3} = 0.3\overline{3}$
14. 0.73 = 3.65 ÷ 5 — Number model: 5 / 5 = 1

Math Journal 2, p. 271

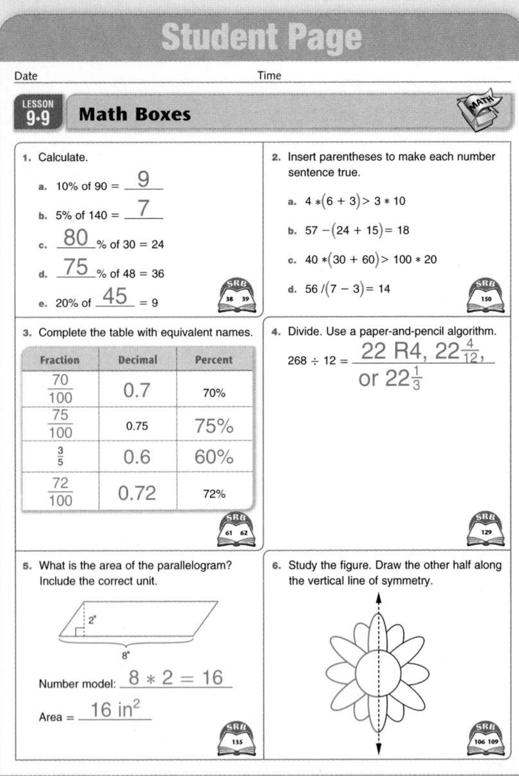
Student Page

Date Time

LESSON 9•9 **Math Boxes**

1. Calculate.
 a. 10% of 90 = 9
 b. 5% of 140 = 7
 c. 80 % of 30 = 24
 d. 75 % of 48 = 36
 e. 20% of 45 = 9

2. Insert parentheses to make each number sentence true.
 a. 4 ∗ (6 + 3) > 3 ∗ 10
 b. 57 − (24 + 15) = 18
 c. 40 ∗ (30 + 60) > 100 ∗ 20
 d. 56 / (7 − 3) = 14

3. Complete the table with equivalent names.

Fraction	Decimal	Percent
$\frac{70}{100}$	0.7	70%
$\frac{75}{100}$	0.75	75%
$\frac{3}{5}$	0.6	60%
$\frac{72}{100}$	0.72	72%

4. Divide. Use a paper-and-pencil algorithm.
 268 ÷ 12 = 22 R4, $22\frac{4}{12}$, or $22\frac{1}{3}$

5. What is the area of the parallelogram? Include the correct unit.
 2" 8"
 Number model: 8 ∗ 2 = 16
 Area = 16 in^2

6. Study the figure. Draw the other half along the vertical line of symmetry.

Math Journal 2, p. 272

2 Ongoing Learning & Practice

▶ Playing *Polygon Pair-Up*

(*Student Reference Book,* p. 258; *Math Masters,* pp. 496 and 497)

Students play *Polygon Pair-Up* to practice identifying properties of polygons. See Lesson 1-6 for additional information.

▶ Math Boxes 9•9

(*Math Journal 2,* p. 272)

Mixed Practice Math Boxes in this lesson are linked with Math Boxes in Lessons 9-5 and 9-7. The skill in Problem 6 previews Unit 10 content.

Writing/Reasoning Have students write a response to the following: *Draw another parallelogram that has the same area as the parallelogram in Problem 5. Does the parallelogram you drew have the same perimeter as the one in Problem 5? Explain your answer.* Sample answer: The perimeter of the parallelogram in Problem 5 is about 20 inches. I cannot tell exactly because the length of the shorter side is not given. The perimeter of the parallelogram that I drew is about 16 inches. They have the same area, but they do not have the same perimeter.

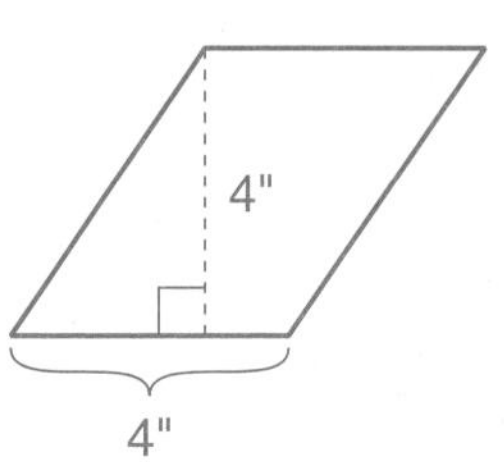

▶ Study Link 9•9

INDEPENDENT ACTIVITY

(*Math Masters,* p. 298)

Home Connection Students use estimation to place the decimal point in the quotient of division problems. They divide decimals by whole numbers.

Study Link Master

Name Date Time

STUDY LINK 9•9 **Dividing Decimals**

For each problem below, the division has been done correctly, but the decimal point is missing in the answer. Correctly place the decimal point in the answer.

1. 88.8 / 6 = 1 4.8
2. 1.35 / 5 = .2 7 0 0
3. 99.84 / 4 = 2 4.9 6
4. 2.58 / 3 = .8 6 0
5. 163.8 / 7 = 2 3.4
6. 233.28 / 4 = 5 8.3 2
7. Explain how you decided where to place the decimal point in Problem 3.
 Sample answer: I rounded 99.84 up and then divided to get an estimate. 100 ÷ 4 = 25, and 24.96 is close to 25.

Try This

Divide. Show your work.

8. 6)25.2 Answer: 4.2
9. 4)154.8 Answer: 38.7
10. 9)5.85 Answer: 0.65

Practice

11. $\frac{7}{8} = \frac{5}{8} + \frac{2}{8}$
12. $\frac{5}{9} - \frac{1}{3} = \frac{2}{9}$
13. $\frac{9}{10} = \frac{7}{10} + \frac{2}{10}$
14. $\frac{9}{10} - \frac{1}{2} = \frac{4}{10}$

Math Masters, p. 298

3 Differentiation Options

READINESS

INDEPENDENT ACTIVITY

Dividing Whole Numbers and Estimating Quotients

15–30 Min

COMPUTATION PRACTICE

(*Math Masters,* p. 299)

To provide experience with whole-number division and estimating quotients, have students complete *Math Masters,* page 299.

READINESS

PARTNER ACTIVITY

Solving Division Number Stories Involving Money

5–15 Min

COMPUTATION PRACTICE

(*Math Masters,* pp. 114 and 428)

To explore division of decimals by whole numbers using a money context, have students use the items on *Math Masters,* page 114 and dollars and cents to model, write, and solve division number stories. Be sure to have students discuss how they handled any remainders. *For example:*

Jen and Carmen bought:

They shared the cost equally. How much did each girl spend?

$(\$3.59 + \$2.99) \div 2 = \$3.29$

ENRICHMENT

PARTNER ACTIVITY

Writing and Solving Division Number Stories with Decimals

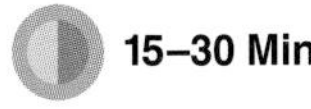

15–30 Min

Portfolio Ideas

To apply students' understanding of division of decimals, have them write and solve number stories involving the division of a decimal by a whole number. Suggest that students write one of each of the following types of division number stories:

- ▷ Partitioning into equal parts
- ▷ Money and equal sharing
- ▷ Calculating an average
- ▷ Calculating a fraction or a percent

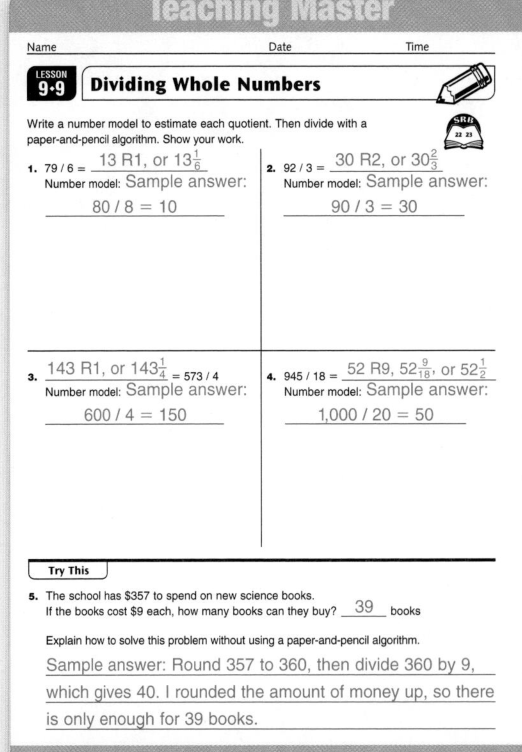

Teaching Master

Name Date Time

LESSON 9•9 **Dividing Whole Numbers**

Write a number model to estimate each quotient. Then divide with a paper-and-pencil algorithm. Show your work.

1. 79 / 6 = 13 R1, or $13\frac{1}{6}$
Number model: Sample answer: 80 / 8 = 10

2. 92 / 3 = 30 R2, or $30\frac{2}{3}$
Number model: Sample answer: 90 / 3 = 30

3. 143 R1, or $143\frac{1}{4}$ = 573 / 4
Number model: Sample answer: 600 / 4 = 150

4. 945 / 18 = 52 R9, $52\frac{9}{18}$, or $52\frac{1}{2}$
Number model: Sample answer: 1,000 / 20 = 50

Try This

5. The school has $357 to spend on new science books. If the books cost $9 each, how many books can they buy? 39 books

Explain how to solve this problem without using a paper-and-pencil algorithm.

Sample answer: Round 357 to 360, then divide 360 by 9, which gives 40. I rounded the amount of money up, so there is only enough for 39 books.

***Math Masters,* p. 299**

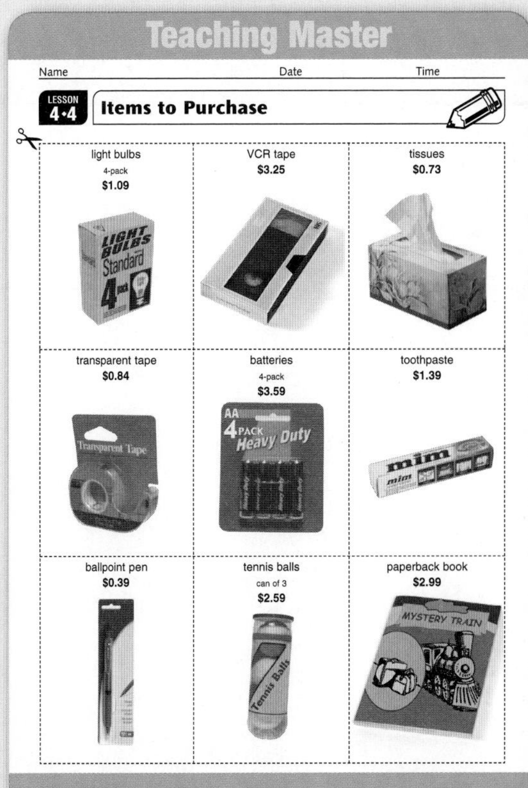

Teaching Master

Name Date Time

LESSON 4•4 **Items to Purchase**

light bulbs 4-pack $1.09	VCR tape $3.25	tissues $0.73
transparent tape $0.84	batteries 4-pack $3.59	toothpaste $1.39
ballpoint pen $0.39	tennis balls can of 3 $2.59	paperback book $2.99

***Math Masters,* p. 114**

9•10 Progress Check 9

Objective To assess students' progress on mathematical content through the end of Unit 9.

1 Looking Back: Cumulative Assessment

Input student data from Progress Check 9 into the **Assessment Management Spreadsheets**.

Materials
- Study Link 9•9
- *Assessment Handbook,* pp. 118–125, 195–199, 224, and 278–281
- markers or crayons; calculator

CONTENT ASSESSED	LESSON(S)	ASSESSMENT ITEMS				
		SELF	ORAL/SLATE	WRITTEN PART A	WRITTEN PART B	OPEN RESPONSE
Find a fraction or a percent of a number. [Number and Numeration Goal 2]	9•1–9•9	1, 2	4	1, 2, 6	11, 12	✓
Rename fractions as decimals and percents. [Number and Numeration Goal 5]	9•1–9•9	3	3	3–5		✓
Use an estimation strategy to divide decimals by whole numbers. [Operations and Computation Goal 6]	9•9	4	1		15, 16	
Use an estimation strategy to multiply decimals by whole numbers. [Operations and Computation Goal 6]	9•8	4	2		13, 14	
Find the area and perimeter of polygons. [Measurement and Reference Frames Goal 2]	9•2, 9•4–9•6, 9•9	5		7–9		
Insert grouping symbols to make number sentences true. [Patterns, Functions, and Algebra Goal 3]	9•5, 9•7, 9•9	6		10		

2 Looking Ahead: Preparing for Unit 10

Math Boxes 9•10

Study Link 9•10: Unit 10 Family Letter

Materials
- *Math Journal 2,* p. 273
- *Math Masters,* pp. 300–303

Getting Started

Math Message • Self Assessment

Complete the Self Assessment. (Assessment Handbook, *page 195*).

Study Link 9·9 Follow-Up

Have small groups of students share the estimation strategies they used to place the decimal point in Problems 1–6.

1 Looking Back: Cumulative Assessment

Math Message Follow-Up

(Self Assessment, *Assessment Handbook,* p. 195)

The Self Assessment offers students the opportunity to reflect upon their progress.

Oral and Slate Assessments

Problems 3 and 4 provide summative information that can be used for grading purposes. Problems 1 and 2 provide formative information that can be useful in planning future instruction.

Oral Assessment

1. On the board, write division number sentences in which a decimal is divided by a whole number. Students explain the strategy that they used to locate the position of the decimal point in the quotient. *Suggestions:*
   - 98.5 / 5 = 1 9 7 19.7
   - 1.96 / 4 = 4 9 0 0 0.49
   - 407.82 / 8 = 5 0 9 7 7 5 50.9775
2. On the board, write multiplication number sentences in which one factor is a whole number and the other factor is a decimal. Students explain the strategy that they used to locate the position of the decimal point in the product. *Suggestions:*
   - 15 * 2.08 = 3 1 2 0 31.20
   - 0.89 * 475 = 4 2 2 7 5 422.75
   - 14 * 0.9 = 1 2 6 12.6

Slate Assessment

3. Write fractions on the board. Students write the equivalent decimal and percent. *Suggestions:*
   - $\frac{3}{10}$ 0.3, 30%
   - $\frac{7}{10}$ 0.7, 70%
   - $\frac{3}{100}$ 0.03, 3%
   - $\frac{1}{2}$ 0.50, 50%
   - $\frac{1}{5}$ 0.20, 20%
   - $\frac{2}{5}$ 0.40, 40%

Assessment Master

Name Date Time

LESSON 9·10 **Self Assessment** Progress Check 9

Think about each skill listed below. Assess your own progress by checking the most appropriate box.

Skills	I can do this on my own and explain how to do it.	I can do this on my own.	I can do this if I get help or look at an example.
1. Solve "fraction-of" problems like these: $\frac{1}{4}$ of 20 $\frac{3}{5}$ of 15			
2. Solve discount number stories.			
3. Rename fractions like these as decimals and percents: $\frac{15}{100}, \frac{6}{10}, \frac{3}{4}, \frac{1}{5}$			
4. Solve decimal multiplication and division problems like these: 4.5 ∗ 7 56.7 / 5 9.82 ∗ 6 345.6 / 4			
5. Find the area and perimeter of rectangles, parallelograms, and triangles.			
6. Use parentheses in number sentences.			

Assessment Handbook, **p. 195**

Assessment Master

LESSON 9·10 **Written Assessment** Progress Check 9

Part A

1. Gloria made 15 out of 20 shots in the school basketball free-throw contest.
   a. What fraction of the shots did she make? $\frac{15}{20}$ or $\frac{3}{4}$
   b. What percent of the shots did she make? 75%
   c. At this rate, how many shots would she make if she took 100 shots? 75 shots
2. Jimmy set a goal of jogging a total of 100 miles over the summer. He filled in the grid at the right to keep track of the miles he ran. During the first two weeks of June, he jogged 20 miles.
   a. What fraction of 100 miles did he jog in 2 weeks? $\frac{20}{100}$ or $\frac{1}{5}$
   b. What percent of 100 miles did he jog? 20%
   c. At this rate, how many weeks will it take him to jog 100 miles? 10 weeks
3. Fill in the table of equivalent fractions, decimals, and percents.

Fraction	Decimal	Percent
$\frac{3}{10}$	0.3	30%
$\frac{1}{2}$	0.5	50%
$\frac{1}{4}$ or $\frac{25}{100}$	0.25	25%
$\frac{3}{4}$	0.75	75%
$\frac{8}{10}$ or $\frac{4}{5}$	0.80	80%
$\frac{5}{5}$	1	100%

Assessment Handbook, **p. 196**

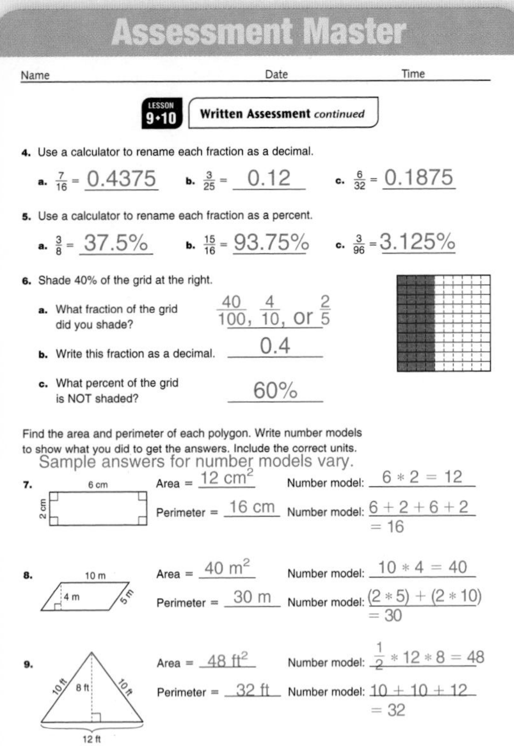
Assessment Master

Name ______ Date ______ Time ______

LESSON 9•10 **Written Assessment** *continued*

4. Use a calculator to rename each fraction as a decimal.

a. $\frac{7}{16}$ = 0.4375 b. $\frac{3}{25}$ = 0.12 c. $\frac{6}{32}$ = 0.1875

5. Use a calculator to rename each fraction as a percent.

a. $\frac{3}{8}$ = 37.5% b. $\frac{15}{16}$ = 93.75% c. $\frac{3}{96}$ = 3.125%

6. Shade 40% of the grid at the right.

a. What fraction of the grid did you shade? $\frac{40}{100}$, $\frac{4}{10}$, or $\frac{2}{5}$

b. Write this fraction as a decimal. 0.4

c. What percent of the grid is NOT shaded? 60%

Find the area and perimeter of each polygon. Write number models to show what you did to get the answers. Include the correct units.
Sample answers for number models vary.

7. (6 cm, 2 cm) Area = 12 cm² Number model: $6 * 2 = 12$
Perimeter = 16 cm Number model: $6 + 2 + 6 + 2 = 16$

8. (10 m, 4 m, 5 m) Area = 40 m² Number model: $10 * 4 = 40$
Perimeter = 30 m Number model: $(2 * 5) + (2 * 10) = 30$

9. (10 ft, 10 ft, 8 ft, 12 ft) Area = 48 ft² Number model: $\frac{1}{2} * 12 * 8 = 48$
Perimeter = 32 ft Number model: $10 + 10 + 12 = 32$

Assessment Handbook, p. 197

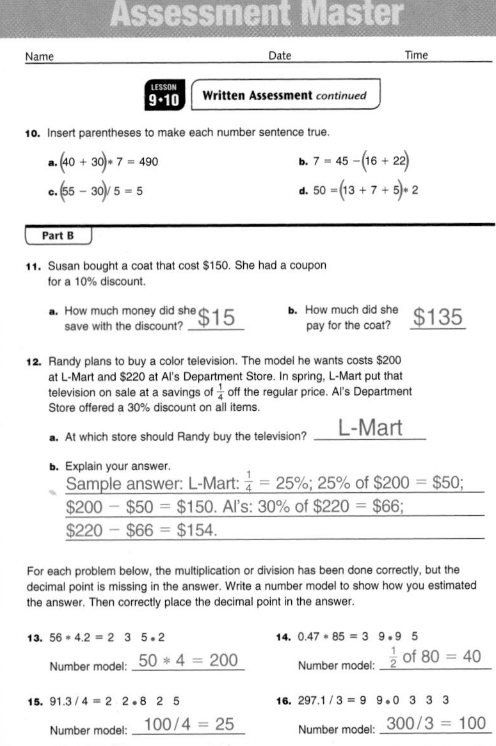
Assessment Master

Name ______ Date ______ Time ______

LESSON 9•10 **Written Assessment** *continued*

10. Insert parentheses to make each number sentence true.

a. $(40 + 30) * 7 = 490$ b. $7 = 45 - (16 + 22)$

c. $(55 - 30) / 5 = 5$ d. $50 = (13 + 7 + 5) * 2$

Part B

11. Susan bought a coat that cost $150. She had a coupon for a 10% discount.

a. How much money did she save with the discount? $15 b. How much did she pay for the coat? $135

12. Randy plans to buy a color television. The model he wants costs $200 at L-Mart and $220 at Al's Department Store. In spring, L-Mart put that television on sale at a savings of $\frac{1}{4}$ off the regular price. Al's Department Store offered a 30% discount on all items.

a. At which store should Randy buy the television? L-Mart

b. Explain your answer.
Sample answer: L-Mart: $\frac{1}{4}$ = 25%; 25% of $200 = $50; $200 − $50 = $150. Al's: 30% of $220 = $66; $220 − $66 = $154.

For each problem below, the multiplication or division has been done correctly, but the decimal point is missing in the answer. Write a number model to show how you estimated the answer. Then correctly place the decimal point in the answer.

13. 56 ∗ 4.2 = 2 3 5.2
Number model: $50 * 4 = 200$

14. 0.47 ∗ 85 = 3 9.9 5
Number model: $\frac{1}{2}$ of 80 = 40

15. 91.3 / 4 = 2 2.8 2 5
Number model: $100 / 4 = 25$

16. 297.1 / 3 = 9 9.0 3 3 3
Number model: $300 / 3 = 100$

Assessment Handbook, p. 198

- $\frac{9}{10}$ 0.9, 90%
- $\frac{1}{4}$ 0.25, 25%
- $\frac{3}{5}$ 0.60, 60%
- $\frac{57}{100}$ 0.57, 57%
- $\frac{3}{4}$ 0.75, 75%
- $\frac{4}{5}$ 0.80, 80%

4. Pose "percent-of" and "fraction-of" problems. *Suggestions:*

- $\frac{1}{3}$ of 90 30
- $\frac{2}{3}$ of 90 60
- $\frac{1}{5}$ of 20 4
- $\frac{4}{5}$ of 20 16
- 25% of 24 6
- 75% of 24 18
- 10% of 50 5
- 30% of 50 15

▶ Written Assessment

INDEPENDENT ACTIVITY

(*Assessment Handbook,* pp. 196–198)

Part A Recognizing Student Achievement

Problems 1–10 provide summative information and may be used for grading purposes.

Problem(s)	Description
1, 2	Write a ratio as a fraction and a percent. Interpret a percent.
3	Fill in a table of equivalent fractions, decimals, and percents.
4	Use a calculator to rename fractions as decimals.
5	Use a calculator to rename fractions as percents.
6	Shade a percent of a region. Write the percent as a fraction and a decimal.
7–9	Find the area and perimeter of a rectangle, parallelogram, and triangle.
10	Insert parentheses to make number sentences true.

Part B Informing Instruction

Problems 11–16 provide formative information that can be useful in planning future instruction.

Problem(s)	Description
11, 12	Use the percent of discount to calculate the discount and sale price of an item.
12	Compare a fraction of a discount and a percent of a discount.
13, 14	Use an estimation strategy to multiply decimals by whole numbers.
15, 16	Use an estimation strategy to divide decimals by whole numbers.

Use the checklists on pages 279 and 281 of the *Assessment Handbook* to record results. Then input the data into the **Assessment Management Spreadsheets** to keep an ongoing record of students' progress toward Grade-Level Goals.

Open Response

INDEPENDENT ACTIVITY

(*Assessment Handbook,* p. 199)

Designing a Floor

The open-response item requires students to apply concepts and skills from Unit 9 to solve a multistep problem. See *Assessment Handbook,* pages 118–122 for rubrics and students' work samples for this problem.

2 Looking Ahead: Preparing for Unit 10

Math Boxes 9·10

INDEPENDENT ACTIVITY

(*Math Journal 2,* p. 273)

Mixed Practice This Math Boxes page previews Unit 10 content.

Study Link 9·10: Unit 10 Family Letter

INDEPENDENT ACTIVITY

(*Math Masters,* pp. 300–303)

Home Connection The Unit 10 Family Letter provides parents and guardians with information and activities related to Unit 10 topics.

Assessment Master

Name Date Time

LESSON 9·10 **Open Response** Progress Check 9

Designing a Floor

Mrs. Wyman is tiling her floor in a colorful pattern. She knows what colors she wants to use and what percent of the floor each color will be.

1. Find how many tiles of each color Mrs. Wyman needs. Show and explain your work.

Color	Percent of Tiles	Number of Tiles
Blue	40%	
Red	25%	
Yellow	20%	
Green	10%	
Orange		
Total		160

See the *Assessment Handbook* for rubrics and students' work samples.

2. Make a design using Mrs. Wyman's tiles on the grid below.

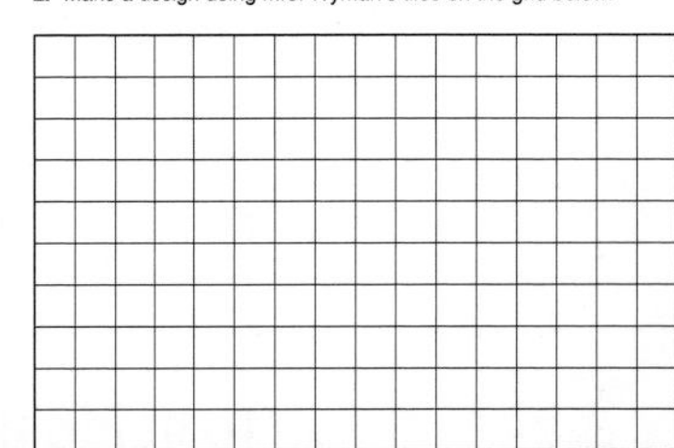

***Assessment Handbook,* p. 199**

Student Page

Date Time

LESSON 9·10 **Math Boxes**

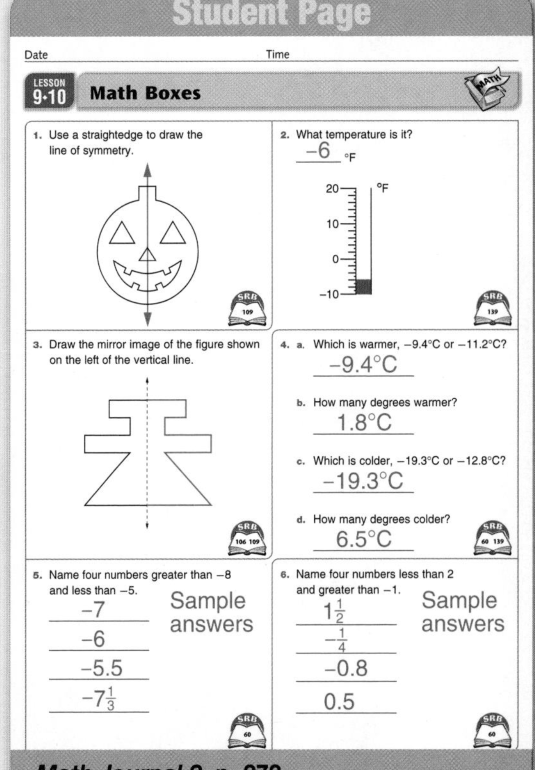

1. Use a straightedge to draw the line of symmetry.

2. What temperature is it? −6 °F

3. Draw the mirror image of the figure shown on the left of the vertical line.

4. a. Which is warmer, −9.4°C or −11.2°C? −9.4°C

b. How many degrees warmer? 1.8°C

c. Which is colder, −19.3°C or −12.8°C? −19.3°C

d. How many degrees colder? 6.5°C

5. Name four numbers greater than −8 and less than −5. Sample answers
−7
−6
−5.5
$-7\frac{1}{3}$

6. Name four numbers less than 2 and greater than −1. Sample answers
$1\frac{1}{2}$
$-\frac{1}{4}$
−0.8
0.5

***Math Journal 2,* p. 273**

Unit 10 Organizer

Reflections and Symmetry

Overview

Unit 10 highlights a return to geometry from the point of view of *transformations* or "motions" of geometric figures. It focuses primarily on reflections and the related topic of symmetry. Unit 10 also introduces formal operations with positive and negative numbers. Unit 10 has three main areas of focus:

- To guide the discovery of basic properties of reflections, involving 2-dimensional figures and the connection with line symmetry,
- To guide the application of reflections, rotations, and translations, and
- To introduce addition involving negative integers.

Linking to the Common Core State Standards

The content of Unit 10 addresses the Common Core State Standards for Mathematics in *Geometry.* The correlation of the Common Core State Standards to the *Everyday Mathematics* Grade 4 lessons begins on page CS1.

Contents

Learning In Perspective

	Lesson Objectives	Links to the Past	Links to the Future
10•1	To guide the exploration of reflections of 2-dimensional figures.	Grade 3: Explore symmetry with geoboards and pattern blocks; complete symmetric figures; identify symmetric shapes and draw lines of symmetry.	Grade 5: Applications and maintenance. Grade 6: Study rotations, rotation symmetry, and point symmetry.
10•2	To guide the exploration of reflections; and to provide practice identifying lines of reflection.	Grade 3: Explore symmetry with geoboards and pattern blocks; complete symmetric figures; identify symmetric shapes and draw lines of symmetry.	Grade 5: Applications and maintenance. Grade 6: Study rotations, rotation symmetry, and point symmetry.
10•3	To guide the discovery of basic properties of reflections.	Grade 3: Explore symmetry with geoboards and pattern blocks; complete symmetric figures; identify symmetric shapes and draw lines of symmetry.	Grade 5: Applications and maintenance. Grade 6: Study rotations, rotation symmetry, and point symmetry.
10•4	To guide exploration of the connection between reflections and line symmetry.	Grade 3: Explore symmetry with geoboards and pattern blocks; complete symmetric figures; identify symmetric shapes and draw lines of symmetry.	Grade 5: Applications and maintenance. Grade 6: Study rotations, rotation symmetry, and point symmetry.
10•5	To guide the application of reflections, rotations, and translations.	Grades 1–3: Use straws, geoboards, and body turns to demonstrate rotations. Grade 3: Model polygons; change the shapes of constructed polygons; perform polygon calisthenics to form polygons and explore their properties.	Grade 5: Transform ordered number pairs and explore the resulting transformations of geometric figures. Explore regular tessellations. Grade 6: Review regular tessellations; introduce notation for tessellations; find semiregular tessellations. Create translation tessellations. Explore topological transformations.
10•6	To introduce addition involving negative integers.	Grade 3: Review uses of positive and negative numbers to relate numbers to a zero point, as in temperatures and elevations, and to record change. Solve number stories about positive and negative numbers.	Grade 4: Play *Credits/Debits Game* (Advanced Version) to practice subtraction of positive and negative integers (Units 11 and 12). Grade 5: Solve addition/subtraction stories with positive and negative numbers. Grade 6: Develop a rule for adding and subtracting positive and negative numbers; practice adding and subtracting positive and negative numbers.

	Key Concepts and Skills	Grade 4 Goals*
10•1	Describe properties of congruent figures.	Geometry Goal 2
	Identify, describe, and sketch reflections of two-dimensional figures.	Geometry Goal 3
	Solve problems involving spatial visualization.	Geometry Goal 3
10•2	Describe properties of congruent figures, right angles, and perpendicular lines.	Geometry Goal 2
	Explore lines of reflection and reflected images.	Geometry Goal 3
	Solve problems involving spatial visualization.	Geometry Goal 3
10•3	Measure length.	Measurement and Reference Frames Goal 1
	Draw and describe congruent figures.	Geometry Goal 2
	Explore basic properties of reflections.	Geometry Goal 3
	Solve problems involving spatial visualization.	Geometry Goal 3
10•4	Identify polygons and describe properties of regular polygons.	Geometry Goal 2
	Identify and draw lines of symmetry.	Geometry Goal 3
	Explore the connection between reflections and line symmetry.	Geometry Goal 3
	Solve problems involving spatial visualization.	Geometry Goal 3
	Describe rules for patterns and use them to solve problems.	Patterns, Functions, and Algebra Goal 1
10•5	Identify and draw congruent figures.	Geometry Goal 2
	Identify, describe, and sketch reflections, rotations, and translations.	Geometry Goal 3
	Extend, describe, and create geometric patterns.	Patterns, Functions, and Algebra Goal 1
10•6	Compare and order integers.	Number and Numeration Goal 6
	Add signed numbers.	Operations and Computation Goal 2
	Identify a line of reflection.	Geometry Goal 3

*See the Appendix for a complete list of Grade 4 Goals.

A Balanced Curriculum

Ongoing Practice

Everyday Mathematics provides numerous opportunities for ongoing practice. These activities are embedded throughout the lessons:

Mental Math and Reflexes activities promote speed and accuracy in mental computation.

Math Boxes offer mixed practice and are paired across lessons as shown in the brackets below. This makes them useful as assessment tools. The last one or two boxes on each page preview the next unit's content.

Mixed practice	[10•1, 10•4], [10•2, 10•5], [10•3, 10•6]
Mixed practice with multiple choice	10•3, 10•4, 10•6
Mixed practice with writing/reasoning opportunity	10•1, 10•3, 10•5, 10•6

Study Links are daily homework assignments that review the content of the lesson and often contain ongoing facts practice or computation practice.

5-Minute Math problems are offered for additional practice in Lesson 10•3.

EM Facts Workshop Game provides online practice of basic facts and computation.

EXTRA PRACTICE **Extra Practice** activities are included in Lessons 10•3, 10•4, and 10•5.

Practice through Games

Games are an essential component of practice in the *Everyday Mathematics* program. Games offer skills practice and promote strategic thinking. See the *Differentiation Handbook* for ways to adapt games to meet students' needs.

Lesson	Game	Skill Practiced
10•1	*Over and Up Squares*	Locating and plotting points on a coordinate grid [MRF Goal 4]
10•2	*Dart Game*	Experimenting with transparent mirrors and reflections [GEO Goal 3]
10•2	*Pocket-Billiards Game*	Experimenting with transparent mirrors and reflections [GEO Goal 3]
10•2	*Angle Tangle*	Estimating and measuring angles [MRF Goal 1]
10•5	*Polygon Pair-Up*	Identifying properties of polygons [GEO Goal 2]
10•6	*Credits/Debits Game*	Adding positive and negative numbers [OC Goal 2]

[NN] Number and Numeration [OC] Operations and Computation [DC] Data and Chance
[MRF] Measurement and Reference Frames [GEO] Geometry [PFA] Patterns, Functions, and Algebra

Problem Solving 

Experts at problem solving and mathematical modeling generally do these things:

- Identify the problem.
- Decide what information is needed to solve the problem.
- Play with and study the data to find patterns and meaning.
- Identify and use mathematical procedures to solve the problem.
- Decide whether the solution makes sense and whether it can be applied to other problems.

The table below lists some of the opportunities in this unit for students to practice these strategies.

Lesson	Activity
10•1	Use the transparent mirror to "move" and draw reflected images of shapes.
10•2	Play games that involve reflections.
10•3	Fold paper to observe reflected images.
10•4	Find lines of symmetry of polygons.
10•5	Create and continue frieze patterns.
10•6	Use credits and debits to practice addition of positive and negative numbers.

Lessons that teach *through* problem solving, not just *about* problem solving

See Chapter 18: Problem Solving in the *Teacher's Reference Manual* for more information.

The Language of Mathematics

Everyday Mathematics provides lesson-specific suggestions to help all students acquire, process, and express mathematical ideas. Throughout Unit 10, there are lesson-specific language development notes that address the needs of English language learners, indicated by ELL.

ELL SUPPORT Activities to support English language learners are in Part 3 of Lessons 10•2 and 10•4.

The *English Learners Handbook* and the *Differentiation Handbook* have suggestions for promoting language development and acquisition of mathematics vocabulary. See Unit 10 in each handbook.

Unit 10 Vocabulary

congruent
credit
debit
frieze pattern
image
line of reflection
line of symmetry
opposite (of a number)
preimage
recessed
reflection
reflection (flip)
rotation (turn)
rotation (turn) symmetry
symmetric
translation (slide)
transparent mirror

Literacy Connection

Lesson 10•1 *Shadows and Reflections,* by Tana Hoban, Greenwillow, 1990

Count Your Way through Japan, by Jim Haskins, Carolrhoda Books, 1987

Count Your Way through Russia, by Jim Haskins, Carolrhoda Books, 1987

How the Second Grade Got $8,205.50 to Visit the Statue of Liberty, by Nathan Zimelman, Albert Whitman & Company, 1992

Reflections, by Ann Jonas, Greenwillow, 1987

For more literacy connections, see the *Home Connection Handbook,* Grades 4–6.

Cross-Curricular Links 

Language Arts – Lesson 10•1
Art – Lessons 10•2, 10•5
Technology – Lessons 10•2, 10•5
Social Studies – Lesson 10•3

Balanced Assessment

Daily Assessments

- **Recognizing Student Achievement** – A daily assessment that is included in every lesson to evaluate students' progress toward the Grade 4 Grade-Level Goals.
- **Informing Instruction** – Notes that appear throughout the unit to help anticipate students' common errors and suggest appropriate problem-solving strategies.

Lesson	Recognizing Student Achievement	Informing Instruction
10•1	Plot points in the first quadrant of a coordinate grid. [MRF Goal 4]	
10•2	Compare fractions with like numerators or like denominators; compare fractions to the benchmark $\frac{1}{2}$. [NN Goal 6]	Find a common factor to use as the interval when labeling an axis.
10•3	Use a transparent mirror to sketch and describe a reflection. [GEO Goal 3]	
10•4	Describe a pattern and use it to solve problems. [PFA Goal 1]	Understand the difference between line symmetry and rotation symmetry.
10•5	Identify and sketch an example of a reflection and identify examples of translations and rotations. [GEO Goal 3]	
10•6	Express the probability of an event as a fraction. [DC Goal 4]	Encourage strategies for adding positive and negative numbers to evolve over time.

[NN] Number and Numeration
[MRF] Measurement and Reference Frames
[OC] Operations and Computation
[GEO] Geometry
[DC] Data and Chance
[PFA] Patterns, Functions, and Algebra

Portfolio Opportunities

Portfolio Ideas

The following lessons provide opportunities to gather samples of students' mathematical writings, drawings, and creations to add balance to the assessment process: Lessons 10•1, 10•2, 10•4, 10•5, and 10•7.

See pages 16 and 17 in the *Assessment Handbook* for more information about portfolios and how to use them.

Unit Assessment

Progress Check 10 – A cumulative assessment of concepts and skills taught in Unit 10 and in previous units, providing information for evaluating students' progress and planning for future instruction. These assessments include oral/slate, written, and open-response activities, as shown below in the sample Progress Check lesson opener.

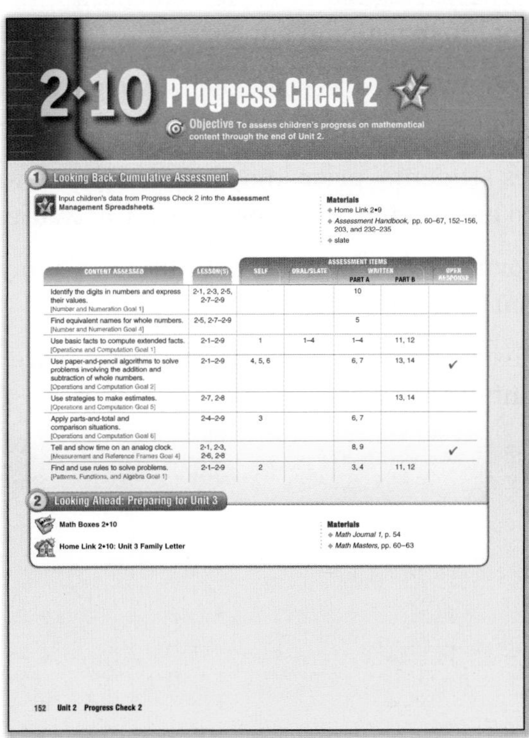

2·10 Progress Check 2

Objective To assess children's progress on mathematical content through the end of Unit 2.

1 Looking Back: Cumulative Assessment

Input children's data from Progress Check 2 into the **Assessment Management Spreadsheets**.

Materials
- Home Link 2•9
- *Assessment Handbook*, pp. 60–67, 152–156, 203, and 232–235
- slate

CONTENT ASSESSED	LESSON(S)	ASSESSMENT ITEMS				
		SELF	ORAL/SLATE	WRITTEN PART A	WRITTEN PART B	OPEN RESPONSE
Identify the digits in numbers and express their values. [Number and Numeration Goal 1]	2·1, 2·3, 2·5, 2·7–2·9			10		
Find equivalent names for whole numbers. [Number and Numeration Goal 4]	2·5, 2·7–2·9			5		
Use basic facts to compute extended facts. [Operations and Computation Goal 1]	2·1–2·9	1	1–4	1–4	11, 12	
Use paper-and-pencil algorithms to solve problems involving the addition and subtraction of whole numbers. [Operations and Computation Goal 2]	2·1–2·9	4, 5, 6		6, 7	13, 14	✓
Use strategies to make estimates. [Operations and Computation Goal 5]	2·7, 2·8				13, 14	
Apply parts-and-total and comparison situations. [Operations and Computation Goal 6]	2·4–2·9	3		6, 7		
Tell and show time on an analog clock. [Measurement and Reference Frames Goal 4]	2·1, 2·3, 2·6, 2·8			8, 9		✓
Find and use rules to solve problems. [Patterns, Functions, and Algebra Goal 1]	2·1–2·9	2		3, 4	11, 12	

2 Looking Ahead: Preparing for Unit 3

Math Boxes 2•10

Home Link 2•10: Unit 3 Family Letter

Materials
- *Math Journal 1*, p. 54
- *Math Masters*, pp. 60–63

152 Unit 2 Progress Check 2

Core Assessment Resources

Assessment Handbook

- **Unit 10 Assessment Overview,** pages 126–133
- **Unit 10 Assessment Masters,** pages 200–205
- **Unit 10 Individual Profiles of Progress,** pages 282, 283, and 302
- **Unit 10 Class Checklists,** pages 284, 285, and 303
- **Math Logs,** pages 306–308
- **Exit Slip,** page 311
- **Other Student Assessment Forms,** pages 304, 305, 309, and 310

Assessment Management Spreadsheets

The Assessment Management Spreadsheets consist of the Digital Class Checklists and Individual Profile of Progress Checklists. Use them to monitor, record, and report student progress.

Addressing All Needs

Differentiated Instruction

Adjusting the Activity – suggests adaptations that target advanced learners, English language learners, or learners who need additional instructional support.

ELL SUPPORT / ELL – provides lesson-specific suggestions to help English language learners understand and process the mathematical content.

READINESS – accesses students' prior knowledge or previews content that prepares students to engage in the lesson's Part 1 activities.

EXTRA PRACTICE – provides additional opportunities to apply the mathematical content of the lesson.

ENRICHMENT – enables students to apply or further explore the mathematical content of the lesson.

Lesson	Adjusting the Activity	ELL Support/ ELL	Readiness	Extra Practice	Enrichment
10•1		•	•		•
10•2	•	•	•		•
10•3	•		•	•	•
10•4	•	•		•	•
10•5	•	•	•	•	•
10•6	•	•	•		

Additional Resources

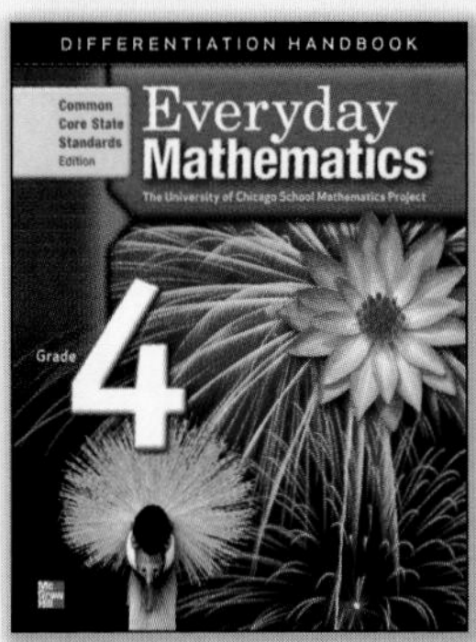

Differentiation Handbook
Provides ideas and strategies for differentiating instruction.
Pages 111–117

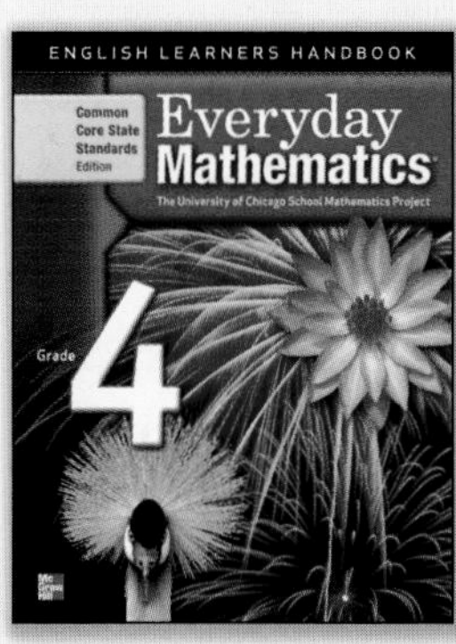

English Learners Handbook
Contains lesson-specific comprehension strategies.
Pages 89–94

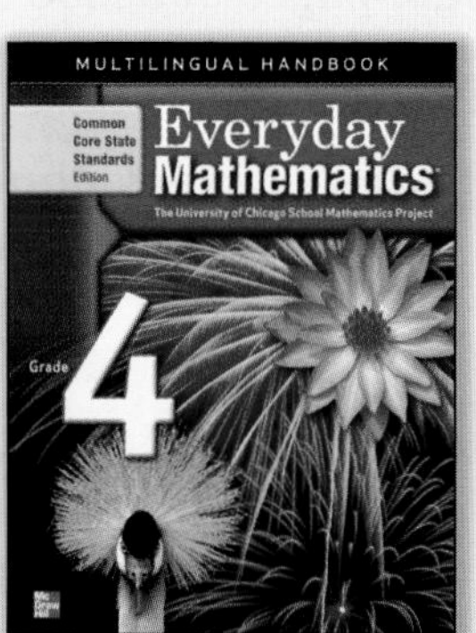

Multilingual Handbook
Previews concepts and vocabulary. It is written in six languages.
Pages 177–188

Planning Tips

Multiage Classroom

Companion Lessons from Grades 3 and 5 can help you meet instructional needs of a multiage classroom. The full Scope and Sequence can be found in the Appendix.

Grade 3	6•3, 6•9	6•9	6•3, 6•9	6•3, 6•9	1•12, 6•3	
Grade 4	**10•1**	**10•2**	**10•3**	**10•4**	**10•5**	**10•6**
Grade 5				3•8	3•8	7•7–7•9, 7•11

Pacing for Success

Pacing depends on a number of factors, such as students' individual needs and how long your school has been using *Everyday Mathematics*. At the beginning of Unit 10, you may want to use tools available at www.everydaymathonline.com to help you set your pace.

Home Support

Unit 10 Family Letter (English/Spanish) provides families with an overview, Do-Anytime Activities, Building Skills through Games, a list of vocabulary, and answers to the daily homework (Study Links). Family Letters in English, Spanish, and seven other languages are also available online.

Study Links are the daily homework assignments. They consist of active projects and ongoing review problems.

Home Support Resources

Home Connection Handbook
Offers ideas and reproducible masters for communicating with families. See Table of Contents for unit information.

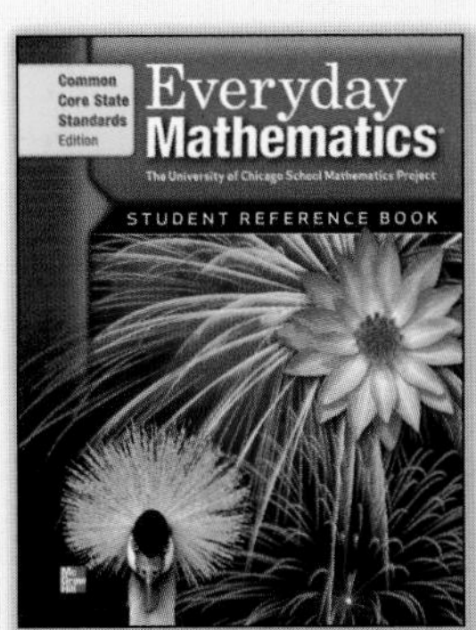

Student Reference Book
Provides a resource for students and parents.

Pages 60, 108, 230, 238, 257, 258, 276, 277, 281, 288–291, 297, 302–305

Technology Resources

Unit 10 Organizer

Materials

Technology Resources www.everydaymathonline.com

ePresentations

eToolkit

Algorithms Practice

EM Facts Workshop Game™

Family Letters

Assessment Management

Common Core State Standards

Curriculum Focal Points

Interactive Teacher's Lesson Guide

Lesson	Masters	Manipulative Kit	Other Items
10•1	Teaching Masters, pp. 304 and 305 Study Link Master, p. 306 Game Master, p. 494 Teaching Aid Master, p. 389	slate; per partnership: 2 six-sided dice, transparent mirror	sheets of paper; colored pencils; crayons*; scissors; *Shadows and Reflections*
10•2	Study Link Master, p. 307 Game Master, p. 457 Teaching Master, p. 308 Teaching Aid Master, p. 389 *Differentiation Handbook,* p. 140	slate; transparent mirror	ruler; large sheets of paper; paints; brushes; dark marker; computer with Internet access; scissors*; protractor; straightedge; Geometry Template
10•3	Teaching Master, p. 309 Study Link Master, p. 310 Teaching Aid Masters, pp. 389, 403, 419–421*, and 447	per partnership: transparent mirror; slate; centimeter cubes; pattern blocks	ruler; blank paper or centimeter grid paper
10•4	Teaching Masters, pp. 311–314, 316, and 317 Teaching Aid Master, p. 389* Study Link Master, p. 315	slate; pattern blocks; per partnership: transparent mirror	scissors; magazines and newspapers; tape; Geometry Template
10•5	Teaching Aid Masters, pp. 389, 403*, and 437 Study Link Master, p. 318 Teaching Master, p. 319 Game Masters, pp. 496 and 497	straws; pattern blocks; slate; per partnership: transparent mirror	straightedge; computer with Internet access; index cards; scissors; overhead pattern blocks*; Geometry Template
10•6	Teaching Master, p. 320 Game Master, p. 468 Transparencies of *Math Masters,* pp. 318* and 321* Study Link Master, p. 322	per partnership: deck of number cards, transparent mirror	masking tape; calculator
10•7	Assessment Masters, pp. 200–205 Study Link Masters, pp. 323–326	slate; transparent mirror	scissors; Geometry Template

*Denotes optional materials

Mathematical Background

The discussion below highlights the major content ideas presented in Unit 10 and helps establish instructional priorities.

Types of Geometry

(Lesson 10•1 and following)

You may remember your high school geometry course as dealing with definitions, axioms, theorems ("Given ..., To Prove ..."), and perhaps straightedge-and-compass constructions. This form of **synthetic geometry** was first developed by Euclid about 300 B.C. and has been the model for teaching geometry ever since.

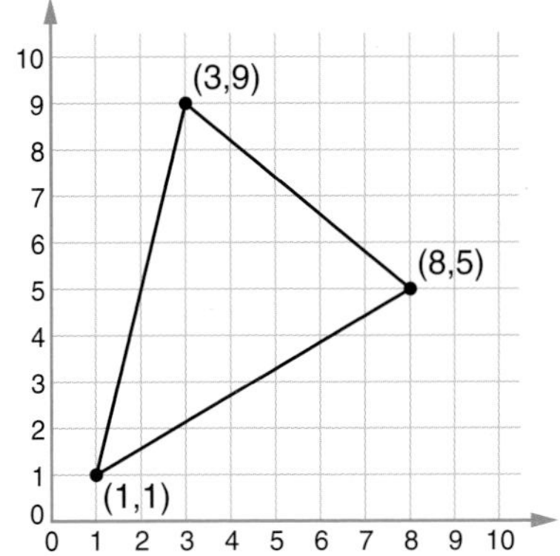

Figure in a coordinate plane

However, there are two modern geometries that cover the same topics:

Analytic geometry The study of figures in a coordinate plane.

Transformation geometry The study of certain operations on figures. These operations, or "transformations," produce figures that are the same shape as (similar to) the original figures, or the same size and shape as (congruent to) the original figures.

These two geometries are probably more useful than synthetic geometry. Both are featured in Grades 4–6 of *Everyday Mathematics,* with this unit introducing the transformation approach.

Learn more about types of geometry in Chapter 13 of the *Teacher's Reference Manual.*

"Isometric" or "Congruence" Transformations

(Lesson 10•1 and following)

You may remember from your high school geometry course the emphasis on **congruent** figures, especially on proving triangles congruent by theorems called "side-angle-side" or "SAS," and so on.

This topic is handled in transformation geometry by **rigid motions** or **isometric transformations,** which do not change the size or shape of figures. These transformations—**translations** (slides), **reflections** (flips), and **rotations** (turns)—can duplicate any figure. (SAS and similar theorems of synthetic geometry apply only to triangles.)

See the *Teacher's Reference Manual,* Section 13.7, for more information about isometric transformations.

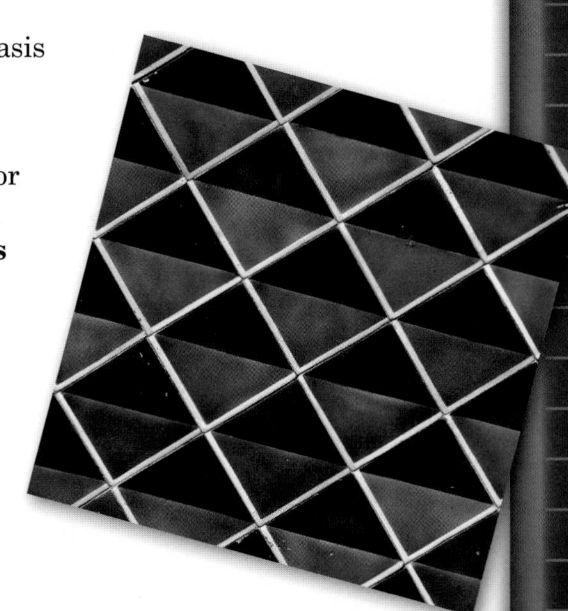

Transparent mirror

Reflections (Flips) and Symmetry with Transparent Mirrors

(Lessons 10•1–10•4)

Everyone is familiar with mirrors and the exact—but reversed—images one sees in them. The device used in this unit, the **transparent mirror,** has an advantage over a regular mirror: It allows students to look through a mirror and reach behind it to touch or trace the mirror image (almost like Alice going "through the looking glass").

As with any new tool, developing the skills for its use takes time, practice, and patience. For accurate placement of images, have students practice these skills:

- Lean down and look directly through the transparent mirror.
- Use the ends of the transparent mirror to keep it perpendicular to the paper.
- Use the inner part of the recessed edge to place the transparent mirror on points or lines or to draw mirror lines.
- Hold the transparent mirror firmly in position with one hand while drawing behind it or along its recessed edge. (This is one of the main skills to be learned.)

It is probably a good idea to acquire or practice these skills yourself before teaching the lessons. Do the mirror exercises on journal pages and masters until you feel comfortable using the transparent mirror.

Project Note

Use Project 4, Making a Quilt, to explore and apply ideas of symmetry, rotation, and reflection in the context of quilts. See the *Differentiation Handbook* for modifications to Project 4.

To learn more about reflections and symmetry with a transparent mirror, refer to Section 13.8 in the *Teacher's Reference Manual.*

Transformations as Design Tools

(Lesson 10◆5)

Geometric patterns are part of many designs—in arts and crafts from around the world, in architecture and engineering, and in paintings and other works of art (sometimes in disguised forms). Lesson 10-5, on **frieze patterns,** encourages students to explore reflections, symmetry, rotations, and translations in order to analyze and create designs. The authors believe that fourth graders will find these design tasks enjoyable. Some of their creations may be quite elegant.

An interesting property of transformations is that two successive reflections across parallel mirror lines are equivalent to one translation. (The original image is reversed in the first reflection, but the mirror image of the first reflection can be a translated image.) Hence one can make friezes either by translating and tracing or by using transparent mirrors twice for each frieze copy.

The authors hope that the principles learned here can be linked to teaching visual arts in your school. Geometry that is useful in both art and practical matters will be applied many times throughout *Everyday Mathematics.*

For more about transformations as design tools, see Section 13.8 in the *Teacher's Reference Manual.*

Operations with Positive and Negative Numbers

(Lesson 10◆6)

Since Kindergarten, *Everyday Mathematics* students have been using positive and negative numbers to identify locations on timelines, number lines, number grids, and thermometers. Since first grade, students have informally used addition and subtraction in going from one place to another and in finding distances. But Lesson 10-6 may be students' first exposure to *operations* with positive and negative numbers. In this lesson, the numbers are limited to integers—whole numbers and their (negative) opposites.

"Credits and debits" number stories are used to help make addition concrete. Single-digit numbers ensure that most problems can be done mentally. It is important in these "accounting" situations to name both the operation and the number.

- "Add +\$3" is read "Add positive 3 dollars" (a credit transaction).
- "Add –\$5" is read "Add negative 5 dollars" (a debit transaction).

This distinguishes the addition operation from the numbers involved.

Later lessons in Grade 4 introduce subtraction of positive and negative numbers and teach the use of the "change sign" key, which enables calculators to work with negative as well as positive numbers. Many practice and review exercises are included. Other operations with positive and negative numbers, as well as applications using them, are featured in Grades 5 and 6.

See Section 10.2.2 of the *Teacher's Reference Manual* for more information about operations with positive and negative numbers.

Confusing Notation for Positive and Negative Numbers (Lesson 10•6)

The use of the same notation with several meanings can be confusing. This is true of the symbol "–":

- The symbol "–" attached to a numeral, as in –3, –0.5, or –37, is read "negative" and is used in naming numbers on the number line ("negative three," "negative five-tenths," "negative thirty-seven").
- The symbol "–" in a number model, preceding a positive or negative number, as in –(+3) or –(–17), is read "opposite of." The opposite of a positive number is a negative number; the opposite of a negative number is a positive number. For example, the "opposite of positive 3" is negative 3, and the "opposite of negative 17" is positive 17.
- The symbol "–" in a number model, as in 17 – 3 = 14, is read **"minus," "subtract,"** or **"take away"** and indicates the familiar subtraction operation.

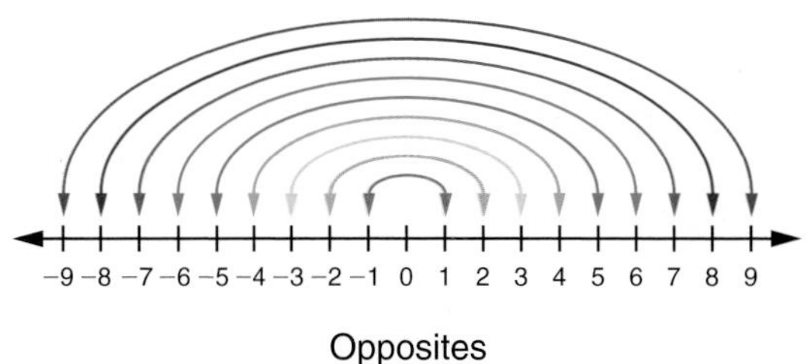

Opposites

Example 17 – 3 = 14 is read "17 minus 3 equals 14."

17 – (+3) = 14 is read "17 minus 3 equals 14."

–(–17) – 3 = 14 is read "the opposite of negative 17 minus 3 equals 14."

17 + (–3) = 14 is read "17 plus negative 3 equals 14."

17 – (–3) = 20 is read "17 minus negative 3 equals 20."

The meanings of the symbol "–" can get quite tangled in number models like –17 – 3 = –20 ("Negative 17 minus 3 equals negative 20") or 12 – –(–4) = 8 ("12 take away the opposite of negative 4 equals 8").

Some mathematics programs of the past tried to reduce confusion by using "–" only for subtraction. Positive and negative numbers were designated with small raised symbols (for example, $^{-}3$, $^{-}7$, $^{+}17$), and opposites were indicated by "opp." But everyday usage and nearly all algebra books continued to use the traditional notation, so students eventually had to reconcile the two notations.

Given the problems associated with both notations, the authors have decided to use the traditional system. Help students sort it out when you read expressions by consistently saying "plus" or "minus" for addition or subtraction, and "positive," "negative," or "opposite" for numbers, as indicated by the context. Encourage students to do likewise when they eventually read expressions to each other and to themselves.

To further explore confusing notation for positive and negative numbers, refer to Section 9.4.1 in the *Teacher's Reference Manual.*

Note

Public or private speech is very helpful in dealing with complexities of meanings. It is verifiable and observable common sense for students to use speech, as well as sight, to sort out complicated symbolic expressions. (This is a key tenet of the learning theory of Lev S. Vygotsky. An excellent article on Vygotskian learning theory is "Why Children Talk to Themselves," by Laura E. Berk, in the November 1994 issue of *Scientific American.*)

10•1 Explorations with a Transparent Mirror

Objective To guide the exploration of reflections of 2-dimensional figures.

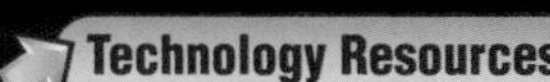

www.everydaymathonline.com

ePresentations

eToolkit

Algorithms Practice

EM Facts Workshop Game™

Family Letters

Assessment Management

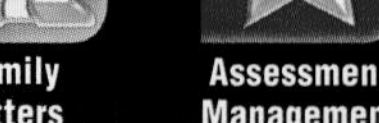

Common Core State Standards

Curriculum Focal Points

Interactive Teacher's Lesson Guide

1 Teaching the Lesson

Key Concepts and Skills

- Describe properties of congruent figures. [Geometry Goal 2]
- Identify, describe, and sketch reflections of two-dimensional figures. [Geometry Goal 3]
- Solve problems involving spatial visualization. [Geometry Goal 3]

Key Activities

Students experiment with reflections using a transparent mirror to move and draw reflected images.

Key Vocabulary

transparent mirror ◆ recessed ◆ preimage ◆ image ◆ congruent

Materials

Math Journal 2, p. 274
Math Masters, pp. 304 and 305
per partnership: 1 transparent mirror ◆ sheets of paper ◆ colored pencils or crayons (optional) ◆ scissors (optional) ◆ slate

2 Ongoing Learning & Practice

Playing *Over and Up Squares*
Student Reference Book, p. 257
Math Masters, p. 494
per partnership: 2 different-colored pencils, 2 six-sided dice
Students practice locating and plotting points on a coordinate grid.

Ongoing Assessment: Recognizing Student Achievement
Use *Math Masters,* page 494.
[Measurement and Reference Frames Goal 4]

Using Coin Values to Add Hundredths
Math Journal 2, pp. 275A and 275B
Students add fractions with 100 in the denominator.

Math Boxes 10•1
Math Journal 2, p. 275
Students practice and maintain skills through Math Box problems.

Study Link 10•1
Math Masters, p. 306
Students practice and maintain skills through Study Link activities.

3 Differentiation Options

READINESS

Exploring Reflections
sheets of paper ◆ scissors
Students fold paper, cut out shapes that contain part of the fold, and predict what the shapes will look like when unfolded.

ENRICHMENT

Exploring Shadows and Reflections
Math Masters, p. 389
Shadows and Reflections
Students explore shadows and reflections.

Advance Preparation

For Part 1, put a box of transparent mirrors near the Math Message. For the optional Enrichment activity in Part 3, obtain ***Shadows and Reflections*** by Tana Hoban (Greenwillow, 1990).

***Teacher's Reference Manual,* Grades 4–6** pp. 42–44, 212

Getting Started

Mental Math and Reflexes

Pose "fraction-of" and "percent-of" problems. *Suggestions:*

●○○	●●○	●●●
$\frac{1}{3}$ of 18 6	$\frac{2}{3}$ of 36 24	$\frac{3}{8}$ of 40 15
$\frac{1}{4}$ of 36 9	$\frac{3}{4}$ of 48 36	$\frac{8}{7}$ of 21 24
50% of 40 20	60% of 60 36	110% of 50 55
25% of 60 15	75% of 36 27	120% of 20 24

Math Message

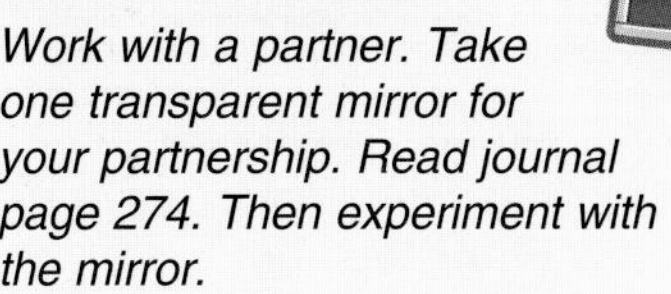

Work with a partner. Take one transparent mirror for your partnership. Read journal page 274. Then experiment with the mirror.

1 Teaching the Lesson

Interactive whiteboard-ready ePresentations are available at www.everydaymathonline.com to help you teach the lesson.

Math Message Follow-Up

WHOLE-CLASS DISCUSSION

ELL

(*Math Journal 2,* p. 274)

Discuss journal page 274. Have students examine the top and bottom edges of the **transparent mirror.** Point out that one side of one edge is **recessed.** (On some transparent mirrors, both edges have a recessed side.) The recessed side can be used as a straightedge.

To support English language learners, discuss the meanings of the words *transparent* and *recessed.* Explain how a transparent mirror differs from a traditional mirror.

Using a Transparent Mirror to "Move" Shapes

WHOLE-CLASS ACTIVITY

Tell students that in this lesson they will have the opportunity to explore with transparent mirrors.

Have students follow this procedure:

1. Draw a squiggle on a sheet of paper.
2. Place the transparent mirror so that the squiggle is between the mirror and your eyes.
3. Look through the mirror.
4. Tell what you see when you look through the transparent mirror. Another squiggle that has the same size and shape as the original squiggle

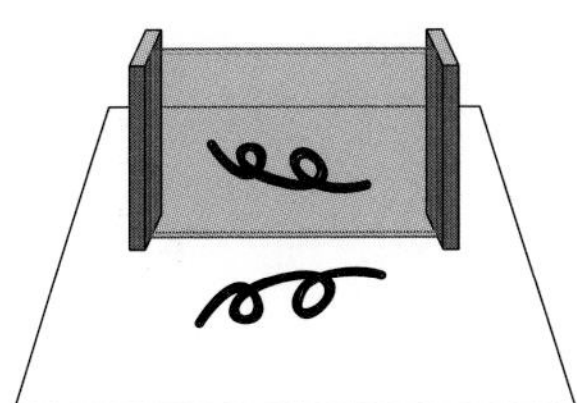

This transparent mirror has two endpieces. Some may have only one end piece.

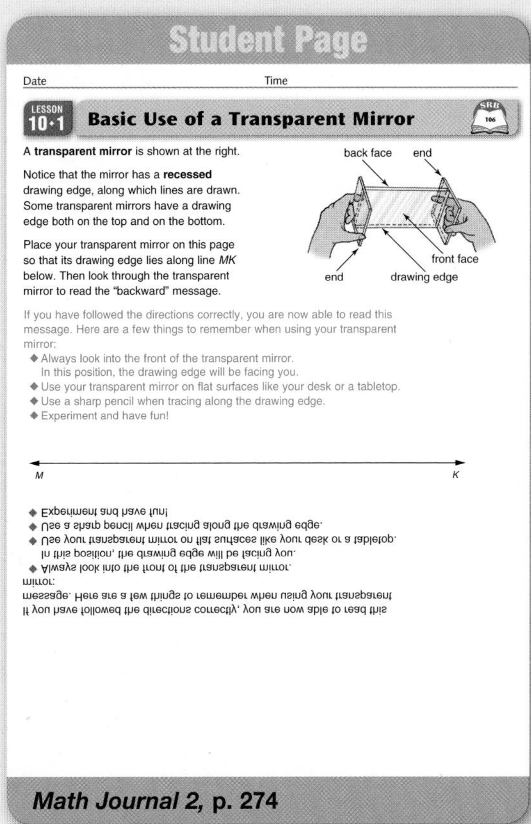

Student Page

Date Time

LESSON 10•1 **Basic Use of a Transparent Mirror**

SRB 106

A **transparent mirror** is shown at the right.

Notice that the mirror has a **recessed** drawing edge, along which lines are drawn. Some transparent mirrors have a drawing edge both on the top and on the bottom.

Place your transparent mirror on this page so that its drawing edge lies along line *MK* below. Then look through the transparent mirror to read the "backward" message.

If you have followed the directions correctly, you are now able to read this message. Here are a few things to remember when using your transparent mirror:

- Always look into the front of the transparent mirror. In this position, the drawing edge will be facing you.
- Use your transparent mirror on flat surfaces like your desk or a tabletop.
- Use a sharp pencil when tracing along the drawing edge.
- Experiment and have fun!

M *K*

Math Journal 2, **p. 274**

Student Page

Date _______________ Time _______________

LESSON 10·1 Using Coins to Add Fractions

In the United States, each coin is worth a fraction of a dollar. For example, the penny is worth $\frac{1}{100}$ of a dollar. The values of some coins can be expressed as a fraction of a dollar in different ways. Two ways to express the value of a quarter are as $\frac{1}{4}$ of a dollar and as $\frac{25}{100}$ of a dollar.

When a coin's value is written as a *unit fraction* (a fraction with a numerator of 1), the denominator tells you how many of those coins are needed to make a dollar. When a coin's value is written as a fraction with a denominator of 100, the numerator tells you how many pennies are needed to equal the value of the coin.

Find the missing numbers to show the value of each coin as a fraction of a dollar.

Coin	Unit fraction	Denominator of 100
Penny:	$\frac{1}{100}$	$\frac{1}{100}$
Nickel:	$\frac{1}{20}$	$\frac{5}{100}$
Dime:	$\frac{1}{10}$	$\frac{10}{100}$
Quarter:	$\frac{1}{4}$	$\frac{25}{100}$
Half Dollar:	$\frac{1}{2}$	$\frac{50}{100}$

For Problems 1–3 on the next page, rewrite the equation to show value of each coin as a unit fraction. Then rename the fractions as hundredths and add to find the total value of the coins.

Example:

Ⓟ + Ⓠ + Ⓝ + Ⓝ + (HD) = ?

Unit fractions: $\frac{1}{100} + \frac{1}{4} + \frac{1}{20} + \frac{1}{20} + \frac{1}{2} = ?$

Hundredths: $\frac{1}{100} + \frac{25}{100} + \frac{5}{100} + \frac{5}{100} + \frac{50}{100} = \frac{86}{100}$, or 86 cents

Math Journal 2, p. 275A

Student Page

Date _______________ Time _______________

LESSON 10·1 Using Coins to Add Fractions *continued*

1. Ⓝ + Ⓓ + Ⓟ + Ⓓ + Ⓠ = ?
   Unit fractions: $\frac{1}{20} + \frac{1}{10} + \frac{1}{100} + \frac{1}{10} + \frac{1}{4} = ?$
   Hundredths: $\frac{5}{100} + \frac{10}{100} + \frac{1}{100} + \frac{10}{100} + \frac{25}{100} = \frac{51}{100}$, or 51 cents
2. Ⓠ + Ⓠ + Ⓓ + Ⓓ + Ⓟ = ?
   Unit fractions: $\frac{1}{4} + \frac{1}{4} + \frac{1}{10} + \frac{1}{10} + \frac{1}{100} = ?$
   Hundredths: $\frac{25}{100} + \frac{25}{100} + \frac{10}{100} + \frac{10}{100} + \frac{1}{100} = \frac{71}{100}$, or 71 cents
3. Ⓟ + Ⓝ + Ⓓ + Ⓠ + (HD) = ?
   Unit fractions: $\frac{1}{100} + \frac{1}{20} + \frac{1}{10} + \frac{1}{4} + \frac{1}{2} = ?$
   Hundredths: $\frac{1}{100} + \frac{5}{100} + \frac{10}{100} + \frac{25}{100} + \frac{50}{100} = \frac{91}{100}$, or 91 cents

For Problems 4–6, the fractions represent coin values. Rename them as hundredths and then add to find the total value.

4. $\frac{1}{2} + \frac{1}{20} + \frac{5}{100} + \frac{10}{100} + \frac{1}{100} + \frac{1}{100}$
   Hundredths: $\frac{50}{100} + \frac{5}{100} + \frac{5}{100} + \frac{10}{100} + \frac{1}{100} + \frac{1}{100} = \frac{72}{100}$, or 72 cents
5. $\frac{1}{2} + \frac{1}{4} + \frac{1}{10} + \frac{1}{20} + \frac{1}{100}$
   Hundredths: $\frac{50}{100} + \frac{25}{100} + \frac{10}{100} + \frac{5}{100} + \frac{1}{100} = \frac{91}{100}$, or 91 cents
6. $\frac{1}{4} + \frac{1}{20} + \frac{1}{20} + \frac{1}{20} + \frac{1}{10}$
   Hundredths: $\frac{25}{100} + \frac{5}{100} + \frac{5}{100} + \frac{5}{100} + \frac{10}{100} = \frac{50}{100}$, or 50 cents
7. Write your own coin problem in the space below. Have your partner solve your problem.
   Answers vary.

Math Journal 2, p. 275B

The original squiggle is known as the **preimage.** The squiggle on the other side of the transparent mirror is called the **image** of the original squiggle. The image and the preimage are **congruent.** Congruent figures have the same size and shape. Two figures are congruent if they match exactly when one is placed on top of the other after a combination of slides, flips, and/or turns.

Language Arts Link Discuss the use of the prefix *pre-* to mean "before." The preimage is the image before it has been reflected in the transparent mirror. Ask students to think of other words that have the prefix *pre-*. Sample answers: *prehistoric, preview,* and *preschool*

Ask students to move the transparent mirror around and observe what happens to the image of the squiggle. Then suggest that students experiment with their mirrors—they can "move" small objects around on their desks.

▶ Using the Transparent Mirror to "Move" Reflected Images

(*Math Masters,* p. 304)

Have partners do the activity on *Math Masters,* page 304. The purpose of the activity is to practice moving the bee around the page. Do not require students to draw the bee at each flower.

▶ Using the Transparent Mirror to Draw Images of Shapes

(*Math Masters,* p. 305)

Students use their transparent mirrors to move a hat, a nose, and a mouth to their appropriate places on the clown face on *Math Masters,* page 305. When each part, as seen through the mirror, is in its desired place, students trace it to complete the picture. They may color and cut out their completed clowns.

2 Ongoing Learning & Practice

Playing *Over and Up Squares*

PARTNER ACTIVITY

(*Student Reference Book,* p. 257; *Math Masters,* p. 494)

Students play *Over and Up Squares* to practice locating and plotting points on a coordinate grid. See Lesson 6-9 for additional information.

Ongoing Assessment: Recognizing Student Achievement

Math Masters Page 494

Use ***Math Masters,* page 494** to assess students' ability to plot points in the first quadrant of a coordinate grid. Students are making adequate progress if they are able to form ordered number pairs from dice rolls and accurately plot them on the *Over and Up Squares* gameboard. Some students may use a strategy to form the ordered number pairs to earn the most points possible.

[Measurement and Reference Frames Goal 4]

Using Coin Values to Add Hundredths

PARTNER ACTIVITY

(*Math Journal 2,* pp. 275A and 275B)

To practice adding fractions with 100 in the denominator, have students express values of coins as unit fractions, then as fractions of a dollar and add.

Math Boxes 10•1

INDEPENDENT ACTIVITY

(*Math Journal 2,* p. 275)

Mixed Practice Math Boxes in this lesson are paired with Math Boxes in Lesson 10-4. The skill in Problem 6 previews Unit 11 content.

Writing/Reasoning Have students write a response to the following: *What strategy did you use to insert the decimal point in Problem 4c?* Sample answer: 0.53 is about $\frac{1}{2}$. Since $\frac{1}{2}$ of 14 is 7, the decimal point goes after the 7 to make 7.42.

Study Link 10•1

INDEPENDENT ACTIVITY

(*Math Masters,* p. 306)

Home Connection Students use a regular mirror to draw the image of a design. They will need a blank piece of paper to complete the activity.

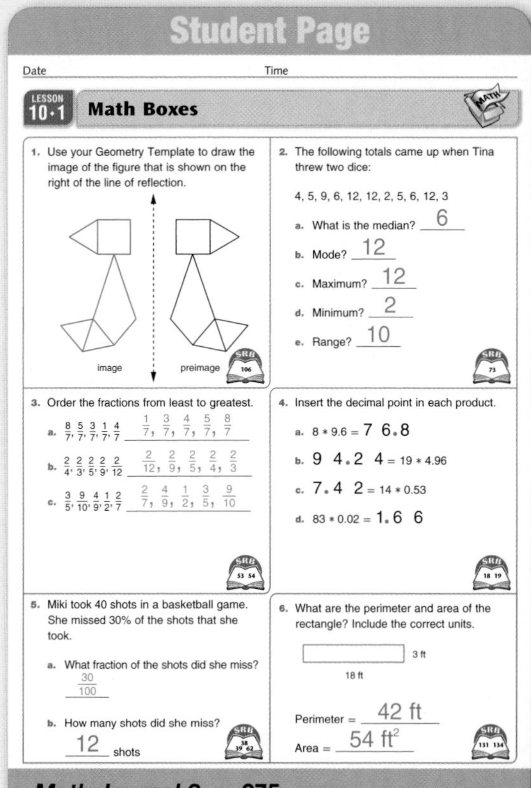

Student Page

Date Time

LESSON 10•1 **Math Boxes**

1. Use your Geometry Template to draw the image of the figure that is shown on the right of the line of reflection.

2. The following totals came up when Tina threw two dice:

4, 5, 9, 6, 12, 12, 2, 5, 6, 12, 3

a. What is the median? 6

b. Mode? 12

c. Maximum? 12

d. Minimum? 2

e. Range? 10

SRB 73

3. Order the fractions from least to greatest.

a. $\frac{8}{7}, \frac{5}{7}, \frac{3}{7}, \frac{1}{7}, \frac{4}{7}$ $\frac{1}{7}, \frac{3}{7}, \frac{4}{7}, \frac{5}{7}, \frac{8}{7}$

b. $\frac{2}{4}, \frac{2}{3}, \frac{2}{5}, \frac{2}{9}, \frac{2}{12}$ $\frac{2}{12}, \frac{2}{9}, \frac{2}{5}, \frac{2}{4}, \frac{2}{3}$

c. $\frac{3}{5}, \frac{9}{10}, \frac{4}{9}, \frac{1}{2}, \frac{2}{7}$ $\frac{2}{7}, \frac{4}{9}, \frac{1}{2}, \frac{3}{5}, \frac{9}{10}$

SRB 53 54

4. Insert the decimal point in each product.

a. 8 ∗ 9.6 = 7 6.8

b. 9 4.2 4 = 19 ∗ 4.96

c. 7.4 2 = 14 ∗ 0.53

d. 83 ∗ 0.02 = 1.6 6

SRB 18 19

5. Miki took 40 shots in a basketball game. She missed 30% of the shots that she took.

a. What fraction of the shots did she miss? $\frac{30}{100}$

b. How many shots did she miss? 12 shots

SRB 38 39 62

6. What are the perimeter and area of the rectangle? Include the correct units.

Perimeter = 42 ft

Area = 54 ft²

SRB 131 134

Math Journal 2, p. 275

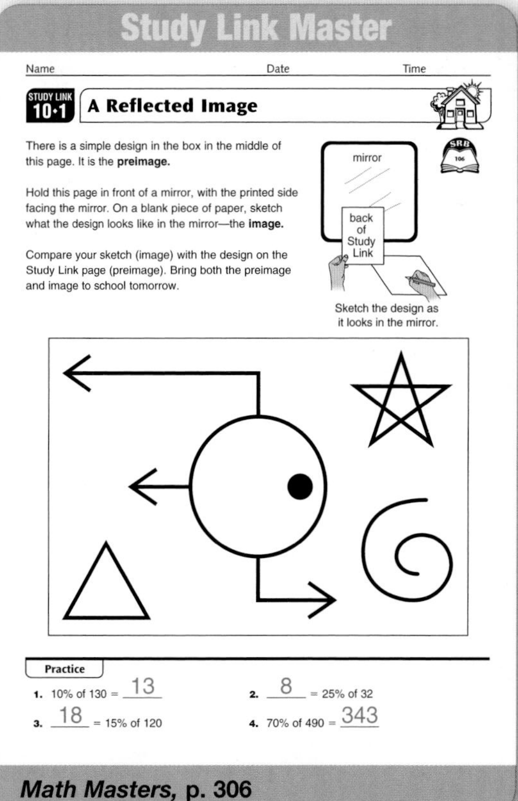

Study Link Master

Name Date Time

STUDY LINK 10•1 **A Reflected Image**

There is a simple design in the box in the middle of this page. It is the **preimage.**

Hold this page in front of a mirror, with the printed side facing the mirror. On a blank piece of paper, sketch what the design looks like in the mirror—the **image.**

Compare your sketch (image) with the design on the Study Link page (preimage). Bring both the preimage and image to school tomorrow.

Practice

1. 10% of 130 = 13

2. 8 = 25% of 32

3. 18 = 15% of 120

4. 70% of 490 = 343

Math Masters, p. 306

3 Differentiation Options

READINESS

PARTNER ACTIVITY

5–15 Min

Exploring Reflections

To explore problems involving spatial visualization, have students fold a piece of paper in half, cut out a shape that contains part of the fold, and draw what they think the complete shape will look like when they unfold it. Students then unfold the shape and compare it with their drawing.

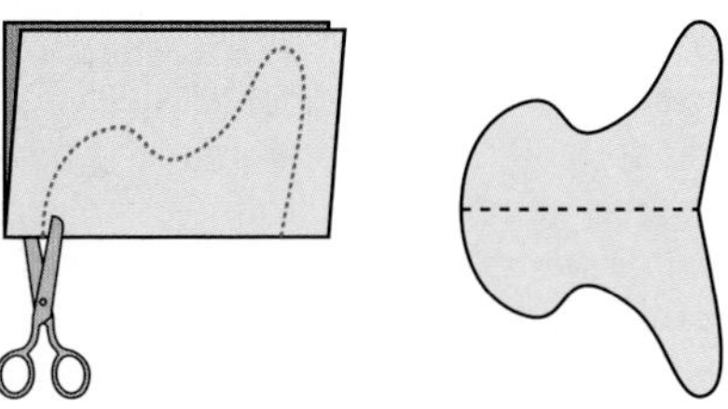

Have students try the activity again, but ask them this time to fold a piece of paper in half and then in half again.

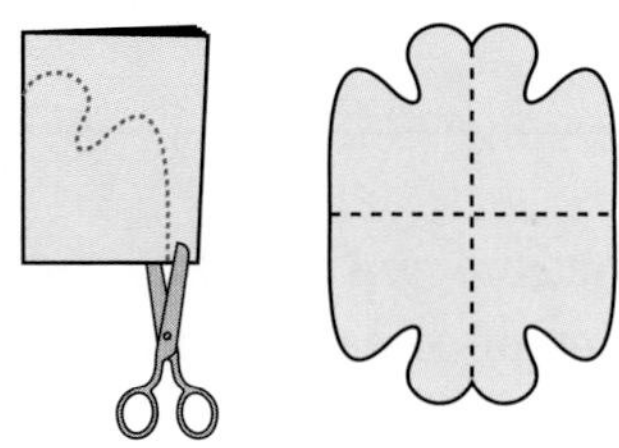

ENRICHMENT

PARTNER ACTIVITY

5–15 Min

Exploring Shadows and Reflections

(*Math Masters,* p. 389)

To apply students' understanding of reflections, have them explore the photographs of nature and city life in ***Shadows and Reflections*** by Tana Hoban (Greenwillow, 1990). On an Exit Slip, ask students to compare the reflections made in class with those in the book. Ask questions such as the following:

- What attributes are unchanged in the photographs?
- What do windows, ponds, and puddles do to reflections?
- Where do you think the different lines of reflection are located?
- How are shadows and reflections similar? How are they different?

10•2 Finding Lines of Reflection

Objectives To guide the exploration of reflections; and to provide practice identifying lines of reflection.

Technology Resources www.everydaymathonline.com

ePresentations

eToolkit

Algorithms Practice

EM Facts Workshop Game™

Family Letters

Assessment Management

Common Core State Standards

Curriculum Focal Points

Interactive Teacher's Lesson Guide

1 Teaching the Lesson

Key Concepts and Skills

- Describe properties of congruent figures, right angles, and perpendicular lines. [Geometry Goal 2]
- Explore lines of reflection and reflected images. [Geometry Goal 3]
- Solve problems involving spatial visualization. [Geometry Goal 3]

Key Activities

Students play games that involve reflections, such as the *Dart Game* and the *Pocket-Billiards Game.* They explore finding the line of reflection of a reflected image.

Ongoing Assessment: Recognizing Student Achievement Use Mental Math and Reflexes. [Number and Numeration Goal 6]

Key Vocabulary

reflection ◆ line of reflection

Materials

Math Journal 2, p. 276 and Activity Sheets 7 and 8
Study Link 10•1
per partnership: 1 transparent mirror ◆ ruler ◆ slate

2 Ongoing Learning & Practice

Playing *Angle Tangle*
Student Reference Book, p. 230
Math Masters, p. 457
straightedge ◆ protractor
Students practice estimating the measures of angles and measuring angles.

Math Boxes 10•2
Math Journal 2, p. 277
Students practice and maintain skills through Math Box problems.

Ongoing Assessment: Informing Instruction See page 802.

Study Link 10•2
Math Masters, p. 307
Geometry Template
Students practice and maintain skills through Study Link activities.

3 Differentiation Options

READINESS

Creating a Paint Reflection
Math Masters, p. 389
large sheets of paper ◆ paints ◆ brushes ◆ dark marker
Students create reflections by painting on half of a sheet of paper and then folding the paper.

ENRICHMENT

Solving Paper-Folding Puzzles
Math Masters, p. 308
scissors (optional)
Students apply their understanding of lines of reflection and reflected images to solve paper-folding puzzles.

ENRICHMENT

Exploring Reflections and Lines of Reflection
computer with Internet access
Students use technology to investigate the mirror as a virtual manipulative.

ELL SUPPORT

Building a Math Word Bank
Differentiation Handbook, p. 140
Students add the term *reflection* to their Math Word Banks.

Advance Preparation

For the optional Readiness activity in Part 3, students will need supplies and space for painting.

***Teacher's Reference Manual,* Grades 4–6** pp. 193, 194, 197, 198

Getting Started

Mental Math and Reflexes 

Have students name and explain the strategy for finding the greater fraction in each fraction pair. *Suggestions:*

●○○ $\frac{3}{4}$ or $\frac{1}{4}$ $\frac{3}{4}$
$\frac{5}{8}$ or $\frac{2}{8}$ $\frac{5}{8}$
$\frac{6}{9}$ or $\frac{6}{7}$ $\frac{6}{7}$

●●○ $\frac{2}{3}$ or $\frac{1}{2}$ $\frac{2}{3}$
$\frac{4}{6}$ or $\frac{1}{2}$ $\frac{4}{6}$
$\frac{3}{9}$ or $\frac{1}{2}$ $\frac{1}{2}$

●●● $\frac{8}{9}$ or $\frac{5}{6}$ $\frac{8}{9}$
$\frac{6}{7}$ or $\frac{4}{5}$ $\frac{6}{7}$
$\frac{1}{7}$ or $\frac{2}{8}$ $\frac{2}{8}$

Math Message

Have you ever played darts or pocket billiards? Discuss the object of each game and some of the rules with a friend.

Study Link 10·1 Follow-Up

Students place Study Link 10-1 and their sketch side by side on their desks. They compare the preimage and the image. Students should note that the image is the opposite or reverse of the preimage.

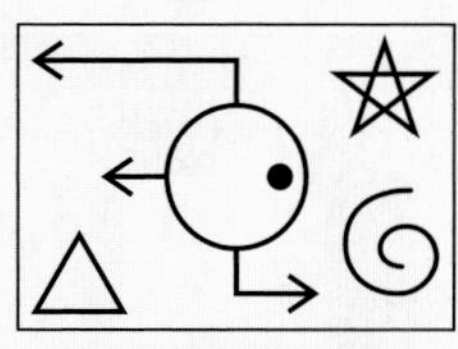

preimage

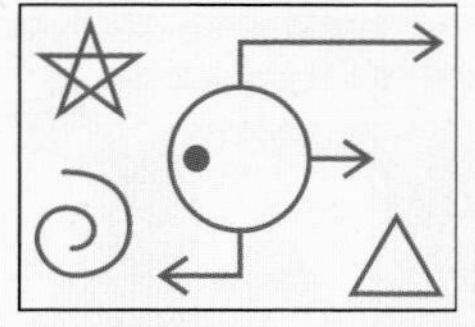

image

Ongoing Assessment: Recognizing Student Achievement

Mental Math and Reflexes 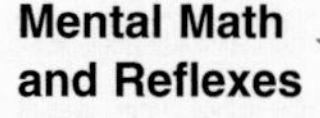 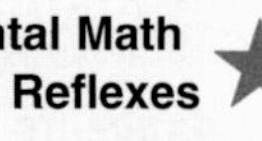

Use **Mental Math and Reflexes** to assess students' ability to compare fractions. Students are making adequate progress if they are able to solve the ●○○ problems, which involve like numerators or like denominators, and the ●●○ problems, which involve comparing fractions to the benchmark $\frac{1}{2}$. Some students may be able to solve the ●●● problems and write about their strategies.

[Number and Numeration Goal 6]

1 Teaching the Lesson

▶ Math Message Follow-Up

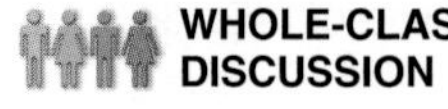

WHOLE-CLASS DISCUSSION

Students briefly share the object and some of the rules of each game with the class. Some students may mention that another name for pocket billiards is *pool*.

NOTE It is not essential that students know the rules or have played these games to understand these activities. However, displaying a dartboard or a picture of a pool table would be helpful to students unfamiliar with the games.

▶ Playing Games that Involve Reflections

PARTNER ACTIVITY

PROBLEM SOLVING

(*Math Journal 2,* p. 276 and Activity Sheets 7 and 8)

Tell students that in this lesson they will experiment with transparent mirrors and reflections by playing two games.

Dart Game

Activity Sheet 7 contains two darts, labeled A and B, and a target. The object is to "hit" the target by reflecting one of the darts with the transparent mirror.

Student Page

Date Time

LESSON 10·2 **Finding Lines of Reflection**

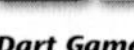

Dart Game

Practice before you play the game on Activity Sheet 7. One partner chooses Dart A and the other partner Dart B. Try to hit the target with your own dart, using the transparent mirror. **Do not practice with your partner's dart.**

Now play the game with your partner.

Directions

Take turns. When it is your turn, use the other dart—the one you did not use for practice. Try to hit the target by placing the transparent mirror on the page, but **do not look through the mirror.** Then both you and your partner look through the mirror to see where the dart hit the target. Keep score.

Pocket-Billiards Game

Practice before you play the game on Activity Sheet 8. Choose a ball (1, 2, 3, or 4) and a pocket (A, B, C, D, E, or F). Try to get the ball into the pocket, using the transparent mirror.

Now play the game with a partner.

Directions

Take turns. When it is your turn, say which ball and which pocket you have picked: for example, "Ball 2 to go into Pocket D." Try to get the ball into the pocket by placing the transparent mirror on the billiard table, **but do not look through the mirror.** Then both you and your partner look through the mirror to check whether the ball has gone into the pocket.

1. How could measuring distances with a ruler help you place the mirror so that the ball goes into the pocket? For example, exactly where can you put the mirror so that Ball 2 will go into Pocket D?
   Since the image and the preimage are equal distances from the mirror, I can measure the distance between the ball and the pocket and place the mirror halfway between the two.

Math Journal 2, p. 276

Students first practice hitting the target. One partner uses Dart A, and the other uses Dart B. Students look through the mirror and move it around until the image of the dart hits the target.

After a little practice, students begin the game. Players switch darts—that is, if they practiced with Dart A, they play the game with Dart B (and vice versa). Now students must place the mirror on the master without looking through the mirror. (There would not be much of a game if they could look through the mirror—it would be easy to hit the bull's eye every time.) Only after placing the mirror on the master may the player look through it to find the score.

Pocket-Billiards Game

Activity Sheet 8 shows the top of a pocket-billiards table. There are six pockets, labeled A–F, and four billiard balls, labeled 1–4. The object is to "sink" a ball into one of the pockets by reflecting the ball with the transparent mirror. As with the *Dart Game,* students practice by looking at the image of a billiard ball through the mirror. Then partners play the game without looking through the mirror. Players should look through the mirror only to check results.

After students have played the game several times, ask them to answer the question at the bottom of journal page 276.

Adjusting the Activity

Have partners devise their own scoring system for the game. It might be as simple as scoring 1 point for each time a ball is sunk into a pocket. Or perhaps each partner gets three tries at sinking a ball into a designated pocket, scoring 5 points if the ball goes in on the first try, 3 points if it goes in on the second try, or 1 point if it goes in on the last try.

AUDITORY • KINESTHETIC • TACTILE • VISUAL

Introducing the Concept of Reflection

WHOLE-CLASS DISCUSSION

Start the discussion by asking the following question:

- In Lesson 10-1, the clown hats were upside down. What would happen if they were drawn right-side up? After being moved to the clown's head, the hats would be upside down.

Introduce the word **reflection**—a flipping motion that makes the image appear to be the "opposite" of the original object. Point out that in a reflection in a mirror, everything is reversed. Explain that the line along the recessed edge of a transparent mirror is called the **line of reflection.**

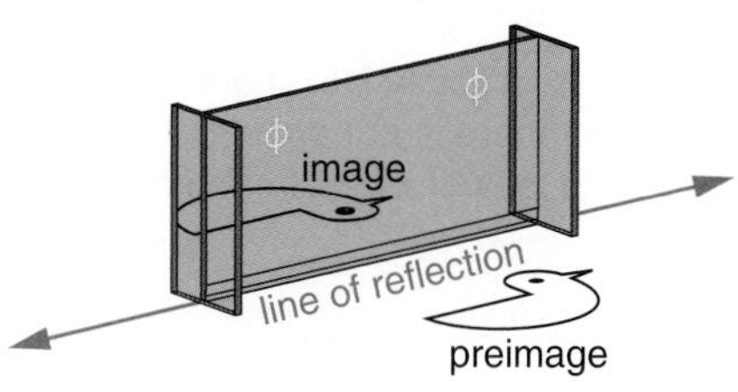

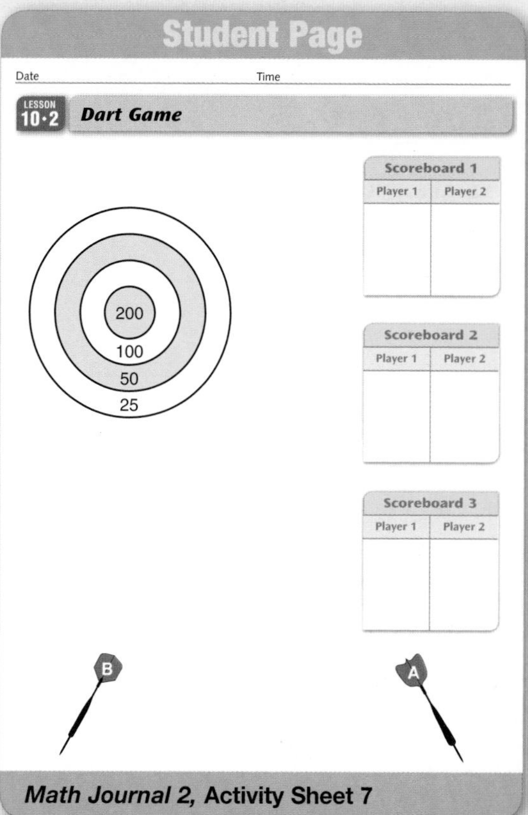

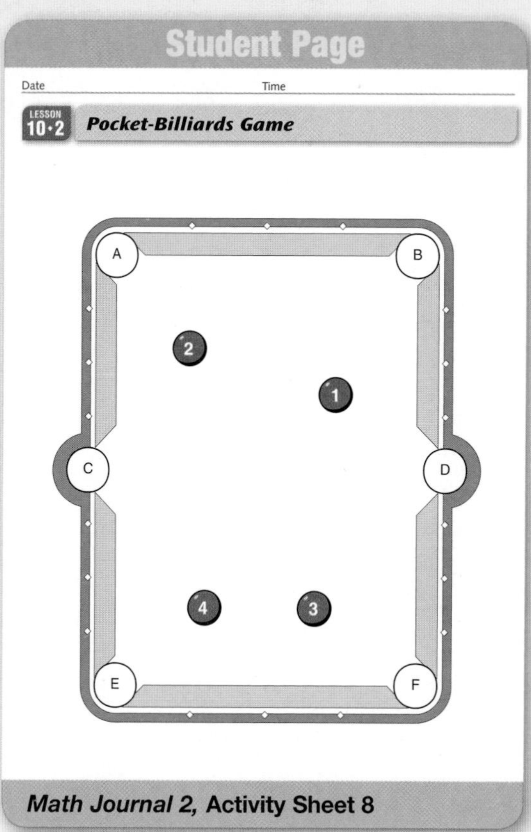

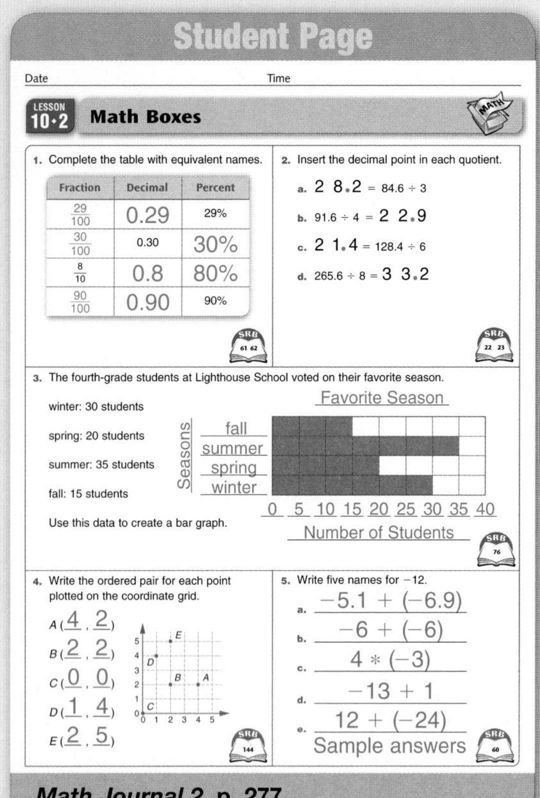
Student Page

Date Time

LESSON 10·2 Math Boxes

1. Complete the table with equivalent names.

Fraction	Decimal	Percent
$\frac{29}{100}$	0.29	29%
$\frac{30}{100}$	0.30	30%
$\frac{8}{10}$	0.8	80%
$\frac{90}{100}$	0.90	90%

SRB 61 62

2. Insert the decimal point in each quotient.

a. 2 8.2 = 84.6 ÷ 3

b. 91.6 ÷ 4 = 2 2.9

c. 2 1.4 = 128.4 ÷ 6

d. 265.6 ÷ 8 = 3 3.2

SRB 22 23

3. The fourth-grade students at Lighthouse School voted on their favorite season.

winter: 30 students

spring: 20 students

summer: 35 students

fall: 15 students

Use this data to create a bar graph.

Favorite Season

Seasons: fall, summer, spring, winter

0 5 10 15 20 25 30 35 40

Number of Students

SRB 76

4. Write the ordered pair for each point plotted on the coordinate grid.

A(4, 2)

B(2, 2)

C(0, 0)

D(1, 4)

E(2, 5)

SRB 144

5. Write five names for −12.

a. −5.1 + (−6.9)

b. −6 + (−6)

c. 4 ∗ (−3)

d. −13 + 1

e. 12 + (−24)

Sample answers

SRB 60

Math Journal 2, p. 277

Have students share their strategies for locating the line of reflection on the pocket-billiards table. Help them see that the mirror must be placed about halfway between the ball and the pocket and that it should be perpendicular (at a right angle) to the invisible line connecting the ball and the pocket. This method works because a reflected object is the same distance from the line of reflection as the original object.

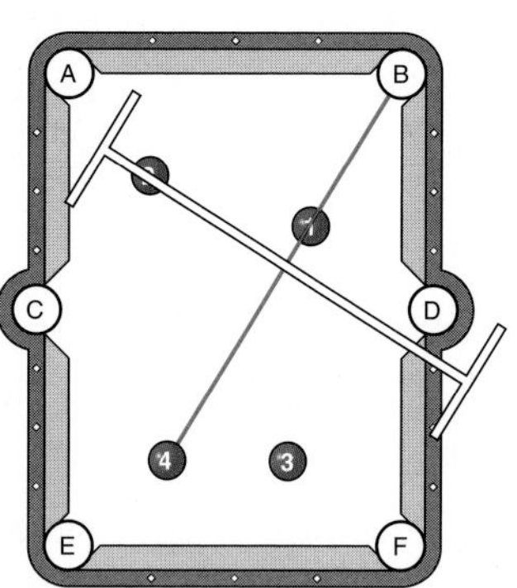

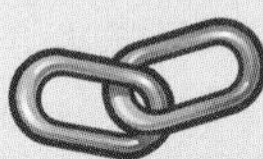

Links to the Future

This is as far as you need to go with this topic for now. With additional experience, students will learn that when an object is reflected, corresponding points on the object and on its reflection image are the same distance from the line of reflection.

2 Ongoing Learning & Practice

▶ Playing *Angle Tangle*

PARTNER ACTIVITY

(*Student Reference Book,* p. 230; *Math Masters,* p. 457)

Students play *Angle Tangle* to practice estimating and measuring angles. See Lesson 6-8 for additional information.

▶ Math Boxes 10·2

INDEPENDENT ACTIVITY

(*Math Journal 2,* p. 277)

Mixed Practice Math Boxes in this lesson are paired with Math Boxes in Lesson 10-5. The skill in Problem 5 previews Unit 11 content.

Ongoing Assessment: Informing Instruction

Watch for students who have difficulty labeling the horizontal axis of the graph in Problem 3 because there is not enough space provided to label it by ones. Encourage them to look at the data and find a common factor to use as the interval.

Study Link 10•2

INDEPENDENT ACTIVITY

(*Math Masters,* p. 307)

Home Connection Students draw lines of reflection between preimages and images. For given preimages, they use the Geometry Template to draw the image on the other side of the line of reflection.

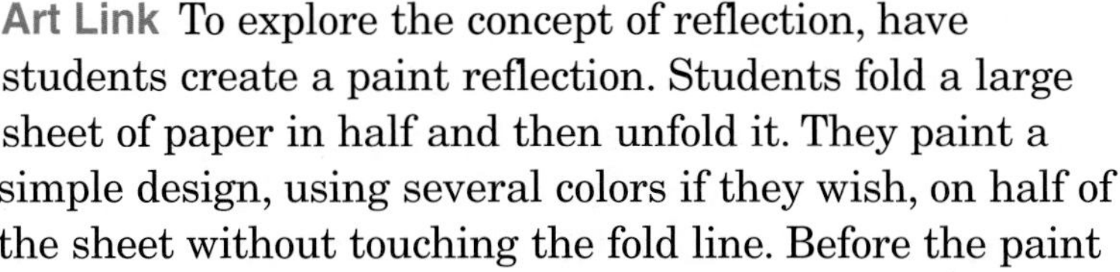

READINESS

INDEPENDENT ACTIVITY

Creating a Paint Reflection

15–30 Min

(*Math Masters,* p. 389)

Art Link To explore the concept of reflection, have students create a paint reflection. Students fold a large sheet of paper in half and then unfold it. They paint a simple design, using several colors if they wish, on half of the sheet without touching the fold line. Before the paint has dried, students refold the paper and unfold it again. The result will be a reflection of the painted design on the other half of the paper.

Have students use a dark marker to highlight the fold line and label it as the *line of reflection.* In addition, have students label the *preimage* and *image.*

Simple design with reflection

Ask students to answer questions such as the following on an Exit Slip:

- What do you notice about your design?
- How are the designs on both sides of the fold alike? How are they different?
- What does the fold represent?
- How would you describe a reflection to someone who did not know what it was?

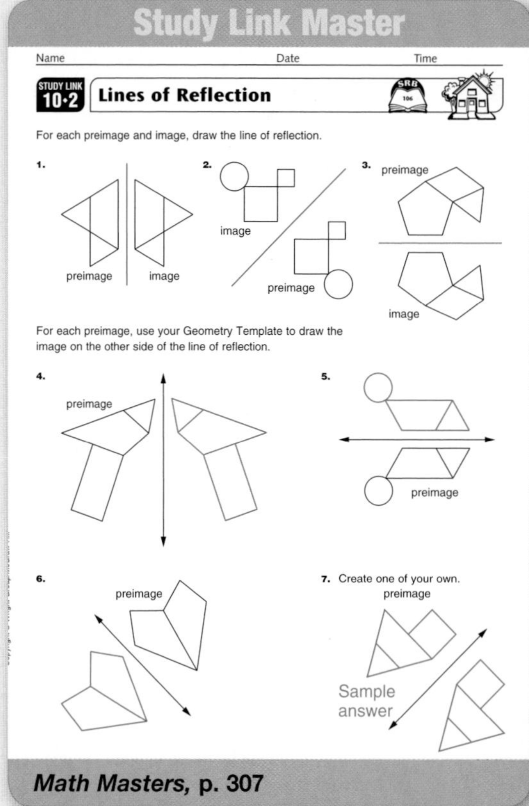

Study Link Master

Name Date Time

STUDY LINK 10•2 **Lines of Reflection**

For each preimage and image, draw the line of reflection.

1. preimage image
2. image preimage
3. preimage image

For each preimage, use your Geometry Template to draw the image on the other side of the line of reflection.

4. preimage
5. preimage
6. preimage
7. Create one of your own. preimage Sample answer

Math Masters, p. 307

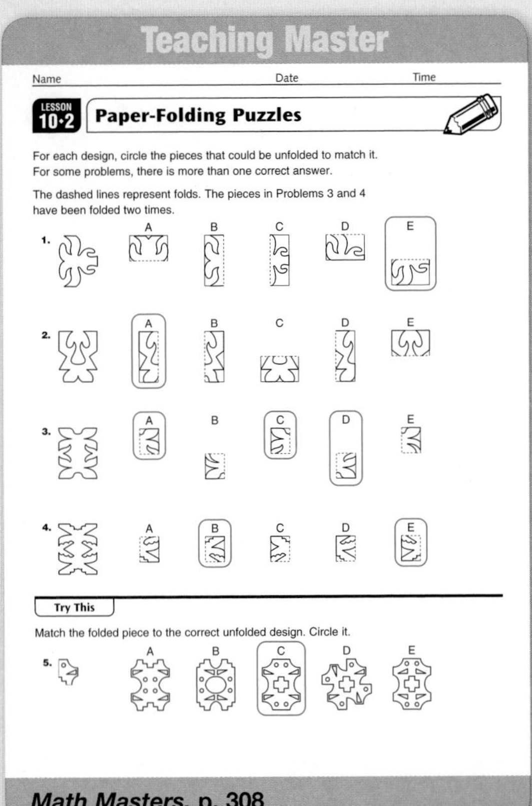

Teaching Master

Name Date Time

LESSON 10•2 **Paper-Folding Puzzles**

For each design, circle the pieces that could be unfolded to match it. For some problems, there is more than one correct answer.

The dashed lines represent folds. The pieces in Problems 3 and 4 have been folded two times.

1. A B C D E

2. A B C D E

3. A B C D E

4. A B C D E

Try This

Match the folded piece to the correct unfolded design. Circle it.

5. A B C D E

Math Masters, p. 308

ENRICHMENT

INDEPENDENT ACTIVITY

5–15 Min

Solving Paper-Folding Puzzles

(*Math Masters,* p. 308)

To apply students' understanding of lines of reflection and reflected images, have them match folded and unfolded designs. Ask students to describe how they used lines of reflection to help them match the designs. Some students may choose to sketch the folded designs and cut them out to check their work. Encourage students to make up their own paper-folding puzzles.

ENRICHMENT

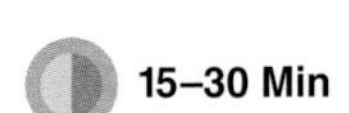
INDEPENDENT ACTIVITY

15–30 Min

Exploring Reflections and Lines of Reflection

Technology Link To apply students' understanding of reflections and lines of reflection, have them investigate the use of a mirror as a virtual manipulative. See the Web site at http://nlvm.usu.edu/en/nav/frames_asid_297_g_2_t_3.html?open=activities. The site is part of the National Library of Virtual Manipulatives for Interactive Mathematics developed by Utah State University. See http://nlvm.usu.edu.

ELL SUPPORT

SMALL-GROUP ACTIVITY

5–15 Min

Building a Math Word Bank

(*Differentiation Handbook,* p. 140)

To provide language support for transformations, have students use the Word Bank Template found on *Differentiation Handbook,* page 140. Ask students to write the term *reflection,* draw a picture representing the term, and write other related words. See the *Differentiation Handbook* for more information.

Planning Ahead

Begin collecting pictures of symmetric objects, such as the front view of an automobile, a table, a window, and a fork. These will be used in an optional ELL Support activity in Lesson 10-4 to start a Line Symmetry Museum.

10•3 Properties of Reflections

Objective To guide the discovery of basic properties of reflections.

www.everydaymathonline.com

ePresentations | eToolkit | Algorithms Practice | EM Facts Workshop Game™ | Family Letters | Assessment Management | Common Core State Standards | Curriculum Focal Points | Interactive Teacher's Lesson Guide

1 Teaching the Lesson

Key Concepts and Skills

- Measure length. [Measurement and Reference Frames Goal 1]
- Draw and describe congruent figures. [Geometry Goal 2]
- Explore basic properties of reflections. [Geometry Goal 3]
- Solve problems involving spatial visualization. [Geometry Goal 3]

Key Activities

Students use a transparent mirror to discover basic properties of reflections. They draw reflected images.

Ongoing Assessment: Recognizing Student Achievement
Use *Math Masters,* page 309.
[Geometry Goal 3]

Key Vocabulary

line of reflection

Materials

Study Link 10•2
Math Masters, p. 309
per partnership: 1 transparent mirror ◆ ruler ◆ slate

2 Ongoing Learning & Practice

World Tour Option: Visiting a Second Country in Region 4
Math Journal 2, pp. 329–331, 338, and 339
Student Reference Book, pp. 276, 277, 281, 288–291, 297, and 302–305
Math Masters, pp. 419–421 (optional)
Students resume the World Tour in Region 4.

Growing Patterns
Math Journal 2, pp. 277A and 277B
Students complete growing patterns.

Math Boxes 10•3
Math Journal 2, p. 278
Students practice and maintain skills through Math Box problems.

Study Link 10•3
Math Masters, p. 310
Students practice and maintain skills through Study Link activities.

3 Differentiation Options

READINESS

Creating Reflections with Pattern Blocks or Centimeter Cubes
Math Masters, pp. 389 and 403
centimeter cubes or pattern blocks ◆ blank paper or centimeter grid paper
Students create designs with pattern blocks or centimeter cubes and reflect the designs.

ENRICHMENT

Exploring Reflections of 3-Dimensional Figures
Math Masters, p. 447
centimeter cubes
Students use centimeter cubes to construct 3-dimensional buildings and their reflections.

EXTRA PRACTICE

5-Minute Math
5-Minute Math™, p. 149
blank paper
Students solve problems involving reflections.

Advance Preparation

***Teacher's Reference Manual,* Grades 4–6** pp. 193, 194, 197, 198

Getting Started

Mental Math and Reflexes

Dictate large numbers for students to write on their slates.
Suggestions:

●○○	●●○	●●●
14,687,320	100,456,892	34,206,408,900
45,318,972	203,541,986	7,940,005,030
89,245,307	106,507,349	49,802,103,062

For each number, ask questions such as the following:

- Which digit is in the millions place?
- What is the value of the digit *x*?
- How many hundred millions are there?

Math Message

Stand facing a partner. One partner poses. The other partner positions his or her body to be the mirror image of the partner. Then switch roles.

Study Link 10·2 Follow-Up

Have students compare answers and share the preimages and images they created for Problem 7.

1 Teaching the Lesson

▶ Math Message Follow-Up

WHOLE-CLASS ACTIVITY

Have partners show their mirror-image poses to the class. Strike your own pose. Have students show the mirror image. Slowly change your pose and challenge students to mirror your changes.

Tell students that in this lesson they will investigate some of the basic properties of reflections.

▶ Examining Relationships between an Object and Its Reflected Image

WHOLE-CLASS ACTIVITY

(*Math Masters,* p. 309)

Tell partnerships to put the recessed edge of the mirror on the line next to the dog's head. When they look directly through the mirror, they will see the image of the dog's head. (It is best to look through the mirror at eye level.) Ask students to carefully draw the image of the dog's head on the paper where they see it through the mirror and describe, on the back of *Math Masters,* page 309, how the drawings are alike and how they are different.

When all students have completed the tasks, bring the class together and lead them in the following exploration:

▷ Point out that the picture of the dog's head to the left of the **line of reflection** is the preimage. Remind students that *pre-* means "before," so they can think of this as the "before image."

▷ Ask: *How are the two drawings alike? How are they different?* Sample answers: The drawings are congruent; they are the same size and shape. They look exactly alike, except that the heads are facing in opposite directions.

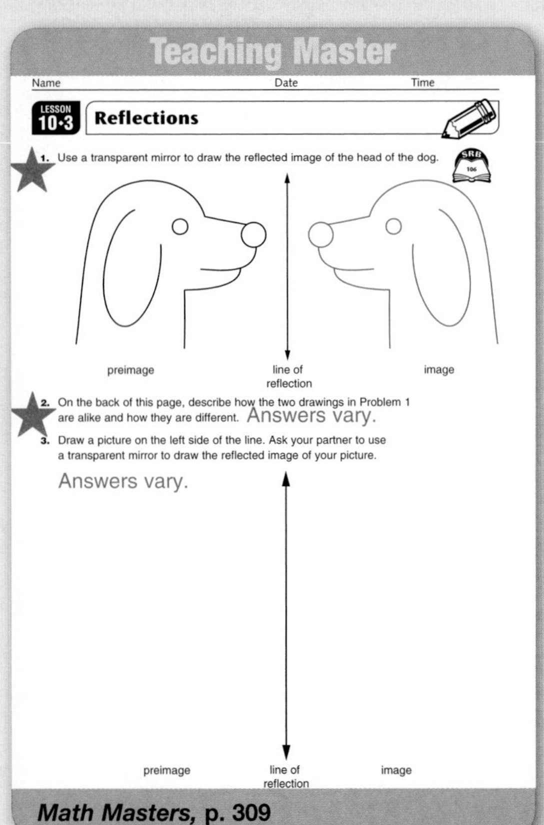
Teaching Master

Name Date Time

LESSON 10·3 **Reflections**

1. Use a transparent mirror to draw the reflected image of the head of the dog.

2. On the back of this page, describe how the two drawings in Problem 1 are alike and how they are different. Answers vary.
3. Draw a picture on the left side of the line. Ask your partner to use a transparent mirror to draw the reflected image of your picture.

Answers vary.

Math Masters, p. 309

- ▷ Have students mark a point A anywhere on the preimage. Then ask them to look through the mirror, mark the image of point A, and label the image A' (“A prime”). Write A' on the board and explain that the little mark by the A is read “prime.” The prime mark shows that A and A' are different, but related, points.

  Check that all students have labeled the corresponding points A and A' on the dogs. The points may be anywhere, but they must be in the same place on the image as on the preimage.

- ▷ Have students use a ruler to measure the distance from point A to the line of reflection and from point A' to the line of reflection. Ask: *What did you find out about the distances?* They are the same.

- ▷ Have students mark and label several other points (B, C, and so on) on the preimage; use the mirror to mark and label the corresponding points (B', C', and so on) on the image; and check with a ruler that corresponding points are the same distance from the line of reflection.

- ▷ Remind students of the *Pocket-Billiards Game*. Ask: *Where did you place the mirror in order to get the ball in the pocket?* Halfway between the ball and the pocket

- ▷ Finally, have each student draw a picture on the left side of the reflection line in the bottom half of the page. Then ask partners to exchange papers and draw the image of their partner's picture.

Ongoing Assessment: Recognizing Student Achievement

Math Masters Page 309 Problems 1 and 2

Use ***Math Masters,* page 309, Problems 1 and 2** to assess students' ability to sketch and describe a reflection. Students are making adequate progress if they are able to use a transparent mirror to accurately draw the reflected image of the dog's head and describe how the preimage and image are alike and different. Some students may describe the relationship of the points on the drawings to the line of reflection.

[Geometry Goal 3]

Folding Paper to Observe Reflected Images

WHOLE-CLASS ACTIVITY

(*Math Masters,* p. 309)

Lead the class through the following procedure:

1. Fold *Math Masters,* page 309 in half lengthwise along the lines of reflection.
2. Hold the folded sheet up to the light to check if the preimage and image in Problem 1 and the preimage and image in Problem 3 match.

Ask: *For each problem, are the preimage and image congruent?* yes *How do you know?* They are the same size and shape.

Student Page

Date Time

LESSON 10·3 Growing Patterns

1. a. Draw the next shape in the pattern.

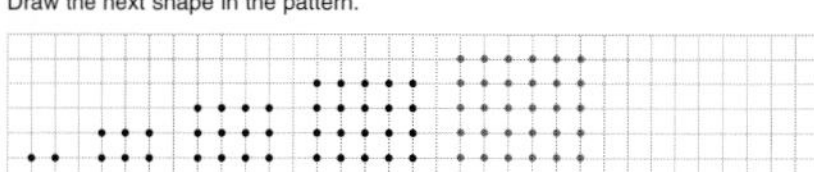

   b. Describe the rule you used to extend the pattern. Sample answer: The number of rows and columns in each rectangle increases by 1 dot.

2. a. Extend the number pattern: 2, 6, 12, 20, 30, 42, 56

   b. Describe the rule you used to extend the pattern. Sample answer: Start with 2. Add 4. Then keep adding the next multiple of 2 to the sum. 2 + **4** = 6; 6 + **6** = 12; 12 + **8** = 20; 20 + **10** = 30; 30 + **12** = 42; 42 + **14** = 56

3. a. Draw the next shape in the pattern.

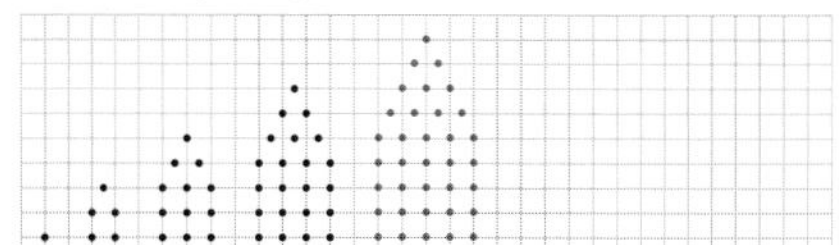

   b. Describe the rule you used to extend the pattern. Sample answer: Each pentagon is made up of a square and a triangle. The number of dots on each side of the square and on each side of the triangle increases by 1.

4. a. Extend the number pattern: 1, 5, 12, 22, 35, 51, 70

   b. Describe the rule you used to extend the pattern. Sample answer: Start with 1. Add 4. Then keep adding 3 more than the number you added before. 1 + **4** = 5; 5 + **7** = 12; 12 + **10** = 22; 22 + **13** = 35; 35 + **16** = 51; 51 + **19** = 70

Math Journal 2, p. 277A

Student Page

Date Time

LESSON 10·3 Growing Patterns *continued*

5. a. Draw the next shape in the pattern.

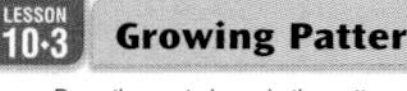
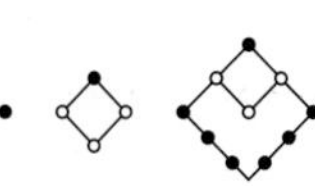
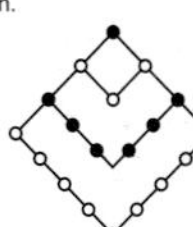

   b. Describe the rule used to extend the pattern. Sample answer: The dots switch back and forth between closed and open. Each time a new set of dots is added, the total number of dots increases by the next multiple of 3.

6. a. Extend the number pattern: 1, 4, 10, 19, 31, 46, 64

   b. Describe the rule used to extend the pattern. Sample answer: Start with 1. Add 3. Then keep adding the next multiple of 3 to the sum. 1 + **3** = 4; 4 + **6** = 10; 10 + **9** = 19; 19 + **12** = 31; 31 + **15** = 46; 46 + **18** = 64

Try This

The numbers in Problem 6 are called *tetragonal numbers.* The shapes in Problem 5 show tetragonal numbers as arrays of dots.

7. a. Make a list of the first 20 tetragonal numbers. Circle the ones digit in each number.

   1, 4, 10, 19, 31, 46, 64, 85, 109, 136, 166, 199, 235, 274, 316, 361, 409, 460, 514, 571

   b. Make a list of the ones digits in the first 20 tetragonal numbers.

   1, 4, 0, 9, 1, 6, 4, 5, 9, 6, 6, 9, 5, 4, 6, 1, 9, 0, 4, 1

   c. Describe any patterns you see in the list of numbers in Part b. The 10th and 11th numbers are 6s. The pattern of numbers ends at the first 6 and then repeats in reverse. It's like there's a line of reflection between the 10th and 11th numbers.

   d. Do you think this pattern will continue? Answers vary. Test your answer.

Math Journal 2, p. 277B

Student Page

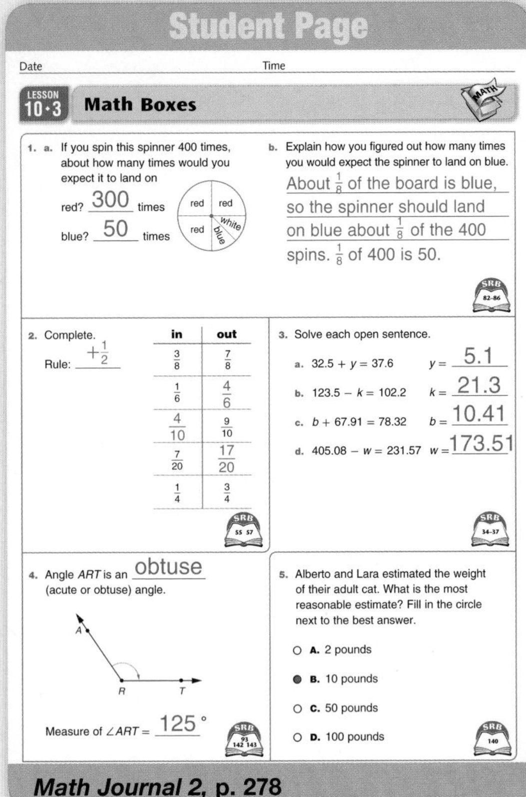
Date Time

LESSON 10·3 **Math Boxes**

1. a. If you spin this spinner 400 times, about how many times would you expect it to land on
   red? 300 times
   blue? 50 times

   b. Explain how you figured out how many times you would expect the spinner to land on blue.
   About $\frac{1}{8}$ of the board is blue, so the spinner should land on blue about $\frac{1}{8}$ of the 400 spins. $\frac{1}{8}$ of 400 is 50.

2. Complete.
   Rule: $+\frac{1}{2}$

in	out
$\frac{3}{8}$	$\frac{7}{8}$
$\frac{1}{6}$	$\frac{4}{6}$
$\frac{4}{10}$	$\frac{9}{10}$
$\frac{7}{20}$	$\frac{17}{20}$
$\frac{1}{4}$	$\frac{3}{4}$

3. Solve each open sentence.
   a. $32.5 + y = 37.6$ $y =$ 5.1
   b. $123.5 - k = 102.2$ $k =$ 21.3
   c. $b + 67.91 = 78.32$ $b =$ 10.41
   d. $405.08 - w = 231.57$ $w =$ 173.51

4. Angle *ART* is an obtuse (acute or obtuse) angle.
   Measure of $\angle ART =$ 125°

5. Alberto and Lara estimated the weight of their adult cat. What is the most reasonable estimate? Fill in the circle next to the best answer.
   - ○ A. 2 pounds
   - ● B. 10 pounds
   - ○ C. 50 pounds
   - ○ D. 100 pounds

Math Journal 2, p. 278

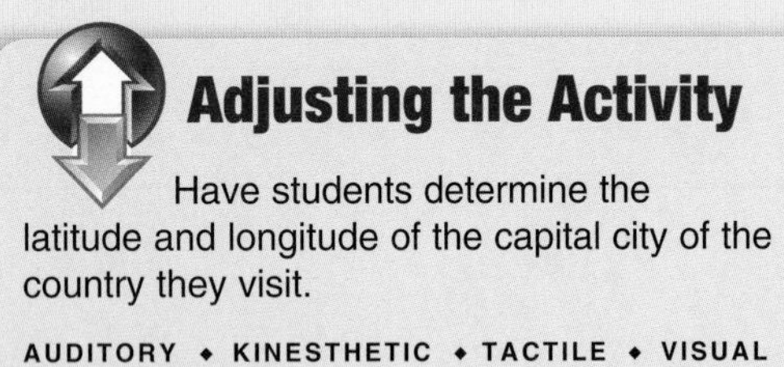
Adjusting the Activity

Have students determine the latitude and longitude of the capital city of the country they visit.

AUDITORY ◆ KINESTHETIC ◆ TACTILE ◆ VISUAL

Study Link Master

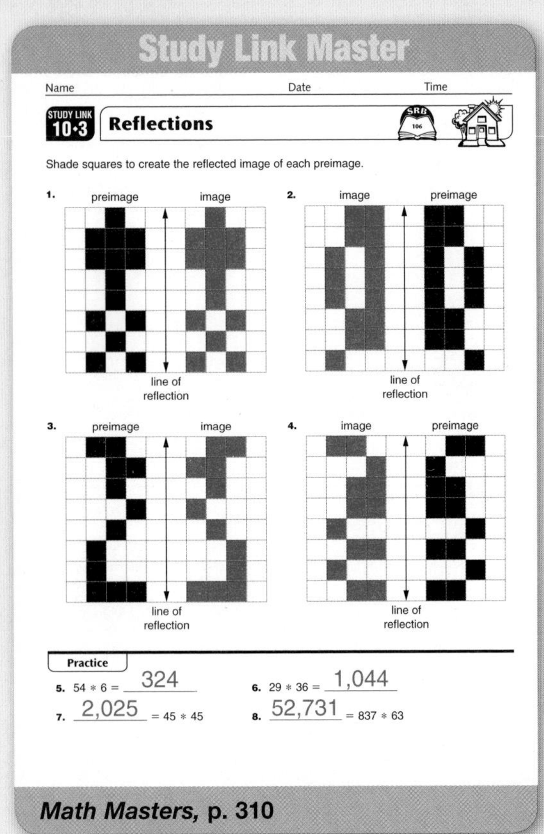
Name Date Time

STUDY LINK 10·3 **Reflections**

Shade squares to create the reflected image of each preimage.

1. preimage image line of reflection
2. image preimage line of reflection
3. preimage image line of reflection
4. image preimage line of reflection

Practice

5. $54 * 6 =$ 324
6. $29 * 36 =$ 1,044
7. 2,025 $= 45 * 45$
8. 52,731 $= 837 * 63$

Math Masters, p. 310

2 Ongoing Learning & Practice

▶ World Tour Option: Visiting a Second Country in Region 4

(*Math Journal 2*, pp. 329–331, 338, and 339; *Student Reference Book*, pp. 276, 277, 281, 288–291, 297, and 302–305; *Math Masters*, pp. 419–421)

Social Studies Link If you have chosen to extend the scope of the World Tour for your class, have small groups visit a second country in Region 4. You may let them choose which countries to visit, or you may assign a country to each group. Remind students to update their Route Log (if they are keeping one) and Route Map and to complete Country Notes for the country they visit.

▶ Growing Patterns

(*Math Journal 2*, pp. 277A and 277B)

Students complete growing patterns of numbers and shapes. Encourage students to discuss the patterns.

After students complete the journal pages, point out that the numbers in Problem 2 are called *rectangular numbers* and the numbers in Problem 4 are called *pentagonal numbers.* The shapes in Problem 1 show the rectangular numbers as arrays of dots. The shapes in Problem 3 are nonregular pentagons.

▶ Math Boxes 10·3

(*Math Journal 2*, p. 278)

Mixed Practice Math Boxes in this lesson are paired with Math Boxes in Lesson 10-6. The skill in Problem 5 previews Unit 11 content.

Writing/Reasoning Have students write a response to the following: *How did you choose the weight for the cat in Problem 5?* Sample answer: I eliminated two of the choices. I knew the cat weighed more than 2 pounds of butter, and some of my friends weigh about 50 pounds. That made 10 pounds the best choice.

▶ Study Link 10·3

(*Math Masters*, p. 310)

Home Connection Students shade grid squares to create images of given preimages. A transparent mirror is not required to do this page.

3 Differentiation Options

READINESS

PARTNER ACTIVITY

5–15 Min

Creating Reflections with Pattern Blocks or Centimeter Cubes

(*Math Masters,* pp. 389 and 403)

To explore reflections using concrete materials, have students use pattern blocks or centimeter cubes to create preimages for a partner to reflect.

- For centimeter cubes, have students fold a sheet of centimeter grid paper in half on a grid line. One partner creates a design on one side of the fold for the other partner to reflect.
- To use pattern blocks, have students fold a blank piece of paper in half to create a line of reflection. One student creates a design on one side of the fold for a partner to reflect on the other side of the fold.

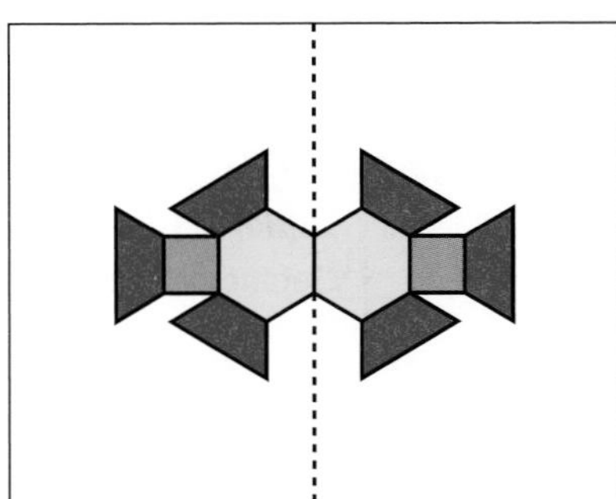

On an Exit Slip, have students explain how they made their reflections.

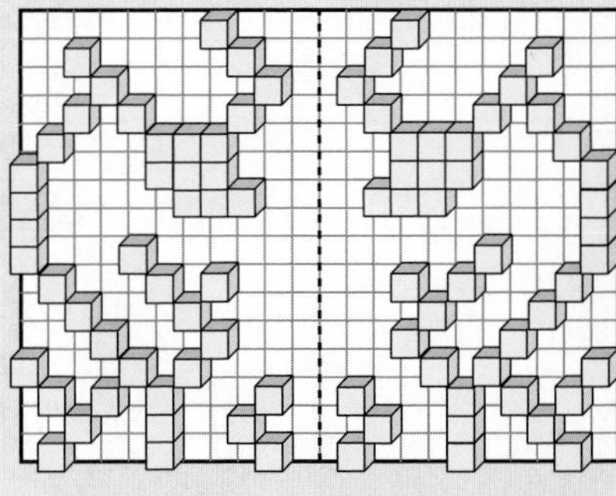

Centimeter cube design with reflection

ENRICHMENT

PARTNER ACTIVITY

15–30 Min

Exploring Reflections of 3-Dimensional Figures

(*Math Masters,* p. 447)

To apply students' understanding of reflections, have partnerships use centimeter cubes to construct a 3-dimensional building, then trade buildings and construct the reflections. Each point in the first building should correspond to a point in the reflected building. Have students draw the original cube building and the reflection of the building on isometric dot paper.

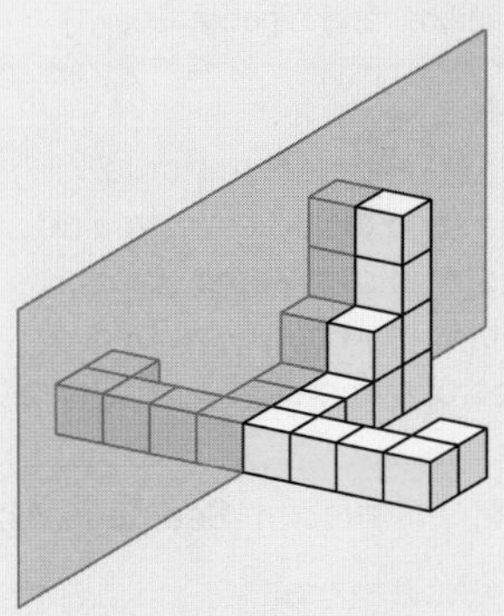

Cube structure with reflection

EXTRA PRACTICE

SMALL-GROUP ACTIVITY

5–15 Min

5-Minute Math

To offer students more experience with reflections, see *5-Minute Math,* page 149.

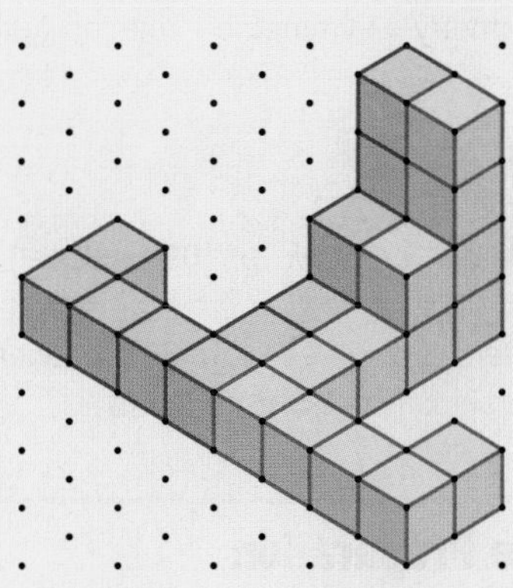

Cube structure and reflection drawn on isometric dot paper

10•4 Line Symmetry

Objective To guide exploration of the connection between reflections and line symmetry.

www.everydaymathonline.com

ePresentations

eToolkit

Algorithms Practice

EM Facts Workshop Game™

Family Letters

Assessment Management

Common Core State Standards

Curriculum Focal Points

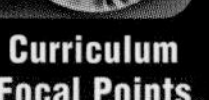

Interactive Teacher's Lesson Guide

1 Teaching the Lesson

Key Concepts and Skills

- Identify polygons and describe properties of regular polygons. [Geometry Goal 2]
- Identify and draw lines of symmetry. [Geometry Goal 3]
- Explore the connection between reflections and line symmetry. [Geometry Goal 3]
- Solve problems involving spatial visualization. [Geometry Goal 3]
- Describe rules for patterns and use them to solve problems. [Patterns, Functions, and Algebra Goal 1]

Key Activities

Students use a transparent mirror to complete symmetric pictures and to find lines of symmetry in symmetric objects. They fold paper to sort polygons by the number of lines of symmetry.

Ongoing Assessment: Informing Instruction See page 812.

Ongoing Assessment: Recognizing Student Achievement Use an Exit Slip (*Math Masters,* p. 389). [Patterns, Functions, and Algebra Goal 1]

Key Vocabulary

line of symmetry ◆ symmetric ◆ rotation (turn) symmetry

Materials

Math Journal 2, p. 279
Student Reference Book, p. 109 (optional)
Study Link 10•3
Math Masters, pp. 311–314; p. 389 (optional)
per partnership: 1 transparent mirror ◆ scissors ◆ slate

2 Ongoing Learning & Practice

Multiplying a Fraction by a Whole Number

Math Journal 2, pp. 280A and 280B
Students practice multiplying fractions by whole numbers.

Math Boxes 10•4

Math Journal 2, p. 280
Students practice and maintain skills through Math Box problems.

Study Link 10•4

Math Masters, p. 315
Students practice and maintain skills through Study Link activities.

3 Differentiation Options

ENRICHMENT
Interpreting a Cartoon

Math Masters, p. 316
Students interpret a cartoon involving line symmetry.

ENRICHMENT
Exploring Rotation or Turn Symmetry

Geometry Template ◆ pattern blocks ◆ tape
Students explore turn or rotation symmetry.

EXTRA PRACTICE
Exploring Line Symmetry

Math Masters, p. 317
Geometry Template ◆ pattern blocks
Students use pattern blocks to create shapes with line symmetry.

ELL SUPPORT
Creating a Line Symmetry Museum

magazines and newspapers ◆ scissors ◆ tape
Students create a Line Symmetry Museum.

Advance Preparation

***Teacher's Reference Manual,* Grades 4–6** pp. 180–185, 200

Getting Started

Mental Math and Reflexes

Write fraction addition problems on the board where tenths are added to tenths, hundredths to hundredths, and tenths to hundredths.
Suggestions:

●○○ $\frac{4}{10} + \frac{1}{10} = \frac{5}{10}$, or $\frac{1}{2}$
$\frac{6}{10} + \frac{3}{10} = \frac{9}{10}$
$\frac{5}{10} + \frac{2}{10} = \frac{7}{10}$
$\frac{3}{10} + \frac{1}{10} = \frac{4}{10}$, or $\frac{2}{5}$

●●○ $\frac{25}{100} + \frac{50}{100} = \frac{75}{100}$, or $\frac{3}{4}$
$\frac{40}{100} + \frac{20}{100} = \frac{60}{100}$, or $\frac{3}{5}$
$\frac{75}{100} + \frac{5}{100} = \frac{80}{100}$, or $\frac{4}{5}$
$\frac{65}{100} + \frac{35}{100} = \frac{100}{100}$, or 1

●●● $\frac{10}{100} + \frac{5}{10} = \frac{60}{100}$, or $\frac{6}{10}$, or $\frac{3}{5}$
$\frac{4}{10} + \frac{40}{100} = \frac{80}{100}$, or $\frac{8}{10}$, or $\frac{4}{5}$
$\frac{90}{100} + \frac{1}{10} = \frac{100}{100}$, or $\frac{10}{10}$, or 1
$\frac{25}{100} + \frac{5}{10} = \frac{75}{100}$, or $\frac{3}{4}$

Math Message

What is symmetry? Be ready to name an object in the classroom that has line symmetry.

Study Link 10·3 Follow-Up

Have partners compare answers and describe how they know each image is a reflection of the preimage.

1 Teaching the Lesson

Math Message Follow-Up

WHOLE-CLASS DISCUSSION

Ask students to share what they know about symmetry. Tell them to indicate "thumbs-up" if they have a similar answer. Then ask students to explain how they know the classroom object that they chose has line symmetry.

Tell students that in this lesson they will investigate how symmetry and reflections are related.

Completing Symmetric Pictures

PARTNER ACTIVITY

(*Math Journal 2,* p. 279; *Math Masters,* p. 311)

Ask students to turn to journal page 279. Partners share a transparent mirror while working on the activities.

Tell the class that each drawing on *Math Masters,* page 311 is only half of a picture. Students are to figure out what each picture would look like if it were complete and then use their transparent mirrors to complete each picture. Remind them to use the recessed edge to draw the line of reflection. Bring the class together to discuss results. Ask the following questions:

- How are these drawings like the dog picture in Lesson 10-3? How are they different? As in the dog picture, there are two sides that look exactly alike (congruent) but are facing in opposite directions. Here, however, the end results are single drawings instead of pairs of drawings.

Point out that here the lines of reflection are in the middle of the pictures or objects—not outside, as in the dog picture. When a line of reflection is in the middle of a picture or object, it is called a **line of symmetry.** In this case, the pictures or objects are said to be **symmetric.**

Adjusting the Activity

ELL

English language learners may find it helpful if you use page 109 in the *Student Reference Book* to summarize the discussion of line symmetry.

AUDITORY ◆ KINESTHETIC ◆ TACTILE ◆ VISUAL

Student Page

Date Time

LESSON 10·4 **Line Symmetry**

You will need *Math Masters,* pages 311–314.

1. The drawings on *Math Masters,* page 311 are only half-pictures. Figure out what each whole picture would show. Then use a transparent mirror to complete each picture. Use the recessed side of the mirror to draw the line of reflection.
2. The pictures on *Math Masters,* page 312 are symmetric.
   a. Use the transparent mirror to draw the line of symmetry for the bat and the turtle.
   b. Cut out the other three pictures and find their lines of symmetry by folding.
   c. Which picture has two lines of symmetry? Bow
3. Cut out each polygon on *Math Masters,* pages 313 and 314. Find all the lines of symmetry for each polygon. Record the results below.

Polygon	Number of Lines of Symmetry
A	3
B	1
C	4
D	2
E	2

Polygon	Number of Lines of Symmetry
F	0
G	1
H	0
I	5
J	6

4. Study the results in the tables above.
   a. How many lines of symmetry are in a regular pentagon (Polygon I)? 5 lines
   b. How many lines of symmetry are in a regular hexagon (Polygon J)? 6 lines
   c. How many lines of symmetry are in a regular octagon? (An octagon has 8 sides.) 8 lines

Math Journal 2, p. 279

Math Masters, p. 311

Adjusting the Activity

The symmetry activities work best if the pictures and polygons on *Math Masters*, pages 312–314 are carefully cut out. If there are students in your class who have difficulty with scissors, consider having a volunteer cut out their shapes for them ahead of time.

AUDITORY ◆ KINESTHETIC ◆ TACTILE ◆ VISUAL

Math Masters, p. 312

NOTE Students may be familiar with line symmetry from previous work but may not have made a connection between line symmetry and reflections. Thinking about line symmetry in terms of reflections is a more powerful approach because it can be generalized to other kinds of symmetry. **Rotation (turn) symmetry,** for example, can be thought of in terms of turns.

▶ Finding Lines of Symmetry

PARTNER ACTIVITY

(*Math Journal 2,* p. 279; *Math Masters,* p. 312)

Students use their transparent mirrors to draw lines of symmetry in the pictures of a bat and a turtle on *Math Masters,* page 312. Then they cut out the other three pictures on the page and find their lines of symmetry by folding. Point out that a picture may have more than one line of symmetry. Have students answer the question in Problem 2c on journal page 279.

Bring the class together to discuss results. Ask: *Which picture has more than one line of symmetry?* The bow

▶ Exploring Lines of Symmetry of Polygons

PARTNER ACTIVITY

(*Math Journal 2,* p. 279; *Math Masters,* pp. 313 and 314)

Students cut out the polygons on *Math Masters,* pages 313 and 314. They find all lines of symmetry for each polygon by folding, and then they record the results in the tables and answer the related questions on journal page 279.

Ongoing Assessment: Informing Instruction

Watch for students who think that Polygon F, the parallelogram, has line symmetry. Many people think this is true because Polygon F does have symmetry; however, it is turn or rotation symmetry, rather than line symmetry. Polygon F cannot be folded (or reflected) so that the two halves match, but it can be turned to match its original shape.

Bring the class together to share results. Students should have found that a regular polygon has the same number of lines of symmetry as it has sides. For example, a regular octagon has 8 sides and 8 lines of symmetry.

Ongoing Assessment: Recognizing Student Achievement

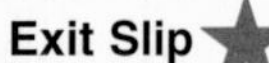

Exit Slip

Use an **Exit Slip** (*Math Masters,* page 389) to assess students' ability to describe a pattern and use it to solve problems. Have students describe patterns they see in Problems 3 and 4 on journal page 279. Students are making adequate progress if they state that a regular polygon has the same number of lines of symmetry as it has sides. Some students may extend the pattern by stating the number of lines of symmetry in additional regular polygons.

[Patterns, Functions, and Algebra Goal 1]

2 Ongoing Learning & Practice

Multiplying a Fraction by a Whole Number

INDEPENDENT ACTIVITY

(*Math Journal 2,* pp. 280A and 280B)

Students practice multiplying fractions by whole numbers.

Math Boxes 10•4

INDEPENDENT ACTIVITY

(*Math Journal 2,* p. 280)

Mixed Practice Math Boxes in this lesson are paired with Math Boxes in Lesson 10-1. The skill in Problem 6 previews Unit 11 content.

Study Link 10•4

INDEPENDENT ACTIVITY

(*Math Masters,* p. 315)

Home Connection Students complete a Venn diagram to identify capital letters of the alphabet that have horizontal and/or vertical line symmetry. They list words with horizontal or vertical line symmetry.

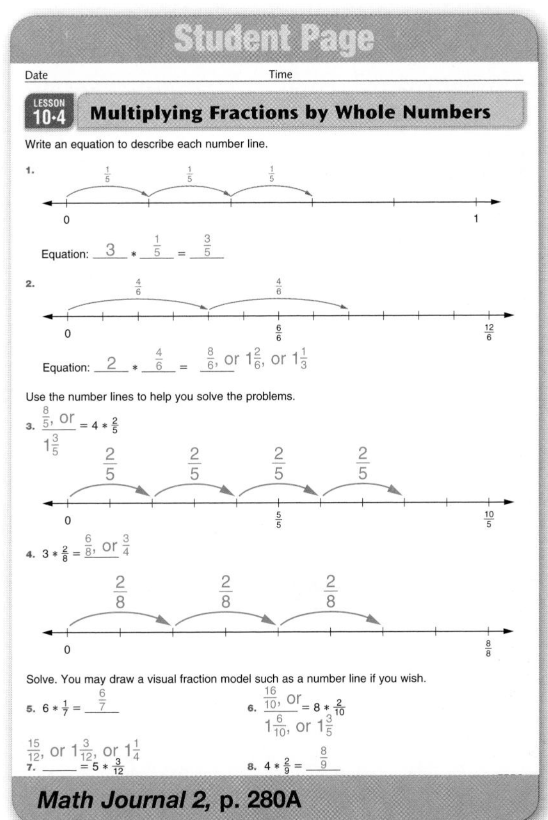

Student Page

Date Time

LESSON 10•4 **Multiplying Fractions by Whole Numbers**

Write an equation to describe each number line.

1. Equation: $3 * \frac{1}{5} = \frac{3}{5}$

2. Equation: $2 * \frac{4}{6} = \frac{8}{6}$, or $1\frac{2}{6}$, or $1\frac{1}{3}$

Use the number lines to help you solve the problems.

3. $\frac{8}{5}$, or $1\frac{3}{5} = 4 * \frac{2}{5}$

4. $3 * \frac{2}{8} = \frac{6}{8}$, or $\frac{3}{4}$

Solve. You may draw a visual fraction model such as a number line if you wish.

5. $6 * \frac{1}{7} = \frac{6}{7}$

6. $\frac{16}{10}$, or $1\frac{6}{10}$, or $1\frac{3}{5} = 8 * \frac{2}{10}$

7. $\frac{15}{12}$, or $1\frac{3}{12}$, or $1\frac{1}{4} = 5 * \frac{3}{12}$

8. $4 * \frac{2}{9} = \frac{8}{9}$

Math Journal 2, p. 280A

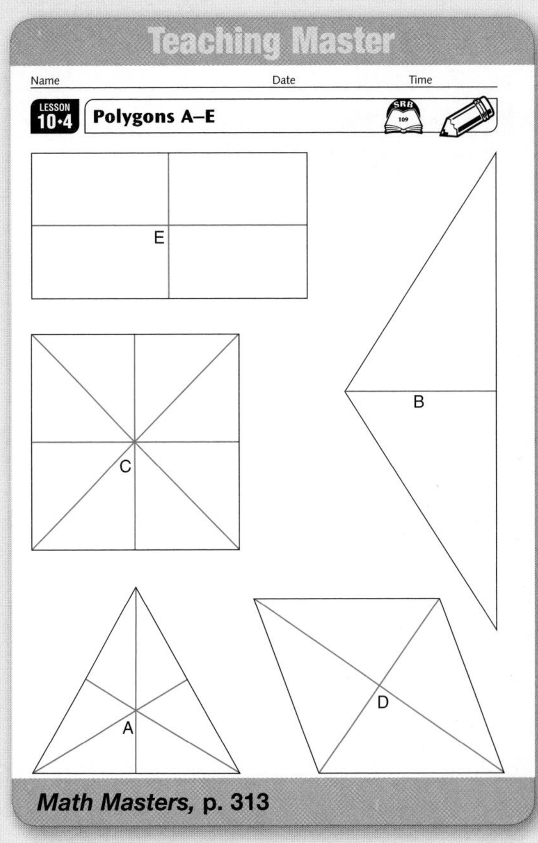

Teaching Master

Name Date Time

LESSON 10•4 **Polygons A–E**

Math Masters, p. 313

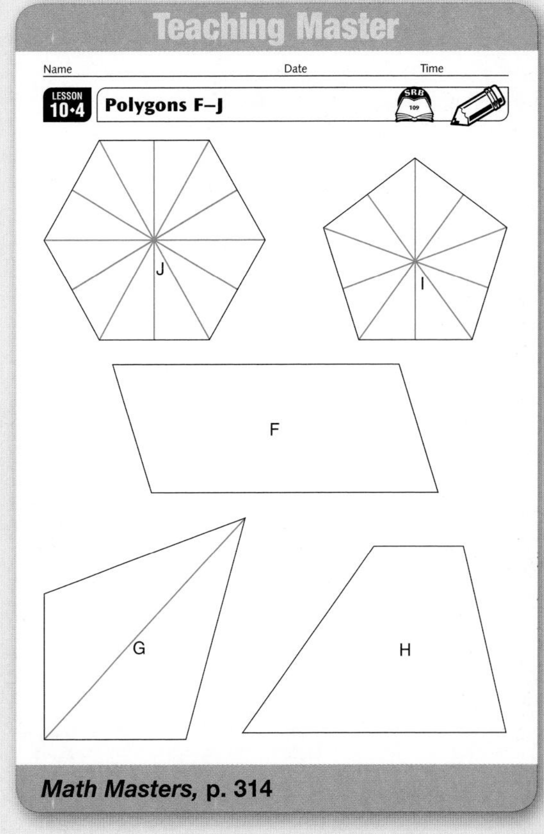

Teaching Master

Name Date Time

LESSON 10•4 **Polygons F–J**

Math Masters, p. 314

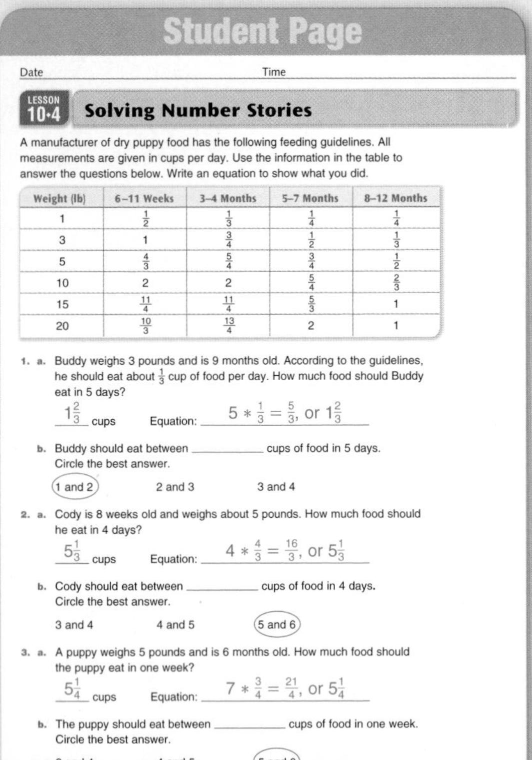

Student Page

Date Time

LESSON 10•4 **Solving Number Stories**

A manufacturer of dry puppy food has the following feeding guidelines. All measurements are given in cups per day. Use the information in the table to answer the questions below. Write an equation to show what you did.

Weight (lb)	6–11 Weeks	3–4 Months	5–7 Months	8–12 Months
1	$\frac{1}{2}$	$\frac{1}{3}$	$\frac{1}{4}$	$\frac{1}{4}$
3	1	$\frac{3}{4}$	$\frac{1}{2}$	$\frac{1}{3}$
5	$\frac{4}{3}$	$\frac{5}{4}$	$\frac{3}{4}$	$\frac{1}{2}$
10	2	2	$\frac{5}{4}$	$\frac{2}{3}$
15	$\frac{11}{4}$	$\frac{11}{4}$	$\frac{5}{3}$	1
20	$\frac{10}{3}$	$\frac{13}{4}$	2	1

1. a. Buddy weighs 3 pounds and is 9 months old. According to the guidelines, he should eat about $\frac{1}{3}$ cup of food per day. How much food should Buddy eat in 5 days?
   $1\frac{2}{3}$ cups Equation: $5 * \frac{1}{3} = \frac{5}{3}$, or $1\frac{2}{3}$
   b. Buddy should eat between ______ cups of food in 5 days. Circle the best answer.
   (1 and 2) 2 and 3 3 and 4
2. a. Cody is 8 weeks old and weighs about 5 pounds. How much food should he eat in 4 days?
   $5\frac{1}{3}$ cups Equation: $4 * \frac{4}{3} = \frac{16}{3}$, or $5\frac{1}{3}$
   b. Cody should eat between ______ cups of food in 4 days. Circle the best answer.
   3 and 4 4 and 5 (5 and 6)
3. a. A puppy weighs 5 pounds and is 6 months old. How much food should the puppy eat in one week?
   $5\frac{1}{4}$ cups Equation: $7 * \frac{3}{4} = \frac{21}{4}$, or $5\frac{1}{4}$
   b. The puppy should eat between ______ cups of food in one week. Circle the best answer.
   3 and 4 4 and 5 (5 and 6)

Math Journal 2, p. 280B

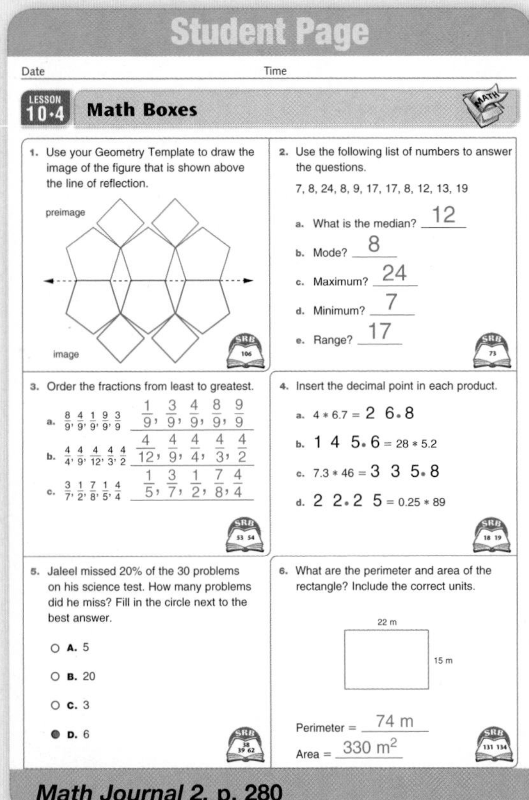

Student Page

Date Time

LESSON 10•4 **Math Boxes**

1. Use your Geometry Template to draw the image of the figure that is shown above the line of reflection.

2. Use the following list of numbers to answer the questions.
   7, 8, 24, 8, 9, 17, 17, 8, 12, 13, 19
   a. What is the median? 12
   b. Mode? 8
   c. Maximum? 24
   d. Minimum? 7
   e. Range? 17
3. Order the fractions from least to greatest.
   a. $\frac{8}{9}, \frac{4}{9}, \frac{1}{9}, \frac{9}{9}, \frac{3}{9}$ — $\frac{1}{9}, \frac{3}{9}, \frac{4}{9}, \frac{8}{9}, \frac{9}{9}$
   b. $\frac{4}{4}, \frac{4}{9}, \frac{4}{12}, \frac{4}{3}, \frac{4}{2}$ — $\frac{4}{12}, \frac{4}{9}, \frac{4}{4}, \frac{4}{3}, \frac{4}{2}$
   c. $\frac{3}{7}, \frac{1}{2}, \frac{7}{8}, \frac{1}{5}, \frac{4}{4}$ — $\frac{1}{5}, \frac{3}{7}, \frac{1}{2}, \frac{7}{8}, \frac{4}{4}$
4. Insert the decimal point in each product.
   a. 4 * 6.7 = 2 6.8
   b. 1 4 5.6 = 28 * 5.2
   c. 7.3 * 46 = 3 3 5.8
   d. 2 2.2 5 = 0.25 * 89
5. Jaleel missed 20% of the 30 problems on his science test. How many problems did he miss? Fill in the circle next to the best answer.
   ○ A. 5
   ○ B. 20
   ○ C. 3
   ● D. 6
6. What are the perimeter and area of the rectangle? Include the correct units.

   Perimeter = 74 m
   Area = 330 m²

Math Journal 2, p. 280

3 Differentiation Options

ENRICHMENT

▶ Interpreting a Cartoon

INDEPENDENT ACTIVITY

5–15 Min

(*Math Masters,* p. 316)

To apply students' understanding of line symmetry, have them interpret a cartoon.

ENRICHMENT

▶ Exploring Rotation or Turn Symmetry

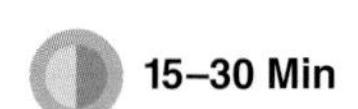
SMALL-GROUP ACTIVITY

15–30 Min

To further explore symmetry, have students use combinations of pattern blocks to perform and analyze transformations. Ask students to tape together a trapezoid and an equilateral triangle pattern block to form a parallelogram.

Ask the following questions:

- Will the parallelogram look exactly the same if it is flipped over? No. If it slanted to the right before the flip, then it will slant to the left after the flip.
- Does the parallelogram have line symmetry? No. Students have already tried folding a parallelogram to find a line of symmetry, and they know that it does not have one.
- Will the parallelogram look exactly the same if it is turned through a $\frac{1}{2}$-turn? yes Have students trace the parallelogram and show that after a $\frac{1}{2}$-turn, the tracing matches the original figure.

Shapes that look the same after they have been turned less than a full turn have rotation or turn symmetry. Have students use pattern blocks and tape to make their own turn-symmetric shapes. Have them use their Geometry Templates to record the shapes they make.

Sample answers:

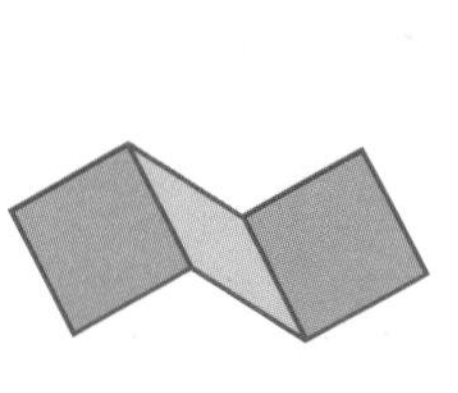

$\frac{1}{2}$-turn symmetry

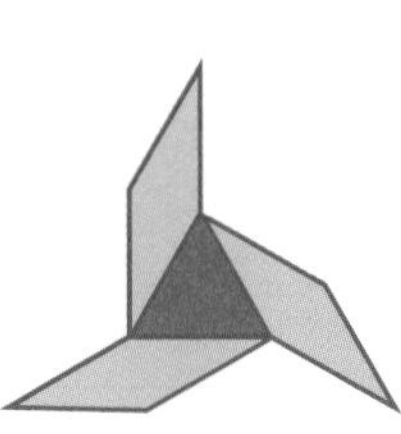

$\frac{1}{3}$-turn symmetry

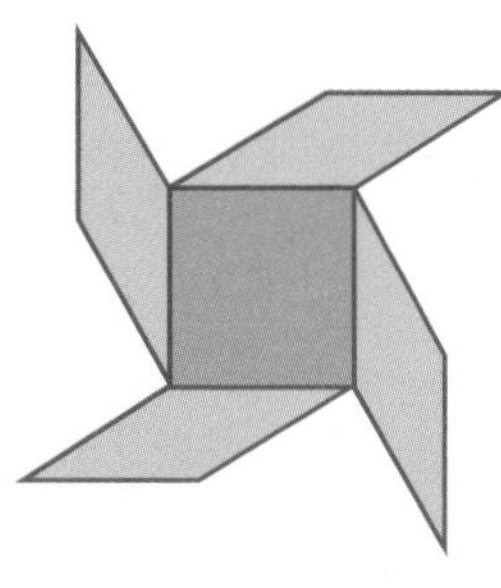

$\frac{1}{4}$-turn symmetry

EXTRA PRACTICE

Exploring Line Symmetry

PARTNER ACTIVITY

15–30 Min

(*Math Masters,* p. 317)

To practice identifying lines of symmetry using a concrete model, have students use combinations of pattern blocks to create figures with a specified number of lines of symmetry.

ELL SUPPORT

Creating a Line Symmetry Museum

SMALL-GROUP ACTIVITY

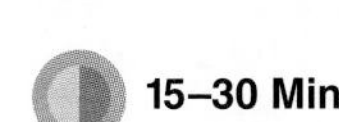

15–30 Min

To provide language support for symmetry, have students bring in pictures of objects with line symmetry to create a Line Symmetry Museum. Have students describe the objects in the pictures and the lines of symmetry they see. They may even draw the lines of symmetry on the pictures. If some of the pictured objects are not perfectly symmetric, consider setting up a section of the museum called Almost Symmetric.

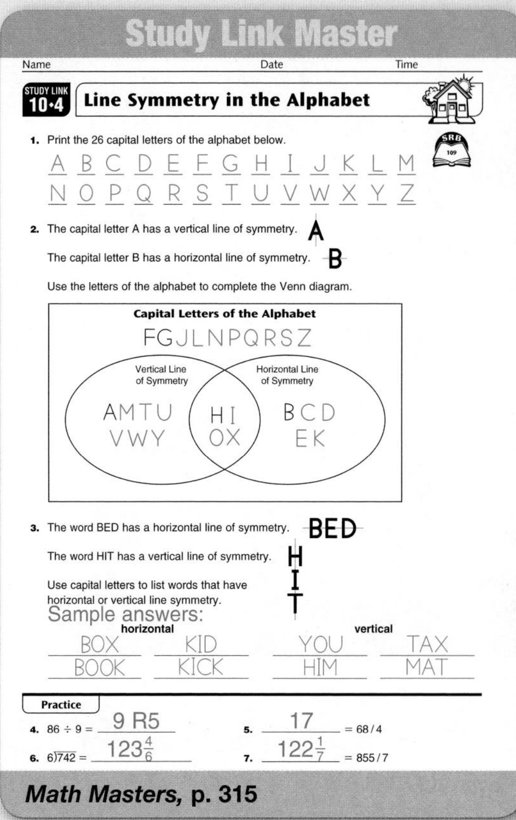

Study Link Master

Name Date Time

STUDY LINK 10•4 **Line Symmetry in the Alphabet**

1. Print the 26 capital letters of the alphabet below.
A B C D E F G H I J K L M
N O P Q R S T U V W X Y Z

2. The capital letter A has a vertical line of symmetry.
The capital letter B has a horizontal line of symmetry.
Use the letters of the alphabet to complete the Venn diagram.

3. The word BED has a horizontal line of symmetry.
The word HIT has a vertical line of symmetry.
Use capital letters to list words that have horizontal or vertical line symmetry.
Sample answers:
horizontal: BOX, KID, BOOK, KICK
vertical: YOU, TAX, HIM, MAT

Practice

4. 86 ÷ 9 = 9 R5
5. 17 = 68 / 4
6. $6\overline{)742}$ = $123\frac{4}{6}$
7. $122\frac{1}{7}$ = 855 / 7

Math Masters, p. 315

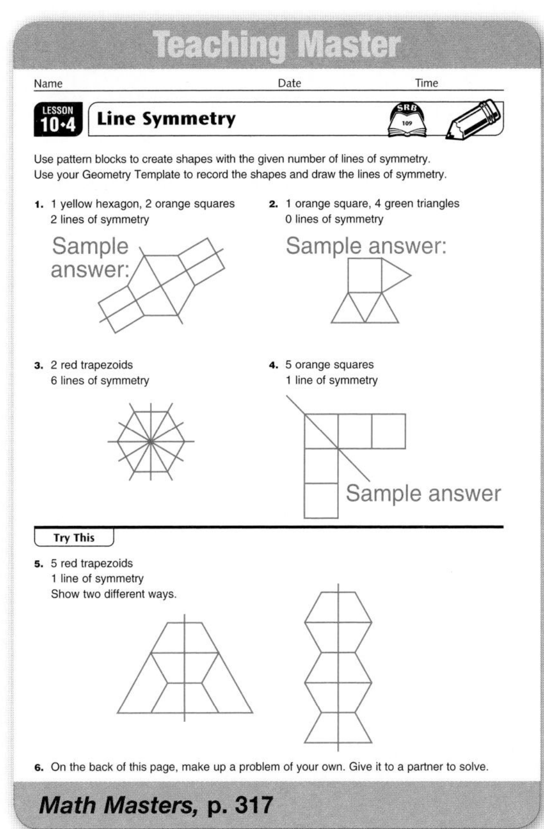

Teaching Master

Name Date Time

LESSON 10•4 **Line Symmetry**

Use pattern blocks to create shapes with the given number of lines of symmetry.
Use your Geometry Template to record the shapes and draw the lines of symmetry.

1. 1 yellow hexagon, 2 orange squares
2 lines of symmetry
Sample answer:

2. 1 orange square, 4 green triangles
0 lines of symmetry
Sample answer:

3. 2 red trapezoids
6 lines of symmetry

4. 5 orange squares
1 line of symmetry
Sample answer

Try This

5. 5 red trapezoids
1 line of symmetry
Show two different ways.

6. On the back of this page, make up a problem of your own. Give it to a partner to solve.

Math Masters, p. 317

Teaching Master

Name Date Time

LESSON 10•4 **Interpreting a Cartoon**

By permission of Rick Detorie and Creators Syndicate, Inc.

1. What answer does Ruthie's brother expect? 4

2. Explain and draw pictures to show why both of Ruthie's answers are correct.
"Up and down, it's three."
"Across, it's zero."

Name Date Time

LESSON 10•4 **Interpreting a Cartoon**

By permission of Rick Detorie and Creators Syndicate, Inc.

1. What answer does Ruthie's brother expect?

2. Explain and draw pictures to show why both of Ruthie's answers are correct.

Math Masters, p. 316

10•5 Frieze Patterns

Objective To guide the application of reflections, rotations, and translations.

Technology Resources www.everydaymathonline.com

ePresentations

eToolkit

Algorithms Practice

EM Facts Workshop Game™

Family Letters

Assessment Management

Common Core State Standards

Curriculum Focal Points

Interactive Teacher's Lesson Guide

1 Teaching the Lesson

Key Concepts and Skills

- Identify and draw congruent figures. [Geometry Goal 2]
- Identify, describe, and sketch reflections, rotations, and translations. [Geometry Goal 3]
- Extend, describe, and create geometric patterns. [Patterns, Functions, and Algebra Goal 1]

Key Activities

Students read about frieze patterns in which a design is repeatedly reflected, rotated, or translated to produce a pattern. They complete frieze patterns and create their own.

Ongoing Assessment: Recognizing Student Achievement Use journal page 281. [Geometry Goal 3]

Key Vocabulary

frieze pattern ◆ reflection (flip) ◆ translation (slide) ◆ rotation (turn)

Materials

Math Journal 2, p. 281
Student Reference Book, p. 108
Study Link 10•4
Math Masters, p. 403 (optional)
overhead or regular pattern blocks (optional) ◆ per partnership: 1 transparent mirror ◆ straightedge ◆ slate

2 Ongoing Learning & Practice

Playing *Polygon Pair-Up*
Student Reference Book, p. 258
Polygon Pair-Up Polygon Cards and Property Cards (*Math Masters,* pp. 496 and 497)
Students practice identifying properties of polygons.

Math Boxes 10•5
Math Journal 2, p. 282
Students practice and maintain skills through Math Box problems.

Study Link 10•5
Math Masters, p. 318
Students practice and maintain skills through Study Link activities.

3 Differentiation Options

READINESS
Exploring Geometric Patterns
Math Masters, p. 389
Geometry Template ◆ pattern blocks
Students use pattern blocks to create and continue geometric patterns.

ENRICHMENT
Exploring Arrangements of Four Straws
Math Masters, p. 437
straws
Students explore different arrangements of four straws.

ENRICHMENT
Exploring Tessellations
computer with Internet access
Students use technology to explore tessellations.

EXTRA PRACTICE
Creating Frieze Patterns
Math Masters, p. 319
index cards ◆ scissors
Students cut out a template and create frieze patterns.

Advance Preparation

***Teacher's Reference Manual,* Grades 4–6** pp. 193, 194, 197, 198

Getting Started

Mental Math and Reflexes

Pose mental subtraction problems. *Suggestions:*

●○○	●●○	●●●
78 – 58 = 20	94 – 85 = 9	150 – 42 = 108
49 – 37 = 12	77 – 58 = 19	283 – 179 = 104
51 – 20 = 31	46 – 27 = 19	402 – 203 = 199
84 – 63 = 21	97 – 59 = 38	731 – 446 = 285

Math Message

Read page 108 in your Student Reference Book. *Be prepared to describe what you notice about the three frieze patterns.*

Study Link 10·4 Follow-Up

Have partnerships compare their Venn diagrams. Students should note that the letter *O* has an infinite number of lines of symmetry if it is printed as a circle.

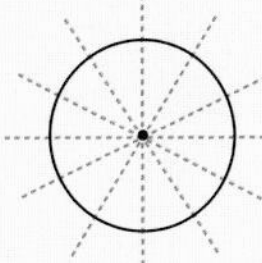

1 Teaching the Lesson

Math Message Follow-Up

WHOLE-CLASS DISCUSSION

(*Student Reference Book,* p. 108)

Ask students to describe what they notice about each of the frieze patterns on *Student Reference Book,* page 108. Have students indicate thumbs-up if they made a similar observation. The discussion should include the following points:

▷ Each pair of horses in the first frieze pattern is the same size and shape, but they face in opposite directions.

▷ The line of reflection for each pair of horses is a vertical line running through the center of the flower.

▷ Each elephant and horse in the second frieze pattern is the same size and shape and faces in the same direction.

▷ Each of the flowers in the third frieze pattern is the same size and shape but is turned in a different direction.

Tell students that in this lesson they will explore examples of frieze patterns to see how designs are created by repeatedly moving figures in three different ways: reflections, translations, and rotations.

Introducing Frieze Patterns

WHOLE-CLASS DISCUSSION

ELL

(*Student Reference Book,* p. 108)

The examples of **frieze patterns** on *Student Reference Book,* page 108 provide an initial exposure to "rigid motions," in which objects retain their shape as they are moved in various ways.

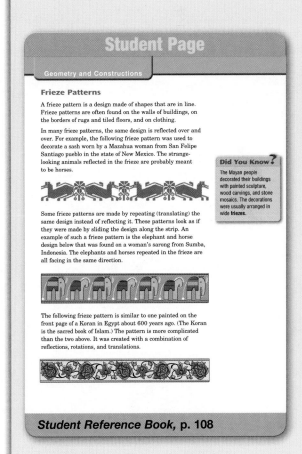

Student Page

Geometry and Constructions

Frieze Patterns

A frieze pattern is a design made of shapes that are in line. Frieze patterns are often found on the walls of buildings, on the borders of rugs and tiled floors, and on clothing.

In many frieze patterns, the same design is reflected over and over. For example, the following frieze pattern was used to decorate a sash worn by a Mazahua woman from San Felipe Santiago pueblo in the state of New Mexico. The strange-looking animals reflected in the frieze are probably meant to be horses.

Some frieze patterns are made by repeating (translating) the same design instead of reflecting it. These patterns look as if they were made by sliding the design along the strip. An example of such a frieze pattern is the elephant and horse design below that was found on a woman's sarong from Sumba, Indonesia. The elephants and horses repeated in the frieze are all facing in the same direction.

The following frieze pattern is similar to one painted on the front page of a Koran in Egypt about 600 years ago. (The Koran is the sacred book of Islam.) The pattern is more complicated than the two above. It was created with a combination of reflections, rotations, and translations.

Did You Know?

The Mayan people decorated their buildings with painted sculpture, wood carvings, and stone mosaics. The decorations were usually arranged in wide **friezes.**

***Student Reference Book,* p. 108**

ELL You may wish to use the less formal terms: **flip** (reflection), **turn** (rotation), and **slide** (translation). To support English language learners, demonstrate the mathematical meanings with gestures.

Through work in the preceding lessons, students should be familiar with **reflections.** (The top frieze on *Student Reference Book,* page 108 was created by reflecting the horse repeatedly across vertical lines of reflection.) The second frieze is an example of another rigid motion—a **translation,** or slide, in which a shape is moved without being turned or flipped. To support English language learners, discuss the everyday and mathematical uses of the word *translation.*

Students should observe a difference between the first and second friezes: In the first frieze, the design is repeated so that alternating designs face in opposite directions. In the second frieze, the designs all face in the same direction.

The third frieze on the *Student Reference Book* page combines slides, flips, and turns in a complex design.

Overhead or regular pattern blocks also can be used to illustrate rigid motions. For example, the pattern below was made by a **rotation** of each figure 90° clockwise, followed by a translation of the figure to the right.

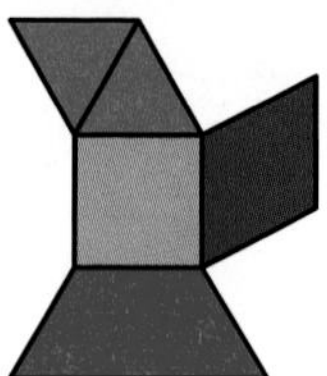
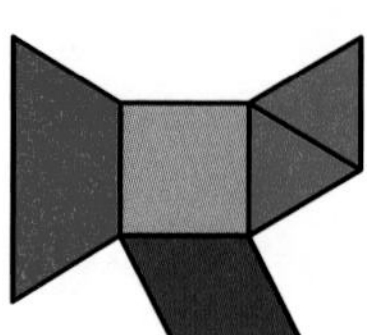

A pattern made by rotations and translations

▶ Drawing Frieze Patterns

(*Math Journal 2,* p. 281)

Art Link Students complete three frieze patterns on journal page 281 and design one of their own.

Adjusting the Activity

ELL

Have students sketch the original design for each frieze pattern on centimeter grid paper (*Math Masters,* page 403). They can use a transparent mirror to check their reflections for Problem 1a and slide and rotate the paper to check their patterns for Problems 1b and 1c.

AUDITORY • KINESTHETIC • TACTILE • VISUAL

Ongoing Assessment: Recognizing Student Achievement

Journal page 281 Problem 1

Use **journal page 281, Problem 1** to assess students' ability to identify and sketch an example of a reflection and identify examples of translations and rotations. Students are making adequate progress if they are able to continue the pattern in Problem 1a and identify the transformations in Problems 1a–1c. Some students may be able to sketch the translations and rotations in Problems 1b and 1c.

[Geometry Goal 3]

Student Page

Date Time

LESSON 10•5 **Frieze Patterns** SRB 108

1. Extend the following frieze patterns. Use a straightedge and your transparent mirror to help you. Then write if you used a reflection, rotation, or translation of the original shape to continue the pattern.

a. reflection

b. translation

c. rotation

2. Create your own frieze pattern. Make a design in the first box. Then repeat the design, using reflections, slides, rotations, or a combination of moves. When you have finished, you may want to color or shade your frieze pattern.

3. Explain how you created your pattern in Problem 2.
Answers vary.

Math Journal 2, p. 281

2 Ongoing Learning & Practice

Playing *Polygon Pair-Up*

INDEPENDENT ACTIVITY

(*Student Reference Book,* p. 258; *Math Masters,* pp. 496 and 497)

Students play *Polygon Pair-Up* to practice identifying properties of polygons. See Lesson 1-6 for additional information.

Math Boxes 10•5

INDEPENDENT ACTIVITY

(*Math Journal 2,* p. 282)

Mixed Practice Math Boxes in this lesson are paired with Math Boxes in Lesson 10-2. The skill in Problem 5 previews Unit 11 content.

Writing/Reasoning Have students write a response to the following: *Calculate the mean number of hours Julia babysat last week and explain your strategy.* Sample answer: I added the hours she babysat each day ($4 + 2\frac{1}{2} + 1 + 1\frac{1}{2} + 3 = 12$) and divided by 5 for the number of days. $12 / 5 = 2\frac{2}{5}$ hours, or 2 hours 24 minutes.

Study Link 10•5

INDEPENDENT ACTIVITY

(*Math Masters,* p. 318)

Home Connection Students extend geometric patterns and create patterns of their own.

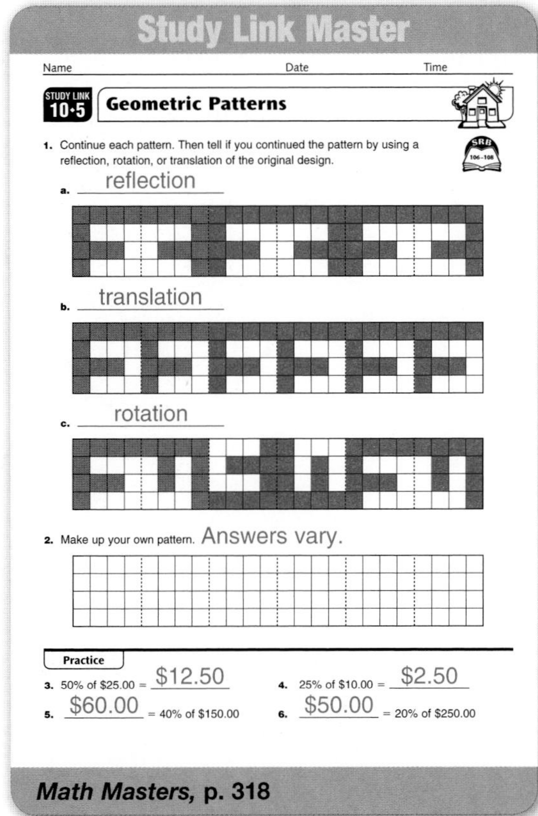

Study Link Master

Name Date Time

STUDY LINK 10•5 **Geometric Patterns**

1. Continue each pattern. Then tell if you continued the pattern by using a reflection, rotation, or translation of the original design. SRB 106–108
   a. reflection
   b. translation
   c. rotation
2. Make up your own pattern. Answers vary.

Practice

3. 50% of \$25.00 = \$12.50
4. 25% of \$10.00 = \$2.50
5. \$60.00 = 40% of \$150.00
6. \$50.00 = 20% of \$250.00

Math Masters, p. 318

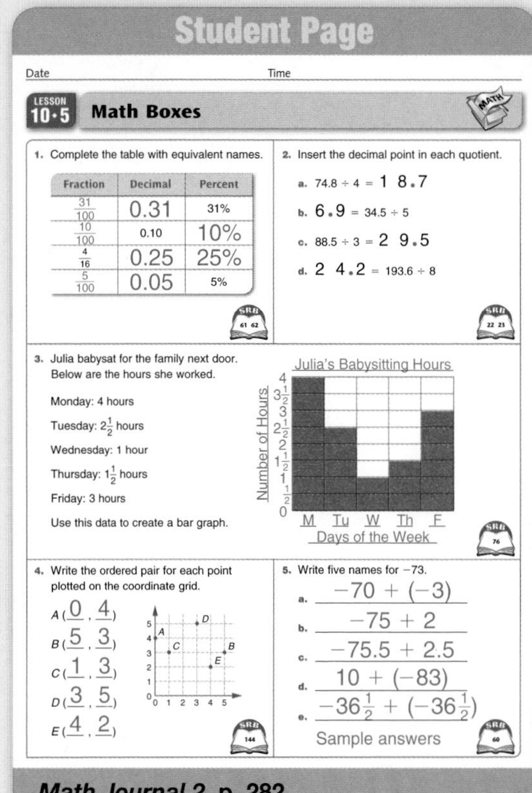

Student Page

Date Time

LESSON 10•5 **Math Boxes**

1. Complete the table with equivalent names.

Fraction	Decimal	Percent
$\frac{31}{100}$	0.31	31%
$\frac{10}{100}$	0.10	10%
$\frac{4}{16}$	0.25	25%
$\frac{5}{100}$	0.05	5%

SRB 61 62

2. Insert the decimal point in each quotient.
   a. 74.8 ÷ 4 = 18.7
   b. 6.9 = 34.5 ÷ 5
   c. 88.5 ÷ 3 = 29.5
   d. 24.2 = 193.6 ÷ 8

SRB 22 23

3. Julia babysat for the family next door. Below are the hours she worked.
   Monday: 4 hours
   Tuesday: $2\frac{1}{2}$ hours
   Wednesday: 1 hour
   Thursday: $1\frac{1}{2}$ hours
   Friday: 3 hours
   Use this data to create a bar graph.

SRB 76

4. Write the ordered pair for each point plotted on the coordinate grid.
   A (0, 4)
   B (5, 3)
   C (1, 3)
   D (3, 5)
   E (4, 2)

SRB 144

5. Write five names for −73.
   a. −70 + (−3)
   b. −75 + 2
   c. −75.5 + 2.5
   d. 10 + (−83)
   e. $-36\frac{1}{2} + (-36\frac{1}{2})$
   Sample answers

SRB 88

Math Journal 2, p. 282

3 Differentiation Options

READINESS

▶ Exploring Geometric Patterns

15–30 Min

(*Math Masters,* p. 389)

Art Link To explore geometric patterns using a concrete model, have students create and continue patterns using pattern blocks. One student begins a pattern. The other students in the group take turns continuing the pattern.

A group drawing can be made of some of the patterns by tracing the blocks or using the Geometry Template. On an Exit Slip, have students describe how they created their pattern using words such as *slide, flip,* or *turn.*

ENRICHMENT

▶ Exploring Arrangements of Four Straws

15–30 Min

(*Math Masters,* p. 437)

To apply students' understanding of congruence, reflections, and rotations, have them investigate 16 possible ways to arrange four straws. Explain the following:

▷ Each straw must connect to the end of at least one other straw, and the straws must connect to form either a straight angle or a right angle.

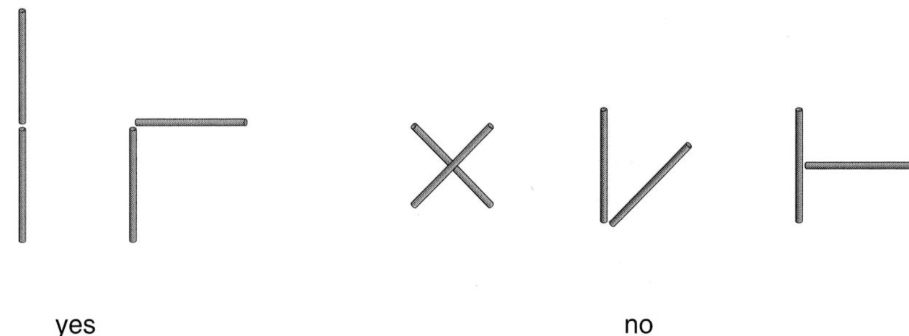

▷ A flipped or rotated figure cannot be counted as a different figure.

Have students record their figures on *Math Masters,* page 437 and explain the strategy they used to find them.

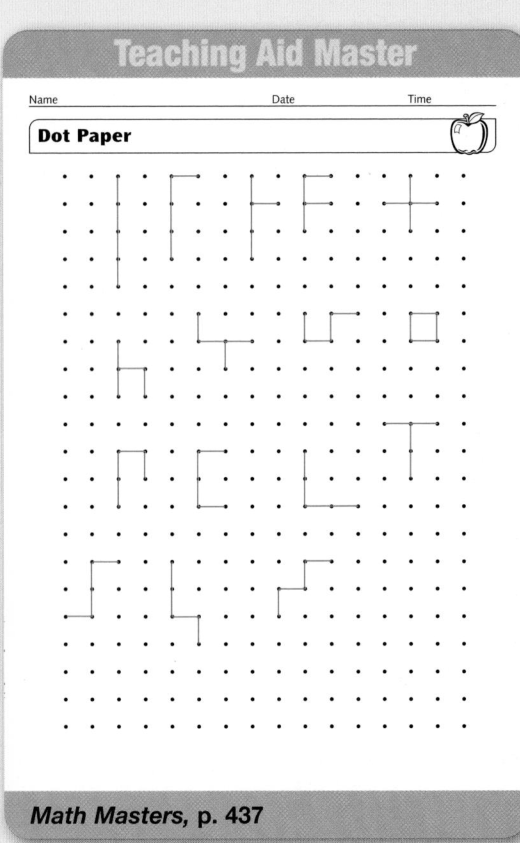

Math Masters, p. 437

ENRICHMENT

INDEPENDENT ACTIVITY

Exploring Tessellations

15–30 Min

Technology Link To apply students' understanding of reflections, rotations, and translations, have them use technology to explore tessellations. See the Web site at http://nlvm.usu.edu/en/nav/frames_asid_163_g_2_t_3.html?open=activities.

Discuss the following points:

- ▷ A *tessellation* is an arrangement of repeated, closed shapes that cover a surface so that no shapes overlap and there are no gaps between the shapes.

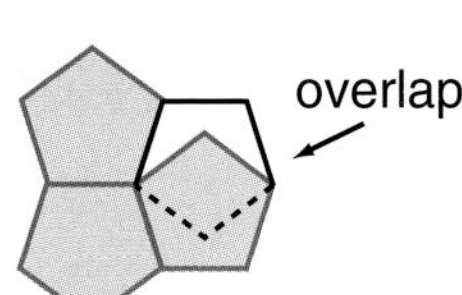

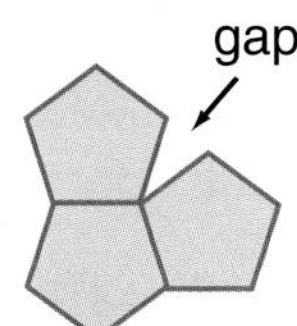

- ▷ Some tessellations repeat only one basic shape. Others combine two or more basic shapes. A *regular tessellation* is a tessellation made up of only one kind of regular polygon.
- ▷ In a tessellation, the basic shapes are reflected, rotated, or translated to fill the surface.

Ask students which of the regular polygons shown on the Web site can be used to create a regular tessellation. There are only three regular tessellations—equilateral triangle, square, and hexagon.

The three regular tessellations

Links to the Future

Students will further explore regular tessellations in *Fifth Grade Everyday Mathematics*. Naming notation, semi-regular tessellations, and Escher-type translation tessellations are introduced in *Sixth Grade Everyday Mathematics.*

EXTRA PRACTICE

INDEPENDENT ACTIVITY

Creating Frieze Patterns

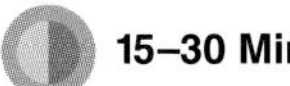

15–30 Min

(*Math Masters,* p. 319)

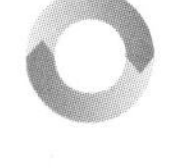

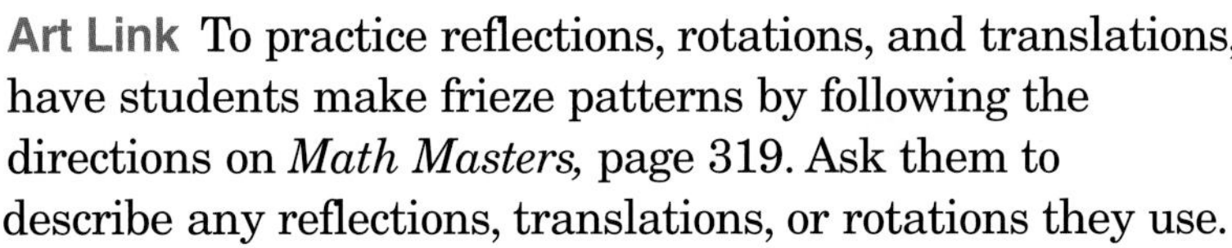

Art Link To practice reflections, rotations, and translations, have students make frieze patterns by following the directions on *Math Masters,* page 319. Ask them to describe any reflections, translations, or rotations they use.

Portfolio Ideas

Teaching Master

Name Date Time

LESSON 10•5 **Making Frieze Patterns**

SRB 106

1. Use an index card as a template for making frieze patterns.
   a. Trim your index card to make a 3-inch by 3-inch square.

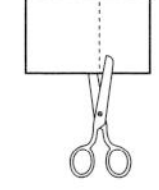

   b. Draw a simple design in the middle of the square.

   c. Cut out your design. If you need to cut through the edge of the index card, then use tape to repair the cut.

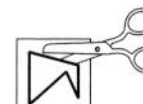

2. Make a frieze pattern with your template.
   a. Draw a long line on a large sheet of paper.
   b. Put your template at the left end of the line.
   c. Trace the shape of the design you cut out. Make a mark on the line at the right edge of the template.
   d. Move your template to the right along the line. Line up the left side of the template with the mark you made on the line.
   e. Repeat Steps c and d. To make more complicated patterns, give your template a turn or a flip every time you move it.

Math Masters, **p. 319**

10•6 Positive and Negative Numbers

Objective To introduce addition involving negative integers.

Technology Resources www.everydaymathonline.com

ePresentations
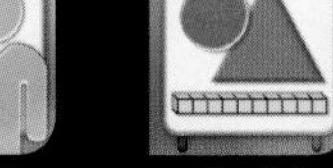
eToolkit

Algorithms Practice

EM Facts Workshop Game™

Family Letters

Assessment Management

Common Core State Standards

Curriculum Focal Points

Interactive Teacher's Lesson Guide

1 Teaching the Lesson

Key Concepts and Skills

- Compare and order integers. [Number and Numeration Goal 6]
- Add signed numbers. [Operations and Computation Goal 2]
- Identify a line of reflection. [Geometry Goal 3]

Key Activities

Students review positive and negative numbers on the number line, thinking of them as reflected across the zero point. They discuss and practice addition of positive and negative numbers as accounting problems, keeping track of "credits" and "debits." They play the *Credits/Debits Game.*

Ongoing Assessment: Informing Instruction See page 825.

Key Vocabulary

opposite (of a number) ◆ credit ◆ debit

Materials

Student Reference Book, pp. 60 and 238
Study Link 10•5
Math Masters, pp. 320 and 468
transparencies of *Math Masters,* pp. 318 and 321 (optional) ◆ per partnership: 1 transparent mirror, deck of number cards (the Everything Math Deck, if available)

2 Ongoing Learning & Practice

Solving Fraction, Decimal, and Percent Problems
Math Journal 2, p. 283
Students solve problems involving fractions, decimals, and percents.

Math Boxes 10•6
Math Journal 2, p. 284
Students practice and maintain skills through Math Box problems.

Ongoing Assessment: Recognizing Student Achievement
Use Math Boxes, Problem 1.
[Data and Chance Goal 4]

Study Link 10•6
Math Masters, p. 322
Students practice and maintain skills through Study Link activities.

3 Differentiation Options

READINESS

Exploring Skip Counts on a Calculator
calculator
Students skip count on a calculator to explore patterns in negative numbers.

READINESS

Using a Number Line to Add Positive and Negative Numbers
masking tape
Students use a number line to add positive and negative integers.

Advance Preparation

For Part 1, make and cut apart copies of *Math Masters,* page 320. Place them near the Math Message.

For the second optional Readiness activity in Part 3, use masking tape to create a life-size number line (–10 to 10) on the floor.

***Teacher's Reference Manual,* Grades 4–6** pp. 71–74, 100–102

Getting Started

Mental Math and Reflexes

Pose problems involving comparisons of integers.
Suggestions:

●○○ Are you better off if you have $3 or owe $10? Have $3
Owe $4 or owe $9? Owe $4
Owe $20 or owe $100? Owe $20

●●○ Which is colder?
–3°C or 10°C? –3°C
–9°C or 19°C? –9°C
–7°C or –11°C? –11°C

●●● Which is greater?
–10 or 8? 8
5 or –1? 5
10 or –10? 10

Math Message

Take a copy of Math Masters, *page 320. Follow the directions and answer the questions. Share 1 transparent mirror with a partner.*

Study Link 10•5 Follow-Up

Review answers. Have students share some of the patterns they created on their own. An overhead transparency of Study Link 10•5 (*Math Masters*, page 318) may be helpful.

1 Teaching the Lesson

Math Message Follow-Up

WHOLE-CLASS DISCUSSION

(*Student Reference Book,* p. 60; *Math Masters,* p. 320)

One way to think about a number line is to imagine the whole numbers reflected across the zero point. Each of these positive numbers picks up a negative sign as it crosses to the other side of zero. The **opposite** of a positive number is a negative number.

Conversely, imagine the negative numbers reflected across the zero point. The sign of each number changes from negative to positive as it crosses to the other side of zero. The opposite of a negative number is a positive number.

NOTE In this "flipping" of the number line, the zero point stays motionless, like the fulcrum of a lever. Zero is the only number that equals its opposite.

When students place the transparent mirror on the line passing through the zero point on *Math Masters,* page 320, the negative numbers appear (reversed) across from the corresponding positive numbers.

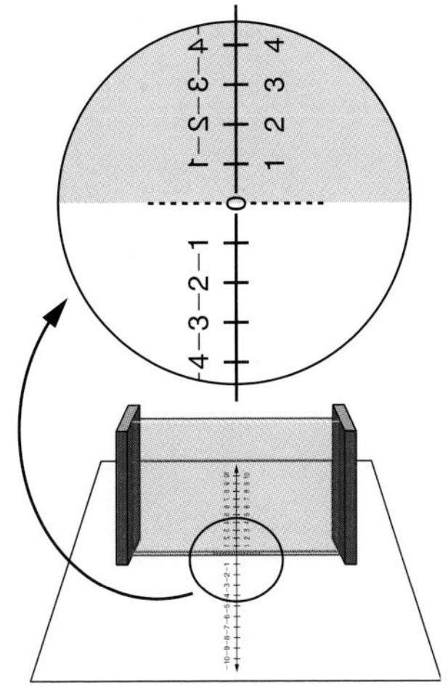

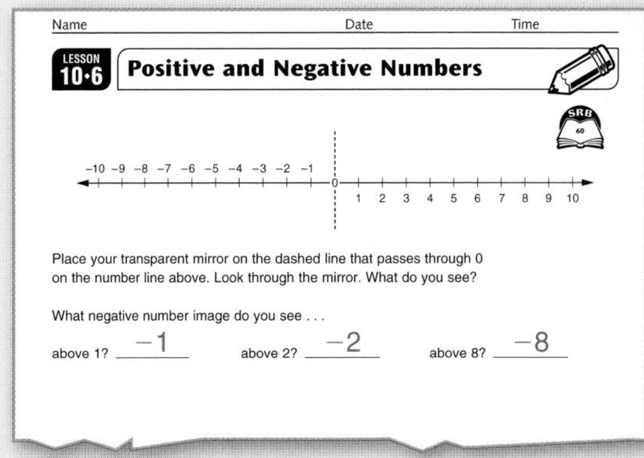

Name Date Time

LESSON 10•6 **Positive and Negative Numbers**

SRB 60

–10 –9 –8 –7 –6 –5 –4 –3 –2 –1 0 1 2 3 4 5 6 7 8 9 10

Place your transparent mirror on the dashed line that passes through 0 on the number line above. Look through the mirror. What do you see?

What negative number image do you see . . .

above 1? –1 above 2? –2 above 8? –8

Math Masters, page 320

Student Page

Fractions

Negative Numbers and Rational Numbers

People have used **counting numbers** (1, 2, 3, and so on) for thousands of years. Long ago people found that the counting numbers did not meet all of their needs. They needed numbers for in-between measures such as $2\frac{1}{2}$ inches and $6\frac{5}{6}$ hours.

Fractions were invented to meet these needs. Fractions can also be renamed as decimals and percents. Most of the numbers you have seen are fractions or can be renamed as fractions.

Examples Rename as fractions: 0, 12, 15.3, 3.75, and 25%.

$0 = \frac{0}{1}$ $12 = \frac{12}{1}$ $15.3 = \frac{153}{10}$ $3.75 = \frac{375}{100}$ $25\% = \frac{25}{100}$

Note

Every **whole number** (0, 1, 2, and so on) can be renamed as a fraction. For example, 0 can be written as $\frac{0}{1}$. And 8 can be written as $\frac{8}{1}$.

However, even fractions did not meet every need. For example, problems such as $5 - 7$ and $2\frac{3}{4} - 5\frac{1}{4}$ have answers that are less than 0 and cannot be named as fractions. (Fractions, by the way they are defined, can never be less than 0.) This led to the invention of **negative numbers.** Negative numbers are numbers that are less than 0. The numbers $-\frac{1}{2}$, -2.75, and -100 are negative numbers. The number -2 is read "negative 2."

Note

Numbers like -2.75 and -100 may not look like negative fractions, but they can be renamed as negative fractions.

$-2.75 = -\frac{11}{4}$, and

$-100 = -\frac{100}{1}$

Negative numbers serve several purposes:

- To express locations such as temperatures below zero on a thermometer and depths below sea level
- To show changes such as yards lost in a football game
- To extend the number line to the left of zero
- To calculate answers to many subtraction problems

The **opposite** of every positive number is a negative number, and the opposite of every negative number is a positive number. The number 0 is neither positive nor negative; 0 is also its own opposite.

The diagram at the right shows this relationship.

The **rational numbers** are all the numbers that can be written or renamed as fractions or as negative fractions.

-7 -6 -5 -4 -3 -2 -1 0 1 2 3 4 5 6 7

Student Reference Book, p. 60

Read and discuss page 60 of the *Student Reference Book* with the class. The diagram on the page is another way of showing that the opposite of every positive number is a negative number, and the opposite of every negative number is a positive number.

▶ Using Credits and Debits to Practice Addition of Positive and Negative Numbers

(*Math Masters*, p. 321)

Display a transparency of *Math Masters,* page 321. Tell students that in this lesson they pretend that they are accountants for a new business. They figure out the "bottom line" as you post transactions.

Discuss **credits** (money received for sales, interest earned, and other income) as *positive additions* to the bottom line, and **debits** (cost of making goods, salaries, and other expenses) as *negative additions* to the bottom line. Explain that you will label credits with a "+" and debits with a "–" to keep track of them as positive and negative numbers.

To support English language learners, clarify any misconceptions about the use of the words *credits, debits,* and *bottom line* in this lesson as compared with students' observations of the use of credit and debit cards at stores.

Be consistent throughout this lesson in "adding" credits and debits as positive and negative numbers, because Lesson 11-6 uses the same format to show "subtraction" of positive and negative numbers—the effect on the bottom line of "taking away" what were thought to be credits or debits.

Following is a suggested series of transactions. Entries in black are reported to the class; entries in color are appropriate student responses. To support English language learners, discuss the meaning of the words *transaction* and *change.*

Transaction	Start	Change	End/Start of Next Transaction
New business, start at \$0	\$0	\$0	\$0
Credit (payment) of \$5 comes in	\$0	add +\$5	+\$5
Credit of \$3	+\$5	add +\$3	+\$8
Debit of \$6	+\$8	add –\$6	+\$2
Debit of \$8 (Be sure to share strategies.)	+\$2	add –\$8	–\$6
Debit of \$3	–\$6	add –\$3	–\$9
Credit of \$5 (At last!)	–\$9	add +\$5	–\$4
Credit of \$6	–\$4	add +\$6	+\$2

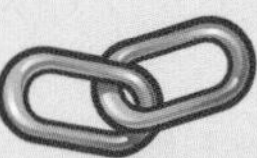

Links to the Future

Students explore subtraction of positive and negative integers in Lesson 11-6. Addition and subtraction of signed numbers is a Grade 5 Goal.

Adjusting the Activity

Have students experiment with their calculators to find out how to enter negative numbers and expressions with negative numbers. On the TI-15 students use the (–) key, and on the Casio *fx*-55, students use the +/– key.

AUDITORY ◆ KINESTHETIC ◆ TACTILE ◆ VISUAL

▸ Playing the *Credits/Debits Game*

PARTNER ACTIVITY

PROBLEM SOLVING

(*Student Reference Book,* p. 238; *Math Masters,* p. 468)

Students play the *Credits/Debits Game* to practice adding positive and negative numbers. They record their work on *Math Masters,* page 468.

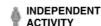

Ongoing Assessment: Informing Instruction

As students play, watch for those who are beginning to devise shortcuts for finding answers. For example, most students will probably count up and back on a number line. Some students may notice that when two positive numbers are added, the result is "more positive"; when two negative numbers are added, the result is "more negative"; and when a positive and a negative number are added, the result is the difference of the two (ignoring the signs) and has the sign of the number that is "bigger" in the sense of being farther from 0.

Do not try too hard to get explanations; these will evolve over time as students have more experience with positive and negative numbers.

Student Page

Games

Credits/Debits Game

Materials □ 1 complete deck of number cards
□ 1 *Credits/Debits Game* Record Sheet for each player (*Math Masters,* p. 468)

Players 2

Skill Addition of positive and negative numbers

Object of the game To have more money after adjusting for credits and debits.

Directions

You are an accountant for a business. Your job is to keep track of the company's current balance. The current balance is also called the "bottom line." As credits and debits are reported, you will record them and then adjust the bottom line.

1. Shuffle the deck and lay it number-side down between the players.
2. The black-numbered cards are the "credits," and the blue- or red-numbered cards are the "debits."
3. Each player begins with a bottom line of +$10.
4. Players take turns. On your turn, do the following:
   - Draw a card. The card tells you the dollar amount and whether it is a credit or debit to the bottom line. Record the credit or debit in your "Change" column.
   - Add the credit or debit to adjust your bottom line.
   - Record the result in your table.
5. At the end of 10 draws each, the player with more money is the winner of the round.

Record Sheet			
	Start	Change	End, and next start
1	+$10		
2			
3			
4			
5			
6			
7			
8			
9			
10			

Each player uses one Record Sheet.

Note
If both players have negative dollar amounts at the end of the round, the player whose amount is closer to 0 wins.

Examples Beth has a "Start" balance of +$20. She draws a black 4. This is a credit of $4, so she records +$4 in the "Change" column. She adds $4 to the bottom line: $20 + $4 = $24. She records +$24 in the "End" column, and +$24 in the "Start" column on the next line.

Alex has a "Start" balance of +$10. He draws a red 12. This is a debit of $12, so he records −$12 in the "Change" column. He adds −$12 to the bottom line: $10+(−$12) = −$2. Alex records −$2 in the "End" column. He also records −$2 in the "Start" column on the next line.

Student Reference Book, p. 238

2 Ongoing Learning & Practice

▸ Solving Fraction, Decimal, and Percent Problems

INDEPENDENT ACTIVITY

(*Math Journal 2,* p. 283)

Students solve problems involving equivalent fractions, decimals, percents, and discounts.

▸ Math Boxes 10·6

INDEPENDENT ACTIVITY

(*Math Journal 2,* p. 284)

Mixed Practice Math Boxes in this lesson are paired with Math Boxes in Lesson 10-3. The skill in Problem 5 previews Unit 11 content.

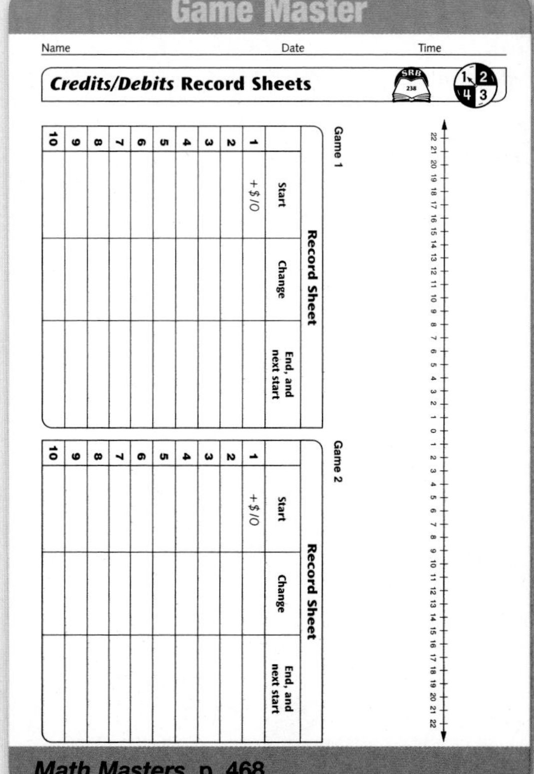

Game Master

Name Date Time

Credits/Debits **Record Sheets**

Game 1

Record Sheet			
	Start	Change	End, and next start
1	+$10		
2			
3			
4			
5			
6			
7			
8			
9			
10			

Game 2

Record Sheet			
	Start	Change	End, and next start
1	+$10		
2			
3			
4			
5			
6			
7			
8			
9			
10			

Math Masters, p. 468

Student Page

Date Time

LESSON 10·6 Review: Fractions, Decimals, and Percents

1. Fill in the missing numbers in the table of equivalent fractions, decimals, and percents.

Fraction	Decimal	Percent
$\frac{4}{10}$	0.4	40%
$\frac{6}{10}$	0.6	60%
$\frac{75}{100}$	0.75	75%

2. Kendra set a goal of saving $50 in 8 weeks. During the first 2 weeks, she was able to save $10.
   a. What fraction of the $50 did she save in the first 2 weeks? $\frac{10}{50}$
   b. What percent of the $50 did she save? 20%
   c. At this rate, how long will it take her to reach her goal? 10 weeks

3. Shade 80% of the square.
   a. What fraction of the square did you shade? $\frac{80}{100}$
   b. Write this fraction as a decimal. 0.8
   c. What percent of the square is *not* shaded? 20%

4. Tanara's new skirt was on sale at 15% off the original price. The original price of the skirt was $60.
   a. How much money did Tanara save with the discount? $9
   b. How much did she pay for the skirt? $51

5. Star Video and Vic's Video Mart sell videos at about the same regular prices. Both stores are having sales. Star Video is selling its videos at $\frac{1}{3}$ off the regular price. Vic's Video Mart is selling its videos at 25% off the regular price. Which store has the better sale? Explain your answer.
   Star Video has the better sale since $\frac{1}{3} = 33\frac{1}{3}\%$, which is more than 25%. So they're taking more off their regular prices.

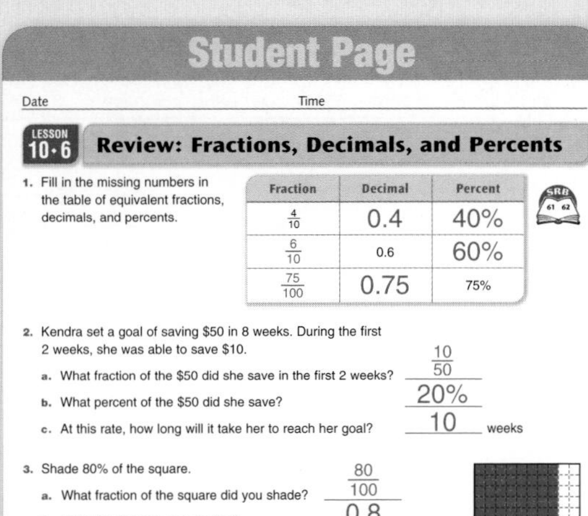

Math Journal 2, p. 283

Student Page

Date Time

LESSON 10·6 Math Boxes

1. a. Make a spinner. Color it so that if you spin it 36 times, you would expect it to land on blue 27 times and red 9 times. Sample answer:

b. Explain how you designed your spinner. Sample answer: If it lands on blue 27 out of the 36 spins, then $\frac{27}{36}$, or $\frac{3}{4}$, of the board should be blue. Likewise, $\frac{9}{36}$, or $\frac{1}{4}$, of the board should be red.

2. Complete.

Rule: $-\frac{1}{4}$

in	out
$\frac{8}{16}$	$\frac{4}{16}$
$\frac{8}{8}$	$\frac{6}{8}$
$\frac{3}{4}$	$\frac{2}{4}$
$\frac{10}{12}$	$\frac{7}{12}$
$\frac{15}{20}$	$\frac{10}{20}$

3. Solve each open sentence.
   a. $67.3 + p = 75.22$ $p =$ 7.92
   b. $6.86 - a = 2.94$ $a =$ 3.92
   c. $x + 5.69 = 7.91$ $x =$ 2.22
   d. $4.6 - n = 0.32$ $n =$ 4.28

4. Angle *RUG* is an acute (acute or obtuse) angle.

Measure of ∠*RUG* = 20 °

5. Sebastian and Joshua estimated the weight of their mother. What is the most reasonable estimate? Fill in the circle next to the best answer.
   ○ **A.** 50 pounds
   ● **B.** 150 pounds
   ○ **C.** 500 pounds
   ○ **D.** 1,000 pounds

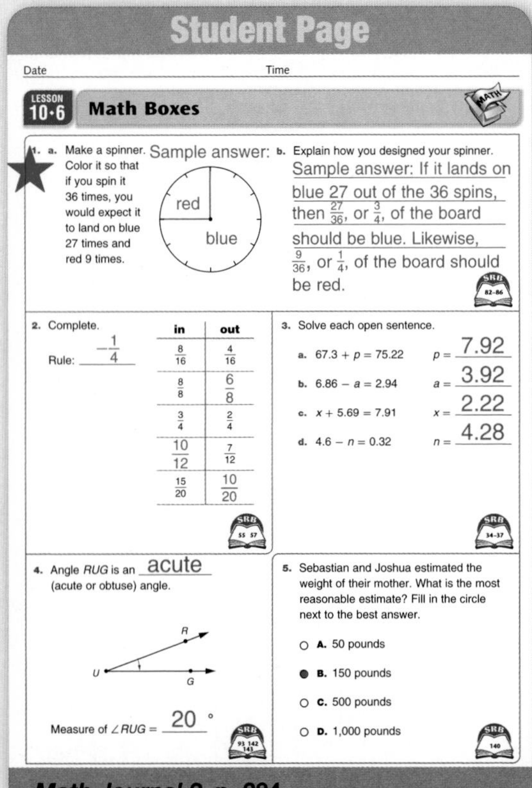

Math Journal 2, p. 284

Writing/Reasoning Have students write a response to the following: *The weights in Problem 5 are expressed in pounds. Make a table to show equivalent weights in ounces for 50; 150; 500; and 1,000 pounds. Then explain how you converted the weights.*

Pounds	Ounces
50	800
150	2,400
500	8,000
1,000	16,000

Sample answer: I know that there are 16 ounces in a pound, so I multiplied each weight by 16 to get the number of ounces.

Ongoing Assessment: Recognizing Student Achievement

Math Boxes Problem 1

Use **Math Boxes, Problem 1** to assess students' ability to express the probability of an event as a fraction. Students are making adequate progress if they design a spinner that is $\frac{1}{4}$ red and $\frac{3}{4}$ blue. Many students will design a spinner that has 3 consecutive parts red and 9 consecutive parts blue. Some students will explore other possibilities—for example, 2 consecutive red parts, followed by 4 blue parts, 1 red part, and 5 blue parts.

[Data and Chance Goal 4]

▶ Study Link 10·6

INDEPENDENT ACTIVITY

(*Math Masters,* p. 322)

Home Connection Students compare and order positive and negative numbers and add positive and negative integers.

3 Differentiation Options

READINESS

SMALL-GROUP ACTIVITY

5–15 Min

▶ Exploring Skip Counts on a Calculator

To explore patterns in negative numbers, have students skip count on the calculator. Ask students to start with 30 and count back by 10s on their calculator as they say the numbers aloud. Stop at –10 and ask the following questions:

- What does the calculator display show after zero? –10
- How do you read this number? negative ten
- Can you predict what number will come next? –20

Have students continue counting back, stopping at –50.

Repeat the routine counting back with other numbers such as 2, 5, 25, and 100. Remind students to clear their calculators after each count.

READINESS

SMALL-GROUP ACTIVITY

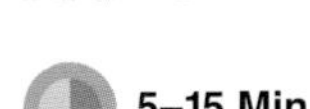

5–15 Min

Using a Number Line to Add Positive and Negative Numbers

To explore addition of positive and negative integers using a number line model, have students act out addition problems by walking on a life-size number line from –10 to 10.

▷ The first number tells students where to start.

▷ The operation sign (+ or –) tells which way to face:

+ means face the positive end of the number line.

– means face the negative end of the number line.

▷ If the second number is negative, then walk backward. Otherwise, walk forward.

▷ The second number (ignoring its sign) tells how many steps to walk.

▷ The number where the student stops is the answer.

Example: –4 + 3

▷ Start at –4.

▷ Face the positive end of the number line.

▷ Walk forward 3 steps.

▷ You are now at –1. So –4 + 3 = –1.

Suggestions:

- –6 + –3 = ? (Start at –6. Face in the positive direction. Walk backward 3 steps. End up at –9.)

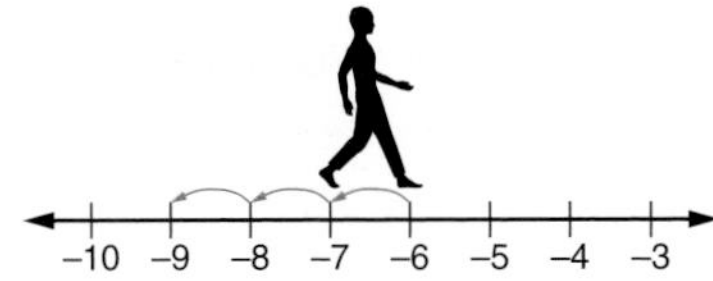

- 4 + –6 = ? (Start at 4. Face in the positive direction. Walk backward 6 steps. End up at –2.)

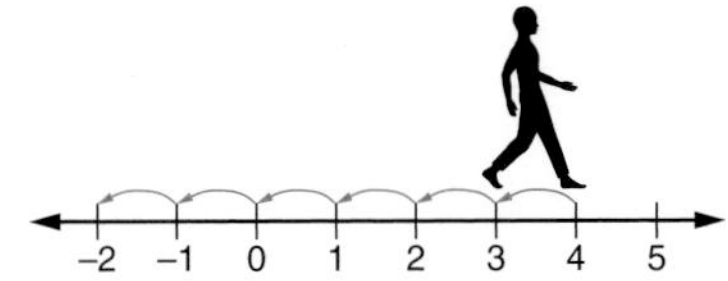

Study Link Master

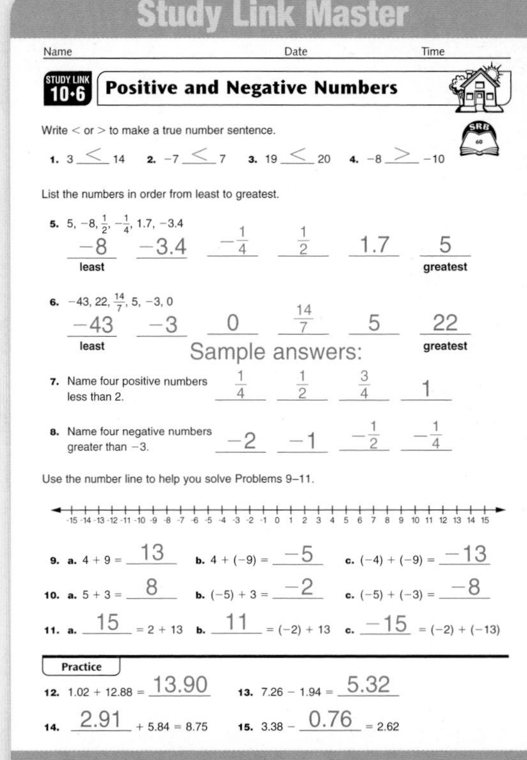

Name　　Date　　Time

STUDY LINK 10•6 **Positive and Negative Numbers**

Write < or > to make a true number sentence.

1. 3 < 14　2. –7 < 7　3. 19 < 20　4. –8 > –10

List the numbers in order from least to greatest.

5. 5, –8, $\frac{1}{2}$, $-\frac{1}{4}$, 1.7, –3.4
–8 (least), –3.4, $-\frac{1}{4}$, $\frac{1}{2}$, 1.7, 5 (greatest)

6. –43, 22, $\frac{14}{7}$, 5, –3, 0
–43 (least), –3, 0, $\frac{14}{7}$, 5, 22 (greatest)

Sample answers:

7. Name four positive numbers less than 2. $\frac{1}{4}$, $\frac{1}{2}$, $\frac{3}{4}$, 1

8. Name four negative numbers greater than –3. –2, –1, $-\frac{1}{2}$, $-\frac{1}{4}$

Use the number line to help you solve Problems 9–11.

-15 -14 -13 -12 -11 -10 -9 -8 -7 -6 -5 -4 -3 -2 -1 0 1 2 3 4 5 6 7 8 9 10 11 12 13 14 15

9. a. 4 + 9 = 13　b. 4 + (–9) = –5　c. (–4) + (–9) = –13

10. a. 5 + 3 = 8　b. (–5) + 3 = –2　c. (–5) + (–3) = –8

11. a. 15 = 2 + 13　b. 11 = (–2) + 13　c. –15 = (–2) + (–13)

Practice

12. 1.02 + 12.88 = 13.90　13. 7.26 – 1.94 = 5.32

14. 2.91 + 5.84 = 8.75　15. 3.38 – 0.76 = 2.62

Math Masters, p. 322

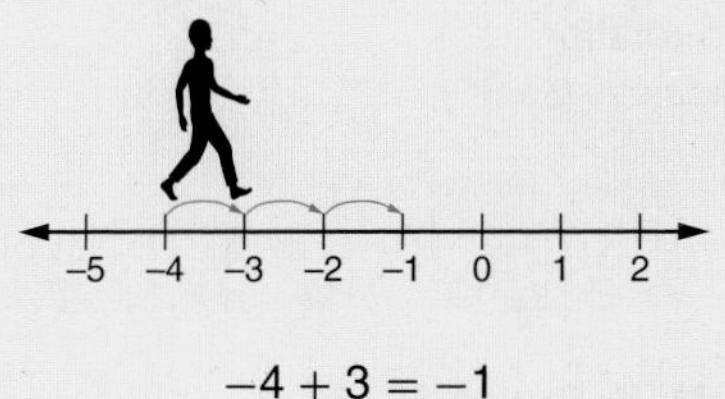

–4 + 3 = –1

10•7 Progress Check 10

Objective To assess students' progress on mathematical content through the end of Unit 10.

1 Looking Back: Cumulative Assessment

Input student data from Progress Check 10 into the **Assessment Management Spreadsheets**.

Materials

- Study Link 10•6
- *Assessment Handbook,* pp. 126–133, 200–205, 225, and 282–285
- slate; scissors; transparent mirror; Geometry Template

CONTENT ASSESSED	LESSON(S)	ASSESSMENT ITEMS				
		SELF	ORAL/SLATE	WRITTEN		OPEN RESPONSE
				PART A	PART B	
Name equivalent fractions, decimals, and percents. [Number and Numeration Goal 5]	10•2, 10•5, 10•6	1	3	9		
Add signed numbers. [Operations and Computation Goal 2]	10•6	2	1		11, 12	
Add and subtract fractions. [Operations and Computation Goal 5]	10•2, 10•3, 10•6		2	10		
Make reasonable estimates for multiplication and division problems. [Operations and Computation Goal 6]	10•1, 10•2, 10•4, 10•5				14	
Measure an angle. [Measurement and Reference Frames Goal 1]	10•2, 10•3, 10•6		4		13	
Locate multiple lines of symmetry in a two-dimensional shape. [Geometry Goal 3]	10•2–10•4	4		1–4		
Identify and sketch examples of reflections; identify examples of translations and rotations. [Geometry Goal 3]	10•1–10•5	3, 5, 6		5–8		✓

2 Looking Ahead: Preparing for Unit 11

Math Boxes 10•7

Study Link 10•7: Unit 11 Family Letter

Materials

- *Math Journal 2,* p. 285
- *Math Masters,* pp. 323–326

Advance Preparation

For the open-response item, students need to cut out the pentominoes on *Assessment Handbook,* page 205.

Getting Started

Math Message • Self Assessment

*Complete the Self Assessment (*Assessment Handbook*, page 200).*

Study Link 10·6 Follow-Up

Have small groups of students compare answers.

1 Looking Back: Cumulative Assessment

Math Message Follow-Up

INDEPENDENT ACTIVITY

(Self Assessment, *Assessment Handbook,* p. 200)

The Self Assessment offers students the opportunity to reflect upon their progress.

Oral and Slate Assessments

WHOLE-CLASS ACTIVITY

Problems 2, 3, and 4 provide summative information and can be used for grading purposes. Problem 1 provides formative information that can be useful in planning future instruction.

Oral Assessment

1. Pose problems that involve the addition of positive and negative numbers. Have students explain their solution strategies. *Suggestions:*
   - $9 + 6 = 15$
   - $-9 + 4 = -5$
   - $8 + (-2) = 6$
   - $0.5 + (-2) = -1.5$
   - $-7 + (-6) = -13$
   - $-\frac{3}{4} + (-\frac{1}{2}) = -1\frac{1}{4}$
2. Pose problems that involve the addition and subtraction of fractions. Have students explain their solution strategies. *Suggestions:*
   - $\frac{1}{4} + \frac{3}{4} = \frac{4}{4}$, or 1
   - $\frac{3}{3} - \frac{1}{3} = \frac{2}{3}$
   - $\frac{2}{9} + \frac{1}{3} = \frac{5}{9}$
   - $\frac{6}{8} - \frac{2}{4} = \frac{2}{8}$
   - $\frac{3}{5} + \frac{1}{10} = \frac{7}{10}$
   - $\frac{11}{12} - \frac{1}{3} = \frac{7}{12}$

Slate Assessment

3. Write fractions on the board. For each fraction, students write the equivalent decimal and percent on their slates. *Suggestions:*
   - $\frac{24}{100}$ 0.24, 24%
   - $\frac{6}{10}$ 0.6, 60%
   - $\frac{1}{4}$ 0.25, 25%
   - $\frac{15}{100}$ 0.15, 15%
   - $\frac{7}{10}$ 0.7, 70%
   - $\frac{2}{5}$ 0.4, 40%
   - $\frac{3}{100}$ 0.03, 3%
   - $\frac{9}{10}$ 0.9, 90%
   - $\frac{2}{2}$ 1, 100%

Assessment Master

Name Date Time

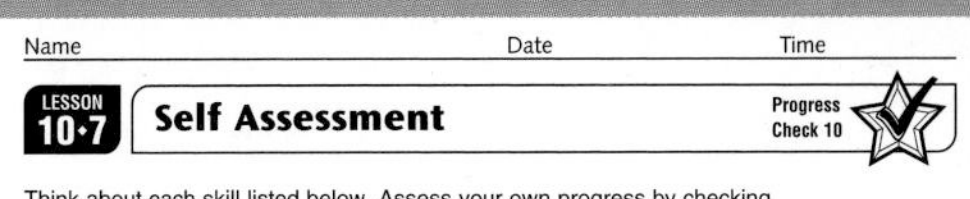

LESSON 10·7 **Self Assessment** Progress Check 10

Think about each skill listed below. Assess your own progress by checking the most appropriate box.

Skills	I can do this on my own and explain how to do it.	I can do this on my own.	I can do this if I get help or look at an example.
1. Give fraction, decimal, and percent equivalencies.			
2. Add positive and negative numbers.			
3. Use a mirror to draw reflections (flips).			
4. Identify shapes with line symmetry, and draw lines of symmetry.			
5. Identify and describe translations (slides).			
6. Identify and describe rotations (turns).			

***Assessment Handbook,* p. 200**

Assessment Master

Name Date Time

LESSON 10·7 **Written Assessment** Progress Check 10

Part A

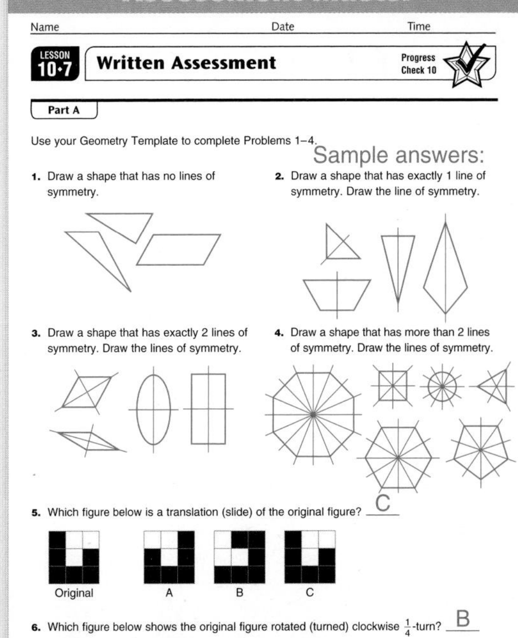

Use your Geometry Template to complete Problems 1–4. Sample answers:

1. Draw a shape that has no lines of symmetry.
2. Draw a shape that has exactly 1 line of symmetry. Draw the line of symmetry.
3. Draw a shape that has exactly 2 lines of symmetry. Draw the lines of symmetry.
4. Draw a shape that has more than 2 lines of symmetry. Draw the lines of symmetry.
5. Which figure below is a translation (slide) of the original figure? C

Original A B C

6. Which figure below shows the original figure rotated (turned) clockwise $\frac{1}{4}$-turn? B

Original A B C

***Assessment Handbook,* p. 201**

Assessment Master

Name ______ Date ______ Time ______

LESSON 10•7 **Written Assessment** *continued*

7. Use a transparent mirror to draw the reflection of the preimage.

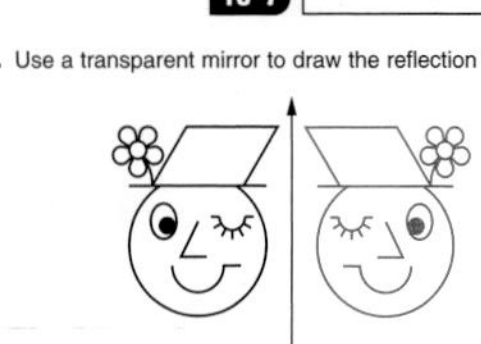

8. Use a transparent mirror to draw the other half of the figure across the line of symmetry.

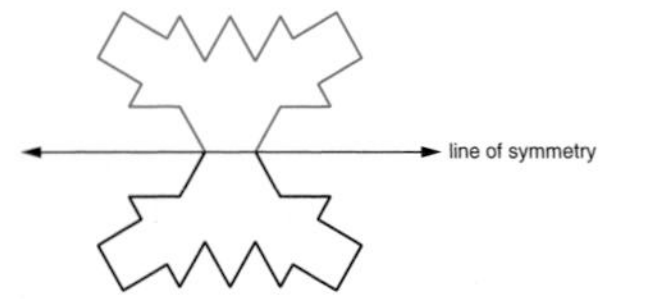

9. Complete the table with equivalent names.

Fraction	Decimal	Percent
$\frac{4}{5}$	0.8	80%
$\frac{20}{100}$, $\frac{2}{10}$, or $\frac{1}{5}$	0.2	20%
$\frac{75}{100}$, or $\frac{3}{4}$	0.75	75%
$\frac{6}{100}$	0.06	6%

10. Add or subtract.

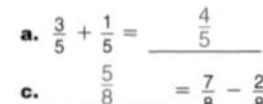

a. $\frac{3}{5} + \frac{1}{5} = \frac{4}{5}$

b. $\frac{7}{12} = \frac{4}{12} + \frac{1}{4}$

c. $\frac{5}{8} = \frac{7}{8} - \frac{2}{8}$

d. $\frac{5}{6} - \frac{1}{2} = \frac{2}{6}$, or $\frac{1}{3}$

Assessment Handbook, p. 202

Use the checklists on pages 283 and 285 of the *Assessment Handbook* to record results. Then input the data into the **Assessment Management Spreadsheets** to keep an ongoing record of students' progress toward Grade-Level Goals.

Assessment Master

Name ______ Date ______ Time ______

LESSON 10•7 **Written Assessment** *continued*

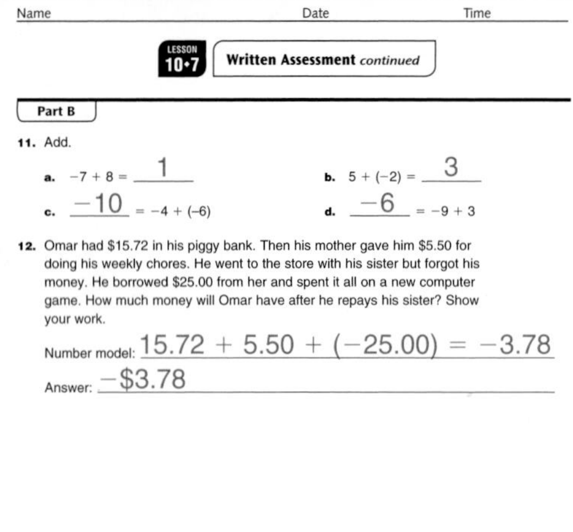

Part B

11. Add.

a. $-7 + 8 = 1$

b. $5 + (-2) = 3$

c. $-10 = -4 + (-6)$

d. $-6 = -9 + 3$

12. Omar had $15.72 in his piggy bank. Then his mother gave him $5.50 for doing his weekly chores. He went to the store with his sister but forgot his money. He borrowed $25.00 from her and spent it all on a new computer game. How much money will Omar have after he repays his sister? Show your work.

Number model: $15.72 + 5.50 + (-25.00) = -3.78$

Answer: $-\$3.78$

13. Angle *TUV* is an acute (acute or obtuse) angle.

Measure of ∠*TUV* = 57°

14. Insert the decimal point in each answer.

a. 9.8 ∗ 6 = 58.8

b. 11.36 = 1.42 ∗ 8

c. 29.46 = 147.3 ÷ 5

d. 36.4 ÷ 8 = 4.55

Assessment Handbook, p. 203

4. Pose problems involving the identification of different types of angles. *Suggestions:*

- Draw an obtuse angle.
- Draw an angle that measures more than 45°.
- Draw a right angle.
- Draw an angle that measures less than 90°.

▶ Written Assessment

(*Assessment Handbook,* pp. 201–203)

Part A Recognizing Student Achievement

Problems 1–10 provide summative information and may be used for grading purposes.

Problem(s)	Description
1–4	Draw shapes with no, one, two, or multiple lines of symmetry.
5	Identify a translation.
6	Identify a rotation.
7	Use a transparent mirror to draw the reflection of the preimage.
8	Use a transparent mirror to draw the other half of the figure across the line of symmetry.
9	Give fraction, decimal, and percent equivalents.
10	Add and subtract fractions.

Part B Informing Instruction

Problems 11–14 provide formative information that can be useful in planning future instruction.

Problem(s)	Description
11	Add positive and negative integers.
12	Solve a number story involving addition of positive and negative numbers.
13	Identify and measure an angle.
14	Estimate the products and quotients of problems involving decimals.

▶ Open Response

(*Assessment Handbook,* pp. 204 and 205)

Exploring Pentominoes

The open-response item requires students to apply concepts and skills from Unit 10 to solve a multistep problem. See *Assessment Handbook,* pages 129–133 for rubrics and students' work samples for this problem.

2 Looking Ahead: Preparing for Unit 11

Math Boxes 10•7

INDEPENDENT ACTIVITY

(*Math Journal 2,* p. 285)

Mixed Practice This Math Boxes page previews Unit 11 content.

Study Link 10•7: Unit 11 Family Letter

INDEPENDENT ACTIVITY

(*Math Masters,* pp. 323–326)

Home Connection The Unit 11 Family Letter provides parents and guardians with information and activities related to Unit 11 topics.

Study Link Masters

Name Date Time

STUDY LINK 10•7 **Unit 11: Family Letter**

3-D Shapes, Weight, Volume, and Capacity

Our next unit introduces several new topics, as well as reviewing some of the work with geometric solids from previous grades and some of the main ideas your child has been studying this past year.

We begin with a lesson on weight and mass, focusing on grams and ounces. Students handle and weigh a variety of objects, trying to develop "weight sense" so that they can estimate weights effectively. The class participates in creating a Gram & Ounce Museum by displaying everyday objects labeled with their weights.

As part of a review of the properties of 3-dimensional shapes (prisms, pyramids, cylinders, and cones), your child will construct models of geometric solids using straws and paper patterns. They will use these models as they discuss vocabulary such as *face, edge,* and *vertex* and compare features of geometric solids.

By experimenting with cubes, the class will develop and apply a formula for finding the volumes of rectangular prisms (solids that look like boxes).

We will consider units of capacity (cups, pints, quarts, gallons, liters, milliliters) and the relationships among them. The class participates in creating a Liter & Milliliter Museum by displaying everyday objets labeled with their capacities.

Your child will also explore subtraction of positive and negative numbers by playing a variation of the *Credits/Debits Game* introduced in Unit 10.

1 kg 1,000 g

In Lesson 11-1, a pan balance is used to measure weight in grams.

Please keep this Family Letter for reference as your child works through Unit 11.

Math Masters, pp. 323–326

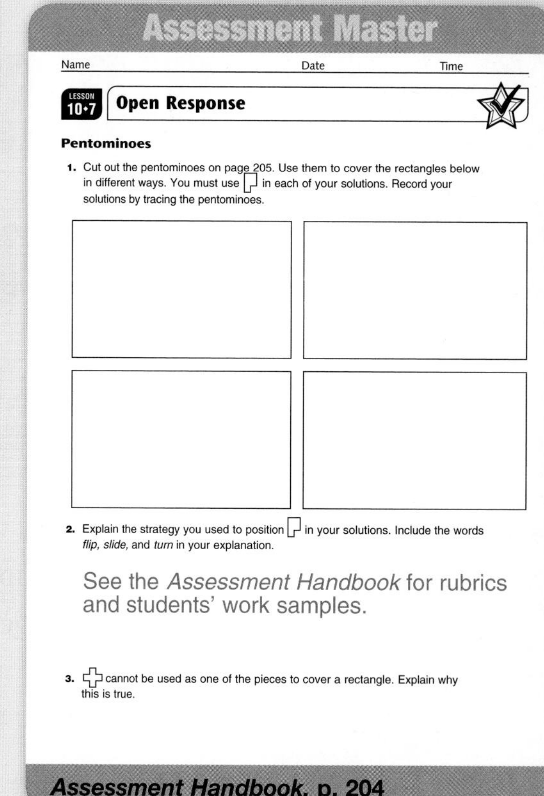

Assessment Master

Name Date Time

LESSON 10•7 **Open Response**

Pentominoes

1. Cut out the pentominoes on page 205. Use them to cover the rectangles below in different ways. You must use [shape] in each of your solutions. Record your solutions by tracing the pentominoes.

2. Explain the strategy you used to position [shape] in your solutions. Include the words *flip, slide,* and *turn* in your explanation.

See the *Assessment Handbook* for rubrics and students' work samples.

3. [shape] cannot be used as one of the pieces to cover a rectangle. Explain why this is true.

***Assessment Handbook,* p. 204**

Assessment Handbook, page 205 includes the 12 pentomino shapes that students cut out and use to solve the open-response item.

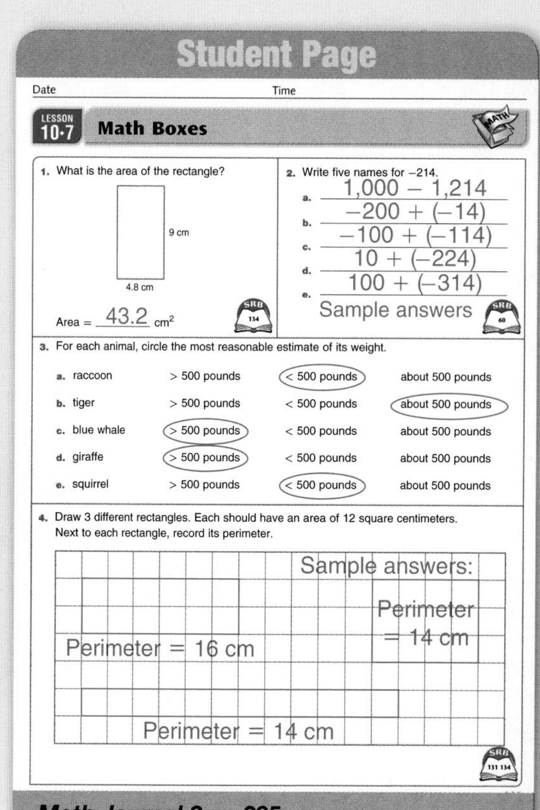

Student Page

Date Time

LESSON 10•7 **Math Boxes**

1. What is the area of the rectangle?

9 cm
4.8 cm

Area = 43.2 cm²

2. Write five names for –214.
a. 1,000 – 1,214
b. –200 + (–14)
c. –100 + (–114)
d. 10 + (–224)
e. 100 + (–314)

Sample answers

3. For each animal, circle the most reasonable estimate of its weight.

a. raccoon	> 500 pounds	(< 500 pounds)	about 500 pounds
b. tiger	> 500 pounds	< 500 pounds	(about 500 pounds)
c. blue whale	(> 500 pounds)	< 500 pounds	about 500 pounds
d. giraffe	(> 500 pounds)	< 500 pounds	about 500 pounds
e. squirrel	> 500 pounds	(< 500 pounds)	about 500 pounds

4. Draw 3 different rectangles. Each should have an area of 12 square centimeters. Next to each rectangle, record its perimeter.

Sample answers:

Perimeter = 16 cm

Perimeter = 14 cm

Perimeter = 14 cm

***Math Journal 2,* p. 285**

Unit 11 Organizer

3-D Shapes, Weight, Volume, and Capacity

Overview

Unit 11 begins with a review of weight that leads into a discussion about the relationship between weight and capacity. Students will review properties of geometric solids and explore concepts and units of volume. Subtraction of negative and positive integers will also be introduced in Unit 11. Unit 11 has four main areas of focus:

- To review grams and ounces as units of weight and mass,
- To identify geometric solids, given their properties,
- To review concepts and units of capacity and volume, and
- To introduce subtraction involving positive and negative integers.

CCSS Linking to the Common Core State Standards

The content of Unit 11 addresses the Common Core State Standards for Mathematics in *Measurement and Data.* The correlation of the Common Core State Standards to the *Everyday Mathematics* Grade 4 lessons begins on page CS1.

Contents

Unit 11 Organizer

Learning In Perspective

	Lesson Objectives	Links to the Past	Links to the Future
11•1	To review grams and ounces as units of mass and weight; and to guide the estimation and measurement of weight in grams and ounces.	Grade 3: Discuss the meaning of weight; review equivalencies between units of weight. Study various kinds of scales with respect to capacity, precision, and use; discuss appropriate scales for weighing different objects; practice reading scales. Guess weights and volumes of objects and check guesses; discuss relationships between weight and volume; order objects by weight and volume.	Grade 5: Convert measurements among units of weight, capacity, and volume in cubic units. Grade 6: Applications and maintenance.
11•2	To review the properties of common geometric solids.	Grade 2: Review names and parts of 3-dimensional objects. Construct and compare pyramids. Grade 3: Identify five basic 3-dimensional shapes (pyramid, prism, cone, cylinder, and sphere) and discuss their characteristics. Construct models of a cube, pyramid, and prism. Classify prisms according to the shapes of their bases. Identify 3-D shapes in the real world.	Grade 5: Use dimensions to compare the volume of rectangular prisms. Grade 6: Solve volume, angle, perimeter, and area problems.
11•3	To provide practice identifying geometric solids given their properties; and to guide the construction of polyhedrons.	Grade 2: Review names and parts of 3-dimensional objects. Construct and compare pyramids. Grade 3: Identify five basic 3-dimensional shapes (pyramid, prism, cone, cylinder, and sphere) and discuss their characteristics. Construct models of a cube, pyramid, and prism. Classify prisms according to the shapes of their bases. Identify 3-D shapes in the real world.	Grade 5: Use dimensions to compare the volume of rectangular prisms. Grade 6: Solve volume, angle, perimeter, and area problems.
11•4	To review concepts and units of volume.	Grade 3: Estimate, then find the volume of boxes by filling them with centimeter cubes. Find the volume of 2-cm, 3-cm, and larger cubes. Find rectangular prisms of a given volume. Use cm cubes to build rectangular prisms with the same volume but different dimensions. Compare the volume of irregular objects by water displacement.	Grade 5: Develop and apply a formula for the volume of a rectangular prism. Extend and apply the volume formula to non-rectangular prisms. Use dimensions to compare the volume of rectangular prisms. Grade 6: Solve volume, angle, perimeter, and area problems.
11•5	To guide the development and use of a formula for finding the volume of a rectangular prism.	Grade 3: Estimate, then find the volume of boxes by filling them with centimeter cubes. Find the volume of 2-cm, 3-cm, and larger cubes. Find rectangular prisms of a given volume. Use cm cubes to build rectangular prisms with the same volume but different dimensions. Compare the volume of irregular objects by water displacement.	Grade 5: Develop and apply a formula for the volume of a rectangular prism. Extend and apply the volume formula to non-rectangular prisms. Use dimensions to compare the volume of rectangular prisms. Grade 6: Solve volume, angle, perimeter, and area problems.
11•6	To review addition of positive and negative integers; and to introduce subtraction of positive and negative integers.	Grade 3: Review positive and negative numbers to relate numbers to a zero point, as in temperatures and elevations, and to record change. Solve number stories about positive and negative numbers.	Grade 5: Solve addition/subtraction stories with positive and negative numbers. Grade 6: Add and subtract positive and negative numbers on a number line; develop a rule for adding and subtracting positive and negative numbers; practice adding and subtracting positive and negative numbers.
11•7	To review units of capacity.	Grade 3: Discuss the meaning of weight; review equivalencies between units of weight. Study various kinds of scales with respect to capacity, precision, and use; discuss appropriate scales for weighing different objects; practice reading scales.	Grade 5: Convert units of liquid capacity to volume in cubic units. Grade 6: Applications and maintenance.

	Key Concepts and Skills	Grade 4 Goals*
11•1	Estimate weight with and without tools.	Measurement and Reference Frames Goal 1
	Describe relationships among metric units of mass and weight.	Measurement and Reference Frames Goal 3
	Convert between metric and customary units of mass and weight.	Measurement and Reference Frames Goal 3
	Extend numeric patterns.	Patterns, Functions, and Algebra Goal 1
11•2	Identify parallel and intersecting line segments and parallel planes.	Geometry Goal 1
	Describe, compare, and classify plane and solid figures.	Geometry Goal 2
	Identify congruent faces.	Geometry Goal 2
	Construct a rectangular prism.	Geometry Goal 2
11•3	Identify parallel and intersecting line segments and parallel faces.	Geometry Goal 1
	Describe, compare, and classify plane and solid figures.	Geometry Goal 2
	Identify congruent faces.	Geometry Goal 2
	Construct polyhedrons; sketch two-dimensional representations of polyhedrons.	Geometry Goal 2
11•4	Use multiplication to solve volume problems.	Operations and Computation Goal 3
	Find the area of the base of a rectangular prism.	Measurement and Reference Frames Goal 2
	Count unit cubes to find the volume of a rectangular prism.	Measurement and Reference Frames Goal 2
	Calculate the surface area of a rectangular prism.	Measurement and Reference Frames Goal 2
	Write number models with parentheses.	Patterns, Functions, and Algebra Goal 3
11•5	Find the area of the base and the surface area of a rectangular prism.	Measurement and Reference Frames Goal 2
	Count unit cubes and use a formula to find the volume of a rectangular prism.	Measurement and Reference Frames Goal 2
	Solve problems involving spatial visualization.	Geometry Goal 3
	Describe a rule for a pattern and use the rule to solve problems.	Patterns, Functions, and Algebra Goal 1
	Write number models with parentheses.	Patterns, Functions, and Algebra Goal 3
11•6	Compare integers.	Number and Numeration Goal 6
	Add and subtract signed numbers.	Operations and Computation Goal 2
	Describe rules for patterns and use them to solve problems.	Patterns, Functions, and Algebra Goal 1
11•7	Use division to solve conversion problems.	Operations and Computation Goal 4
	Describe relationships among units of capacity.	Measurement and Reference Frames Goal 3

*See the Appendix for a complete list of Grade 4 Goals.

A Balanced Curriculum

Ongoing Practice

Everyday Mathematics provides numerous opportunities for ongoing practice. These activities are embedded throughout the lessons:

Mental Math and Reflexes activities promote speed and accuracy in mental computation.

Math Boxes offer mixed practice and are paired across lessons as shown in the brackets below. This makes them useful as assessment tools. The last one or two boxes on each page preview the next unit's content.

Mixed practice	[11•1, 11•3], [11•2, 11•4, 11•6], [11•5, 11•7]
Mixed practice with multiple choice	11•2, 11•4, 11•6
Mixed practice with writing/reasoning opportunity	11•2, 11•4, 11•5

Study Links are daily homework assignments that review the content of the lesson and often contain ongoing facts practice or computation practice.

5-Minute Math problems are offered for additional practice in Lessons 11•1, 11•6, and 11•7.

EM Facts Workshop Game provides online practice of basic facts and computation.

EXTRA PRACTICE **Extra Practice** activities are included in Lessons 11•1, 11•2, 11•3, 11•6, and 11•7.

Practice through Games

Games are an essential component of practice in the *Everyday Mathematics* program. Games offer skills practice and promote strategic thinking. See the *Differentiation Handbook* for ways to adapt games to meet students' needs.

Lesson	Game	Skill Practiced
11•4	*Credits/Debits Game*	Adding positive and negative numbers [OC Goal 2]
11•5	*Chances Are*	Using probability language to describe the likelihood of an event [DC Goal 3]
11•6	*Credits/Debits Game* (Advanced Version)	Adding and subtracting positive and negative numbers [OC Goal 2]

[NN] Number and Numeration [OC] Operations and Computation [DC] Data and Chance
[MRF] Measurement and Reference Frames [GEO] Geometry [PFA] Patterns, Functions, and Algebra

Problem Solving 

Experts at problem solving and mathematical modeling generally do these things:

- Identify the problem.
- Decide what information is needed to solve the problem.
- Play with and study the data to find patterns and meaning.
- Identify and use mathematical procedures to solve the problem.
- Decide whether the solution makes sense and whether it can be applied to other problems.

The table below lists some of the opportunities in this unit for students to practice these strategies.

Lessons that teach *through* problem solving, not just *about* problem solving

Lesson	Activity
11•1	Estimate weights and convert between metric and customary weights.
11•2	Model geometric solids.
11•3	Solve geometry riddles, use straws and twist-ties to model polyhedrons, and draw cube models.
11•4	Use cubes to find the volume of a rectangular prism.
11•5	Solve cube stacking problems and derive a formula for the volume of a rectangular prism.
11•6	Use credits and debits to practice subtraction of positive and negative numbers.

See Chapter 18: Problem Solving in the *Teacher's Reference Manual* for more information.

The Language of Mathematics

Everyday Mathematics provides lesson-specific suggestions to help all students acquire, process, and express mathematical ideas. Throughout Unit 11, there are lesson-specific language development notes that address the needs of English language learners, indicated by ELL.

ELL SUPPORT Activities to support English language learners are in Part 3 of Lessons 11•2, 11•4, and 11•7.

The *English Learners Handbook* and the *Differentiation Handbook* have suggestions for promoting language development and acquisition of mathematics vocabulary. See Unit 11 in each handbook.

Unit 11 Vocabulary

capacity	milliliter
cone	ounce
congruent	pint
cube	polyhedron
cubic units	prism
cup	pyramid
curved surface	quart
cylinder	rectangular prism
dimensions	regular polyhedron
dodecahedron	sphere
edge	square pyramid
face	surface area
flat surface	tetrahedron
formula	triangular prism
gallon	triangular pyramid
geometric solid	vertex (vertices)
gram	volume
liter	

Literacy Connection

A Grain of Rice, by Helena Clare Pittman, Scholastic Inc., 1997
Mummy Math: An Adventure in Geometry, by Cindy Neuschwander, Square Fish, 2009
Is a Blue Whale the Biggest Thing There Is?, by Robert E. Wells, Albert Whitman, 1993
Fannie in the Kitchen: The Whole Story from Soup to Nuts of How Fannie Farmer Invented Recipes with Precise Measurements, by Deborah Hopkinson, Aladdin, 2004

For more literacy connections, see the *Home Connection Handbook,* Grades 4–6.

Cross-Curricular Links 

Social Studies – Lesson 11•1 **Technology** – Lessons 11•2, 11•4 **Language Arts** – Lesson 11•3

Balanced Assessment

Daily Assessments

- **Recognizing Student Achievement** – A daily assessment that is included in every lesson to evaluate students' progress toward the Grade 4 Grade-Level Goals.
- **Informing Instruction** – Notes that appear throughout the unit to help anticipate students' common errors and suggest appropriate problem-solving strategies.

Lesson	Recognizing Student Achievement	Informing Instruction
11•1	Describe a translation. [GEO Goal 3]	Notice the difference between the ounces number line and the grams number line.
11•2	Describe a rectangular prism. [GEO Goal 2]	
11•3	Find multiples of whole numbers less than 10. [NN Goal 3]	
11•4	Demonstrate automaticity with multiplication facts and proficiency with division facts. [OC Goal 3]	
11•5	Find the volume of stacks of centimeter cubes. [MRF Goal 2]	Use visible cubes to help determine the volume of a box.
11•6	Identify an example of a rotation. [GEO Goal 3]	Look for shortcut strategies when subtracting negative numbers.
11•7	Describe the relationships among U.S. customary units of length and among metric units of length. [MRF Goal 3]	Understand the scale to read a bar graph correctly.

[NN] Number and Numeration
[MRF] Measurement and Reference Frames
[OC] Operations and Computation
[GEO] Geometry
[DC] Data and Chance
[PFA] Patterns, Functions, and Algebra

Portfolio Opportunities

The following lessons provide opportunities to gather samples of students' mathematical writings, drawings, and creations to add balance to the assessment process: Lessons 11•2, 11•3, 11•4, 11•5, and 11•8.

See pages 16 and 17 in the *Assessment Handbook* for more information about portfolios and how to use them.

Unit Assessment

Progress Check 11 – A cumulative assessment of concepts and skills taught in Unit 11 and in previous units, providing information for evaluating students' progress and planning for future instruction. These assessments include oral/slate, written, and open-response activities, as shown below in the sample Progress Check lesson opener.

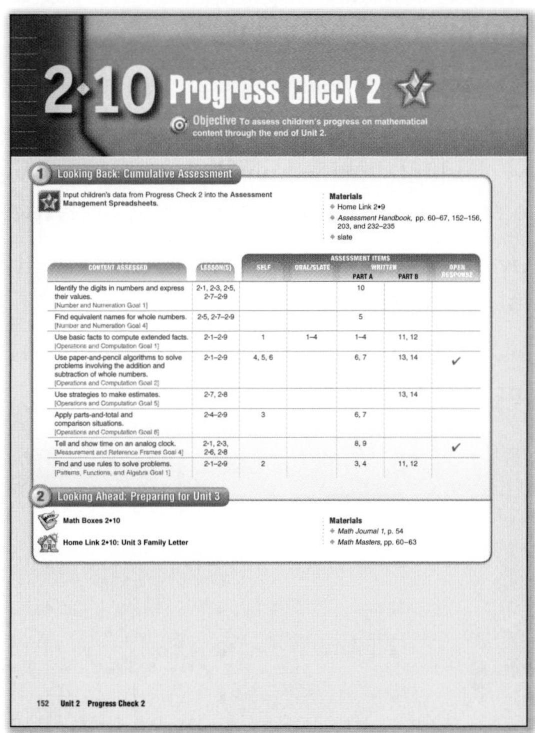

2·10 Progress Check 2

Objective To assess children's progress on mathematical content through the end of Unit 2.

1 Looking Back: Cumulative Assessment

Input children's data from Progress Check 2 into the Assessment Management Spreadsheets.

Materials
- Home Link 2•9
- *Assessment Handbook,* pp. 60–67, 152–156, 203, and 232–235
- slate

Content Assessed	Lesson(s)	Assessment Items: Self	Oral/Slate	Written: Part A	Written: Part B	Open Response
Identify the digits in numbers and express their values. [Number and Numeration Goal 1]	2·1, 2·3, 2·5, 2·7–2·9			10		
Find equivalent names for whole numbers. [Number and Numeration Goal 4]	2·5, 2·7–2·9			5		
Use basic facts to compute extended facts. [Operations and Computation Goal 1]	2·1–2·9	1	1–4	1–4	11, 12	
Use paper-and-pencil algorithms to solve problems involving the addition and subtraction of whole numbers. [Operations and Computation Goal 2]	2·1–2·9	4, 5, 6		6, 7	13, 14	✓
Use strategies to make estimates. [Operations and Computation Goal 5]	2·7, 2·8				13, 14	
Apply parts-and-total and comparison situations. [Operations and Computation Goal 6]	2·4–2·9	3		6, 7		
Tell and show time on an analog clock. [Measurement and Reference Frames Goal 4]	2·1, 2·3, 2·6, 2·8			8, 9		✓
Find and use rules to solve problems. [Patterns, Functions, and Algebra Goal 1]	2·1–2·9	2		3, 4	11, 12	

2 Looking Ahead: Preparing for Unit 3

Math Boxes 2•10

Home Link 2•10: Unit 3 Family Letter

Materials
- *Math Journal 1,* p. 54
- *Math Masters,* pp. 60–63

152 Unit 2 Progress Check 2

Core Assessment Resources

Assessment Handbook

- **Unit 11 Assessment Overview,** pages 134–141
- **Unit 11 Assessment Masters,** pages 206–210
- **Unit 11 Individual Profiles of Progress,** pages 286, 287, and 302
- **Unit 11 Class Checklists,** pages 288, 289, and 303
- **Math Logs,** pages 306–308
- **Exit Slip,** page 311
- **Other Student Assessment Forms,** pages 304, 305, 309, and 310

Assessment Management Spreadsheets

The Assessment Management Spreadsheets consist of the Digital Class Checklists and Individual Profile of Progress Checklists. Use them to monitor, record, and report student progress.

Addressing All Needs

Differentiated Instruction

Adjusting the Activity – suggests adaptations that target advanced learners, English language learners, or learners who need additional instructional support.

ELL SUPPORT / **ELL** – provides lesson-specific suggestions to help English language learners understand and process the mathematical content.

READINESS – accesses students' prior knowledge or previews content that prepares students to engage in the lesson's Part 1 activities.

EXTRA PRACTICE – provides additional opportunities to apply the mathematical content of the lesson.

ENRICHMENT – enables students to apply or further explore the mathematical content of the lesson.

Lesson	Adjusting the Activity	ELL Support/ ELL	Readiness	Extra Practice	Enrichment
11•1	•	•	•	•	
11•2		•		•	•
11•3	•	•	•	•	•
11•4	•	•	•		•
11•5	•	•	•		•
11•6	•	•	•	•	
11•7	•	•	•	•	

Additional Resources

Differentiation Handbook
Provides ideas and strategies for differentiating instruction.
Pages 118–124

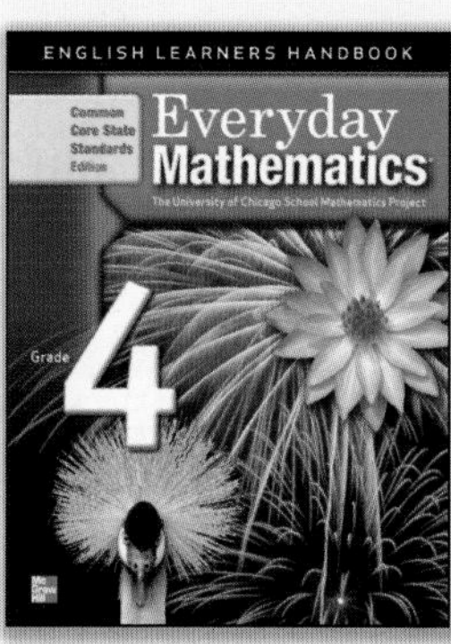

English Learners Handbook
Contains lesson-specific comprehension strategies.
Pages 95–101

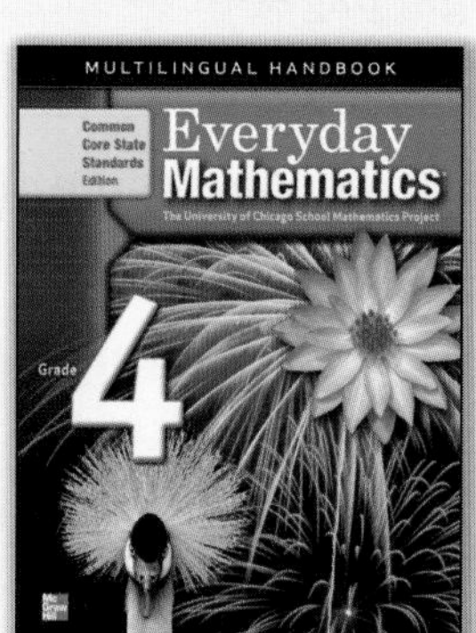

Multilingual Handbook
Previews concepts and vocabulary. It is written in six languages.
Pages 189–202

Planning Tips

Multiage Classroom

Companion Lessons from Grades 3 and 5 can help you meet instructional needs of a multiage classroom. The full Scope and Sequence can be found in the Appendix.

Grade 3	10•3	10•4		10•2	10•4	10•2, 10•4	10•5
Grade 4	**11•1**	**11•2**	**11•3**	**11•4**	**11•5**	**11•6**	**11•7**
Grade 5	11•6	11•1, 11•2		11•5	9•8	7•9	9•10, 11•6

Pacing for Success

Pacing depends on a number of factors, such as students' individual needs and how long your school has been using *Everyday Mathematics*. At the beginning of Unit 11, you may want to use tools available at www.everydaymathonline.com to help you set your pace.

Home Support

Unit 11 Family Letter (English/Spanish) provides families with an overview, Do-Anytime Activities, Building Skills through Games, a list of vocabulary, and answers to the daily homework (Study Links). Family Letters in English, Spanish, and seven other languages are also available online.

Study Links are the daily homework assignments. They consist of active projects and ongoing review problems.

Home Support Resources

Home Connection Handbook
Offers ideas and reproducible masters for communicating with families. See Table of Contents for unit information.

Student Reference Book
Provides a resource for students and parents.

Pages 101, 102, 137, 236–239, 276, 277, 281, 292, 293, 297, 302–305

Technology Resources

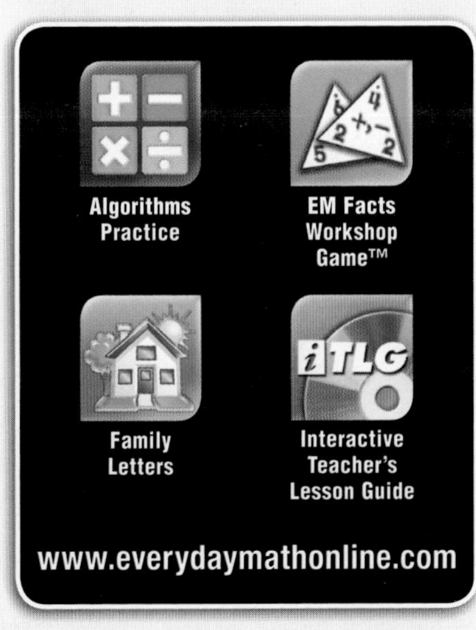

Materials

Technology Resources www.everydaymathonline.com

ePresentations

eToolkit

Algorithms Practice

EM Facts Workshop Game™

Family Letters

Assessment Management

Common Core State Standards

Curriculum Focal Points

Interactive Teacher's Lesson Guide

Lesson	Masters	Manipulative Kit	Other Items
11•1	Transparency of *Math Masters,* p. 448* Study Link Master, p. 327 Teaching Aid Masters, pp. 389 and 419–421*	balance or scale	standard masses; index cards; nickels; pennies and quarters*; liter bottles of water*; chart paper*; objects to weigh
11•2	Study Link Master, p. 328 Teaching Aid Masters, pp. 389 and 390	straws and twist-ties; per group: balance or scale capable of measuring 1 ounce	models of geometric solids; Class Data Pad*; pennies, nickels, dimes, and quarters; computer with Internet access
11•3	Teaching Aid Masters, pp. 389, 411, 414, 416*, 444, 452*, and 453* Study Link Master, p. 329	straws and twist-ties; slate; set of polyhedral dice*	models of geometric solids; blank paper; straightedge; transparent tape; dictionary*; pen or colored pencil; scissors; 30 objects of various shapes
11•4	Teaching Aid Masters, pp. 389 and 403 Study Link Master, p. 330 Game Master, p. 468 *Differentiation Handbook,* p. 140	base-10 blocks; centimeter cubes; metersticks; slate; deck of number cards	tape; scissors; traffic cones and string*; computer with Internet access*
11•5	Study Link Master, p. 331 Game Masters, pp. 462–466 Teaching Master, p. 332 Teaching Aid Master, p. 388 or 389	centimeter cubes; slate	centimeter ruler; interlocking cubes; sheet of notebook paper; scissors; stick-on notes
11•6	Game Master, p. 469 Transparency of *Math Masters,* p. 321* Study Link Master, p. 333	per partnership: deck of number cards; slate; number line*	per partnership: 1 penny; masking tape
11•7	Study Link Master, p. 334 Teaching Aid Master, p. 389 *Differentiation Handbook,* p. 140	slate; per partnership: eyedropper, liter pitcher, graduated beaker	measuring cup; empty milk cartons (pint, quart, $\frac{1}{2}$ gallon, gallon); pourable substance, such as sand; chart paper*; empty containers of various sizes; index cards; per partnership: 2 liters of water
11•8	Assessment Masters, pp. 206–210 Study Link Masters, pp. 335–338	slate; centimeter cubes	

*Denotes optional materials

Mathematical Background

The discussion below highlights the major content ideas presented in Unit 11 and helps establish instructional priorities.

Weight (Lesson 11◆1)

Students review weight as measured in grams and ounces, estimate the weight of objects, and check their estimates by actually weighing the objects. The minimum equipment required is one pan balance and a set of standard masses; however, a variety of scales is desirable. An important activity is setting up a Gram and Ounce Museum, displaying everyday objects labeled with their weights.

See Section 14.6 in the *Teacher's Reference Manual* for more information about weight and mass.

Geometric Solids (Lessons 11◆2 and 11◆3)

Work and play with 2-dimensional figures and 3-dimensional shapes are essential at every level of *Everyday Mathematics.* The reviews, reminders, and constructions in Lessons 11-2 and 11-3 are intended for enjoyment, as well as for preparation for the study of volume that begins in Lesson 11-4. In keeping with the program's philosophy, the study of volume continues through *Fifth* and *Sixth Grade Everyday Mathematics.*

The authors refer to certain 3-dimensional shapes as "geometric solids." By definition, such shapes are not, in fact, "solid" but consist only of the enclosing surfaces. That is, cylinders, cones, prisms, and so on, are empty rather than full. The interior points are not included unless there is a specific reference to a shape and its interior.

Further complication occurs when a straw construction is used to model a geometric solid: Only the frames of the surfaces appear, not the surfaces themselves. Such ambiguities are harmless in informal discourse. Periodically remind students that a geometric solid is made up of surfaces; however, it is not necessary to enforce the definition at this time. *Fifth* and *Sixth Grade Everyday Mathematics* will include work with exact mathematical definitions, especially in geometry.

More information about geometric solids can be found in Section 13.5.1 of the *Teacher's Reference Manual.*

Project Note

Use Project 6, Building and Viewing Structures, to build structures with cubes given "blueprints" or side views of the structures and to represent structures with diagrams. See the *Differentiation Handbook* for modifications to Project 6.

Subtraction of Positive and Negative Numbers (Lesson 11•6)

Throughout *Everyday Mathematics,* students have been using positive and negative numbers to record information from various reference frames (thermometers, timelines, number lines, number grids). Recording reference-frame information using positive and negative numbers is one of the main applications of such numbers in everyday life, including the areas of science and technology. Positive and negative numbers are also used as exponents and as positive or negative factors in expressing "slopes" or "rates" in coordinate graphs, equations, and formulas.

Situations that involve addition, subtraction, multiplication, or division of positive and negative numbers are rare. However, it may be useful to compare what happens when these operations are performed on only positive numbers with what happens when they are performed on both positive and negative numbers. Furthermore, for students who will be taking algebra and more advanced mathematics courses later, operational skills involving the entire set of positive and negative rational numbers are essential.

The approach to subtraction of positive and negative numbers in Lesson 11-6 parallels the approach to addition in Lesson 10-6. Again, the context is bookkeeping for a small business. "Credits" are represented by positive numbers and "debits" by negative numbers. Transactions are recorded in a ledger with the headings "Start," "Change," and "End." There is one new element: Occasionally, mistakes in recording are made and must be corrected. Corrections are done by subtracting (that is, removing or taking away) credits or debits that have been recorded "by mistake."

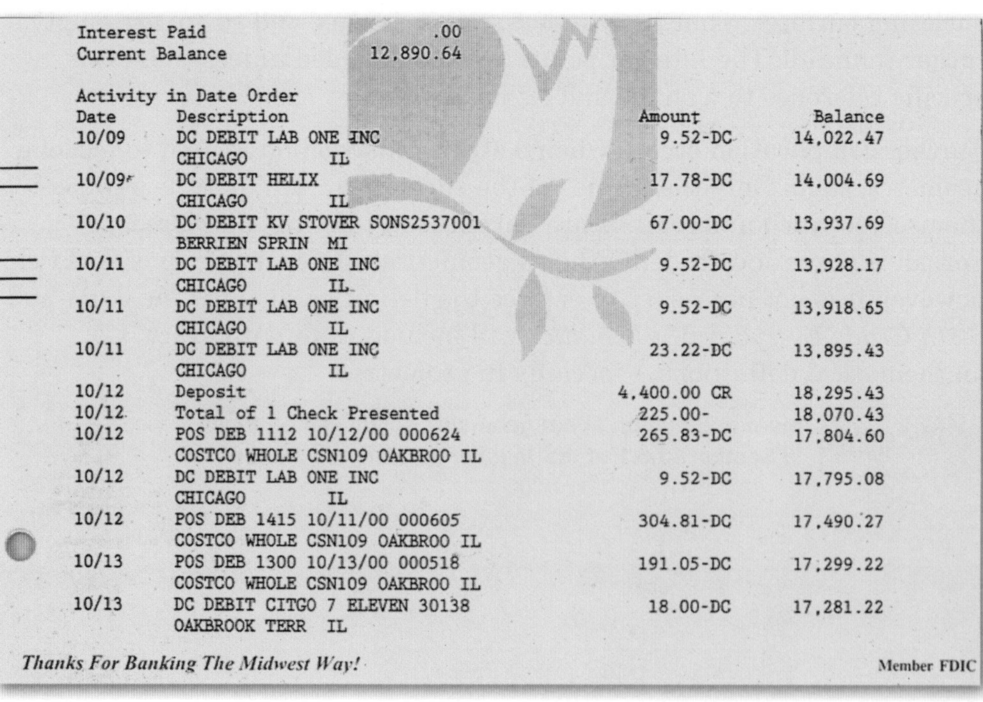

Interest Paid .00
Current Balance 12,890.64

Activity in Date Order

Date	Description	Amount	Balance
10/09	DC DEBIT LAB ONE INC CHICAGO IL	9.52-DC	14,022.47
10/09	DC DEBIT HELIX CHICAGO IL	17.78-DC	14,004.69
10/10	DC DEBIT KV STOVER SONS2537001 BERRIEN SPRIN MI	67.00-DC	13,937.69
10/11	DC DEBIT LAB ONE INC CHICAGO IL	9.52-DC	13,928.17
10/11	DC DEBIT LAB ONE INC CHICAGO IL	9.52-DC	13,918.65
10/11	DC DEBIT LAB ONE INC CHICAGO IL	23.22-DC	13,895.43
10/12	Deposit	4,400.00 CR	18,295.43
10/12	Total of 1 Check Presented	225.00-	18,070.43
10/12	POS DEB 1112 10/12/00 000624 COSTCO WHOLE CSN109 OAKBROO IL	265.83-DC	17,804.60
10/12	DC DEBIT LAB ONE INC CHICAGO IL	9.52-DC	17,795.08
10/12	POS DEB 1415 10/11/00 000605 COSTCO WHOLE CSN109 OAKBROO IL	304.81-DC	17,490.27
10/13	POS DEB 1300 10/13/00 000518 COSTCO WHOLE CSN109 OAKBROO IL	191.05-DC	17,299.22
10/13	DC DEBIT CITGO 7 ELEVEN 30138 OAKBROOK TERR IL	18.00-DC	17,281.22

Thanks For Banking The Midwest Way! Member FDIC

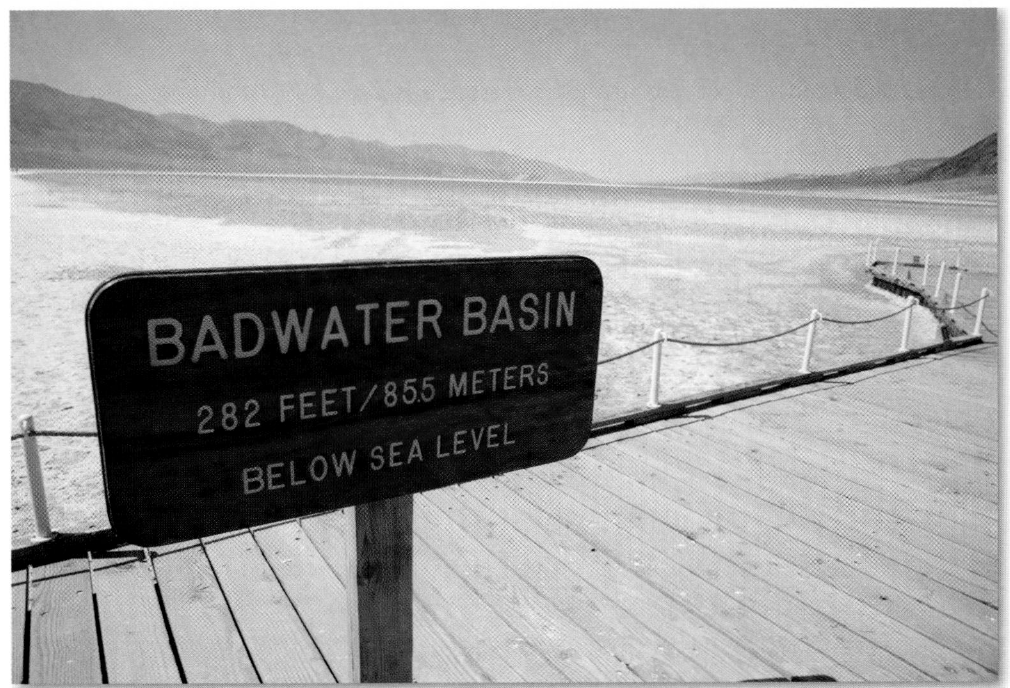

It should become apparent that taking away a credit (a positive number) leaves a business worse off, and taking away a debit (a negative number) leaves it better off. This is the central idea of the lesson. That is, when you subtract a negative number, your answer is greater than the number you started with. For example, $10 - (-5) = 15$ (not 5). This illustrates the following, very helpful procedure for subtraction:

> To subtract a number (whether positive or negative), add the opposite of the number.

While some students may discover this procedure, it would be premature to teach it at this time. This initial exploration of subtraction involving both positive and negative numbers is for fun and familiarization—mastery is not expected.

$+6 - (+3) = +6 + (-3) = +3$

$+8 - (-2) = +8 + (+2) = +10$

$-5 - (+2) = -5 + (-2) = -7$

$-12 - (-8) = -12 + (+8) = -4$

$+7 - (+10) = +7 + (-10) = -3$

$+6 - (-11) = +6 + (+11) = +17$

$-3 - (+4) = -3 + (-4) = -7$

$-5 - (-9) = -5 + (+9) = +4$

See Section 10.2.2 of the *Teacher's Reference Manual* for more information about adding and subtracting positive and negative numbers.

Volume (Lessons 11•4 and 11•5)

Volume is a measure of the amount of space inside a 3-dimensional shape. In Lessons 11-4 and 11-5, students develop the concept of volume by building 3-dimensional structures with identical cubes, or by filling open boxes with such cubes, and then counting the cubes. If the shape is a rectangular prism, a natural strategy is to build one layer of cubes, count the number of cubes in that layer, and then multiply that number by the number of layers needed to fill the prism. Since the number of cubes in one layer corresponds to the area of the base (often represented by the formula $A = l * w$), this process can be linked to the two standard formulas for the volume of a rectangular prism:

A big cube base-10 block has 10 layers, with $10 * 10 = 100$ cubes in each layer. $V = 100 \text{ cm}^2 * 10 \text{ cm} = 1{,}000 \text{ cm}^3$

$V = l * w * h$ (volume equals the product of the length and width of the rectangular base and the height perpendicular to that base)

$V = B * h$ (volume equals the product of the area of the base and the height perpendicular to that base)

The former is commonly used in textbooks and on standardized tests; the latter is used in many mathematics courses and technical applications. *Everyday Mathematics* uses both formulas, but the authors prefer $V = B * h$ because it can be used for prisms other than rectangular prisms, as well as for cylinders.

The Mathematical Background for Unit 8 suggests that students be encouraged to think of the area of a rectangle in terms of "painting" the surface inside the rectangle. Similarly, students can think of the volume of a prism in terms of the base rising along the "sides" of the prism until the prism is filled to the top. As an illustration of this idea, the open-response problem in Lesson 11-8 asks students to imagine a large amount of rain falling into their classroom. Assuming that the classroom floor is rectangular, the rainwater will rise, forming a rectangular prism whose height becomes greater and greater as more rain falls. Students find the volume of the rain and the weight of the water.

More about volume can be found in Section 14.5 of the *Teacher's Reference Manual.*

Units of Volume and Capacity

(Lessons 11•4 and 11•7)

It is important to note that, like other measures, volume and capacity are expressed with both numbers and units. Usually, volume units are *cubic units,* based on some linear measure; for example, cubic centimeters, cubic inches, cubic meters, cubic yards, and so on. In everyday life, it is common to express capacities in units that are not cubic units: teaspoons, cups, pints, U.S. or Imperial gallons, liters, barrels, bushels, and so on. These standards were developed centuries ago to measure things poured into or out of containers, such as liquids, grains, fruits, salt, and so on. Every locality had its own system of measures, and a variety of standards persists even today. For example, in the United States, *pint* has different meanings for dry and liquid measures and still another meaning in England. *Ounce* can refer to *fluid ounce* (a unit of capacity, about 1.8 cubic inches), *avoirdupois ounce* (a familiar unit of weight, about 28 grams), or *troy ounce* (a specialized unit of weight, about 31 grams).

In spite of these kinds of ambiguities, traditional units for capacity continue to be used in everyday life. Along with the liter, they have been the main focus of the discussion of capacity since *Kindergarten Everyday Mathematics.*

Section 14.5 of the *Teacher's Reference Manual* has more information about units of volume and capacity.

Continuation of the World Tour

(Lesson 11•1)

Students return to North America by flying to Mexico City, Mexico. North America is the final region on the World Tour.

11•1 Weight

Objectives To review grams and ounces as units of mass and weight; and to guide the estimation and measurement of weight in grams and ounces.

Technology Resources www.everydaymathonline.com

ePresentations

eToolkit

Algorithms Practice

EM Facts Workshop Game™

Family Letters

Assessment Management

Common Core State Standards

Curriculum Focal Points

Interactive Teacher's Lesson Guide

1 Teaching the Lesson

Key Concepts and Skills

- Estimate weight with and without tools. [Measurement and Reference Frames Goal 1]
- Describe relationships among metric units of mass and weight. [Measurement and Reference Frames Goal 3]
- Convert between metric and customary units of mass and weight. [Measurement and Reference Frames Goal 3]
- Extend numeric patterns. [Patterns, Functions, and Algebra Goal 1]

Key Activities

Students review measuring weight in ounces and grams and start a classroom Gram and Ounce Museum. They estimate weights and practice converting between grams and ounces.

Ongoing Assessment: Informing Instruction See page 851.

Key Vocabulary

gram ◆ ounce

Materials

Math Journal 2, pp. 286 and 287
transparency of *Math Masters,* p. 448 (optional) ◆ balance or scale ◆ standard masses ◆ index cards ◆ nickels ◆ pennies and quarters (optional) ◆ liter bottles of water (optional) ◆ chart paper (optional)

2 Ongoing Learning & Practice

Updating the World Tour

Math Journal 2, pp. 329–331, 340, and 341
Student Reference Book, pp. 276, 277, 281, 292, 293, 297, and 302–305
Math Masters, pp. 419–421 (optional)
Students continue the World Tour, traveling to Region 5.

Math Boxes 11•1

Math Journal 2, p. 288
Students practice and maintain skills through Math Box problems.

Ongoing Assessment: Recognizing Student Achievement
Use Math Boxes, Problem 1a.
[Geometry Goal 3]

Study Link 11•1

Math Masters, p. 327
Students practice and maintain skills through Study Link activities.

3 Differentiation Options

READINESS

Ordering Weights

Math Masters, p. 389
5 objects to weigh ◆ balance or scale
Students order objects by weight.

EXTRA PRACTICE

Estimating Weights

objects to weigh ◆ scale
Students estimate weights of objects.

EXTRA PRACTICE

5-Minute Math

5-Minute Math™, p. 134
Students convert among units of weight.

Advance Preparation

Give each student a nickel to use in the Math Message. In preparation for the Gram and Ounce Museum in Part 1, gather different kinds of scales, balances, and standard mass sets. See the note on page 850 for additional information.

***Teacher's Reference Manual,* Grades 4–6** pp. 13, 44–46, 216–218, 225, 236, 237

Getting Started

Mental Math and Reflexes

Write pairs of fractions on the board. Have students indicate "thumbs-up" if the fractions are equivalent. *Suggestions:*

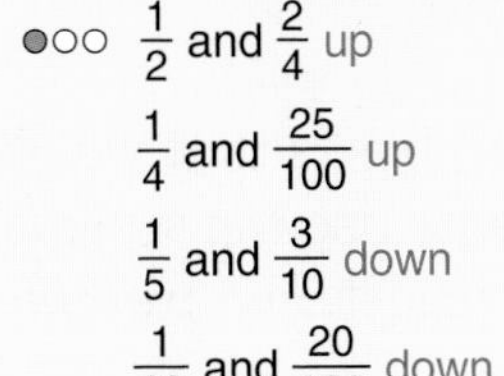

●○○	●●○	●●●
$\frac{1}{2}$ and $\frac{2}{4}$ up	$\frac{3}{4}$ and $\frac{6}{8}$ up	$\frac{14}{21}$ and $\frac{2}{3}$ up
$\frac{1}{4}$ and $\frac{25}{100}$ up	$\frac{4}{5}$ and $\frac{9}{10}$ down	$\frac{12}{20}$ and $\frac{2}{5}$ down
$\frac{1}{5}$ and $\frac{3}{10}$ down	$\frac{2}{3}$ and $\frac{3}{9}$ down	$\frac{8}{40}$ and $\frac{1}{5}$ up
$\frac{1}{10}$ and $\frac{20}{100}$ down	$\frac{7}{8}$ and $\frac{70}{80}$ up	$\frac{18}{54}$ and $\frac{1}{3}$ up

Math Message

A nickel weighs about 5 grams. Look around the classroom. Find objects you think weigh about:

1 gram
10 grams
25 grams
100 grams

Teaching the Lesson

Math Message Follow-Up

WHOLE-CLASS ACTIVITY

Demonstrate or have students demonstrate how to use a scale or balance to weigh some of the objects identified by students for the weights given. *For example:*

1 gram	centimeter cube
10 grams	hexagon pattern block
25 grams	compass
100 grams	calculator

For greater accuracy in weighing small objects, weigh several at once and divide to find the weight of a single object.

Review the relationship betwen **grams** and kilograms (1,000 grams = 1 kilogram) and other metric units of mass, including the milligram ($\frac{1}{1,000}$ gram) and the metric ton (1,000 kilograms). Ask:

- What might be measured in milligrams? Sample answer: medicine
- In grams? Sample answer: food
- In kilograms? Sample answer: body weight
- In metric tons? Sample answer: whale

Discuss the difference between *weight* and *mass*. Ask questions such as the following:

- If you went to the moon and weighed yourself, would you weigh more or less than you do on Earth? less Why? Gravity is weaker on the moon than it is on Earth.
- If your weight on the moon is not the same as on Earth, what does remain the same? mass
- Would you rather have a bowling ball dropped on your toe on Earth or on the moon? Explain. On the moon, because the weight of the bowling ball is less on the moon so it would hurt less.

Interactive whiteboard-ready ePresentations are available at www.everydaymathonline.com to help you teach the lesson.

NOTE In everyday language, the terms *weight* and *mass* are used more or less interchangeably. One may, for example, try to lose *weight* in order to improve one's body *mass* index. But in technical and scientific contexts, *weight* and *mass* are quite different. In such contexts, *weight* refers to the force of gravity on an object, whereas *mass* is a measure of the amount of matter in an object. Mass and weight are proportional—an object with twice the mass, for example, weighs twice as much—so the distinction between them is subtle and was not understood even by scientists until relatively recently. So, for example, units such as grams and pounds, which have been in use for hundreds of years, are often used for both mass and weight, and the context must be used to sort out what is being measured. See Section 14.6 of the *Teacher's Reference Manual* for a further discussion of the differences between weight and mass.

NOTE The distinction between mass and weight is tricky, so do not expect students to grasp it right away. Return to questions such as these throughout this unit as the occasion arises.

- Can you think of an activity where your weight changes but your mass stays the same? Sample answers: skydiving; jumping off a diving platform; riding on an elevator that is either starting to move or coming to a stop
- Would an astronaut be able to move a large satellite easily since it is weightless in outer space? No, because the satellite is still massive and resists being moved.

Review **ounces** by asking students to name objects that weigh about 1, 4, 8, 16, and 32 ounces. Have students use the scale or balance to weigh some of the objects they suggest. *For example:*

1 ounce	chalk/white board eraser
4 ounces	calculator
8 ounces	pad of paper; 50 sheets
16 ounces	*Student Math Journal*
32 ounces	*Student Reference Book*

Review the relationship between ounces and pounds (16 ounces = 1 pound) and pounds and tons (2,000 pounds = 1 ton). Ask:

- What might be measured in ounces? Sample answer: letters
- In pounds? Sample answer: body weight
- In tons? Sample answer: trucks

Adjusting the Activity

ELL

Display a poster in the classroom to remind students of weight equivalencies and approximate comparisons. Consider adding pictures of items for the weights listed to provide a reference for students. *For example:*

Metric Units
1 gram (g) = 1,000 milligrams (mg)
1 kilogram (kg) = 1,000 grams
1 metric ton (t) = 1,000 kilograms

U.S. Customary Units
1 pound (lb) = 16 ounces (oz)
1 ton (T) = 2,000 pounds

Rules of Thumb
1 kilogram equals about 2.2 pounds.
1 ounce equals about 30 grams.

AUDITORY ◆ KINESTHETIC ◆ TACTILE ◆ VISUAL

NOTE Use a variety of measuring tools for the Gram and Ounce Museum (for example, a bathroom scale, a diet scale, and a spring scale) so students can measure a range of weights. The minimum equipment is a rocker balance or pan balance and a set of standard masses. Use commercial standard masses, or

- for metric standard masses, use nickels (about 5 grams each) and pennies dated 1983 or later (about 2.5 grams each).
- for customary standard masses, use quarters (about 0.2 ounce each).

To make larger standard masses for weighing heavier objects, coins, washers, or other objects can be taped together or placed in resealable plastic bags.

▶ Setting up a Gram and Ounce Museum

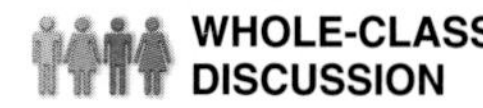
WHOLE-CLASS DISCUSSION

Introduce a project to create a museum of objects of different weights measured in grams and ounces. Use index cards to label objects in the museum and record their weights. The measuring tools available determine the range of weights you can display. For example, if you are limited to one balance and coins as standard masses, then aim for a modest weight range (possibly up to 500 grams or 16 ounces). If you also have a scale or a balance that can accommodate larger weights, then expand the range of weights.

Discuss the goals for the collection, the kinds of objects to be collected, and the procedures for adding objects to the museum. For example, if you have a scale that is precise enough to weigh objects to the nearest gram, you might decide to try to find an object for every number of grams from 1 to 100. Because this will be a large collection, you might focus on common items like rocks.

The procedure for adding items should probably be managed by students. Ask students to bring in objects for the museum over the next week or two. To ensure accuracy and to assess students' skill in weighing different objects, require that every item added to the museum be weighed by two or three students working independently.

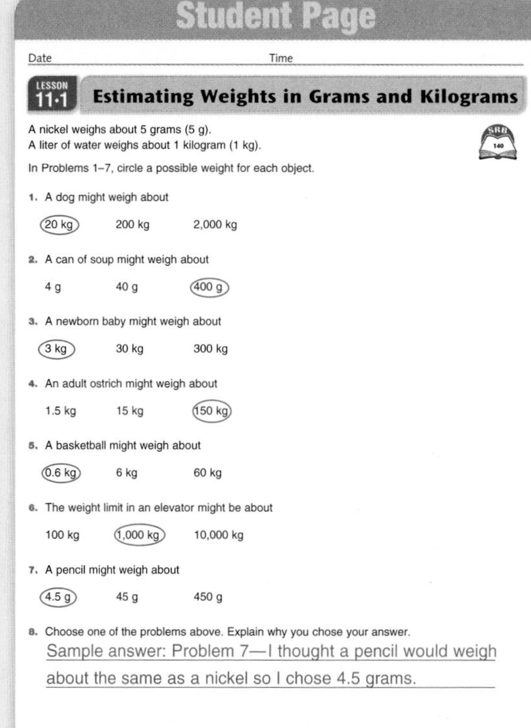
Student Page

Date Time

LESSON 11·1 **Estimating Weights in Grams and Kilograms**

A nickel weighs about 5 grams (5 g).
A liter of water weighs about 1 kilogram (1 kg).

In Problems 1–7, circle a possible weight for each object.

1. A dog might weigh about
   (20 kg) 200 kg 2,000 kg
2. A can of soup might weigh about
   4 g 40 g (400 g)
3. A newborn baby might weigh about
   (3 kg) 30 kg 300 kg
4. An adult ostrich might weigh about
   1.5 kg 15 kg (150 kg)
5. A basketball might weigh about
   (0.6 kg) 6 kg 60 kg
6. The weight limit in an elevator might be about
   100 kg (1,000 kg) 10,000 kg
7. A pencil might weigh about
   (4.5 g) 45 g 450 g
8. Choose one of the problems above. Explain why you chose your answer.
   Sample answer: Problem 7—I thought a pencil would weigh about the same as a nickel so I chose 4.5 grams.

Math Journal 2, p. 286

Estimating Weights

(*Math Journal 2,* p. 286)

PARTNER ACTIVITY
PROBLEM SOLVING

Students estimate the weights of different objects. Partners should discuss the possibilities and come to an agreement about which measure is the most reasonable for each object.

Adjusting the Activity

ELL

Have a handful of nickels and a couple of liter bottles of water available so students have an opportunity to hold the different weights, compare them, and use this information to make better estimates.

AUDITORY ◆ KINESTHETIC ◆ TACTILE ◆ VISUAL

Converting between Metric and Customary Weights

(*Math Journal 2,* p. 287; *Math Masters,* p. 448)

PARTNER ACTIVITY
PROBLEM SOLVING

Students use a double-scale number line to convert between grams and ounces. Use a transparency of *Math Masters,* page 448 to demonstrate how to use the number line.

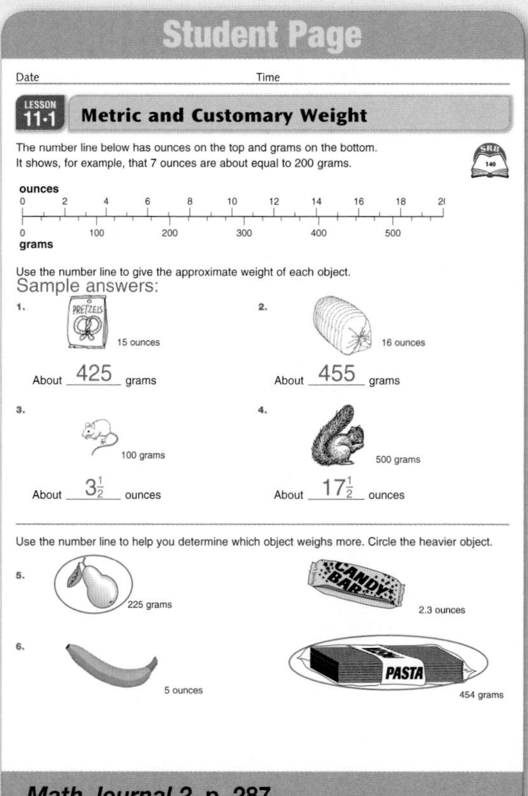
Student Page

Date Time

LESSON 11·1 **Metric and Customary Weight**

The number line below has ounces on the top and grams on the bottom. It shows, for example, that 7 ounces are about equal to 200 grams.

ounces: 0 2 4 6 8 10 12 14 16 18 20
grams: 0 100 200 300 400 500

Use the number line to give the approximate weight of each object.
Sample answers:

1. 15 ounces — About 425 grams
2. 16 ounces — About 455 grams
3. 100 grams — About $3\frac{1}{2}$ ounces
4. 500 grams — About $17\frac{1}{2}$ ounces

Use the number line to help you determine which object weighs more. Circle the heavier object.

5. 225 grams (circled); 2.3 ounces
6. 5 ounces; 454 grams (circled)

Math Journal 2, p. 287

Ongoing Assessment: Informing Instruction

Watch for students who do not notice that the ounces number line has a different scale than the grams number line. Have students cover the grams portion of the double-scale number line with a sheet of paper while they label the tick marks on the ounces number line. Then have them reverse the procedure.

Student Page

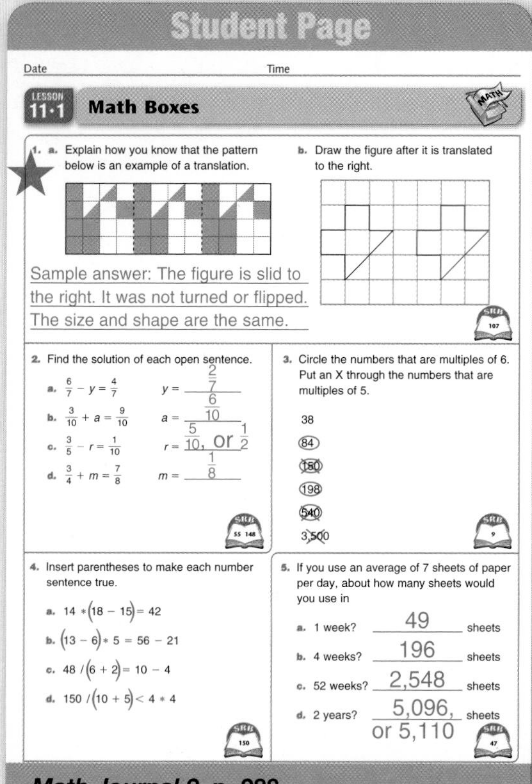
Date Time

LESSON 11·1 **Math Boxes**

1. a. Explain how you know that the pattern below is an example of a translation.

Sample answer: The figure is slid to the right. It was not turned or flipped. The size and shape are the same.

b. Draw the figure after it is translated to the right.

2. Find the solution of each open sentence.

a. $\frac{6}{7} - y = \frac{4}{7}$ $y = \frac{2}{7}$

b. $\frac{3}{10} + a = \frac{9}{10}$ $a = \frac{6}{10}$

c. $\frac{3}{5} - r = \frac{1}{10}$ $r = \frac{5}{10}$, or $\frac{1}{2}$

d. $\frac{3}{4} + m = \frac{7}{8}$ $m = \frac{1}{8}$

3. Circle the numbers that are multiples of 6. Put an X through the numbers that are multiples of 5.

38, (84), (150), (198), (540), 3,500

4. Insert parentheses to make each number sentence true.

a. 14 * (18 − 15) = 42

b. (13 − 6) * 5 = 56 − 21

c. 48 / (6 + 2) = 10 − 4

d. 150 / (10 + 5) < 4 * 4

5. If you use an average of 7 sheets of paper per day, about how many sheets would you use in

a. 1 week? 49 sheets

b. 4 weeks? 196 sheets

c. 52 weeks? 2,548 sheets

d. 2 years? 5,096, or 5,110 sheets

Math Journal 2, p. 288

Study Link Master

Name Date Time

STUDY LINK 11·1 **The World's Largest Foods**

Food	Weight	Date	Location
Apple	3 pounds 11 ounces	October 1997	Linton, England
Bagel	714 pounds	July 1998	Mattoon, Illinois
Bowl of pasta	7,355 pounds	February 2004	Hartford, New York
Chocolate bar	5,026 pounds	March 2000	Turin, Italy
Garlic	2 pounds 10 ounces	1985	Eureka, California
Gingerbread man	372.13 pounds	November 2003	Vancouver, Canada
Hamburger	6,040 pounds	September 1999	Sac, Montana
Ice cream sundae	22.59 tons	July 1988	Alberta, Canada
Pumpkin	1,337 pounds	October 2002	Topsfield, Massachusetts
Taco	1,654 pounds	March 2003	Mexicali, Mexico

Source: www.guinnessworldrecords.com

Use the information in the table to solve the following problems.

1. The largest apple weighed 59 ounces.

2. A typical hamburger weighs about 4 ounces. The largest hamburger weighed 96,640 ounces.

3. Which 2 foods together weigh about a ton? bagel and pumpkin Or, gingerbread man and taco

4. A kilogram is a little more than 2 pounds. Which 4 foods each weigh more than 1,000 kilograms? Pasta, chocolate bar, hamburger, ice cream sundae

5. On the back of this page, use data from the table to write and solve your own problem. Answers vary.

Practice

6. −\$75 + \$25 = −\$50

7. −\$75 = −\$45 + (−\$30)

8. \$0 = −\$60 + \$60

9. \$55 + (−\$25) = \$30

Math Masters, p. 327

2 Ongoing Learning & Practice

▶ Updating the World Tour

INDEPENDENT ACTIVITY

(*Math Journal 2,* pp. 329–331, 340, and 341; *Student Reference Book,* pp. 276, 277, 281, 292, 293, 297, and 302–305; *Math Masters,* pp. 419–421)

Social Studies Link Students follow the established World Tour routine:

▷ They update the Route Map by drawing a line segment connecting Beijing, China, and Mexico City, Mexico.

▷ They use the World Tour section of the *Student Reference Book* to locate facts about Mexico and Mexico City, and fill in the Country Notes pages for this country and capital.

▷ If they are keeping a Route Log, they update it.

▶ Math Boxes 11·1

(*Math Journal 2,* p. 288)

Mixed Practice Math Boxes in this lesson are paired with Math Boxes in Lesson 11-3. The skill in Problem 5 previews Unit 12 content.

Ongoing Assessment: Recognizing Student Achievement

Math Boxes Problem 1a ★

Use **Math Boxes, Problem 1a** to assess students' ability to describe a translation. Students are making adequate progress if they state that the pattern is an example of a translation because the original figure moved or slid to the right, without being turned or flipped, and that the size and shape of the figure remained the same. Some students might be able to sketch an example of a translation in Problem 1b.

[Geometry Goal 3]

▶ Study Link 11·1

(*Math Masters,* p. 327)

Home Connection Students convert among ounces, pounds, and tons as they solve problems involving some of the world's largest foods.

3 Differentiation Options

READINESS

SMALL-GROUP ACTIVITY

15–30 Min

Ordering Weights

(*Math Masters,* p. 389)

To explore estimating and ordering weights, have students hold and compare the weights of five objects and then place them in order from lightest to heaviest. Ask students to record the estimated order on an Exit Slip. Then have the group use a balance or scale to check their estimates and record the actual order and weights on the Exit Slip.

Discuss how this activity uses the force of gravity as a guide to ordering objects by weight. In the Space Shuttle, the objects would be weightless, but their masses would be the same as they are on Earth. Ask students how they might order a set of objects by mass in the Space Shuttle. Sample answer: One method would be to give each object a push to set it in motion. The more an object resists being set in motion, the more massive it is. So the harder an object is to push, the more mass it has.

EXTRA PRACTICE

SMALL-GROUP ACTIVITY

15–30 Min

Estimating Weights

To practice estimating weights of objects with and without tools, have students estimate the weights of objects by holding them and by comparing the weights to benchmarks. Then have students use a scale to determine the actual weight.

Consider having students do this activity in teams. Have students devise a scoring system to determine the winning team.

EXTRA PRACTICE

SMALL-GROUP ACTIVITY

5–15 Min

5-Minute Math

To offer students more experience with units of weight, see *5-Minute Math,* page 134.

Planning Ahead

Have models of the following geometric solids available for Lesson 11-2: rectangular prism, triangular prism, square pyramid, cylinder, cone, and sphere. Gather examples from everyday objects or make them from *Math Masters,* pages 449–451.

11·2 Geometric Solids

Objective To review the properties of common geometric solids.

Technology Resources www.everydaymathonline.com

ePresentations

eToolkit

Algorithms Practice

EM Facts Workshop Game™

Family Letters

Assessment Management

Common Core State Standards

Curriculum Focal Points

Interactive Teacher's Lesson Guide

1 Teaching the Lesson

Key Concepts and Skills

- Identify parallel and intersecting line segments and parallel planes. [Geometry Goal 1]
- Describe, compare, and classify plane and solid figures. [Geometry Goal 2]
- Identify congruent faces. [Geometry Goal 2]
- Construct a rectangular prism. [Geometry Goal 2]

Key Activities

Students review common geometric solids—including prisms, pyramids, cylinders, cones, and spheres—and investigate their properties. Students construct rectangular prisms using straws and twist-ties.

Ongoing Assessment: Recognizing Student Achievement Use journal page 290. [Geometry Goal 2]

Key Vocabulary

geometric solid ◆ rectangular prism ◆ cylinder ◆ triangular prism ◆ cone ◆ sphere ◆ square pyramid ◆ face ◆ congruent ◆ curved surface ◆ edge ◆ vertex (vertices) ◆ cube ◆ flat surface

Materials

Math Journal 2, pp. 289 and 290
Student Reference Book, p. 101
Study Link 11•1
models of geometric solids (See Planning Ahead in Lesson 11•1.) ◆ straws and twist-ties ◆ Class Data Pad (optional)

2 Ongoing Learning & Practice

Making a 1-Ounce Weight
Math Journal 2, p. 291
per group: balance or scale capable of measuring 1 ounce, pennies, nickels, dimes, and quarters
Students determine how many of each U.S. coin are needed to make a 1-ounce weight.

Math Boxes 11•2
Math Journal 2, p. 292
Students practice and maintain skills through Math Box problems.

Study Link 11•2
Math Masters, p. 328
Students practice and maintain skills through Study Link activities.

3 Differentiation Options

ENRICHMENT
Exploring Euler's Polyhedral Formula
Math Masters, p. 389
computer with Internet access
Students explore the relationships among the number of vertices, faces, and edges of polyhedrons.

EXTRA PRACTICE
Comparing Geometric Solids
Math Masters, p. 390
models of geometric solids
Students use a Venn diagram to compare geometric solids.

ELL SUPPORT
Creating a Word Wall
Students create a Word Wall of geometry vocabulary.

Advance Preparation

For Part 1, construct a cube with 16 twist-ties and 12 straws, all the same length. In four boxes, place enough twist-ties and full-size, $\frac{1}{2}$-size, and $\frac{3}{4}$-size straws so that each pair of students can have 16 twist-ties and 8 straws of each length.

***Teacher's Reference Manual,* Grades 4–6** pp. 42–44, 52, 187, 190–192

Getting Started

Mental Math and Reflexes

Write large numbers on the board, and have volunteers read them aloud. *Suggestions:*

●○○	●●○	●●●
7,540,312	43,290,517	1,206,598,346
2,560,371	831,247,906	2,165,307,498
16,436,280	372,815,206	172,039,598,563

Ask questions like the following:

- What is the value of the digit *x*?
- Which digit is in the millions place?

Math Message

Complete journal page 289.

Study Link 11·1 Follow-Up

Ask small groups of students to compare answers and to pose and solve the problems they created.

1 Teaching the Lesson

Math Message Follow-Up

WHOLE-CLASS ACTIVITY

ELL

(*Math Journal 2,* p. 289)

Display models of the six **geometric solids—rectangular prism, cylinder, triangular prism, cone, sphere,** and **square pyramid—**pictured on journal page 289.

Begin with the rectangular prism. To support English language learners, attach a tag and label it. Hold it up and ask the class to share examples of rectangular prisms in the classroom. You may wish to keep a list on the board or the Class Data Pad. Repeat this procedure for the remaining solids.

When all of the solids have been discussed, ask students the following questions:

- Which solids were easy to find? Probably the rectangular prism, cylinder, and sphere
- Which were hard to find? Probably the pyramid, triangular prism, and cone
- Why do you think some solids are more common than others? Probably because they are easier to make or are more useful for storing things

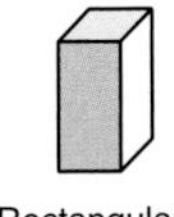
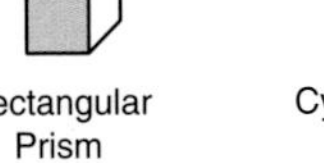

Rectangular Prism

Cylinder

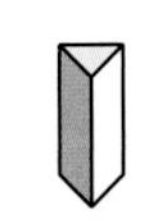

Triangular Prism

Cone

Sphere

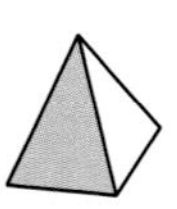

Square Pyramid

Pictures of geometric solids

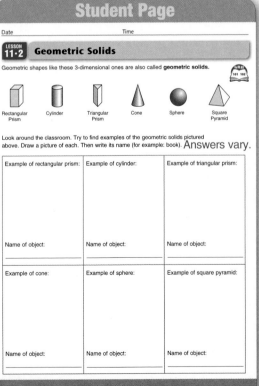

Student Page

Date Time

LESSON 11·2 **Geometric Solids**

Geometric shapes like these 3-dimensional ones are also called **geometric solids.** SRB 101 102

Rectangular Prism, Cylinder, Triangular Prism, Cone, Sphere, Square Pyramid

Look around the classroom. Try to find examples of the geometric solids pictured above. Draw a picture of each. Then write its name (for example: book). Answers vary.

Example of rectangular prism:	Example of cylinder:	Example of triangular prism:
Name of object:	Name of object:	Name of object:
Example of cone:	Example of sphere:	Example of square pyramid:
Name of object:	Name of object:	Name of object:

Math Journal 2, p. 289

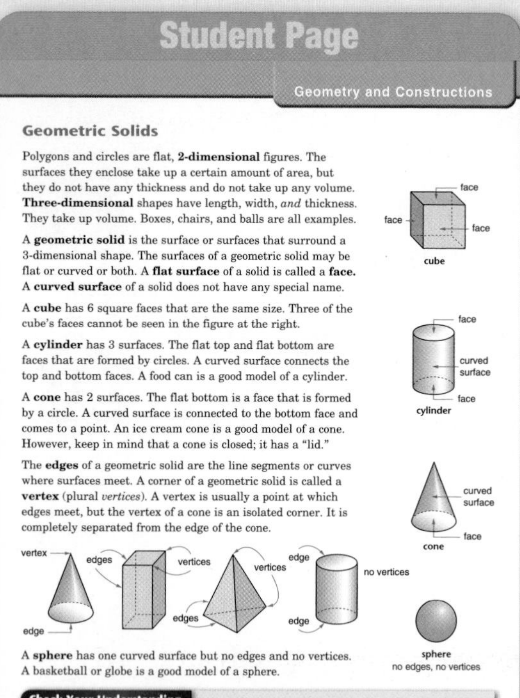

Student Page

Geometry and Constructions

Geometric Solids

Polygons and circles are flat, **2-dimensional** figures. The surfaces they enclose take up a certain amount of area, but they do not have any thickness and do not take up any volume. **Three-dimensional** shapes have length, width, *and* thickness. They take up volume. Boxes, chairs, and balls are all examples.

A **geometric solid** is the surface or surfaces that surround a 3-dimensional shape. The surfaces of a geometric solid may be flat or curved or both. A **flat surface** of a solid is called a **face.** A **curved surface** of a solid does not have any special name.

A **cube** has 6 square faces that are the same size. Three of the cube's faces cannot be seen in the figure at the right.

A **cylinder** has 3 surfaces. The flat top and flat bottom are faces that are formed by circles. A curved surface connects the top and bottom faces. A food can is a good model of a cylinder.

A **cone** has 2 surfaces. The flat bottom is a face that is formed by a circle. A curved surface is connected to the bottom face and comes to a point. An ice cream cone is a good model of a cone. However, keep in mind that a cone is closed; it has a "lid."

The **edges** of a geometric solid are the line segments or curves where surfaces meet. A corner of a geometric solid is called a **vertex** (plural *vertices*). A vertex is usually a point at which edges meet, but the vertex of a cone is an isolated corner. It is completely separated from the edge of the cone.

A **sphere** has one curved surface but no edges and no vertices. A basketball or globe is a good model of a sphere.

Check Your Understanding

1. **a.** How are cylinders and cones alike? **b.** How do they differ?
2. **a.** How are spheres and cones alike? **b.** How do they differ?

Check your answers on page 343.

Student Reference Book, **p. 101**

▶ Reviewing Vocabulary for Geometric Solids

WHOLE-CLASS DISCUSSION

ELL

(*Math Journal 2,* p. 289; *Student Reference Book,* p. 101)

Use the display models of the six geometric solids and *Student Reference Book,* page 101 to review vocabulary associated with geometric solids. To support English language learners, discuss the meaning of each term. Pose questions like the following:

- Which of these geometric solids has 6 **faces**? Rectangular prism
- Which solids have **congruent** faces? Rectangular prism, cylinder, triangular prism, square pyramid
- Which solids have a **curved surface**? Sphere, cone, and cylinder
- Which has the most **edges**? Rectangular prism
- Which two have the fewest **vertices** (corners)? Cylinder and sphere What is the singular form of the word *vertices*? vertex
- Which has two faces and one curved surface? cylinder

Have students look around the classroom and point out the faces, edges, and vertices of objects that have shapes similar to those in the display.

Links to the Future

Encourage students to use the geometry vocabulary, but do not expect them to be precise at this time.

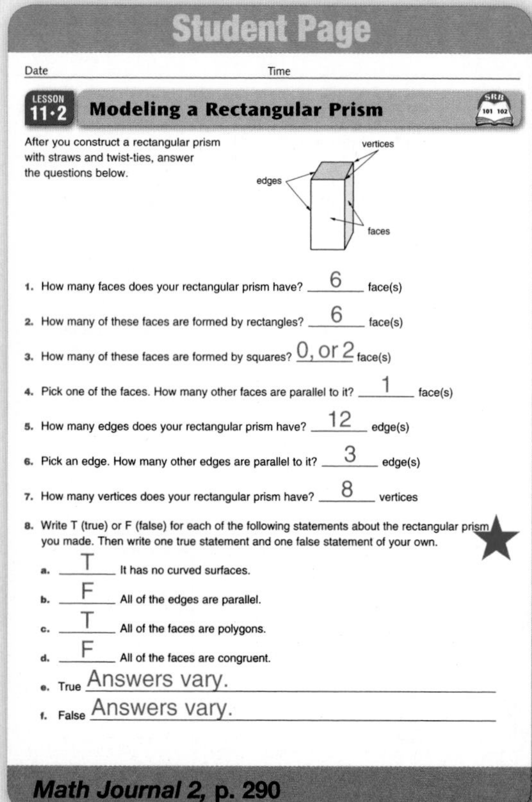

Student Page

Date Time

LESSON 11·2 **Modeling a Rectangular Prism**

SRB 101 102

After you construct a rectangular prism with straws and twist-ties, answer the questions below.

1. How many faces does your rectangular prism have? 6 face(s)
2. How many of these faces are formed by rectangles? 6 face(s)
3. How many of these faces are formed by squares? 0, or 2 face(s)
4. Pick one of the faces. How many other faces are parallel to it? 1 face(s)
5. How many edges does your rectangular prism have? 12 edge(s)
6. Pick an edge. How many other edges are parallel to it? 3 edge(s)
7. How many vertices does your rectangular prism have? 8 vertices
8. Write T (true) or F (false) for each of the following statements about the rectangular prism you made. Then write one true statement and one false statement of your own.
   a. T It has no curved surfaces.
   b. F All of the edges are parallel.
   c. T All of the faces are polygons.
   d. F All of the faces are congruent.
   e. True Answers vary.
   f. False Answers vary.

Math Journal 2, **p. 290**

▶ Modeling Geometric Solids

PARTNER ACTIVITY

PROBLEM SOLVING

(*Math Journal 2,* p. 290)

Show the class the **cube** you constructed out of straws. (*See Advance Preparation.*) Point out that it shows only the edges of the faces. It is a "frame" for the geometric solid; the **flat surfaces** of the cube must be imagined.

Ask students what geometric solid this construction represents. Cube, or rectangular prism Demonstrate how the vertices are put together.

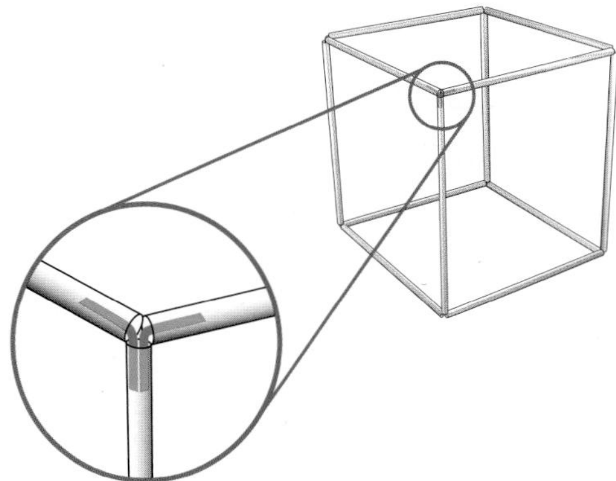

Cube made out of straws and twist-ties

Distribute straws and twist-ties. (*See Advance Preparation.*) Have partners work together to make a rectangular prism. One way is to start with a rectangle and build up. Have the straw cube, as well as other models of rectangular prisms, available for inspection. When their rectangular prism is finished, partners should complete journal page 290.

NOTE Problem 3 on journal page 290 asks students to identify the number of square faces in the rectangular prisms they have made. Depending on the straw sizes used, the prisms will have either 0 or 2 square faces. Students cannot construct cubes (which have 6 square faces) because they have only 8 straws of each length per partnership.

Ongoing Assessment: Recognizing Student Achievement

Journal page 290 Problem 8

Use **journal page 290, Problem 8** to assess students' ability to describe a rectangular prism. Students are making adequate progress if they are able to correctly identify the given statements as true or false and write their own true and false statements. Some students may write statements that involve comparisons among geometric solids.

[Geometry Goal 2]

2 Ongoing Learning & Practice

Making a 1-Ounce Weight

SMALL-GROUP ACTIVITY

(*Math Journal 2,* p. 291)

Students use a balance or scale to determine how many of each available type of U.S. coin are needed to make a 1-ounce weight. Students can display the results of their experiments in the Gram & Ounce Museum.

Student Page

Date Time

Making a 1-Ounce Weight

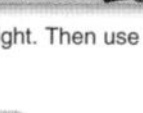

1. Estimate how many of each coin you think it will take to make a 1-ounce weight. Then use a balance or scale to determine exactly how many of each coin are needed.

Coin	Estimated Number of Coins	Actual Number of Coins
penny	Answers vary.	11 or 12
nickel		5 or 6
dime		12 or 13
quarter		5

2. Describe how you estimated how many of each coin it might take to make a 1-ounce weight.
Sample answer: I know there are about 28 g in 1 ounce, and a nickel weighs 5 g. Therefore, 6 nickels should weigh 30 g ($5 * 6 = 30$), so 6 nickels equal about 1 ounce. I estimate that pennies weigh $\frac{1}{2}$ as much as nickels, so it should take twice as many pennies, which is 12. Dimes are smaller than pennies, so I guessed 15 dimes. Quarters are heavier than nickels, so I guessed 4.

Try This

3. About what fraction of an ounce does each coin weigh? Sample answers:
1 penny = $\frac{1}{12}$ oz 1 nickel = $\frac{1}{6}$ oz 1 dime = $\frac{1}{13}$ oz 1 quarter = $\frac{1}{5}$ oz

Explain how you found your answers.
Sample answer: I used the number of coins that equal 1 oz as the denominator. For example, because 12 pennies equal 1 oz, 1 penny equals $\frac{1}{12}$ oz.

Math Journal 2, p. 291

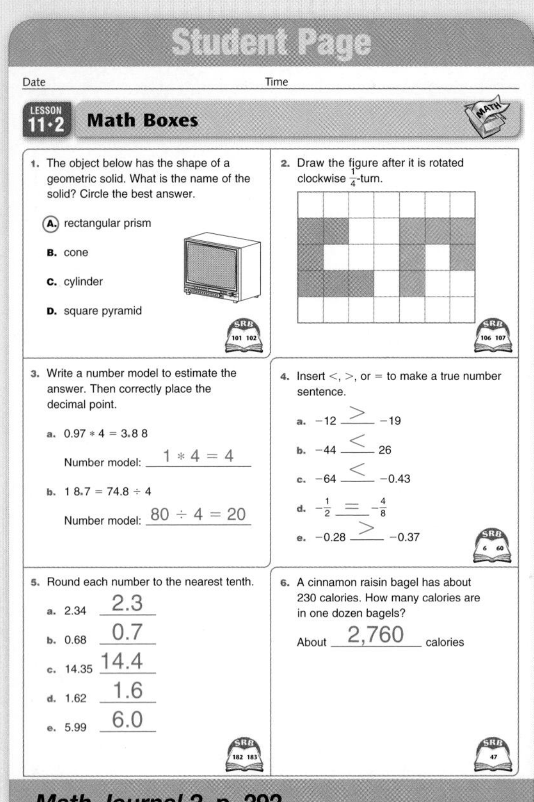
Student Page

Date Time

LESSON 11·2 Math Boxes

1. The object below has the shape of a geometric solid. What is the name of the solid? Circle the best answer.

(A.) rectangular prism
B. cone
C. cylinder
D. square pyramid

SRB 101 102

2. Draw the figure after it is rotated clockwise $\frac{1}{4}$-turn.

SRB 106 107

3. Write a number model to estimate the answer. Then correctly place the decimal point.

a. 0.97 ∗ 4 = 3.8 8
Number model: 1 ∗ 4 = 4

b. 1 8.7 = 74.8 ÷ 4
Number model: 80 ÷ 4 = 20

4. Insert <, >, or = to make a true number sentence.

a. −12 > −19
b. −44 < 26
c. −64 < −0.43
d. $-\frac{1}{2}$ = $-\frac{4}{8}$
e. −0.28 > −0.37

SRB 6 60

5. Round each number to the nearest tenth.

a. 2.34 2.3
b. 0.68 0.7
c. 14.35 14.4
d. 1.62 1.6
e. 5.99 6.0

SRB 182 183

6. A cinnamon raisin bagel has about 230 calories. How many calories are in one dozen bagels?

About 2,760 calories

SRB 47

Math Journal 2, p. 292

▶ Math Boxes 11·2

INDEPENDENT ACTIVITY

(*Math Journal 2,* p. 292)

Mixed Practice Math Boxes in this lesson are linked with Math Boxes in Lessons 11-4 and 11-6. The skills in Problems 5 and 6 preview Unit 12 content.

Writing/Reasoning Have students write a response to the following: *For Problem 6, how would you determine the number of calories in $3\frac{1}{2}$ bagels?* Sample answer: Multiply the number of calories in 1 bagel by 3; 230 ∗ 3 = 690. Then divide the number of calories in 1 bagel by 2; 230 / 2 = 115. Add the quotient to the number of calories in 3 bagels; 115 + 690 = 805.

▶ Study Link 11·2

(*Math Masters,* p. 328)

Home Connection Students identify geometric solids represented by various objects. They also identify the vertices and the number of edges in two geometric solids.

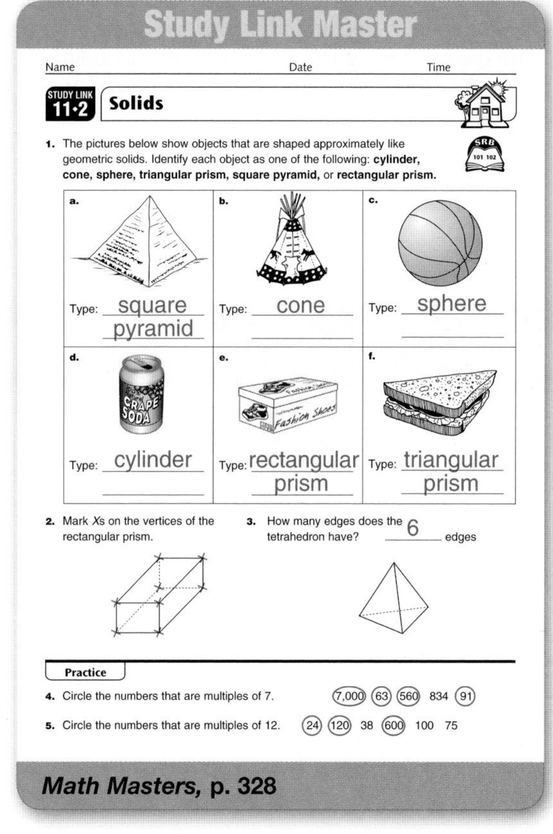
Study Link Master

Name Date Time

STUDY LINK 11·2 Solids

1. The pictures below show objects that are shaped approximately like geometric solids. Identify each object as one of the following: **cylinder, cone, sphere, triangular prism, square pyramid,** or **rectangular prism.**

SRB 101 102

a. Type: square pyramid	b. Type: cone	c. Type: sphere
d. Type: cylinder	e. Type: rectangular prism	f. Type: triangular prism

2. Mark Xs on the vertices of the rectangular prism.

3. How many edges does the tetrahedron have? 6 edges

Practice

4. Circle the numbers that are multiples of 7. (7,000) (63) (560) 834 (91)

5. Circle the numbers that are multiples of 12. (24) (120) 38 (600) 100 75

Math Masters, p. 328

3 Differentiation Options

ENRICHMENT

INDEPENDENT ACTIVITY

Exploring Euler's Polyhedral Formula

15–30 Min

(*Math Masters,* p. 389)

Technology Link To apply students' ability to describe solid figures, have them explore the relationships among vertices, edges, and faces of polyhedrons at http://nlvm.usu.edu/en/nav/frames_asid_128_g_2_t_3.html?open=instructions.

On an Exit Slip, ask students to record their observations and draw a conclusion. Sample answer: The sum of the numbers of faces and vertices is 2 more than the number of edges: $E + 2 = F + V$.

Euler's polyhedral formula states that the number of vertices minus the number of edges plus the number of faces is always equal to 2.
$V - E + F = 2$

NOTE The Web site is part of the National Library of Virtual Manipulatives for Interactive Mathematics developed by Utah State University. See http://nlvm.usu.edu.

EXTRA PRACTICE

Comparing Geometric Solids

(*Math Masters,* p. 390)

To practice comparing the attributes of solid figures, have students choose two geometric solids and use them to complete the Venn diagram on *Math Masters,* page 390.

ELL SUPPORT

Creating a Word Wall

To provide language support for geometry vocabulary, have students illustrate definitions of key geometric terms for a classroom display.

NOTE It might appear that there is an overwhelming number of geometry terms to know and understand. Each of these terms should be discussed in the context of solving problems and should relate to students' experiences. Teaching these terms in isolation or reducing them to a vocabulary list that needs to be memorized will not produce successful results in most cases. Students should have opportunities to work with each of these terms, build models of them, write them, and discuss them.

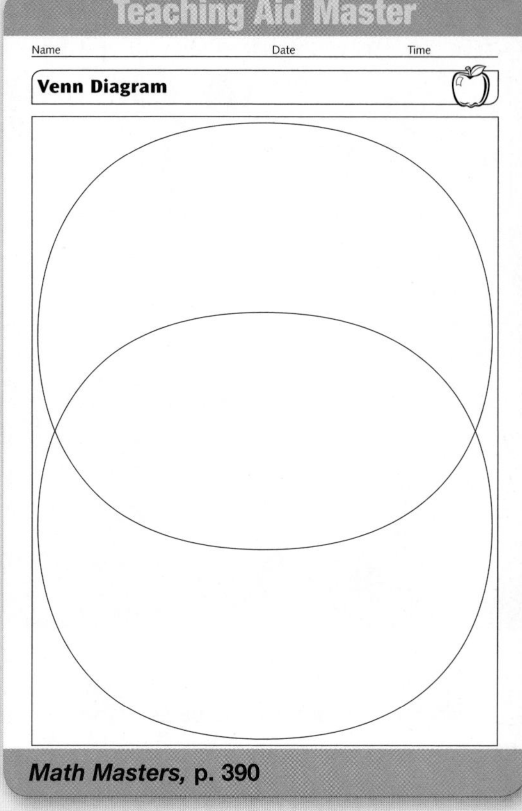

Math Masters, p. 390

11•3 Constructing Geometric Solids

Objectives To provide practice identifying geometric solids given their properties; and to guide the construction of polyhedrons.

Technology Resources www.everydaymathonline.com

ePresentations

eToolkit

Algorithms Practice

EM Facts Workshop Game™

Family Letters

Assessment Management

Common Core State Standards

Curriculum Focal Points

Interactive Teacher's Lesson Guide

1 Teaching the Lesson

Key Concepts and Skills

- Identify parallel and intersecting line segments and parallel faces. [Geometry Goal 1]
- Describe, compare, and classify plane and solid figures. [Geometry Goal 2]
- Identify congruent faces. [Geometry Goal 2]
- Construct polyhedrons; sketch two-dimensional representations of polyhedrons. [Geometry Goal 2]

Key Activities

Students practice identifying geometric solids by solving riddles about their properties. Students construct polyhedrons with straws and twist-ties. Students explore ways to draw a cube.

Key Vocabulary

pyramid ◆ prism ◆ polyhedron ◆ regular polyhedron ◆ triangular pyramid ◆ tetrahedron ◆ dodecahedron

Materials

Math Journal 2, pp. 293–295
Student Reference Book, p. 102
Study Link 11•2
Math Masters, pp. 452 and 453 (optional)
models of geometric solids (See Planning Ahead in Lesson 11•1.) ◆ straws and twist-ties (See Lesson 11•2.) ◆ blank paper ◆ straightedge ◆ transparent tape ◆ slate ◆ set of polyhedral dice (optional) ◆ dictionary (optional)

2 Ongoing Learning & Practice

Plotting Book Heights

Math Journal 2, pp. 295A and 295B
Students plot book heights on a line plot.

Math Boxes 11•3

Math Journal 2, p. 296
Students practice and maintain skills through Math Box problems.

Ongoing Assessment: Recognizing Student Achievement

Use Math Boxes, Problem 3a.
[Number and Numeration Goal 3]

Study Link 11•3

Math Masters, p. 329
Students practice and maintain skills through Study Link activities.

3 Differentiation Options

READINESS

Sorting Geometric Solids

30 objects of various shapes
Students sort common objects by their properties.

ENRICHMENT

Creating Cube Nets

Math Masters, pp. 389 and 444
scissors
Students find all possible cube nets.

EXTRA PRACTICE

Taking a 50-Facts Test

Math Masters, pp. 411 and 414; p. 416 (optional)
pen or colored pencil
Students take a 50-facts test. They use a line graph to record individual and optional class scores.

Advance Preparation

For Part 1, you need the geometric solids from Lesson 11•2, plus a triangular pyramid and a cube. Use everyday objects or make them from *Math Masters,* pages 452 and 453. For the optional Readiness activity in Part 3, use cans, egg cartons, party hats, paper cups, tubes, and boxes.

***Teacher's Reference Manual,* Grades 4–6** pp. 187–189

Getting Started

Mental Math and Reflexes

Pose problems involving the multiplication of a fraction by a whole number. Have students find each product. *Suggestions:*

●○○	●●○	●●●
$4 * \frac{1}{2} = 2$	$5 * \frac{3}{5} = 3$	$5 * \frac{1}{2} = 2\frac{1}{2}$
$24 * \frac{1}{8} = 3$	$9 * \frac{2}{3} = 6$	$14 * \frac{1}{3} = 4\frac{2}{3}$
$30 * \frac{1}{6} = 5$	$16 * \frac{3}{4} = 12$	$10 * \frac{3}{4} = 7\frac{2}{4}$, or $7\frac{1}{2}$

Math Message

Open your Student Reference Book *to page 102. Solve the following riddle: I have the same number of faces as vertices. What am I?*

Study Link 11·2 Follow-Up

Have partners compare answers. Ask:

- How many pairs of parallel faces does the rectangular prism have? 3
- How many pairs of parallel faces does the tetrahedron have? 0

1 Teaching the Lesson

▶ Math Message Follow-Up

WHOLE-CLASS DISCUSSION

(*Student Reference Book,* p. 102)

All of the **pyramids** shown at the top of page 102 of the *Student Reference Book* have the same number of faces as vertices. Pyramids are named for the shape of their base. All of the remaining faces are triangles that meet at a vertex.

Pose another riddle: *I have 6 faces. All of my faces are rectangles. What am I?* Rectangular prism **Prisms** are named for the shape of their two parallel bases. Emphasize that a **polyhedron** (plural *polyhedrons* or *polyhedra*) is a geometric solid whose surfaces are all formed by polygons. A polyhedron does not have any curved surfaces.

Display the six geometric solids from Lesson 11-2 and the triangular pyramid and cube. Ask: *Which of these solids are NOT polyhedrons?* Cylinder, sphere, cone

A polyhedron is a **regular polyhedron** if

▷ each face is formed by a regular polygon;

▷ the faces all have the same size and shape; and

▷ each vertex looks exactly the same as every other vertex.

Ask: *Which of these solids are regular polyhedrons?* Cube and **triangular pyramid,** or **tetrahedron**

NOTE *Triangular pyramid* and *tetrahedron* are two names for the same geometric solid. When people refer to a tetrahedron, they often mean a regular tetrahedron. Not all tetrahedrons (triangular pyramids) are regular, however.

Student Page

Geometry and Constructions

Polyhedrons

A **polyhedron** is a geometric solid whose surfaces are all formed by polygons. These surfaces are the faces of the polyhedron. A polyhedron does not have any curved surfaces.

Pyramids and **prisms** are two important kinds of polyhedrons.

Did You Know?
A rhombicuboctahedron has 26 faces. Eighteen of them are squares and 8 are triangles.

Polyhedrons That Are Pyramids

base — triangular pyramid; base — square pyramid; base — pentagonal pyramid; base — hexagonal pyramid

The shaded face of each pyramid above is called the **base** of the pyramid. The shape of the base is used to name the pyramid. For example, the base of a square pyramid has a square shape. The faces of a pyramid that are not the base are all shaped like triangles and meet at the same vertex.

Polyhedrons That Are Prisms

base, base — triangular prism; base, base — rectangular prism; base, base — pentagonal prism; base, base — hexagonal prism

The two shaded faces of each prism above are called the **bases** of the prism. The bases of a prism are the same size and shape. They are parallel. All other faces join the bases and are shaped like parallelograms.

The shape of the bases of a prism is used to name the prism. For example, the bases of a pentagonal prism have the shape of a pentagon.

Many polyhedrons are not pyramids or prisms. Some are illustrated below.

Polyhedrons That Are NOT Pyramids or Prisms

Student Reference Book, p. 102

Adjusting the Activity

Distribute a set of polyhedral dice. Ask students to find the name of each die and determine the die that is not a regular polyhedron. The names of the dice are as follows: tetrahedron, octahedron, decahedron, dodecahedron, icosahedron. The decahedron is not a regular polygon because its faces are not regular polygons.

AUDITORY ◆ KINESTHETIC ◆ TACTILE ◆ VISUAL

▶ Solving Geometry Riddles

WHOLE-CLASS ACTIVITY

Tell students that in this lesson they will explore the properties of polyhedrons by solving more riddles like the one in the Math Message.

Pose additional riddles for students to solve. You might read one clue at a time and have students guess each time. When all clues have been given, ask a student to come up and display the correct solid, or a picture of it in the *Student Reference Book,* and name it. Ask the student to explain why it is that particular solid.

Language Arts Link Consider having students look up the word parts *tetra-, -hedron, poly-, octa-, deca-,* and *dodeca-* in the dictionary to give them a better understanding of the origins and meanings of geometric terms.

Riddle 1

I am a geometric solid.
I have six faces.
All of my faces are squares.
What am I? cube

Riddle 2

I am a geometric solid.
I have two surfaces.
My base is formed by a circle.
I come to a point at the top.
What am I? cone

Riddle 3

I am a polyhedron.
I have the fewest number of faces of all the polyhedrons.
All of my faces are triangular.
I come to a point at the top.
What am I? Triangular pyramid, or tetrahedron

Riddle 4

I am a polyhedron.
My faces are pentagons.
I am useful for calendars.
My picture is on page 103 of the *Student Reference Book.*
What am I? dodecahedron

Student Page

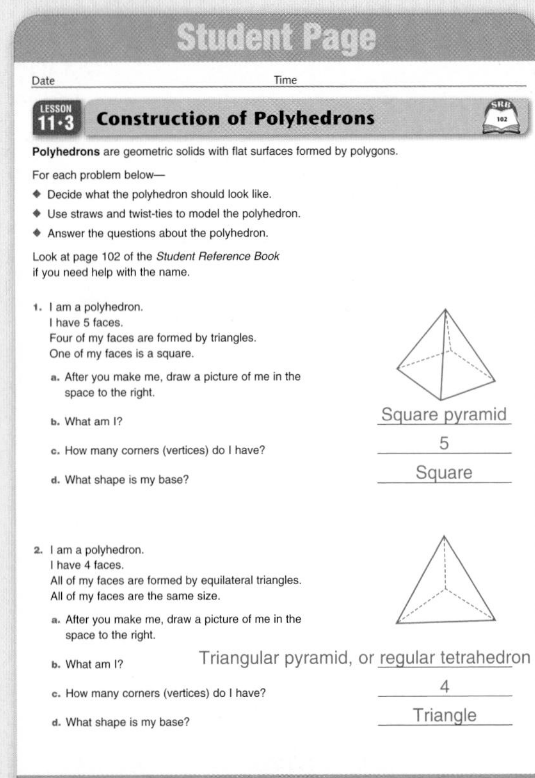
Date Time

LESSON 11·3 **Construction of Polyhedrons** SRB 102

Polyhedrons are geometric solids with flat surfaces formed by polygons.

For each problem below—
- Decide what the polyhedron should look like.
- Use straws and twist-ties to model the polyhedron.
- Answer the questions about the polyhedron.

Look at page 102 of the *Student Reference Book* if you need help with the name.

1. I am a polyhedron.
I have 5 faces.
Four of my faces are formed by triangles.
One of my faces is a square.
   a. After you make me, draw a picture of me in the space to the right.
   b. What am I? Square pyramid
   c. How many corners (vertices) do I have? 5
   d. What shape is my base? Square

2. I am a polyhedron.
I have 4 faces.
All of my faces are formed by equilateral triangles.
All of my faces are the same size.
   a. After you make me, draw a picture of me in the space to the right.
   b. What am I? Triangular pyramid, or regular tetrahedron
   c. How many corners (vertices) do I have? 4
   d. What shape is my base? Triangle

Math Journal 2, p. 293

Riddle 5

I am a polyhedron.
I have two triangular bases.
My other faces are rectangles.
Sometimes I am used for keeping doors open.
What am I? Triangular prism

Riddle 6

I am a geometric solid.
I have only one surface.
My one surface is curved.
I have no base.
What am I? sphere

Using Straws and Twist-Ties to Model Polyhedrons

(*Math Journal 2,* p. 293)

Remind students how the straws and twist-ties were used to make frames for cubes and rectangular prisms in Lesson 11-2. Students should work with partners to construct polyhedrons and answer the riddles on journal page 293. Although students' constructions might differ in size, the shapes should have the same properties.

Drawing Cube Models

(*Math Journal 2,* pp. 294 and 295)

Have students follow the directions on journal pages 294 and 295 to draw cubes in three different ways. Tell students to practice on blank paper and then tape their best example of each method on the bottom of journal page 295. Ask students to share any other method they use to draw a cube.

2 Ongoing Learning & Practice

Plotting Book Heights

INDEPENDENT ACTIVITY

(*Math Journal 2,* pp. 295A and 295B)

Students plot book heights in fractions of an inch on a line plot. Then they use the line plot to solve fraction and mixed-number addition and subtraction problems.

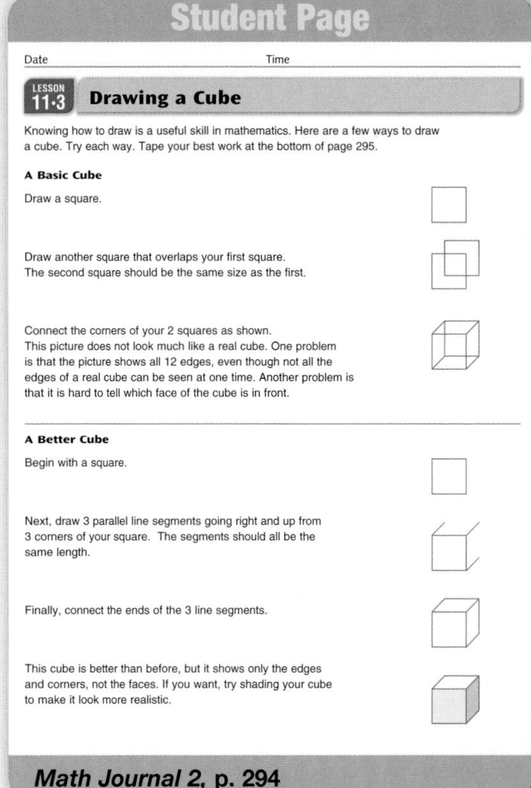

Student Page

Date Time

LESSON 11·3 **Drawing a Cube**

Knowing how to draw is a useful skill in mathematics. Here are a few ways to draw a cube. Try each way. Tape your best work at the bottom of page 295.

A Basic Cube

Draw a square.

Draw another square that overlaps your first square. The second square should be the same size as the first.

Connect the corners of your 2 squares as shown. This picture does not look much like a real cube. One problem is that the picture shows all 12 edges, even though not all the edges of a real cube can be seen at one time. Another problem is that it is hard to tell which face of the cube is in front.

A Better Cube

Begin with a square.

Next, draw 3 parallel line segments going right and up from 3 corners of your square. The segments should all be the same length.

Finally, connect the ends of the 3 line segments.

This cube is better than before, but it shows only the edges and corners, not the faces. If you want, try shading your cube to make it look more realistic.

***Math Journal 2,* p. 294**

If possible, have several geometric solids available for students to handle as they work in their journals.

AUDITORY ◆ KINESTHETIC ◆ TACTILE ◆ VISUAL

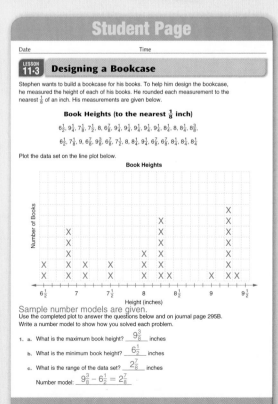

Student Page

Date Time

LESSON 11·3 **Designing a Bookcase**

Stephen wants to build a bookcase for his books. To help him design the bookcase, he measured the height of each of his books. He rounded each measurement to the nearest $\frac{1}{8}$ of an inch. His measurements are given below.

Book Heights (to the nearest $\frac{1}{8}$ inch)

$6\frac{1}{2}, 9\frac{1}{4}, 7\frac{1}{8}, 7\frac{1}{2}, 8, 6\frac{7}{8}, 9\frac{1}{4}, 9\frac{1}{4}, 9\frac{1}{4}, 9\frac{1}{4}, 9\frac{1}{4}, 8\frac{1}{4}, 8, 8\frac{1}{4}, 8\frac{3}{8},$

$6\frac{1}{2}, 7\frac{1}{8}, 9, 6\frac{7}{8}, 9\frac{3}{8}, 6\frac{7}{8}, 7\frac{1}{2}, 8, 8\frac{1}{4}, 9\frac{1}{4}, 6\frac{7}{8}, 6\frac{7}{8}, 8\frac{1}{4}, 8\frac{1}{4}, 8\frac{1}{4}$

Plot the data set on the line plot below.

Book Heights

Number of Books

$6\frac{1}{2}$ 7 $7\frac{1}{2}$ 8 $8\frac{1}{2}$ 9 $9\frac{1}{2}$

Height (inches)

Sample number models are given.

Use the completed plot to answer the questions below and on journal page 295B. Write a number model to show how you solved each problem.

1. a. What is the maximum book height? $9\frac{3}{8}$ inches

b. What is the minimum book height? $6\frac{1}{2}$ inches

c. What is the range of the data set? $2\frac{7}{8}$ inches

Number model: $9\frac{3}{8} - 6\frac{1}{2} = 2\frac{7}{8}$

***Math Journal 2,* p. 295A**

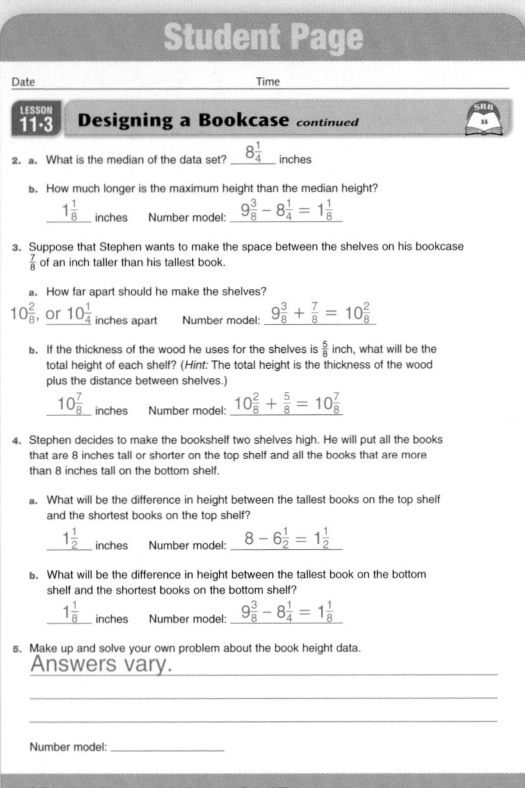

Student Page

Date Time

LESSON 11·3 **Designing a Bookcase** *continued*

2. a. What is the median of the data set? $8\frac{1}{4}$ inches

b. How much longer is the maximum height than the median height?

$1\frac{1}{8}$ inches Number model: $9\frac{3}{8} - 8\frac{1}{4} = 1\frac{1}{8}$

3. Suppose that Stephen wants to make the space between the shelves on his bookcase $\frac{7}{8}$ of an inch taller than his tallest book.

a. How far apart should he make the shelves?

$10\frac{2}{8}$, or $10\frac{1}{4}$ inches apart Number model: $9\frac{3}{8} + \frac{7}{8} = 10\frac{2}{8}$

b. If the thickness of the wood he uses for the shelves is $\frac{5}{8}$ inch, what will be the total height of each shelf? (*Hint:* The total height is the thickness of the wood plus the distance between shelves.)

$10\frac{7}{8}$ inches Number model: $10\frac{2}{8} + \frac{5}{8} = 10\frac{7}{8}$

4. Stephen decides to make the bookshelf two shelves high. He will put all the books that are 8 inches tall or shorter on the top shelf and all the books that are more than 8 inches tall on the bottom shelf.

a. What will be the difference in height between the tallest books on the top shelf and the shortest books on the top shelf?

$1\frac{1}{2}$ inches Number model: $8 - 6\frac{1}{2} = 1\frac{1}{2}$

b. What will be the difference in height between the tallest book on the bottom shelf and the shortest books on the bottom shelf?

$1\frac{1}{8}$ inches Number model: $9\frac{3}{8} - 8\frac{1}{4} = 1\frac{1}{8}$

5. Make up and solve your own problem about the book height data.

Answers vary.

Number model: ______

Math Journal 2, p. 295B

Math Boxes 11·3

(*Math Journal 2,* p. 296)

Mixed Practice Math Boxes in this lesson are paired with Math Boxes in Lesson 11-1. The skill in Problem 5 previews Unit 12 content.

Ongoing Assessment: Recognizing Student Achievement

Math Boxes Problem 3a

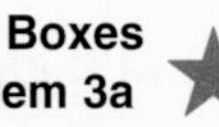

Use **Math Boxes, Problem 3a** to assess students' ability to find multiples of whole numbers less than 10. Students are making adequate progress if they are able to name the first ten multiples of 6. Some students might be able to solve Problem 3b, which involves finding multiples of whole numbers greater than 10.

[Number and Numeration Goal 3]

Study Link 11·3

INDEPENDENT ACTIVITY

(*Math Masters,* p. 329)

Home Connection Students solve riddles about geometric solids.

3 Differentiation Options

READINESS

SMALL-GROUP ACTIVITY

Sorting Geometric Solids

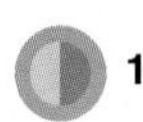

15–30 Min

To investigate attributes of geometric solids, have students sort common household items into groups based on appearance and discuss how the objects in each group are the same and how they are different. Then have one student sort the items according to a different attribute and ask the other students to determine how they were sorted.

Finally, have students sort the objects by use. Ask questions such as the following:

- Which containers would be easiest to pack together in a box?
- Why might containers for liquids and dry materials have different shapes?
- Why might the word *container* be a good description for most of the objects?

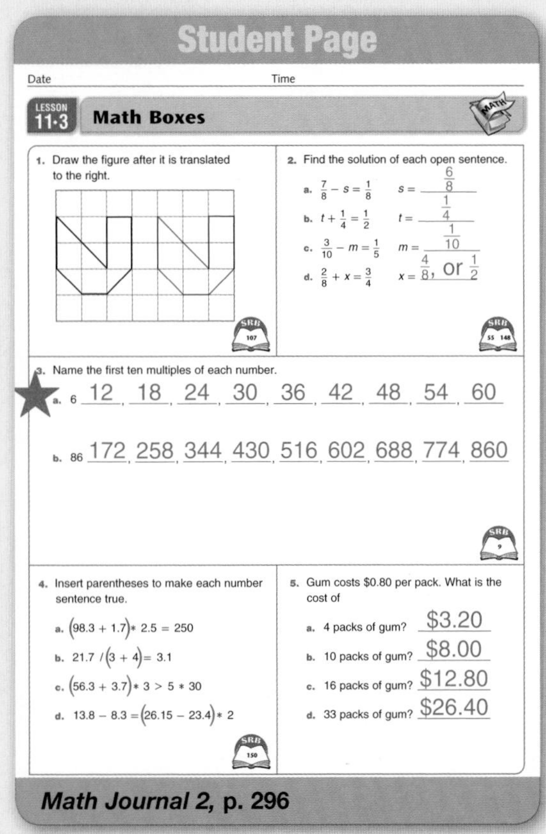

Student Page

Date Time

LESSON 11·3 **Math Boxes**

1. Draw the figure after it is translated to the right.

2. Find the solution of each open sentence.

a. $\frac{7}{8} - s = \frac{1}{8}$ $s = \frac{6}{8}$

b. $t + \frac{1}{4} = \frac{1}{2}$ $t = \frac{1}{4}$

c. $\frac{3}{10} - m = \frac{1}{5}$ $m = \frac{1}{10}$

d. $\frac{2}{8} + x = \frac{3}{4}$ $x = \frac{4}{8}$, or $\frac{1}{2}$

3. Name the first ten multiples of each number.

a. 6 12, 18, 24, 30, 36, 42, 48, 54, 60

b. 86 172, 258, 344, 430, 516, 602, 688, 774, 860

4. Insert parentheses to make each number sentence true.

a. (98.3 + 1.7) ∗ 2.5 = 250

b. 21.7 / (3 + 4) = 3.1

c. (56.3 + 3.7) ∗ 3 > 5 ∗ 30

d. 13.8 – 8.3 = (26.15 – 23.4) ∗ 2

5. Gum costs $0.80 per pack. What is the cost of

a. 4 packs of gum? $3.20

b. 10 packs of gum? $8.00

c. 16 packs of gum? $12.80

d. 33 packs of gum? $26.40

Math Journal 2, p. 296

ENRICHMENT

SMALL-GROUP ACTIVITY

Creating Cube Nets

15–30 Min

(*Math Masters,* pp. 389 and 444)

To apply students' understanding of attributes of geometric solids, have them find all possible *nets,* or patterns of squares that can be folded to form a cube. (*See margin.*) Students should record their nets on 1-inch grid paper (*Math Masters,* page 444).

Students should eliminate any nets that are duplicates when reflected or rotated in their unfolded state.

Eleven nets are possible:

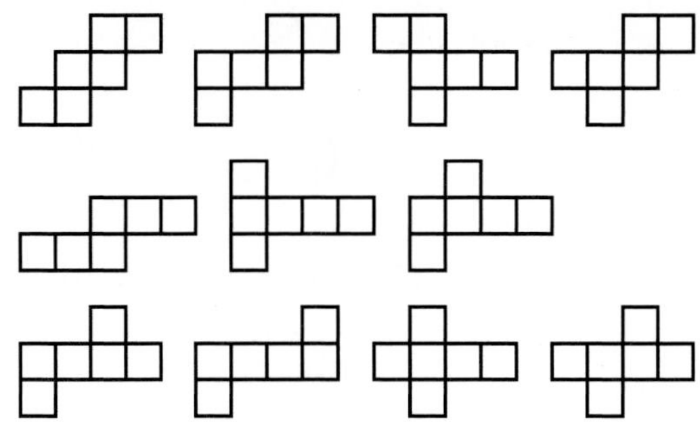

On an Exit Slip, have students describe common features of nets that will and will not result in cubes. Sample answer: Nets that will result in cubes have 6 squares and 14 sides. Nets that will not result in cubes have fewer than 6 squares, have 4 squares that share a single vertex, or have more than 4 squares in a single row.

EXTRA PRACTICE

SMALL-GROUP ACTIVITY

Taking a 50-Facts Test

5–15 Min

(*Math Masters,* pp. 411, 414, and 416)

See Lesson 3-4 for details regarding the administration of a 50-facts test and the recording and graphing of individual and optional class results.

Study Link Master

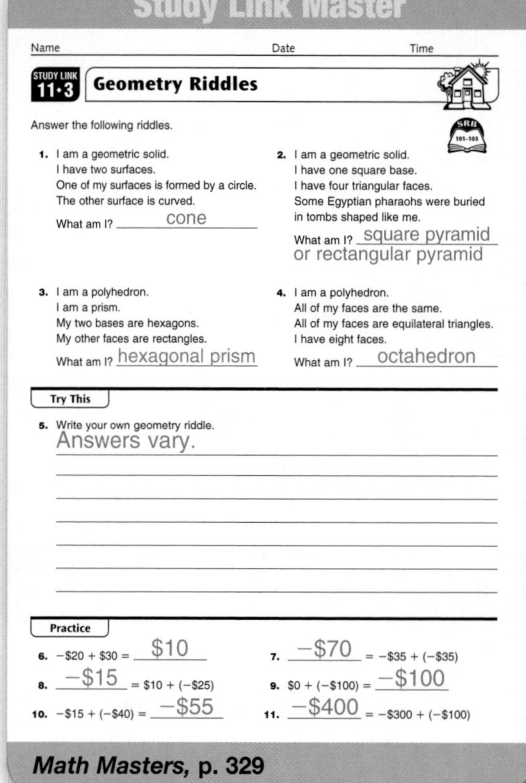

Name ______ Date ______ Time ______

STUDY LINK 11•3 **Geometry Riddles**

Answer the following riddles.

1. I am a geometric solid.
I have two surfaces.
One of my surfaces is formed by a circle.
The other surface is curved.
What am I? cone

2. I am a geometric solid.
I have one square base.
I have four triangular faces.
Some Egyptian pharaohs were buried in tombs shaped like me.
What am I? square pyramid or rectangular pyramid

3. I am a polyhedron.
I am a prism.
My two bases are hexagons.
My other faces are rectangles.
What am I? hexagonal prism

4. I am a polyhedron.
All of my faces are the same.
All of my faces are equilateral triangles.
I have eight faces.
What am I? octahedron

Try This

5. Write your own geometry riddle.
Answers vary.

Practice

6. −\$20 + \$30 = \$10
7. −\$70 = −\$35 + (−\$35)
8. −\$15 = \$10 + (−\$25)
9. \$0 + (−\$100) = −\$100
10. −\$15 + (−\$40) = −\$55
11. −\$400 = −\$300 + (−\$100)

Math Masters, p. 329

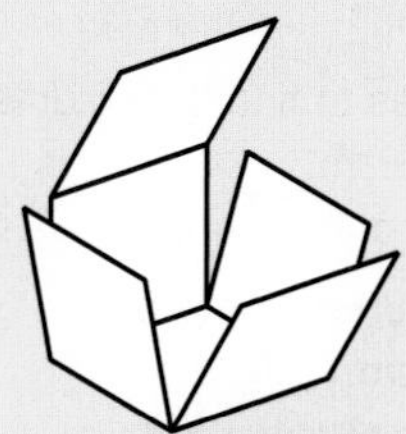

Folding a net to form a cube

11•4 A Volume Exploration

Objective To review concepts and units of volume.

www.everydaymathonline.com

ePresentations

eToolkit

Algorithms Practice

EM Facts Workshop Game™

Family Letters

Assessment Management

Common Core State Standards

Curriculum Focal Points

Interactive Teacher's Lesson Guide

1 Teaching the Lesson

Key Concepts and Skills

- Use multiplication to solve volume problems. [Operations and Computation Goal 3]
- Find the area of the base of a rectangular prism. [Measurement and Reference Frames Goal 2]
- Count unit cubes to find the volume of a rectangular prism. [Measurement and Reference Frames Goal 2]
- Calculate the surface area of a rectangular prism. [Measurement and Reference Frames Goal 2]
- Write number models with parentheses. [Patterns, Functions, and Algebra Goal 3]

Key Activities

Students use base-10 blocks and metersticks to visualize the sizes of metric cubic units. They make and fill open boxes with centimeter cubes to determine their volume.

Ongoing Assessment: Recognizing Student Achievement Use Mental Math and Reflexes. [Operations and Computation Goal 3]

Key Vocabulary

cubic units ◆ volume ◆ dimensions ◆ surface area

Materials

Student Reference Book, p. 137
Study Link 11•3 ◆ *Math Masters,* p. 403
base-10 blocks ◆ centimeter cubes ◆ tape ◆ metersticks ◆ slate ◆ scissors ◆ traffic cones and string (optional) ◆ computer with Internet access (optional)

2 Ongoing Learning & Practice

Playing the *Credits/Debits Game*
Student Reference Book, p. 238
Math Masters, p. 468
per partnership: deck of number cards (the Everything Math Deck, if available)
Students practice addition of integers.

Math Boxes 11•4
Math Journal 2, p. 297
Students practice and maintain skills through Math Box problems.

Study Link 11•4
Math Masters, p. 330
Students practice and maintain skills through Study Link activities.

3 Differentiation Options

READINESS

Finding Rectangular Prisms
Math Masters, p. 389
24 centimeter cubes
Students use 24 cubes to build as many rectangular prisms as possible, each with a different base.

ENRICHMENT

Exploring Penticubes
Math Masters, p. 389
5 centimeter cubes
Students create penticubes and compare their surface areas.

ELL SUPPORT

Building a Math Word Bank
Differentiation Handbook, p. 140
Students add the terms *volume* and *cubic units* to their Math Word Banks.

Advance Preparation

For the cubic meter demonstration in Part 1, you need 3 metersticks; for the alternative demonstration, you need 4 metersticks, 4 traffic cones, and string; or 2 metersticks, 2 traffic cones, string, and tape. See the illustrations on pages 868 and 869.

***Teacher's Reference Manual,* Grades 4–6** pp. 222–225, 233–237

Getting Started

Mental Math and Reflexes 

FACTS PRACTICE

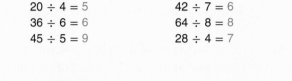

Pose multiplication and division facts. *Suggestions:*

●○○	●●○	●●●
2 ∗ 4 = 8	30 ∗ 9 = 270	90 ∗ 90 = 8,100
5 ∗ 7 = 35	4 ∗ 80 = 320	80 ∗ 70 = 5,600
10 ∗ 6 = 60	60 ∗ 40 = 2,400	60 ∗ 900 = 54,000
20 ÷ 4 = 5	42 ÷ 7 = 6	48 ÷ 6 = 8
36 ÷ 6 = 6	64 ÷ 8 = 8	63 ÷ 7 = 9
45 ÷ 5 = 9	28 ÷ 4 = 7	72 ÷ 9 = 8

Math Message

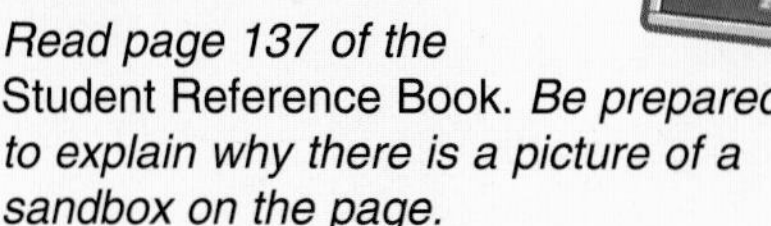

Read page 137 of the Student Reference Book. *Be prepared to explain why there is a picture of a sandbox on the page.*

Study Link 11·3 Follow-Up

Working in small groups, have students compare answers and pose the riddle they wrote.

Ongoing Assessment: Recognizing Student Achievement

Mental Math and Reflexes ★

Use **Mental Math and Reflexes** to assess students' ability to solve multiplication and division facts. Students are making adequate progress if they demonstrate automaticity with the multiplication facts and proficiency with the division facts. Some students may demonstrate automaticity with the division facts.

[Operations and Computation Goal 3]

1 Teaching the Lesson

Math Message Follow-Up

WHOLE-CLASS DISCUSSION

(*Student Reference Book,* p. 137)

Review the information on *Student Reference Book,* page 137. Once students explain the significance of the picture of the sandbox, ask them to give other examples in which it is useful to know the volume of an object. *For example:*

▷ Buying a cooler—to decide whether it is big enough to hold the food for a camping trip

▷ Renting a car—to decide if the trunk is large enough to hold the family's luggage

Tell students that in this lesson they will review units of volume and explore how to use cubes to find the volume of a rectangular prism.

Student Page

Measurement

Volume and Capacity

Volume

The **volume** of a solid object such as a brick or a ball is a measure of *how much space the object takes up.* The volume of a container such as a freezer is a measure of *how much the container will hold.*

Volume is measured in **cubic units.** A base-10 cube has sides that are 1 centimeter long; it is called a **cubic centimeter.** A cube with 1-inch sides is called a **cubic inch.**

Other cubic units are used to measure large volumes. A **cubic foot** has 1-foot sides. A **cubic yard** has 1-yard sides and can hold 27 cubic feet. A **cubic meter** has 1-meter sides and can hold more than 35 cubic feet.

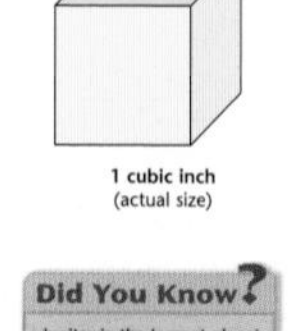

1 cubic centimeter (actual size)

1 cubic inch (actual size)

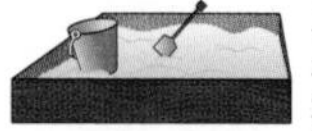

The volume of an object can be very useful to know. Suppose you wanted to buy sand to fill an empty sandbox. To estimate how much sand to buy, you would measure the length, width, and height of the sandbox. The length, width, and height are called the **dimensions** of the box. You would then use these dimensions to calculate how many cubic feet (or cubic yards) of sand to order. You could do similar calculations to determine how much concrete would be needed to build a patio, or how much gravel to buy for a path in the backyard.

Capacity

We often measure things that are poured into or out of containers such as liquids, grains, salt, and so on. The volume of a container that is filled with a liquid or a solid that can be poured is often called its **capacity.**

Capacity is usually measured in units such as **gallons, quarts, pints, cups, fluid ounces, liters,** and **milliliters.** These are standard units, but they are not cubic units.

The tables at the right compare different units of capacity.

Did You Know?

Jupiter is the largest planet in the solar system. The volume of Jupiter is 1,300 times the volume of Earth.

U.S. Customary Units
1 gallon (gal) = 4 quarts (qt)
1 gallon = 2 half-gallons
1 half-gallon = 2 quarts
1 quart = 2 pints (pt)
1 pint = 2 cups (c)
1 cup = 8 fluid ounces (fl oz)
1 pint = 16 fluid ounces
1 quart = 32 fluid ounces
1 half-gallon = 64 fluid ounces
1 gallon = 128 fluid ounces

Metric Units
1 liter (L) = 1,000 milliliters (mL)
1 milliliter = $\frac{1}{1,000}$ liter

***Student Reference Book,* p. 137**

▶ Visualizing Metric Cubic Units

Discuss the following:

▷ Linear measurements are usually given in standard units (such as feet or meters), and area measurements are often given in squares of those units (such as square feet or square meters). Many volume measurements are given in cubes of standard units, or **cubic units.**

▷ The area of a closed 2-dimensional figure is the number of unit squares and fractions of unit squares needed to cover the interior of the figure. The **volume** of a 3-dimensional object is the number of unit cubes and fractions of unit cubes needed to fill the space taken up by the object. To support English language learners, discuss the everyday and mathematical meanings of *volume.*

Use base-10 blocks and metersticks to help students visualize the sizes of various metric cubic units.

▷ Hold up a cm cube. Point out that each edge is 1 centimeter long, so the volume of a cm cube is 1 cubic centimeter.

▷ Hold up a "big cube." Explain that each edge is 10 centimeters, or 1 decimeter, long, so the volume of a big cube is 1 cubic decimeter.

Ask: *How many cubic centimeters are in 1 cubic decimeter?* Have students use base-10 blocks to "prove" their answers. There are 10 cubic centimeters in 1 long; there are 10 longs, or 100 cubic centimeters, in 1 flat. You can fill a cubic decimeter container with 10 flats, or 1,000 cubic centimeters. Therefore, 1 cubic decimeter equals 1,000 cubic centimeters.

You will not have enough base-10 blocks to build a 1-meter cube, but you can help students visualize such a cube using one of these methods:

Method 1: Place two metersticks on a flat surface at right angles to each other. Hold up a third meterstick perpendicular to the other metersticks so that all three sticks meet in one corner.

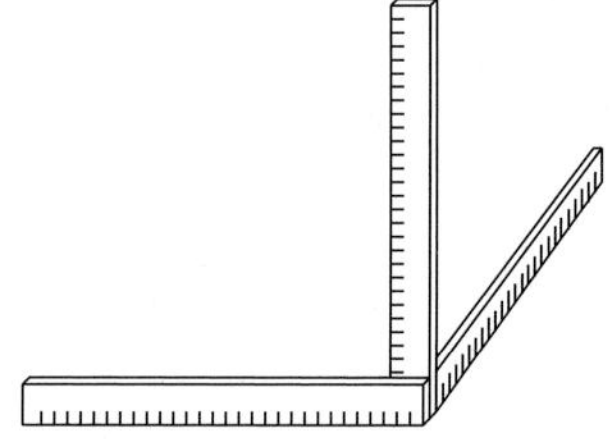

With the help of this partial frame, students can imagine a cube whose edges are the length of a meterstick. The volume of this cube is 1 cubic meter.

Method 2: Place four hollow traffic cones on the floor at the corners of a square with 1-meter sides. Put a meterstick through the top of each cone so that each stick stands straight up. Connect the tops of the metersticks with string to form a square. The string should be as close to the top of the metersticks as possible. (*See margin.*)

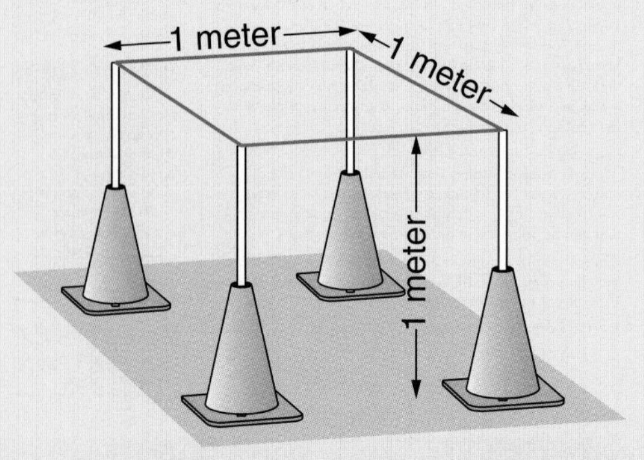

Method 3: A variation of the above method uses two cones and two metersticks. Place the cones 1 meter from a wall and 1 meter apart. Connect the tops of the metersticks with string. Run a string from the top of each meterstick to the wall at a height of 1 meter, and tape the string to the wall.

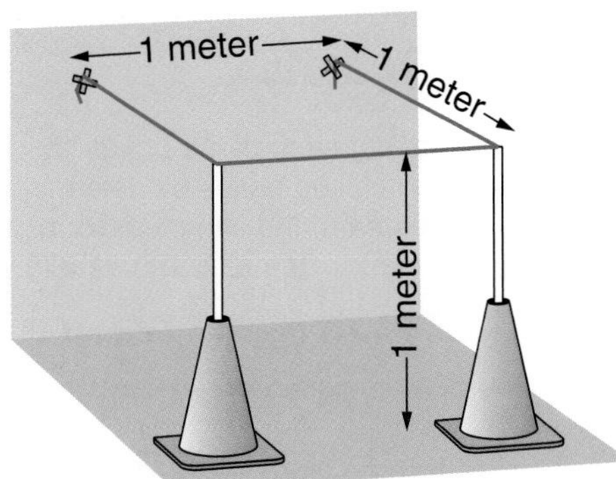

Adjusting the Activity

Ask: *How many cubic decimeters are in 1 cubic meter?* 1,000 *How many cubic centimeters are in 1 cubic meter?* 100 ∗ 100 ∗ 100 = 1,000,000

AUDITORY ◆ KINESTHETIC ◆ TACTILE ◆ VISUAL

Remind students of alternative ways of writing square units: square m, sq m, or m^2; square cm, sq cm, or cm^2; and square in., sq in., or in^2. Similarly, cubic units may be written as m^3, cm^3, or in^3. These are read as "cubic meter," "cubic centimeter," and "cubic inch."

Using Cubes to Find the Volume of a Rectangular Prism

(*Math Masters,* p. 403)

Model the following activity for students before they work in partnerships to make their own boxes:

1. On a sheet of centimeter grid paper (*Math Masters,* page 403), draw a pattern for an open box. For example, the bottom of the box might be a rectangle 4 centimeters long and 3 centimeters wide, and the box might be 2 centimeters high.
2. Cut out the pattern. Fold up the sides, and tape them together.
3. Fill the box with centimeter cubes. The number of cubes needed to fill the box is the volume of the box.

Partners may make boxes with any **dimensions** they choose, but the height must be at least 2 centimeters.

NOTE To help students visualize 2-dimensional nets as 3-dimensional shapes, see www.everydaymathonline.com.

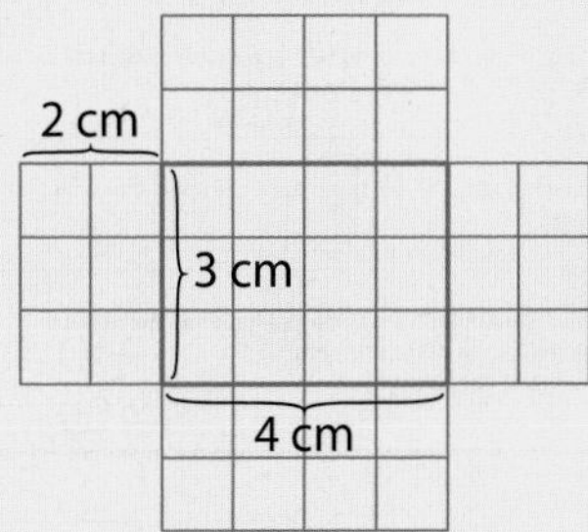

Pattern for open box

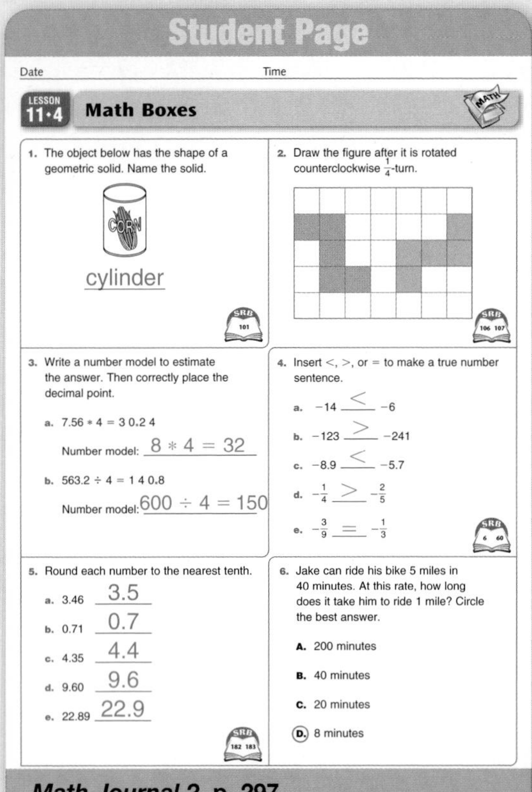

Student Page

Date Time

LESSON 11•4 **Math Boxes**

1. The object below has the shape of a geometric solid. Name the solid.

   cylinder

2. Draw the figure after it is rotated counterclockwise $\frac{1}{4}$-turn.

3. Write a number model to estimate the answer. Then correctly place the decimal point.

   a. 7.56 ∗ 4 = 3 0.2 4

   Number model: $8 * 4 = 32$

   b. 563.2 ÷ 4 = 1 4 0.8

   Number model: $600 \div 4 = 150$

4. Insert <, >, or = to make a true number sentence.

   a. $-14 < -6$

   b. $-123 > -241$

   c. $-8.9 < -5.7$

   d. $-\frac{1}{4} > -\frac{2}{5}$

   e. $-\frac{3}{9} = -\frac{1}{3}$

5. Round each number to the nearest tenth.

   a. 3.46 3.5

   b. 0.71 0.7

   c. 4.35 4.4

   d. 9.60 9.6

   e. 22.89 22.9

6. Jake can ride his bike 5 miles in 40 minutes. At this rate, how long does it take him to ride 1 mile? Circle the best answer.

   A. 200 minutes

   B. 40 minutes

   C. 20 minutes

   (D.) 8 minutes

Math Journal 2, p. 297

Technology Link Alternatively, have students visit the Web site at http://illuminations.nctm.org/ActivityDetail.aspx?ID=6 to create boxes of varying dimensions and manipulate and count unit cubes, rows of unit cubes, or layers of unit cubes.

Adjusting the Activity

Have students imagine that each of the boxes has a lid. Have them calculate the **surface area** of the closed boxes by determining the sum of the areas of the faces. The surface area of the sample box on page 869 is 52 square centimeters: $(2 * (2 * 3)) + (2 * (2 * 4)) + (2 * (3 * 4)) = 52$.

AUDITORY ♦ KINESTHETIC ♦ TACTILE ♦ VISUAL

2 Ongoing Learning & Practice

▶ Playing the *Credits/Debits Game*

PARTNER ACTIVITY

(*Student Reference Book,* p. 238; *Math Masters,* p. 468)

Students play the *Credits/Debits Game* to practice adding positive and negative numbers. See Lesson 10-6 for additional information.

▶ Math Boxes 11•4

INDEPENDENT ACTIVITY

(*Math Journal 2,* p. 297)

Mixed Practice Math Boxes in this lesson are linked with Math Boxes in Lessons 11-2 and 11-6. The skills in Problems 5 and 6 preview Unit 12 content.

Writing/Reasoning Have students write a response to the following: *How did you round each number to the nearest tenth in Problem 5?* Sample answer: I found the digit in the tenths place. Then I looked at the digit to the right. If it was less than 5, I kept the digit in the tenths place the same. If the number was 5 or greater, I rounded up the number in the tenths place.

▶ Study Link 11•4

INDEPENDENT ACTIVITY

(*Math Masters,* p. 330)

Home Connection Students cut out and assemble an open box. They search for items at home that have volumes equal to about $\frac{1}{2}$ of, the same as, and 2 times the volume of the open box.

Study Link Master

Name Date Time

STUDY LINK 11•4 **Volume**

Cut out the pattern below and tape it together to form an open box.

1. Find and record two items in your home that have volumes equal to about $\frac{1}{2}$ of the volume of the open box.

   Answers vary.

2. Find and record two items in your home that have about the same volume as the open box.

   Answers vary.

3. Find and record two items in your home that have volumes equal to about 2 times the volume of the open box.

   Answers vary.

Practice

4. $96 \div 4 =$ 24

5. $86 / 5 =$ 17 R1, or $17\frac{1}{5}$

6. $\frac{232}{8} =$ 29

7. $4\overline{)358} =$ 89 R2, or $89\frac{2}{4}$, or $89\frac{1}{2}$

TAB TAB TAB TAB

Math Masters, p. 330

3 Differentiation Options

READINESS

PARTNER ACTIVITY

Finding Rectangular Prisms

15–30 Min

(*Math Masters,* p. 389)

To explore the concept of volume, have students use 24 centimeter cubes to build as many rectangular prisms as possible, each with a different base. The area of the base must be greater than 1 cm^2, and the height of the prism must be greater than 1 cm.

Have students create a table on an Exit Slip (*Math Masters,* page 389) to organize their work. The table should include the area of the base, the height, and the volume of each prism they make. Remind students to include the units. (*See margin.*)

Example:

Area of Base (sq cm)	Height (cm)	Volume (cu cm)
2	12	24
12	2	24
3	8	24
8	3	24
4	6	24
6	4	24

ENRICHMENT

PARTNER ACTIVITY

Exploring Penticubes

15–30 Min

(*Math Masters,* p. 389)

Portfolio Ideas

To investigate volume and **surface area,** have students build *penticubes,* which are 3-dimensional figures with a volume of 5 cubic units. They are constructed from 5 cubes connected by at least one face. There are 29 possible penticubes.

Have students compare the surface areas of the penticubes and describe on an Exit Slip (*Math Masters,* page 389) anything they notice about the figures with similar surface areas. Expect responses such as the following:

- ▷ All but two of the penticubes have a surface area of 22 square units. The penticubes that are circled to the right have a surface area of 20 square units.
- ▷ If a cube touches only 1 other cube face, then the surface area of that individual cube is 5 square units. If a cube touches two faces, then the surface area of that individual cube is 4 square units.
- ▷ The more faces the cubes touch, the smaller the surface area is. For example, in the circled penticubes, 4 of the cubes touch 2 or 3 faces each, thereby creating a smaller surface area.

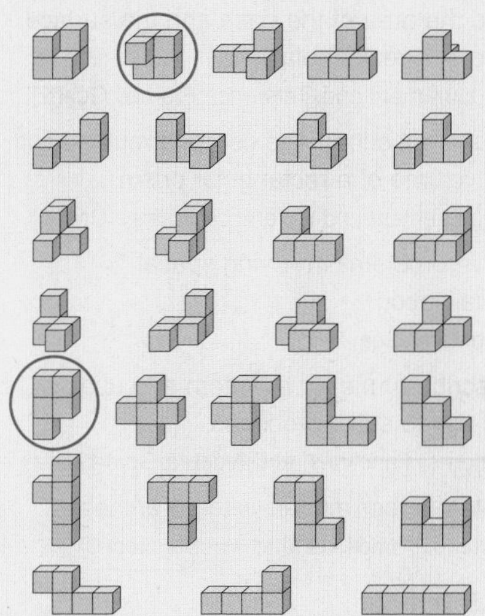

There are 29 possible penticubes.

ELL SUPPORT

SMALL-GROUP ACTIVITY

Building a Math Word Bank

5–15 Min

(*Differentiation Handbook,* p. 140)

To provide language support for volume, have students use the Word Bank Template found on *Differentiation Handbook,* page 140. Ask students to write the terms *volume* and *cubic units,* draw pictures relating to each term, and write other related words. See the *Differentiation Handbook* for more information.

11•5 A Formula for the Volume of Rectangular Prisms

Objective To guide the development and use of a formula for finding the volume of a rectangular prism.

Technology Resources www.everydaymathonline.com

ePresentations

eToolkit

Algorithms Practice

EM Facts Workshop Game™

Family Letters

Assessment Management

Common Core State Standards

Curriculum Focal Points

Interactive Teacher's Lesson Guide

1 Teaching the Lesson

Key Concepts and Skills

- Find the area of the base and the surface area of a rectangular prism. [Measurement and Reference Frames Goal 2]
- Count unit cubes and use a formula to find the volume of a rectangular prism. [Measurement and Reference Frames Goal 2]
- Solve problems involving spatial visualization. [Geometry Goal 3]
- Describe a rule for a pattern and use the rule to solve problems. [Patterns, Functions, and Algebra Goal 1]
- Write number models with parentheses. [Patterns, Functions, and Algebra Goal 3]

Key Activities

Students solve cube-stacking problems and use the results to derive a formula for the volume of a rectangular prism.

Ongoing Assessment: Informing Instruction See page 874.

Ongoing Assessment: Recognizing Student Achievement Use journal page 302. [Measurement and Reference Frames Goal 2]

Key Vocabulary

rectangular prism • volume • formula

Materials

Math Journal 2, pp. 298 and 300–302
Study Link 11•4
centimeter cubes • centimeter ruler • slate

2 Ongoing Learning & Practice

Playing *Chances Are*
Student Reference Book, pp. 236 and 237
Math Masters, p. 464
Chances Are Event and Probability Cards (*Math Masters,* pp. 462, 463, 465, and 466)
Students practice using probability language to describe the likelihood of an event.

Math Boxes 11•5
Math Journal 2, p. 299
Students practice and maintain skills through Math Box problems.

Study Link 11•5
Math Masters, p. 331
Students practice and maintain skills through Study Link activities.

3 Differentiation Options

READINESS

Solving Spatial-Visualization Puzzles
Math Masters, p. 332
interlocking cubes • stick-on notes
Students use interlocking cubes to build cube stacks and solve spatial visualization problems.

ENRICHMENT

Estimating the Volume of a Sheet of Paper
Math Masters, p. 388 or 389
sheet of notebook paper • scissors
Students estimate the volume of a sheet of notebook paper.

Advance Preparation

***Teacher's Reference Manual,* Grades 4–6** pp. 13, 222–225

Getting Started

Mental Math and Reflexes

Pose mental addition problems. *Suggestions:*

●○○ 16 + 4 = 20
25 + 5 = 30
11 + 9 = 20
37 + 3 = 40

●●○ 18 + 19 = 37
49 + 17 = 66
48 + 16 = 64
32 + 18 = 50

●●● 253 + 29 = 282
76 + 149 = 225
126 + 259 = 385
644 + 39 = 683

Math Message

Complete journal page 298.

Study Link 11·4 Follow-Up

Working in small groups, have students describe the items in their home that had volumes equal to about $\frac{1}{2}$ of, the same as, and 2 times the volume of the open box. Ask students to use centimeter cubes to determine the volume of the box. 96 cm^3 Ask: *Suppose the box had a lid. What would be the surface area of the closed box?* 136 cm^2

1 Teaching the Lesson

▶ Math Message Follow-Up

(*Math Journal 2,* p. 298)

Algebraic Thinking Review the answers on journal page 298. Discuss the use of variables to stand for quantities such as length and width. Two formulas that students are likely to give are $A = l * w$ and $A = b * h$. To support English language learners, write the two formulas on the board.

Tell students that in this lesson they will apply their knowledge of area formulas to develop a formula for finding the volume of a rectangular prism.

▶ Solving Cube-Stacking Problems

PARTNER ACTIVITY

(*Math Journal 2,* pp. 300 and 301)

Each problem on journal pages 300 and 301 shows a picture of a box that is partially filled with cubes. Students find the number of cubes needed to completely fill each box and record the results in the table on journal page 300.

Fill in the column for Box 1 with the class. You might wish to use the following prompts:

- How many cubes can be placed along the longer side of the box? 8 Along the shorter side? 4
- How many cubes are needed to cover the bottom of the box? 32
- How many layers of cubes are needed to fill the box? 5 How can you tell? There are 5 cubes in the stack.
- How many cubes are needed to fill the box? There are 5 layers with 32 cubes in each layer, and 5 * 32 = 160, so 160 cubes are needed to fill the box.

Have students complete the rest of the problems with partners.

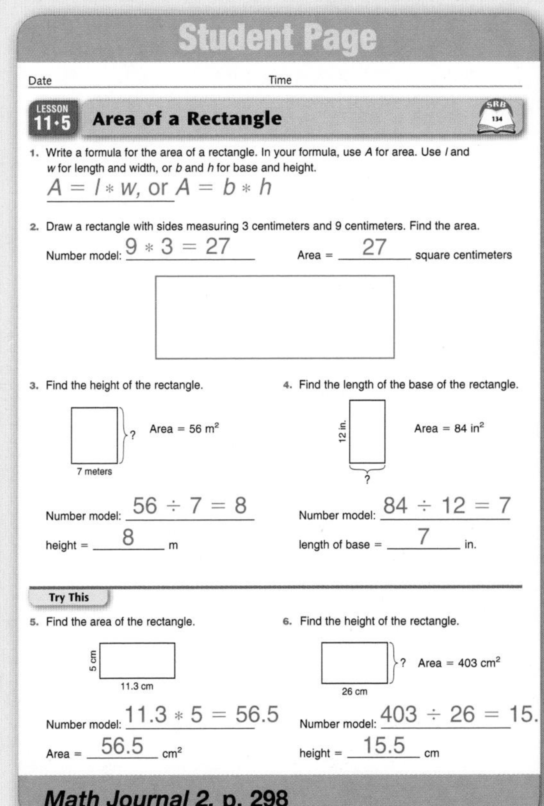

Student Page

Date Time

LESSON 11·5 **Area of a Rectangle**

1. Write a formula for the area of a rectangle. In your formula, use *A* for area. Use *l* and *w* for length and width, or *b* and *h* for base and height.
$A = l * w$, or $A = b * h$

2. Draw a rectangle with sides measuring 3 centimeters and 9 centimeters. Find the area.
Number model: $9 * 3 = 27$ Area = 27 square centimeters

3. Find the height of the rectangle.

Number model: $56 \div 7 = 8$
height = 8 m

4. Find the length of the base of the rectangle.

Number model: $84 \div 12 = 7$
length of base = 7 in.

Try This

5. Find the area of the rectangle.

Number model: $11.3 * 5 = 56.5$
Area = 56.5 cm^2

6. Find the height of the rectangle.

Number model: $403 \div 26 = 15.$
height = 15.5 cm

***Math Journal 2,* p. 298**

Ongoing Assessment: Informing Instruction

Watch for students who try to find the volume by counting only the cubes shown in the picture. Remind them that the cubes that are shown will help determine the height of the box and the number of cubes needed to cover the bottom, but that the volume of the box is the total number of cubes needed to fill the box.

▶ Deriving a Formula for the Volume of a Rectangular Prism

(*Math Journal 2,* pp. 300 and 301)

Algebraic Thinking Remind students that geometric solids, such as those pictured on journal pages 300 and 301, are called **rectangular prisms.** Review the properties of rectangular prisms. To support English language learners, write students' responses on the board. *For example:*

- ▷ A rectangular prism has 6 rectangular faces, 12 edges, and 8 corners.
- ▷ Pairs of opposite faces are congruent.
- ▷ *Any face* of a rectangular prism can be designated as the base of the prism. The height of the prism is the distance between the base and the face opposite the base.

Allow students 10 to 15 minutes to complete the journal pages. Then bring the class together to discuss students' results.

Draw a rectangular prism on the board and label the base and height, as shown.

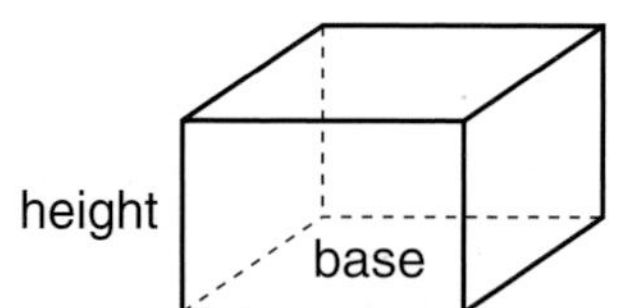

Ask students to look for a pattern in the table on journal page 300. To find the total number of cubes needed to fill each box, multiply the number of cubes needed to cover the bottom of the box by the number of cubes in the tallest stack.

NOTE The properties to the right are true of *right* rectangular prisms. The *oblique* rectangular prism shown below has only two rectangular faces. In *Fourth Grade Everyday Mathematics,* the term *rectangular prism* will refer only to a right rectangular prism.

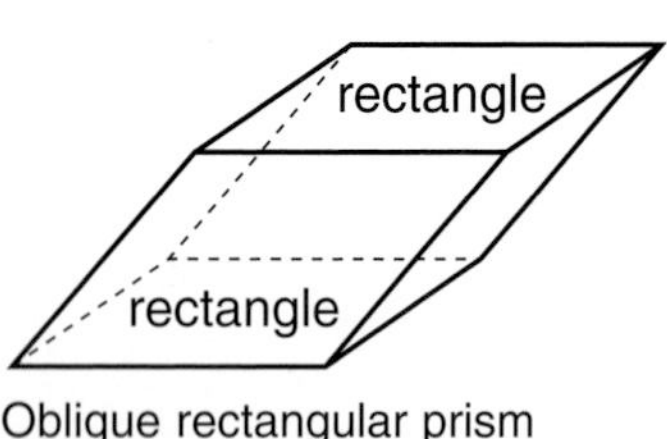

Oblique rectangular prism

Student Page

Date Time

LESSON 11•5 **Cube-Stacking Problems** SRB 138

Each picture at the bottom of this page and on the next page shows a box that is partially filled with cubes. The cubes in each box are the same size. Each box has at least one stack of cubes that goes to the top.

Your task is to find the total number of cubes needed to completely fill each box.

Record your answers in the table below.

Table of Volumes

Placement of Cubes	Box 1	Box 2	Box 3	Box 4	Box 5	Box 6
Number of cubes needed to cover the bottom	32	40	24	16	35	25
Number of cubes in the tallest stack (Be sure to count the bottom cube.)	5	7	4	5	6	5
Total number of cubes needed to fill the box	160	280	96	80	210	125

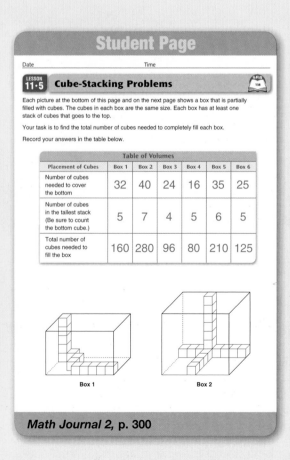

Box 1 Box 2

Math Journal 2, p. 300

Then call students' attention to the following relationships:

- ▷ The number of cubes needed to cover the bottom of the box is the same as the number of squares needed to cover the base—that is, the area of the base of the box.
- ▷ The number of cubes in the tallest stack is the same as the height of the box.
- ▷ Therefore, you can find the **volume** of a rectangular prism by multiplying the area of a base by the height of the prism.

Volume of a rectangular prism = area of base $*$ height

Written with variables, this becomes $V = B * h$, where V is the volume of the rectangular prism, B is the area of the base, and h is the height of the prism.

Have students record the **formula** at the bottom of journal page 301.

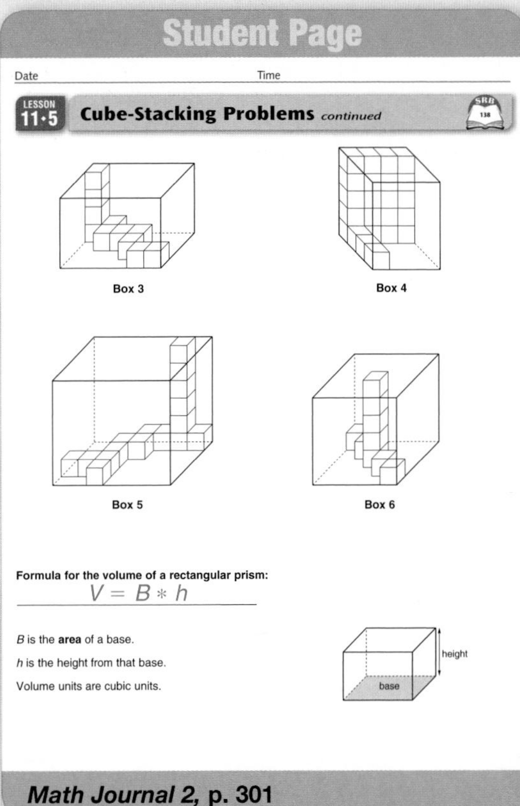

Student Page

Date Time

LESSON 11•5 **Cube-Stacking Problems** *continued* SRB 138

Box 3 Box 4

Box 5 Box 6

Formula for the volume of a rectangular prism: $V = B * h$

B is the **area** of a base.

h is the height from that base.

Volume units are cubic units.

***Math Journal 2,* p. 301**

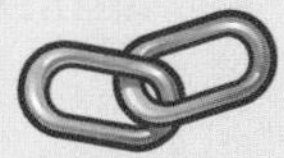

Links to the Future

Use of a formula to calculate the volume of a prism is a Grade 5 Goal.

▶ Finding Volume

PARTNER ACTIVITY

(*Math Journal 2,* p. 302)

Students find the volume of stacks of centimeter cubes and calculate the volume of rectangular prisms. Ask students to explain the strategies they used to solve the problems. *For example:*

- ▷ **Problem 2:** A portion of the top layer is missing. Calculate the volume of a completed rectangular prism and subtract the missing blocks. Alternatively, determine the volume of the complete prism as shown and add the partial layer of cubes.
- ▷ **Problem 3:** There is one complete layer of cubes with three identical stacks on top. Add the volume of the bottom layer to the volume of the three stacks to determine the total volume.

NOTE Traditionally, lowercase letters are used in formulas to represent length, and uppercase letters are used to represent area or volume. For example, b stands for the length of the base of a polygon, and B stands for the area of the base of a geometric solid.

Adjusting the Activity

ELL

Have students use centimeter cubes to build the stacks and rectangular prisms on journal page 302.

AUDITORY ◆ KINESTHETIC ◆ TACTILE ◆ VISUAL

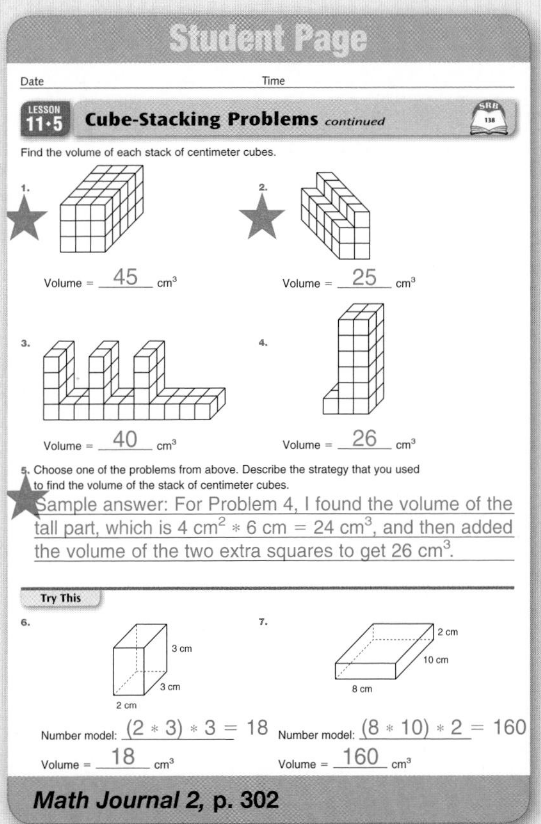

Student Page

Date Time

LESSON 11•5 **Cube-Stacking Problems** *continued* SRB 138

Find the volume of each stack of centimeter cubes.

1. Volume = 45 cm^3

2. Volume = 25 cm^3

3. Volume = 40 cm^3

4. Volume = 26 cm^3

5. Choose one of the problems from above. Describe the strategy that you used to find the volume of the stack of centimeter cubes.
Sample answer: For Problem 4, I found the volume of the tall part, which is $4 \text{ cm}^2 * 6 \text{ cm} = 24 \text{ cm}^3$, and then added the volume of the two extra squares to get 26 cm^3.

Try This

6.
Number model: $(2 * 3) * 3 = 18$
Volume = 18 cm^3

7.
Number model: $(8 * 10) * 2 = 160$
Volume = 160 cm^3

***Math Journal 2,* p. 302**

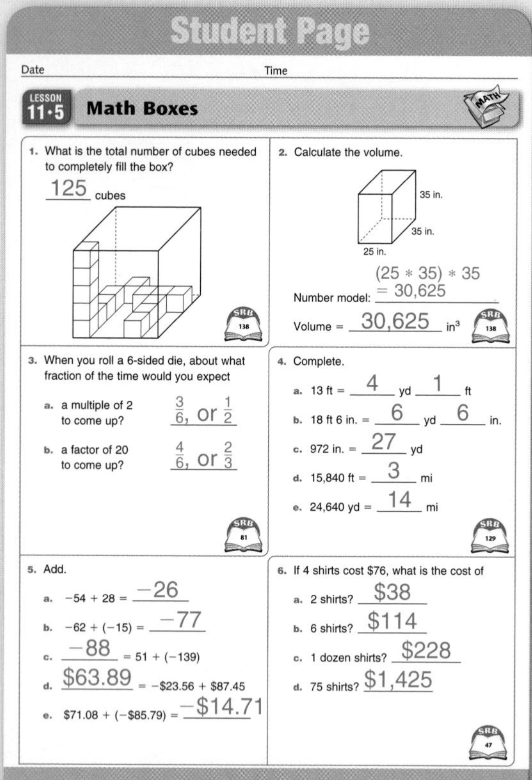

Student Page

Date Time

LESSON 11·5 **Math Boxes**

1. What is the total number of cubes needed to completely fill the box?
125 cubes

2. Calculate the volume.
35 in., 35 in., 25 in.
Number model: (25 ∗ 35) ∗ 35 = 30,625
Volume = 30,625 in³

3. When you roll a 6-sided die, about what fraction of the time would you expect
a. a multiple of 2 to come up? 3/6, or 1/2
b. a factor of 20 to come up? 4/6, or 2/3

4. Complete.
a. 13 ft = 4 yd 1 ft
b. 18 ft 6 in. = 6 yd 6 in.
c. 972 in. = 27 yd
d. 15,840 ft = 3 mi
e. 24,640 yd = 14 mi

5. Add.
a. −54 + 28 = −26
b. −62 + (−15) = −77
c. −88 = 51 + (−139)
d. $63.89 = −$23.56 + $87.45
e. $71.08 + (−$85.79) = −$14.71

6. If 4 shirts cost $76, what is the cost of
a. 2 shirts? $38
b. 6 shirts? $114
c. 1 dozen shirts? $228
d. 75 shirts? $1,425

Math Journal 2, p. 299

Ongoing Assessment: Recognizing Student Achievement

Journal page 302 Problems 1, 2, and 5

Use **journal page 302, Problems 1, 2, and 5** to assess students' ability to find the volume of stacks of centimeter cubes. Students are making adequate progress if they are able to build the stacks with actual centimeter cubes or look at the pictures to find the volume and then describe the strategy used. Some students may be able to solve Problems 3 and 4, which involve more difficult arrangements of cubes, and Problems 6 and 7, which involve representations of rectangular prisms that do not show individual cubes.

[Measurement and Reference Frames Goal 2]

2 Ongoing Learning & Practice

▶ Playing *Chances Are*

PARTNER ACTIVITY

(*Student Reference Book,* pp. 236 and 237; *Math Masters,* pp. 462–466)

Students play *Chances Are* to practice using probability language to describe the likelihood of an event. See Lesson 7-11 for additional information.

▶ Math Boxes 11·5

INDEPENDENT ACTIVITY

(*Math Journal 2,* p. 299)

Mixed Practice Math Boxes in this lesson are paired with Math Boxes in Lesson 11-7. The skill in Problem 6 previews Unit 12 content.

Writing/Reasoning Have students write a response to the following: *Use probability terms to describe the likelihood of each of the events in Problem 3. Explain your choice of language.* Sample answer: There is a 50-50 chance of rolling a multiple of 2 because 2, 4, and 6 are multiples of 2. There are 3 favorable outcomes out of 6 possible outcomes. It is likely that a factor of 20 will come up. 1, 2, 4, and 5 are factors of 20. There are 4 favorable outcomes out of 6 possible outcomes.

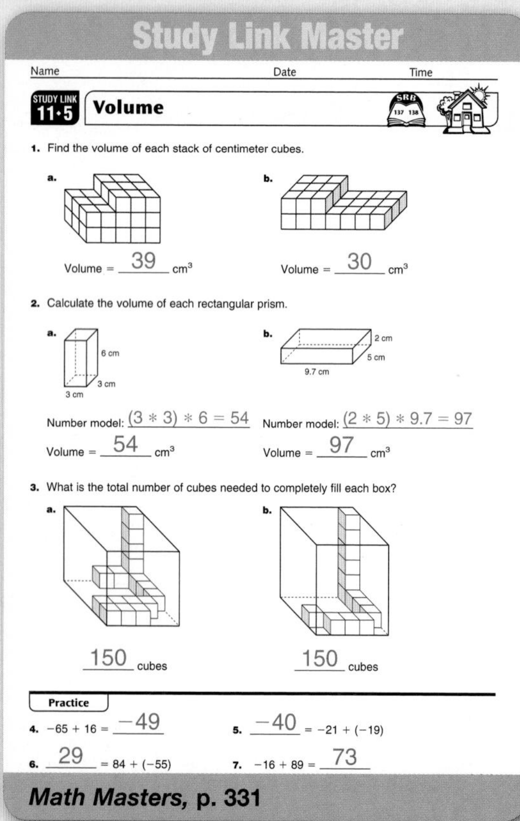

Study Link Master

Name Date Time

STUDY LINK 11·5 **Volume**

1. Find the volume of each stack of centimeter cubes.
a. Volume = 39 cm³
b. Volume = 30 cm³

2. Calculate the volume of each rectangular prism.
a. 6 cm, 3 cm, 3 cm
Number model: (3 ∗ 3) ∗ 6 = 54
Volume = 54 cm³
b. 2 cm, 5 cm, 9.7 cm
Number model: (2 ∗ 5) ∗ 9.7 = 97
Volume = 97 cm³

3. What is the total number of cubes needed to completely fill each box?
a. 150 cubes
b. 150 cubes

Practice

4. −65 + 16 = −49
5. −40 = −21 + (−19)
6. 29 = 84 + (−55)
7. −16 + 89 = 73

Math Masters, p. 331

▶ Study Link 11·5

INDEPENDENT ACTIVITY

(*Math Masters,* p. 331)

Home Connection Students find the volume of stacks of centimeter cubes, calculate the volume of rectangular prisms, and determine the number of cubes that are needed to fill boxes.

3 Differentiation Options

READINESS

Solving Spatial-Visualization Puzzles

PARTNER ACTIVITY

15–30 Min

(*Math Masters,* p. 332)

To explore the representation of 3-dimensional figures with 2-dimensional drawings, have students use interlocking cubes to build cube stacks and solve spatial-visualization problems.

ENRICHMENT

Estimating the Volume of a Sheet of Paper

INDEPENDENT ACTIVITY

5–15 Min

(*Math Masters,* p. 388 or 389)

Algebraic Thinking To apply students' understanding of volume, have them estimate the volume of a sheet of notebook paper. In a Math Log or on an Exit Slip, have students write a brief report describing their strategy. One possible strategy is given below.

1. Cut the sheet of paper into 1-inch squares.
2. Stack the squares into a neat pile. Measure the height of the pile of squares. About $\frac{1}{4}$-inch high The area of the base of the pile is 1 square inch.
3. Use the formula: $V = B * h$

   $V = 1 * \frac{1}{4}$

   $V = \frac{1}{4}$
4. The volume of a sheet of notebook paper is about 0.25 cubic inches.

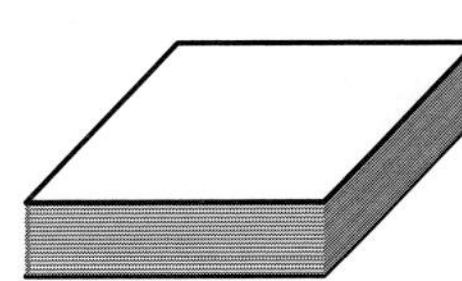
1-inch squares cut from a single sheet of paper

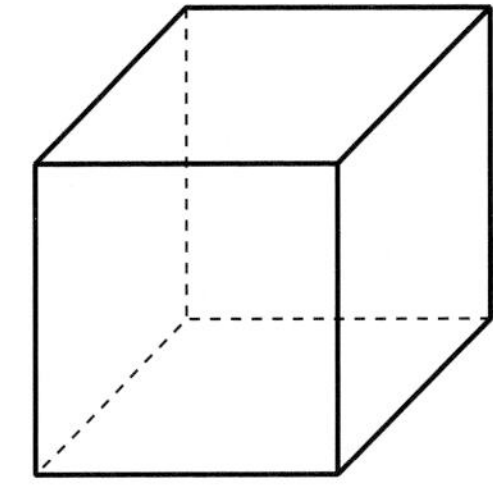
1-inch cube

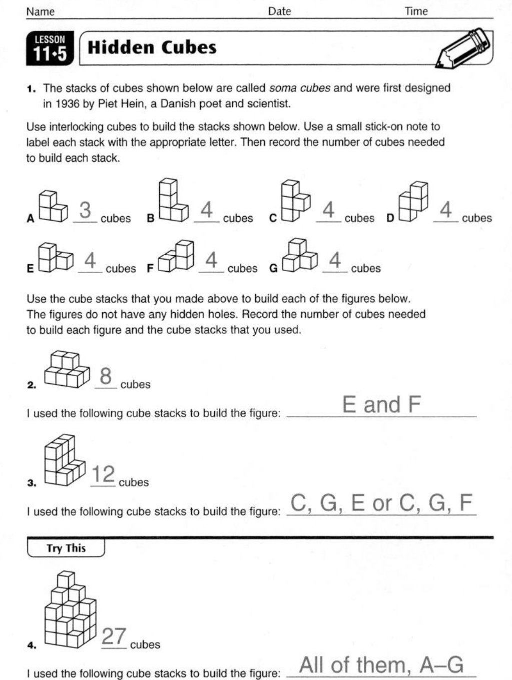

Teaching Master

Name Date Time

LESSON 11•5 **Hidden Cubes**

1. The stacks of cubes shown below are called *soma cubes* and were first designed in 1936 by Piet Hein, a Danish poet and scientist.

Use interlocking cubes to build the stacks shown below. Use a small stick-on note to label each stack with the appropriate letter. Then record the number of cubes needed to build each stack.

A 3 cubes B 4 cubes C 4 cubes D 4 cubes

E 4 cubes F 4 cubes G 4 cubes

Use the cube stacks that you made above to build each of the figures below. The figures do not have any hidden holes. Record the number of cubes needed to build each figure and the cube stacks that you used.

2. 8 cubes

I used the following cube stacks to build the figure: E and F

3. 12 cubes

I used the following cube stacks to build the figure: C, G, E or C, G, F

Try This

4. 27 cubes

I used the following cube stacks to build the figure: All of them, A–G

Math Masters, p. 332

11•6 Subtraction of Positive and Negative Numbers

Objectives To review addition of positive and negative integers; and to introduce subtraction of positive and negative integers.

Technology Resources www.everydaymathonline.com

ePresentations

eToolkit

Algorithms Practice

EM Facts Workshop Game™

Family Letters

Assessment Management

Common Core State Standards

Curriculum Focal Points

Interactive Teacher's Lesson Guide

1 Teaching the Lesson

Key Concepts and Skills

- Compare integers.
  [Number and Numeration Goal 6]
- Add and subtract signed numbers.
  [Operations and Computation Goal 2]
- Describe rules for patterns and use them to solve problems.
  [Patterns, Functions, and Algebra Goal 1]

Key Activities

Students discuss and practice subtraction of positive and negative integers, and review addition of such numbers, in the context of an accounting problem. Students play the *Credits/Debits Game* (Advanced Version).

Ongoing Assessment: Informing Instruction See page 881.

Materials

Student Reference Book, p. 239
Study Link 11•5
Math Masters, p. 469
transparency of *Math Masters,* p. 321 (optional) ◆ per partnership: 1 penny, deck of number cards (the Everything Math Deck, if available) ◆ slate ◆ number line (optional)

2 Ongoing Learning & Practice

Summarizing the Gram & Ounce Museum
Math Journal 2, p. 303
Students summarize the Gram & Ounce museum.

Math Boxes 11•6
Math Journal 2, p. 304
Students practice and maintain skills through Math Box problems.

Ongoing Assessment: Recognizing Student Achievement
Use Math Boxes, Problem 2.
[Geometry Goal 3]

Study Link 11•6
Math Masters, p. 333
Students practice and maintain skills through Study Link activities.

3 Differentiation Options

READINESS

Using a Number Line to Subtract Positive and Negative Numbers
masking tape
Students use a number line to subtract positive and negative numbers.

EXTRA PRACTICE

5-Minute Math
5-Minute Math™, pp. 100 and 189
Students practice adding and subtracting positive and negative numbers.

Advance Preparation

For the optional Readiness activity in Part 3, use masking tape to create a life-size number line (–10 to 10) on the floor.

***Teacher's Reference Manual,* Grades 4–6** pp. 71–74, 100–102

Getting Started

Mental Math and Reflexes

Pose problems involving the addition of positive and negative numbers. *Suggestions:*

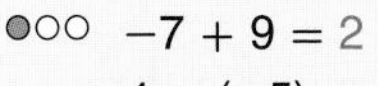

●○○ $-7 + 9 = 2$
$4 + (-5) = -1$
$6 + (-8) = -2$

●●○ $20 + (-30) = -10$
$70 + (-50) = 20$
$10 + (-90) = -80$

●●● $\frac{1}{2} + (-\frac{1}{4}) = \frac{1}{4}$
$-\frac{1}{3} + (-\frac{1}{3}) = -\frac{2}{3}$
$\frac{2}{8} + (-\frac{1}{2}) = -\frac{2}{8}$, or $-\frac{1}{4}$

Math Message

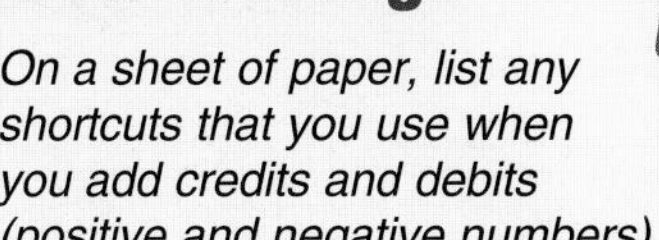

On a sheet of paper, list any shortcuts that you use when you add credits and debits (positive and negative numbers).

Study Link 11•5 Follow-Up

Have volunteers write number models on the board to show how they calculated the volume of each figure.

1 Teaching the Lesson

Math Message Follow-Up

WHOLE-CLASS DISCUSSION

Ask students to share any shortcuts they devised for adding positive and negative numbers the last time they used credits and debits. *For example:*

- ▷ When two positive numbers are added, the result is "more positive."
- ▷ When two negative numbers are added, the result is "more negative."
- ▷ When a positive and a negative number are added, the result is the difference of the two addends (ignoring the signs); the sign in the answer is that of whichever addend is "bigger."

Using Credits and Debits to Practice Subtraction of Positive and Negative Numbers

WHOLE-CLASS ACTIVITY

(*Math Masters,* p. 321)

Links to the Future

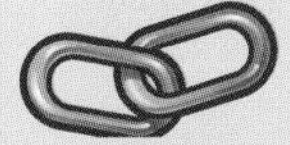

Addition and subtraction of signed numbers is a Grade 5 Goal.

Tell students that in this lesson they will pretend to be accountants, as they did in Lesson 10-6. They record what happens as they help start a business and keep track of the "bottom line" by posting credits and debits.

Teaching Master

Name Date Time

LESSON 10•6 **Ledger**

Transaction	Start	Change	End/Start of Next Transaction

−10 −9 −8 −7 −6 −5 −4 −3 −2 −1 0 1 2 3 4 5 6 7 8 9 10

Math Masters, p. 321

Student Page

Games

Credits/Debits Game (Advanced Version)

Materials
- □ 1 complete deck of number cards
- □ 1 penny
- □ 1 *Credits/Debits Game* (Advanced Version) Record Sheet for each player (*Math Masters,* p. 469)

Players 2

Skill Addition and subtraction of positive and negative numbers

Object of the game To have more money after adding and subtracting credits and debits.

Directions

1. Shuffle the deck and lay it number-side down between the players.
2. The black-numbered cards are the "credits," and the blue- or red-numbered cards are the "debits."
3. The heads side of the coin tells you to **add** a credit or debit to the bottom line. The tails side of the coin tells you to **subtract** a credit or debit from the bottom line.
4. Each player begins with a bottom line of +$10.
5. Players take turns. On your turn, do the following:
   - Flip the coin. This tells you whether to add or subtract.
   - Draw a card. The card tells you what amount in dollars (positive or negative) to add or subtract from your bottom line. Red or blue numbers are negative numbers. Black numbers are positive numbers.
   - Record the results in your table.
6. Scoring is the same as in the *Credits/Debits Game*.

Record Sheet

	Start	Change		End, and next start
		Addition or Subtraction	Credit or Debit	
1	+$10			
2				
3				
4				
5				
6				
7				
8				
9				
10				

Each player uses one Record Sheet.

Examples Max has a "Start" balance of $5. His coin lands heads up and he records + in the "Addition or Subtraction" column. He draws a red 9 and records −$9 in the "Credit or Debit" column. Max adds: $5 + (−$9) = −$4. He records −$4 in the "End" balance column and also in the "Start" column on the next line.

Beth has a "Start" balance of −$20. Her coin lands tails up, which means subtract. She draws a black 2 (+$2). She subtracts: −$20 − (+$2) = −$22. Her "End" balance is −$22.

***Student Reference Book,* p. 239**

Inform students that this is a new business, and there are some kinks in the accounting system; sometimes the credits or debits are not reported correctly. The subtraction of positive and negative numbers can be understood as the taking away or subtracting from the bottom line what were considered to be credits or debits.

- ▷ When a debit (negative number) is taken away or subtracted, the result is an increase in the bottom line.
- ▷ When a credit (positive number) is taken away or subtracted, the result is a decrease in the bottom line.

Remind students that you are labeling credits with "+" and debits with "–" to help keep track of them as positive or negative numbers. When credits and debits come in, the class will figure out the bottom line as you post transactions on an overhead transparency of *Math Masters,* page 321.

Following is a suggested series of transactions. Entries in black would be reported to the class; entries in color are appropriate student responses.

Event	Start	Change	End, and next start
New business. Start at $0.	$0	$0	$0
Credit (payment) of $8 comes in.	$0	add +$8	+$8
Credit of $3	+$8	add +$3	+$11
Debit of $4	+$11	add −$4	+$7
Credit of $3 was an error. Adjust account.	+$7	subtract +$3	+$4
Debit of $6	+$4	add −$6	−$2
Credit of $5	−$2	add +$5	+$3
Debit of $4 was an error. Adjust account.	+$3	subtract −$4	+$7
Debit of $6 was an error. Adjust account.	+$7	subtract −$6	+$13

NOTE Try to consistently use the terms *positive* and *negative* for numbers and amounts and *add* or *subtract* for operations. It is important to be consistent in *subtracting* the credits and debits as positive and negative numbers when there is an error.

Game Master

Name Date Time

Credits/Debits Game (Advanced Version) Record Sheets

SRB 239

Game 1

	Start	Change		End, and next start
		Addition or Subtraction	Credit or Debit	
1				
2				
3				
4				
5				
6				
7				
8				
9				
10				

Game 2

	Start	Change		End, and next start
		Addition or Subtraction	Credit or Debit	
1				
2				
3				
4				
5				
6				
7				
8				
9				
10				

***Math Masters,* p. 469**

▶ Playing the *Credits/Debits Game* (Advanced Version)

(*Student Reference Book,* p. 239; *Math Masters,* p. 469)

Have students read the rules for the *Credits/Debits Game* (Advanced Version) on page 239 of the *Student Reference Book.* Play one round as a class to be sure that students understand how the game is played. Have students record their steps on *Math Masters,* page 469.

Adjusting the Activity

ELL

Encourage students to use a class number line to assist in subtracting the debits and credits.

AUDITORY ♦ KINESTHETIC ♦ TACTILE ♦ VISUAL

Ongoing Assessment: Informing Instruction

Watch for students who are beginning to devise shortcuts for finding answers. For example, some students may notice that subtracting a negative number is the same as adding a positive number. Do not expect students to explain these strategies; explanations will evolve over time as students acquire experience manipulating positive and negative numbers.

2 Ongoing Learning & Practice

Summarizing the Gram & Ounce Museum

PARTNER ACTIVITY

(*Math Journal 2,* p. 303)

Have partners discuss the Gram & Ounce Museum before completing journal page 303.

Math Boxes 11·6

INDEPENDENT ACTIVITY

(*Math Journal 2,* p. 304)

Mixed Practice Math Boxes in this lesson are linked with Math Boxes in Lessons 11-2 and 11-4. The skills in Problems 5 and 6 preview Unit 12 content.

Ongoing Assessment: Recognizing Student Achievement

Math Boxes Problem 2

Use **Math Boxes, Problem 2** to assess students' ability to identify an example of a rotation. Students are making adequate progress if they are able to correctly identify what the figure would look like if it were rotated clockwise $\frac{1}{2}$-turn. Some students may be able to determine the degree of rotation for each figure.

[Geometry Goal 3]

Student Page

Date Time

LESSON 11·6 **Gram and Ounce Museum**

1. a. What was the heaviest item in the class Gram and Ounce Museum? ______
   b. How much did it weigh? ______ grams ______ ounces Answers vary.
2. a. What was the lightest item in the class Gram and Ounce Museum? ______
   b. How much did it weigh? ______ grams ______ ounces Answers vary.

Complete.

3. 6 g = 6,000 mg
4. 7 g = 7,000 mg
5. 3 kg = 3,000 g
6. 8 kg = 8,000 g
7. 2.9 g = 2,900 mg
8. 4.5 kg = 4,500 g
9. 6 lb = 96 oz
10. 9 lb = 144 oz
11. 3.5 lb = 56 oz
12. 8 T = 16,000 lb

Use the Rules of Thumb below to solve Problems 13–15. Write number models to show how you estimated.

Rules of Thumb
1 kilogram equals about 2.2 pounds
1 ounce equals about 30 grams

Sample answers:

13. A video camera weighs about 120 grams. About how many ounces is that?
    Number model: $120 \div 30 = 4$ 4 oz
14. A baby weighs about 3.5 kilograms at birth. About how many pounds is that?
    Number model: $3.5 * 2.2 = 7.7$ 7.7 lb
15. An African elephant weighs 11,023 pounds. About how many kilograms is that?
    Number model: $11{,}000 \div 2.2 = 5{,}000$ 5,000 kg

Math Journal 2, p. 303

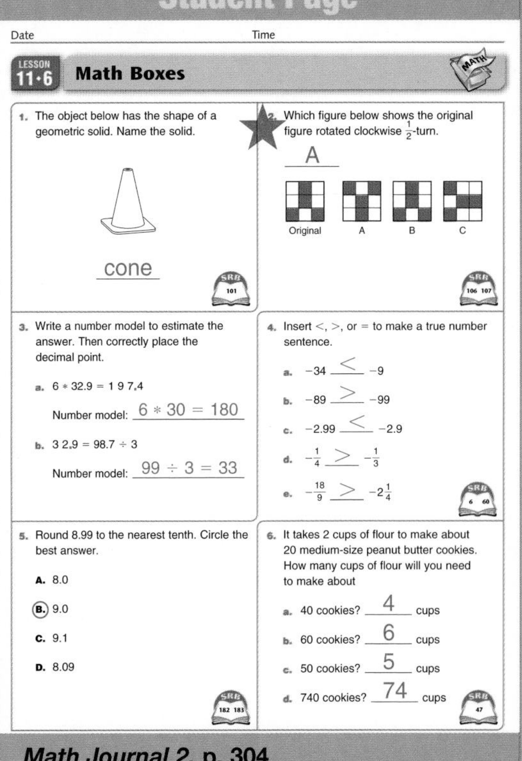

Student Page

Date Time

LESSON 11·6 **Math Boxes**

1. The object below has the shape of a geometric solid. Name the solid.
   cone
2. Which figure below shows the original figure rotated clockwise $\frac{1}{2}$-turn.
   A
   Original A B C
3. Write a number model to estimate the answer. Then correctly place the decimal point.
   a. 6 ∗ 32.9 = 1 9 7.4
   Number model: $6 * 30 = 180$
   b. 3 2.9 = 98.7 ÷ 3
   Number model: $99 \div 3 = 33$
4. Insert <, >, or = to make a true number sentence.
   a. $-34 < -9$
   b. $-89 > -99$
   c. $-2.99 < -2.9$
   d. $-\frac{1}{4} > -\frac{1}{3}$
   e. $-\frac{18}{9} > -2\frac{1}{4}$
5. Round 8.99 to the nearest tenth. Circle the best answer.
   A. 8.0
   (B.) 9.0
   C. 9.1
   D. 8.09
6. It takes 2 cups of flour to make about 20 medium-size peanut butter cookies. How many cups of flour will you need to make about
   a. 40 cookies? 4 cups
   b. 60 cookies? 6 cups
   c. 50 cookies? 5 cups
   d. 740 cookies? 74 cups

Math Journal 2, p. 304

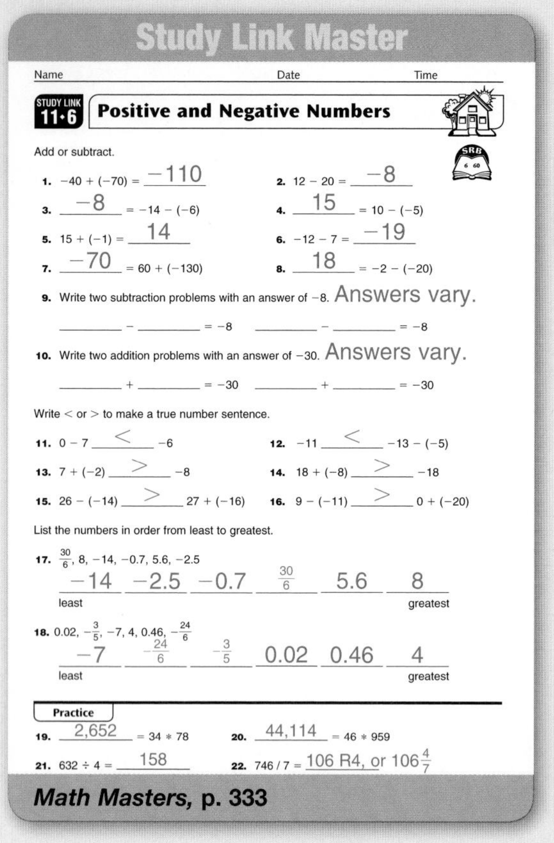

Name Date Time

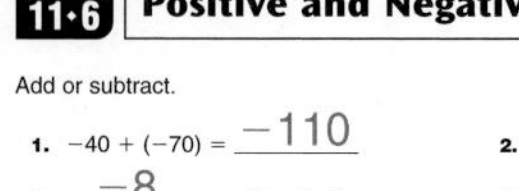

STUDY LINK 11·6 Positive and Negative Numbers

Add or subtract.

1. $-40 + (-70) =$ −110
2. $12 - 20 =$ −8
3. −8 $= -14 - (-6)$
4. 15 $= 10 - (-5)$
5. $15 + (-1) =$ 14
6. $-12 - 7 =$ −19
7. −70 $= 60 + (-130)$
8. 18 $= -2 - (-20)$
9. Write two subtraction problems with an answer of −8. Answers vary.

   ____ − ____ = −8 ____ − ____ = −8

10. Write two addition problems with an answer of −30. Answers vary.

   ____ + ____ = −30 ____ + ____ = −30

Write < or > to make a true number sentence.

11. $0 - 7$ < -6
12. -11 < $-13 - (-5)$
13. $7 + (-2)$ > -8
14. $18 + (-8)$ > -18
15. $26 - (-14)$ > $27 + (-16)$
16. $9 - (-11)$ > $0 + (-20)$

List the numbers in order from least to greatest.

17. $\frac{30}{6}$, 8, −14, −0.7, 5.6, −2.5

   −14, −2.5, −0.7, $\frac{30}{6}$, 5.6, 8
   least … greatest

18. 0.02, $-\frac{3}{5}$, −7, 4, 0.46, $-\frac{24}{6}$

   −7, $-\frac{24}{6}$, $-\frac{3}{5}$, 0.02, 0.46, 4
   least … greatest

Practice

19. 2,652 $= 34 * 78$
20. 44,114 $= 46 * 959$
21. $632 \div 4 =$ 158
22. $746 / 7 =$ 106 R4, or $106\frac{4}{7}$

Math Masters, p. 333

Study Link 11·6

INDEPENDENT ACTIVITY

(*Math Masters*, p. 333)

Home Connection Students add and subtract positive and negative integers and compare and order positive and negative numbers.

3 Differentiation Options

READINESS

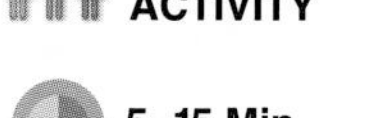

SMALL-GROUP ACTIVITY

5–15 Min

Using a Number Line to Subtract Positive and Negative Numbers

To explore subtraction of positive and negative numbers using a number line model, have students act out subtraction problems by walking on a life-size number line from –10 to 10.

▷ The first number tells students where to start.

▷ The operation sign – means face toward the negative end of the number line.

▷ If the second number is negative, then walk backward. Otherwise, walk forward.

▷ The second number tells how many steps to walk.

▷ The number where the student stops is the answer.

Example: $-2 - (+3)$

▷ Start at -2.

▷ Face toward the negative end of the number line.

▷ Walk forward 3 steps.

▷ You are now at -5. So $-2 - (+3) = -5$.

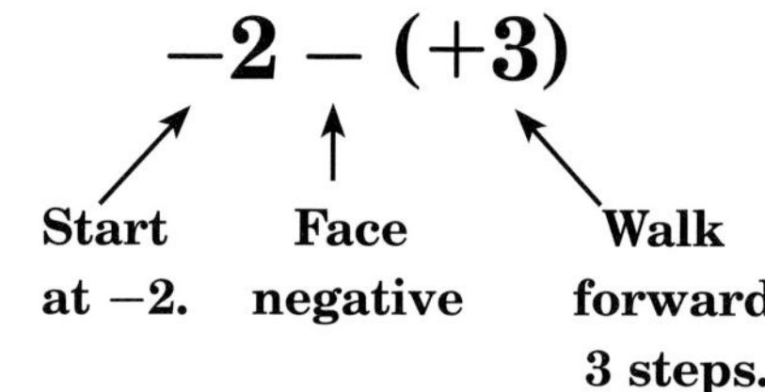

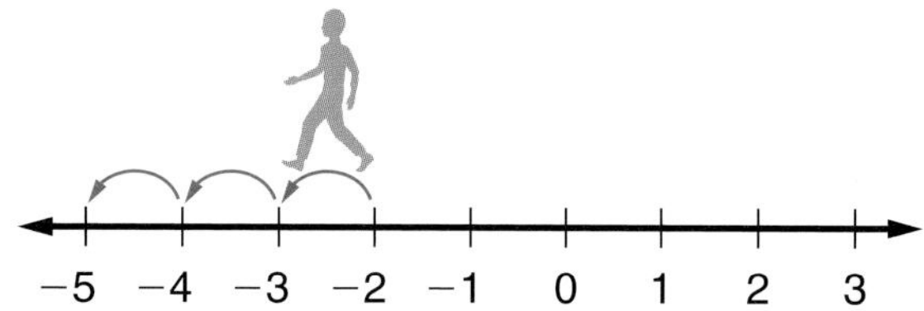

Example: $5 - (-2)$

▷ Start at 5.

▷ Face toward the negative end of the number line.

▷ Walk backward 2 steps.

▷ You are now at 7. So $5 - (-2) = 7$.

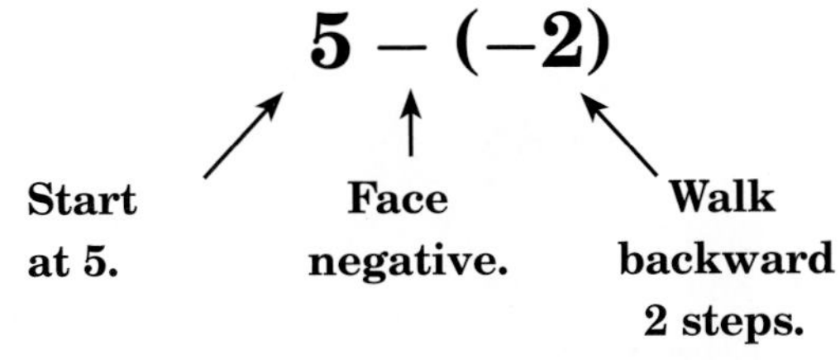

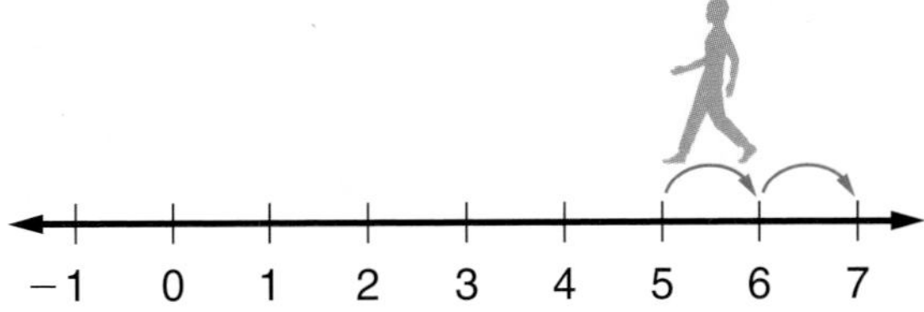

Suggestions:

- $-2 - (-3) = ?$ (Start at –2. Face in the negative direction. Walk backward 3 steps. End up at 1.)
- $4 - (-5) = ?$ (Start at 4. Face in the negative direction. Walk backward 5 steps. End up at 9.)

EXTRA PRACTICE

SMALL-GROUP ACTIVITY

5-Minute Math

5–15 Min

To offer students more experience with adding and subtracting positive and negative numbers, see *5-Minute Math,* pages 100 and 189.

11•7 Capacity

Objective To review units of capacity.

Technology Resources www.everydaymathonline.com

ePresentations

eToolkit

Algorithms Practice

EM Facts Workshop Game™

Family Letters

Assessment Management

Common Core State Standards

Curriculum Focal Points

Interactive Teacher's Lesson Guide

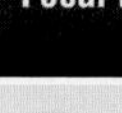

1 Teaching the Lesson

Key Concepts and Skills

- Use division to solve conversion problems.
  [Operations and Computation Goal 4]
- Describe relationships among units of capacity.
  [Measurement and Reference Frames Goal 3]

Key Activities

Students review equivalencies between units of capacity. They start a classroom Liter and Milliliter Museum. Students compare capacities by measuring.

Key Vocabulary

cup ◆ pint ◆ quart ◆ gallon ◆ capacity ◆ liter ◆ milliliter

Materials

Math Journal 2, pp. 305, 305A, and 305B
Student Reference Book, p. 137
Study Link 11•6
measuring cup ◆ empty milk cartons (pint, quart, $\frac{1}{2}$ gallon, gallon) ◆ chart paper (optional) ◆ per group: 1 eyedropper, 1 liter pitcher, 1 graduated beaker, 2 liters of water ◆ slate ◆ index cards ◆ containers of various capacities

2 Ongoing Learning & Practice

Creating a Bar Graph
Math Journal 2, p. 306
Student Reference Book, p. 302
Students create a bar graph to display population data.

Ongoing Assessment: Informing Instruction See page 887.

Math Boxes 11•7
Math Journal 2, p. 307
Students practice and maintain skills through Math Box problems.

Ongoing Assessment: Recognizing Student Achievement
Use Math Boxes, Problem 4.
[Measurement and Reference Frames Goal 3]

Study Link 11•7
Math Masters, p. 334
Students practice and maintain skills through Study Link activities.

3 Differentiation Options

READINESS

Estimating Capacity
Math Masters, p. 389
empty containers of various sizes ◆ pourable substance, such as sand
Students sort containers according to capacity.

EXTRA PRACTICE

5-Minute Math
5-Minute Math™, p. 132
Students convert among customary units of capacity.

ELL SUPPORT

Building a Math Word Bank
Differentiation Handbook, p. 140
Students add the term *capacity* to their Math Word Banks.

Advance Preparation

In preparation for the Liter and Milliliter Museum in Part 1, gather containers of various capacities. See page 886 for more information.

For Part 1, you will also need a 1-liter pitcher filled with water, a milliliter of water held in an eyedropper (20 drops), and 5 additional containers of varying capacities (under 2 liters).

For the optional Readiness activity in Part 3, identify several containers by letter (A, B, C, …), designating a middle-size container as the target capacity.

***Teacher's Reference Manual,* Grades 4–6** pp. 13, 44–46, 216–218, 222–225, 233–237

Getting Started

Mental Math and Reflexes

Pose problems involving the multiplication of a fraction by a whole number. Have students find each product in simplest form. *Suggestions:*

●○○ $10 * \frac{1}{2} = 5$
$18 * \frac{1}{6} = 3$
$36 * \frac{1}{9} = 4$

●●○ $10 * \frac{7}{10} = 7$
$12 * \frac{3}{4} = 9$
$24 * \frac{3}{8} = 9$

●●● $7 * \frac{1}{2} = 3\frac{1}{2}$
$12 * \frac{1}{5} = 2\frac{2}{5}$
$6 * \frac{3}{8} = 2\frac{1}{4}$

Math Message

Fill in the missing numbers in the Math Message problems at the top of journal page 305.

Study Link 11·6 Follow-Up

Have partners compare answers and strategies. Ask volunteers to share the number sentences they wrote for Problems 9 and 10.

1 Teaching the Lesson

Math Message Follow-Up

WHOLE-CLASS DISCUSSION

ELL

(*Math Journal 2,* p. 305)

Display the cup, pint, quart, half-gallon, and gallon containers. Ask students to identify each. Review the answers to the Math Message. To support English language learners, have students model the equivalencies by pouring water or another substance from one container into the other.

Ask: *Did anyone figure out the meaning of the picture next to the Math Message problems?* The "frame" is in the shape of the letter *G.* It represents the word *gallon.* Inside the *G,* there are four *Q*s. Each *Q* represents the word *quart.* Inside each *Q,* there are two *P*s. Each *P* represents the word *pint.* Inside each *P,* there are two *C*s. Each *C* represents the word *cup.*

Explain that **cup, pint, quart,** and **gallon** are units of capacity in the U.S. customary system. **Capacity** is a measure of the amount of liquid or other substance a container can hold. Capacity is a type of volume measure. Tell students that the liter is a unit of capacity in the metric system. A liter and a quart container will hold approximately the same amount of liquid.

Adjusting the Activity

ELL

Have students create a poster of the gallon frame shown on journal page 305 and display it as a reminder of equivalent capacities in the U.S. customary system.

AUDITORY ◆ KINESTHETIC ◆ TACTILE ◆ VISUAL

Student Page

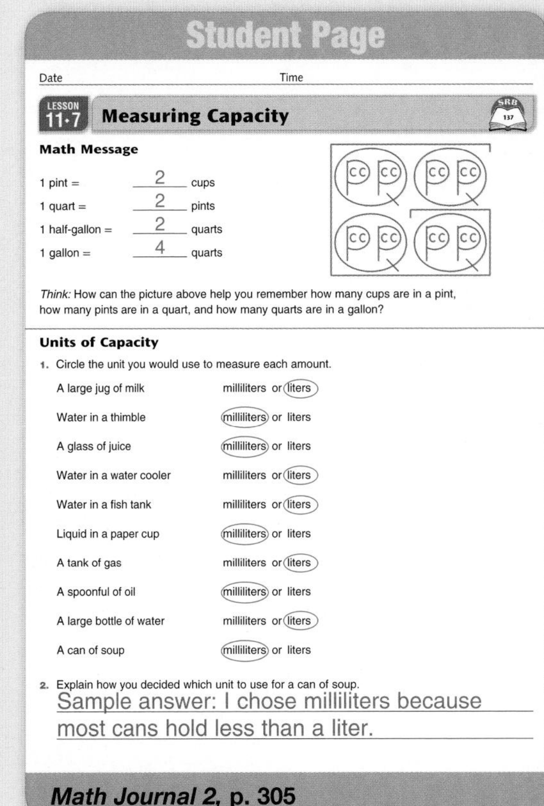

Date Time

LESSON 11·7 **Measuring Capacity**

Math Message

1 pint = 2 cups
1 quart = 2 pints
1 half-gallon = 2 quarts
1 gallon = 4 quarts

Think: How can the picture above help you remember how many cups are in a pint, how many pints are in a quart, and how many quarts are in a gallon?

Units of Capacity

1. Circle the unit you would use to measure each amount.

A large jug of milk	milliliters or (liters)
Water in a thimble	(milliliters) or liters
A glass of juice	(milliliters) or liters
Water in a water cooler	milliliters or (liters)
Water in a fish tank	milliliters or (liters)
Liquid in a paper cup	(milliliters) or liters
A tank of gas	milliliters or (liters)
A spoonful of oil	(milliliters) or liters
A large bottle of water	milliliters or (liters)
A can of soup	(milliliters) or liters

2. Explain how you decided which unit to use for a can of soup.
Sample answer: I chose milliliters because most cans hold less than a liter.

Math Journal 2, p. 305

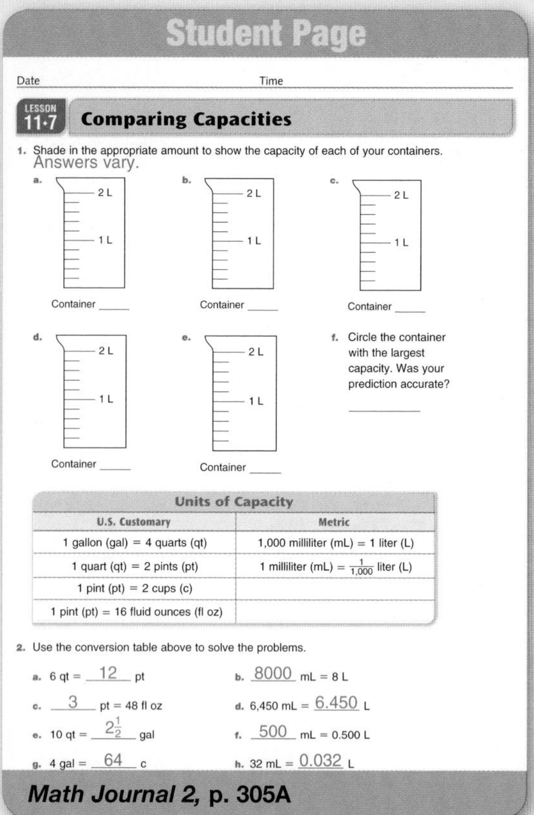

Student Page

Date ______ Time ______

LESSON 11·7 **Comparing Capacities**

1. Shade in the appropriate amount to show the capacity of each of your containers. Answers vary.

a. 2 L, 1 L — Container ______
b. 2 L, 1 L — Container ______
c. 2 L, 1 L — Container ______
d. 2 L, 1 L — Container ______
e. 2 L, 1 L — Container ______
f. Circle the container with the largest capacity. Was your prediction accurate? ______

Units of Capacity	
U.S. Customary	Metric
1 gallon (gal) = 4 quarts (qt)	1,000 milliliter (mL) = 1 liter (L)
1 quart (qt) = 2 pints (pt)	1 milliliter (mL) = $\frac{1}{1,000}$ liter (L)
1 pint (pt) = 2 cups (c)	
1 pint (pt) = 16 fluid ounces (fl oz)	

2. Use the conversion table above to solve the problems.

a. 6 qt = 12 pt
b. 8000 mL = 8 L
c. 3 pt = 48 fl oz
d. 6,450 mL = 6.450 L
e. 10 qt = $2\frac{1}{2}$ gal
f. 500 mL = 0.500 L
g. 4 gal = 64 c
h. 32 mL = 0.032 L

Math Journal 2, p. 305A

Measuring Capacity in Metric Units

(*Math Journal 2,* p. 305; *Student Reference Book,* p. 137)

Tell students that a **liter** is a metric unit of capacity. Liquids such as water, soft drinks, and fuel are often measured in liters. Smaller amounts of liquid are often measured in **milliliters.** Have students read *Student Reference Book,* page 137 and discuss the essay with a partner.

Review the relationship between liters and milliliters (1 liter = 1,000 milliliters). Show students the eyedropper and explain that it holds 20 drops of water, which is equivalent to 1 milliliter. Then show them the 1-liter pitcher and explain that this is 1 liter, or 1,000 milliliters. Explain that 1,000 eyedroppers full of water are needed to fill the 1-liter pitcher. Record the following number sentence on the board to illustrate the relationship between these two metric units:

1 liter (L) = 1,000 milliliters (mL)

Now have students complete journal page 305 to practice determining the appropriate unit for measuring capacity.

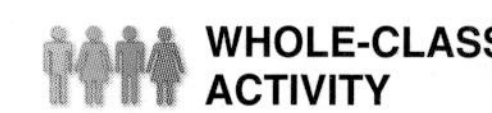

Setting up a Liter and Milliliter Museum

Introduce a project to explore a museum of objects that have different capacities measured in milliliters and liters. Use index cards to label objects in the museum with their capacities. The measuring tools available will determine the range of capacities. Keep a variety of measuring tools near the Liter and Milliliter Museum (for example, an eyedropper, liter pitcher, a measuring cup with a scale in mL, and graduated cylinders of various sizes) so students can measure a wide range of capacities.

Discuss the goals for the collection, the kinds of objects to be collected, and the procedures for adding objects to the museum.

The procedure for adding items should probably be managed by students. Ask students to bring in objects for the museum over the next week or two. This project will continue into the next unit. To ensure accuracy and to assess students' skill in finding the capacity of different objects, require that every item added to the museum be measured by two or three students working independently.

This project will be revisited in Lesson 12-7.

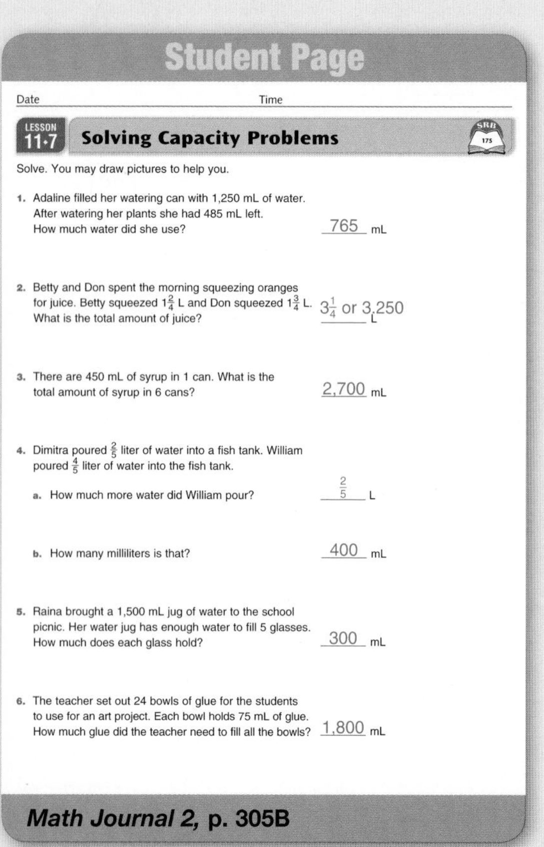

Student Page

Date ______ Time ______

LESSON 11·7 **Solving Capacity Problems** SRB 175

Solve. You may draw pictures to help you.

1. Adaline filled her watering can with 1,250 mL of water. After watering her plants she had 485 mL left. How much water did she use? 765 mL

2. Betty and Don spent the morning squeezing oranges for juice. Betty squeezed $1\frac{2}{4}$ L and Don squeezed $1\frac{3}{4}$ L. What is the total amount of juice? $3\frac{1}{4}$ or 3,250 L

3. There are 450 mL of syrup in 1 can. What is the total amount of syrup in 6 cans? 2,700 mL

4. Dimitra poured $\frac{2}{5}$ liter of water into a fish tank. William poured $\frac{4}{5}$ liter of water into the fish tank.

a. How much more water did William pour? $\frac{2}{5}$ L

b. How many milliliters is that? 400 mL

5. Raina brought a 1,500 mL jug of water to the school picnic. Her water jug has enough water to fill 5 glasses. How much does each glass hold? 300 mL

6. The teacher set out 24 bowls of glue for the students to use for an art project. Each bowl holds 75 mL of glue. How much glue did the teacher need to fill all the bowls? 1,800 mL

Math Journal 2, p. 305B

Comparing Capacity Using Metric Measures

(*Math Journal 2,* p. 305A)

Have students compare the capacity of 5 different size containers. Ask students to predict which containers have the largest and smallest capacities. Then have the students use various measuring tools and water to find and compare the capacities of the five containers and to determine if their predictions were correct. Students shade in the pitchers on journal page 305A to record the capacities. Encourage students to develop personal references for units of capacity as they make and check their predictions.

Solving Capacity Number Stories

PARTNER ACTIVITY

(*Math Journal 2,* p. 305B)

Have students solve the capacity number stories on journal page 305B.

2 Ongoing Learning & Practice

Creating a Bar Graph

INDEPENDENT ACTIVITY

(*Math Journal 2,* p. 306; *Student Reference Book,* p. 302)

Students create a bar graph to display population data.

Ongoing Assessment: Informing Instruction

Watch for students who make incorrect statements for Problem 2, such as "About twice as many people live in New York City as Calcutta." Point out that the vertical scale for the number of people in each city begins at 10 million. The bar for New York City may be twice the height of the bar for Calcutta, but the population of New York City is approximately 18 million, and the population of Calcutta is approximately 13 million.

Math Boxes 11•7

INDEPENDENT ACTIVITY

(*Math Journal 2,* p. 307)

Mixed Practice Math Boxes in this lesson are paired with Math Boxes in Lesson 11-5. The skill in Problem 6 previews Unit 12 content.

Ongoing Assessment: Recognizing Student Achievement

Math Boxes Problem 4

Use **Math Boxes, Problem 4** to assess students' ability to describe the relationships among U.S. customary units of length and among metric units of length. Students are making adequate progress if they are able to complete the equivalencies correctly. Some students may include number models to explain their work.

[Measurement and Reference Frames Goal 3]

Student Page

Date Time

LESSON 11•7 **Largest Cities by Population**

1. Use the data in the Largest Cities by Population table at the top of *Student Reference Book,* page 302 to complete the bar graph. Round each figure to the nearest million.

Largest Cities by Population

Number of People (in millions): 10, 12, 14, 16, 18, 20, 22, 24, 26, 28, 30, 32, 34, 36

Cities: Tokyo, Mexico City, New York City, São Paulo, Mumbai (Bombay), Calcutta, Shanghai

2. Make three statements comparing the cities in the bar graph.

Example: *About 21 million more people live in Tokyo than in Shanghai.*

Sample answers: About the same number of people live in Mexico City and New York City; about 1 million more people live in São Paulo than Mumbai; about twice as many people live in Tokyo as São Paulo.

Math Journal 2, p. 306

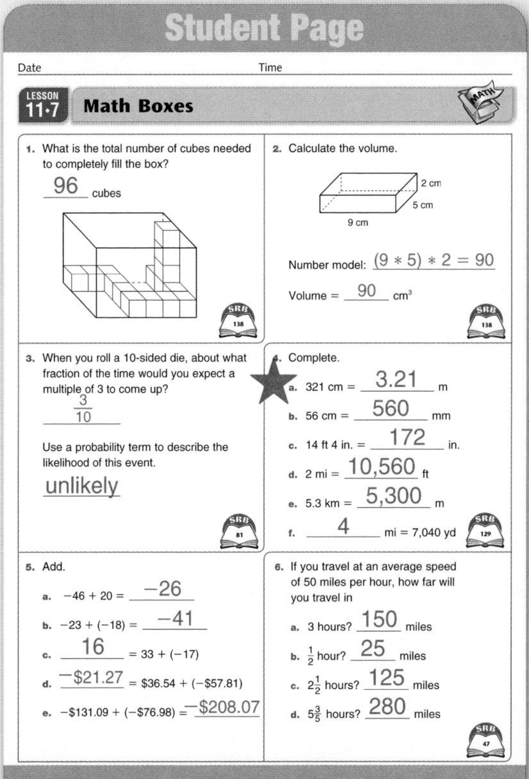

Student Page

Date Time

LESSON 11•7 **Math Boxes**

1. What is the total number of cubes needed to completely fill the box?
96 cubes

2. Calculate the volume.
2 cm, 5 cm, 9 cm
Number model: (9 ∗ 5) ∗ 2 = 90
Volume = 90 cm³

3. When you roll a 10-sided die, about what fraction of the time would you expect a multiple of 3 to come up?
$\frac{3}{10}$
Use a probability term to describe the likelihood of this event.
unlikely

4. Complete.
a. 321 cm = 3.21 m
b. 56 cm = 560 mm
c. 14 ft 4 in. = 172 in.
d. 2 mi = 10,560 ft
e. 5.3 km = 5,300 m
f. 4 mi = 7,040 yd

5. Add.
a. −46 + 20 = −26
b. −23 + (−18) = −41
c. 16 = 33 + (−17)
d. −$21.27 = $36.54 + (−$57.81)
e. −$131.09 + (−$76.98) = −$208.07

6. If you travel at an average speed of 50 miles per hour, how far will you travel in
a. 3 hours? 150 miles
b. $\frac{1}{2}$ hour? 25 miles
c. $2\frac{1}{2}$ hours? 125 miles
d. $5\frac{3}{5}$ hours? 280 miles

Math Journal 2, p. 307

▶ Study Link 11•7

INDEPENDENT ACTIVITY

(*Math Masters,* p. 334)

Home Connection Students find containers that hold less than 1 pint, 1 pint, 1 quart, and more than 1 quart. They solve problems about equivalent capacities.

3 Differentiation Options

READINESS

SMALL-GROUP ACTIVITY

▶ Estimating Capacity

5–15 Min

(*Math Masters,* p. 389)

To explore capacity, have students sort empty containers (identified by letter) according to whether they will hold more than, less than, or about the same as a target container. Ask students to label three columns on an Exit Slip (*Math Masters,* page 389) *more than, less than,* and *about the same*. Have them sort the containers according to the categories.

Provide students with a pourable substance such as sand, rice, pasta, or beans to check their estimates. Have students rearrange the groups as necessary.

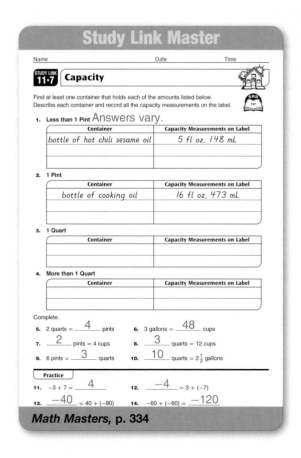

Study Link Master

Name Date Time

STUDY LINK 11•7 **Capacity**

Find at least one container that holds each of the amounts listed below. Describe each container and record all the capacity measurements on the label.

SRB 137

1. Less than 1 Pint Answers vary.

Container	Capacity Measurements on Label
bottle of hot chili sesame oil	5 fl oz, 148 mL

2. 1 Pint

Container	Capacity Measurements on Label
bottle of cooking oil	16 fl oz, 473 mL

3. 1 Quart

Container	Capacity Measurements on Label

4. More than 1 Quart

Container	Capacity Measurements on Label

Complete.

5. 2 quarts = 4 pints
6. 3 gallons = 48 cups
7. 2 pints = 4 cups
8. 3 quarts = 12 cups
9. 6 pints = 3 quarts
10. 10 quarts = $2\frac{1}{2}$ gallons

Practice

11. $-3 + 7 =$ 4
12. -4 $= 3 + (-7)$
13. -40 $= 40 + (-80)$
14. $-60 + (-60) =$ -120

Math Masters, p. 334

EXTRA PRACTICE

5-Minute Math

5–15 Min

To offer students more experience with units of capacity, see *5-Minute Math,* page 132.

ELL SUPPORT

Building a Math Word Bank

5–15 Min

(*Differentiation Handbook,* p. 140)

To provide language support for capacity, have students use the Word Bank Template found on *Differentiation Handbook,* page 140. Ask students to write the term *capacity,* draw pictures relating to the term, and write other related words. See the *Differentiation Handbook* for more information.

11·8 Progress Check 11

Objective To assess students' progress on mathematical content through the end of Unit 11.

1 Looking Back: Cumulative Assessment

Input student data from Progress Check 11 into the **Assessment Management Spreadsheets**.

Materials
- Study Link 11•7
- *Assessment Handbook,* pp. 134–141, 206–210, 226, and 286–289
- slate; centimeter cubes

CONTENT ASSESSED	LESSON(S)	ASSESSMENT ITEMS				
		SELF	ORAL/SLATE	WRITTEN PART A	WRITTEN PART B	OPEN RESPONSE
Add and subtract signed numbers. [Operations and Computation Goal 2]	11•3, 11•5–11•7	1, 2			15–22	
Multiply and divide whole numbers and decimals. [Operations and Computation Goal 4]	11•1–11•4, 11•6				23–26	
Round decimals to the nearest tenth. [Operations and Computation Goal 6]	11•2, 11•4, 11•6, 11•7		1			
Make reasonable estimates for whole number and decimal multiplication problems; explain how the estimates were obtained. [Operations and Computation Goal 6]	11•7					✔
Describe events using basic probability terms. [Data and Chance Goal 3]	11•5, 11•7	3		12		
Estimate weight with and without tools. [Measurement and Reference Frames Goal 1]	11•1, 11•2, 11•6, 11•7			11		
Describe and use strategies to find the volume of a rectangular prism. [Measurement and Reference Frames Goal 2]	11•4, 11•5, 11•7	4, 5	2	7–10	13, 14	✔
Describe relationships among units of weight, length, and capacity. [Measurement and Reference Frames Goal 3]	11•1, 11•4, 11•5, 11•7		3, 4			✔
Identify, describe, compare, and classify plane and solid figures. [Geometry Goal 2]	11•2–11•6	6	2	1–6		

2 Looking Ahead: Preparing for Unit 12

Math Boxes 11•8

Study Link 11•8: Unit 12 Family Letter

Materials
- *Math Journal 2,* p. 308
- *Math Masters,* pp. 335–338

Getting Started

Math Message • Self Assessment

Complete the Self Assessment (Assessment Handbook, *page 206*).

Study Link 11·8 Follow-Up

Have small groups of students compare the containers they found.

1 Looking Back: Cumulative Assessment

Math Message Follow-Up

INDEPENDENT ACTIVITY

(Self Assessment, *Assessment Handbook,* p. 206)

The Self Assessment offers students the opportunity to reflect upon their progress.

Oral and Slate Assessments

WHOLE-CLASS ACTIVITY

Problems 1 and 3 provide summative information and can be used for grading purposes. Problems 2 and 4 provide formative information that can be useful in planning future instruction.

Oral Assessment

1. Have students round each number to the nearest tenth and explain how they did it. *Suggestions:*
    - 4.36 4.4
    - 18.03 18.0
    - 9.97 10.0
    - 2.79 2.8
    - 1.62 1.6
    - 1.006 1.0

2. Provide centimeter cubes. Ask students to build rectangular prisms with given volumes or dimensions. *Suggestions:*
    - volume = 24 cm^3
    - volume = 30 cm^3
    - length of base = 5 cm
width of base = 4 cm
height of prism = 2 cm
    - length of base = 3 cm
width of base = 2 cm
height of prism = 3 cm

Slate Assessment

3. Pose problems involving equivalent measures. *Suggestions:*
    - 13 ft = _4_ yd _1_ ft
    - 74 in. = _2_ yd _2_ in.
    - _30_ ft = 10 yd
    - _60_ mm = 6 cm
    - 89 mm = _8.9_ cm
    - 4 cm = _0.04_ m

4. Pose problems involving equivalent capacities. *Suggestions:*
    - 6 cups = _3_ pints
    - _8_ cups = 2 quarts
    - 2 gallons = _8_ quarts
    - 3 quarts = _6_ pints
    - $4\frac{1}{2}$ gallons = 18 quarts
    - $5\frac{1}{2}$ quarts = 11 pints

Assessment Master

Name Date Time

LESSON 11·8 **Self Assessment** Progress Check 11

Think about each skill listed below. Assess your own progress by checking the most appropriate box.

Skills	I can do this on my own and explain how to do it.	I can do this on my own.	I can do this if I get help or look at an example.
1. Add positive and negative numbers.			
2. Subtract positive and negative numbers.			
3. Describe events using terms such as: *certain, likely, very unlikely,* and *impossible.*			
4. Count cubes to find the volume of a rectangular prism.			
5. Use a formula to find the volume of a rectangular prism.			
6. Identify, describe, and compare solid figures such as: *rectangular prisms, pyramids,* and *cones.*			

Assessment Handbook, **p. 206**

Assessment Master

Name Date Time

LESSON 11·8 **Written Assessment** Progress Check 11

Part A

1. Each object below has the shape of a geometric solid. Name the geometric solid.

a. sphere

b. cylinder

2. How many faces does the pentagonal pyramid have? _6_ faces

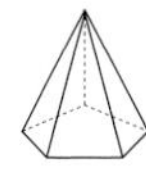

3. Mark Xs on the vertices of the triangular prism.

4. How many edges does the rectangular pyramid have? _8_ edges

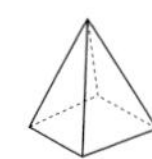

5. Name the shape of the base of the pyramid below. _hexagon_

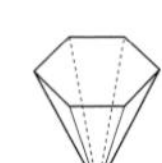

6. Describe the geometric solid to the right. Use the words *vertex, base, face, edge,* and *congruent* in your description.
Sample answer: This is a triangular prism with 6 vertices, 9 edges, and 5 faces. It has 3 rectangular faces and 2 congruent triangular bases.

Assessment Handbook, **p. 207**

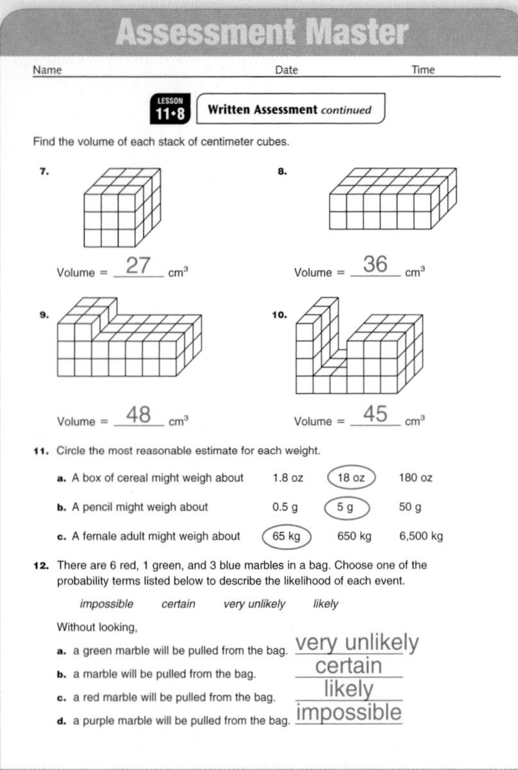

Assessment Master

Name Date Time

LESSON 11•8 **Written Assessment** *continued*

Find the volume of each stack of centimeter cubes.

7. Volume = 27 cm^3

8. Volume = 36 cm^3

9. Volume = 48 cm^3

10. Volume = 45 cm^3

11. Circle the most reasonable estimate for each weight.

a. A box of cereal might weigh about 1.8 oz (18 oz) 180 oz

b. A pencil might weigh about 0.5 g (5 g) 50 g

c. A female adult might weigh about (65 kg) 650 kg 6,500 kg

12. There are 6 red, 1 green, and 3 blue marbles in a bag. Choose one of the probability terms listed below to describe the likelihood of each event.

impossible *certain* *very unlikely* *likely*

Without looking,

a. a green marble will be pulled from the bag. very unlikely

b. a marble will be pulled from the bag. certain

c. a red marble will be pulled from the bag. likely

d. a purple marble will be pulled from the bag. impossible

***Assessment Handbook*, p. 208**

NOTE In *Fourth Grade Everyday Mathematics,* the term *triangular prism* refers only to a right triangular prism. In Problem 6, the triangular prism has 2 congruent triangular bases and 3 rectangular faces. If students are not sure whether the prism is right or oblique, however, they may state that the 3 faces are parallelograms, which is also correct.

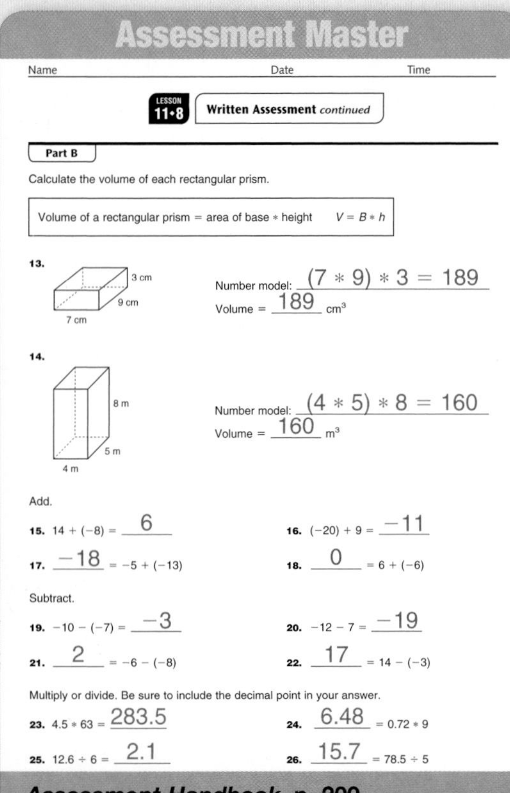

Assessment Master

Name Date Time

LESSON 11•8 **Written Assessment** *continued*

Part B

Calculate the volume of each rectangular prism.

Volume of a rectangular prism = area of base ∗ height $V = B * h$

13. (3 cm, 9 cm, 7 cm) Number model: $(7 * 9) * 3 = 189$ Volume = 189 cm^3

14. (8 m, 5 m, 4 m) Number model: $(4 * 5) * 8 = 160$ Volume = 160 m^3

Add.

15. $14 + (-8) = 6$

16. $(-20) + 9 = -11$

17. $-18 = -5 + (-13)$

18. $0 = 6 + (-6)$

Subtract.

19. $-10 - (-7) = -3$

20. $-12 - 7 = -19$

21. $2 = -6 - (-8)$

22. $17 = 14 - (-3)$

Multiply or divide. Be sure to include the decimal point in your answer.

23. $4.5 * 63 = 283.5$

24. $6.48 = 0.72 * 9$

25. $12.6 \div 6 = 2.1$

26. $15.7 = 78.5 \div 5$

***Assessment Handbook*, p. 209**

▶ Written Assessment

INDEPENDENT ACTIVITY

(*Assessment Handbook,* pp. 207–209)

Part A Recognizing Student Achievement

Problems 1–12 provide summative information and may be used for grading purposes.

Problem(s)	Description
1	Name the geometric solid.
2	Identify pentagonal pyramid faces.
3	Mark the vertices of a triangular prism.
4	Identify rectangular pyramid edges.
5	Name the base of a pyramid.
6	Describe a triangular prism.
7–10	Find the volume of a stack of cm cubes.
11	Make reasonable weight estimates.
12	Use probability terms to describe events.

Part B Informing Instruction

Problems 13–26 provide formative information that can be useful in planning future instruction.

Problem(s)	Description
13, 14	Use a volume formula.
15–18	Add signed numbers.
19–22	Subtract signed numbers.
23–26	Multiply and divide using decimals.

Use the checklists on pages 287 and 289 of the *Assessment Handbook* to record results. Then input the data into the **Assessment Management Spreadsheets** to keep an ongoing record of students' progress toward Grade-Level Goals.

▶ Open Response

INDEPENDENT ACTIVITY

(*Assessment Handbook,* p. 210)

Record Rainfall

The open-response item requires students to apply concepts and skills from Unit 11 to solve a multistep problem. See *Assessment Handbook,* pages 137–141 for rubrics and students' work samples for this problem.

Looking Ahead: Preparing for Unit 12

Math Boxes 11•8

INDEPENDENT ACTIVITY

(*Math Journal 2,* p. 308)

Mixed Practice This page previews Unit 12 content.

Study Link 11•8: Unit 12 Family Letter

INDEPENDENT ACTIVITY

(*Math Masters,* pp. 335–338)

Home Connection The Unit 12 Family Letter provides parents and guardians with information and activities related to Unit 12 topics.

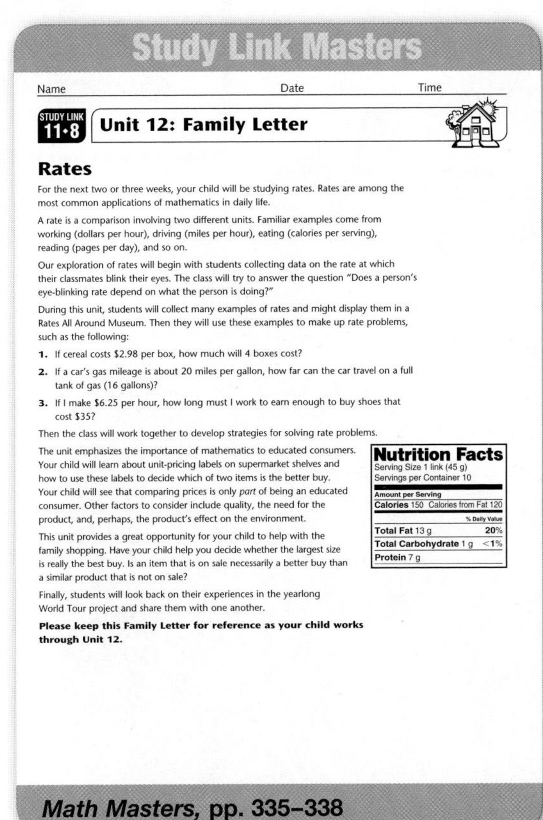

Study Link Masters

Name Date Time

STUDY LINK 11•8 **Unit 12: Family Letter**

Rates

For the next two or three weeks, your child will be studying rates. Rates are among the most common applications of mathematics in daily life.

A rate is a comparison involving two different units. Familiar examples come from working (dollars per hour), driving (miles per hour), eating (calories per serving), reading (pages per day), and so on.

Our exploration of rates will begin with students collecting data on the rate at which their classmates blink their eyes. The class will try to answer the question "Does a person's eye-blinking rate depend on what the person is doing?"

During this unit, students will collect many examples of rates and might display them in a Rates All Around Museum. Then they will use these examples to make up rate problems, such as the following:

1. If cereal costs $2.98 per box, how much will 4 boxes cost?
2. If a car's gas mileage is about 20 miles per gallon, how far can the car travel on a full tank of gas (16 gallons)?
3. If I make $6.25 per hour, how long must I work to earn enough to buy shoes that cost $35?

Then the class will work together to develop strategies for solving rate problems.

The unit emphasizes the importance of mathematics to educated consumers. Your child will learn about unit-pricing labels on supermarket shelves and how to use these labels to decide which of two items is the better buy. Your child will see that comparing prices is only *part* of being an educated consumer. Other factors to consider include quality, the need for the product, and, perhaps, the product's effect on the environment.

Nutrition Facts
Serving Size 1 link (45 g)
Servings per Container 10
Amount per Serving
Calories 150 Calories from Fat 120
% Daily Value
Total Fat 13 g **20%**
Total Carbohydrate 1 g **<1%**
Protein 7 g

This unit provides a great opportunity for your child to help with the family shopping. Have your child help you decide whether the largest size is really the best buy. Is an item that is on sale necessarily a better buy than a similar product that is not on sale?

Finally, students will look back on their experiences in the yearlong World Tour project and share them with one another.

Please keep this Family Letter for reference as your child works through Unit 12.

Math Masters, **pp. 335–338**

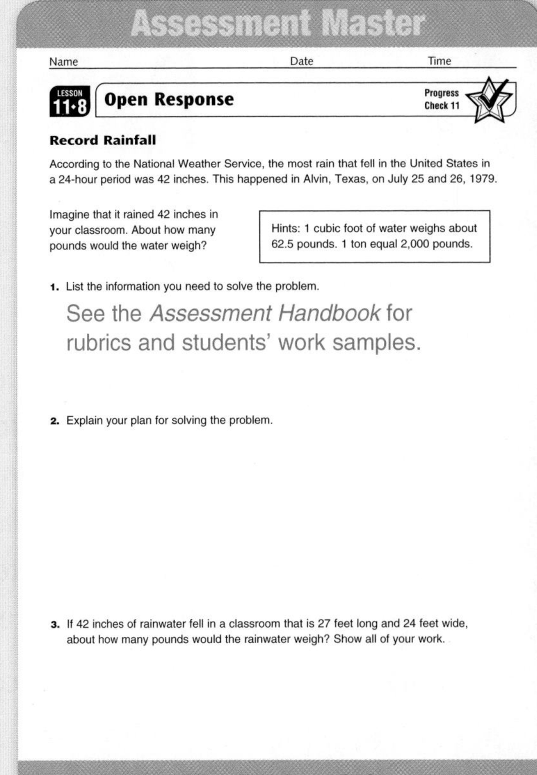

Assessment Master

Name Date Time

LESSON 11•8 **Open Response** Progress Check 11

Record Rainfall

According to the National Weather Service, the most rain that fell in the United States in a 24-hour period was 42 inches. This happened in Alvin, Texas, on July 25 and 26, 1979.

Imagine that it rained 42 inches in your classroom. About how many pounds would the water weigh?

Hints: 1 cubic foot of water weighs about 62.5 pounds. 1 ton equal 2,000 pounds.

1. List the information you need to solve the problem.

See the *Assessment Handbook* for rubrics and students' work samples.

2. Explain your plan for solving the problem.

3. If 42 inches of rainwater fell in a classroom that is 27 feet long and 24 feet wide, about how many pounds would the rainwater weigh? Show all of your work.

Assessment Handbook, **p. 210**

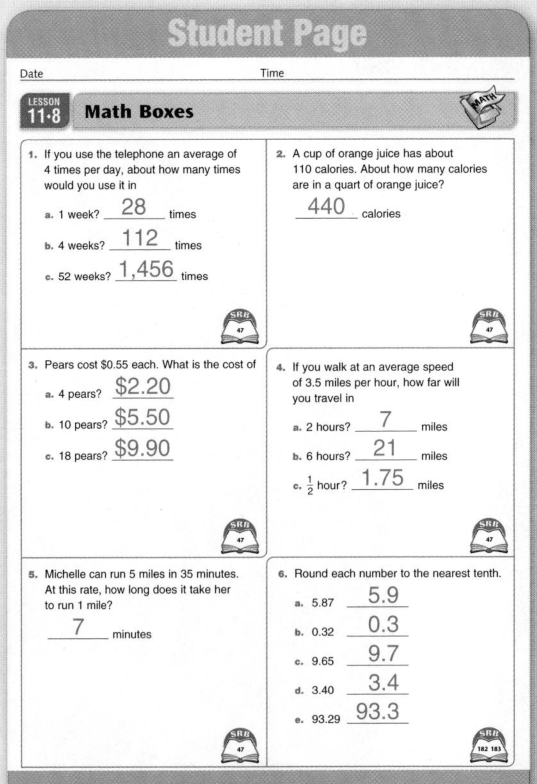

Student Page

Date Time

LESSON 11•8 **Math Boxes**

1. If you use the telephone an average of 4 times per day, about how many times would you use it in
   a. 1 week? 28 times
   b. 4 weeks? 112 times
   c. 52 weeks? 1,456 times

SRB 47

2. A cup of orange juice has about 110 calories. About how many calories are in a quart of orange juice?
   440 calories

SRB 47

3. Pears cost $0.55 each. What is the cost of
   a. 4 pears? $2.20
   b. 10 pears? $5.50
   c. 18 pears? $9.90

SRB 47

4. If you walk at an average speed of 3.5 miles per hour, how far will you travel in
   a. 2 hours? 7 miles
   b. 6 hours? 21 miles
   c. $\frac{1}{2}$ hour? 1.75 miles

SRB 47

5. Michelle can run 5 miles in 35 minutes. At this rate, how long does it take her to run 1 mile?
   7 minutes

SRB 47

6. Round each number to the nearest tenth.
   a. 5.87 5.9
   b. 0.32 0.3
   c. 9.65 9.7
   d. 3.40 3.4
   e. 93.29 93.3

SRB 182 183

Math Journal 2, **p. 308**

Unit 12 Organizer

Rates

Overview

In Unit 12, students focus on rates. The use of rates is prevalent in the everyday world. The ability to handle rate, ratio, and proportion problems with ease is an indication of good "number sense" and "measurement sense." *Everyday Mathematics* takes the position that the key to understanding rates is repeated exposure to their many uses in everyday life. Unit 12 has three main areas of focus:

- To introduce rates and provide practice collecting and comparing rate data,
- To provide practice solving rate problems, to provide practice comparing unit prices and identifying information needed for comparison shopping, and
- To reflect on this year's World Tour experiences.

SPEED
LIMIT
25

Linking to the Common Core State Standards

CCSS

The content of Unit 12 addresses the Common Core State Standards for Mathematics in *Measurement and Data.* The correlation of the Common Core State Standards to the *Everyday Mathematics* Grade 4 lessons begins on page CS1.

Contents

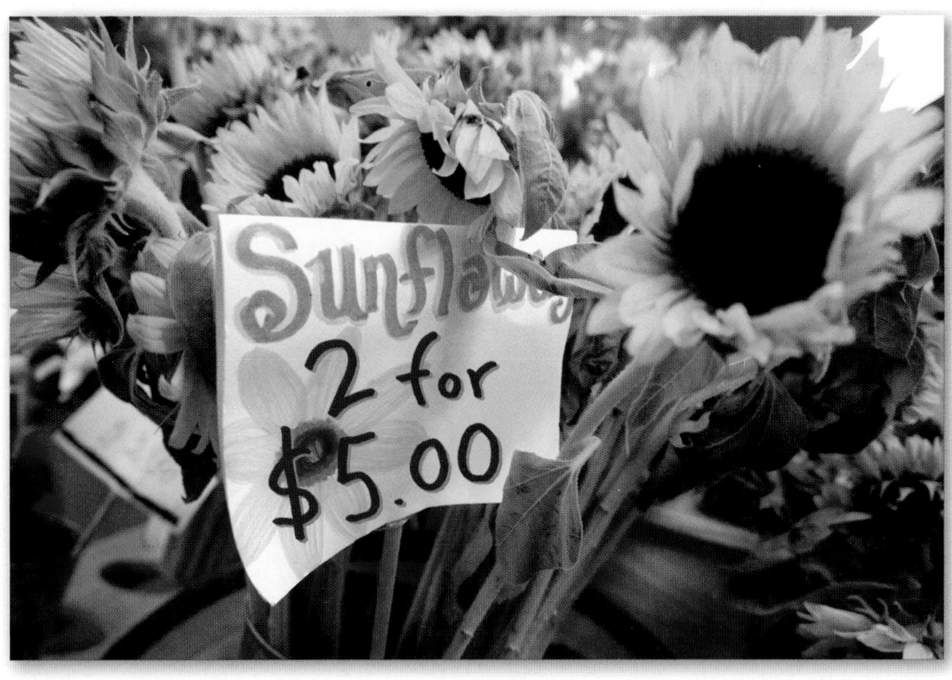

Learning In Perspective

	Lesson Objectives	Links to the Past	Links to the Future
12•1	To introduce rates; and to provide practice collecting and comparing rate data.	Grades 2 and 3: Collect, organize, interpret, and display data.	Grades 5 and 6: Collect, organize, interpret, and display data.
12•2	To provide practice using a rate table to record rate information; and to provide practice solving rate problems.	Grades 2 and 3: Organize data in tables. Solve "What's My Rule?" problems.	Grade 5: Represent rates with formulas, tables of values, and graphs. Solve rate and ratio number stories. Grade 6: Estimate travel time based on rate information. Model rate and ratio problems with proportions; solve proportions by cross multiplication and other methods.
12•3	To provide practice checking the validity of data by converting the data to more accessible rates.	Grades 2 and 3: Collect, organize, interpret, and display data.	Grades 5 and 6: Collect, organize, interpret, and display data.
12•4	To introduce calculating the unit price for a product; and to provide practice comparing unit prices and identifying information needed for comparison shopping.	Grade 2: Solve comparison number stories; use comparison diagrams and write number models. Grade 3: Practice multiplication in number stories. Compare estimated costs to exact costs. Make up and solve problems about costs of multiple items.	Grade 5: Review the meaning and uses of rates; represent rates with formulas, tables of values, and graphs. Solve rate and ratio number stories. Measure heart rates. Grade 6: Model rate and ratio problems with proportions; solve proportions by cross multiplication and other methods.
12•5	To provide practice calculating and comparing unit prices that involve fractions of cents.	Grade 2: Solve comparison number stories; use comparison diagrams and write number models. Grade 3: Practice multiplication in number stories. Compare estimated costs to exact costs. Make up and solve problems about costs of multiple items.	Grade 5: Review the meaning and uses of rates; represent rates with formulas, tables of values, and graphs. Solve rate and ratio number stories. Measure heart rates. Grade 6: Model rate and ratio problems with proportions; solve proportions by cross multiplication and other methods.
12•6	To reflect on this year's World Tour experiences.	Grade 3: Collect and record sunrise/sunset data once a week throughout the school year.	Grade 5: Complete a yearlong American Tour project to explore mathematical aspects of the history, demographics, politics, and environment of the United States.

	Key Concepts and Skills	Grade 4 Goals*
12•1	Describe examples of rates.	Operations and Computation Goal 7
	Collect and organize data to create a table.	Data and Chance Goal 1
	Find the median and mean of a data set.	Data and Chance Goal 2
	Use data to draw conclusions and make predictions.	Data and Chance Goal 2
	Write a number sentence with parentheses.	Patterns, Functions, and Algebra Goal 3
12•2	Find multiples.	Number and Numeration Goal 3
	Solve multiplication and division facts.	Operations and Computation Goal 3
	Multiply and divide decimals by whole numbers.	Operations and Computation Goal 4
	Use repeated addition and scaling to model multiplication problems.	Operations and Computation Goal 7
	Use patterns and rules to solve rate problems.	Patterns, Functions, and Algebra Goal 1
12•3	Find multiples.	Number and Numeration Goal 3
	Divide whole numbers.	Operations and Computation Goal 4
	Round decimals and whole numbers.	Operations and Computation Goal 6
	Convert between rates.	Operations and Computation Goal 7
	Analyze and interpret data.	Data and Chance Goal 2
12•4	Find multiples.	Number and Numeration Goal 3
	Multiply and divide decimals by whole numbers.	Operations and Computation Goal 4
	Use repeated addition and scaling to model multiplication problems.	Operations and Computation Goal 7
	Analyze and interpret data.	Data and Chance Goal 2
	Use patterns and rules to solve rate problems.	Patterns, Functions, and Algebra Goal 1
12•5	Compare decimals.	Number and Numeration Goal 6
	Divide decimals by whole numbers.	Operations and Computation Goal 4
	Round decimals.	Operations and Computation Goal 6
	Use repeated addition and scaling to solve rate problems.	Operations and Computation Goal 7
12•6	Solve problems involving addition of whole numbers.	Operations and Computation Goal 2
	Solve problems involving division of multidigit whole numbers; interpret the remainder.	Operations and Computation Goal 4

*See the Appendix for a complete list of Grade 4 Goals.

A Balanced Curriculum

Ongoing Practice

Everyday Mathematics provides numerous opportunities for ongoing practice. These activities are embedded throughout the lessons:

Mental Math and Reflexes activities promote speed and accuracy in mental computation.

Math Boxes offer mixed practice and are paired across lessons as shown in the brackets below. This makes them useful as assessment tools.

Mixed practice	[12•1, 12•3], [12•2, 12•4, 12•6], [12•5, 12•7]
Mixed practice with multiple choice	12•1, 12•4, 12•6
Mixed practice with writing/reasoning opportunity	12•2, 12•3, 12•5

Study Links are daily homework assignments that review the content of the lesson and often contain ongoing facts practice or computation practice.

5-Minute Math problems are offered for additional practice in Lessons 12•5 and 12•6.

EM Facts Workshop Game provides online practice of basic facts and computation.

EXTRA PRACTICE **Extra Practice** activities are included in Lessons 12•2, 12•5, and 12•6.

Practice through Games

Games are an essential component of practice in the *Everyday Mathematics* program. Games offer skills practice and promote strategic thinking. See the *Differentiation Handbook* for ways to adapt games to meet students' needs.

Lesson	Game	Skill Practiced
12•2	*Credits/Debits Game* (Advanced Version)	Adding and subtracting positive and negative integers [OC Goal 2]
12•4	*Name That Number*	Representing numbers in different ways [NN Goal 4 and PFA Goal 3]
12•5	*Fraction Top-It*	Comparing and ordering fractions [NN Goal 6]

[NN] Number and Numeration
[MRF] Measurement and Reference Frames
[OC] Operations and Computation
[GEO] Geometry
[DC] Data and Chance
[PFA] Patterns, Functions, and Algebra

Problem Solving 

Experts at problem solving and mathematical modeling generally do these things:

- Identify the problem.
- Decide what information is needed to solve the problem.
- Play with and study the data to find patterns and meaning.
- Identify and use mathematical procedures to solve the problem.
- Decide whether the solution makes sense and whether it can be applied to other problems.

The table below lists some of the opportunities in this unit for students to practice these strategies.

Lesson	Activity
12•1	Compare eye-blinking rates for when a person is reading and at rest.
12•2	Solve rate problems.
12•3	Use rates to determine if data makes sense.
12•4	Calculate and compare unit prices.
12•5	Solve problems involving unit prices.

Lessons that teach *through* problem solving, not just *about* problem solving

See Chapter 18: Problem Solving in the *Teacher's Reference Manual* for more information.

The Language of Mathematics

Everyday Mathematics provides lesson-specific suggestions to help all students acquire, process, and express mathematical ideas. Throughout Unit 12, there are lesson-specific language development notes that address the needs of English language learners, indicated by ELL.

ELL SUPPORT Activities to support English language learners are in Part 3 of Lessons 12•1 and 12•3.

The *English Learners Handbook* and the *Differentiation Handbook* have suggestions for promoting language development and acquisition of mathematics vocabulary. See Unit 12 in each handbook.

Unit 12 Vocabulary

comparison shopping
consumer
per
products
rate
rate table
services
unit price
unit rate

Literacy Connection

Lesson 12•2 *Each Orange Had 8 Slices: A Counting Book,* by Paul Giganti, Greenwillow Books, 1999

If Dogs Were Dinosaurs, by David M. Schwartz, Scholastic Inc., 2005

If You Hopped Like a Frog, by David M. Schwartz, Scholastic Inc., 1999

The Grapes of Math, by Greg Tang, Scholastic Paperbacks, 2004

For more literacy connections, see the *Home Connection Handbook,* Grades 4–6.

Cross-Curricular Links 

Social Studies – Lessons 12•1, 12•6
Literature – Lesson 12•2
Consumer – Lessons 12•4, 12•5
Science – Lesson 12•5

Balanced Assessment

Daily Assessments

- **Recognizing Student Achievement** – A daily assessment that is included in every lesson to evaluate students' progress toward the Grade 4 Grade-Level Goals.
- **Informing Instruction** – Notes that appear throughout the unit to help anticipate students' common errors and suggest appropriate problem-solving strategies.

Lesson	Recognizing Student Achievement	Informing Instruction
12•1	Write number sentences comparing two numbers between 100 and –100. [NN Goal 6]	
12•2	Describe the rule for a pattern and use that rule to solve problems. [PFA Goal 1]	Note the similarities between a rate table and a "What's My Rule?" table.
12•3	Use given data to create a line graph. [DC Goal 1]	Note that a problem may be missing information or contain unnecessary information.
12•4	Insert parentheses in number sentences to make them true. [PFA Goal 3]	Do not assume that the lower-cost package is the better buy.
12•5	Use scaling to model multiplication and division. [OC Goal 7]	
12•6	Demonstrate automaticity with multiplication facts through 10 * 10. [OC Goal 3]	

[NN] Number and Numeration [OC] Operations and Computation [DC] Data and Chance
[MRF] Measurement and Reference Frames [GEO] Geometry [PFA] Patterns, Functions, and Algebra

Portfolio Opportunities

The following lessons provide opportunities to gather samples of students' mathematical writings, drawings, and creations to add balance to the assessment process: Lessons 12•1, 12•2, 12•3, 12•5, and 12•7.

See pages 16 and 17 in the *Assessment Handbook* for more information about portfolios and how to use them.

Unit Assessment

Progress Check 12 – A cumulative assessment of concepts and skills taught in Unit 12 and in previous units, providing information for evaluating students' progress. These assessments include oral/slate, written, and open-response activities, as shown below in the sample Progress Check lesson opener.

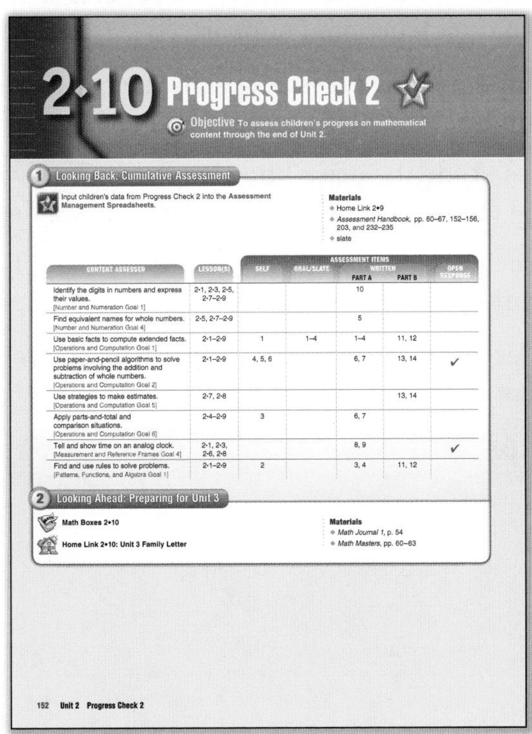

2·10 Progress Check 2

Objective To assess children's progress on mathematical content through the end of Unit 2.

1 Looking Back: Cumulative Assessment

Input children's data from Progress Check 2 into the Assessment Management Spreadsheets.

Materials
- Home Link 2•9
- *Assessment Handbook,* pp. 60–67, 152–156, 203, and 232–235
- slate

CONTENT ASSESSED	LESSON(S)	ASSESSMENT ITEMS				
		SELF	ORAL/SLATE	WRITTEN PART A	WRITTEN PART B	OPEN RESPONSE
Identify the digits in numbers and express their values. [Number and Numeration Goal 1]	2·1, 2·3, 2·5, 2·7–2·9			10		
Find equivalent names for whole numbers. [Number and Numeration Goal 4]	2·5, 2·7–2·9			5		
Use basic facts to compute extended facts. [Operations and Computation Goal 1]	2·1–2·9	1	1–4	1–4	11, 12	
Use paper-and-pencil algorithms to solve problems involving the addition and subtraction of whole numbers. [Operations and Computation Goal 2]	2·1–2·9	4, 5, 6		6, 7	13, 14	✓
Use strategies to make estimates. [Operations and Computation Goal 5]	2·7, 2·8				13, 14	
Apply parts-and-total and comparison situations. [Operations and Computation Goal 6]	2·4–2·9	3		6, 7		
Tell and show time on an analog clock. [Measurement and Reference Frames Goal 4]	2·1, 2·3, 2·6, 2·8			8, 9		✓
Find and use rules to solve problems. [Patterns, Functions, and Algebra Goal 1]	2·1–2·9	2		3, 4	11, 12	

2 Looking Ahead: Preparing for Unit 3

Math Boxes 2•10

Home Link 2•10: Unit 3 Family Letter

Materials
- *Math Journal 1,* p. 54
- *Math Masters,* pp. 60–63

152 Unit 2 Progress Check 2

Core Assessment Resources

Assessment Handbook

- **Unit 12 Assessment Overview,** pages 142–149
- **Unit 12 Assessment Masters,** pages 211–215
- **Unit 12 Individual Profiles of Progress,** pages 290, 291, and 302
- **Unit 12 Class Checklists,** pages 292, 293, and 303
- **End-of-Year Assessment,** pages 150, 151, and 234–241
- **Quarterly Checklist: Quarter 4,** pages 300 and 301
- **Math Logs,** pages 306–308
- **Exit Slip,** page 311
- **Other Student Assessment Forms,** pages 304, 305, 309, and 310

Assessment Management Spreadsheets

The Assessment Management Spreadsheets consist of the Digital Class Checklists and Individual Profile of Progress Checklists. Use them to monitor, record, and report student progress.

Addressing All Needs

Differentiated Instruction

Adjusting the Activity – suggests adaptations that target advanced learners, English language learners, or learners who need additional instructional support.

ELL SUPPORT / ELL – provides lesson-specific suggestions to help English language learners understand and process the mathematical content.

READINESS – accesses students' prior knowledge or previews content that prepares students to engage in the lesson's Part 1 activities.

EXTRA PRACTICE – provides additional opportunities to apply the mathematical content of the lesson.

ENRICHMENT – enables students to apply or further explore the mathematical content of the lesson.

Lesson	Adjusting the Activity	ELL Support/ ELL	Readiness	Extra Practice	Enrichment
12•1	•	•	•		•
12•2	•	•	•	•	•
12•3		•			•
12•4		•	•		•
12•5	•		•	•	•
12•6	•		•	•	

Additional Resources

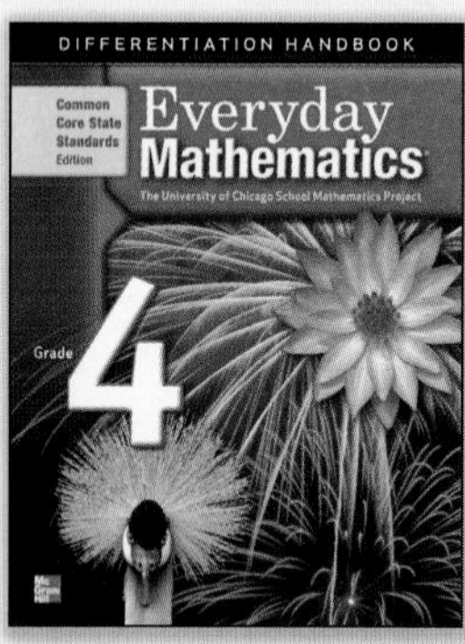

Differentiation Handbook
Provides ideas and strategies for differentiating instruction.
Pages 125–131

English Learners Handbook
Contains lesson-specific comprehension strategies.
Pages 102–107

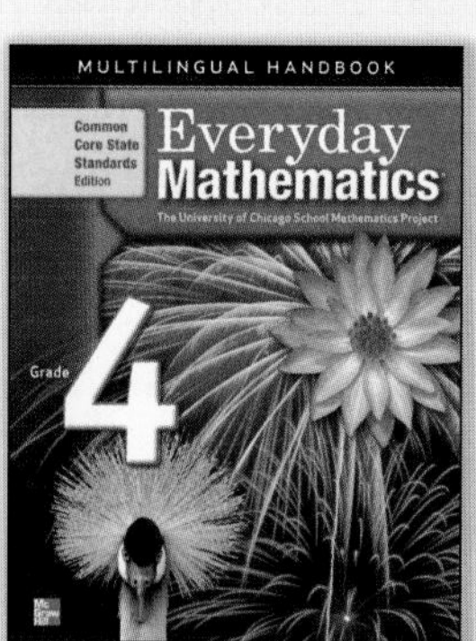

Multilingual Handbook
Previews concepts and vocabulary. It is written in six languages.
Pages 203–214

Planning Tips

Multiage Classroom

Companion Lessons from Grades 3 and 5 can help you meet instructional needs of a multiage classroom. The full Scope and Sequence can be found in the Appendix.

Grade 3	2•6		2•6	7•7, 9•5	7•7, 9•5	
Grade 4	**12•1**	**12•2**	**12•3**	**12•4**	**12•5**	**12•6**
Grade 5		12•5	12•6, 12•8		8•9, 12•4	

Pacing for Success

Pacing depends on a number of factors, such as students' individual needs and how long your school has been using *Everyday Mathematics*. At the beginning of Unit 12, you may want to use tools available at www.everydaymathonline.com to help you set your pace.

Home Support

Unit 12 Family Letter (English/Spanish) provides families with an overview, Do-Anytime Activities, Building Skills through Games, a list of vocabulary, and answers to the daily homework (Study Links). Family Letters in English, Spanish, and seven other languages are also available online.

Study Links are the daily homework assignments. They consist of active projects and ongoing review problems.

▶ Home Support Resources

Home Connection Handbook
Offers ideas and reproducible masters for communicating with families. See Table of Contents for unit information.

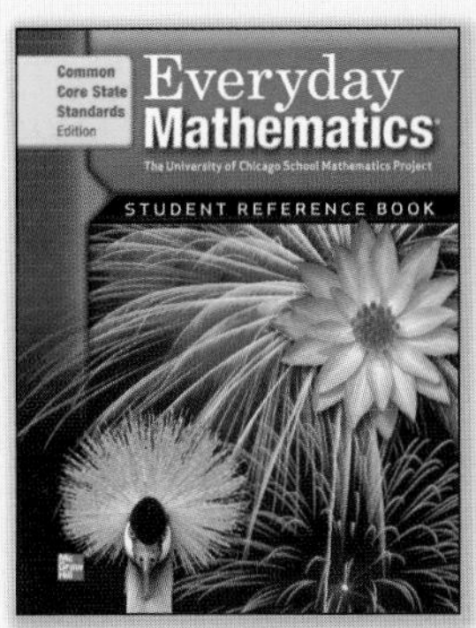

Student Reference Book
Provides a resource for students and parents.
Pages 239, 247, 254, 271, 297, 299, 301

Technology Resources

Algorithms Practice

EM Facts Workshop Game™

Family Letters

Interactive Teacher's Lesson Guide

www.everydaymathonline.com

Unit 12 Organizer

Materials

Technology Resources www.everydaymathonline.com

ePresentations

eToolkit

Algorithms Practice

EM Facts Workshop Game™

Family Letters

Assessment Management

Common Core State Standards

Curriculum Focal Points

Interactive Teacher's Lesson Guide

Lesson	Masters	Manipulative Kit	Other Items
12•1	Teaching Aid Masters, pp. 403 and 423 Study Link Master, p. 339 Teaching Master, p. 340	slate	timer or clock with a second hand; index cards*; chart paper; colored pencils or crayons; calculator*
12•2	Teaching Aid Masters, pp. 388, 389*, 443, and 454 Transparency of *Math Masters,* p. 454* Study Link Master, p. 341 Game Master, p. 469	slate; per partnership: deck of number cards	per partnership: penny; *Each Orange Had 8 Slices: A Counting Book;* colored pencils or crayons; straightedge
12•3	Study Link Master, p. 342 Teaching Masters, pp. 343 and 344	slate	straightedge; calculator
12•4	Teaching Aid Masters, pp. 428 and 454* Study Link Master, p. 345 Game Master, p. 489 Teaching Master, p. 346	slate; coins; per partnership: deck of number cards	calculator; products to test
12•5	Study Link Master, p. 347 Game Master, p. 506 Teaching Masters, pp. 348–351 Teaching Aid Master, p. 428	slate; coins	overhead calculator*; supermarket ads; Fraction Cards; calculator
12•6	Teaching Aid Masters, pp. 389, 412, 414, 415, 416*, and 417* Study Link Master, p. 352 Teaching Master, p. 353	slate	pen or colored pencil; calculator
12•7	Assessment Masters, pp. 211–215 and 234–241* Study Link Masters, pp. 354–357	slate	calculator

*Denotes optional materials

Mathematical Background

The discussion below highlights the major content areas presented in Unit 12 and helps establish instructional priorities.

Solving Rate Problems (Lesson 12♦2)

After students have discussed examples of rates in Lesson 12-1, they begin to solve rate problems in Lesson 12-2. Rate tables, which some students may recognize as a special kind of "What's My Rule?" table, are also introduced as an aid to problem solving. By completing such tables, students develop a sense that rate problems usually involve a search for equivalent rates, leading to the solution of problems. As you and your students make up and solve problems, three basic types of rate problems should emerge. These types are illustrated by the following examples:

1. Bill's new car can travel 35 miles on 1 gallon of gasoline. At this rate, how far can the car travel on 7 gallons of gasoline?

In this problem, a unit rate (35 miles per gallon) is given, and the solution is an equivalent rate obtained by multiplication: If the car can travel 35 miles on 1 gallon, it can travel 7 times as far on 7 gallons. $7 * 35 = 245$ miles per 7 gallons.

2. Jennifer received an allowance of \$8 in 4 weeks. At this rate, how much allowance did she receive per week?

In this problem, a rate that is not a unit rate (\$8 in 4 weeks) is given, and the solution is an equivalent unit rate obtained by division: If Jennifer received \$8 in 4 weeks, she received $\frac{1}{4}$ of \$8 in 1 week. $\$8 / 4 = \$2$ per week.

3. A gray whale's heart beats 24 times in 3 minutes. At this rate, how many times does a gray whale's heart beat in 2 minutes?

In this problem, a rate that is not a unit rate (24 beats in 3 minutes) is given, and the solution is an equivalent rate that is not a unit rate. The solution can be obtained by first finding the equivalent unit rate by division and then using the unit rate to find the solution by multiplication: If the gray whale's heart beats 24 times in 3 minutes, it beats $\frac{1}{3}$ of 24 times in 1 minute ($24 / 3 = 8$) and twice as many times in 2 minutes ($2 * 8 = 16$ beats per 2 minutes).

To learn more about solving rate problems, see Section 9.3.3 in the *Teacher's Reference Manual.*

The Unit-Rate Strategy

(Lessons 12•2 and 12•3)

The strategy illustrated in the last example—in which rate information given for a *number* of things is converted to the equivalent *unit* rate, from which other equivalent rates are calculated—is a powerful one. This strategy is practiced throughout the unit in various pricing and purchasing exercises, where students explore the "reasonableness" of rate estimates involving very large numbers. While there are other, more advanced strategies for dealing with rates, this basic strategy is perhaps the most universally useful one and the one advocated by many science and mathematics educators. (See *Sci-Math,* by Madeline P. Goodstein, Addison-Wesley, 1983.)

The authors recommend frequent, brief practice sessions for solving such problems. Use them as Mental Math and Reflexes routines. Even a single problem, followed by a brief sharing of solutions, should help your students improve their problem-solving skills.

Units Analysis in Rate Problems

(Lesson 12•3 and following)

Scientists and science educators often complain that mathematics teaching does not prepare students for the study of science. One of their main criticisms is that too much teaching of arithmetic deals strictly with numbers and ignores the role of units of measure that are nearly always attached to those numbers. With this problem in mind, the authors of *Everyday Mathematics* have insisted, starting in Kindergarten, that nearly every number must come with a count or measure unit. You might want to extend the work with units to a basic strategy used throughout the natural sciences, called units analysis. This strategy involves combining and canceling units in calculations involving measures.

Examples:

- There are 6 rows of chairs with 4 chairs per row. How many chairs are there in all?

  $6 \text{ rows} * \frac{4 \text{ chairs}}{1 \text{ row}} = 24 \text{ chairs}$

  The "row" units cancel in much the same way as do numbers in the numerators and denominators in the multiplication of fractions.

- Marsha earned \$56 for 8 hours of work. How much did she earn per hour?

  $\frac{56 \text{ dollars}}{8 \text{ hours}} = 7 \text{ dollars per hour}$

  Dollars divided by hours = dollars per hour

You can begin to show the rate units as "word fractions" that come from the rate fractions. As with many new emphases in *Everyday Mathematics,* initial exposure involves simply calling these strategies to the attention of students, without expecting them to use them, or even to fully understand them.

More can be learned about units analysis in Section 9.3.3 of the *Teacher's Reference Manual.*

Comparison Shopping

(Lessons 12•4 and 12•5)

Lessons 12-4 and 12-5 deal with a specific application of the unit-rate strategy—calculating unit prices in order to compare the costs of similar items. This application has become so commonplace that most supermarkets display unit-price labels along with the price of the items on their shelves. Students collect real data from newspaper ads, visits to grocery stores, and other places of business; represent them symbolically, usually in fraction form; and convert them to decimal form by doing the indicated division. Performing these operations with a calculator will usually result in an answer with more decimal places than are needed. Hence, these activities also provide practice with simplifying complicated results by rounding.

You may need to review problems involving dollars and cents. For example, if a 3-pound bag of apples costs $1.49, the unit price is obtained by dividing $1.49 by 3. On a calculator, this result may be displayed as 0.4966666667. The digit in the first place to the right of the decimal point represents dimes, the second digit represents pennies, and the third digit represents tenths of cents. In this problem then, the calculator display is interpreted as 4 dimes, 9 pennies, 6 tenths of a cent, and so on. This is equivalent to 49.7 cents when rounded to the nearest tenth of a cent.

See the *Teacher's Reference Manual,* Section 9.3.3, for more about comparison shopping.

Project Note

Use Project 5, Which Soft Drink is the Best Buy?, to calculate the unit price of various soft drinks and decide which is the best buy. See the *Differentiation Handbook* for modifications to Project 5.

World Tour Wrap-Up (Lesson 12•6)

Students have participated in the World Tour project for most of the school year. Be sure to reserve time for at least one sharing session, in which students describe and compare their experiences from the World Tour.

To learn more about the World Tour project see Section 1.2.7 in the *Teacher's Reference Manual.*

12•1 Introducing Rates

Objectives To introduce rates; and to provide practice collecting and comparing rate data.

www.everydaymathonline.com

ePresentations

eToolkit

Algorithms Practice

EM Facts Workshop Game™

Family Letters

Assessment Management

Common Core State Standards

Curriculum Focal Points

Interactive Teacher's Lesson Guide

1 Teaching the Lesson

Key Concepts and Skills

- Describe examples of rates. [Operations and Computation Goal 7]
- Collect and organize data to create a table. [Data and Chance Goal 1]
- Find the median and mean of a data set. [Data and Chance Goal 2]
- Use data to draw conclusions and make predictions. [Data and Chance Goal 2]
- Write a number sentence with parentheses. [Patterns, Functions, and Algebra Goal 3]

Key Activities

Students collect data on how many times classmates blink in one minute. They compare median blinking rates for students at rest and for students who are reading. Students list examples of rates.

Key Vocabulary

rate ◆ per

Materials

Math Journal 2, p. 309
Student Reference Book, pp. 271 and 299
Math Masters, p. 423
timer or clock with a second hand ◆ index cards (optional) ◆ slate ◆ calculator (optional)

2 Ongoing Learning & Practice

Identifying Fractions and Decimals on Number Lines
Math Journal 2, p. 310
Students fill in missing fractions and decimals on number lines.

Math Boxes 12•1
Math Journal 2, p. 311
Students practice and maintain skills through Math Box problems.

Ongoing Assessment: Recognizing Student Achievement
Use Math Boxes, Problems 4a–4c.
[Number and Numeration Goal 6]

Study Link 12•1
Math Masters, p. 339
Students practice and maintain skills through Study Link activities.

3 Differentiation Options

READINESS
Finding the Median and Mean of a Data Set
Math Masters, p. 340
Students analyze the median and mean of a data set.

ENRICHMENT
Creating Side-by-Side Bar Graphs
Math Masters, p. 403
colored pencils or crayons
Students create a side-by-side (double) bar graph to display eye blinking rates.

ELL SUPPORT
Creating a Rates All Around Museum
chart paper ◆ colored pencils or crayons
Students create a Rates All Around Museum.

Advance Preparation

For Part 1, read the description of the eye-blinking experiment before class and decide how best to conduct it. For the optional ELL Support activity in Part 3, post chart paper for a Rates All Around Museum.

***Teacher's Reference Manual,* Grades 4–6** pp. 13, 64–68, 160, 168, 169

Getting Started

Mental Math and Reflexes

Pose rate problems. Have copies of the multiplication/division diagram (*Math Masters,* page 423) available for student use. *Suggestions:*

●○○ There are 9 stickers per sheet. How many stickers on
5 sheets? 45 stickers
7 sheets? 63 stickers
9 sheets? 81 stickers

●●○ There are 40 books per shelf. How many books on
10 shelves? 400 books
30 shelves? 1,200 books
50 shelves? 2,000 books

●●● Pencils cost $1.20 per box. What is the cost of
4 boxes? $4.80
6 boxes? $7.20
11 boxes? $13.20

Math Message

Find the median for each set of numbers.

a. 4, 9, 3, 12, 15, 9, 7

b. 2, 10, 6, 9

1 Teaching the Lesson

Interactive whiteboard-ready ePresentations are available at www.everydaymathonline.com to help you teach the lesson.

▶ Math Message Follow-Up

WHOLE-CLASS DISCUSSION

The median of a set of numbers is the middle number when the numbers are listed in order from smallest to largest or from largest to smallest. Nine is the median of the first set of numbers because in the ordered list 3, 4, 7, $\underline{9}$, 9, 12, 15, the number 9 is the middle number.

If there is an even number of numbers in the set, the median is the mean (average) of the two middle numbers. In the ordered list 2, $\underline{6}$, $\underline{9}$, 10, there are two middle numbers. The median is $(6 + 9) / 2$, or $7\frac{1}{2}$.

Adjusting the Activity

Ask students to find the mean of each data set and write a number model with parentheses to describe their strategy.

▷ $(3 + 4 + 7 + 9 + 9 + 12 + 15) / 7 = 8.4286$

▷ $(2 + 6 + 9 + 10) / 4 = 6.75$

Students should note that the median and the mean for a set of data usually are not equal, but the two are often close.

AUDITORY ◆ KINESTHETIC ◆ TACTILE ◆ VISUAL

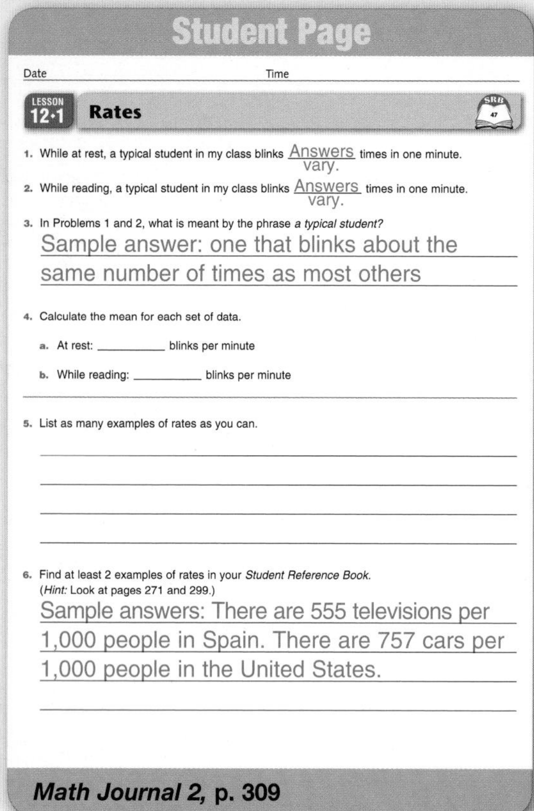
Student Page

Date Time

LESSON 12·1 **Rates**

1. While at rest, a typical student in my class blinks Answers vary. times in one minute.
2. While reading, a typical student in my class blinks Answers vary. times in one minute.
3. In Problems 1 and 2, what is meant by the phrase *a typical student?*
Sample answer: one that blinks about the same number of times as most others
4. Calculate the mean for each set of data.
a. At rest: ______ blinks per minute
b. While reading: ______ blinks per minute
5. List as many examples of rates as you can.
6. Find at least 2 examples of rates in your *Student Reference Book.* (*Hint:* Look at pages 271 and 299.)
Sample answers: There are 555 televisions per 1,000 people in Spain. There are 757 cars per 1,000 people in the United States.

***Math Journal 2,* p. 309**

▶ Collecting Eye-Blinking Data

Take half the class aside, outside the hearing range of the other half. Tell these students that they are going to collect data on their classmates' eye-blinking rates, but they must do so secretly. Explain the procedure they are to follow:

▷ Each student in the data-collecting group—Group A—is paired with a student in the other group—Group B. Partners sit across from each other and, at your signal, they look at each other.

▷ While looking at each other, students in Group A count the number of times their partners in Group B blink in one minute. At the end of one minute, you give the signal to stop. Students in Group A secretly write the number of times their partner blinked in one minute.

▷ Next, instruct the students in Group B to open a book. At your signal, the students in Group B start reading, while the students in Group A again count their partners' number of blinks. Again, you give the signal to stop at the end of one minute.

▷ The students in Group A then write the number of times their partners blinked while reading for one minute.

Tell students in Group A that they will follow this procedure so that their partners remain unaware of what is taking place. Otherwise, they might blink unnaturally.

Bring the class together and conduct the experiment.

▶ Comparing Eye-Blinking Rates

WHOLE-CLASS ACTIVITY

PROBLEM SOLVING

(*Math Journal 2,* p. 309)

Ask one of the students in Group A to describe the experiment. Have students in Group B speculate about whether a person blinks more often while reading or at rest, or whether the number of blinks remains about the same.

Take a vote and ask students to discuss why they voted the way they did. Make a table on the board and record each student's blinking rates on a separate line. (*See margin.*)

Ask partners to find the median for each set of data, record them in Problems 1 and 2 in their journals, and describe what is meant in Problem 3 by the phrase "a typical student."

Number of Blinks in 1 Minute

At Rest	Reading
14	10
18	1
2	2

Table for recording blinking rates (sample data provided)

Adjusting the Activity

ELL

Have students record the numbers in each column of the table on separate index cards. They can then order the index cards to find the middle value for each data group.

AUDITORY ◆ KINESTHETIC ◆ TACTILE ◆ VISUAL

Bring the class together to discuss the results. Ask:

- Why might a person's blinking rate vary, depending on the activity? Sample answer: A person may concentrate more and blink less when reading.
- What might be some other factors that can affect blinking rates? Sample answers: Brightness of light; how tired a person is; whether a person wears glasses or contact lenses; whether a person is interested or bored
- Based on the data, can you make a prediction about a person's blinking rate while exercising? Sample answer: When a person concentrates on moving certain muscles, he or she may blink less. However, if a person is exercising outdoors, the wind and sunlight may make the person blink more.

Listing Examples of Rates

(*Math Journal 2,* p. 309; *Student Reference Book,* pp. 271 and 299)

The number of times a person blinks in one minute is an example of a **rate.** A rate tells how many there are of one thing for a certain number of another thing. Rates often contain the word ***per,*** which means "for each," such as in *15 blinks per minute* or *55 miles per hour*. A rate can be written with a slash to represent the word *per,* as in \$2.25/lb.

Ask students to list other examples of rates in Problem 5 in their journals. You might suggest a few categories:

▷ Food: calories per serving

▷ Packaging: paper clips per box

▷ Price: dollars per pound

▷ Transportation: miles per hour

▷ Sports: minutes per half in basketball

Social Studies Link In Problem 6, have students record at least two examples of rates from pages 271 and 299 of the *Student Reference Book* World Tour section. Bring students together to share their examples. Throughout the unit, encourage the class to find other examples of rates and display them in a Rates All Around Museum. See the optional ELL Support activity in Part 3.

Student Page

Date Time

LESSON 12•1 Counting with Fractions and Decimals

Fill in the missing fractions on the number lines below.

1. 0, $\frac{1}{3}$, $\frac{2}{3}$, 1

2. 0, $\frac{1}{6}$, $\frac{2}{6}$, $\frac{3}{6}$, $\frac{4}{6}$, $\frac{5}{6}$, 1

3. 0, $\frac{1}{8}$, $\frac{2}{8}$, $\frac{3}{8}$, $\frac{4}{8}$, $\frac{5}{8}$, $\frac{6}{8}$, $\frac{7}{8}$, 1

Fill in the missing decimals on the number lines below.

4. 2, 2.5, 3, 3.5, 4

Try This

5. 7, 7.25, 7.50, 7.75, 8

6. −2, −1.5, −1, −0.5, 0, 0.5, 1

***Math Journal 2,* p. 310**

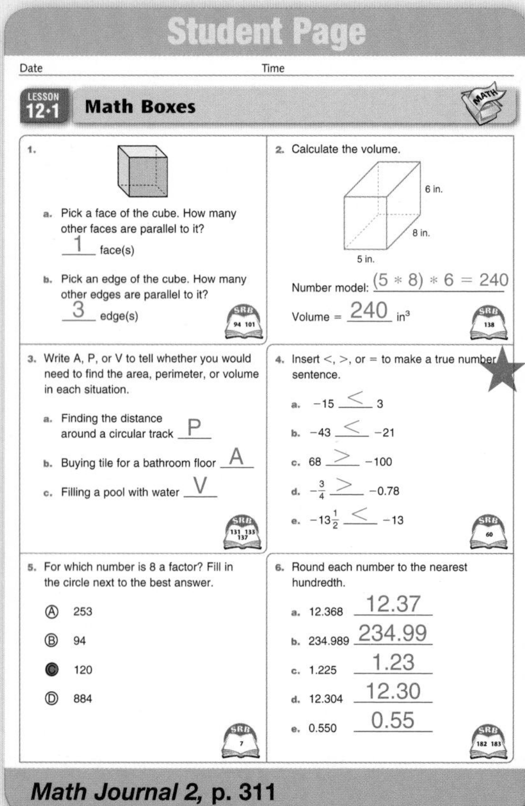
Student Page

Date Time

LESSON 12•1 Math Boxes

1. a. Pick a face of the cube. How many other faces are parallel to it? 1 face(s)
   b. Pick an edge of the cube. How many other edges are parallel to it? 3 edge(s)

2. Calculate the volume. (6 in., 8 in., 5 in.)
   Number model: (5 ∗ 8) ∗ 6 = 240
   Volume = 240 in³

3. Write A, P, or V to tell whether you would need to find the area, perimeter, or volume in each situation.
   a. Finding the distance around a circular track P
   b. Buying tile for a bathroom floor A
   c. Filling a pool with water V

4. Insert <, >, or = to make a true number sentence.
   a. −15 < 3
   b. −43 < −21
   c. 68 > −100
   d. $-\frac{3}{4}$ > −0.78
   e. $-13\frac{1}{2}$ < −13

5. For which number is 8 a factor? Fill in the circle next to the best answer.
   Ⓐ 253
   Ⓑ 94
   ● 120
   Ⓓ 884

6. Round each number to the nearest hundredth.
   a. 12.368 12.37
   b. 234.989 234.99
   c. 1.225 1.23
   d. 12.304 12.30
   e. 0.550 0.55

***Math Journal 2,* p. 311**

2 Ongoing Learning & Practice

▶ Identifying Fractions and Decimals on Number Lines

INDEPENDENT ACTIVITY

(*Math Journal 2,* p. 310)

Students fill in the missing fractions and decimals on number lines.

▶ Math Boxes 12•1

INDEPENDENT ACTIVITY

(*Math Journal 2,* p. 311)

Mixed Practice Math Boxes in this lesson are paired with Math Boxes in Lesson 12-3.

Ongoing Assessment: Recognizing Student Achievement

Math Boxes Problems 4a–4c ★

Use **Math Boxes, Problems 4a–4c** to assess students' ability to compare integers between 100 and −100. Students are making adequate progress if they insert <, >, or = to make true number sentences. Some students may be able to solve Problems 4d and 4e, which involve the comparison of rational numbers.

[Number and Numeration Goal 6]

▶ Study Link 12•1

INDEPENDENT ACTIVITY

(*Math Masters,* p. 339)

Home Connection Students look for examples of rates in newspapers, in magazines, and on labels and bring them to class.

3 Differentiation Options

READINESS

INDEPENDENT ACTIVITY

▶ Finding the Median and Mean of a Data Set

5–15 Min

(*Math Masters,* p. 340)

To provide experience finding the median and calculating the mean of a data set, have students complete *Math Masters,* page 340.

ENRICHMENT

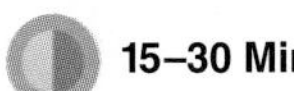

Creating Side-by-Side Bar Graphs

(*Math Masters,* p. 403)

Portfolio Ideas

To apply students' ability to organize and compare data, have them create a side-by-side (double) bar graph to display the eye-blinking rates for students at rest and while reading. Remind students to choose a reasonable title and labels for the graph and to include a key for the color-coded bars. *For example:*

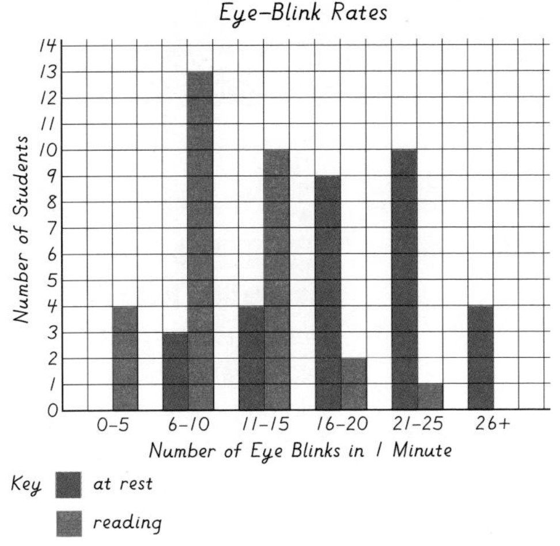

When students have completed their graphs, ask:

- Why might it be useful to show data in a side-by-side graph like this rather than two individual bar graphs? Sample answer: When the two bars are side by side, you can immediately compare the rates without looking at the numbers.
- How did you determine the scale to use for the vertical and horizontal axes? Sample answer: I decided to clump the number of eye blinks into categories of 0–5, 6–10, 11–15, 16–20, and 26+ on the horizontal axis, because the chart would be too crowded with the individual data.

ELL SUPPORT

Creating a Rates All Around Museum

To provide language support for rates, have students create a Rates All Around Museum. Ask them to read the numbers and describe some of the ways that rates are used in the museum; for example, what the numbers mean or the units attached to the rates.

Study Link Master

Name Date Time

STUDY LINK 12·1 **Examples of Rates**

1. Look for examples of rates in newspapers, in magazines, and on labels.
Study the two examples below, and then list some of the examples you find. If possible, bring your samples to class.

Example: Label on a can of corn says "Servings Per Container $3\frac{1}{2}$"

Nutrition Facts
Serving Size 110 g
Servings Per Container 3 1/2

Example: Lightbulbs come in packages of 4 bulbs. The package doesn't say so, but there are always 4 bulbs in each package.

Example: ______

Example: ______

Example: ______

Practice

2. $\frac{4}{5} - \frac{1}{5} = \frac{3}{5}$

3. $\frac{1}{8} = \frac{7}{8} - \frac{3}{4}$

4. $\frac{9}{9}$, or 1 $= \frac{1}{9} + \frac{8}{9}$

5. $\frac{1}{3} + \frac{3}{6} = \frac{5}{6}$

Math Masters, p. 339

Teaching Master

Name Date Time

LESSON 12·1 **Median and Mean**

Anthony's first 4 test scores for his weekly 20-word spelling tests were 80%, 90%, 100%, and 75%.

1. What is Anthony's *median* score? 85 %

2. What score must Anthony get on his next test to maintain his median score? 85 % Explain your answer.
Sample answer: Any other score would result in a change in median.

3. Anthony would like to raise his *mean* score to 90% or higher. If he takes one more spelling test, can he do it? No Explain your answer.
Even if he makes 100% on the next test, his average will be (80 + 90 + 100 + 75 + 100) / 5 = 89%.

Name Date Time

LESSON 12·1 **Median and Mean**

Anthony's first 4 test scores for his weekly 20-word spelling tests were 80%, 90%, 100%, and 75%.

1. What is Anthony's *median* score? ______%

2. What score must Anthony get on his next test to maintain his median score? ______% Explain your answer.

3. Anthony would like to raise his *mean* score to 90% or higher. If he takes one more spelling test, can he do it? ______ Explain your answer.

Math Masters, p. 340

12•2 Solving Rate Problems

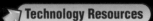

Objectives To provide practice using a rate table to record rate information; and to provide practice solving rate problems.

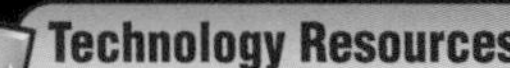

www.everydaymathonline.com

ePresentations

eToolkit

Algorithms Practice

EM Facts Workshop Game™

Family Letters

Assessment Management

Common Core State Standards

Curriculum Focal Points

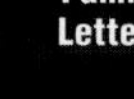
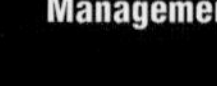
Interactive Teacher's Lesson Guide

1 Teaching the Lesson

Key Concepts and Skills

- Find multiples. [Number and Numeration Goal 3]
- Solve multiplication and division facts. [Operations and Computation Goal 3]
- Multiply and divide decimals by whole numbers. [Operations and Computation Goal 4]
- Use repeated addition and scaling to model multiplication problems. [Operations and Computation Goal 7]
- Use patterns and rules to solve rate problems. [Patterns, Functions, and Algebra Goal 1]

Key Activities

Students use a version of the "What's My Rule?" table, called a *rate table,* to solve rate problems.

Ongoing Assessment: Informing Instruction See page 917.

Ongoing Assessment: Recognizing Student Achievement Use an Exit Slip (*Math Masters,* page 389). [Patterns, Functions, and Algebra Goal 1]

Key Vocabulary

rate table ◆ unit rate

Materials

Math Journal 2, pp. 312 and 313
Study Link 12•1
Math Masters, p. 389 (optional)
transparency of *Math Masters,* p. 454 (optional) ◆ slate

2 Ongoing Learning & Practice

Playing the *Credits/Debits Game* (Advanced Version)
Student Reference Book, p. 239
Math Masters, p. 469
per partnership: penny, complete deck of number cards (the Everything Math Deck, if available)
Students practice adding and subtracting integers.

Math Boxes 12•2
Math Journal 2, p. 314
Students practice and maintain skills through Math Box problems.

Study Link 12•2
Math Masters, p. 341
Students practice and maintain skills through Study Link activities.

3 Differentiation Options

READINESS
Illustrating Rate Problems
Math Masters, p. 388
Each Orange Had 8 Slices: A Counting Book
colored pencils or crayons
Students describe and illustrate situations involving rate problems.

ENRICHMENT
Representing Rates with Line Graphs
Math Journal 2, pp. 312 and 313
Math Masters, p. 443
straightedge
Students plot points corresponding to a linear relationship on graph paper and connect the points using a straight line.

EXTRA PRACTICE
Solving Rate Problems
Math Masters, p. 454
Students use rate tables to solve rate problems.

Advance Preparation

For Part 1, make an overhead transparency of *Math Masters,* page 454 or draw several blank rate tables on the board. For the optional Readiness activity in Part 3, you need a copy of ***Each Orange Had 8 Slices: A Counting Book*** by Paul Giganti, Jr. (Greenwillow Books, 1999).

***Teacher's Reference Manual,* Grades 4–6** pp. 19, 64–68

Getting Started

Mental Math and Reflexes 

Pose measurement conversion problems. *Suggestions:*

●○○ 1 foot is 12 inches. How many inches are in
2 feet? 24
3 feet? 36
5 feet? 60

●●○ 1 gallon is 16 cups. How many cups are in
5 gallons? 80
10 gallons? 160
100 gallons? 1,600

●●● 1 liter is 1,000 milliliters. How many milliliters are in
$2\frac{1}{4}$ liters? 2,250
$8\frac{1}{2}$ liters? 8,500
$12\frac{3}{4}$ liters? 12,750

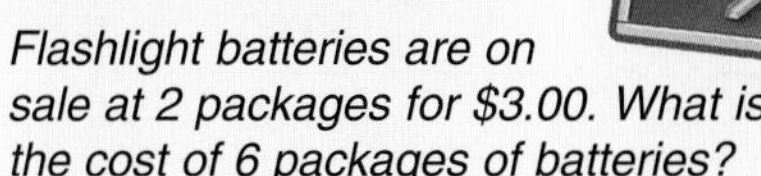

Math Message

Flashlight batteries are on sale at 2 packages for $3.00. What is the cost of 6 packages of batteries?

Study Link 12·1 Follow-Up

Ask students to share the examples of rates they have brought from home and to add them to the Rates All Around Museum, if you have one. Encourage students to continue to look for examples of rates.

1 Teaching the Lesson

Math Message Follow-Up

Ask students to share solution strategies. Draw pictures on the board to illustrate their strategies.

Some possible strategies might include the following:

▷ 6 packages is 3 times as much as 2 packages.

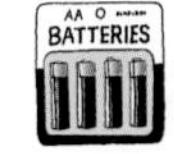
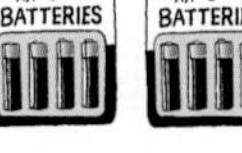
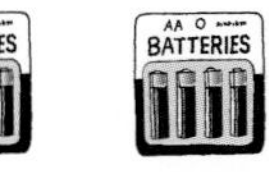

$3.00 + $3.00 + $3.00 = $9.00

▷ If 2 packages cost $3.00, then 1 package costs half as much: $\frac{1}{2}$ of $3.00 = $1.50. Six packages cost 6 times as much as 1 package: 6 ∗ $1.50 = $9.00.

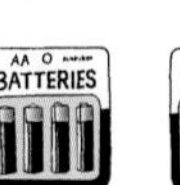

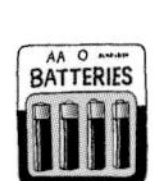

$1.50 + $1.50 + $1.50 + $1.50 + $1.50 + $1.50 = $9.00

Tell students that in this lesson they will use rate tables to help them organize information in rate problems.

Batteries: 2 packages/$3.00

Packages	Cost
1	$1.50
2	$3.00
3	$4.50
4	$6.00
5	$7.50
6	$9.00
7	$10.50
8	$12.00
9	$13.50

Rate Table

NOTE The *unit rate* is a version of the rate that tells how many of some thing for each 1 of a second thing. For example, 27 minutes for 9 buttons is not a unit rate; 3 minutes for 1 button is a unit rate. Similarly, $3.00 for 2 packages is not a unit rate; $1.50 for 1 package is a unit rate. It is usually easier to fill in the other cells of a rate table if the unit rate is filled in first.

▶ Introducing Rate Tables

Algebraic Thinking The information provided by a rate can be extended to show other equivalent rates. Make a **rate table** and fill in the cost of 2 packages and 6 packages of batteries. (*See margin.*) Students should recognize this as a "What's My Rule?" table: The *in* numbers (packages) are known; most of the *out* numbers (cost) are to be found.

Fill in the rest of the table with the help of the class. As you do so, ask questions such as the following:

- If 2 packages cost $3.00, how can you find the cost of 1 package? Divide $3.00 by 2.
- How can you find the cost of 3 packages? Multiply the cost of 1 package by 3: 3 ∗ $1.50 = $4.50. Or add the cost of 1 package to the cost of 2 packages: $3.00 + $1.50 = $4.50.
- How can you find the cost of 8 packages? Multiply the cost of 2 packages by 4: 4 ∗ $3.00 = $12.00.

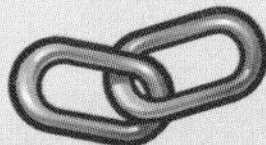

Links to the Future

Representing rates with tables of values, formulas, and graphs is a Grade 5 Goal.

▶ Solving Rate Problems

(*Math Masters,* p. 454)

Algebraic Thinking Use an overhead transparency of *Math Masters,* page 454 or the blank rate tables you have drawn on the board.

1. Enter the given rate in a rate table.
2. Fill in the rest of the cells in the rate table.
3. Answer the question posed in the problem.

Example:

Mr. Rankin sews buttons on shirts. He sewed 9 buttons in 27 minutes. At that rate, how many buttons did he sew after 15 minutes?

1. Make a rate table and enter the given rate: 9 buttons in 27 minutes.

Buttons	1	2	3	4	5	6	7	8	9
Minutes									27

2. Fill in the rest of the cells in the rate table.

   a. Fill in the cell for 1 button first; this is called a **unit rate.**

Buttons	1	2	3	4	5	6	7	8	9
Minutes	3								27

   b. Then fill in the other cells.

Buttons	1	2	3	4	5	6	7	8	9
Minutes	3	6	9	12	15	18	21	24	27

3. Answer the question posed in the problem: At that rate, Mr. Rankin sewed 5 buttons after 15 minutes.

Work with the class to solve these problems:

- A building has a height of 60 feet. If each story is 12 feet high, how many stories does the building have? 5 stories. The unit rate 12 ft/1 story is given. To support English language learners, discuss the meaning of *story* in this context.
- DeAndre receives $4 per week as an allowance. If he saves all his money, how much will he have after one year? $208. The unit rate $4/1 week is given.
- In one week, Jill mowed 12 lawns and made $72. If she charged each customer the same amount, how much did she charge per lawn? $6. The given rate $72 per 12 lawns is not a unit rate. Division is needed to find the unit rate: $72 \div 12 =$ $6 per 1 lawn. How much had she earned after she mowed 4 lawns? $24. Since the unit rate is $6 per lawn, multiplication is used to find an equivalent rate: $4 * 6 =$ $24 per 4 lawns or repeated addition $6 + 6 + 6 + 6 =$ $24 per 4 lawns.

Ongoing Assessment: Informing Instruction

Watch for students who note that a rate table is like a "What's My Rule?" table turned on its side. Encourage students to consider the strategies they used to complete "What's My Rule?" tables and to find the rules when they are solving rate problems.

Practicing with Rate Problems

PARTNER ACTIVITY

(*Math Journal 2,* pp. 312 and 313)

Assign journal pages 312 and 313. The unit rate is given for Problem 1. For the remaining problems, students should find the unit rate first and then fill in the remainder of the rate table. For Problem 7, have students discuss their solution strategies.

Adjusting the Activity

Ask students to state a rule for finding the number of buttons sewn in a given number of minutes. Divide the number of minutes by 3. Now ask students to use variables to state the rule as a formula. Sample answer: $b = m / 3$, where b is the number of buttons sewn and m is the number of minutes

AUDITORY ◆ KINESTHETIC ◆ TACTILE ◆ VISUAL

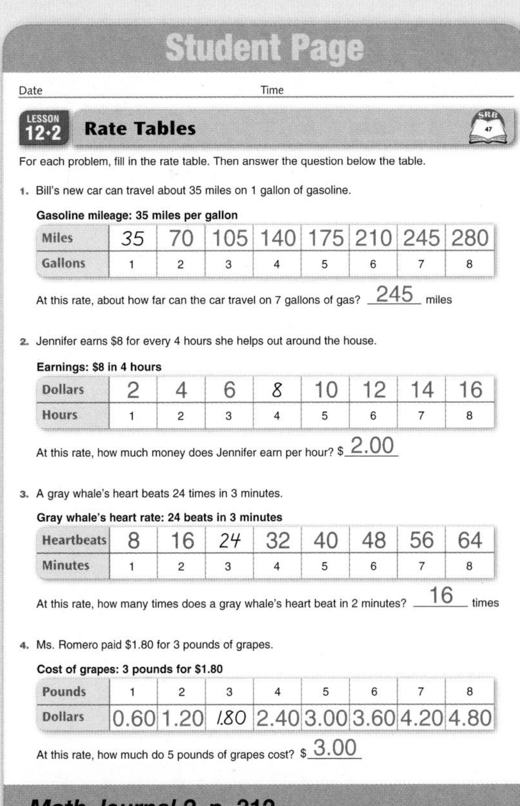

Student Page

Date Time

LESSON 12·2 **Rate Tables**

SRB 47

For each problem, fill in the rate table. Then answer the question below the table.

1. Bill's new car can travel about 35 miles on 1 gallon of gasoline.

Gasoline mileage: 35 miles per gallon

Miles	35	70	105	140	175	210	245	280
Gallons	1	2	3	4	5	6	7	8

At this rate, about how far can the car travel on 7 gallons of gas? 245 miles

2. Jennifer earns $8 for every 4 hours she helps out around the house.

Earnings: $8 in 4 hours

Dollars	2	4	6	8	10	12	14	16
Hours	1	2	3	4	5	6	7	8

At this rate, how much money does Jennifer earn per hour? $2.00

3. A gray whale's heart beats 24 times in 3 minutes.

Gray whale's heart rate: 24 beats in 3 minutes

Heartbeats	8	16	24	32	40	48	56	64
Minutes	1	2	3	4	5	6	7	8

At this rate, how many times does a gray whale's heart beat in 2 minutes? 16 times

4. Ms. Romero paid $1.80 for 3 pounds of grapes.

Cost of grapes: 3 pounds for $1.80

Pounds	1	2	3	4	5	6	7	8
Dollars	0.60	1.20	1.80	2.40	3.00	3.60	4.20	4.80

At this rate, how much do 5 pounds of grapes cost? $3.00

Math Journal 2, p. 312

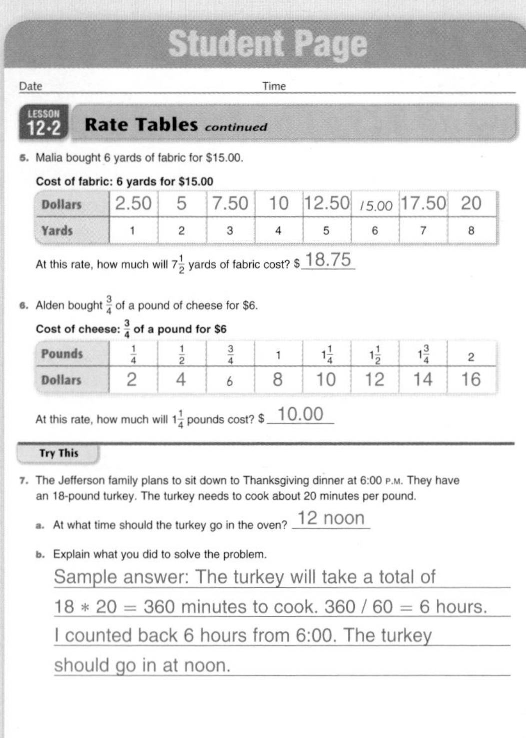

Student Page

Date Time

LESSON 12·2 **Rate Tables** *continued*

5. Malia bought 6 yards of fabric for $15.00.

Cost of fabric: 6 yards for $15.00

Dollars	2.50	5	7.50	10	12.50	15.00	17.50	20
Yards	1	2	3	4	5	6	7	8

At this rate, how much will $7\frac{1}{2}$ yards of fabric cost? $ 18.75

6. Alden bought $\frac{3}{4}$ of a pound of cheese for $6.

Cost of cheese: $\frac{3}{4}$ of a pound for $6

Pounds	$\frac{1}{4}$	$\frac{1}{2}$	$\frac{3}{4}$	1	$1\frac{1}{4}$	$1\frac{1}{2}$	$1\frac{3}{4}$	2
Dollars	2	4	6	8	10	12	14	16

At this rate, how much will $1\frac{1}{4}$ pounds cost? $ 10.00

Try This

7. The Jefferson family plans to sit down to Thanksgiving dinner at 6:00 P.M. They have an 18-pound turkey. The turkey needs to cook about 20 minutes per pound.

a. At what time should the turkey go in the oven? 12 noon

b. Explain what you did to solve the problem.

Sample answer: The turkey will take a total of 18 * 20 = 360 minutes to cook. 360 / 60 = 6 hours. I counted back 6 hours from 6:00. The turkey should go in at noon.

Math Journal 2, p. 313

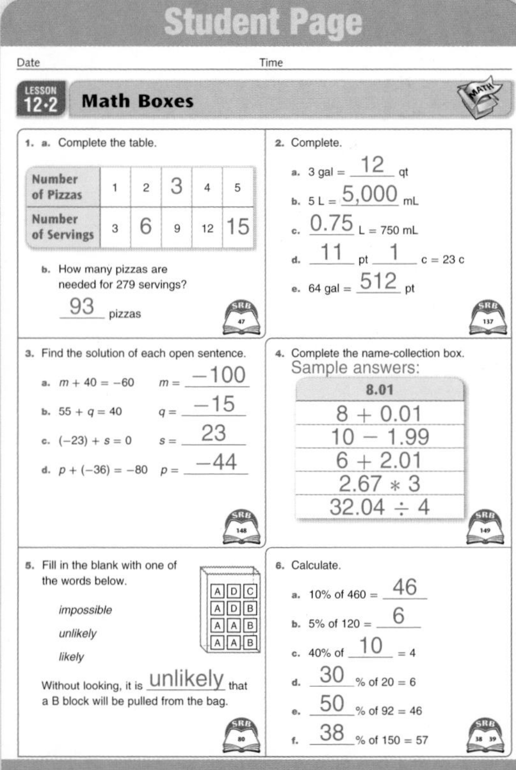

Student Page

Date Time

LESSON 12·2 **Math Boxes**

1. a. Complete the table.

Number of Pizzas	1	2	3	4	5
Number of Servings	3	6	9	12	15

b. How many pizzas are needed for 279 servings? 93 pizzas

2. Complete.

a. 3 gal = 12 qt

b. 5 L = 5,000 mL

c. 0.75 L = 750 mL

d. 11 pt 1 c = 23 c

e. 64 gal = 512 pt

3. Find the solution of each open sentence.

a. $m + 40 = -60$ $m =$ −100

b. $55 + q = 40$ $q =$ −15

c. $(-23) + s = 0$ $s =$ 23

d. $p + (-36) = -80$ $p =$ −44

4. Complete the name-collection box. Sample answers:

8.01
8 + 0.01
10 − 1.99
6 + 2.01
2.67 * 3
32.04 ÷ 4

5. Fill in the blank with one of the words below.

impossible
unlikely
likely

Without looking, it is unlikely that a B block will be pulled from the bag.

6. Calculate.

a. 10% of 460 = 46

b. 5% of 120 = 6

c. 40% of 10 = 4

d. 30 % of 20 = 6

e. 50 % of 92 = 46

f. 38 % of 150 = 57

Math Journal 2, p. 314

Exit Slip ★

Ongoing Assessment: Recognizing Student Achievement

Use an **Exit Slip** (*Math Masters,* page 389) to assess students' ability to describe a rule for a pattern and use the rule to solve problems. Have students describe the pattern in the rate table in Problem 3 on journal page 312. Students are making adequate progress if their explanation demonstrates an understanding of the pattern; that is, the numbers in the top row of the rate table are all multiples of 8, and each number in the top row can be found by multiplying the number in the bottom row by 8. Some students may note that they can use the pattern to find values for numbers not given in the table. For example, a gray whale's heart beats 120 times in 15 minutes, or 36 times in $4\frac{1}{2}$ minutes.

[Patterns, Functions, and Algebra Goal 1]

2 Ongoing Learning & Practice

▶ Playing the *Credits/Debits Game* (Advanced Version)

(*Student Reference Book,* p. 239; *Math Masters,* p. 469)

Students play the *Credits/Debits Game* (Advanced Version) to practice adding and subtracting integers. See Lesson 11-6 for additional information.

▶ Math Boxes 12·2

(*Math Journal 2,* p. 314)

Mixed Practice Math Boxes in this lesson are linked with Math Boxes in Lessons 12-4 and 12-6.

Portfolio Ideas

Writing/Reasoning Have students write a response to the following: *Look carefully at the bag of blocks in Problem 5. Describe two events that are equally likely. Express the probability of each event as a fraction.* Sample answers: Pulling a B block and pulling a C *or* D block are equally likely events. The probability of each event is $\frac{3}{12}$, or $\frac{1}{4}$. Pulling an A block and pulling a B, C, *or* D block are equally likely events. The probability of each event is $\frac{6}{12}$, or $\frac{1}{2}$.

▶ Study Link 12·2

(*Math Masters,* p. 341)

Home Connection Students solve problems involving rates. In some problems, students need to calculate the unit rate when it is not given.

3 Differentiation Options

READINESS

PARTNER ACTIVITY

Illustrating Rate Problems

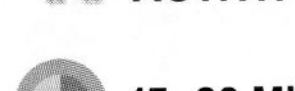

15–30 Min

(*Math Masters,* p. 388)

Literature Link To explore rate situations using a visual model, have students read ***Each Orange Had 8 Slices: A Counting Book*** by Paul Giganti, Jr. (Greenwillow Books, 1999). Ask students to use rate language to describe each situation. For example: "Two juicy oranges. Eight slices *per* orange. Two seeds *per* slice."

In a Math Log, have students illustrate their own rate situation and use rate language to describe it.

ENRICHMENT

INDEPENDENT ACTIVITY

Representing Rates with Line Graphs

5–15 Min

(*Math Journal 2,* pp. 312 and 313; *Math Masters,* p. 443)

To further explore representing rates with line graphs, have students choose a problem on journal page 312 or 313 and display the values found in the rate table on a line graph. Remind students to choose a reasonable title and labels for the graph.

Students should notice that when the dots on the graph are connected, they form a straight line. Discuss how to obtain values from the graph. In the example to the right, to find out how much money Jennifer earns in $2\frac{1}{2}$ hours, move along the horizontal axis to $2\frac{1}{2}$, which is halfway between 2 and 3 hours, and mark the point on the line that is directly above $2\frac{1}{2}$. Then move left from there to 5 on the vertical axis. Thus, Jennifer earns $5.00 in $2\frac{1}{2}$ hours.

NOTE Continuous quantities can be divided into smaller and smaller amounts. Measures, such as the height and weight of a student in your class, are continuous quantities. Discrete quantities are countable things that cannot be broken up into smaller amounts, such as the number of students in your class. The rates in this lesson can be represented by line graphs, since most of the variables represent continuous, not discrete, quantities.

EXTRA PRACTICE

INDEPENDENT ACTIVITY

Solving Rate Problems

5–15 Min

(*Math Masters,* p. 454)

Algebraic Thinking To provide practice solving rate problems, have students use rate tables to record given rate information and generate equivalent rates. Use *Math Masters,* page 454 to create problems to meet the needs of individual students, or have students create and solve their own problems.

Study Link Master

Name Date Time

STUDY LINK 12·2 **Rates**

Solve the problems.

1. Hotels R Us charges $45 per night for a single room. At that rate, how much does a single room cost *per week?* $ 315
2. The Morales family spends about $84 each week for food. On average, how much do they spend *per day?* $ 12
3. Sharon practices playing the piano the same amount of time each day. She practiced a total of 4 hours on Monday and Tuesday combined. At that rate, how many hours would she practice *in a week?* 14 hours

Hours	2	4	6	8	10	12	14
Days	1	2	3	4	5	6	7

Try This

4. People in the United States spend an average of 6 hours and 4 minutes each week reading newspapers.
   a. That's how many minutes *per week?* 364 minutes per week
   b. At that rate, how much time does an average person spend reading newspapers in a *3-day period?* 156 minutes

Minutes	52	104	156	208	260	312	364
Days	1	2	3	4	5	6	7

Practice

5. 9,096 = 24 * 379
6. 870 * 63 = 54,810
7. 652 ÷ 8 = 81 R4
8. 546 ÷ 42 = 13

Math Masters, p. 341

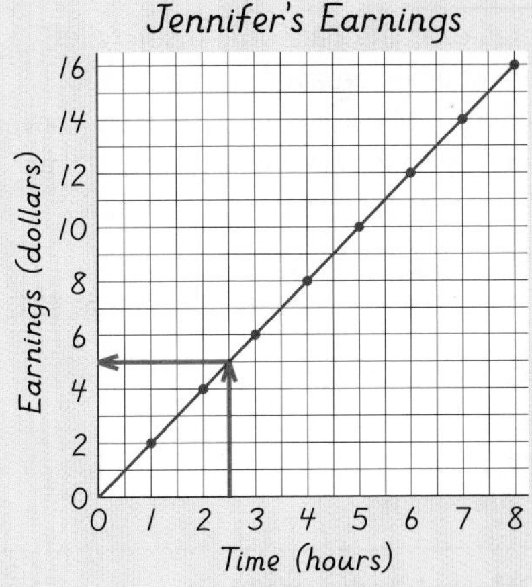

12·3 Converting between Rates

Objective To provide practice checking the validity of data by converting the data to more accessible rates.

 www.everydaymathonline.com

 ePresentations
 eToolkit
 Algorithms Practice
 EM Facts Workshop Game™
 Family Letters
 Assessment Management
 Common Core State Standards
 Curriculum Focal Points

 Interactive Teacher's Lesson Guide

1 Teaching the Lesson

Key Concepts and Skills

- Find multiples. [Number and Numeration Goal 3]
- Divide whole numbers. [Operations and Computation Goal 4]
- Round decimals and whole numbers. [Operations and Computation Goal 6]
- Convert between rates. [Operations and Computation Goal 7]
- Analyze and interpret data. [Data and Chance Goal 2]

Key Activities

Students examine data on the estimated number of times an average person does something in his or her lifetime. They convert the rates to ones with smaller units of time that can be understood more easily.

 **Ongoing Assessment: Informing Instruction** See page 921.

Materials

Math Journal 2, pp. 316 and 317
Study Link 12•2
calculator ◆ slate

2 Ongoing Learning & Practice

Using a Line Graph to Display Data
Math Journal 2, p. 318
straightedge
Students create and interpret a line graph.

 **Ongoing Assessment: Recognizing Student Achievement**
Use journal page 318.
[Data and Chance Goal 1]

 **Math Boxes 12·3**
Math Journal 2, p. 315
Students practice and maintain skills through Math Box problems.

 **Study Link 12·3**
Math Masters, p. 342
Students practice and maintain skills through Study Link activities.

3 Differentiation Options

ENRICHMENT
Calculating Mammal Speeds
Math Masters, pp. 343 and 344
Students calculate speeds to see which mammal would win a race.

ELL SUPPORT
Analyzing Life Expectancy Data
Student Reference Book, p. 301
Students analyze life expectancy or average lifetime data.

Additional Information

The data for sleep, TV watching, and laughter found in this lesson are from ***The Compass in Your Nose and Other Astonishing Facts about Humans*** by Marc McCutcheon (Tarcher Putnam, 1989). The authors made up the "data" about the number of breaths in a lifetime.

 ***Teacher's Reference Manual,* Grades 4–6** pp. 13, 64–68, 160, 168, 169

Getting Started

Mental Math and Reflexes

Pose rate problems. *Suggestions:*

●○○ There are 7 oranges per bag. How many oranges in

5 bags? 35 oranges

8 bags? 56 oranges

11 bags? 77 oranges

How many bags for 49 oranges? 7 bags

●●○ There are 13 olives in one jar. How many olives in

3 jars? 39 olives

6 jars? 78 olives

12 jars? 156 olives

How many jars for 65 olives? 5 jars

●●● One batch of cookies contains 3.5 ounces of nuts. How many ounces of nuts in

4 batches? 14 ounces

7 batches? 24.5 ounces

13 batches? 45.5 ounces

How many batches contain 35 ounces of nuts? 10 batches

Math Message

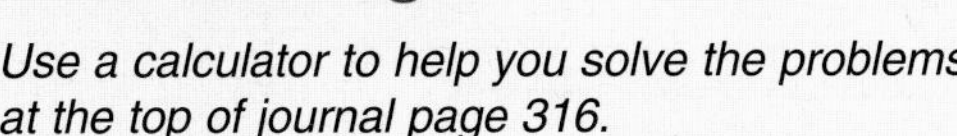

Use a calculator to help you solve the problems at the top of journal page 316.

Study Link 12·2 Follow-Up

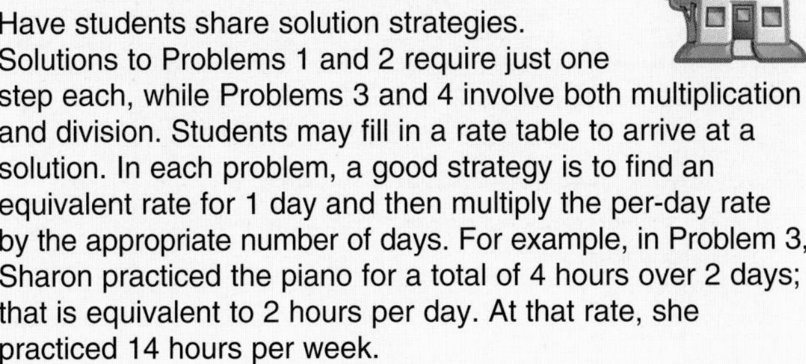

Have students share solution strategies. Solutions to Problems 1 and 2 require just one step each, while Problems 3 and 4 involve both multiplication and division. Students may fill in a rate table to arrive at a solution. In each problem, a good strategy is to find an equivalent rate for 1 day and then multiply the per-day rate by the appropriate number of days. For example, in Problem 3, Sharon practiced the piano for a total of 4 hours over 2 days; that is equivalent to 2 hours per day. At that rate, she practiced 14 hours per week.

1 Teaching the Lesson

▶ Math Message Follow-Up

(*Math Journal 2,* p. 316)

Algebraic Thinking Show the following rate table on the board:

Years	1	2	5	10	75
Days	365	730	1,825	3,650	27,375

Since there are about 365 days in 1 year (366 in leap years), there must be about 27,375 (75 * 365) days in 75 years. Each day has 24 hours, so there are 657,000 (24 * 27,375) hours in 75 years. Some students may have multiplied the number of days in a year by 24 to find the total number of hours per year and then multiplied by 75 to find the total number of hours in 75 years; (365 * 24) * 75 = 657,000.

Ongoing Assessment: Informing Instruction

Watch for students who note that the problem was missing information required to solve it—the number of days per year and the number of hours per day. Remind students that in other cases a problem might contain unnecessary information.

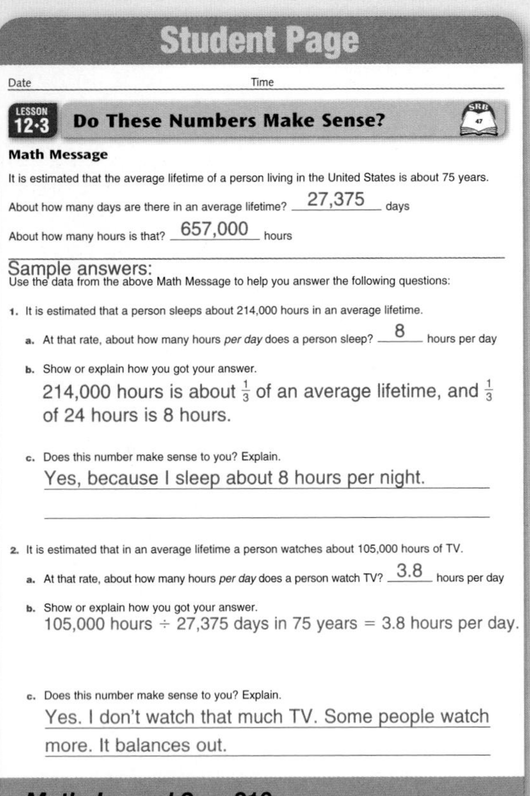

Student Page

Date Time

LESSON 12·3 **Do These Numbers Make Sense?**

Math Message

It is estimated that the average lifetime of a person living in the United States is about 75 years.

About how many days are there in an average lifetime? 27,375 days

About how many hours is that? 657,000 hours

Sample answers:

Use the data from the above Math Message to help you answer the following questions:

1. It is estimated that a person sleeps about 214,000 hours in an average lifetime.
   a. At that rate, about how many hours *per day* does a person sleep? 8 hours per day
   b. Show or explain how you got your answer.
      214,000 hours is about $\frac{1}{3}$ of an average lifetime, and $\frac{1}{3}$ of 24 hours is 8 hours.
   c. Does this number make sense to you? Explain.
      Yes, because I sleep about 8 hours per night.
2. It is estimated that in an average lifetime a person watches about 105,000 hours of TV.
   a. At that rate, about how many hours *per day* does a person watch TV? 3.8 hours per day
   b. Show or explain how you got your answer.
      105,000 hours ÷ 27,375 days in 75 years = 3.8 hours per day.
   c. Does this number make sense to you? Explain.
      Yes. I don't watch that much TV. Some people watch more. It balances out.

***Math Journal 2,* p. 316**

▶ Exploring Methods for Checking Data

(*Math Journal 2,* p. 316)

Tell students that in this lesson they will examine data on the estimated number of times an average person does something in his or her lifetime. They will convert the rates to ones with smaller units of time so that they can be understood more easily.

Write the following statement on the board: *In an average lifetime, a person sleeps about 214,000 hours.*

Ask students how the information might have been found.

- Is it likely that people actually keep track of how long they sleep each night of their lives? It is more likely that many people are observed for a short period of time, and then this information is used to make an estimate for a lifetime.

Explain that this information was found in a reference book, but that it is important to decide whether this number makes sense. Reference books can sometimes be misleading or wrong.

Ask for suggestions on how to check whether this number makes sense.

- Would the number be easier to understand if you calculated about how many hours a person sleeps in a year? In a night?

Divide the class into partnerships. Ask students to calculate about how many hours a person sleeps per day based on a lifetime total and record the strategy they used in Problem 1 on journal page 316. Students should assume a lifetime of 75 years and the stated lifetime sleep total of 214,000 hours. Bring the class together to share solution strategies. Three possible approaches:

▷ Divide 214,000 by 75 to find the number of hours of sleep per year. About 2,853 hours Then divide the result by 365 to find the number of hours of sleep per day. 7.8 hours, rounded to the nearest tenth of an hour

▷ Divide 214,000 by 27,375 (the number of days in 75 years) to find the number of hours of sleep per day. 7.8 hours, rounded to the nearest tenth of an hour

▷ Round 27,375 to 27,000. (This is acceptable since the 75-year life expectancy figure is itself an estimate.) Then divide 214,000 by 27,000 (or, more simply, 214 by 27, since both numbers are "thousands"). The quotient is very close to 8.

Thus, according to the lifetime data, a typical person sleeps about 8 hours per day. Does this result make sense? yes

Students record the results for Problem 1 on journal page 316.

▸ Checking whether Data Make Sense

(*Math Journal 2,* pp. 316 and 317)

Assign Problems 2–5 on journal pages 316 and 317. Bring the class together to share solution strategies. Discuss which of the data in these problems make sense.

Problem 2: Divide 105,000 by 27,375—the number of days in 75 years—to find the number of hours of TV watched per day. 3.8 hours per day, rounded to the nearest tenth

▷ Opinions will probably vary on whether 3.8 hours of TV seems reasonable, based on students' experience. There is no right or wrong answer; what is important is that students think about whether this number makes sense.

▷ Students should be cautioned about predicting lifetime experience based on their own personal viewing habits. The typical child ages 6 to 11 watches about half the number of hours of TV per day as the typical adult.

Problem 3: Divide 540,000 by 27,375 to find the number of laughs per day. About 20

▷ Students usually think that 20 laughs per day is too high. If time allows, the class can consider why the estimate is so high. It may be that every giggle and chuckle is counted as a laugh; including these would raise the rate per day. There are many people who laugh continuously as they converse; their frequent laughs might balance out the infrequent laughs of all others and raise the average rate to 20 laughs per day.

Problem 4: Students might have calculated several different rates. Some of these rates are difficult to interpret because the time period is so long.

▷ Divide 95 million by 27,375 to find the number of breaths per day. 3,470 It is hard to know if 3,470 breaths per day makes sense.

▷ Divide 95 million by 657,000 to find the number of breaths per hour. About 145 This hourly rate is easier to interpret. Some students may decide at this point that the rate is too low and does not make sense.

▷ Divide the hourly rate of 145 breaths per hour by 60 to find the number of breaths per minute. About 2.4 All students should realize that this minute rate is too small and does not make sense; most people take 10 to 15 breaths per minute.

Links to the Future

In *Sixth Grade Everyday Mathematics,* students explore the validity of data presented in the form of pictographs and line graphs.

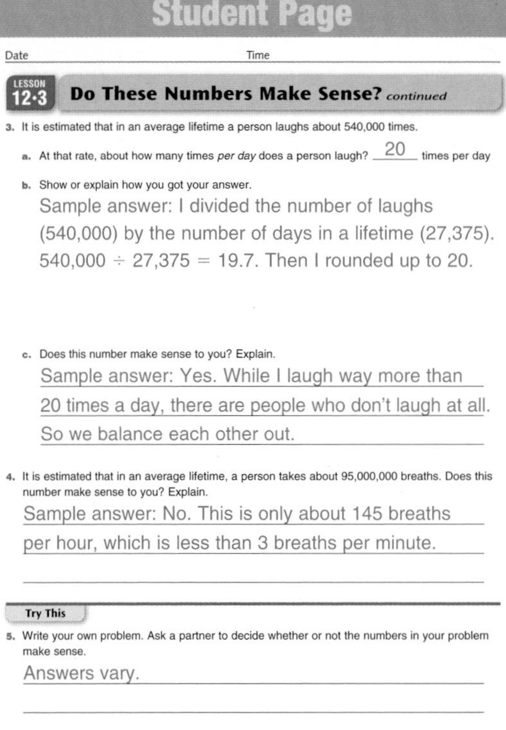

Student Page

Date Time

LESSON 12·3 **Do These Numbers Make Sense?** *continued*

3. It is estimated that in an average lifetime a person laughs about 540,000 times.

a. At that rate, about how many times *per day* does a person laugh? 20 times per day

b. Show or explain how you got your answer.
Sample answer: I divided the number of laughs (540,000) by the number of days in a lifetime (27,375). 540,000 ÷ 27,375 = 19.7. Then I rounded up to 20.

c. Does this number make sense to you? Explain.
Sample answer: Yes. While I laugh way more than 20 times a day, there are people who don't laugh at all. So we balance each other out.

4. It is estimated that in an average lifetime, a person takes about 95,000,000 breaths. Does this number make sense to you? Explain.
Sample answer: No. This is only about 145 breaths per hour, which is less than 3 breaths per minute.

Try This

5. Write your own problem. Ask a partner to decide whether or not the numbers in your problem make sense.
Answers vary.

***Math Journal 2,* p. 317**

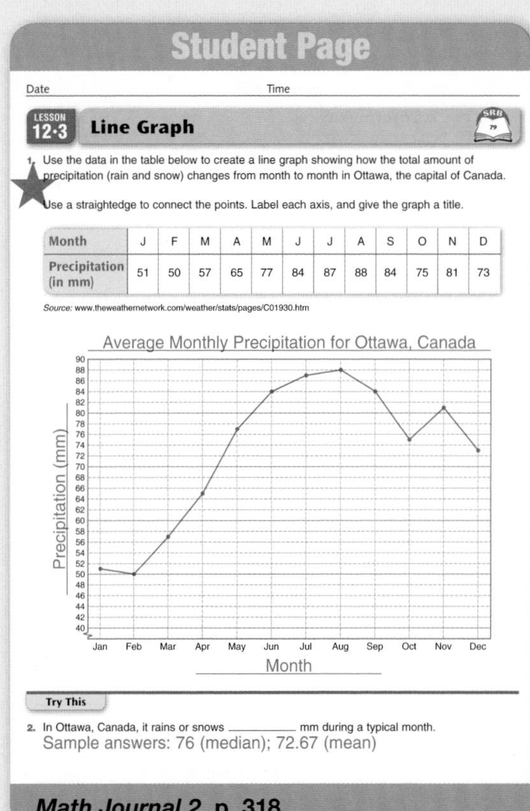

Student Page

Date Time

LESSON 12·3 **Line Graph**

1. Use the data in the table below to create a line graph showing how the total amount of precipitation (rain and snow) changes from month to month in Ottawa, the capital of Canada. Use a straightedge to connect the points. Label each axis, and give the graph a title.

Month	J	F	M	A	M	J	J	A	S	O	N	D
Precipitation (in mm)	51	50	57	65	77	84	87	88	84	75	81	73

Source: www.theweathernetwork.com/weather/stats/pages/C01930.htm

Try This

2. In Ottawa, Canada, it rains or snows ______ mm during a typical month.
Sample answers: 76 (median); 72.67 (mean)

***Math Journal 2,* p. 318**

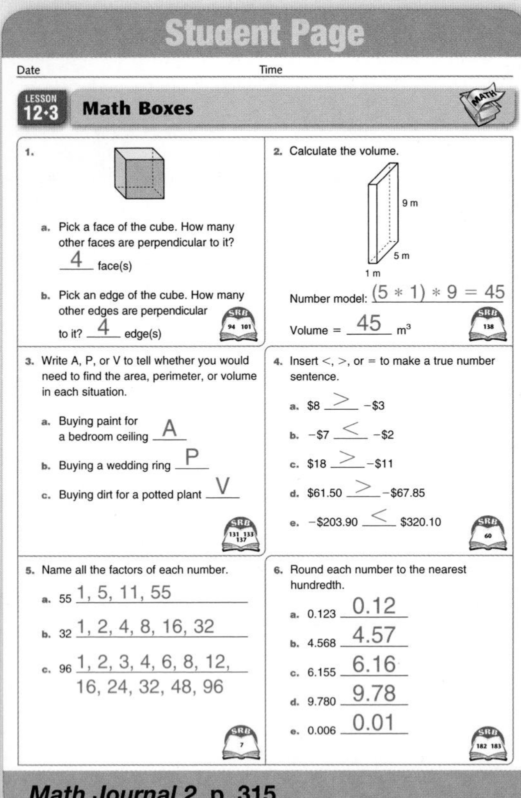
Student Page

Date Time

LESSON 12·3 **Math Boxes**

1.
a. Pick a face of the cube. How many other faces are perpendicular to it? 4 face(s)
b. Pick an edge of the cube. How many other edges are perpendicular to it? 4 edge(s)

2. Calculate the volume.
9 m, 5 m, 1 m
Number model: (5 ∗ 1) ∗ 9 = 45
Volume = 45 m^3

3. Write A, P, or V to tell whether you would need to find the area, perimeter, or volume in each situation.
a. Buying paint for a bedroom ceiling A
b. Buying a wedding ring P
c. Buying dirt for a potted plant V

4. Insert <, >, or = to make a true number sentence.
a. $8 > –$3
b. –$7 < –$2
c. $18 > –$11
d. $61.50 > –$67.85
e. –$203.90 < $320.10

5. Name all the factors of each number.
a. 55 1, 5, 11, 55
b. 32 1, 2, 4, 8, 16, 32
c. 96 1, 2, 3, 4, 6, 8, 12, 16, 24, 32, 48, 96

6. Round each number to the nearest hundredth.
a. 0.123 0.12
b. 4.568 4.57
c. 6.155 6.16
d. 9.780 9.78
e. 0.006 0.01

Math Journal 2, p. 315

2 Ongoing Learning & Practice

Using a Line Graph to Display Data

INDEPENDENT ACTIVITY

(*Math Journal 2,* p. 318)

Students use a table of data to create a line graph displaying the average monthly precipitation in Ottawa, Canada.

Ongoing Assessment: Recognizing Student Achievement

Journal page 318 Problem 1

Use **journal page 318, Problem 1** to assess students' ability to use given data to create a line graph. Students are making adequate progress if they can accurately plot the average amount of precipitation for each month, connect the points with line segments, and provide a label for each axis and a title for the graph. Some students may be able to determine typical monthly precipitation in Problem 2 by finding the median of the monthly data. 75 mm Other students may find the mean. 72.67 mm

[Data and Chance Goal 1]

Math Boxes 12·3

INDEPENDENT ACTIVITY

(*Math Journal 2,* p. 315)

Mixed Practice Math Boxes in this lesson are paired with Math Boxes in Lesson 12-1.

Portfolio Ideas

Writing/Reasoning Have students write a response to the following: *In Problem 5, explain how you knew that you had listed all of the factors of a number.* Sample answer: I started with 1 and the number itself. Then I found all of the other factor pairs of that number. When I found a turn-around fact, I knew that I had all of the factors of the number.

Study Link 12·3

INDEPENDENT ACTIVITY

(*Math Masters,* p. 342)

Home Connection Students solve rate problems involving the activities of mammals.

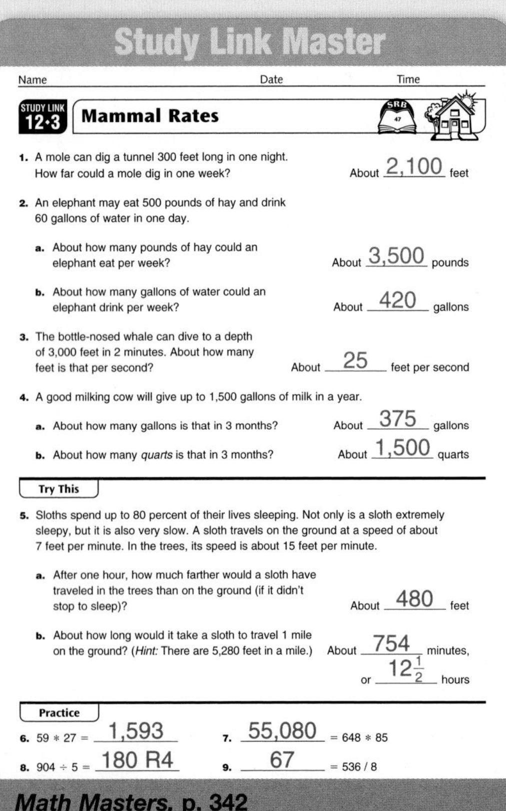
Study Link Master

Name Date Time

STUDY LINK 12·3 **Mammal Rates**

1. A mole can dig a tunnel 300 feet long in one night. How far could a mole dig in one week? About 2,100 feet
2. An elephant may eat 500 pounds of hay and drink 60 gallons of water in one day.
a. About how many pounds of hay could an elephant eat per week? About 3,500 pounds
b. About how many gallons of water could an elephant drink per week? About 420 gallons
3. The bottle-nosed whale can dive to a depth of 3,000 feet in 2 minutes. About how many feet is that per second? About 25 feet per second
4. A good milking cow will give up to 1,500 gallons of milk in a year.
a. About how many gallons is that in 3 months? About 375 gallons
b. About how many *quarts* is that in 3 months? About 1,500 quarts

Try This

5. Sloths spend up to 80 percent of their lives sleeping. Not only is a sloth extremely sleepy, but it is also very slow. A sloth travels on the ground at a speed of about 7 feet per minute. In the trees, its speed is about 15 feet per minute.
a. After one hour, how much farther would a sloth have traveled in the trees than on the ground (if it didn't stop to sleep)? About 480 feet
b. About how long would it take a sloth to travel 1 mile on the ground? (*Hint:* There are 5,280 feet in a mile.) About 754 minutes, or $12\frac{1}{2}$ hours

Practice

6. 59 ∗ 27 = 1,593
7. 55,080 = 648 ∗ 85
8. 904 ÷ 5 = 180 R4
9. 67 = 536 / 8

Math Masters, p. 342

3 Differentiation Options

ENRICHMENT

PARTNER ACTIVITY

Calculating Mammal Speeds

15–30 Min

(*Math Masters,* pp. 343 and 344)

To apply students' understanding of rates, have them predict and then calculate which mammal would win a 300-foot race—an elephant, a cheetah, or a fourth grader. Students must determine rates in feet per second to plot the positions of the two other contestants on the race course when the winner crosses the finish line.

NOTE Students should not be overly concerned about the feasibility of such a race.

ELL SUPPORT

SMALL-GROUP ACTIVITY

Analyzing Life Expectancy Data

5–15 Min

(*Student Reference Book,* p. 301)

To provide language support for average lifetime data, have students analyze the life expectancy table on *Student Reference Book,* page 301. *Life expectancy,* or *average lifetime,* is defined as the average number of years a person can expect to live. Data for males and females are given separately because women usually live longer than men.

Record statements like the following on the board and have students fill in the missing numbers and words:

▷ Men in Spain (Region 2) are expected to live 76 years.

▷ Women live 84 years in Canada (Region 5).

▷ The average lifetime is the same for men and women in Sample answers: Kenya (Region 1), South Africa (Region 1), and Bangladesh (Region 4).

Teaching Master

Name ______ Date ______ Time ______

LESSON 12·3 **Mammal 100-Yard Dash**

It could not happen, of course, but suppose that you, an elephant, and a cheetah were to race a distance of 100 yards, or 300 feet. Which of you would win? Which would come in second? Third? Answers vary for 1 and 2.

1. My Prediction: First ______ Second ______ Third ______

2. On the diagram below, show the winner crossing the finish line. Estimate where you think the second-place and third-place mammals would be when the fastest mammal wins. Write "C" for the cheetah, "E" for the elephant, and "Me" for yourself.

0 30 60 90 120 150 180 210 240 270 300 feet
Start Finish

3. What information would help you predict the winner?
Sample answer: It would help to know the speed of an average fourth grader, an elephant, and a cheetah.

4. Complete the table below by using the "last race results" to find each mammal's top sprint speed in feet per second.

Mammal	Last Race Results	Top Sprint Speed (approximate)
Fourth Grader	84 yards in 12 seconds	21 ft/sec
Cheetah	2,448 inches in 2 seconds	102 ft/sec
Elephant	36 yards in 3 seconds	36 ft/sec

Math Masters, p. 343

NOTE To have students use a rate to calculate the distance a turtle travels and graph the results, see www.everydaymathonline.com.

Teaching Master

Name ______ Date ______ Time ______

LESSON 12·3 **Mammal 100-Yard Dash** *continued*

5. According to the ft/sec rates, how would the 300-foot race among an elephant, a cheetah, and a fourth grader turn out?
First Cheetah Second Elephant Third Me

6. About how long would it take for the winner of the race to run 300 feet? About 3 seconds

7. By the time the winner crosses the finish line, how far would the other mammals have run?
Second-place mammal About 100 feet
Third-place mammal About 60 feet

8. Would it be a close race? No

9. On the diagram below, show which mammal will win the race and where the other two mammals will be when the winner crosses the finish line.

Me E C
0 30 60 90 120 150 180 210 240 270 300 feet
Start Finish

10. About how many times faster is the first-place mammal than
a. the second-place mammal? 3
b. the third-place mammal? 5

11. The top sprint speed for a squirrel is 18 feet per second. Does this mean that you could catch a squirrel by running after it? Explain.
Sample answer: No. I can run in a straight line faster than a squirrel can, but they rarely run in straight lines when I chase them.

Math Masters, p. 344

12•4 Comparison Shopping: Part 1

Objectives To introduce calculating the unit price for a product; and to provide practice comparing unit prices and identifying information needed for comparison shopping.

Technology Resources www.everydaymathonline.com

ePresentations

eToolkit

Algorithms Practice

EM Facts Workshop Game™

Family Letters

Assessment Management

Common Core State Standards

Curriculum Focal Points

Interactive Teacher's Lesson Guide

1 Teaching the Lesson

Key Concepts and Skills

- Find multiples.
  [Number and Numeration Goal 3]
- Multiply and divide decimals by whole numbers.
  [Operations and Computation Goal 4]
- Use repeated addition and scaling to model multiplication problems.
  [Operations and Computation Goal 7]
- Analyze and interpret data.
  [Data and Chance Goal 2]
- Use patterns and rules to solve rate problems.
  [Patterns, Functions, and Algebra Goal 1]

Key Activities

Students calculate the unit prices of various products. They calculate and compare the unit prices of two products to decide which is the better buy.

Ongoing Assessment: Informing Instruction See page 929.

Key Vocabulary

consumer ◆ products ◆ services ◆ comparison shopping ◆ unit price

Materials

Math Journal 2, pp. 319 and 320
Study Link 12•3
Math Masters, p. 454 (optional)
calculator ◆ slate

2 Ongoing Learning & Practice

Playing *Name That Number*
Student Reference Book, p. 254
Math Masters, p. 489
per partnership: complete deck of number cards (the Everything Math Deck, if available)
Students practice representing numbers in different ways.

Ongoing Assessment: Recognizing Student Achievement
Use *Math Masters,* page 489.
[Patterns, Functions, and Algebra Goal 3]

Converting Units of Measure
Math Journal 2, pp. 319A and 319B
Students convert among units of measure.

Math Boxes 12•4
Math Journal 2, p. 321
Students practice and maintain skills through Math Box problems.

Study Link 12•4
Math Masters, p. 345
Students practice and maintain skills through Study Link activities.

3 Differentiation Options

READINESS

Finding Unit Prices
Math Masters, pp. 346 and 428
coins
Students use a concrete model to determine unit prices.

ENRICHMENT

Testing Products
products to test
Students test products and then analyze and interpret the data.

Advance Preparation

***Teacher's Reference Manual,* Grades 4–6** pp. 13, 64–68, 160, 168, 169

Getting Started

Mental Math and Reflexes

Pose measurement conversion problems. *Suggestions:*

●○○ 1 hour is 60 minutes. How many minutes are in
- 2 hours? 120
- 4 hours? 240
- 7 hours? 420

●●○ 1 pound is 16 ounces. How many ounces are in
- 2 pounds? 32
- 30 pounds? 480
- 100 pounds? 1,600

●●● 1 kilogram is 1,000 grams. How many grams are in
- $3\frac{1}{2}$ kilograms? 3,500
- $7\frac{1}{4}$ kilograms? 7,250
- $15\frac{1}{2}$ kilograms 15,500

Math Message

Read and complete journal page 319.

Study Link 12·3 Follow-Up

Have small groups compare answers.

1 Teaching the Lesson

Math Message Follow-Up

(*Math Journal 2,* p. 319)

Students share their definitions of the word ***consumer.*** Sample answer: A person who acquires products or uses services

Pose questions such as the following, and list students' responses on the board.

- What are some **products** and **services** you have used recently? Sample answers: Products: food, clothing, school supplies; Services: public transportation, school, the postal service, utilities such as the telephone or electricity
- What are some of the qualities of a smart consumer? Sample answers: Makes thoughtful decisions based on the quality, price, and effect of the product or service on the environment, as well as on personal needs and taste
- What information might you want to know before choosing a baseball camp? Sample answers: The qualifications of the counselors, the types of activities offered, the location of the camp, the cost
- How would you go about getting the information you need to select the best product? Sample answers: Ask people who have used the products, read articles about the products in consumer magazines, compare prices. This kind of research is called **comparison shopping.**

Student Page

Date Time

LESSON 12·4 Product Testing

Some publications ask their readers to test many different kinds of products. The results of the tests are then published to help readers make wise buying decisions. One example is the former *Consumer Reports for Kids Online.* It featured articles previously published in *Zillions,* a child's version of *Consumer Reports.* In one test, 99 readers field tested several backpack models. The readers considered fit, back friendliness, and comfort as they tried to decide which brand was the best buy. In another test, a team of young people compared 40 brands of jeans in their search for a brand that would not shrink in length.

When a reader wrote to complain about a board game she bought, the staff sent board games to young people in every part of the country. Testers were asked to play each game several times and then to report what they liked and disliked about the game.

Answers vary.

1. If you were testing a board game, what are some of the features you would look for?
2. When readers of the magazine tested backpacks, they considered fit, back friendliness, and comfort in determining the best one. Which of these factors is the most important to you? Why?
3. What is a **consumer**? Be prepared to share your definition with the class.

Math Journal 2, **p. 319**

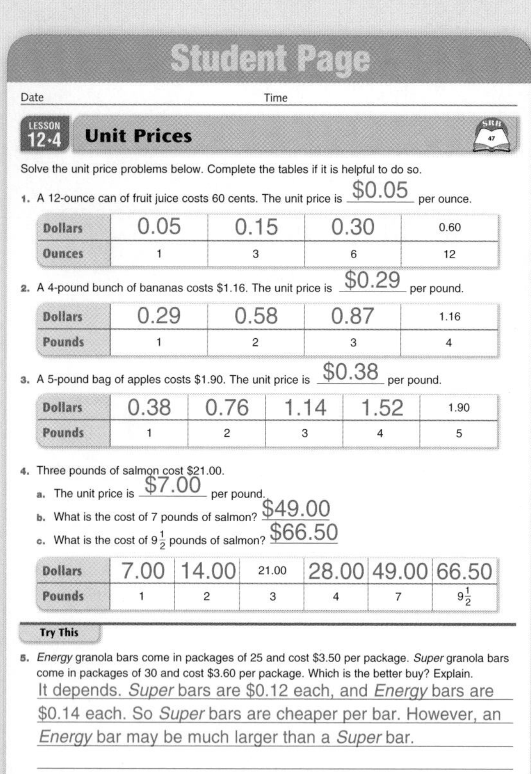

Student Page

Date Time

LESSON 12·4 **Unit Prices**

Solve the unit price problems below. Complete the tables if it is helpful to do so.

1. A 12-ounce can of fruit juice costs 60 cents. The unit price is $0.05 per ounce.

Dollars	0.05	0.15	0.30	0.60
Ounces	1	3	6	12

2. A 4-pound bunch of bananas costs $1.16. The unit price is $0.29 per pound.

Dollars	0.29	0.58	0.87	1.16
Pounds	1	2	3	4

3. A 5-pound bag of apples costs $1.90. The unit price is $0.38 per pound.

Dollars	0.38	0.76	1.14	1.52	1.90
Pounds	1	2	3	4	5

4. Three pounds of salmon cost $21.00.
   a. The unit price is $7.00 per pound.
   b. What is the cost of 7 pounds of salmon? $49.00
   c. What is the cost of $9\frac{1}{2}$ pounds of salmon? $66.50

Dollars	7.00	14.00	21.00	28.00	49.00	66.50
Pounds	1	2	3	4	7	$9\frac{1}{2}$

Try This

5. *Energy* granola bars come in packages of 25 and cost $3.50 per package. *Super* granola bars come in packages of 30 and cost $3.60 per package. Which is the better buy? Explain.
   It depends. *Super* bars are $0.12 each, and *Energy* bars are $0.14 each. So *Super* bars are cheaper per bar. However, an *Energy* bar may be much larger than a *Super* bar.

***Math Journal 2,* p. 320**

Student Page

Date Time

LESSON 12·4 **Converting Units of Measure**

1 pound (lb) = 16 ounces (oz)
1 ton (T) = 2,000 pounds (lb)

Complete the conversions between ounces, pounds, and tons.
Write the information you needed to make the conversion.

1. 5 lb = 80 oz   1 lb = 16 oz
2. $\frac{1}{2}$ lb = 8 oz   1 lb = 16 oz
3. 129 lb = 2,064 oz   1 lb = 16 oz
4. 2 T = 4,000 lb   1 T = 2,000 lb
5. $6\frac{1}{4}$ T = 12,500 lb   1 T = 2,000 lb
6. 112 oz = 7 lb   1 lb = 16 oz
7. 20,000 lb = 10 T   1 T = 2,000 lb
8. 4,240 oz = 265 lb   1 lb = 16 oz
9. 3,000 lb = $1\frac{1}{2}$ T   1 T = 2,000 lb
10. $1\frac{1}{4}$ lb = 20 oz   1 lb = 16 oz

Complete the table.

11.

Ounces	Pounds	Tons
160,000	10,000	5
304,000	19,000	9.5
16,000	1,000	$\frac{1}{2}$

***Math Journal 2,* p. 319A**

▶ Introducing Unit Prices

(*Math Masters,* p. 454)

NOTE Although the sequence of lessons on unit pricing focuses on the arithmetic of buying products and services, it is also important to discuss the more general aspects of what it means to be a consumer.

Throughout the sequence of lessons on unit pricing, remind students that comparison shopping is not simply a matter of determining which of several comparable products or services is the cheapest. There are other important factors that enter into making wise decisions.

Consumer Link The **unit price** is the cost of an item per unit of measure. Give several examples and write them in rate tables so that students will understand that unit prices are rates. To support English language learners, help students make connections between the terms *unit fraction* and *unit rate* from prior lessons and the term *unit price. Suggestions:*

- A 10-pound bag of potatoes costs $5.00. The unit price is the cost of 1 pound. $0.50

Dollars	0.50	5.00
Pounds	1	10

- A package of 6 pens costs $4.20. The unit price is the cost of 1 pen. $0.70

Dollars	0.70	4.20
Pens	1	6

- A dozen bagels cost $3.60. The unit price is the cost of 1 bagel. $0.30

Dollars	0.30	3.60
Bagels	1	12

Ask how the unit price is calculated from the cost information that is given. Divide the cost by the number of units or items. For example, $\$5.00 \div 10 = \$0.50$, $\$4.20 \div 6 = \$0.70$, and $\$3.60 \div 12 = \$0.30$. Explain that finding the unit price is like solving an equal-sharing problem: Division is used to find the cost of each unit, item, or share.

Now pose several practice problems on comparison shopping. Work through these as a class, and encourage students to use calculators. Calculate unit prices for similar items, and then compare these unit prices to determine which item is the better buy. Point out that unit prices are not easily compared unless they are *for the same unit.* (For example, $3.20/1 lb and $0.10/1 oz are not easily compared, but $0.20/1 oz and $0.10/1 oz are.)

Suggestions:

▷ Lightbulbs

Brand A: package of 4 bulbs for $2.08

Brand B: package of 6 bulbs for $3.00

Brand A: $0.52/1 bulb; Brand B: $0.50/1 bulb; Brand B is the better buy.

▷ Crackers

Brand A: 1-pound box for $2.40

Brand B: 24-ounce box for $3.84

Brand A: $0.15/1 oz; Brand B: $0.16/1 oz; Brand A is the better buy.

Calculating and Comparing Unit Prices

(*Math Journal 2,* p. 320)

Have partners complete Problems 1–5 on journal page 320.

Ongoing Assessment: Informing Instruction

Watch for students who assume that the lower-cost package of *Energy* granola bars in Problem 5 is the better buy. Have students compare quantities and explain that even though the price of the package may be lower, the price per granola bar may be higher because there are not as many bars in the package or the size of the bars is smaller.

2 Ongoing Learning & Practice

Playing *Name That Number*

(*Student Reference Book,* p. 254; *Math Masters,* p. 489)

Students play *Name That Number* to practice representing numbers in different ways. See Lesson 2-2 for additional information.

Ongoing Assessment: Recognizing Student Achievement

Math Masters Page 489

Use ***Math Masters,* page 489** to assess students' ability to insert grouping symbols to make true number sentences. Students are making adequate progress if they are able to use parentheses in number sentences to show combinations of numbers and operations that name the target numbers. Some students may be able to use nested parentheses in their number sentences.

[Patterns, Functions, and Algebra Goal 3]

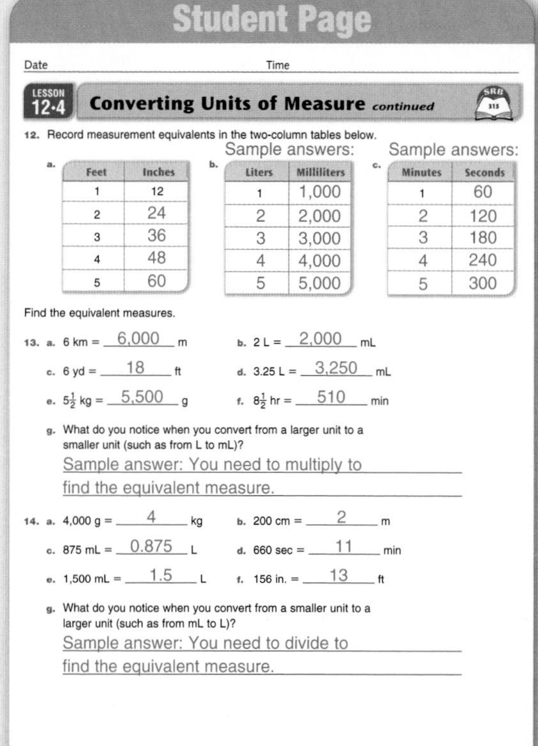

Student Page

Date Time

LESSON 12•4 **Converting Units of Measure** *continued*

12. Record measurement equivalents in the two-column tables below.

a.

Feet	Inches
1	12
2	24
3	36
4	48
5	60

b. Sample answers:

Liters	Milliliters
1	1,000
2	2,000
3	3,000
4	4,000
5	5,000

c. Sample answers:

Minutes	Seconds
1	60
2	120
3	180
4	240
5	300

Find the equivalent measures.

13. a. 6 km = 6,000 m b. 2 L = 2,000 mL

c. 6 yd = 18 ft d. 3.25 L = 3,250 mL

e. $5\frac{1}{2}$ kg = 5,500 g f. $8\frac{1}{2}$ hr = 510 min

g. What do you notice when you convert from a larger unit to a smaller unit (such as from L to mL)?
Sample answer: You need to multiply to find the equivalent measure.

14. a. 4,000 g = 4 kg b. 200 cm = 2 m

c. 875 mL = 0.875 L d. 660 sec = 11 min

e. 1,500 mL = 1.5 L f. 156 in. = 13 ft

g. What do you notice when you convert from a smaller unit to a larger unit (such as from mL to L)?
Sample answer: You need to divide to find the equivalent measure.

Math Journal 2, p. 319B

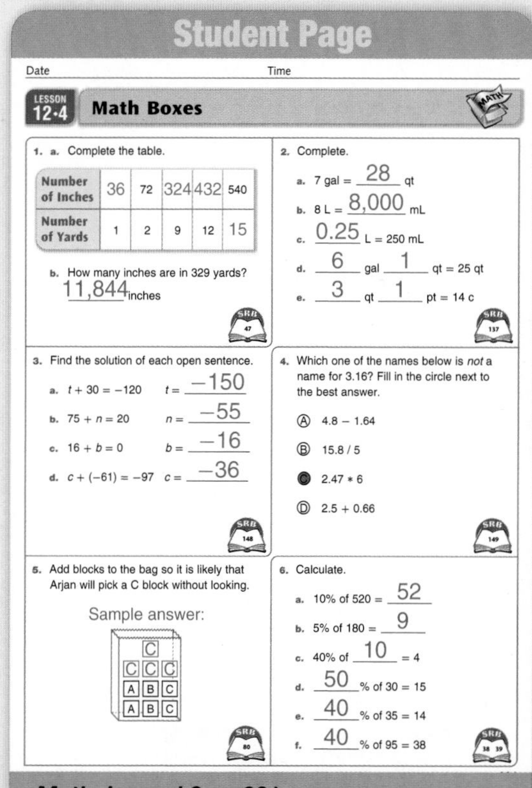

Student Page

Date Time

LESSON 12•4 **Math Boxes**

1. a. Complete the table.

Number of Inches	36	72	324	432	540
Number of Yards	1	2	9	12	15

b. How many inches are in 329 yards? 11,844 inches

2. Complete.
a. 7 gal = 28 qt
b. 8 L = 8,000 mL
c. 0.25 L = 250 mL
d. 6 gal 1 qt = 25 qt
e. 3 qt 1 pt = 14 c

3. Find the solution of each open sentence.
a. $t + 30 = -120$ $t =$ −150
b. $75 + n = 20$ $n =$ −55
c. $16 + b = 0$ $b =$ −16
d. $c + (-61) = -97$ $c =$ −36

4. Which one of the names below is *not* a name for 3.16? Fill in the circle next to the best answer.
Ⓐ 4.8 − 1.64
Ⓑ 15.8 / 5
● 2.47 ∗ 6
Ⓓ 2.5 + 0.66

5. Add blocks to the bag so it is likely that Arjan will pick a C block without looking.
Sample answer:
C; C C C; A B C; A B C

6. Calculate.
a. 10% of 520 = 52
b. 5% of 180 = 9
c. 40% of 10 = 4
d. 50 % of 30 = 15
e. 40 % of 35 = 14
f. 40 % of 95 = 38

Math Journal 2, p. 321

Study Link Master

Name Date Time

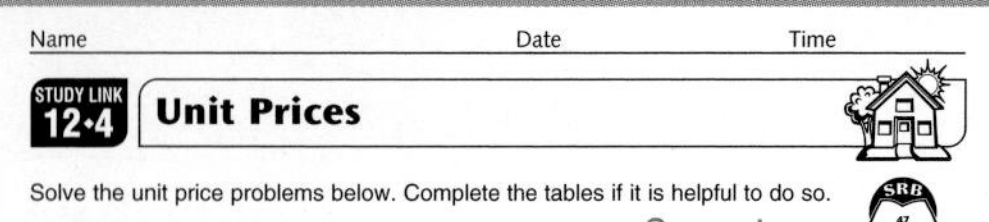
STUDY LINK 12•4 **Unit Prices**

Solve the unit price problems below. Complete the tables if it is helpful to do so.

1. A 12-oz bag of pretzels costs 96 cents. The unit price is 8 cents per ounce.

Dollars	0.08	0.24	0.72	0.96
Ounces	1	3	9	12

2. A package of 3 rolls of paper towels costs $2.07. The unit price is $0.69 per roll.

Dollars	0.69	1.38	2.07
Rolls	1	2	3

3. A 4-liter bottle of water costs $1.40. The unit price is $0.35 per liter.

Dollars	0.35	0.70	1.05	1.40
Liters	1	2	3	4

4. Choose 4 items from newspaper ads. In the table below, record the name, price, and quantity of each item. Leave the Unit Price column blank.

Item	Quantity	Price	Unit Price
Golden Sun Raisins	24 ounces	$2.99	12.4 cents per ounce
Answers vary.			

Practice

Name the factor pairs for each number.

5. 12 1, 12; 2, 6; 3, 4
6. 50 1, 50; 2, 25; 5, 10

Math Masters, p. 345

Teaching Master

Name Date Time

LESSON 12•4 **Stock-Up Sale**

Party Town is having a summer stock-up sale. The ad below shows the original price of each item and the sale price if you buy a certain number of items. Use bills and coins to help you find the stock-up price per item.

1. Party Music CDs $8.00 each. Stock-Up Price: Buy 5 for $25.00. You pay $5.00 per CD.
2. String in a Can $3.00 each. Stock-Up Price: Buy 8 for $16.00. You pay $2.00 per can.
3. Mylar Balloon $1.99 each. Stock-Up Price: Buy 12 for $14.40. You pay $1.20 per balloon.
4. Piñata $14.99 each. Stock-Up Price: Buy 3 for $29.97. You pay $9.99 per piñata.
5. Glow bracelets $2.50 each. Stock-Up Price: Buy 6 for $10.50. You pay $1.75 per bracelet.
6. Party Hats $9.99 for a package of 45. Stock-Up Price: Buy 4 packages for $19.96. You pay $4.99 per package.

Math Masters, p. 346

▶ Converting Units of Measure

INDEPENDENT ACTIVITY

(*Math Journal 2,* pp. 319A and 319B)

Students convert among units of weight, capacity, length, and time. They look for patterns in how they make the conversions.

▶ Math Boxes 12•4

INDEPENDENT ACTIVITY

(*Math Journal 2,* p. 321)

Mixed Practice Math Boxes in this lesson are linked with Math Boxes in Lessons 12-2 and 12-6.

▶ Study Link 12•4

INDEPENDENT ACTIVITY

(*Math Masters,* p. 345)

Home Connection Students calculate unit prices. They also look for supermarket ads in newspapers and record the information contained in four of them. In Lesson 12-5 students will calculate the unit prices of these items.

3 Differentiation Options

READINESS

PARTNER ACTIVITY

▶ Finding Unit Prices

5–15 Min

(*Math Masters,* pp. 346 and 428)

To explore unit prices using a concrete model, have students determine the unit prices for items sold during a summer stock-up sale. Encourage students to use bills (*Math Masters,* page 428) and coins to act out dividing the stock-up price by the number of items to find the unit price.

ENRICHMENT

PARTNER ACTIVITY

▶ Testing Products

30+ Min

To apply students' ability to analyze and interpret data, have students create guidelines for testing a product such as colored markers. They may want to consider factors such as brightness, cost, and drying time. Encourage students to use a scale to rate each criterion for each brand. *For example:* 4 = excellent, 3 = good, 2 = not so good, 1 = poor. Have students test three brands of the chosen product using their guidelines. Students should tally and report their findings with a chart or graph.

12•5 Comparison Shopping: Part 2

Objective To provide practice calculating and comparing unit prices that involve fractions of cents.

Technology Resources www.everydaymathonline.com

Presentations

eToolkit

Algorithms Practice

EM Facts Workshop Game™

Family Letters

Assessment Management

Common Core State Standards

Curriculum Focal Points

Interactive Teacher's Lesson Guide

1 Teaching the Lesson

Key Concepts and Skills

- Compare decimals.
  [Number and Numeration Goal 6]
- Divide decimals by whole numbers.
  [Operations and Computation Goal 4]
- Round decimals.
  [Operations and Computation Goal 6]
- Use repeated addition and scaling to solve rate problems.
  [Operations and Computation Goal 7]

Key Activities

Students share unit-price label information they collected on visits to supermarkets and use the information collected from supermarket ads to calculate unit prices. Students calculate unit prices involving fractions of cents.

Ongoing Assessment: Recognizing Student Achievement
Use journal page 322.
[Operations and Computation Goal 7]

Materials

Math Journal 2, p. 322
Study Link 12•4
calculator ◆ slate ◆ supermarket ads ◆ overhead calculator (optional)

2 Ongoing Learning & Practice

Playing *Fraction Top-It*
Fraction Cards (*Math Journal 2,* Activity Sheets 5 and 6)
Student Reference Book, p. 247
Math Masters, p. 506
Students practice comparing and ordering fractions.

Investigating Liters and Milliliters
Math Journal 2, pp. 322A and 322B
Students solve capacity problems.

Math Boxes 12•5
Math Journal 2, p. 323
Students practice and maintain skills through Math Box problems.

Study Link 12•5
Math Masters, p. 347
Students practice and maintain skills through Study Link activities.

3 Differentiation Options

READINESS

Solving Comparison Shopping Problems
Math Masters, pp. 348 and 428
coins
Students explore comparison shopping problems.

ENRICHMENT

Measuring Air Pressure with a Barometer
Student Reference Book, p. 297
Math Masters, pp. 349–351
Students explore how barometric pressure can be used to determine elevation.

EXTRA PRACTICE

5-Minute Math
5-Minute Math™, pp. 27, 29, 105, 109, 191, and 192
Students solve rate problems.

Advance Preparation

***Teacher's Reference Manual,* Grades 4–6** pp. 19, 29–35, 64–68

Getting Started

Mental Math and Reflexes

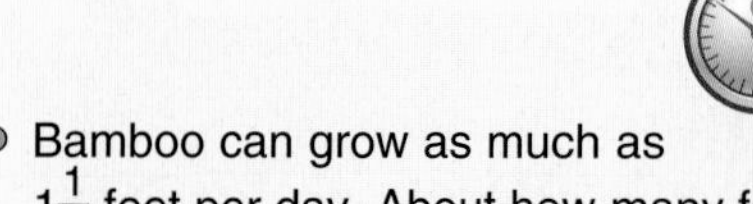

Pose rate problems. *Suggestions:*

●○○ Plums are on sale at 10 for $1.20. How much for
1 plum? 12 cents
5 plums? 60 cents
8 plums? 96 cents
How many plums for $2.40? 20 plums

●●○ Juice boxes are on sale at 12 for $6. How much for
1 juice box? 50 cents
7 juice boxes? $3.50
25 juice boxes? $12.50
How many juice boxes for $5.00? 10 juice boxes

●●● Bamboo can grow as much as $1\frac{1}{2}$ feet per day. About how many feet might it grow in
12 hours? $\frac{3}{4}$ foot
3 days? $4\frac{1}{2}$ feet
1 week? $10\frac{1}{2}$ feet
How many days would it take to grow $7\frac{1}{2}$ feet? 5 days

Math Message

Use a calculator to help you solve the division problems at the top of journal page 322.

Study Link 12·4 Follow-Up

Have students compare answers to Problems 1–3. Problem 4 will be discussed later in the lesson.

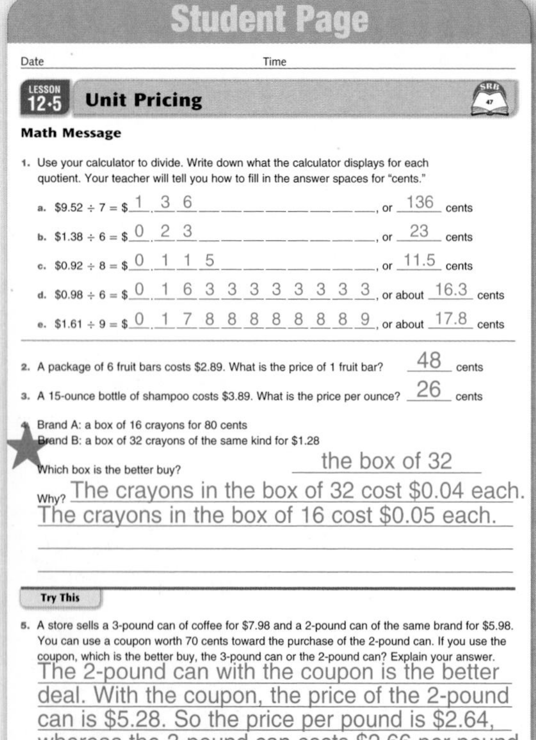

Student Page

Date Time

LESSON 12·5 **Unit Pricing** SRB 47

Math Message

1. Use your calculator to divide. Write down what the calculator displays for each quotient. Your teacher will tell you how to fill in the answer spaces for "cents."
   a. $9.52 ÷ 7 = $1.36, or 136 cents
   b. $1.38 ÷ 6 = $0.23, or 23 cents
   c. $0.92 ÷ 8 = $0.115, or 11.5 cents
   d. $0.98 ÷ 6 = $0.1633333333, or about 16.3 cents
   e. $1.61 ÷ 9 = $0.1788888889, or about 17.8 cents
2. A package of 6 fruit bars costs $2.89. What is the price of 1 fruit bar? 48 cents
3. A 15-ounce bottle of shampoo costs $3.89. What is the price per ounce? 26 cents
4. Brand A: a box of 16 crayons for 80 cents
   Brand B: a box of 32 crayons of the same kind for $1.28
   Which box is the better buy? the box of 32
   Why? The crayons in the box of 32 cost $0.04 each. The crayons in the box of 16 cost $0.05 each.

Try This

5. A store sells a 3-pound can of coffee for $7.98 and a 2-pound can of the same brand for $5.98. You can use a coupon worth 70 cents toward the purchase of the 2-pound can. If you use the coupon, which is the better buy, the 3-pound can or the 2-pound can? Explain your answer.
   The 2-pound can with the coupon is the better deal. With the coupon, the price of the 2-pound can is $5.28. So the price per pound is $2.64, whereas the 3-pound can costs $2.66 per pound.

Math Journal 2, p. 322

1 Teaching the Lesson

▶ Math Message Follow-Up

(*Math Journal 2,* p. 322)

The 11-digit TI-15 display will show the following amounts:

a. 1.36 **b.** 0.23
c. 0.115 **d.** 0.1633333333
e. 0.1788888889

The 8-digit Casio *fx*-55 display will show the following amounts:

a. 1.36 **b.** 0.23
c. 0.115 **d.** 0.1633333
e. 0.1788888

Students may find it difficult to interpret the calculator displays as money amounts in Problems 1c–1e. Tell students that unit-price calculations will often result in decimals with many places. To convert them to amounts in cents, they can proceed as follows:

1. Ignore all but the first 3 digits following the decimal point.
2. Read the first 2 digits following the decimal point as cents.
3. Read the third digit following the decimal point as tenths of a cent.

Examples:

▷ Problem 1c: $0.115 is 11.5 cents, or $11\frac{1}{2}$ cents.

▷ Problem 1d: $0.1633333333 is about 16.3 cents; the last 7 digits are ignored.

▷ Problem 1e: $0.1788888889 is about 17.8 cents; the last 7 digits are ignored.

Have students fill in the answer spaces for "cents" for these five division problems.

Adjusting the Activity

Have students round decimals more precisely by ignoring all but the first 4 digits following the decimal point. If the fourth digit is less than 5, delete it. If the fourth digit is 5 or greater, increase the third digit by 1, and delete the fourth digit.

Examples:

▷ Problem 1d: $0.1633333333 → $0.1633 (4th digit is less than 5) → $0.163, or 16.3 cents

▷ Problem 1e: $0.1788888889 → $0.1788 (4th digit is 5 or more) → $0.179, or 17.9 cents

AUDITORY ◆ KINESTHETIC ◆ TACTILE ◆ VISUAL

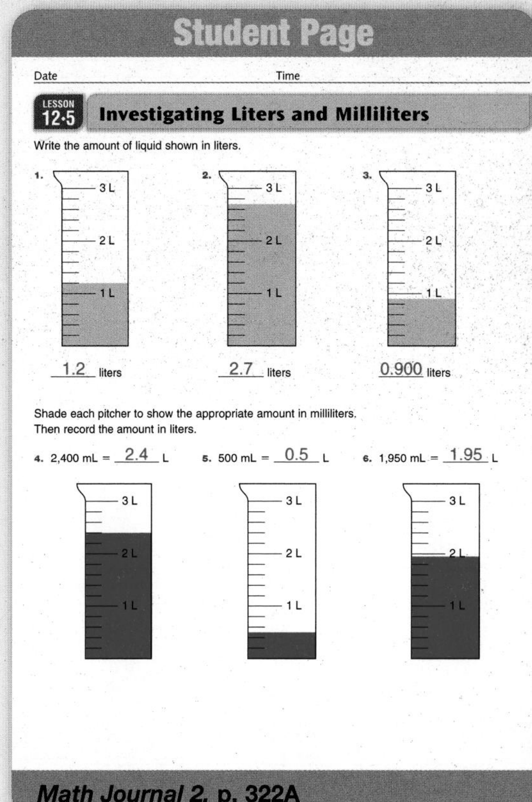

Student Page

Date Time

LESSON 12·5 Investigating Liters and Milliliters

Write the amount of liquid shown in liters.

1. 1.2 liters

2. 2.7 liters

3. 0.900 liters

Shade each pitcher to show the appropriate amount in milliliters. Then record the amount in liters.

4. 2,400 mL = 2.4 L

5. 500 mL = 0.5 L

6. 1,950 mL = 1.95 L

Math Journal 2, p. 322A

Calculating Unit Prices for Supermarket Items

PARTNER ACTIVITY

(*Math Masters,* p. 345)

Consumer Link Students share some of the ad information they recorded at the bottom of Study Link 12-4. Ask them to use their calculators to find the unit price of each item. Students should record each unit price as cents and tenths of a cent in the fourth column of the Study Link table.

Choose one of the students' items to demonstrate on the overhead calculator that the unit price can always be calculated from the given price information in a single step: Divide the price (cost) by the quantity (number of items or units).

Solving Problems Involving Unit Pricing

INDEPENDENT ACTIVITY

(*Math Journal 2,* p. 322)

Have students solve Problems 2–5 on journal page 322.

Ongoing Assessment: Recognizing Student Achievement

Journal page 322 Problem 4

Use **journal page 322, Problem 4** to assess students' ability to use scaling to model multiplication and division. Students are making adequate progress if they are able to use division to calculate unit prices and then determine the better buy. Some students may use multiplication or division to determine the better buy. For example, $2 * \$0.80 = \$1.60$; the cost of two 16-crayon boxes (32 crayons) is more than the cost of one box of 32 crayons. $\$1.28 \div 2 = \$0.64$; the cost of half a 32-crayon box (16 crayons) is less than the cost of a box of 16 crayons.

[Operations and Computation Goal 7]

Student Page

Date Time

LESSON 12·5 Investigating Liters and Milliliters *continued*

Solve. You may draw pictures to help you.

Maria Elena's store sells soup in various sized containers.

Size of Container	Amount	Price
Extra small	250 mL	$1.50
Small	500 mL	$2.45
Medium	1 L	$4.80
Large	1.5 L	$6.25
Extra large	2 L	$8.50

1. How much more soup does the extra large container hold than the extra small? 1.75 L, or 1,750 mL

2. Lucius bought 1 extra small, 1 medium, and 3 small containers of soup. How many liters of soup did he buy? 2.75 L

3. Kamu bought 3 large containers of soup. She needs 4,000 mL of soup.
   a. Does she have enough? yes
   b. If so, how much extra soup does she have? 0.5 L, or 500 mL

4. Sally bought 1 extra small, 1 small, and 2 extra large containers of soup. How much money did she spend? $20.95

5. Rocco wants to spend $8 or less on soup but he wants to get the most for his money.
   a. What's the greatest amount of soup he could buy? 1.75 L
   b. How much would he spend? $7.75

6. Write and solve your own problem.
   Answers vary.

Math Journal 2, p. 322B

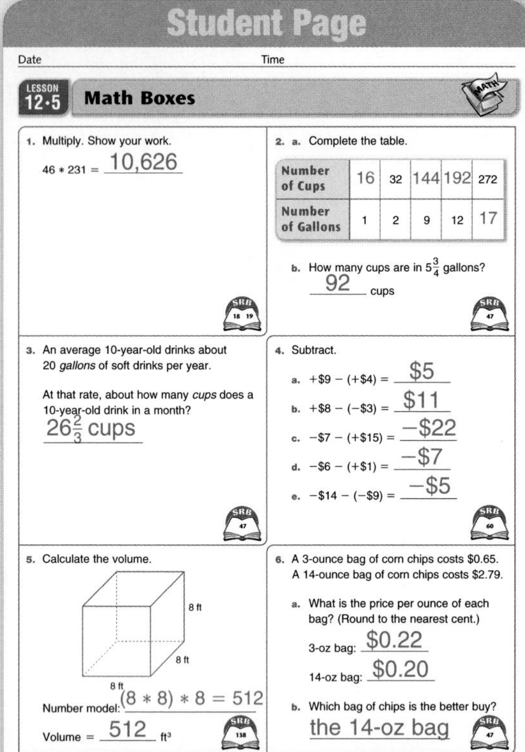

Student Page

Date Time

LESSON 12·5 **Math Boxes**

1. Multiply. Show your work.

46 * 231 = 10,626

2. a. Complete the table.

Number of Cups	16	32	144	192	272
Number of Gallons	1	2	9	12	17

b. How many cups are in $5\frac{3}{4}$ gallons? 92 cups

SRB 18 19

SRB 47

3. An average 10-year-old drinks about 20 *gallons* of soft drinks per year.

At that rate, about how many *cups* does a 10-year-old drink in a month?

$26\frac{2}{3}$ cups

4. Subtract.

a. +$9 − (+$4) = $5

b. +$8 − (−$3) = $11

c. −$7 − (+$15) = −$22

d. −$6 − (+$1) = −$7

e. −$14 − (−$9) = −$5

SRB 47

SRB 60

5. Calculate the volume.

8 ft, 8 ft, 8 ft

Number model: (8 ∗ 8) ∗ 8 = 512

Volume = 512 ft³

SRB 138

6. A 3-ounce bag of corn chips costs $0.65. A 14-ounce bag of corn chips costs $2.79.

a. What is the price per ounce of each bag? (Round to the nearest cent.)

3-oz bag: $0.22

14-oz bag: $0.20

b. Which bag of chips is the better buy? the 14-oz bag

SRB 47

Math Journal 2, p. 323

2 Ongoing Learning & Practice

▶ Playing *Fraction Top-It*

(*Math Journal 2,* Activity Sheets 5 and 6; *Student Reference Book,* p. 247; *Math Masters,* p. 506)

Students play *Fraction Top-It* to practice comparing and ordering fractions. See Lesson 7-10 for additional information.

▶ Investigating Liters and Milliliters

(*Math Journal 2,* pp. 322A and 322B)

Students solve capacity problems. They use a measurement scale to find measures in milliliters and liters. Then they solve number stories about the menu in a soup store.

▶ Math Boxes 12·5

(*Math Journal 2,* p. 323)

Mixed Practice Math Boxes in this lesson are paired with Math Boxes in Lesson 12-7.

Writing/Reasoning Have students write a response to the following: *Describe how you solved Problem 2b and how you might check your answer.* Sample answer: I multiplied 5 by 16 to get 80—the number of cups in 5 gallons. Then, $\frac{3}{4}$ of a gallon (16 cups) is equal to 12 cups. 80 + 12 = 92 cups. I can use the relationship between multiplication and division to check my answer: 92 / 16 = $5\frac{3}{4}$ and 92 / 5.75 = 16.

▶ Study Link 12·5

(*Math Masters,* p. 347)

Home Connection Students solve problems involving unit pricing.

Study Link Master

Name Date Time

STUDY LINK 12·5 **Unit Pricing**

SRB 47

1. A package of 3 muffins costs $1.89. What is the price *per muffin?* $0.63

2. A 5-pound bag of rice costs $1.85. What is the price *per pound?* $0.37

3. Chewy worms are sold at $2.40 per pound. What is the price *per ounce?* $0.15

4. A 6-pack of bagels costs $2.11. What is the price *per bagel?* $0.35

5. A 2-pound bag of frozen corn costs $2.03. What is the price *per pound?* $1.02

6. A store sells yogurt in two sizes: The 8-ounce cup costs 72 cents, and the 6-ounce cup costs 60 cents. Which is the better buy? Explain your answer.

Sample answer: The 8-ounce cup is the better buy. The yogurt is 9 cents per ounce in the 8-ounce cup, whereas the yogurt costs 10 cents per ounce in the 6-ounce cup.

7. Make up your own "better buy" problem. Then solve it.

Answers vary.

Practice

Name all the factors.

8. 42 1, 2, 3, 6, 7, 14, 21, 42

9. 23 1, 23

Math Masters, p. 347

3 Differentiation Options

READINESS

PARTNER ACTIVITY

Solving Comparison Shopping Problems

5–15 Min

(*Math Masters,* pp. 348 and 428)

To explore solving rate problems in a comparison-shopping context, have students draw pictures and use bills (*Math Masters,* page 428) and coins to solve problems in which a unit rate is compared to a non-unit rate. Encourage students to use estimation strategies as well.

ENRICHMENT

Measuring Air Pressure with a Barometer

15–30 Min

(*Student Reference Book,* p. 297; *Math Masters,* pp. 349–351)

Science Link To apply students' understanding of rates, have them use rates in the context of barometric pressure to solve elevation problems. After reading *Math Masters,* pages 349 and 350, ask students to complete *Math Masters,* page 351 by using rate information to find the elevation of various places on the island of Hawaii.

Additionally, have students look up the elevation for the capital city of each Region 5 country on *Student Reference Book,* page 297. Ask them to compute and record the approximate average barometric pressure for each city.

EXTRA PRACTICE

SMALL-GROUP ACTIVITY

5-Minute Math

5–15 Min

To offer students more experience calculating rates, see *5-Minute Math,* pages 27, 29, 105, 109, 191, and 192.

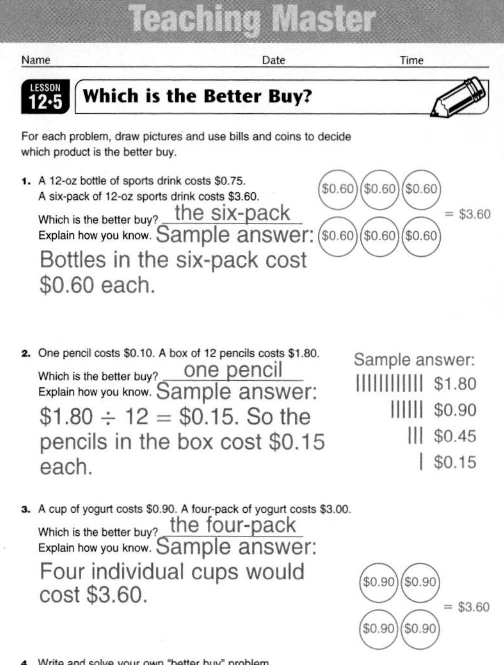

Teaching Master

Name Date Time

LESSON 12·5 **Which is the Better Buy?**

For each problem, draw pictures and use bills and coins to decide which product is the better buy.

1. A 12-oz bottle of sports drink costs $0.75. A six-pack of 12-oz sports drink costs $3.60.
Which is the better buy? the six-pack
Explain how you know. Sample answer: Bottles in the six-pack cost $0.60 each.
$0.60 $0.60 $0.60 $0.60 $0.60 $0.60 = $3.60

2. One pencil costs $0.10. A box of 12 pencils costs $1.80.
Which is the better buy? one pencil
Explain how you know. Sample answer: $1.80 ÷ 12 = $0.15. So the pencils in the box cost $0.15 each.
Sample answer: |||||||||||| $1.80; |||||| $0.90; ||| $0.45; | $0.15

3. A cup of yogurt costs $0.90. A four-pack of yogurt costs $3.00.
Which is the better buy? the four-pack
Explain how you know. Sample answer: Four individual cups would cost $3.60.
$0.90 $0.90 $0.90 $0.90 = $3.60

4. Write and solve your own "better buy" problem.
Answers vary.

Math Masters, p. 348

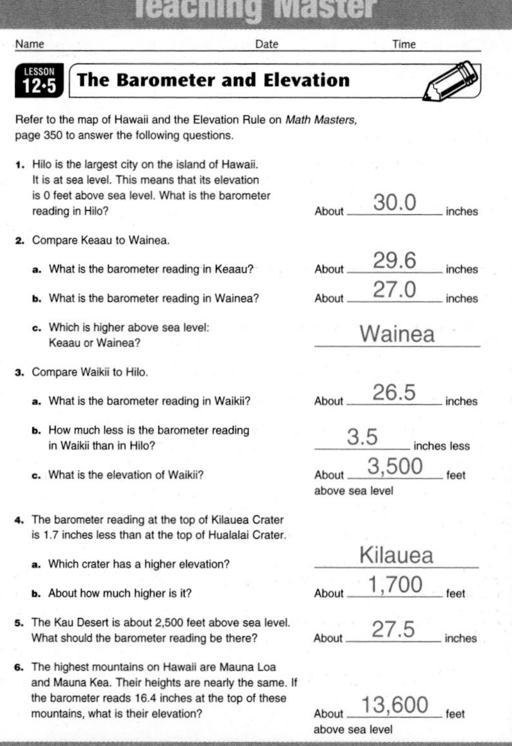

Teaching Master

Name Date Time

LESSON 12·5 **The Barometer and Elevation**

Refer to the map of Hawaii and the Elevation Rule on *Math Masters,* page 350 to answer the following questions.

1. Hilo is the largest city on the island of Hawaii. It is at sea level. This means that its elevation is 0 feet above sea level. What is the barometer reading in Hilo? About 30.0 inches
2. Compare Keaau to Wainea.
   a. What is the barometer reading in Keaau? About 29.6 inches
   b. What is the barometer reading in Wainea? About 27.0 inches
   c. Which is higher above sea level: Keaau or Wainea? Wainea
3. Compare Waikii to Hilo.
   a. What is the barometer reading in Waikii? About 26.5 inches
   b. How much less is the barometer reading in Waikii than in Hilo? 3.5 inches less
   c. What is the elevation of Waikii? About 3,500 feet above sea level
4. The barometer reading at the top of Kilauea Crater is 1.7 inches less than at the top of Hualalai Crater.
   a. Which crater has a higher elevation? Kilauea
   b. About how much higher is it? About 1,700 feet
5. The Kau Desert is about 2,500 feet above sea level. What should the barometer reading be there? About 27.5 inches
6. The highest mountains on Hawaii are Mauna Loa and Mauna Kea. Their heights are nearly the same. If the barometer reads 16.4 inches at the top of these mountains, what is their elevation? About 13,600 feet above sea level

Math Masters, p. 351

12•6 World Tour Wrap-Up

Objective To reflect on this year's World Tour experiences.

Technology Resources www.everydaymathonline.com

ePresentations

eToolkit

Algorithms Practice

EM Facts Workshop Game™

Family Letters

Assessment Management

Common Core State Standards

Curriculum Focal Points

Interactive Teacher's Lesson Guide

1 Teaching the Lesson

Key Concepts and Skills

- Solve problems involving addition of whole numbers. [Operations and Computation Goal 2]
- Solve problems involving division of multidigit whole numbers; interpret the remainder. [Operations and Computation Goal 4]

Key Activities

Students reflect on and discuss their World Tour experiences.

Ongoing Assessment: Recognizing Student Achievement Use Mental Math and Reflexes. [Operations and Computation Goal 3]

Materials

Math Journal 1, p. 171 (optional); pp. 174–181
Math Journal 2, pp. 324, 325, and 330–341; p. 329 (optional)
Study Link 12•5
calculator ◆ slate

2 Ongoing Learning & Practice

Solving Rate Problems

Math Journal 2, p. 326
Students solve number stories involving rates.

Summarizing the Liter & Milliliter Museum

Students summarize the Liter and Milliliter museum.

Math Boxes 12•6

Math Journal 2, p. 327
Students practice and maintain skills through Math Box problems.

Study Link 12•6

Math Masters, p. 352
Students practice and maintain skills through Study Link activities.

3 Differentiation Options

READINESS

Interpreting the Remainder

Math Masters, p. 353
Students solve division problems and interpret remainders.

EXTRA PRACTICE

50-Facts Test Wrap-Up

Math Masters, pp. 389, 412, 414, and 415; pp. 416 and 417 (optional)
pen or colored pencil
Students take a 50-facts test and review individual and optional class progress.

EXTRA PRACTICE

5-Minute Math

5-Minute Math™, pp. 34, 37, 38, and 41
Students solve problems involving the mean and median of a data set.

Advance Preparation

***Teacher's Reference Manual,* Grades 4–6** pp. 13, 14

Getting Started

Mental Math and Reflexes   

Pose multiplication facts and extended facts. *Suggestions:*

●○○	●●○	●●●
4 * 7 = 28	8 * 9 = 72	20 * 90 = 1,800
5 * 4 = 20	7 * 9 = 63	50 * 60 = 3,000
6 * 7 = 42	8 * 8 = 64	80 * 70 = 5,600

Math Message 

Complete Problems 1–4 on journal page 324.

Study Link 12·5 Follow-Up 

Ask small groups of students to compare answers. Have them share the "better buy" problems they made up and solved. For Problems 8 and 9, ask students if either of the numbers are prime and how they know. 23 is prime because its only factors are 1 and itself.

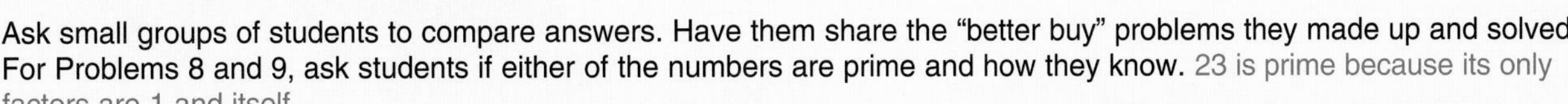

Ongoing Assessment: Recognizing Student Achievement

Mental Math and Reflexes ★

Use **Mental Math and Reflexes** to assess students' automaticity with multiplication facts. Students are making adequate progress if they demonstrate automaticity with the ●○○ and ●●○ problems. Some students may demonstrate automaticity with the extended facts in the ●●● problems.

[Operations and Computation Goal 3]

1 Teaching the Lesson

▶ Math Message Follow-Up

WHOLE-CLASS DISCUSSION

(*Math Journal 2,* p. 324)

Discuss the answers to Problems 2–4.

Problem 2: If students have kept the optional Route Log, they can quickly calculate the total distance they have traveled. Students who did not keep a Route Log can calculate the total distance using the Air Mileage Chart on the Route Map.

Problem 3: Divide the total distance by 5,000 and ignore the decimal remainder. For example, if the calculator displays a quotient of 18.938..., this means that although you are close to having earned 19 coupons, you have flown enough miles to earn only 18 coupons.

Problem 4: Divide the number of coupons earned by 5. Again, ignore the decimal remainder.

Adjusting the Activity

If some students traveled to more countries than others, have the class find the median distance flown and the number of round-trip tickets earned for that distance.

AUDITORY ◆ KINESTHETIC ◆ TACTILE ◆ VISUAL

Student Page

Date Time

LESSON 12·6 Looking Back on the World Tour

Math Message

It is time to complete the World Tour. Answers vary.

1. Fly to Washington, D.C., and then travel to your hometown. Mark the final leg of the tour on the Route Map on *Math Journal 2,* pages 330 and 331.
2. What is the total distance you have traveled? ______ miles
3. The airline has given you a coupon for every 5,000 miles you have traveled. Suppose you did all your traveling by plane on the same airline. How many coupons have you earned on the World Tour? ______ coupons
4. You can trade in 5 coupons for one free round-trip ticket to fly anywhere in the continental United States. How many round-trip tickets have you earned on the World Tour? ______ round-trip tickets

Refer to "My Country Notes" in your journals (*Math Journal 1,* pages 174–181 and *Math Journal 2,* pages 332–341) as you answer the following questions.

5. If you could travel all over the world for a whole year, what information would you need in order to plan your trip?

Math Journal 2, p. 324

Student Page

Date ____________ Time ____________

LESSON 12•6 **Looking Back on the World Tour** *continued*

6. To which country would you most like to travel in your lifetime? Explain your answer.
Answers vary.

7. On your travels, you would have the opportunity to learn about many different cultures. What would you want to share with people from other countries about *your* culture?

8. What are some things you have enjoyed on the World Tour?

9. What is something about the World Tour you would like to add or change?

Math Journal 2, p. 325

Student Page

Date ____________ Time ____________

LESSON 12•6 **Rates**

1. David Fischer of Chicago, Illinois, jumped rope 56 times in 60 seconds. If he could continue at this rate, about how many jumps would he do in 13 minutes?
About 728 jumps
Source: Guinness World Records, www.guinnessworldrecords.com

2. Some scientists recommend that the average person drink about 8 eight-ounce cups of water per day. At this rate, about how many cups of water would a person drink in 2 weeks?
About 112 cups

3. On average, Americans eat about 20 pounds of pasta per year.
   a. Does this 20 pounds per year seem reasonable to you? Yes
   Explain. 20 pounds = 320 ounces. That is about 26 oz per month—about 4 servings.
   b. At this rate, about how many pounds of pasta would an American eat in 23 years?
   About 460 pounds
   Source: Sicilian Culture, www.sicilianculture.com/food/pasta.htm

4. Thirty-six buses would be needed to carry the passengers and crew of three 747 jumbo jets.
   a. Fill in the rate table.

Buses	12	24	36	180	252
Jets	1	2	3	15	21

   b. How many jets would be needed to carry the passengers on 264 buses? 22

5. A man in India grew one of his thumbnails until it was 114 centimeters long. Fingernails grow about 2.5 centimeters each year. At this rate, about how many years did it take the man in India to grow his thumbnail?
About 45.6 years

Math Journal 2, p. 326

▶ Reflecting on the World Tour

PARTNER ACTIVITY

(*Math Journal 2,* pp. 324 and 325)

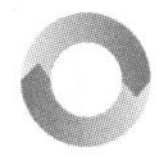

Social Studies Link Students discuss their World Tour experiences with their partners and record their impressions.

Students might want to refer to their Route Logs (*Math Journal 1,* page 171 and *Math Journal 2,* page 329) and their Country Notes (*Math Journal 1,* pages 174–181 and *Math Journal 2,* pages 332–341) to refresh their memories.

2 Ongoing Learning & Practice

▶ Solving Rate Problems

INDEPENDENT ACTIVITY

(*Math Journal 2,* p. 326)

Algebraic Thinking Students solve rate problems, complete a rate table, and decide whether or not a statistic seems reasonable.

▶ Summarizing the Liter & Milliliter Museum

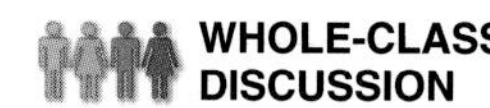
WHOLE-CLASS DISCUSSION

Discuss the Liter and Milliliter museum. Ask questions like the following:

- Which item had the largest capacity? What was its capacity?
- Which item had the smallest capacity? What was its capacity?

▶ Math Boxes 12•6

INDEPENDENT ACTIVITY

(*Math Journal 2,* p. 327)

Mixed Practice Math Boxes in this lesson are linked with Math Boxes in Lessons 12-2 and 12-4.

▶ Study Link 12•6

INDEPENDENT ACTIVITY

(*Math Masters,* p. 352)

Home Connection Students solve a variety of problems involving data from different countries. Problem 1 involves finding the difference of two numbers. Problem 2 is a "times as many" problem. Problem 3 calls for finding the percent of a number and Problem 4 for finding a fraction of a number. Problem 5 involves finding the landmarks for a data set.

3 Differentiation Options

READINESS

PARTNER ACTIVITY

Interpreting the Remainder

5–15 Min

(*Math Masters,* p. 353)

To provide experience interpreting the remainder of a division problem, have students complete *Math Masters,* page 353. Remind students that depending upon the situation, a remainder is handled in different ways.

▷ The remainder might be regarded as a fractional or decimal part of the whole. For example, leftover parts of a dollar can be converted into cents.

▷ The remainder might indicate that the quotient should be rounded up to the next-larger whole number to obtain the answer. For example, if 30 people need to be transported in vans that hold 8 people each, it makes sense to order 4 vans rather than 3.75 vans.

▷ The remainder might be ignored because it represents a "leftover" amount that cannot be split up further. For example, leftover people or cars cannot be split up easily.

▷ The remainder might be ignored, and the answer is the quotient. For example, if CDs are $9 and I have $50, I can only buy 5 CDs.

Teaching Master

Name Date Time

LESSON 12•6 **Interpreting the Remainder**

Draw a picture to illustrate the problem. Then solve the problem.
Sample pictures

1. The roller coaster holds 24 people per ride. There are 65 people waiting in line. How many times does the roller coaster need to run before everyone in line gets a turn to ride?

Number model: $65 \div 24 \rightarrow 2$ R17

Picture: 24, 24, 17

Answer: 3 times

What did you do about the remainder? Circle the answer.

Ignored it.

Reported it as a fraction or decimal.

(Rounded the answer up.)

Why?
Sample answer: After two runs, there were still 17 people who hadn't had a turn to ride. Another run was needed, so I rounded up.

2. Cedric's teacher is ordering pizza for an end-of-year party. He has $35.00 to spend. A large cheese pizza costs $8.00. How many pizzas can he order?

Number model: $35 \div 8 \rightarrow 4$ R3

Picture: ($8) ($8) ($8) ($8) $3

Answer: 4 pizzas

What did you do about the remainder? Circle the answer.

(Ignored it.)

Reported it as a fraction or decimal.

Rounded the answer up.

Why?
Sample answer: The three dollars left can't buy any more pizzas. So I ignored it.

Math Masters, p. 353

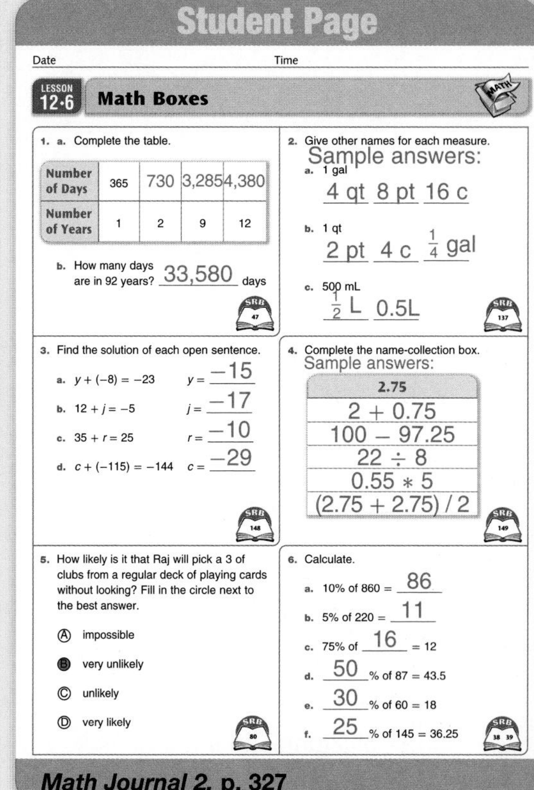

Student Page

Date Time

LESSON 12•6 **Math Boxes**

1. a. Complete the table.

Number of Days	365	730	3,285	4,380
Number of Years	1	2	9	12

b. How many days are in 92 years? 33,580 days

2. Give other names for each measure. Sample answers:
a. 1 gal 4 qt 8 pt 16 c
b. 1 qt 2 pt 4 c $\frac{1}{4}$ gal
c. 500 mL $\frac{1}{2}$ L 0.5L

3. Find the solution of each open sentence.
a. $y + (-8) = -23$ $y = -15$
b. $12 + j = -5$ $j = -17$
c. $35 + r = 25$ $r = -10$
d. $c + (-115) = -144$ $c = -29$

4. Complete the name-collection box. Sample answers:

2.75
2 + 0.75
100 − 97.25
22 ÷ 8
0.55 * 5
(2.75 + 2.75) / 2

5. How likely is it that Raj will pick a 3 of clubs from a regular deck of playing cards without looking? Fill in the circle next to the best answer.
Ⓐ impossible
● very unlikely
Ⓒ unlikely
Ⓓ very likely

6. Calculate.
a. 10% of 860 = 86
b. 5% of 220 = 11
c. 75% of 16 = 12
d. 50 % of 87 = 43.5
e. 30 % of 60 = 18
f. 25 % of 145 = 36.25

Math Journal 2, p. 327

Algorithm Project To teach U.S. traditional long division, see Algorithm Project 8 on page A37.

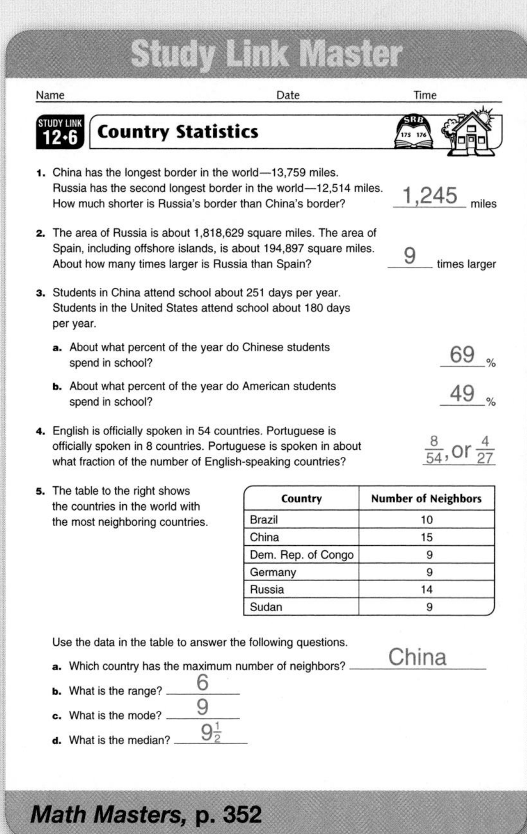

Study Link Master

Name Date Time

STUDY LINK 12•6 **Country Statistics**

1. China has the longest border in the world—13,759 miles. Russia has the second longest border in the world—12,514 miles. How much shorter is Russia's border than China's border? 1,245 miles

2. The area of Russia is about 1,818,629 square miles. The area of Spain, including offshore islands, is about 194,897 square miles. About how many times larger is Russia than Spain? 9 times larger

3. Students in China attend school about 251 days per year. Students in the United States attend school about 180 days per year.
a. About what percent of the year do Chinese students spend in school? 69 %
b. About what percent of the year do American students spend in school? 49 %

4. English is officially spoken in 54 countries. Portuguese is officially spoken in 8 countries. Portuguese is spoken in about what fraction of the number of English-speaking countries? $\frac{8}{54}$, or $\frac{4}{27}$

5. The table to the right shows the countries in the world with the most neighboring countries.

Country	Number of Neighbors
Brazil	10
China	15
Dem. Rep. of Congo	9
Germany	9
Russia	14
Sudan	9

Use the data in the table to answer the following questions.
a. Which country has the maximum number of neighbors? China
b. What is the range? 6
c. What is the mode? 9
d. What is the median? $9\frac{1}{2}$

Math Masters, p. 352

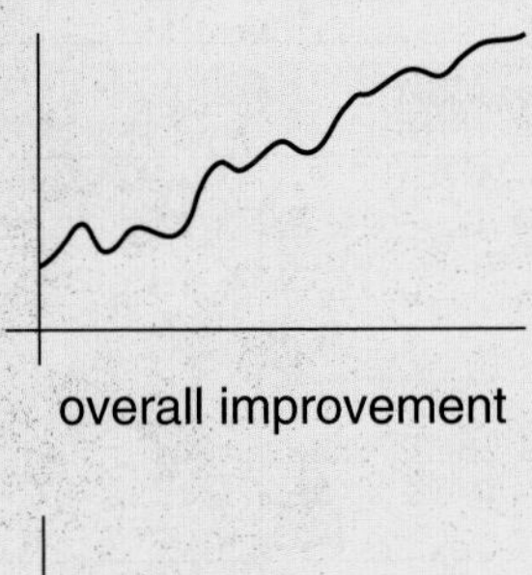

overall improvement

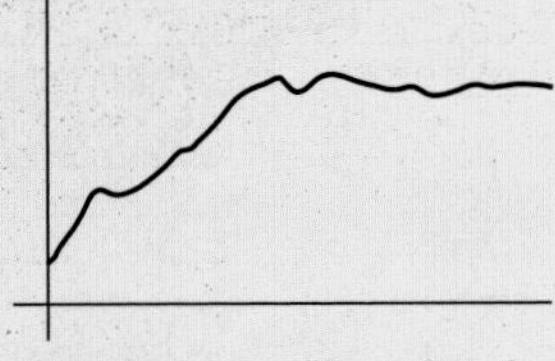

improve and maintain

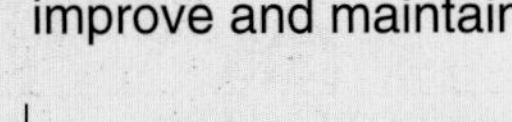

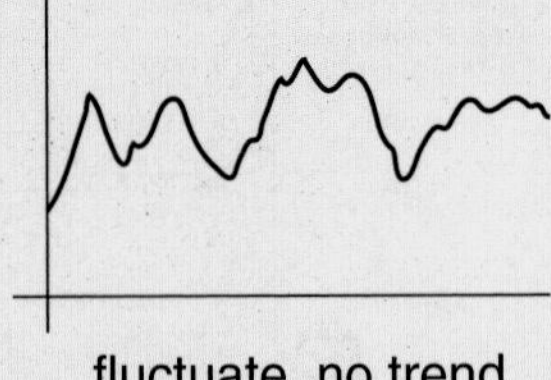

fluctuate, no trend

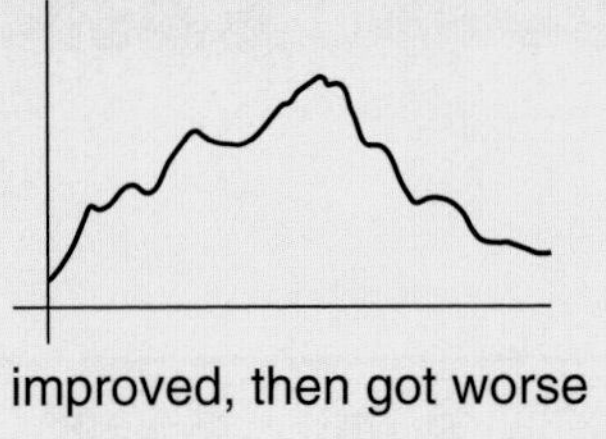

improved, then got worse

EXTRA PRACTICE

▶ 50-Facts Test Wrap-Up

FACTS PRACTICE

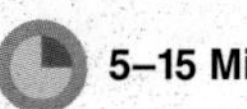

(*Math Masters,* pp. 412 and 414–417)

See Lesson 3-4 for details regarding the administration of a 50-facts test and the recording and graphing of individual and optional class results.

If students have been graphing the class scores, ask them to compare the median and mean on the class line graph. Most likely the landmarks are close together. Discuss the progress of other landmarks over time. For example, did the range widen, narrow, or remain the same? Answers vary. Discuss the overall class profile. (*See margin for examples.*)

On an Exit Slip, have students give their individual graphs a title such as those given in the margin and justify the title by describing the shape of the graphs.

EXTRA PRACTICE

▶ *5-Minute Math*

To offer students more experience with the mean and median of a data set, see *5-Minute Math,* pages 34, 37, 38, and 41.

12•7 Progress Check 12

Objective To assess students' progress on mathematical content through the end of Unit 12.

1 Looking Back: Cumulative Assessment

The **End-of-Year Assessment** in the *Assessment Handbook* is a written assessment that you may use to assess students' proficiency with Grade-Level Goals.

Input student data from Progress Check 12 and the End-of-Year Assessment into the **Assessment Management Spreadsheets**.

Materials

- Study Link 12•6
- *Assessment Handbook,* pp. 142–149, 211–215, 227, and 290–293
- End-of-Year Assessment (*Assessment Handbook,* pp. 150, 151, 234–241, and 244–245)
- slate; calculator

CONTENT ASSESSED	LESSON(S)	ASSESSMENT ITEMS				
		SELF	ORAL/SLATE	WRITTEN		OPEN RESPONSE
				PART A	PART B	
Find whole-number factors of numbers. [Number and Numeration Goal 3]	12•1, 12•3–12•5	1		4, 5		
Compare and order fractions. [Number and Numeration Goal 6]	12•1, 12•5	2			11	
Compare and order integers. [Number and Numeration Goal 6]	12•1, 12•3			6, 7		
Add and subtract signed numbers. [Operations and Computation Goal 2]	12•2, 12•4–12•6	3, 4	1			
Add and subtract decimals. [Operations and Computation Goal 2]	12•2, 12•4					✓
Solve problems involving division. [Operations and Computation Goal 4]	12•2–12•6					✓
Use scaling to model rate situations. [Operations and Computation Goal 7]	12•2–12•6	5	3, 4	1–3	13, 14	✓
Analyze and interpret data. [Data and Chance Goal 2]	12•3–12•6				12	
Find the volumes of rectangular prisms. [Measurement and Reference Frames Goal 2]	12•1, 12•3, 12•5			9		
Convert among units of capacity. [Measurement and Reference Frames Goal 3]	12•2, 12•4–12•6	6	2	8		
Solve open sentences. [Patterns, Functions, and Algebra Goal 2]	12•2, 12•4, 12•6	7		10		

2 Looking Ahead: Preparing for Grade 5

Math Boxes 12•7

Study Link 12•7: End-of-Year Family Letter

Materials

- *Math Journal 2,* p. 328
- *Math Masters,* pp. 354–357

Getting Started

Math Message • Self Assessment

Complete the Self Assessment
(Assessment Handbook, *page 211*).

Study Link 12·6 Follow-Up

Briefly review students' answers.

1 Looking Back: Cumulative Assessment

▶ Math Message Follow-Up

INDEPENDENT ACTIVITY

(Self Assessment, *Assessment Handbook,* p. 211)

The Self Assessment offers students the opportunity to reflect upon their progress.

▶ Oral and Slate Assessments

Problems 2, 3, and 4 provide summative information and can be used for grading purposes. Problem 1 provides formative information.

Oral Assessment

1. Pose addition and subtraction problems involving positive and negative integers. Have students explain their solution strategies. *Suggestions:*
   - $6 + (-8) = -2$
   - $15 - (-12) = 27$
   - $20 + (-15) = 5$
   - $-10 - (12) = -22$
   - $-7 - (-9) = 2$
   - $-12 + (-18) = -30$
   - $-20 - (14) = -34$
   - $-16 + 15 = -1$
2. Have students show "thumbs-up" if the two quantities are equivalent and "thumbs-down" if they are not. *Suggestions:*
   - 4 quarts and 1 gallon up
   - 1 pint and 3 cups down
   - 1 liter and 1,000 mL up
   - 3 pints and $1\frac{1}{2}$ quarts up
   - 3 liters and 300 mL down
   - $2\frac{1}{2}$ gallons and 10 quarts up

Assessment Master

Name Date Time

LESSON 12·7 **Self Assessment** Progress Check 12

Think about each skill listed below. Assess your own progress by checking the most appropriate box.

Skills	I can do this on my own and explain how to do it.	I can do this on my own.	I can do this if I get help or look at an example.
1. Find factors and factor pairs.			
2. Compare and order positive and negative fractions.			
3. Add positive and negative numbers.			
4. Subtract positive and negative numbers.			
5. Solve rate problems.			
6. Convert among units of capacity.			
7. Solve open sentences.			

Assessment Handbook, p. 211

Slate Assessment

3. Pose rate problems. Encourage students to use rate tables if necessary. *Suggestions:*
   - If 1 pound of apples costs 40 cents, what is the cost of 5 pounds? $2.00
   - Roberto earns $3 per hour babysitting. How much does he earn in 4 hours? $12 In $2\frac{1}{2}$ hours? $7.50
   - The Hole-in-One shop sells used golf balls for $2.40 per dozen. What is the cost of 1 golf ball? $0.20 Of 4 golf balls? $0.80 Of $\frac{1}{2}$-dozen golf balls? $1.20
   - Mitchell walks at the rate of about 3 miles per hour. At that rate, what distance will he walk in 20 minutes? About 1 mile In $\frac{1}{2}$ hour? About $1\frac{1}{2}$ miles In 10 minutes? About $\frac{1}{2}$ mile In 3 hours? About 9 miles In $1\frac{1}{3}$ hours? About 4 miles
   - Caroline reads about 25 pages per hour. About how many pages could she read in 3 hours? 75 pages In 5 hours? 125 pages In $1\frac{1}{2}$ hours? $37\frac{1}{2}$ pages
   - Carlos eats about 3 servings of fruit per day. About how many servings is that in 4 days? 12 servings In 1 week? 21 servings In 4 weeks? 84 servings
   - Hamburgers cost 70 cents each. What is the cost of 2 hamburgers? $1.40 Of 4 hamburgers? $2.80 Of 1 dozen hamburgers? $8.40
4. Pose problems involving unit prices. Encourage students to use rate tables if necessary. Have them round their answers to the nearest tenth of a cent. *Suggestions:*
   - A 6-pack of cola costs $2.40. What is the price per can? 40 cents
   - A box of 8 pieces of chalk costs 64 cents. What is the cost of 1 piece of chalk? 8 cents
   - A 46-ounce can of pineapple juice costs $1.75. What is the price per ounce? 3.8 cents
   - A 6-ounce can of tomato paste costs 34 cents. What is the price per ounce? 5.7 cents
   - An 8-pack of yogurt costs $4.00. What is the cost per container? $0.50
   - Twelve bars of soap cost $3.60. What is the price per bar? $0.30
   - A 15-ounce can of green beans costs 90 cents. What is the price per ounce? 6 cents

Assessment Master

Name Date Time

LESSON 12•7 **Written Assessment** Progress Check 12

Part A

1. The Davis family drove 280 miles to visit relatives. It took 5 hours. At that rate, about how many miles did the Davises drive in 3 hours? About 168 miles

Fill in the rate table, if needed.

Hours	1	2	3	4	5
Miles	56	112	168	224	280

2. Jan earned $19.50 last week for mowing 3 lawns. At that rate, what would Jan earn for mowing 5 lawns? $32.50

Fill in the rate table, if needed.

Lawns	1	2	3	4	5
Dollars	6.50	13	19.50	26	32.50

3. Tina works 7 hours per day, 5 days per week. She earns $56.00 per day.
   a. How much does she earn per hour? $8
   b. How much does she earn per week? $280
4. List the factor pairs of 40.
   1 and 40   4 and 10
   2 and 20   5 and 8
5. Name all the factors of 64.
   1, 2, 4, 8, 16, 32, 64

Assessment Handbook, p. 212

Assessment Master

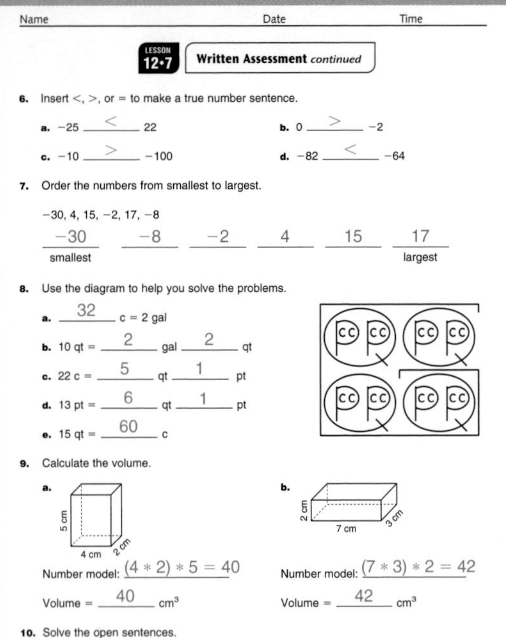

Name Date Time

LESSON 12•7 **Written Assessment** *continued*

6. Insert <, >, or = to make a true number sentence.

a. −25 <u><</u> 22 b. 0 <u>></u> −2

c. −10 <u>></u> −100 d. −82 <u><</u> −64

7. Order the numbers from smallest to largest.

−30, 4, 15, −2, 17, −8

−30 (smallest), −8, −2, 4, 15, 17 (largest)

8. Use the diagram to help you solve the problems.

a. 32 c = 2 gal

b. 10 qt = 2 gal 2 qt

c. 22 c = 5 qt 1 pt

d. 13 pt = 6 qt 1 pt

e. 15 qt = 60 c

9. Calculate the volume.

a. 5 cm, 4 cm, 2 cm

Number model: $(4 * 2) * 5 = 40$

Volume = 40 cm³

b. 2 cm, 7 cm, 3 cm

Number model: $(7 * 3) * 2 = 42$

Volume = 42 cm³

10. Solve the open sentences.

a. $0.930 + 3.59 = y$ $y =$ 4.52 b. $51.9 + b = 69.07$ $b =$ 17.17

c. $1.89 - 0.206 = q$ $q =$ 1.684 d. $1.46 = k - 0.028$ $k =$ 1.488

Assessment Handbook, p. 213

INDEPENDENT ACTIVITY

▶ Written Assessment

(*Assessment Handbook,* pp. 212–214)

Part A Recognizing Student Achievement

Problems 1–10 provide summative information and may be used for grading purposes.

Problem(s)	Description
1–3	Solve rate problems.
4, 5	Find factors and factor pairs.
6	Compare integers.
7	Order integers.
8	Find equivalent capacities.
9	Calculate volume.
10	Solve open sentences.

Part B Informing Instruction

Problems 11–14 provide formative information.

Problem	Description
11	Compare and order fractions.
12	Determine the reasonableness of a statistic.
13	Determine which box of cereal is the better buy.
14	Make informed consumer decisions.

Use the checklists on pages 291 and 293 of the *Assessment Handbook* to record results. Then input the data into the **Assessment Management Spreadsheets** to keep an ongoing record of students' progress toward Grade-Level Goals.

Assessment Master

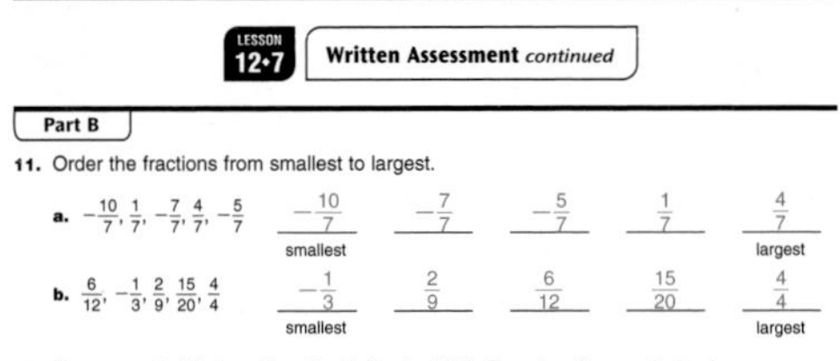

Name Date Time

LESSON 12•7 **Written Assessment** *continued*

Part B

11. Order the fractions from smallest to largest.

a. $-\frac{10}{7}, \frac{1}{7}, -\frac{7}{7}, \frac{4}{7}, -\frac{5}{7}$ — $-\frac{10}{7}$ (smallest), $-\frac{7}{7}$, $-\frac{5}{7}$, $\frac{1}{7}$, $\frac{4}{7}$ (largest)

b. $\frac{6}{12}, -\frac{1}{3}, \frac{2}{9}, \frac{15}{20}, \frac{4}{4}$ — $-\frac{1}{3}$ (smallest), $\frac{2}{9}$, $\frac{6}{12}$, $\frac{15}{20}$, $\frac{4}{4}$ (largest)

12. It was reported that on New Year's Day in 1907, Theodore Roosevelt shook hands with 8,513 people. Does this seem reasonable? Explain your answer.

Sample answer: Yes. If he shook hands for 18 hours that day, it would be about 8 hands per minute. That's a lot of hands, but it seems like a president might do that.

13. A store charges $1.58 for a 20-ounce box of Puff Flakes cereal and $1.72 for a 24-ounce box of the same cereal. Which is the better buy?

the 24-oz box

Explain why.

Sample answer: The cereal in the 20-oz box costs 7.9 cents per ounce, while the same cereal in the 24-oz box costs 7.17 cents per ounce.

14. Joey goes to Doreen's Delicious Doughnuts to buy doughnuts for the class party. What is the least amount of money he will have to pay for 30 doughnuts?

$12.10

Explain. Sample answer:

At Doreen's the bigger the package, the cheaper the doughnut. Joey should buy two dozens for $4.80 per dozen and one half-dozen for $2.50, for a total of $4.80 + $4.80 + $2.50 = $12.10.

Assessment Handbook, p. 214

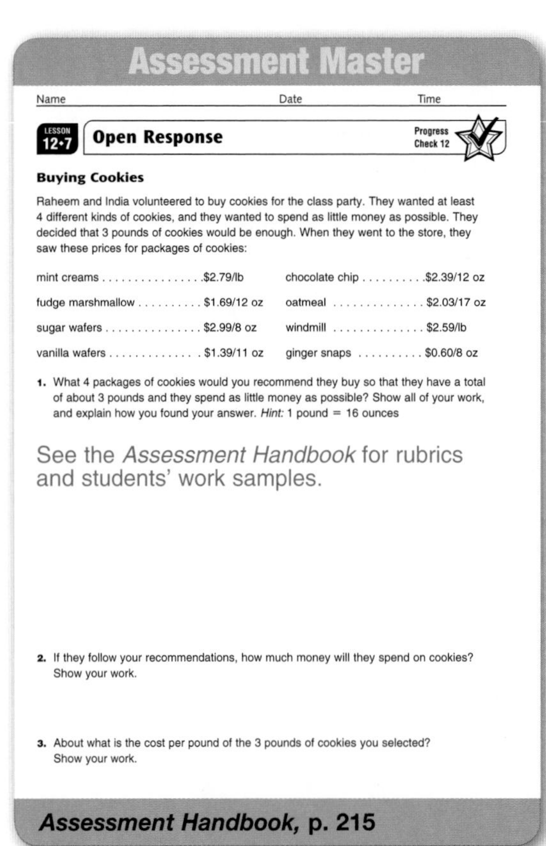

Assessment Master

Name Date Time

LESSON 12•7 **Open Response** Progress Check 12

Buying Cookies

Raheem and India volunteered to buy cookies for the class party. They wanted at least 4 different kinds of cookies, and they wanted to spend as little money as possible. They decided that 3 pounds of cookies would be enough. When they went to the store, they saw these prices for packages of cookies:

mint creams	$2.79/lb	chocolate chip	$2.39/12 oz
fudge marshmallow	$1.69/12 oz	oatmeal	$2.03/17 oz
sugar wafers	$2.99/8 oz	windmill	$2.59/lb
vanilla wafers	$1.39/11 oz	ginger snaps	$0.60/8 oz

1. What 4 packages of cookies would you recommend they buy so that they have a total of about 3 pounds and they spend as little money as possible? Show all of your work, and explain how you found your answer. *Hint:* 1 pound = 16 ounces

See the *Assessment Handbook* for rubrics and students' work samples.

2. If they follow your recommendations, how much money will they spend on cookies? Show your work.

3. About what is the cost per pound of the 3 pounds of cookies you selected? Show your work.

Assessment Handbook, p. 215

Open Response

INDEPENDENT ACTIVITY

(*Assessment Handbook,* p. 215)

Buying Cookies

The open-response item requires students to apply concepts and skills from Unit 12 to solve a multistep problem. See *Assessment Handbook,* pages 145–149 for rubrics and students' work samples for this problem.

End-of-Year Assessment

INDEPENDENT ACTIVITY

(*Assessment Handbook,* pp. 150, 151, and 234–241)

The End-of-Year Assessment (*Assessment Handbook,* pages 234–241) provides an additional assessment opportunity that you may use as part of your balanced assessment plan. This assessment covers many of the important concepts and skills presented in *Fourth Grade Everyday Mathematics.* It should be used along with ongoing and periodic assessments. Please see pages 150 and 151 in the *Assessment Handbook* for further information.

2 Looking Ahead: Preparing for Grade 5

Math Boxes 12•7

INDEPENDENT ACTIVITY

(*Math Journal 2,* p. 328)

Mixed Practice Math Boxes in this lesson are paired with Math Boxes in Lesson 12-5.

Study Link 12•7: End-of-Year Family Letter

INDEPENDENT ACTIVITY

(*Math Masters,* pp. 354–357)

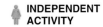

Home Connection The End-of-Year Family Letter thanks family members for their participation in *Fourth Grade Everyday Mathematics,* suggests activities that can be done at home during the vacation, and provides a preview of *Fifth Grade Everyday Mathematics.*

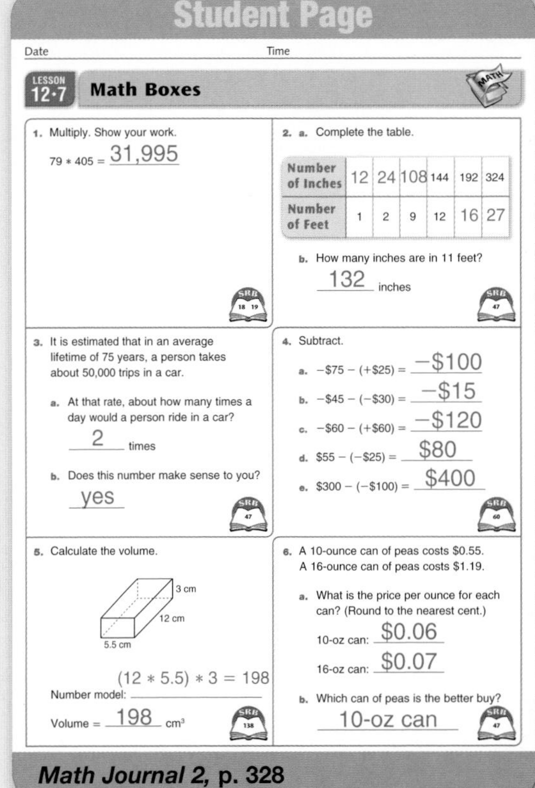

Student Page

Date Time

LESSON 12•7 **Math Boxes**

1. Multiply. Show your work.

79 * 405 = 31,995

2. a. Complete the table.

Number of Inches	12	24	108	144	192	324
Number of Feet	1	2	9	12	16	27

b. How many inches are in 11 feet?

132 inches

3. It is estimated that in an average lifetime of 75 years, a person takes about 50,000 trips in a car.

a. At that rate, about how many times a day would a person ride in a car?

2 times

b. Does this number make sense to you?

yes

4. Subtract.

a. −$75 − (+$25) = −$100

b. −$45 − (−$30) = −$15

c. −$60 − (+$60) = −$120

d. $55 − (−$25) = $80

e. $300 − (−$100) = $400

5. Calculate the volume.

3 cm, 12 cm, 5.5 cm

Number model: (12 ∗ 5.5) ∗ 3 = 198

Volume = 198 cm³

6. A 10-ounce can of peas costs $0.55. A 16-ounce can of peas costs $1.19.

a. What is the price per ounce for each can? (Round to the nearest cent.)

10-oz can: $0.06

16-oz can: $0.07

b. Which can of peas is the better buy?

10-oz can

Math Journal 2, p. 328

Study Link Masters

Name Date Time

STUDY LINK 12•7 **Family Letter**

Congratulations!

By completing *Fourth Grade Everyday Mathematics,* your child has accomplished a great deal. Thank you for all of your support.

This Family Letter is a resource to use throughout your child's vacation. It includes an extended list of Do-Anytime Activities, directions for games that can be played at home, a list of mathematics-related books to check out over vacation, and a sneak preview of what your child will be learning in *Fifth Grade Everyday Mathematics.* Enjoy the vacation!

Do-Anytime Activities

Mathematics means more when it is rooted in real-life situations. To help your child review many of the concepts he or she has learned in fourth grade, we suggest the following activities for you and your child to do together over vacation. These activities will help your child build on the skills he or she has learned this year and help prepare him or her for *Fifth Grade Everyday Mathematics.*

1. Have your child practice any multiplication and division facts that he or she has not yet mastered. Include some quick drills.
2. Provide items for your child to measure. Have your child use personal references, as well as U.S. customary and metric measuring tools.
3. Use newspapers and magazines as sources of numbers, graphs, and tables that your child may read and discuss.
4. Have your child practice multidigit multiplication and division using the algorithms that he or she is most comfortable with.
5. Ask your child to look at advertisements and find the sale prices of items using the original prices and rates of discount or find rates of discount using original prices and sale prices. Have your child use a calculator and calculate unit prices to determine best or better buys.
6. Continue the World Tour by reading about other countries.

Math Masters, pp. 354–357

Appendices

Contents

Project 1

Making a Cutaway Globe

Objective To reinforce work with latitude and longitude.

Technology Resources www.everydaymathonline.com

eToolkit

Algorithms Practice

EM Facts Workshop Game™

Family Letters

Assessment Management

Common Core State Standards

Curriculum Focal Points

Interactive Teacher's Lesson Guide

1 Doing the Project

Recommended Use After Unit 6

Key Concepts and Skills

- Identify 90° and 180° angles.
  [Measurement and Reference Frames Goal 1]
- Use degree measurements to mark lines of latitude and longitude.
  [Measurement and Reference Frames Goal 1]
- Use latitude and longitude to locate points on the global grid system.
  [Measurement and Reference Frames Goal 4]
- Identify semicircles.
  [Geometry Goal 2]

Key Activities

Students work with partners to construct a cutaway version of a globe. Then they use latitude and longitude to locate various places on their globe.

Materials

- *Math Masters,* pp. 360 and 361
- transparent tape
- scissors
- straightedge
- 2 or 3 standard-size paper clips
- globe

2 Extending the Project

Students find the point on the globe that is polar opposite to their hometown and name the latitude and longitude for that point.

Students examine latitude and longitude on the Web.

Materials

- computer with Internet access

Advance Preparation

In order for the cutaway globe to work properly, *Math Masters,* page 360 must be copied on cardstock or similar paper. Before beginning the project, you may want to cut apart *Math Masters,* page 360 and follow the instructions that follow to construct a cutaway globe.

You need a globe. You also need to know the approximate latitude and longitude of your school, or use the area where it is located, or a nearby city's latitude and longitude. These can be estimated from the globe or a map in the *Student Reference Book.* They can also be found at several Internet sites; see the end of this project.

It will be helpful if you recruit one or two parents or students to help as students construct their models.

1 Doing the Project

▸ Constructing a Cutaway Globe

PARTNER ACTIVITY

(*Math Masters,* pp. 360 and 361)

Divide the class into partnerships and distribute *Math Masters,* page 360. There are two sets of circles and semicircles on the sheet. Students will use them to construct models of two hemispheres and then assemble them to form a full globe. The directions for making the cutaway globe are on *Math Masters,* page 361. You may want to have students read and follow the directions on their own while you and your helpers circulate. Or you may prefer to demonstrate the construction while students follow along and construct their models.

Directions:

1. Carefully cut out one of the circles A along the dashed lines.
2. Cut out one of the semicircles B. Cut the slit marked at 90° on the semicircle.
3. Lay semicircle B on circle A so that the base of the semicircle aligns with the 0° to 180° diameter shown on circle A. Tape the pieces together on both sides of the semicircle. Move semicircle B so that it is perpendicular to circle A.

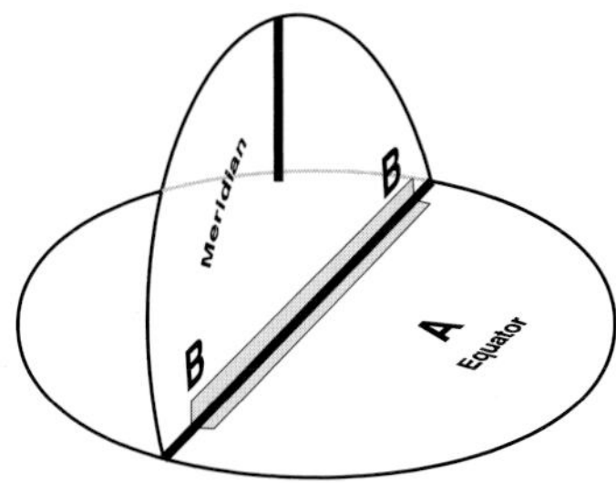

4. Cut out one of the semicircles C. Cut the slit marked at the bottom of the 90° line. Fold the semicircle in half along the 90° line. Fold it back and forth several times to make a good crease. Set semicircle C aside for later use.

Tell students that they have made a cutaway model of the Northern Hemisphere. The circumference of circle A corresponds to the equator. Ask them to point out the North Pole and the prime meridian. (Note that semicircle B shows only the northern half of the prime meridian. The rest of the semicircle is the northern half of the 180° longitude semicircle.)

Ask: *What part of the globe is at the center of circle A?* The center of the globe

Call attention to the degree labels on circle A. The labels from 0° to 180° on each side of the prime meridian correspond to the degree labels along the equator.

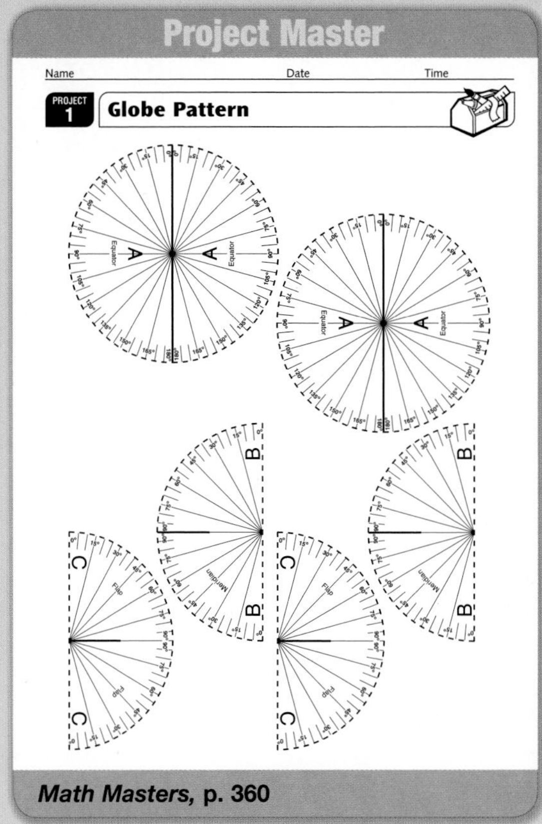

Project Master

Name Date Time

PROJECT 1 **Globe Pattern**

Math Masters, p. 360

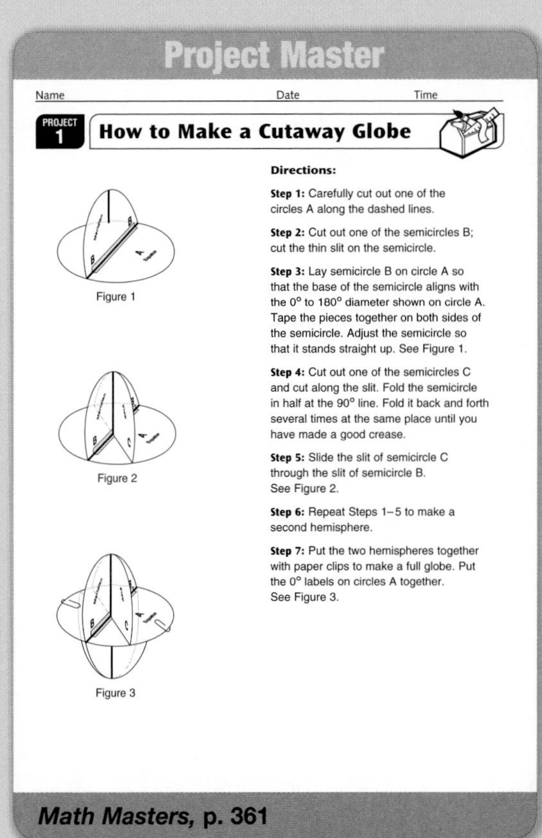

Project Master

Name Date Time

PROJECT 1 **How to Make a Cutaway Globe**

Directions:

Step 1: Carefully cut out one of the circles A along the dashed lines.

Step 2: Cut out one of the semicircles B; cut the thin slit on the semicircle.

Step 3: Lay semicircle B on circle A so that the base of the semicircle aligns with the 0° to 180° diameter shown on circle A. Tape the pieces together on both sides of the semicircle. Adjust the semicircle so that it stands straight up. See Figure 1.

Step 4: Cut out one of the semicircles C and cut along the slit. Fold the semicircle in half at the 90° line. Fold it back and forth several times at the same place until you have made a good crease.

Step 5: Slide the slit of semicircle C through the slit of semicircle B. See Figure 2.

Step 6: Repeat Steps 1–5 to make a second hemisphere.

Step 7: Put the two hemispheres together with paper clips to make a full globe. Put the 0° labels on circles A together. See Figure 3.

Figure 1

Figure 2

Figure 3

Math Masters, p. 361

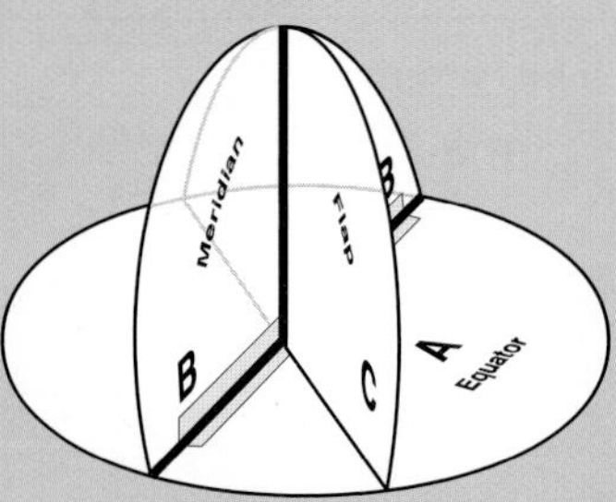

Figure 1

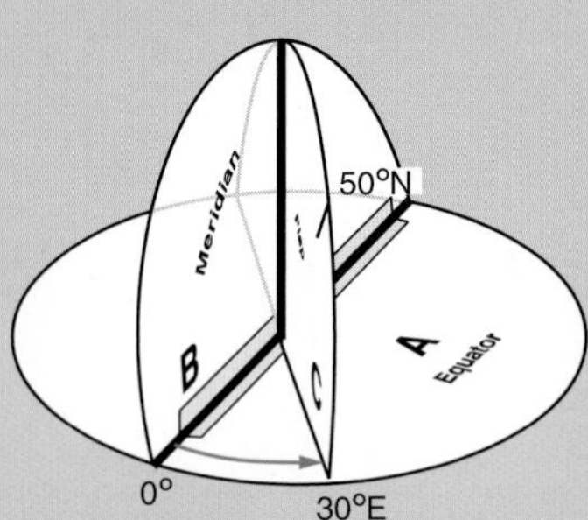

Figure 2

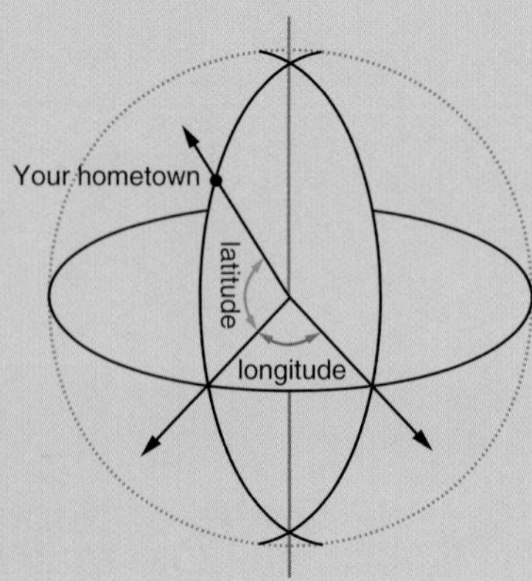

Figure 3

On semicircle B, degree labels from 0° to 90° start at each end of the base. They represent degrees of latitude north of the equator.

Now ask students to take semicircle C, which they had set aside, and slide the slit of this semicircle through the slit of semicircle B (*See Figure 1.*) If necessary, lengthen the slits for a good fit.

Demonstrate how this movable semicircle can be used to show any combination of latitude and longitude.

Example: Find 50° North, 30° East.

1. With the prime meridian facing the class, find the 30° East mark on circle A. Rotate the right flap of the movable semicircle C to that position.
2. Then, without moving flap C, point to the 50° North mark on it.

The model now shows the location of 50° North, 30° East. Find this location on the globe and compare it with the location on the model. (*See Figure 2.*)

Ask a volunteer to give the approximate latitude and longitude of an important place—preferably the school, hometown, or nearby city. If not already known, these can be estimated from the globe or maps in the *Student Reference Book.* Write them on the board.

Direct students to mark this location on their models by doing the following. (*See Figure 3.*)

1. Move Flap C to show the longitude (east or west on the equator). Then draw a line along the base of the flap.

   This hand-drawn line, along with the base of the prime meridian flap (Flap B), forms an angle on circle A.

   Ask: *What does the degree measure of the angle represent?* The number of degrees of longitude

2. Make a dot on the edge of the flap to show the latitude of the location identified on the board. Draw a line from the center of the model to the dot. This line, along with the base of the flap, forms a second angle.

   Ask: *What does the degree measure of the angle represent?* The number of degrees of latitude north from the equator

NOTE At this point, it is not necessary for students to be able to state that degrees of latitude and longitude are measures of angles whose vertices are at the center of Earth. It is enough that by drawing the angles, students become aware of this fact.

Making a Full Cutaway Globe

Next, ask students to make a second hemisphere out of the remaining circle and semicircles on *Math Masters,* page 360.

Then show how to make a complete cutaway globe—that is, one that shows both the Northern and Southern Hemispheres. (*See Figure 4.*) Partners use paper clips to fasten the bases of their models together, making sure to align the 0° longitude marks on both hemispheres. With this full globe, they can practice finding locations in both hemispheres.

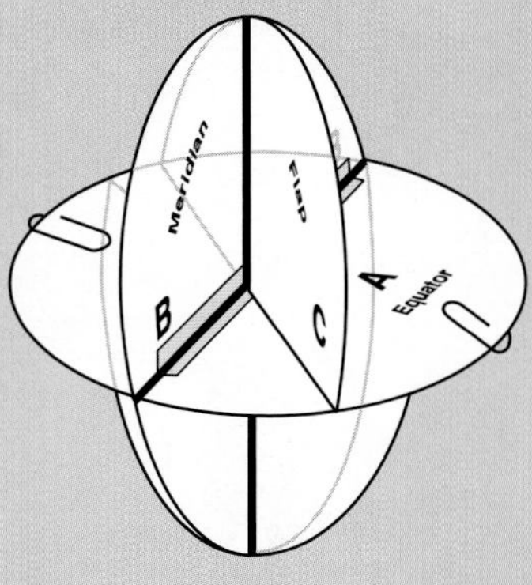

Figure 4

On the board, write other latitude/longitude pairs in the Northern Hemisphere. Ask students to move the flaps on their models to find these locations. Then have them guess on which continent these are located. Check on the globe. *For example:*

20°N,	20°E	Africa
15°N,	105°E	Southeast Asia
45°N,	100°W	North America
50°N,	5°E	Northern Europe
0°S,	60°W	South America

2 Extending the Project

Digging a Tunnel

Ask students to imagine digging a straight tunnel from their hometown through the center of Earth to the surface on the opposite side. Ask them to show the opposite point on their models and to name its latitude and longitude. Have them share strategies. Suggest other starting points for the tunnel.

Looking Up Latitudes and Longitudes

Invite students to look up latitudes and longitudes on the Internet.

For locations in the United States:

- kids.earth.nasa.gov/trmm/locator.html
- www.census.gov/geo/www/gazetteer/gazette.html

For locations in the United States and elsewhere:

- www.infoplease.com/ipa/A0001769.html
- www.indo.com/cgi-bin/dist

The last site also allows you to calculate the distance between locations.

Project 2

Using a Magnetic Compass

Objective To introduce reading a magnetic compass and finding directions.

Technology Resources www.everydaymathonline.com

eToolkit

Algorithms Practice

EM Facts Workshop Game™

Family Letters

Assessment Management

Common Core State Standards

Curriculum Focal Points

Interactive Teacher's Lesson Guide

1 Doing the Project

Recommended Use After Unit 6

Key Concepts and Skills

- Identify degree measurements to find the direction from north on a compass. [Measurement and Reference Frames Goal 1]
- Draw a line segment. [Geometry Goal 1]
- Identify clockwise rotations. [Geometry Goal 3]

Key Activities

Students learn how to orient and read a magnetic compass. Then, working in small groups, they use a magnetic compass to practice finding the direction of objects in relation to north.

Key Vocabulary

compass bearing ◆ magnetic north

Materials

- *Math Masters,* p. 362; p. 363 (optional)

Per group:

- magnetic compass
- 10-foot string
- tape

2 Extending the Project

Students make a floating compass with a steel sewing needle, a bar magnet, a piece of cork, and a dish of water.

Students further investigate orienteering through reading books and Web sites.

Materials

- steel sewing needle
- bar magnet
- piece of cork
- dish of water
- liquid detergent
- *Basic Essentials: Map and Compass*
- computer with Internet access

Advance Preparation

For Part 1, you need a magnetic compass and a copy of *Math Masters,* page 362 for a classroom demonstration. Try to obtain additional compasses for the group activity. Each group of four will need a 10-foot length of string.

For the optional activity in Part 2, you can use ***Basic Essentials: Map and Compass*** by Cliff Jacobson (Falcon, 2007).

1 Doing the Project

Introducing the Magnetic Compass

Gather the class around an open space in the classroom. If you have more than one magnetic compass, distribute them for students to examine.

Prompt discussion along the following lines:

- Does anyone know how a magnetic compass works? Earth behaves like a huge magnet. The compass needle is a tiny magnet. Earth's magnetic field exerts a force or pull on the compass needle so that the needle points north.
- How do you use a magnetic compass? Lay the compass flat on a surface or hold it level to the ground. Make sure that there are no metal objects or magnets near the compass. The compass needle will settle down and point north.

Using a Magnetic Compass

(*Math Masters,* p. 362)

Show students a method for describing the direction of an object from a given point.

1. A paper compass (*Math Masters,* page 362) is laid on a flat surface so that the 0° mark points north.
2. A string is stretched from the center of the paper compass toward the object, making it possible to describe the direction of the object in relation to north.

You will need a magnetic compass to orient the paper compass so that it points north. Here is one way to do it:

1. Lay the paper compass flat on the floor.
2. Place the magnetic compass on the paper compass so that the center of the magnetic compass is over the center of the paper compass. Make sure the letter *N* on both compasses points in the same direction.
3. Gently rotate the paper with the magnetic compass on it until the needle on the magnetic compass points to the letter *N.* Tape the paper compass in place.

Now select a location in the classroom—for example, the class globe. Demonstrate how to find the direction of the globe from the compass, using north as a reference.

1. Have a student hold down one end of a piece of string on the center of the paper compass.
2. Ask another student to pull the string as far as possible in the direction of the object you selected, keeping the string at floor level.

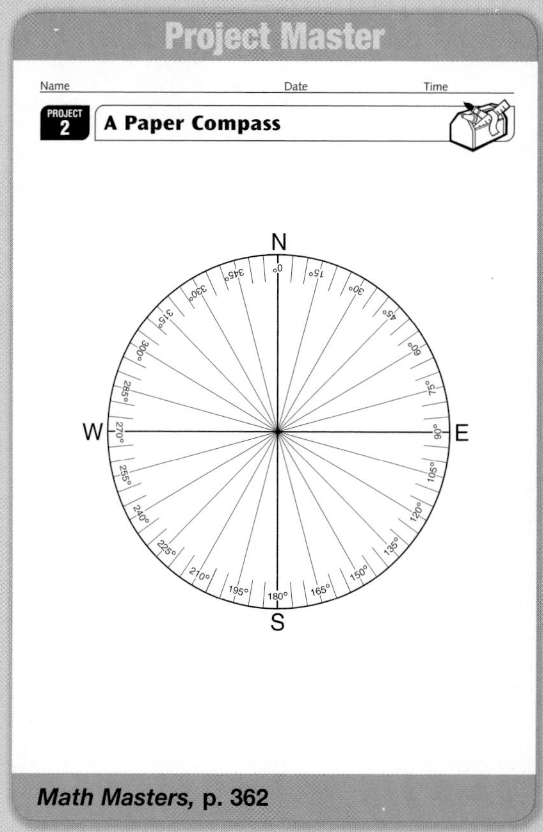

Math Masters, p. 362

NOTE Depending on one's location, a compass may not show "true" north. The U.S. Geological Survey (USGS) maintains a Web site on the National Geomagnetism Program: http://geomag.usgs.gov. Its FAQ page gives basic information and can guide you to the models and calculations that show the variation between "true" and magnetic north for a given location. The National Geophysical Data Center (NGDC) maintains archives of geomagnetic data, models, software, and other information. Their general Web page and FAQ might be helpful: www.ngdc.noaa.gov/geomag

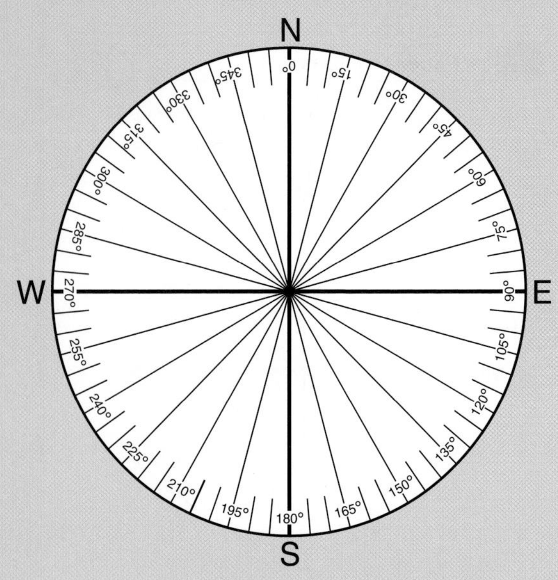

Use a paper compass to determine compass bearings of objects in the classroom.

3. Read the number of degrees at the mark where the string crosses the edge of the paper compass. This gives the direction of the object, using north as a reference. For example, "The globe is 120° clockwise from north," or "The globe has a **compass bearing** of 120°."

Emphasize that this method measures the amount of clockwise rotation from **magnetic north.**

Choose other objects or locations in the classroom. Ask pairs of students to find the objects' direction from north, using the metho just described.

▶ Measuring Direction

SMALL-GROUP ACTIVITY

(*Math Masters,* p. 362)

Divide the class into groups of four. Pass out a length of string to each group and a magnetic compass to as many groups as possible. If there are not enough compasses to go around, groups can share.

Ask each group to lay its copy of *Math Masters,* page 362 flat on the desktop and orient it toward north, as described earlier. Then tape the paper compass to the desktop.

Each group now uses its string to find the direction of each corner of the room on its taped paper compass. Students indicate the direction of each corner by drawing a line segment along the string from the center of the paper compass to the edge. Have students record next to each line segment the number of degrees from north.

Bring the class together to share results. Ask: *Why do the results differ from group to group?* The direction of any particular location depends on the point from which the direction is measured. For example, the direction of the classroom globe will vary, depending on where one is standing in the classroom.

2 Extending the Project

Making a Compass

INDEPENDENT ACTIVITY

(*Math Masters,* p. 363)

Math Masters, page 363 provides a brief history of compasses and the directions for making a floating compass with a steel sewing needle, bar magnet, piece of cork, and dish of water.

Finding Out about Compasses and Orienteering

INDEPENDENT ACTIVITY

Invite students to learn more about the history and uses of compasses by looking in encyclopedias and books such as ***Basic Essentials: Map and Compass*** by Cliff Jacobson (Falcon, 2007).

Through scouting or camping, some students may be familiar with using a compass to follow a course and might be interested in describing their experiences to the class.

The competitive sport of orienteering involves using a detailed map and a compass to navigate around a course with designated control points. The winner of the competition is the participant who visits the control points in order and in the shortest amount of time. The International Orienteering Federation has a Web site at www.orienteering.org.

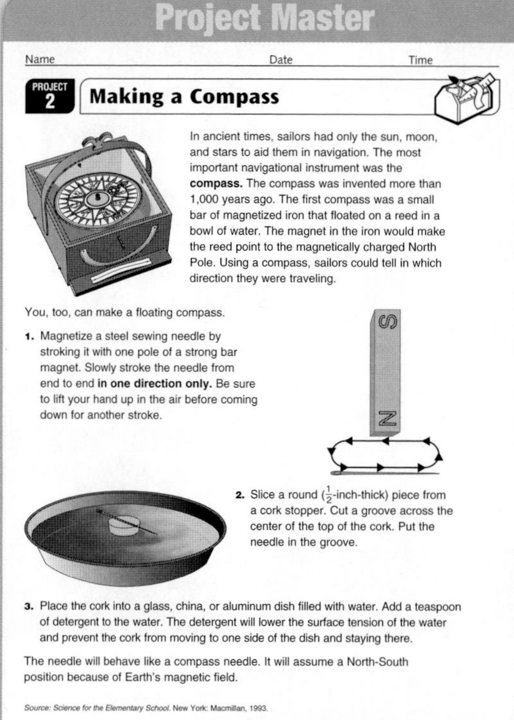

Project Master

Name Date Time

PROJECT 2 **Making a Compass**

In ancient times, sailors had only the sun, moon, and stars to aid them in navigation. The most important navigational instrument was the **compass.** The compass was invented more than 1,000 years ago. The first compass was a small bar of magnetized iron that floated on a reed in a bowl of water. The magnet in the iron would make the reed point to the magnetically charged North Pole. Using a compass, sailors could tell in which direction they were traveling.

You, too, can make a floating compass.

1. Magnetize a steel sewing needle by stroking it with one pole of a strong bar magnet. Slowly stroke the needle from end to end **in one direction only.** Be sure to lift your hand up in the air before coming down for another stroke.

2. Slice a round ($\frac{1}{2}$-inch-thick) piece from a cork stopper. Cut a groove across the center of the top of the cork. Put the needle in the groove.
3. Place the cork into a glass, china, or aluminum dish filled with water. Add a teaspoon of detergent to the water. The detergent will lower the surface tension of the water and prevent the cork from moving to one side of the dish and staying there.

The needle will behave like a compass needle. It will assume a North-South position because of Earth's magnetic field.

Source: Science for the Elementary School. New York: Macmillan, 1993.

Math Masters, **p. 363**

Project

3 A Carnival Game

Objectives To provide opportunities to analyze a cube-tossing game; and to invent a profitable variation.

Technology Resources www.everydaymathonline.com

eToolkit

Algorithms Practice

EM Facts Workshop Game™

Family Letters

Assessment Management

Common Core State Standards

Curriculum Focal Points

Interactive Teacher's Lesson Guide

1 Doing the Project

Recommended Use After Unit 7

Key Concepts and Skills

- Solve problems involving extended multiplication facts.
  [Operations and Computation Goal 3]
- Collect and organize data.
  [Data and Chance Goal 1]
- Conduct a cube-drop experiment.
  [Data and Chance Goal 4]
- Compare predicted results and experimental results; use results to predict future events.
  [Data and Chance Goal 4]

Key Activities

Students make a "quilt" out of the 10-by-10 grids they colored in Lesson 7•12. They use their quilt as a target mat for a cube-tossing game.

Then students work in small groups to invent a variation of the game that will show a profit.

Materials

- *Math Journal 2,* p. 215 (optional)
- *Math Masters,* pp. 238 and 242 (as completed by the student, if available); pp. 364 and 365
- calculator
- centimeter cube
- scissors
- transparent tape

2 Extending the Project

Students make up their own games.

Materials

- none

Advance Preparation

You need the data for 1,000 cube drops collected in Lesson 7•12 on *Math Masters,* page 242. If this was not done, combine 20 students' results on 50 drops as described in Part 3 of Lesson 7•12, or generate the data with the students from their results on *Math Journal 2,* page 215. Write this information, including percents for each color, on the board.

Students need their completed copies of *Math Masters,* page 238. If these are not available, copy the master and have students color it as described in the project.

1 Doing the Project

Introducing a Carnival Game

SMALL-GROUP ACTIVITY

(*Math Journal 2,* p. 215; *Math Masters,* pp. 238 and 364)

Constructing a Class "Quilt" Mat

Have students take out the grid they colored on *Math Masters,* page 238. If this is not available, have students color the grid on a blank copy of the master according to the specifications shown on the table. (*See margin.*) They may color the squares in any way they want. The colors may form a pattern or a picture, or they may be arranged randomly.

If there are fewer than 20 students in your class, divide the class into groups of four. If there are 20 or more, divide the class into groups of five. (Any "leftover" students form their own group.) Ask students in each group to cut out their hundreds grids and tape them together to form one row of hundreds grids. (For example, a group of four will make a row of four grids.)

Bring the groups together. Have them tape their rows together to form a rectangular (or nearly rectangular) quilt. For example, a class of 20 would form a quilt with four rows, each row with five grids.

Becoming Familiar with the Game

Introduce the carnival game on *Math Masters,* page 364. A player pays 10¢ for each cube the player tosses onto the class "quilt" mat. The player may win a prize, depending on the color on which the cube lands.

Ask students to complete Problem 1. Bring the class together to compare results.

Tell the class that the table on the board contains the combined results of 50 cube drops by 20 students in Lesson 7-12. Since $20 * 50 = 1{,}000$, the table shows the number of times, and percent of total times, that a cube landed on each color out of 1,000 drops.

Suggest that the carnival game could be run at a school fair or similar event to raise money for the class—for a party, equipment, or other purposes. Have students complete Problem 2 to find out how much money the class could earn if students sold 1,000 tickets and the results were the same as those on the board.

If you wish, have students actually play the game.

Project Master

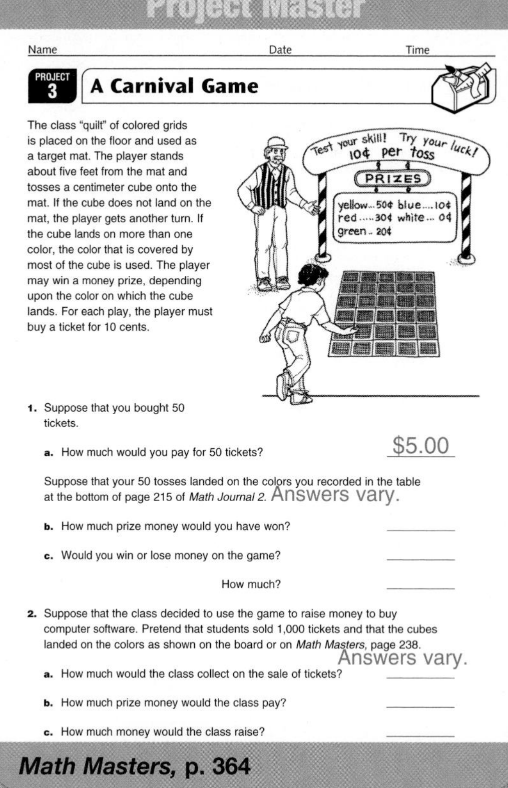

Name Date Time

PROJECT 3 **A Carnival Game**

The class "quilt" of colored grids is placed on the floor and used as a target mat. The player stands about five feet from the mat and tosses a centimeter cube onto the mat. If the cube does not land on the mat, the player gets another turn. If the cube lands on more than one color, the color that is covered by most of the cube is used. The player may win a money prize, depending upon the color on which the cube lands. For each play, the player must buy a ticket for 10 cents.

1. Suppose that you bought 50 tickets.
   a. How much would you pay for 50 tickets? $5.00

   Suppose that your 50 tosses landed on the colors you recorded in the table at the bottom of page 215 of *Math Journal 2.* Answers vary.

   b. How much prize money would you have won? ____
   c. Would you win or lose money on the game? ____
   How much? ____

2. Suppose that the class decided to use the game to raise money to buy computer software. Pretend that students sold 1,000 tickets and that the cubes landed on the colors as shown on the board or on *Math Masters,* page 238. Answers vary.
   a. How much would the class collect on the sale of tickets? ____
   b. How much prize money would the class pay? ____
   c. How much money would the class raise? ____

Math Masters, p. 364

How to Color the Grid	
Color	**Number of Squares**
yellow	1
red	4
green	10
blue	35
white	50
Total	100

NOTE If you want the taped rows to form a rectangle or square, you may have to ask students to color additional grids.

Project Master

Name Date Time

PROJECT 3 **A Carnival Game** *continued*

3. Work with your group to make up your own version of the carnival game.

a. Record how much you would charge for a ticket and what the prizes would be for each color.

Ticket Price	Prizes
______ per toss	yellow ______
	red ______
	green ______
	blue ______
	white ______

b. Use the results for 1,000 cube drops shown on the board or on *Math Masters,* page 242 to answer the following questions: Answers vary.

Would the class have won or lost money? ______

How much? ______

4. Suppose that the class ran your game on Parents' Night. Answers vary.

a. How many tickets do you estimate the class would sell? ______

b. How much money would the class get from ticket sales? ______

c. About how much money should you expect to pay in prizes? ______

d. About how much money should the class expect to earn? ______

***Math Masters,* p. 365**

▶ Inventing a Variation on the Carnival Game

(*Math Masters,* p. 365)

By now, students should have a fairly good understanding of the rules of the carnival game and the factors that affect the game's profitability. Tell them that each group is to invent its own version of the game. Spend a few minutes discussing things students need to take into consideration, such as the following:

- How much should you charge for a ticket?
- Which colors should win prizes?
- What should the prizes be?
- How will your decisions affect the number of tickets sold?
- Will you make more money if you charge a lot for a ticket and offer large prizes? Or will a high ticket price discourage people from buying tickets?

Students can complete this project over the next few days. Groups can post their ticket prices and prizes near the mat and play each other's games in their free time. To find the total amount of money the class would earn, follow this procedure: Multiply the number of times a cube lands on each color by the amount of the prize for that color. Then add the amounts won for each color.

Example:

Cube lands on		**Prizes**
yellow	1 time	$1 * 50¢ = \$0.50$
red	2 times	$2 * 30¢ = \$0.60$
green	6 times	$6 * 20¢ = \$1.20$
blue	11 times	$11 * 10¢ = \$1.10$
white	30 times	$30 * 0¢ = \$0.00$
	Total:	\$3.40

The 50 tickets cost \$5.00 (50 ∗ 10¢). The players win only \$3.40. The class earns \$1.60; (\$5.00 − \$3.40 = \$1.60).

Have students complete *Math Masters,* page 365.

2 Extending the Project

▶ Creating Other Games

Invite students to make up their own games, establish prices and prizes, and use expected results to calculate prizes paid and profits earned.

Project 4

Making a Quilt

Objective To guide students as they explore and apply ideas of pattern, symmetry, rotation, and reflection in the context of quilts.

Technology Resources www.everydaymathonline.com

eToolkit

Algorithms Practice

EM Facts Workshop Game™

Family Letters

Assessment Management

Common Core State Standards

Curriculum Focal Points

Interactive Teacher's Lesson Guide

1 Doing the Project

Recommended Use After Unit 10

Key Concepts and Skills

- Identify squares, triangles, and rectangles.
  [Geometry Goal 2]
- Identify lines of symmetry; create patterns with a specified number of lines of symmetry.
  [Geometry Goal 3]
- Identify and use rotations and translations.
  [Geometry Goal 3]
- Identify and extend visual patterns.
  [Patterns, Functions, and Algebra Goal 1]

Key Activities

Students apply their knowledge of symmetry and rotations to make a paper quilt.

Key Vocabulary

patwork quilt ◆ 9-Patch Pattern ◆ quilting bee

Materials

- *Math Masters,* pp. 366–374 (one per student); p. 375 (at least three copies per student)
- markers, crayons, or colored pencils; or paper of various colors
- one-hole punch
- paste or glue
- scissors
- straightedge
- yarn
- crepe paper (optional)

2 Extending the Project

Students learn more about quilts through literature.

Materials

- *Eight Hands Round: A Patchwork Alphabet*

Advance Preparation

Students need yarn to assemble their quilts. If you wish, collect colored paper or wrapping paper to be cut up for "patches." You may want to make overhead transparencies of *Math Masters,* pages 367 and 371. If you can laminate the patches, the quilt will last longer and look more finished.

For the optional activity in Part 2, obtain copies of ***Eight Hands Round: A Patchwork Alphabet*** by Ann Whitford Paul (HarperCollins, 1996).

Project Master

Name ______ Date ______ Time ______

PROJECT 4 **Patchwork Quilts** 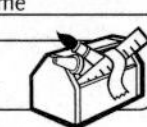

Throughout American history, women have worked together to make **patchwork quilts.** Because cloth was expensive and scarce, quilts were often made out of pieces of worn-out clothing or leftovers from another project. The quilters began by sewing together pieces of different colors, shapes, and textures to create a square pattern. Then they made more "patchwork" squares with the same pattern. When they had enough squares, they sewed them together to form the top of the quilt. Next they added a layer of wool fleece or cotton, called *batting,* and a cloth backing. They made a "sandwich" of the three layers—the backing on the bottom, the batting in the middle, and the patchwork on the top. They stretched the "sandwich" on a wooden frame and sewed the three layers together with tiny stitches.

The quilt was put together at a party, called a **quilting bee.** While cutting and sewing, the women would tell stories and share what went on in their lives. When the quilt was finished, the men joined the women for supper and dancing.

Buggy Wheel

Many patchwork patterns have become traditions. Their names and designs have come from the everyday lives of the people who created them. For example, the "Buggy Wheel" pattern was probably inspired by a trip in a buggy. Along with walking and riding horses, buggies were a popular form of transportation in early America.

Does and Darts

Although early quilters may not have studied geometry in school, we can see geometry in many of their designs. Patchwork quilting involves the cutting of fabric into various geometric shapes and sewing them together into patterns. The pattern may be repeated over and over to form a quilt, or it may be rotated or reflected as the patches are assembled. Many patchwork patterns, such as the "Buggy Wheel" and "Does and Darts," are symmetric. Others, such as the "Crazy Quilt," seem to have been created at random.

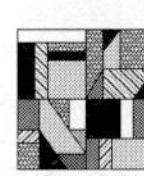
Crazy Quilt

The beauty of a quilt lies in its uniqueness. No two patches need ever be the same because there are many possible arrangements of fabrics and colors.

Math Masters, p. 366

1 Doing the Project

▶ Learning about Quilts

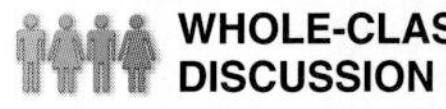
WHOLE-CLASS DISCUSSION

(*Math Masters,* p. 366)

Have students read the article about quilts on *Math Masters,* page 366. Then ask them to discuss it. The discussion should include the following points:

- ▷ Quilting patterns often reflect the lives of the people who create them.
- ▷ Quilting patterns display some of the geometric transformations that students have been studying, such as reflections and rotations, and the symmetries based on these transformations.
- ▷ **Patchwork quilts** were made from available scraps sewn into a square pattern.

Tell students that during this project they will learn more about quilting patterns, and they will use this knowledge to make their own paper quilts.

▶ Examining Lines of Symmetry in Quilting Patterns

PARTNER ACTIVITY

(*Math Masters,* p. 367)

Introduce the activity with a discussion of the Pinwheel Pattern at the top of *Math Masters,* page 367. Students should notice the following details:

- ▷ The original, uncolored pattern has four lines of symmetry.
- ▷ This pattern may be colored in many different ways.
- ▷ The number of lines of symmetry varies, depending on the coloring scheme.

Working with a partner, students examine three other basic patterns and various coloring schemes based on these patterns. Then students draw all the lines of symmetry for each.

After a few minutes, bring the class together and go over the answers. It may be helpful to refer to an overhead transparency of *Math Masters,* page 367.

Project Master

Name ______ Date ______ Time ______

PROJECT 4 **Symmetric Patterns**

Each pattern to the right of the "Pinwheel" pattern below has been colored in a different way. Notice how each color arrangement changes the number of lines of symmetry.

Pinwheel Pattern

lines of symmetry: 4 | 2 | 1 | 0

For each pattern below, draw all the lines of symmetry and record the number of lines of symmetry.

1. Bow-Tie Pattern

lines of symmetry: 4 | 1 | 2 | 2

2. Ohio Star Pattern

lines of symmetry: 4 | 4 | 0 | 0

3. Pineapple Log Cabin Pattern

lines of symmetry: 4 | 4 | 4 | 0

Math Masters, p. 367

Designing 9-Patch Patterns

(*Math Masters,* pp. 368–370)

Tell the class that there is a special kind of quilting pattern called the **9-Patch Pattern.** Students will design such patterns of colored squares, triangles, and rectangles.

To make the various pieces, students follow the directions on *Math Masters,* page 368 for coloring the squares on *Math Masters,* page 369. Then they cut the squares into triangles and rectangles as directed on *Math Masters,* page 368.

To assemble a 9-Patch Pattern, students use the 3-by-3 grid on *Math Masters,* page 370. They experiment with different ways to arrange the triangles and rectangles they cut out.

When students have completed a pattern, have them copy it onto a grid on *Math Masters,* page 368. Students should make at least one pattern with four lines of symmetry, one with two lines of symmetry, and one with no lines of symmetry.

Project Master

Name Date Time

PROJECT 4 **Traditional 9-Patch Patterns**

Some patterns, called **9-Patch Patterns,** look like they are made up of 9 squares. You can make your own 9-Patch Pattern on a 3-by-3 grid.

Take out *Math Masters,* pages 369 and 370. Color 6 squares on *Math Masters,* page 369 in one color and the other 6 in a different color. Cut out the 12 squares. Then make triangles by cutting 6 of the squares in half along a diagonal. Make rectangles by cutting the other 6 squares in half along a line through the middle.

Now arrange some of the pieces on the grid on *Math Masters,* page 370 to make a pattern. Follow the directions below. When you have completed a pattern, draw and color it on one of the 3-by-3 grids below.

1. Make one or two patterns having 4 lines of symmetry.
   Answers vary.
2. Make one or two patterns having 2 lines of symmetry.
   Answers vary.
3. Make one or two patterns having no lines of symmetry.
   Answers vary.

Math Masters, p. 368

Math Masters, p. 369

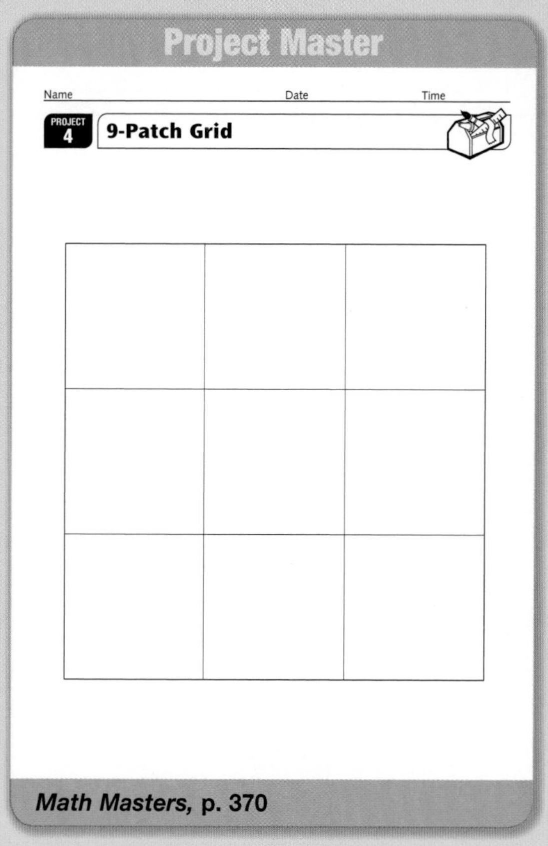

Math Masters, p. 370

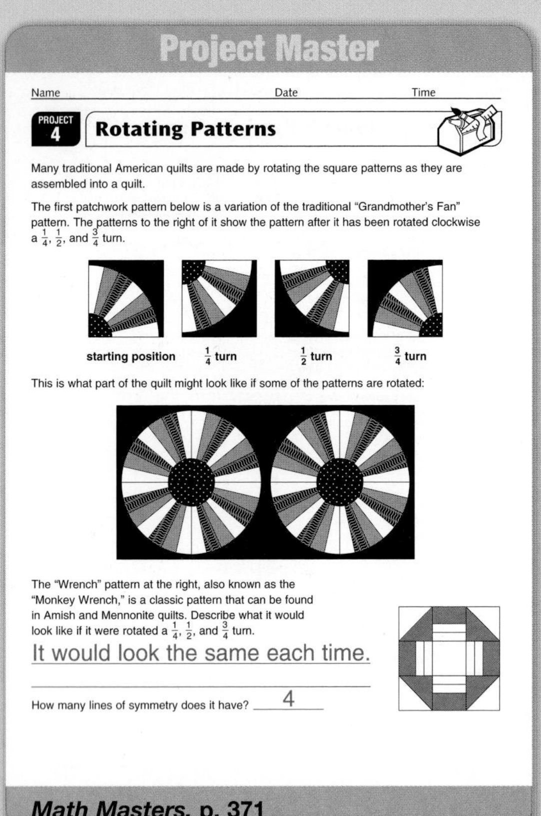

Project Master

Name Date Time

PROJECT 4 **Rotating Patterns**

Many traditional American quilts are made by rotating the square patterns as they are assembled into a quilt.

The first patchwork pattern below is a variation of the traditional "Grandmother's Fan" pattern. The patterns to the right of it show the pattern after it has been rotated clockwise a $\frac{1}{4}$, $\frac{1}{2}$, and $\frac{3}{4}$ turn.

starting position | $\frac{1}{4}$ turn | $\frac{1}{2}$ turn | $\frac{3}{4}$ turn

This is what part of the quilt might look like if some of the patterns are rotated:

The "Wrench" pattern at the right, also known as the "Monkey Wrench," is a classic pattern that can be found in Amish and Mennonite quilts. Describe what it would look like if it were rotated a $\frac{1}{4}$, $\frac{1}{2}$, and $\frac{3}{4}$ turn.

It would look the same each time.

How many lines of symmetry does it have? 4

Math Masters, p. 371

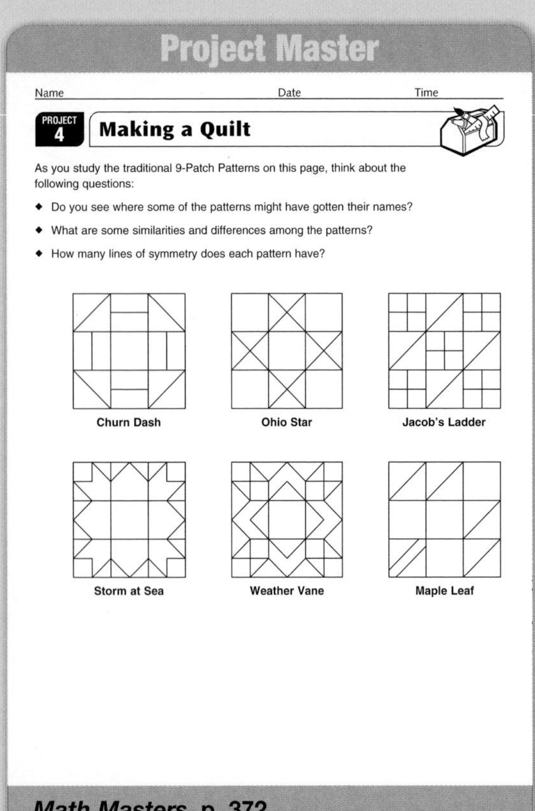

Project Master

Name Date Time

PROJECT 4 **Making a Quilt**

As you study the traditional 9-Patch Patterns on this page, think about the following questions:

- Do you see where some of the patterns might have gotten their names?
- What are some similarities and differences among the patterns?
- How many lines of symmetry does each pattern have?

Churn Dash | Ohio Star | Jacob's Ladder

Storm at Sea | Weather Vane | Maple Leaf

Math Masters, p. 372

▶ Looking at Rotations of Patterns

(*Math Masters,* p. 371)

Briefly review rotations. Ask students to place a closed journal or other book on their desks. Then have them rotate it through various turns. *For example:*

- ▷ Clockwise $\frac{1}{2}$ turn
- ▷ Counterclockwise $\frac{1}{2}$ turn
- ▷ Clockwise $\frac{1}{4}$ turn
- ▷ Counterclockwise $\frac{3}{4}$ turn

Finally, go over *Math Masters,* page 371 with the class. You may want to use an overhead transparency of the master.

▶ Making a Paper Patchwork Quilt

(*Math Masters,* pp. 372–375)

Ask students to examine the traditional 9-Patch Patterns on *Math Masters,* page 372. Like the patterns students created previously, each of these patterns is based on a grid of nine squares. Ask students to speculate about the origin of some of the names, to comment on similarities and differences between the patterns, and to identify the lines of symmetry in each pattern.

Divide the class into groups of three and tell students that they are going to make a patchwork quilt out of paper. Go over the directions for making the quilt on *Math Masters,* page 373. Emphasize these requirements:

- ▷ The pattern that a group chooses may not have more than two lines of symmetry.
- ▷ When the group assembles the quilt, at least one of the patches should be rotated through a $\frac{1}{4}$, $\frac{1}{2}$, or $\frac{3}{4}$ turn.

Then students proceed as follows:

1. Each student cuts out the 3-by-3 grid of squares, including the border with the dots, from three copies of *Math Masters,* page 375.

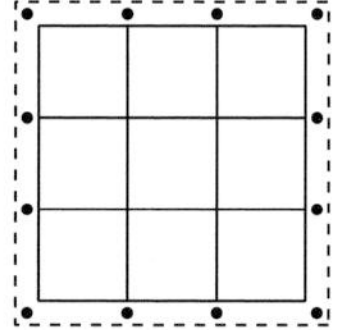

2. Each student cuts out the pieces on *Math Masters,* page 374.
3. Each group chooses one of the patterns on *Math Masters,* page 372 and decides on a coloring scheme.
4. Each student then copies the agreed-upon pattern onto each of the 3-by-3 grids he or she cut out. The pieces cut out from *Math Masters,* page 374 can be used as templates to help in drawing the pattern.

5. Students color each pattern according to the agreed-upon coloring scheme. Alternatively, the pieces cut out from *Math Masters,* page 374 can be traced onto colored paper or wrapping paper. The tracings can be cut out and glued onto the 3-by-3 grid.
6. The students punch holes through each dot on the borders of the 3-by-3 grids. If you have access to a laminating machine, laminate the squares before students punch the holes. The quilts will look more finished and will last longer.

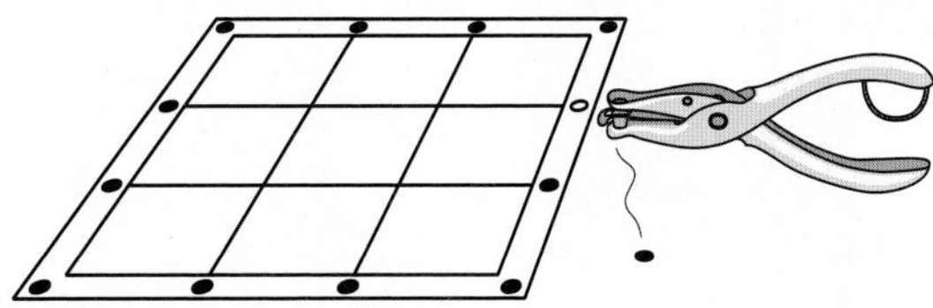

7. When all 3-by-3 "patches" have been completed, students in each group assemble them into a patchwork quilt. They lay the patterns on the floor and arrange them so that the borders of the squares overlap and the holes line up. Students use yarn to fasten the square patterns together by weaving the yarn in and out of the holes.
8. The quilt may be decorated with a ruffle made out of crepe paper. The crepe paper should be pleated and glued around the edges of the quilt.

Summarizing the Project

WHOLE-CLASS ACTIVITY

Ask each group to present its finished quilt to the class and describe how it was designed and put together. Students should point out lines of symmetry, reflections, and rotations in the pattern.

2 Extending the Project

Finding Out about Quilts

INDEPENDENT ACTIVITY

Invite students to learn more about quilts by looking in encyclopedias and books such as ***Eight Hands Round: A Patchwork Alphabet*** by Ann Whitford Paul (HarperCollins, 1996). This informative book speculates on the origins of the names of early American patchwork patterns for each letter in the alphabet.

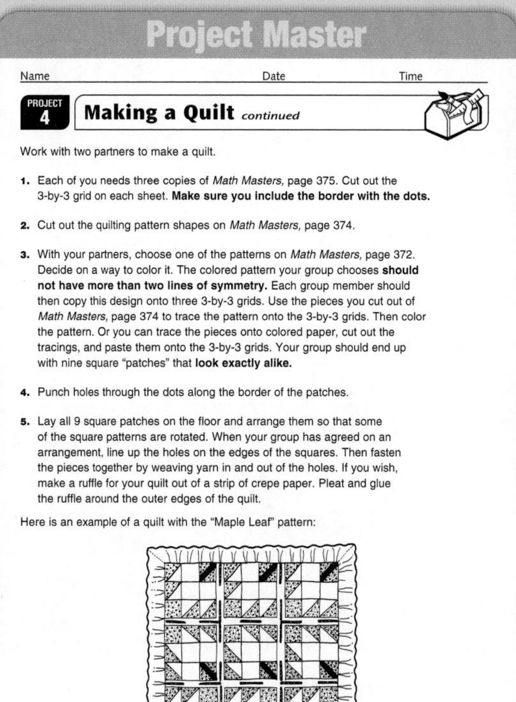

Project Master

Name Date Time

PROJECT 4 **Making a Quilt** *continued*

Work with two partners to make a quilt.

1. Each of you needs three copies of *Math Masters,* page 375. Cut out the 3-by-3 grid on each sheet. **Make sure you include the border with the dots.**
2. Cut out the quilting pattern shapes on *Math Masters,* page 374.
3. With your partners, choose one of the patterns on *Math Masters,* page 372. Decide on a way to color it. The colored pattern your group chooses **should not have more than two lines of symmetry.** Each group member should then copy this design onto three 3-by-3 grids. Use the pieces you cut out of *Math Masters,* page 374 to trace the pattern onto the 3-by-3 grids. Then color the pattern. Or you can trace the pieces onto colored paper, cut out the tracings, and paste them onto the 3-by-3 grids. Your group should end up with nine square "patches" that **look exactly alike.**
4. Punch holes through the dots along the border of the patches.
5. Lay all 9 square patches on the floor and arrange them so that some of the square patterns are rotated. When your group has agreed on an arrangement, line up the holes on the edges of the squares. Then fasten the pieces together by weaving yarn in and out of the holes. If you wish, make a ruffle for your quilt out of a strip of crepe paper. Pleat and glue the ruffle around the outer edges of the quilt.

Here is an example of a quilt with the "Maple Leaf" pattern:

Math Masters, p. 373

NOTE Students are making a 9-Patch Pattern quilt, but this is by no means the only method of quilting. In the spirit of the traditional **quilting bee,** you may wish to serve refreshments after students have completed their quilts.

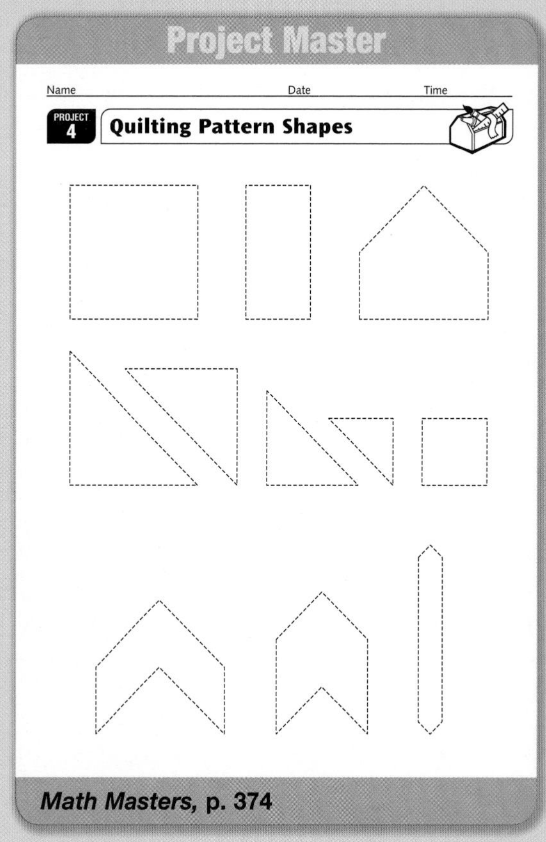

Project Master

Name Date Time

PROJECT 4 **Quilting Pattern Shapes**

Math Masters, p. 374

Project 5

Which Soft Drink Is the Best Buy?

Objective To guide students as they calculate the unit price of various soft drinks and decide which is the best buy.

Technology Resources www.everydaymathonline.com

eToolkit

Algorithms Practice

EM Facts Workshop Game™

Family Letters

Assessment Management

Common Core State Standards

Curriculum Focal Points

Interactive Teacher's Lesson Guide

1 Doing the Project

Recommended Use During or after Unit 12

Key Concepts and Skills

- Round to the nearest fluid ounce.
  [Operations and Computation Goal 6]
- Calculate unit price.
  [Operations and Computation Goal 7]
- Collect and organize data.
  [Data and Chance Goal 1]
- Draw conclusions from data.
  [Data and Chance Goal 2]
- Convert among units of capacity.
  [Measurement and Reference Frames Goal 3]

Key Activities

Students collect soft-drink cups from local businesses and record the prices charged for various sizes of soft drinks. They work in groups to determine which place offers the best soft-drink value.

Key Vocabulary

capacity

Materials

- *Math Masters,* pp. 376 and 377
- soft-drink cups
- measuring cup (fluid ounces)
- about 2 quarts or 2 liters of water or other pourable substance
- stick-on labels
- calculator

2 Extending the Project

Students read magazines and Web sites about consumer issues.

Materials

- computer with Internet access

Advance Preparation

A week or so before beginning the project, divide the class into groups of four or five. Each group is responsible for collecting soft-drink cups of various sizes (small, medium, large) from local businesses (restaurants, fast-food franchises, movie theaters, sports events, concerts, carnivals, and so on)—preferably three different sizes from each of three different places per group. Students should rinse out each cup and label it with its source and price. Collect additional cups for students who may need more. Since it is difficult to write on the surface of some cups, give each group a set of stick-on labels on which to write the information.

Gather enough measuring cups so that each group has one. Each group will also need about 2 liters or 2 quarts of water or other pourable substance, such as sand, navy or lima beans, or unpopped popcorn.

1 Doing the Project

Introducing the Soft-Drink Project

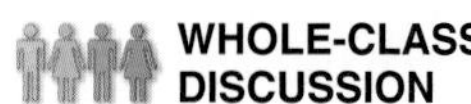
WHOLE-CLASS DISCUSSION

Ask students to share the experiences they had buying soft drinks in various sizes at fast-food restaurants, movie theaters, sports events, concerts, carnivals, and so on.

Then ask students for suggestions for deciding which places and which sizes of soft-drink cups offer the best value.

- How can you use the information you have recorded to make this determination?
- What other information do you need?
- How would you gather this information?

Carrying Out the Project

SMALL-GROUP ACTIVITY

(*Math Masters,* pp. 376 and 377)

These groups can be the same as those that collected the cups. Give each group a measuring cup and enough water or other pourable substance to carry out the investigation. (If possible, each group should work with three sets of three different-sized cups, each set from a different business.)

Students find out how much each container conveniently holds (not filled to the brim). They should round the **capacity** to the nearest fluid ounce. When calculating the price per ounce, ask them to round the answer to the nearest tenth of a cent. Then have students record all information on *Math Masters,* page 376.

After students have finished collecting the data and calculating the unit prices, have each group use *Math Masters,* page 377 to prepare a report describing the data collected and the conclusions drawn from the data. The report might include tables and pictorial representations of the data (for example, bar graphs).

NOTE

1 cup = 8 fluid ounces (fl oz)

1 pint = 2 cups = 16 fl oz

1 quart = 2 pints = 32 fl oz

1 gallon = 4 quarts = 128 fl oz

Project Master

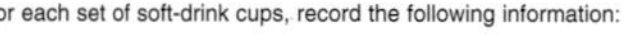

Name Date Time

PROJECT 5 **Which Soft Drink Would You Buy?**

For each set of soft-drink cups, record the following information:

- The name of the place from which the cups come
- The size of the cup (small, medium, or large)
- The price
- The capacity in fluid ounces

Then calculate each unit price in cents per fluid ounce, rounded to the nearest tenth of a cent. Answers vary.

Soft-Drink Cups from

Size	Price	Capacity (fl oz)	Unit Price (¢/fl oz)

Soft-Drink Cups from

Size	Price	Capacity (fl oz)	Unit Price (¢/fl oz)

Soft-Drink Cups from

Size	Price	Capacity (fl oz)	Unit Price (¢/fl oz)

Math Masters, p. 376

Project Master

Name ____________ Date ____________ Time ____________

PROJECT 5 **Consumer Report: Best Soft-Drink Prices**

Imagine that you have been assigned by *Kids' Consumer Reports* to investigate and report on the prices of soft drinks. Use the information your group recorded on *Math Masters*, page 376 to prepare a group report for the magazine. Your report might contain graphs, tables, and pictures. Try to answer some of the following questions in your report:

- Do small (or medium or large) cups at different places contain the same amount?
- Are prices similar for similar sizes? (For example, are the small-size drinks about the same price at different places?)
- Which places have the least expensive soft drinks? The most expensive soft drinks?
- Is the largest size always the best value?
- Which types of businesses offer better values? (For example, do restaurants generally offer better values than movie theaters?)
- What would you recommend to consumers? Do some places offer free refills? If so, how would this affect your recommendation?

Answers vary.

***Math Masters,* p. 377**

Discussing the Results

WHOLE-CLASS DISCUSSION

(*Math Masters,* pp. 376 and 377)

Bring the groups together to present their reports. After all the reports have been heard, ask students what conclusions they can draw from their consumer survey. For example, ask: *Is getting the best value the only reason for choosing a particular size?*

2 Extending the Project

Looking at Consumer Magazines

INDEPENDENT ACTIVITY

Invite students to look at *Consumer Reports* or other consumer magazines that may be available in the school or local library or on the Internet. Students might report on how measurements of various items are reported—such as dimensions, weight, and capacity—and whether measurements or unit prices are used in determining best buys.

Project

6 Building and Viewing Structures

Objectives To provide practice building structures with cubes, given "blueprints" or side views of the structures; and to provide practice representing structures with diagrams.

Technology Resources www.everydaymathonline.com

eToolkit

Algorithms Practice

EM Facts Workshop Game™

Family Letters

Assessment Management

Common Core State Standards

Curriculum Focal Points

Interactive Teacher's Lesson Guide

1 Doing the Project

Recommended Use During or after Unit 11

Key Concepts and Skills

- Describe and compare plane and solid figures.
  [Geometry Goal 2]
- Describe 3-D objects from different perspectives.
  [Geometry Goal 2]
- Use manipulatives to solve problems involving spatial visualization.
  [Geometry Goal 2]
- Identify and describe reflections of 3-D structures.
  [Geometry Goal 3]

Key Activities

Students build structures with centimeter cubes on a 4-by-4 grid. They record what they see at eye level for two or more sides of the structure.

Key Vocabulary

blueprint

Materials

- *Math Masters,* pp. 378–380
- at least 25 centimeter cubes (or other size cubes)
- scissors

2 Extending the Project

Students build additional structures.

Materials

- centimeter cubes

Advance Preparation

This project can be done with cubes of any size, as long as students use cubes that are all the same size. If students use cubes other than cm cubes, you will need to make and distribute copies of a Blueprint Mat like the one on *Math Masters,* page 378. It should show squares that are the size of one face of the cubes being used.

Prepare four direction signs for a class demonstration and label them as follows:

↑BACK↑ ↑FRONT↑ ↑LEFT SIDE↑ ↑RIGHT SIDE↑

Arrange a table so that one student can sit at each of the four sides. There should be space on all sides of the table so that the rest of the class can gather around it. Place the direction signs and a copy of *Math Masters,* page 378 on the table.

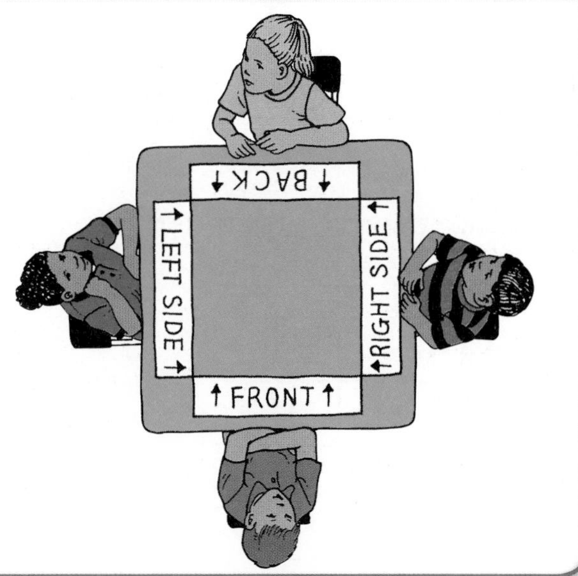

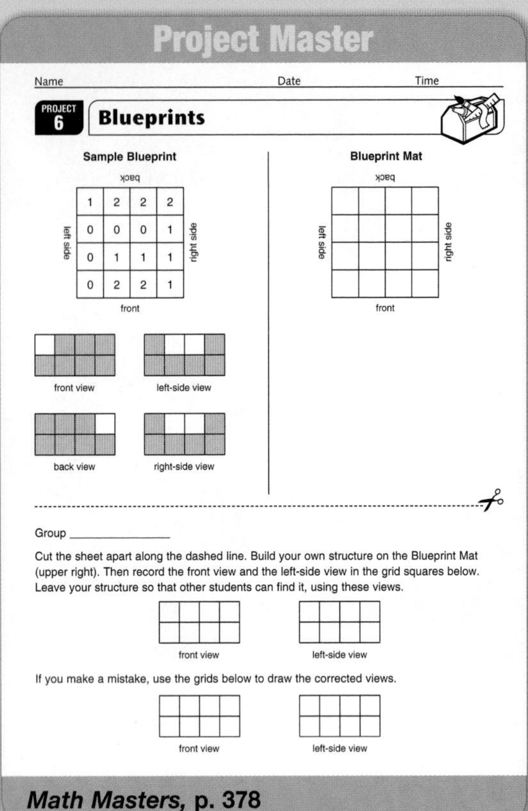
Project Master

Name Date Time

PROJECT 6 **Blueprints**

Sample Blueprint

back

1	2	2	2
0	0	0	1
0	1	1	1
0	2	2	1

left side / right side / front

front view / left-side view

back view / right-side view

Blueprint Mat

back / left side / right side / front

Group

Cut the sheet apart along the dashed line. Build your own structure on the Blueprint Mat (upper right). Then record the front view and the left-side view in the grid squares below. Leave your structure so that other students can find it, using these views.

front view / left-side view

If you make a mistake, use the grids below to draw the corrected views.

front view / left-side view

***Math Masters,* p. 378**

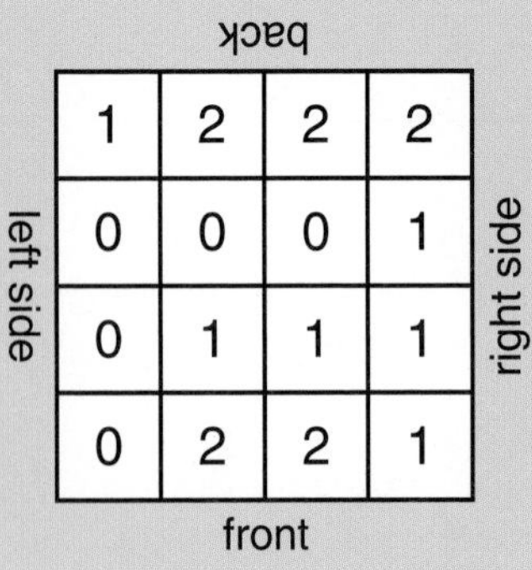

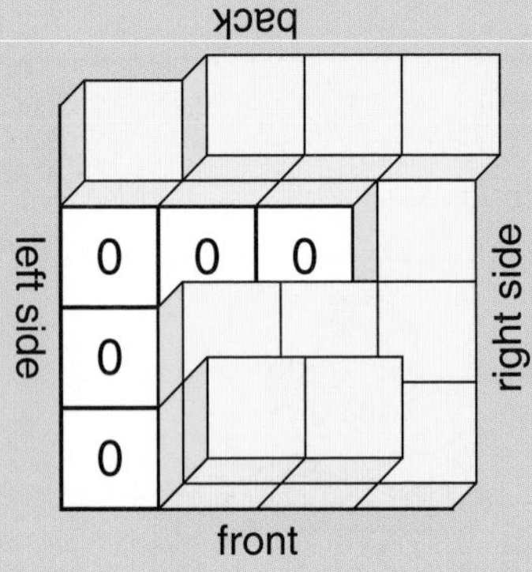

Building a structure on the blueprint

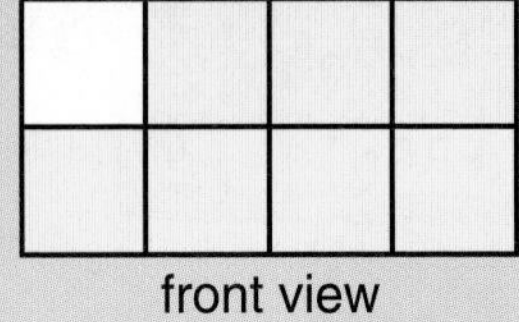

1 Doing the Project

▶ Building a Structure and Recording Four Views of It

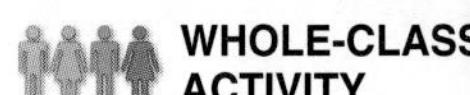

(*Math Masters,* p. 378)

Seat four students at the demonstration table and gather the rest of the class around it. Explain how to use the sample **blueprint** (*Math Masters,* page 378, top left) to build a structure out of cm cubes:

> The number in each square tells how many cubes to stack on the square: Stack 2 cubes on each 2-square, 1 cube on each 1-square, and no cubes on each 0-square.

After students have built the structure, have the student who is seated on the FRONT side of the blueprint stoop down so that the structure is at eye level. The student will then see the front view of the structure.

Ask the student to verify that this view of the structure looks like the shaded grid below the blueprint labeled "front view" (on *Math Masters,* page 378). Be sure to mention that the shaded squares do not show *only* what is in the *front* row of the structure. For example, the *front* row has *no* cubes in the first square on the left. Yet, the last row has *one* cube in that position, so the viewer sees *one* cube, not zero cubes. Similarly, the front row has one cube in the last square on the right. But since the back row has two cubes in that position, the viewer sees two cubes, not one cube.

Ask the other three students at the demonstration table to verify that the appropriate shaded grid below the blueprint (on *Math Masters,* page 378) represents what they actually see. Then ask them to change seats and verify each of the other three views. Let other students do the same, or divide the class into groups of four and ask each group to replicate the structure and verify the views.

Relating the Views of Opposite Sides

(*Math Masters,* pp. 378 and 379)

Have partners share cubes. Students work on the tasks on *Math Masters,* page 379 independently and then compare each other's work. Have students follow the blueprint on *Math Masters,* page 379 but build it on the Blueprint Mat on *Math Masters,* page 378. Bring the class together to discuss the results. Ask questions like the following:

- Is it possible to build two different structures from the same blueprint? no
- How are the views of opposite sides alike? They have the same number of shaded squares.
- How do they differ? The shading pattern is reversed.

Building Structures Based on Two Views

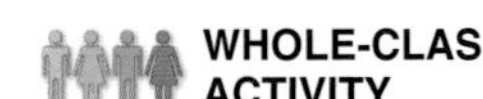

(*Math Masters,* p. 378)

In this activity, each student builds a structure on the Blueprint Mat on *Math Masters,* page 378 (upper right) and then draws the front and left-side views on two grids at the bottom of the page. Then students cut off the lower portion of the master and give it to you. Redistribute these sheets so that no student gets his or her own sheet. Students then walk around and try to find the structures recorded on their sheets.

There are a number of ways to organize this activity. Here is a suggested procedure:

1. Ask students to cut *Math Masters,* page 378 into two parts along the dashed line.
2. Divide the class into two groups—Group A and Group B. Ask students to write their group letter on the lower portion of the master.
3. Each student designs and builds a structure on the Blueprint Mat and draws the front and left-side views on the lower portion of *Math Masters,* page 378.
4. When students have completed Step 3, they raise their hands to signal that they are ready to have you check their work. If students made a mistake, have them correct their work on the second set of grids.
5. After everyone's work has been checked, students hand in the lower portion of the master.
6. Pass out these sheets randomly—Group A's sheets to students in Group B and Group B's sheets to students in Group A. Students then walk about the classroom and try to identify the structures that match their sheets.

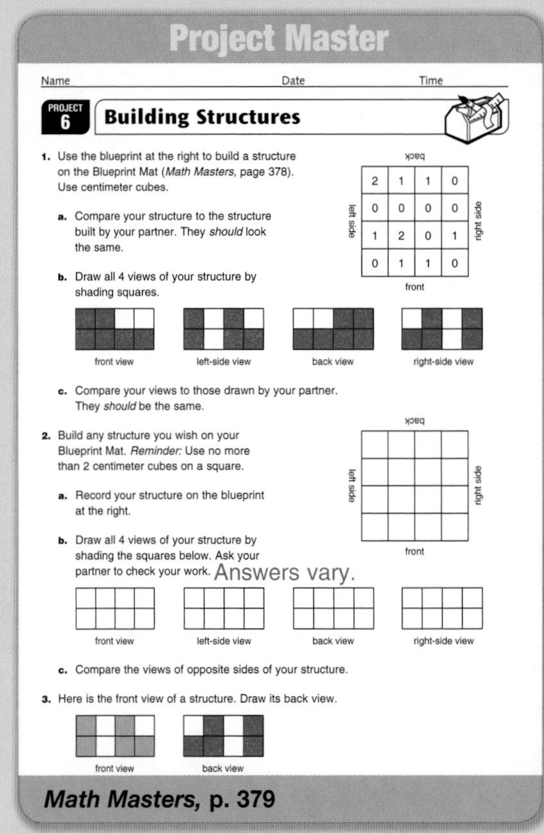

Project Master

Name Date Time

PROJECT 6 **Building Structures**

1. Use the blueprint at the right to build a structure on the Blueprint Mat (*Math Masters,* page 378). Use centimeter cubes.

   a. Compare your structure to the structure built by your partner. They *should* look the same.

   b. Draw all 4 views of your structure by shading squares.

back

2	1	1	0
0	0	0	0
1	2	0	1
0	1	1	0

left side / right side / front

front view, left-side view, back view, right-side view

   c. Compare your views to those drawn by your partner. They *should* be the same.

2. Build any structure you wish on your Blueprint Mat. *Reminder:* Use no more than 2 centimeter cubes on a square.

   a. Record your structure on the blueprint at the right.

   b. Draw all 4 views of your structure by shading the squares below. Ask your partner to check your work. Answers vary.

back / left side / right side / front

front view, left-side view, back view, right-side view

   c. Compare the views of opposite sides of your structure.

3. Here is the front view of a structure. Draw its back view.

front view, back view

Math Masters, p. 379

▶ Drawing a Structure

INDEPENDENT ACTIVITY

(*Math Masters,* p. 380)

Ask students to solve Problem 1 on *Math Masters,* page 380. Tell them to build the structure with their cubes if it will help.

Go over the answers. Remind students that the shading patterns for views of opposite sides are reversed. The back view should be the reverse of the front view, and the left-side view should be the reverse of the right-side view.

▶ Building Structures Specified by Views of Two Adjacent Sides

(*Math Masters,* pp. 378 and 380)

In Problems 2 and 3 on *Math Masters,* page 380, students are given a front view and a left-side view of a structure. They build structures based on these views and make a blueprint for each structure.

From these activities, students should conclude that it is possible to build different structures from the same two adjacent views (Problem 4a). Furthermore, if students know two adjacent views, they can draw the other two views (see *Math Masters,* page 378). Therefore, it is usually possible to build different structures from the same four views (Problem 4b).

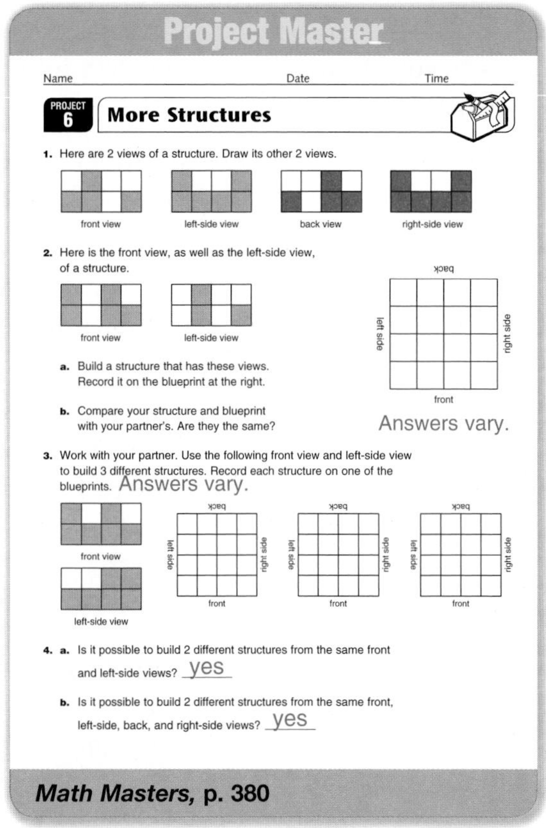

Project Master

Name Date Time

PROJECT 6 **More Structures**

1. Here are 2 views of a structure. Draw its other 2 views.

front view left-side view back view right-side view

2. Here is the front view, as well as the left-side view, of a structure.

front view left-side view

back / left side / right side / front

a. Build a structure that has these views. Record it on the blueprint at the right.

b. Compare your structure and blueprint with your partner's. Are they the same? Answers vary.

3. Work with your partner. Use the following front view and left-side view to build 3 different structures. Record each structure on one of the blueprints. Answers vary.

front view

left-side view

back / left side / right side / front

4. a. Is it possible to build 2 different structures from the same front and left-side views? yes

b. Is it possible to build 2 different structures from the same front, left-side, back, and right-side views? yes

Math Masters, p. 380

2 Extending the Project

Building More Structures

INDEPENDENT ACTIVITY

It is not always possible to build two different structures from the same two adjacent views, as shown in the following example:

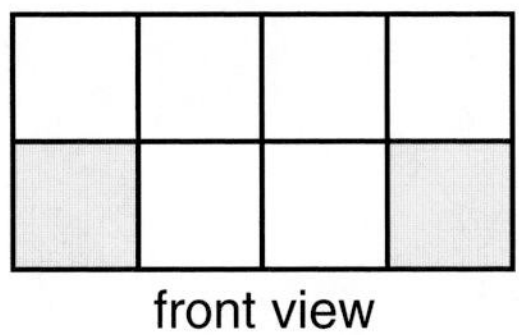
front view

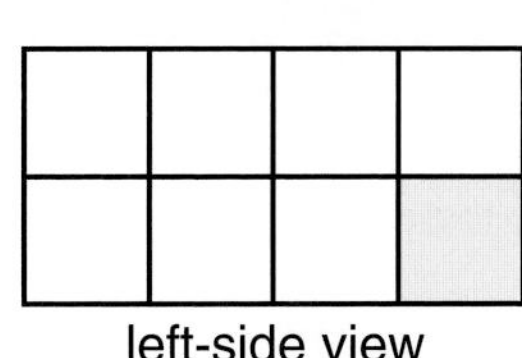
left-side view

Ask students to build the structure above and then try to find another different structure that matches the blueprint. There is only one possible structure, shown in the following blueprint:

back

left side

0	0	0	0
0	0	0	0
0	0	0	0
1	0	0	1

right side

front

Invite students to build and represent structures with blueprint grids other than 4 by 4 (for example, 5 by 5, 4 by 6, and so on) and heights greater than two cubes.

Project

7 Numbers, Mayan Style

 **Objectives** To introduce the Mayan numeration system; and to provide practice converting between Mayan numerals and base-ten numerals.

Technology Resources www.everydaymathonline.com

eToolkit

Algorithms Practice

EM Facts Workshop Game™

Family Letters

Assessment Management

Common Core State Standards

Curriculum Focal Points

Interactive Teacher's Lesson Guide

1 Doing the Project

Recommended Use During or after Unit 5

Key Concepts and Skills

- Identify places in whole numbers and the values of the digits in those places. [Number and Numeration Goal 1]
- Use symbolic notation to represent numbers in base-twenty. [Number and Numeration Goal 1]
- Use extended multiplication facts to convert base-twenty numerals to base-ten numerals. [Operations and Computation Goal 3]
- Use division to convert base-ten numerals to base-twenty numerals. [Operations and Computation Goal 4]

Key Activities

Students work with partners to convert between Mayan numerals and base-ten numerals.

Materials

- *Math Masters,* p. 381
- *Student Reference Book,* p. 293
- map of North America

2 Extending the Project

Students further investigate Mayan numeration through literature.

Materials

- *Secrets of Ancient Cultures: The Maya—Activities and Crafts from a Mysterious Land*
- *The Maya (True Books)*

Advance Preparation

For the optional activity in Part 2, obtain copies of ***Secrets of Ancient Cultures: The Maya—Activities and Crafts from a Mysterious Land*** by Arlette N. Braman and Michelle Nidenoff (Wiley, 2003) and ***The Maya (True Books)*** by Stefanie Takacs (Children's Press, 2004).

1 Doing the Project

Comparing the Mayan Place-Value System to Our Place-Value System

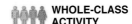

WHOLE-CLASS ACTIVITY

(*Math Masters,* p. 381)

Have students read the article "Numbers, Mayan Style" on *Math Masters,* page 381. Ask a volunteer to locate where the Maya lived on a classroom map or on page 293 of the World Tour section of the *Student Reference Book*.

Review our base-ten place-value numeration system. For example, in the numeral 2,457, the digit 2 stands for 2 [1,000s], the digit 4 for 4 [100s], and so on. (*See margin.*)

2 [1,000s] =	2,000
4 [100s] =	400
5 [10s] =	50
7 [1s] =	+ 7
	2,457

If necessary, try a few additional examples to make sure that students understand how our place-value system works before comparing it to the Mayan system.

Next, discuss the Mayan place-value system.

- How many symbols did the Maya use in their numerals? 3
- What are the three symbols? (shell) ● ——
- How many symbols are used in our place-value system? 10

Refer to the example of the Mayan numeral for 837 on *Math Masters,* page 381. Point out each of the "places." Remind students that Mayan numerals read from top to bottom. Students should notice the space that is left between each place. If this space is not shown clearly, it is easy to mistake the place a symbol is in.

- Can there be more than one symbol in a place in the Mayan system? Yes. In the Mayan system, a single dot is one symbol. So two dots are two symbols in one place.
- In our place-value system, can there be more than one symbol in a place? no
- In Mayan numerals, how is the value of the symbols in a place determined? By adding the values of all the symbols in that place

Remind students that in our place-value system, the value of a place is 10 times the value of the preceding place. Thus, the values of the first three places in a numeral for a whole number, from right to left, are 1, 10, and 10 ∗ 10 (or 100). In the Mayan system, the value of a place is 20 times the value of the preceding place. Thus, the values of the first three places, from bottom to top, are 1, 20, and 20 ∗ 20 (or 400).

- What is the value of the next (fourth) place in the Mayan system? 20 ∗ 20 ∗ 20 = 8,000

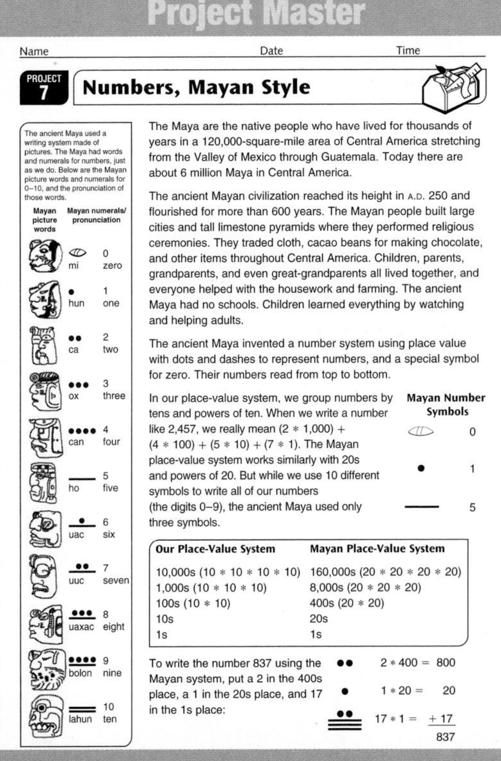

Project Master

Name Date Time

PROJECT 7 **Numbers, Mayan Style**

The ancient Maya used a writing system made of pictures. The Maya had words and numerals for numbers, just as we do. Below are the Mayan picture words and numerals for 0–10, and the pronunciation of those words.

Mayan numerals/pronunciation	
mi	0 zero
hun	1 one
ca	2 two
ox	3 three
can	4 four
ho	5 five
uac	6 six
uuc	7 seven
uaxac	8 eight
bolon	9 nine
lahun	10 ten

The Maya are the native people who have lived for thousands of years in a 120,000-square-mile area of Central America stretching from the Valley of Mexico through Guatemala. Today there are about 6 million Maya in Central America.

The ancient Mayan civilization reached its height in A.D. 250 and flourished for more than 600 years. The Mayan people built large cities and tall limestone pyramids where they performed religious ceremonies. They traded cloth, cacao beans for making chocolate, and other items throughout Central America. Children, parents, grandparents, and even great-grandparents all lived together, and everyone helped with the housework and farming. The ancient Maya had no schools. Children learned everything by watching and helping adults.

The ancient Maya invented a number system using place value with dots and dashes to represent numbers, and a special symbol for zero. Their numbers read from top to bottom.

In our place-value system, we group numbers by tens and powers of ten. When we write a number like 2,457, we really mean (2 ∗ 1,000) + (4 ∗ 100) + (5 ∗ 10) + (7 ∗ 1). The Mayan place-value system works similarly with 20s and powers of 20. But while we use 10 different symbols to write all of our numbers (the digits 0–9), the ancient Maya used only three symbols.

Mayan Number Symbols: (shell) 0; ● 1; —— 5

Our Place-Value System	Mayan Place-Value System
10,000s (10 ∗ 10 ∗ 10 ∗ 10)	160,000s (20 ∗ 20 ∗ 20 ∗ 20)
1,000s (10 ∗ 10 ∗ 10)	8,000s (20 ∗ 20 ∗ 20)
100s (10 ∗ 10)	400s (20 ∗ 20)
10s	20s
1s	1s

To write the number 837 using the Mayan system, put a 2 in the 400s place, a 1 in the 20s place, and 17 in the 1s place:

2 ∗ 400 =	800
1 ∗ 20 =	20
17 ∗ 1 =	+ 17
	837

Math Masters, p. 381

Write each Mayan numeral with digits. Then add.

1. 2,106

= 5 [400s] = 2,000

= 5 [20s] = 100

= 6 [1s] = 6

2. 2,476

= 6 [400s] = 2,400

= 3 [20s] = 60

= 16 [1s] = 16

3. 20,023

= 2 [8,000s] = 16,000

= 10 [400s] = 4,000

= 1 [20] = 20

= 3 [1s] = 3

Try This

4. Write each base-10 numeral as a Mayan numeral.

a. 153 

b. 1,594  

▶ Converting between Mayan and Base-Ten Numerals

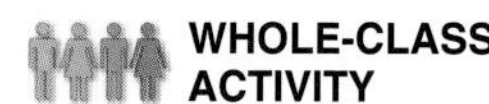

Write the problem below on the board. Discuss how the Mayan numeral in this problem is converted to a base-ten numeral. Then convert several more Mayan numerals as a class. *For example:*

●●●	3 [400s] =	1,200
●●	2 [20s] =	40
●●●●	9 [1s] =	+ 9
		1,249
●●●●	9 [20s] =	180
●●●●	19 [1s] =	+ 19
		199

You might also have students make up Mayan numerals for the class to convert.

On the board, write Problems 1–4 shown in the margin. For Problems 1–3, have students write each Mayan numeral with digits and then add. Go over the answers with the class.

For Problem 4, students will write each base-ten numeral as a Mayan numeral. Conversions of base-ten numerals to Mayan numerals involve division. Following are answers for Problem 4.

a. 153

How many [20s] are in 153?

The remainder is 13.

20)153
–140
13

7 ●●

7 [20s] in 153

13 [1s] ●●●

b. 1,594

How many [400s] are in 1,594?

400)1,594
–1,200
394

3 ●●●

3 [400s] in 1,594

How many [20s] are in 394?

The remainder is 14.

20)394
–380
14

19 ●●●●

19 [20s] in 394

14 [1s] ●●●●

2 Extending the Project

Learning More about the Maya

INDEPENDENT ACTIVITY

Invite students to find out more about the Maya in encyclopedias and in books such as ***Secrets of Ancient Cultures: The Maya—Activities and Crafts from a Mysterious Land*** by Arlette N. Braman and Michelle Nidenoff (Wiley, 2003) and ***The Maya (True Books)*** by Stefanie Takacs (Children's Press, 2004).

This would be a good opportunity to have students use the Internet to research and compare the Mayan numeral system with other numeral systems, for example, the Roman or Babylonian numeral system (which uses a base of 60).

Hindu-Arabic	0	1	2	3	4	5	6	7	8	9	10
Babylonian		▼	▼▼	▼▼▼	▼▼▼▼	▼▼▼ ▼▼	▼▼▼ ▼▼▼	▼▼▼▼ ▼▼▼	▼▼▼▼ ▼▼▼▼	▼▼▼▼▼ ▼▼▼▼	<
Egyptian		𓏺	𓏻	𓏼	𓏽	𓏾	𓏿	𓐀	𓐁	𓐂	𓎆
Mayan	𝋠	𝋡	𝋢	𝋣	𝋤	𝋥	𝋦	𝋧	𝋨	𝋩	𝋪
Greek		α	β	Υ	δ	ϵ	ϕ	ζ	η	θ	ι
Roman		I	II	III	IV	V	VI	VII	VIII	IX	X

Students may also want to explore other base systems, such as base five, which is used by people in Kenya. The chart below describes this "one-hand system."

Base-Five Symbol	Base-Five Grouping	Base-Five Symbol
0_{five}		0 fingers
1_{five}	X	1 finger
2_{five}	XX	2 fingers
3_{five}	XXX	3 fingers
4_{five}	XXXX	4 fingers
10_{five}	(XXXXX)	1 hand and 0 fingers
11_{five}	(XXXXX) X	1 hand and 1 finger
12_{five}	(XXXXX) XX	1 hand and 2 fingers
13_{five}	(XXXXX) XXX	1 hand and 3 fingers
14_{five}	(XXXXX) XXXX	1 hand and 4 fingers
20_{five}	(XXXXX) (XXXXX)	2 hands and 0 fingers

Algorithm
1
Project

U.S. Traditional Addition

Objective To introduce U.S. traditional addition.

Technology Resources www.everydaymathonline.com

eToolkit

Algorithms Practice

EM Facts Workshop Game™

Family Letters

Assessment Management

Common Core State Standards

Curriculum Focal Points

Interactive Teacher's Lesson Guide

1 Doing the Project

Recommended Use After Lesson 2•7

Key Concepts and Skills

- Identify places in whole numbers and the values of the digits in those places. [Number and Numeration Goal 1]
- Use addition facts to find sums of multidigit whole numbers. [Operations and Computation Goal 1]
- Add multidigit whole numbers. [Operations and Computation Goal 2]
- Write and solve addition number stories. [Operations and Computation Goal 2]

Key Activities

Students explore and practice U.S. traditional addition with multidigit whole numbers.

Key Vocabulary

U.S. traditional addition

Materials

- *Math Journal 1* or *2,* pp. 1P–4P
- *Student Reference Book,* p. 24A

2 Extending the Project

Students solve multidigit addition problems, first using the focus algorithm (partial-sums addition) and then using any algorithm they wish.

Materials

- Online Additional Practice, pp. 4A–4D
- *Student Reference Book,* pp. 10, 11, and 24A

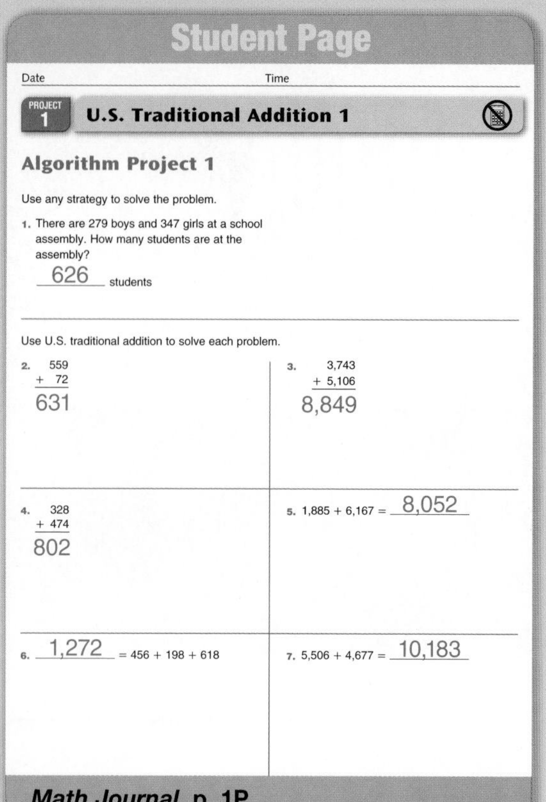

Student Page

Date Time

PROJECT 1 **U.S. Traditional Addition 1**

Algorithm Project 1

Use any strategy to solve the problem.

1. There are 279 boys and 347 girls at a school assembly. How many students are at the assembly?
626 students

Use U.S. traditional addition to solve each problem.

2. 559 + 72 = 631

3. 3,743 + 5,106 = 8,849

4. 328 + 474 = 802

5. 1,885 + 6,167 = 8,052

6. 1,272 = 456 + 198 + 618

7. 5,506 + 4,677 = 10,183

Math Journal, p. 1P

1 Doing the Project

▶ Solving an Addition Problem

INDEPENDENT ACTIVITY

(*Math Journal 1* or *2,* p. 1P)

Ask students to solve Problem 1 on journal page 1P. Tell them they may use any methods they wish, but they may not use calculators.

▶ Discussing Solutions

WHOLE-CLASS ACTIVITY

(*Math Journal 1* or *2,* p. 1P)

Discuss students' solutions to Problem 1 on journal page 1P. 279 + 347 = 626 students Expect that students will use several different methods, including column addition and partial-sums addition. Some students may also use U.S. traditional addition. *Possible strategies:*

▷ Using column addition

	100s	10s	1s
	2	**7**	**9**
	+ **3**	**4**	**7**
Add the numbers in each column.	5	11	16
Trade 10 ones for 1 ten.	5	12	6
Trade 10 tens for 1 hundred.	**6**	**2**	**6**

▷ Using partial-sums addition

		279
		+ 347
Add the 100s.	200 + 300 →	500
Add the 10s.	70 + 40 →	110
Add the 1s.	9 + 7 →	16
Add the partial sums.	500 + 110 + 16 →	**626**

▷ Using U.S. traditional addition

```
  1 1
  2 7 9
+ 3 4 7
  6 2 6
```

▶ Introducing U.S. Traditional Addition

After you have discussed students' solutions, and even if one or more students used **U.S. traditional addition,** demonstrate it as described below.

Example 1: 279 + 347

Step 1:

Add the 1s: 9 + 7 = 16.
16 = 1 ten + 6 ones
Write 6 in the 1s place below the line.
Write 1 above the numbers in the 10s place.

```
    1
  2 7 9
+ 3 4 7
      6
```

Step 2:

$$\begin{array}{r} 1\,1 \\ 2\,\mathbf{7}\,9 \\ +\ 3\,\mathbf{4}\,7 \\ \hline \mathbf{2}\,6 \end{array}$$

Add the 10s: 1 + 7 + 4 = 12.
12 tens = 1 hundred + 2 tens
Write 2 in the 10s place below the line.
Write 1 above the numbers in the 100s place.

Step 3:

$$\begin{array}{r} \mathbf{1}\,1 \\ \mathbf{2}\,7\,9 \\ +\ \mathbf{3}\,4\,7 \\ \hline \mathbf{6}\,2\,6 \end{array}$$

Add the 100s: 1 + 2 + 3 = 6.
Write 6 in the 100s place below the line.

279 + 347 = 626
There are 626 students at the assembly.

NOTE Throughout the discussion of U.S. traditional addition, be sure that students understand the values of the digits. For instance, in Step 2 of Example 1, 1 + 7 + 4 = 12 means 1 ten + 7 tens + 4 tens = 12 tens (1 hundred + 2 tens) or 10 + 70 + 40 = 120.

Example 2: 8,654 + 4,789

Step 1:

$$\begin{array}{r} \mathbf{1} \\ 8\,6\,5\,\mathbf{4} \\ +\ 4\,7\,8\,\mathbf{9} \\ \hline \mathbf{3} \end{array}$$

Add the 1s: 4 + 9 = 13.
13 = 1 ten + 3 ones
Write 3 in the 1s place below the line.
Write 1 above the numbers in the 10s place.

Step 2:

$$\begin{array}{r} \mathbf{1}\,1 \\ 8\,6\,\mathbf{5}\,4 \\ +\ 4\,7\,\mathbf{8}\,9 \\ \hline \mathbf{4}\,3 \end{array}$$

Add the 10s: 1 + 5 + 8 = 14.
14 tens = 1 hundred + 4 tens
Write 4 in the 10s place below the line.
Write 1 above the numbers in the 100s place.

Step 3:

$$\begin{array}{r} \mathbf{1}\,\mathbf{1}\,1 \\ 8\,\mathbf{6}\,5\,4 \\ +\ 4\,\mathbf{7}\,8\,9 \\ \hline \mathbf{4}\,4\,3 \end{array}$$

Add the 100s: 1 + 6 + 7 = 14.
14 hundreds = 1 thousand + 4 hundreds
Write 4 in the 100s place below the line.
Write 1 above the numbers in the 1,000s place.

Step 4:

$$\begin{array}{r} \mathbf{1}\,1\,1 \\ \mathbf{8}\,6\,5\,4 \\ +\ \mathbf{4}\,7\,8\,9 \\ \hline \mathbf{1}\,\mathbf{3}\,4\,4\,3 \end{array}$$

Add the 1,000s: 1 + 8 + 4 = 13.
13 thousands = 1 ten thousand + 3 thousands
Write 3 in the 1,000s place below the line.
Write 1 in the 10,000s place below the line.

8,654 + 4,789 = 13,443

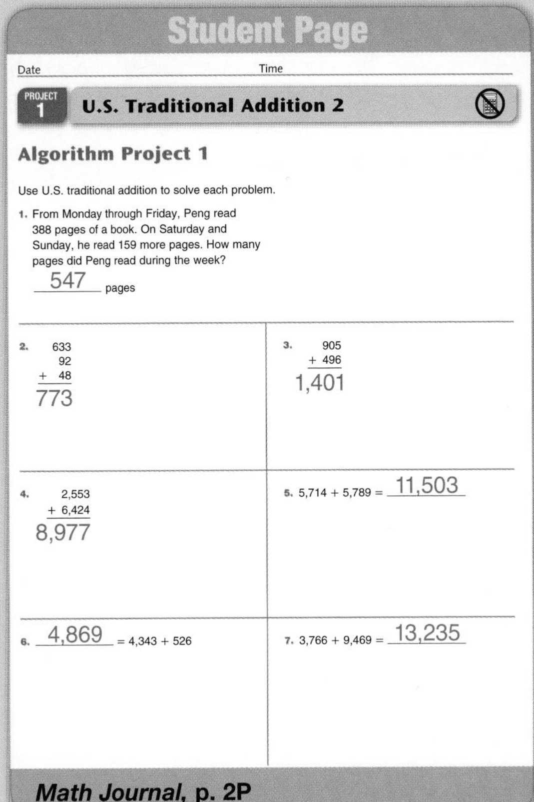
Student Page

Date Time

PROJECT 1 **U.S. Traditional Addition 2**

Algorithm Project 1

Use U.S. traditional addition to solve each problem.

1. From Monday through Friday, Peng read 388 pages of a book. On Saturday and Sunday, he read 159 more pages. How many pages did Peng read during the week?
547 pages

2. 633 + 92 + 48 = 773

3. 905 + 496 = 1,401

4. 2,553 + 6,424 = 8,977

5. 5,714 + 5,789 = 11,503

6. 4,869 = 4,343 + 526

7. 3,766 + 9,469 = 13,235

Math Journal, p. 2P

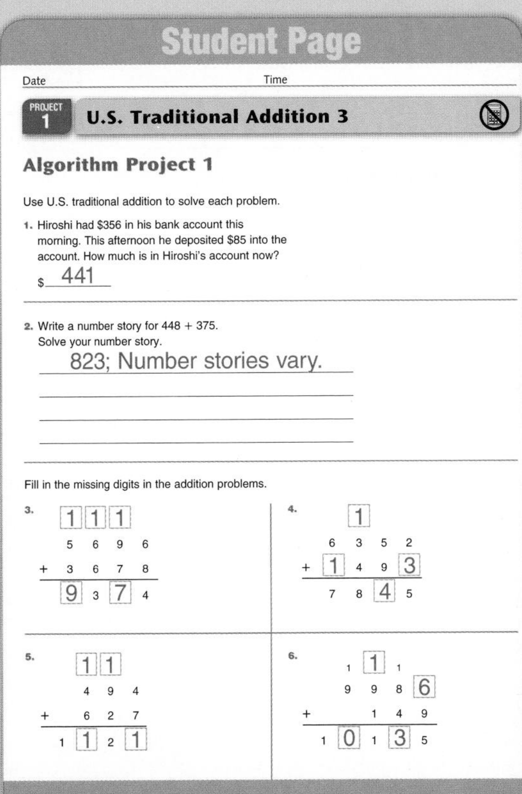
Student Page

Date Time

PROJECT 1 **U.S. Traditional Addition 3**

Algorithm Project 1

Use U.S. traditional addition to solve each problem.

1. Hiroshi had $356 in his bank account this morning. This afternoon he deposited $85 into the account. How much is in Hiroshi's account now?
$ 441

2. Write a number story for 448 + 375.
Solve your number story.
823; Number stories vary.

Fill in the missing digits in the addition problems.

3. 1 1 1 / 5 6 9 6 / + 3 6 7 8 / 9 3 7 4

4. 1 / 6 3 5 2 / + 1 4 9 3 / 7 8 4 5

5. 1 1 / 4 9 4 / + 6 2 7 / 1 1 2 1

6. 1 1 1 / 9 9 8 6 / + 1 4 9 / 1 0 1 3 5

Math Journal, p. 3P

Student Page

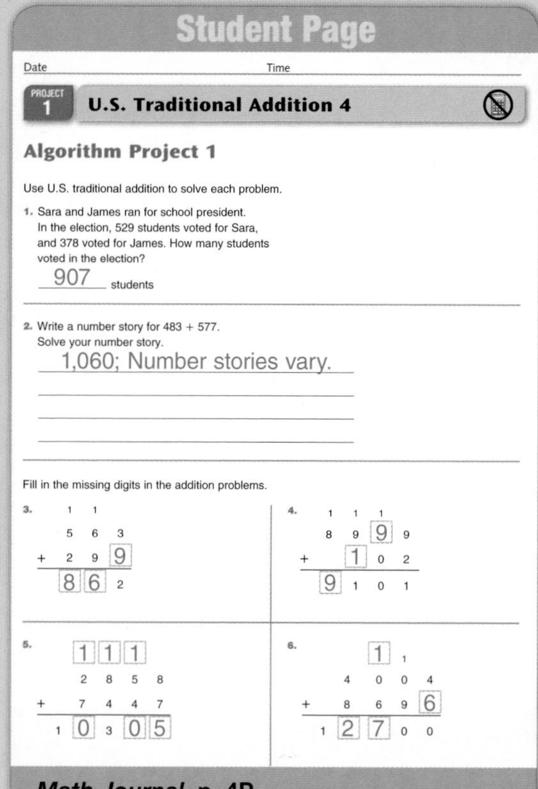

Date Time

PROJECT 1 **U.S. Traditional Addition 4**

Algorithm Project 1

Use U.S. traditional addition to solve each problem.

1. Sara and James ran for school president. In the election, 529 students voted for Sara, and 378 voted for James. How many students voted in the election?
907 students

2. Write a number story for 483 + 577. Solve your number story.
1,060; Number stories vary.

Fill in the missing digits in the addition problems.

3.
```
   1 1
   5 6 3
+  2 9 9
   8 6 2
```

4.
```
   1 1 1
   8 9 9 9
+  1 0 2
   9 1 0 1
```

5.
```
   1 1 1
   2 8 5 8
+  7 4 4 7
 1 0 3 0 5
```

6.
```
   1   1
   4 0 0 4
+  8 6 9 6
 1 2 7 0 0
```

Math Journal, p. 4P

Go to www.everydaymathonline.com to access the additional practice pages.

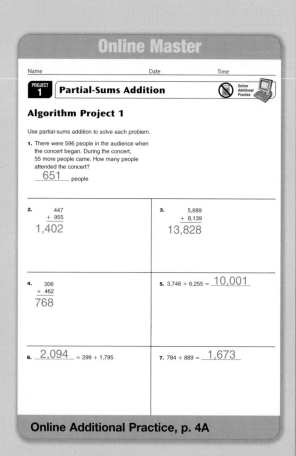

Online Master

Name Date Time

PROJECT 1 **Partial-Sums Addition** Online Additional Practice

Algorithm Project 1

Use partial-sums addition to solve each problem.

1. There were 596 people in the audience when the concert began. During the concert, 55 more people came. How many people attended the concert?
651 people

2. 447 + 955 = 1,402

3. 5,689 + 8,139 = 13,828

4. 306 + 462 = 768

5. 3,746 + 6,255 = 10,001

6. 2,094 = 299 + 1,795

7. 784 + 889 = 1,673

Online Additional Practice, p. 4A

You may want to work several more examples with the whole class.

Suggestions:

▷ 56 + 49 = ? 105

▷ 774 + 68 = ? 842

▷ 482 + 315 = ? 797

▷ 6,556 + 3,984 = ? 10,540

▷ 528 + 933 + 295 = ? 1,756

▷ 5,088 + 6,515 = ? 11,603

▶ Practicing U.S. Traditional Addition

(*Math Journal 1* or *2,* pp. 1P–4P; *Student Reference Book,* p. 24A)

When students are ready, have them solve Problems 2–7 on journal page 1P. They may find the example on *Student Reference Book,* page 24A helpful.

Journal pages 2P–4P provide students with additional practice using U.S. traditional addition. Use these journal pages as necessary.

2 Extending the Project

▶ Solving Multidigit Addition Problems

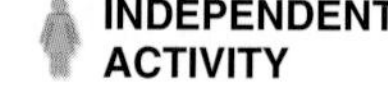

(Online Additional Practice, pp. 4A–4D; *Student Reference Book,* pp. 10, 11, and 24A)

Online practice pages 4A–4D provide students with additional practice solving multidigit addition problems. Use these pages as necessary.

Encourage students to use the focus algorithm (partial-sums addition) to solve the problems on practice page 4A. Invite them to use any algorithm they wish to solve the problems on the remaining pages.

Students may find the examples on *Student Reference Book,* pages 10, 11, and 24A helpful.

Algorithm **2** Project

U.S. Traditional Addition: Decimals

Objective To introduce U.S. traditional addition with decimals.

Technology Resources www.everydaymathonline.com

eToolkit

Algorithms Practice

EM Facts Workshop Game™

Family Letters

Assessment Management

Common Core State Standards

Curriculum Focal Points

Interactive Teacher's Lesson Guide

1 Doing the Project

Recommended Use After Lesson 4•5

Key Concepts and Skills

- Identify places in whole numbers and decimals and the values of the digits in those places.
  [Number and Numeration Goal 1]
- Use addition facts to find sums of decimals.
  [Operations and Computation Goal 1]
- Add decimals.
  [Operations and Computation Goal 2]
- Write and solve addition number stories with decimals.
  [Operations and Computation Goal 2]

Key Activities

Students explore and practice U.S. traditional addition with decimals.

Materials

- *Math Journal 1* or *2,* pp. 5P–8P
- *Student Reference Book,* p. 40A
- \$1 and \$10 bills (*Math Masters,* p. 428; optional)
- dimes and pennies (optional)
- base-10 blocks (optional)

2 Extending the Project

Students solve decimal addition problems, first using the focus algorithm (partial-sums addition) and then using any algorithm they choose.

Materials

- Online Additional Practice, pp. 8A–8D
- *Student Reference Book,* pp. 34–36 and 40A

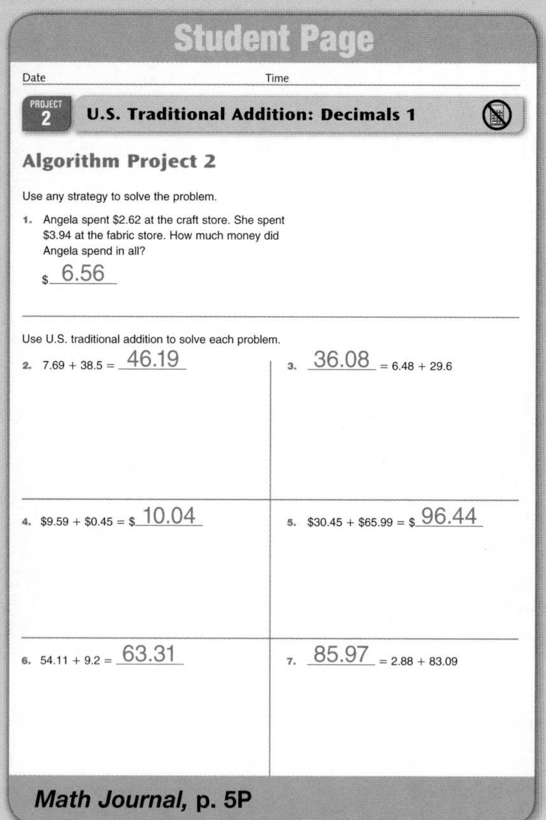
Student Page

Date Time

PROJECT 2 **U.S. Traditional Addition: Decimals 1**

Algorithm Project 2

Use any strategy to solve the problem.

1. Angela spent $2.62 at the craft store. She spent $3.94 at the fabric store. How much money did Angela spend in all?

$ 6.56

Use U.S. traditional addition to solve each problem.

2. 7.69 + 38.5 = 46.19
3. 36.08 = 6.48 + 29.6
4. $9.59 + $0.45 = $ 10.04
5. $30.45 + $65.99 = $ 96.44
6. 54.11 + 9.2 = 63.31
7. 85.97 = 2.88 + 83.09

Math Journal, p. 5P

1 Doing the Project

Solving a Decimal Addition Problem

(*Math Journal 1* or *2,* p. 5P)

Ask students to solve Problem 1 on journal page 5P. Tell them they may use base-10 blocks, play money, paper and pencil, or any other tools they wish, except calculators.

Discussing Solutions

(*Math Journal 1* or *2,* p. 5P)

Discuss students' solutions to Problem 1 on journal page 5P. $2.62 + $3.94 = $6.56 Expect that students will use several different methods, including base-10 blocks, play money, and partial-sums addition. Some students may also use U.S. traditional addition. *Possible strategies:*

▷ Modeling with base-10 blocks

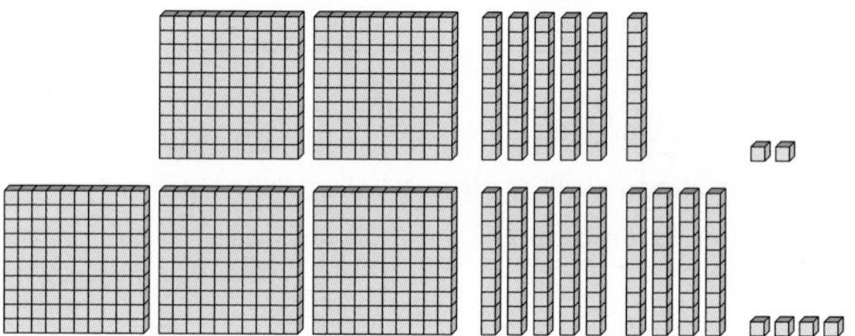

Show 2.62 and 3.94 with blocks.

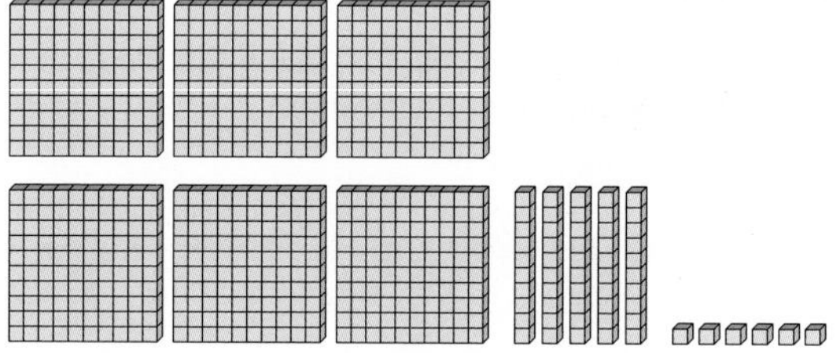

Trade 10 longs for 1 flat.

$2.62 + $3.94 = $6.56

▷ Using shorthand pictures of base-10 blocks

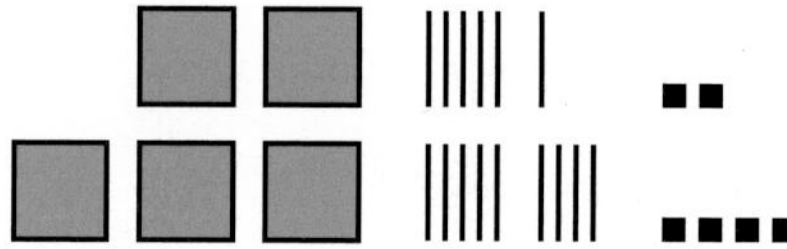

Draw a picture for each number.

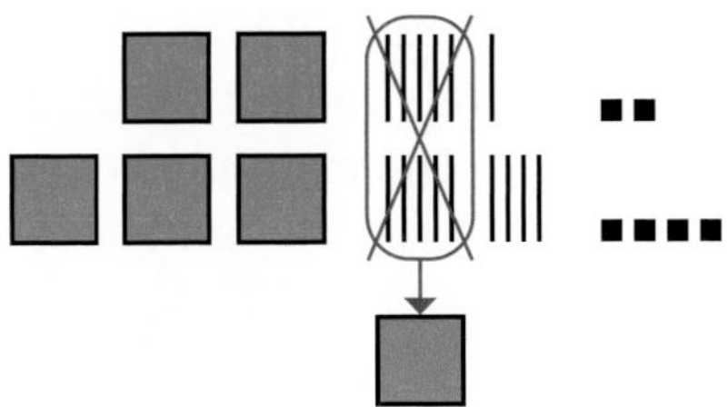

Draw a ring around 10 longs and trade them for 1 flat.

This drawing shows 6.56.

\$2.62 + \$3.94 = \$6.56

▷ Using partial-sums addition

		2.62
		+ 3.94
Add the 1s.	2 + 3 →	5.00
Add the 0.1s.	0.6 + 0.9 →	1.50
Add the 0.01s.	0.02 + 0.04 →	0.06
Add the partial sums.	5.00 + 1.50 + 0.06 →	**6.56**

▷ Using U.S. traditional addition

$$\begin{array}{r} {}^{1} \\ 2.62 \\ +\,3.94 \\ \hline 6.56 \end{array}$$

Introducing U.S. Traditional Addition for Decimals

WHOLE-CLASS ACTIVITY

After you have discussed students' solutions, and even if one or more students used U.S. traditional addition, demonstrate it again as described below.

Example 1: \$2.62 + \$3.94

Step 1:

Start with the 0.01s: 2 + 4 = 6.

$$\begin{array}{r} 2.6\mathbf{2} \\ +\,3.9\mathbf{4} \\ \hline \mathbf{6} \end{array}$$

Step 2:

Add the 0.1s: 6 + 9 = 15.
15 tenths = 1 whole + 5 tenths

$$\begin{array}{r} \mathbf{1} \\ 2.\mathbf{6}2 \\ +\,3.\mathbf{9}4 \\ \hline \mathbf{5}6 \end{array}$$

Step 3:

Add the 1s: 1 + 2 + 3 = 6.
Remember to include the decimal point in the answer.

$$\begin{array}{r} \mathbf{1} \\ \mathbf{2}.62 \\ +\,\mathbf{3}.94 \\ \hline \mathbf{6}.56 \end{array}$$

\$2.62 + \$3.94 = \$6.56

Angela spent \$6.56 in all.

NOTE Throughout the discussion of U.S. traditional addition, be sure that students understand the values of the digits. For instance, in Step 1 of Example 1, 2 + 4 = 6 means 2 hundredths + 4 hundredths = 6 hundredths, or 0.02 + 0.04 = 0.06. The same structure applies to the carry digits.

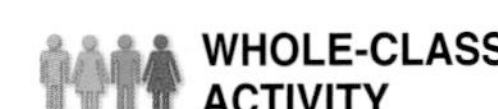

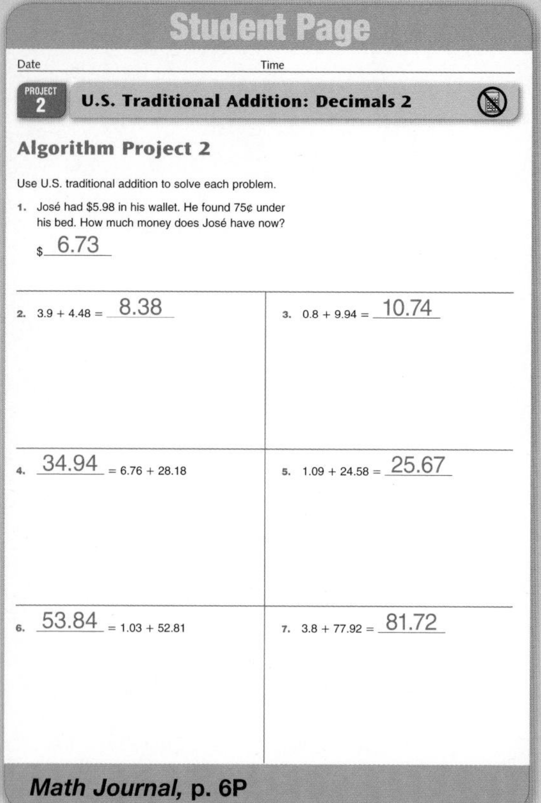

Student Page

Date Time

PROJECT 2 **U.S. Traditional Addition: Decimals 2**

Algorithm Project 2

Use U.S. traditional addition to solve each problem.

1. José had $5.98 in his wallet. He found 75¢ under his bed. How much money does José have now?
$ 6.73

2. 3.9 + 4.48 = 8.38
3. 0.8 + 9.94 = 10.74
4. 34.94 = 6.76 + 28.18
5. 1.09 + 24.58 = 25.67
6. 53.84 = 1.03 + 52.81
7. 3.8 + 77.92 = 81.72

Math Journal, p. 6P

Student Page

Date Time

PROJECT 2 **U.S. Traditional Addition: Decimals 3**

Algorithm Project 2

Use U.S. traditional addition to solve each problem.

1. There is a flower growing in Kayla's garden. It was 22.48 centimeters tall. In three months, it grew 8.6 centimeters. How tall is the flower now?
31.08 centimeters

2. Write a number story for $3.80 + $5.12. Solve your number story.
$8.92; Number stories vary.

Fill in the missing digits in the addition problems.

3. 3.85 + 6.67 = 10.52
4. 49.09 + 6.91 = 56.00
5. 29.42 + 0.97 = 30.39
6. 71.44 + 12.86 = 84.30

Math Journal, p. 7P

Be sure that students understand how to properly line up the places when adding decimals so that tenths are added to tenths, ones to ones, and so on. In the example below, write 4.6 as 4.60 so that both numbers have the same number of digits after the decimal point.

Example 2: 9.82 + 4.6

Step 1:

Start with the 0.01s: 2 + 0 = 2.

$$\begin{array}{r} 9.8\mathbf{2} \\ +\,4.6\mathbf{0} \\ \hline \mathbf{2} \end{array}$$

Step 2:

Add the 0.1s: 8 + 6 = 14.
14 tenths = 1 whole + 4 tenths

$$\begin{array}{r} 1 \\ 9.\mathbf{8}2 \\ +\,4.\mathbf{6}0 \\ \hline \mathbf{4}2 \end{array}$$

Step 3:

Add the 1s: 1 + 9 + 4 = 14.
14 ones = 1 ten + 4 ones
Remember to include the decimal point in the answer.

$$\begin{array}{r} 1 \\ \mathbf{9}.82 \\ +\,\mathbf{4}.60 \\ \hline \mathbf{14}.42 \end{array}$$

9.82 + 4.6 = 14.42

You may want to work several more examples with the whole class.

Suggestions:

- ▷ 25.3 + 5.78 = ? 31.08
- ▷ 10.3 + 7.55 = ? 17.85
- ▷ 59.4 + 3.65 = ? 63.05
- ▷ $1.99 + $45.63 = ? $47.62
- ▷ 36.55 + 9.8 = ? 46.35
- ▷ $45.09 + $38.71 = ? $83.80

▶ Practicing U.S. Traditional Addition for Decimals

(*Math Journal 1* or *2,* pp. 5P–8P; *Student Reference Book,* p. 40A)

When students are ready, have them solve Problems 2–7 on journal page 5P. They may find the example on *Student Reference Book,* page 40A helpful.

Journal pages 6P–8P provide students with additional practice using U.S. traditional addition. Use these journal pages as necessary.

2 Extending the Project

Solving Decimal Addition Problems

INDEPENDENT ACTIVITY

(Online Additional Practice, pp. 8A–8D; *Student Reference Book,* pp. 34–36 and 40A)

Online practice pages 8A–8D provide students with additional practice solving decimal addition problems. Use these pages as necessary.

Encourage students to use the focus algorithm (partial-sums addition) to solve the problems on practice page 8A. Invite them to use any algorithm they wish to solve the problems on the remaining pages.

Students may find the examples on *Student Reference Book,* pages 34–36 and 40A helpful.

Go to www.everydaymathonline.com to access the additional practice pages.

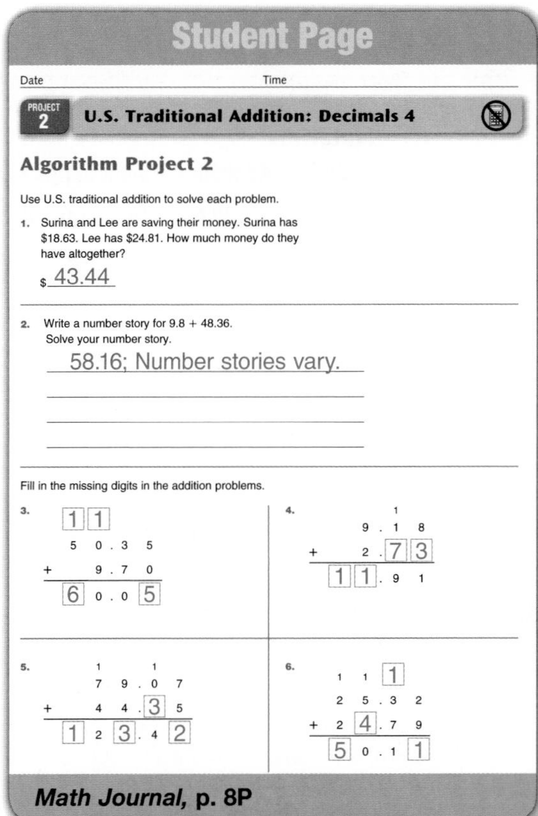

Student Page

Date Time

PROJECT 2 **U.S. Traditional Addition: Decimals 4**

Algorithm Project 2

Use U.S. traditional addition to solve each problem.

1. Surina and Lee are saving their money. Surina has $18.63. Lee has $24.81. How much money do they have altogether?
$ 43.44

2. Write a number story for 9.8 + 48.36. Solve your number story.
58.16; Number stories vary.

Fill in the missing digits in the addition problems.

3. 50.35 + 9.70 = 60.05 (carries: 1 1)

4. 9.18 + 2.73 = 11.91 (carry: 1)

5. 79.07 + 44.35 = 123.42 (carries: 1 1)

6. 25.32 + 24.79 = 50.11 (carries: 1 1 1)

Math Journal, p. 8P

Online Master

Name Date Time

PROJECT 2 **Partial-Sums Addition: Decimals**

Online Additional Practice

Algorithm Project 2

Use partial-sums addition to solve the problems.

1. Malik had $89.72 in the bank. He earned $14 this week. How much money does Malik have now?
$ 103.72

2. 99.01 = 67.12 + 31.89

3. 18.68 + 5.7 = 24.38

4. 2.08 + 9.9 = 11.98

5. $72.81 + $7.71 = $ 80.52

6. 17.83 = 4.11 + 13.72

7. 67.42 = 5.59 + 61.83

Online Additional Practice, p. 8A

Algorithm
3
Project

U.S. Traditional Subtraction

Objective To introduce U.S. traditional subtraction.

Technology Resources www.everydaymathonline.com

eToolkit

Algorithms Practice

EM Facts Workshop Game™

Family Letters

Assessment Management

Common Core State Standards

Curriculum Focal Points

Interactive Teacher's Lesson Guide

1 Doing the Project

Recommended Use After Lesson 2•9

Key Concepts and Skills

- Identify places in whole numbers and the values of the digits in those places.
  [Number and Numeration Goal 1]
- Use subtraction facts to find differences of multidigit whole numbers.
  [Operations and Computation Goal 1]
- Subtract multidigit numbers.
  [Operations and Computation Goal 2]
- Write and solve subtraction number stories.
  [Operations and Computation Goal 2]

Key Activities

Students explore and practice U.S. traditional subtraction with multidigit whole numbers.

Key Vocabulary

U.S. traditional subtraction

Materials

- *Math Journal 1* or *2,* pp. 9P–12P
- *Student Reference Book,* p. 24B
- play money (optional)
- base-10 blocks (optional)

2 Extending the Project

Students solve multidigit subtraction problems, first using the focus algorithm (trade-first subtraction) and then using any algorithm they choose.

Materials

- Online Additional Practice, pp. 12A–12D
- *Student Reference Book,* pp. 12–15 and 24B

1 Doing the Project

Solving a Subtraction Problem

INDEPENDENT ACTIVITY

(*Math Journal 1* or *2,* p. 9P)

Ask students to solve Problem 1 on journal page 9P. Tell them they may use base-10 blocks, play money, paper and pencil, or any other tools they wish, except calculators.

Discussing Solutions

(*Math Journal 1* or *2,* p. 9P)

Discuss students' solutions to Problem 1 on journal page 9P. 625 – 379 = 246 shirts Expect that students will use several different methods. Some may use base-10 blocks, play money, or other manipulatives. Others may use paper-and-pencil methods, including the same-change rule, counting up, partial-differences subtraction, and trade-first subtraction. Some students may also use U.S. traditional subtraction. *Possible strategies:*

▷ Using the same-change rule

$$\begin{array}{r} \mathbf{625} \\ -\ \mathbf{379} \\ \hline \end{array} \quad \begin{array}{l} \text{(add 21)} \\ \text{(add 21)} \end{array} \quad \begin{array}{r} 646 \\ -\ 400 \\ \hline \mathbf{246} \end{array}$$

▷ Counting up

$$379 \xrightarrow{+1} 380 \xrightarrow{+20} 400 \xrightarrow{+200} 600 \xrightarrow{+25} 625$$

$$\begin{array}{l} 379 + \boxed{1} = 380 \\ 380 + \boxed{20} = 400 \\ 400 + \boxed{200} = 600 \\ 600 + \boxed{25} = 625 \end{array}$$

1 + 20 + 200 + 25 = 246

625 – 379 = 246

▷ Using partial-differences subtraction

		625
		– 379
Subtract the 100s.	600 – 300 →	+ 300
Subtract the 10s.	20 – 70 →	– 50
Subtract the 1s.	5 – 9 →	– 4
Find the total.	300 – 50 – 4 →	**246**

▷ Using trade-first subtraction

	11	
5	~~1~~	15
~~6~~	~~2~~	~~5~~
– 3	7	9
2	4	6

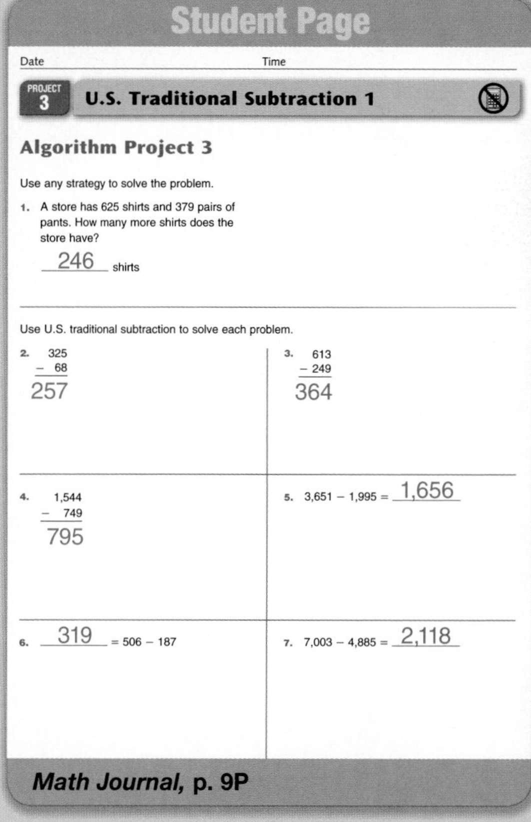
Student Page

Date Time

PROJECT 3 **U.S. Traditional Subtraction 1**

Algorithm Project 3

Use any strategy to solve the problem.

1. A store has 625 shirts and 379 pairs of pants. How many more shirts does the store have?
   246 shirts

Use U.S. traditional subtraction to solve each problem.

2. 325 – 68 = 257
3. 613 – 249 = 364
4. 1,544 – 749 = 795
5. 3,651 – 1,995 = 1,656
6. 319 = 506 – 187
7. 7,003 – 4,885 = 2,118

Math Journal, p. 9P

▷ Using U.S. traditional subtraction

	11	
5	~~1~~	15
~~6~~	~~2~~	~~5~~
− 3	7	9
2	4	6

NOTE Trade-first subtraction resembles U.S. traditional subtraction, except that in trade-first subtraction, as the name implies, all the trading is done before any subtractions are carried out, allowing the person to concentrate on one task at a time.

▶ Introducing U.S. Traditional Subtraction

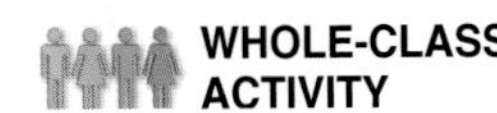

After you have discussed students' solutions, and even if one or more students used **U.S. traditional subtraction,** demonstrate it again as described below.

Example 1: 625 – 379

Step 1:

Start with the 1s.

Since 9 > 5, you need to regroup.

Trade 1 ten for 10 ones:
625 = 6 hundreds + 1 ten + 15 ones.

Subtract the 1s: 15 – 9 = 6.

	1	**15**
6	~~**2**~~	~~**5**~~
− 3	7	**9**
		6

Step 2:

Go to the 10s.

Since 7 > 1, you need to regroup.

Trade 1 hundred for 10 tens:
625 = 5 hundreds + 11 tens + 15 ones.

Subtract the 10s: 11 – 7 = 4.

	11	
5	~~**1**~~	15
~~**6**~~	~~2~~	~~5~~
− 3	**7**	9
	4	6

Step 3:

Go to the 100s. You don't need to regroup.

Subtract the 100s: 5 – 3 = 2.

625 – 379 = 246

There are 246 more shirts than pairs of pants.

	11	
5	~~1~~	15
~~6~~	~~2~~	~~5~~
− **3**	7	9
2	4	6

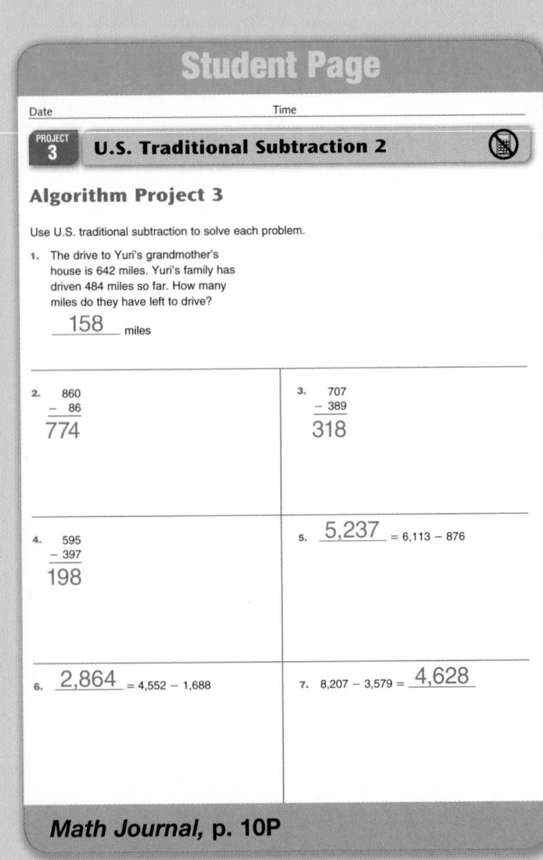

Student Page

Date Time

PROJECT 3 **U.S. Traditional Subtraction 2**

Algorithm Project 3

Use U.S. traditional subtraction to solve each problem.

1. The drive to Yuri's grandmother's house is 642 miles. Yuri's family has driven 484 miles so far. How many miles do they have left to drive?
158 miles

2. 860 − 86 = 774

3. 707 − 389 = 318

4. 595 − 397 = 198

5. 5,237 = 6,113 − 876

6. 2,864 = 4,552 − 1,688

7. 8,207 − 3,579 = 4,628

Math Journal, p. 10P

Example 2: 802 – 457

Step 1:

Start with the 1s.

Since 7 > 2, you need to regroup.

There are no tens in 802, so trade 1 hundred for 10 tens and then trade 1 ten for 10 ones: 802 = 7 hundreds + 9 tens + 12 ones.

Subtract the 1s: 12 – 7 = 5.

	9	
7	~~**10**~~	**12**
~~**8**~~	~~**0**~~	~~**2**~~
– 4	5	**7**
		5

Step 2:

Go to the 10s. You don't need to regroup.

Subtract the 10s: 9 – 5 = 4.

	9	
7	~~10~~	12
~~8~~	~~0~~	~~2~~
– 4	**5**	7
	4	5

Step 3:

Go to the 100s. You don't need to regroup.

Subtract the 100s: 7 – 4 = 3.

802 – 457 = 345

	9	
7	~~10~~	12
~~8~~	~~0~~	~~2~~
– **4**	5	7
3	4	5

You may want to work several more examples with the whole class.

Suggestions:

▷ 75 – 48 = ? 27

▷ 711 – 36 = ? 675

▷ 342 – 148 = ? 194

▷ 402 – 327 = ? 75

▷ 7,243 – 2,977 = ? 4,266

▷ 6,004 – 4,735 = ? 1,269

Practicing U.S. Traditional Subtraction

PARTNER ACTIVITY

(*Math Journal 1* or *2,* pp. 9P–12P; *Student Reference Book,* p. 24B)

When students are ready, have them solve Problems 2–7 on journal page 9P. They may find the example on *Student Reference Book,* page 24B helpful.

Journal pages 10P–12P provide students with additional practice using U.S. traditional subtraction. Use these journal pages as necessary.

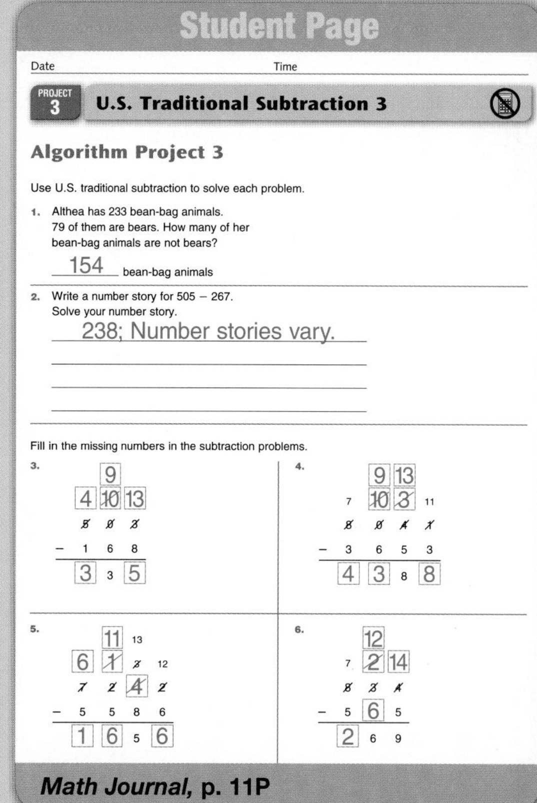
Student Page

Date Time

PROJECT 3 **U.S. Traditional Subtraction 3**

Algorithm Project 3

Use U.S. traditional subtraction to solve each problem.

1. Althea has 233 bean-bag animals. 79 of them are bears. How many of her bean-bag animals are not bears?
154 bean-bag animals

2. Write a number story for 505 – 267. Solve your number story.
238; Number stories vary.

Fill in the missing numbers in the subtraction problems.

3.
9
4 10 13
~~5~~ ~~0~~ ~~3~~
– 1 6 8
3 3 5

4.
9 13
7 10 3 11
~~8~~ ~~0~~ ~~4~~ ~~1~~
– 3 6 5 3
4 3 8 8

5.
11 13
6 1 3 12
~~7~~ ~~2~~ ~~4~~ ~~2~~
– 5 5 8 6
1 6 5 6

6.
12
7 2 14
~~8~~ ~~3~~ ~~4~~
– 5 6 5
2 6 9

Math Journal, p. 11P

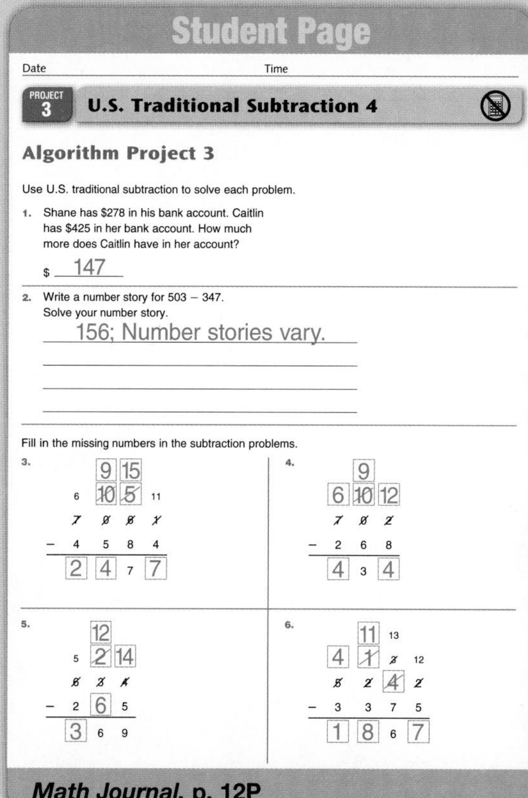
Student Page

Date Time

PROJECT 3 **U.S. Traditional Subtraction 4**

Algorithm Project 3

Use U.S. traditional subtraction to solve each problem.

1. Shane has $278 in his bank account. Caitlin has $425 in her bank account. How much more does Caitlin have in her account?
$ 147

2. Write a number story for 503 – 347. Solve your number story.
156; Number stories vary.

Fill in the missing numbers in the subtraction problems.

3.
9 15
6 10 5 11
~~7~~ ~~0~~ ~~6~~ ~~1~~
– 4 5 8 4
2 4 7 7

4.
9
6 10 12
~~7~~ ~~0~~ ~~2~~
– 2 6 8
4 3 4

5.
12
5 2 14
~~6~~ ~~3~~ ~~4~~
– 2 6 5
3 6 9

6.
11 13
4 1 3 12
~~5~~ ~~2~~ ~~4~~ ~~2~~
– 3 3 7 5
1 8 6 7

Math Journal, p. 12P

Go to www.everydaymathonline.com to access the additional practice pages.

2 Extending the Project

Solving Multidigit Subtraction Problems

(Online Additional Practice, pp. 12A–12D; *Student Reference Book*, pp. 12–15 and 24B)

Online practice pages 12A–12D provide students with additional practice solving multidigit subtraction problems. Use these pages as necessary.

Encourage students to use the focus algorithm (trade-first subtraction) to solve the problems on practice page 12A. Invite them to use any algorithm they wish to solve the problems on the remaining pages.

Students may find the examples on *Student Reference Book,* pages 12–15 and 24B helpful.

Online Master

Name Date Time

PROJECT 3 **Trade-First Subtraction** Online Additional Practice

Algorithm Project 3

Use trade-first subtraction to solve each problem.

1. Mai's book has 316 pages. She has read 77 pages so far. How many pages does Mai have left to read?
   239 pages

2. 384 − 295 = 89

3. 512 − 144 = 368

4. 2,171 − 688 = 1,483

5. 6,645 − 3,896 = 2,749

6. 629 = 804 − 175

7. 7,006 − 5,117 = 1,889

Online Additional Practice, p. 12A

Algorithm

Project

U.S. Traditional Subtraction: Decimals

Objective To introduce U.S. traditional subtraction with decimals.

Technology Resources www.everydaymathonline.com

eToolkit

Algorithms Practice

EM Facts Workshop Game™

Family Letters

Assessment Management

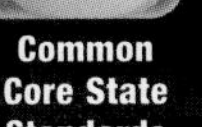
Common Core State Standards

Curriculum Focal Points

Interactive Teacher's Lesson Guide

1 Doing the Project

Recommended Use After Lesson 4•5

Key Concepts and Skills

- Identify places in whole numbers and decimals and the values of the digits in those places.
  [Number and Numeration Goal 1]
- Use subtraction facts to find differences of decimals.
  [Operations and Computation Goal 1]
- Subtract decimals.
  [Operations and Computation Goal 2]
- Write and solve subtraction number stories with decimals.
  [Operations and Computation Goal 2]

Key Activities

Students explore and practice U.S. traditional subtraction with decimals.

Materials

- *Math Journal 1* or *2,* pp. 13P–16P
- *Student Reference Book,* p. 40B
- \$1 and \$10 bills (*Math Masters,* p. 428; optional)
- dimes and pennies (optional)
- base-10 blocks (optional)

2 Extending the Project

Students solve decimal subtraction problems, first using the focus algorithm (trade-first subtraction) and then using any algorithm they choose.

Materials

- Online Additional Practice, pp. 16A–16D
- *Student Reference Book,* pp. 34–37 and 40B

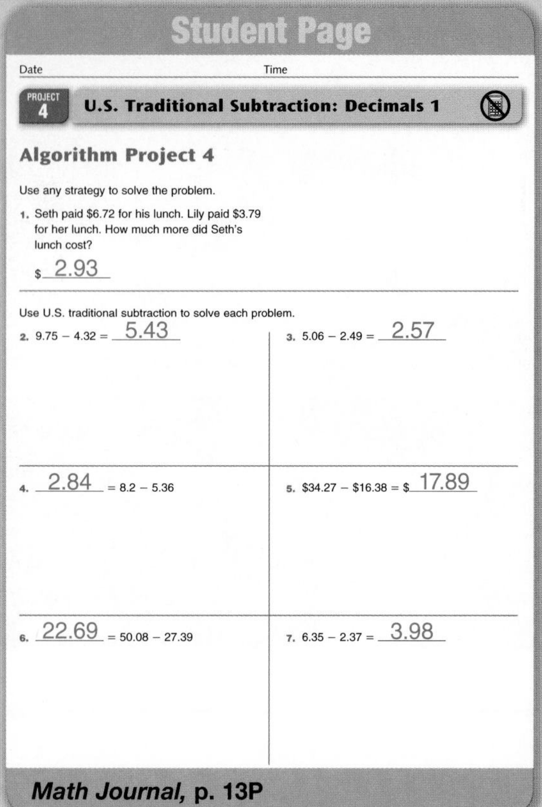

Student Page

Date Time

PROJECT 4 **U.S. Traditional Subtraction: Decimals 1**

Algorithm Project 4

Use any strategy to solve the problem.

1. Seth paid $6.72 for his lunch. Lily paid $3.79 for her lunch. How much more did Seth's lunch cost?
$ 2.93

Use U.S. traditional subtraction to solve each problem.

2. 9.75 – 4.32 = 5.43
3. 5.06 – 2.49 = 2.57
4. 2.84 = 8.2 – 5.36
5. $34.27 – $16.38 = $ 17.89
6. 22.69 = 50.08 – 27.39
7. 6.35 – 2.37 = 3.98

***Math Journal*, p. 13P**

1 Doing the Project

▶ Solving a Decimal Subtraction Problem

INDEPENDENT ACTIVITY

(*Math Journal 1* or *2,* p.13P)

Ask students to solve Problem 1 on journal page 13P. Tell them they may use base-10 blocks, play money, paper and pencil, or any other tools they wish, except calculators.

▶ Discussing Solutions

WHOLE-CLASS ACTIVITY

(*Math Journal 1* or *2,* p. 13P)

Discuss students' solutions to Problem 1 on journal page 13P. $6.72 – $3.79 = $2.93 Expect that students will use several different methods, including modeling with base-10 blocks, counting up, using partial-differences subtraction, and using trade-first subtraction. Some students may also use U.S. traditional subtraction. *Possible strategies:*

▷ Modeling with base-10 blocks

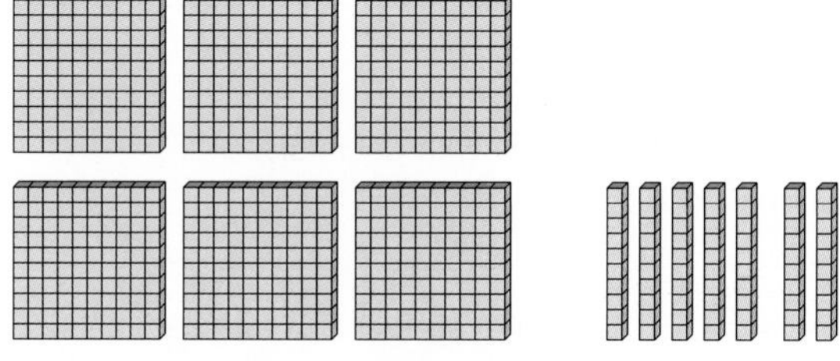

Show 6.72 with blocks.

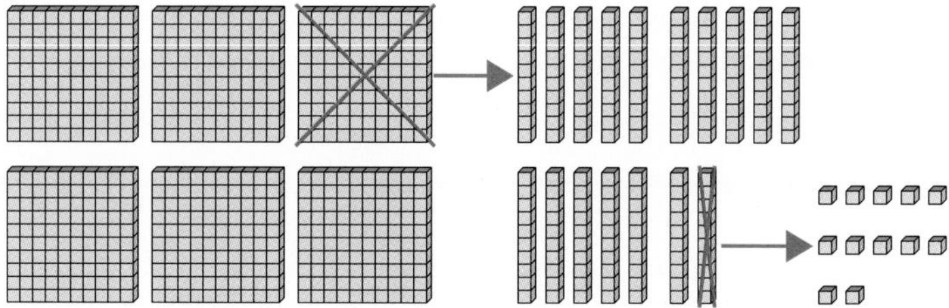

You want to take away 3.79. To do this, you need to first trade 1 flat for 10 longs and 1 long for 10 cubes.

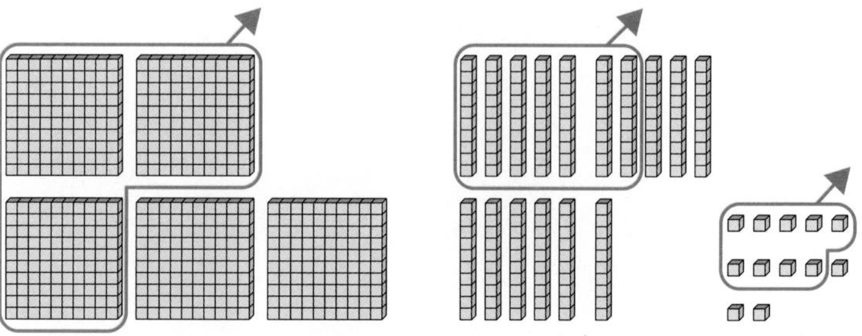

Now remove 3 flats, 7 longs, and 9 cubes (3.79). Two flats, 9 longs, and 3 cubes are left. These blocks show 2.93.

▷ Using shorthand pictures of base-10 blocks (*See margin.*)

▷ Counting up

3.79	
+ (0.01)	
3.80	
+ (0.20)	0.01
4.00	0.20
+ (2.72)	+ 2.72
6.72	2.93

\$6.72 − \$3.79 = \$2.93

▷ Using partial-differences subtraction

		6. 7 2
		− 3. 7 9
Subtract the 1s.	6 − 3 →	3. 0 0
Subtract the 0.1s.	0.7 − 0.7 →	0. 0 0
Subtract the 0.01s.	0.02 − 0.09 →	− 0. 0 7
Find the total.	3 − 0.07 →	**2. 9 3**

▷ Using trade-first subtraction

1s	0.1s	0.01s
	16	
5	~~6~~	12
~~6~~.	~~7~~	~~2~~
− 3.	7	9
2.	9	3

▷ Using U.S. traditional subtraction

1s	0.1s	0.01s
	16	
5	~~6~~	12
~~6~~.	~~7~~	~~2~~
− 3.	7	9
2.	9	3

NOTE Trade-first subtraction resembles U.S. traditional subtraction, except that in trade-first subtraction, as the name implies, all the trading is done before any subtractions are carried out, allowing the person to concentrate on one task at a time.

Introducing U.S. Traditional Subtraction for Decimals

WHOLE-CLASS ACTIVITY

After you have discussed students' solutions, and even if one or more students used U.S. traditional subtraction, demonstrate it again as described on the next page.

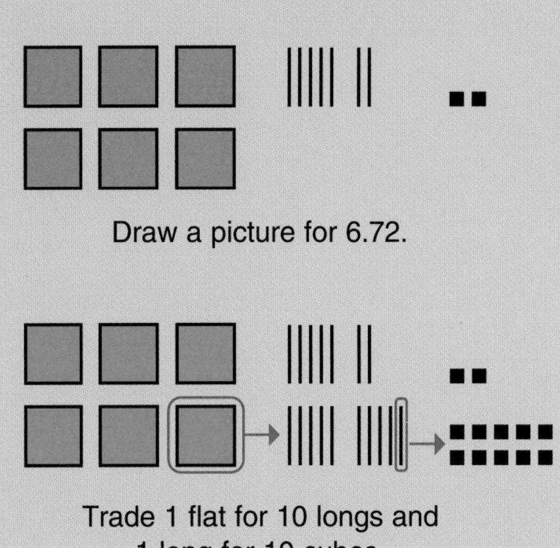

Draw a picture for 6.72.

Trade 1 flat for 10 longs and 1 long for 10 cubes.

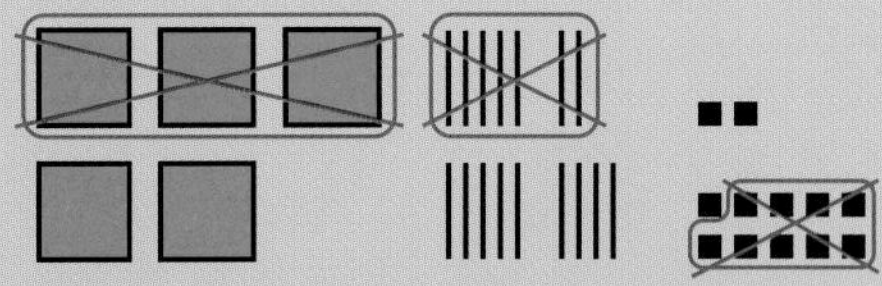

Remove 3 flats, 7 longs, and 9 cubes. The drawing shows 2.93.

Example 1: $6.72 – $3.79

Step 1:

Start with the 0.01s.

Since 9 > 2, you need to regroup.

Trade 1 tenth for 10 hundredths:
6.72 = 6 ones + 6 tenths + 12 hundredths.

Subtract the 0.01s: 12 – 9 = 3.

$$\begin{array}{r} \mathbf{6}\ \mathbf{12} \\ 6\ .\ \not{7}\ \not{2} \\ -\ 3\ .\ 7\ \mathbf{9} \\ \hline \mathbf{3} \end{array}$$

Step 2:

Go to the 0.1s.

Since 7 > 6, you need to regroup.

Trade 1 one for 10 tenths:
6.72 = 5 ones + 16 tenths + 12 hundredths.

Subtract the 0.1s: 16 – 7 = 9.

$$\begin{array}{r} \mathbf{16} \\ \mathbf{5}\ \ \not{6}\ \ 12 \\ \not{6}\ .\ \not{7}\ \not{2} \\ -\ 3\ .\ \mathbf{7}\ 9 \\ \hline \mathbf{9}\ \ 3 \end{array}$$

Step 3:

Go to the 1s. You don't need to regroup.

Subtract the 1s: 5 – 3 = 2.

Remember to include the decimal point in the answer.

$$\begin{array}{r} 16 \\ 5\ \ \not{6}\ \ 12 \\ \not{6}\ .\ \not{7}\ \not{2} \\ -\ \mathbf{3}\ .\ 7\ 9 \\ \hline \mathbf{2}\ \mathbf{.}\ 9\ 3 \end{array}$$

$6.72 – $3.79 = $2.93

Seth's lunch cost $2.93 more than Lily's lunch.

Example 2: 46.03 – 27.48

Step 1:

Start with the 0.01s.

Since 8 > 3, you need to regroup.

There are no tenths in 46.03, so trade 1 one for 10 tenths and then trade 1 tenth for 10 hundredths: 46.03 = 4 tens + 5 ones + 9 tenths + 13 hundredths.

Subtract the 0.01s: 13 – 8 = 5.

$$\begin{array}{r} \mathbf{9} \\ \mathbf{5}\ \ \not{10}\ \ \mathbf{13} \\ 4\ \ \not{6}\ .\ \not{0}\ \not{3} \\ -\ 2\ \ 7\ .\ 4\ \mathbf{8} \\ \hline \mathbf{5} \end{array}$$

Step 2:

Go to the 0.1s.

You don't need to regroup.

Subtract the 0.1s: 9 – 4 = 5.

$$\begin{array}{r} \mathbf{9} \\ 5\ \ \not{10}\ \ 13 \\ 4\ \ \not{6}\ .\ \not{0}\ \not{3} \\ -\ 2\ \ 7\ .\ \mathbf{4}\ 8 \\ \hline \mathbf{5}\ \ 5 \end{array}$$

Step 3:

Go to the 1s.

Since 7 > 5, you need to regroup.

Trade 1 ten for 10 ones: 46.03 = 3 tens + 15 ones + 9 tenths + 13 hundredths.

Subtract the ones: 15 – 7 = 8.

$$\begin{array}{r} \mathbf{15}\ \ 9 \\ \mathbf{3}\ \ \not{5}\ \ \not{10}\ \ 13 \\ \not{4}\ \ \not{6}\ .\ \not{0}\ \not{3} \\ -\ 2\ \ \mathbf{7}\ .\ 4\ 8 \\ \hline \mathbf{8}\ \ 5\ \ 5 \end{array}$$

Step 4:

Go to the 10s.
You don't need to regroup.
Subtract the 10s: 3 – 2 = 1.
Remember to include the decimal point in the answer.

```
   15  9
 3  5 10 13
 4  6 . 0  3
-2  7 . 4  8
-----------
 1  8 . 5  5
```

46.03 – 27.48 = 18.55

Example 3: 7.1 – 3.86

Step 1:

Write the problem in columns.
Be sure to line up the places correctly.
Since 3.86 has two decimal places, write 7.1 as 7.10.

```
  7 . 1  0
- 3 . 8  6
----------
```

Step 2:

Start with the 0.01s.
Since 6 > 0, you need to regroup.
Trade 1 tenth for 10 hundredths:
7.10 = 7 ones + 0 tenths + 10 hundredths.
Subtract the 0.01s: 10 – 6 = 4.

```
        0 10
  7 . 1  0
- 3 . 8  6
----------
         4
```

Step 3:

Go to the 0.1s.
Since 8 > 0, you need to regroup.
Trade 1 one for 10 tenths:
7.10 = 6 ones + 10 tenths + 10 hundredths.
Subtract the 0.1s: 10 – 8 = 2.

```
       10
  6     0 10
  7 . 1  0
- 3 . 8  6
----------
      2  4
```

Step 4:

Go to the 1s. You don't need to regroup.
Subtract the 1s: 6 – 3 = 3.
Remember to include the decimal point in the answer.

```
       10
  6     0 10
  7 . 1  0
- 3 . 8  6
----------
  3 . 2  4
```

7.1 – 3.86 = 3.24

You may want to work several more examples with the whole class.

Suggestions:

▷ $8.49 – $6.35 = ? $2.14

▷ 5.61 – 3.74 = ? 1.87

▷ 7.06 – 4.98 = ? 2.08

▷ 3.9 – 2.62 = ? 1.28

▷ $28.74 – $19.86 = ? $8.88

▷ 40.07 – 26.39 = ? 13.68

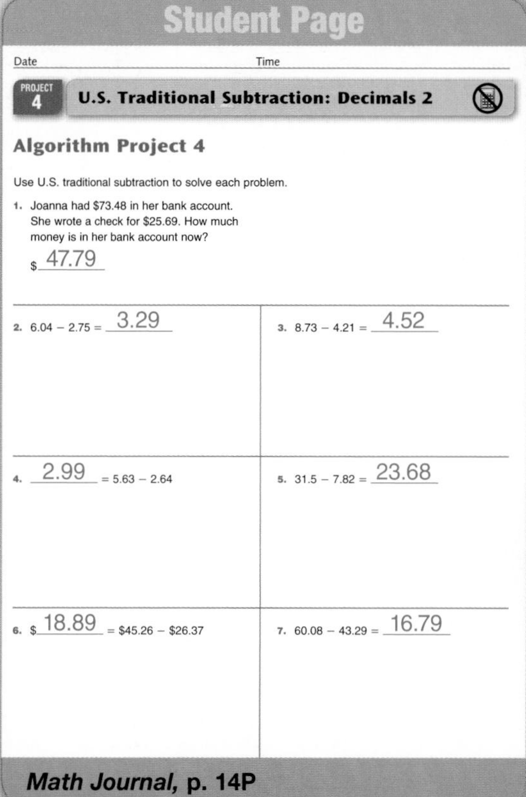
Student Page

Date Time

PROJECT 4 **U.S. Traditional Subtraction: Decimals 2**

Algorithm Project 4

Use U.S. traditional subtraction to solve each problem.

1. Joanna had $73.48 in her bank account. She wrote a check for $25.69. How much money is in her bank account now?
$ 47.79

2. 6.04 – 2.75 = 3.29

3. 8.73 – 4.21 = 4.52

4. 2.99 = 5.63 – 2.64

5. 31.5 – 7.82 = 23.68

6. $ 18.89 = $45.26 – $26.37

7. 60.08 – 43.29 = 16.79

Math Journal, p. 14P

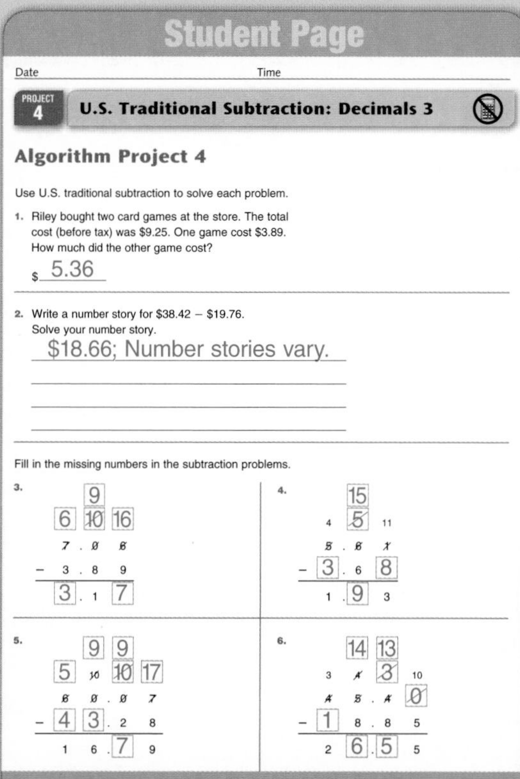
Student Page

Date Time

PROJECT 4 **U.S. Traditional Subtraction: Decimals 3**

Algorithm Project 4

Use U.S. traditional subtraction to solve each problem.

1. Riley bought two card games at the store. The total cost (before tax) was $9.25. One game cost $3.89. How much did the other game cost?
$ 5.36

2. Write a number story for $38.42 – $19.76. Solve your number story.
$18.66; Number stories vary.

Fill in the missing numbers in the subtraction problems.

Math Journal, p. 15P

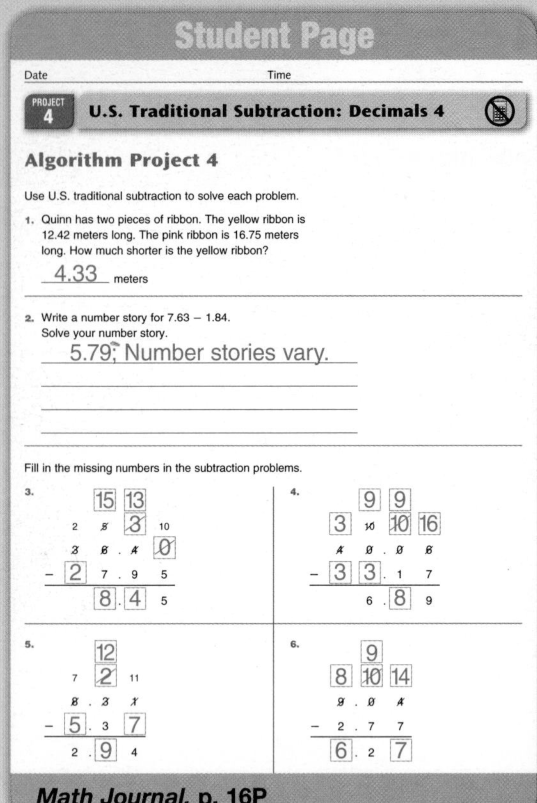

▶ Practicing U.S. Traditional Subtraction for Decimals

(*Math Journal 1* or *2,* pp. 13P–16P; *Student Reference Book,* p. 40B)

When students are ready, have them solve Problems 2–7 on journal page 13P. They may find the example on *Student Reference Book,* page 40B helpful.

Journal pages 14P–16P provide students with additional practice using U.S. traditional subtraction. Use these journal pages as necessary.

2 Extending the Project

▶ Solving Decimal Subtraction Problems

(Online Additional Practice, pp. 16A–16D; *Student Reference Book,* pp. 34–37 and 40B)

Online practice pages 16A–16D provide students with additional practice solving decimal subtraction problems. Use these pages as necessary.

Encourage students to use the focus algorithm (trade-first subtraction) to solve the problems on practice page 16A. Invite them to use any algorithm they wish to solve the problems on the remaining pages.

Students may find the examples on *Student Reference Book,* pages 34–37 and 40B helpful.

Go to www.everydaymathonline.com to access the additional practice pages.

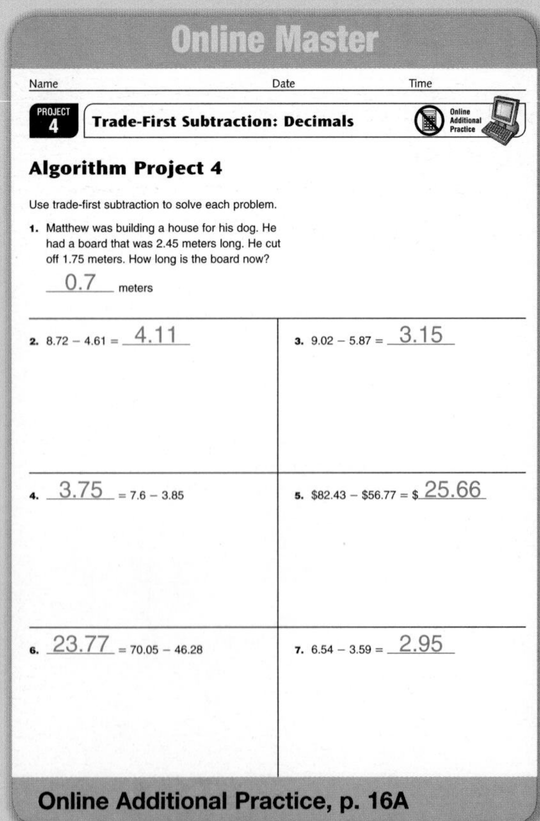

Algorithm 5 Project

U.S. Traditional Multiplication

Objective To introduce U.S. traditional multiplication.

Technology Resources www.everydaymathonline.com

eToolkit

Algorithms Practice

EM Facts Workshop Game™

Family Letters

Assessment Management

Common Core State Standards

Curriculum Focal Points

Interactive Teacher's Lesson Guide

1 Doing the Project

Recommended Use After Lesson 5•7

Key Concepts and Skills

- Identify places in whole numbers and the values of the digits in those places. [Number and Numeration Goal 1]
- Use multiplication facts to find products of multidigit whole numbers. [Operations and Computation Goal 3]
- Multiply multidigit whole numbers. [Operations and Computation Goal 4]
- Write and solve multiplication number stories. [Operations and Computation Goal 4]

Key Activities

Students explore and practice U.S. traditional multiplication with multidigit whole numbers.

Key Vocabulary

U.S. traditional multiplication

Materials

- *Math Journal 1* or *2,* pp. 17P–20P
- *Student Reference Book,* pp. 24C and 24D

2 Extending the Project

Students solve multidigit multiplication problems, first using the focus algorithm (partial-products multiplication) and then using any algorithm they choose.

Materials

- Online Additional Practice, pp. 20A–20D
- *Student Reference Book,* pp. 18, 19, 24C, and 24D

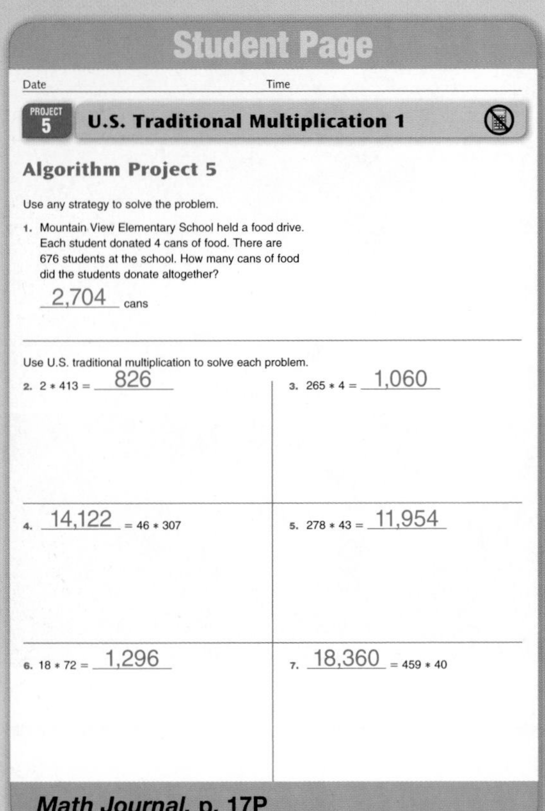
Student Page

Date Time

PROJECT 5 **U.S. Traditional Multiplication 1**

Algorithm Project 5

Use any strategy to solve the problem.

1. Mountain View Elementary School held a food drive. Each student donated 4 cans of food. There are 676 students at the school. How many cans of food did the students donate altogether?
2,704 cans

Use U.S. traditional multiplication to solve each problem.

2. 2 ∗ 413 = 826
3. 265 ∗ 4 = 1,060
4. 14,122 = 46 ∗ 307
5. 278 ∗ 43 = 11,954
6. 18 ∗ 72 = 1,296
7. 18,360 = 459 ∗ 40

Math Journal, p. 17P

1 Doing the Project

▶ Solving a Multiplication Problem

INDEPENDENT ACTIVITY

(*Math Journal 1* or *2,* p. 17P)

Ask students to solve Problem 1 on journal page 17P. Tell them they may use any methods they wish, except calculators.

▶ Discussing Solutions

WHOLE-CLASS ACTIVITY

(*Math Journal 1* or *2,* p. 17P)

Discuss students' solutions to Problem 1 on journal page 17P. 4 ∗ 676 = 2,704 cans Expect that students will use several different methods, including partial-products multiplication and lattice multiplication. Some students may also use U.S. traditional multiplication. *Possible strategies:*

▷ Using partial-products multiplication

$$\begin{array}{rr} & 676 \\ & *\quad\;\; 4 \\ \hline 4 * 600 \rightarrow & 2400 \\ 4 * 70 \rightarrow & 280 \\ 4 * 6 \rightarrow & +\quad 24 \\ \hline & 2704 \end{array}$$

▷ Using lattice multiplication

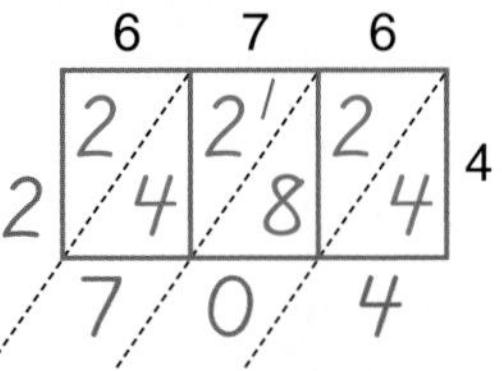

▷ Using U.S. traditional multiplication

$$\begin{array}{r} {\scriptstyle 3\,2}\;\; \\ 676 \\ *\quad\;\; 4 \\ \hline 2704 \end{array}$$

▸ Introducing U.S. Traditional Multiplication

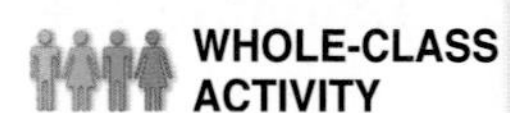
WHOLE-CLASS ACTIVITY

After you have discussed students' solutions, and even if one or more students used **U.S. traditional multiplication,** demonstrate it again as described below.

Example 1: 4 ∗ 676

Step 1:

Multiply the ones.
4 ∗ 6 ones = 24 ones = 2 tens + 4 ones
Write 4 in the 1s place below the line.
Write 2 above the 7 in the 10s place.

```
    2
  676
*   4
-----
    4
```

Step 2:

Multiply the tens.
4 ∗ 7 tens = 28 tens
Remember the 2 tens from Step 1.
28 tens + 2 tens = 30 tens in all
30 tens = 3 hundreds + 0 tens
Write 0 in the 10s place below the line.
Write 3 above the 6 in the 100s place.

```
   32
  676
*   4
-----
   04
```

Step 3:

Multiply the hundreds.
4 ∗ 6 hundreds = 24 hundreds
Remember the 3 hundreds from Step 2.
24 hundreds + 3 hundreds = 27 hundreds
27 hundreds = 2 thousands + 7 hundreds
Write 7 in the 100s place below the line.
Write 2 in the 1,000s place below the line.

```
   32
  676
*   4
-----
 2704
```

4 ∗ 676 = 2,704

The students donated 2,704 cans.

NOTE U.S. traditional multiplication is so familiar that the details of its working may appear more meaningful than they are. Consider the following example:

```
   12
   35
  147
*  38
-----
 1176
+4410
-----
 5586
```

Many people, when asked why the "2" carried from "3 ∗ 7" is written in the 10s place, will explain that it stands for "2 tens." But this "2" really means "2 hundreds" since the "3" is really "3 tens." U.S. traditional multiplication is efficient—though not as efficient as a calculator—but it is not, despite its familiarity, conceptually transparent.

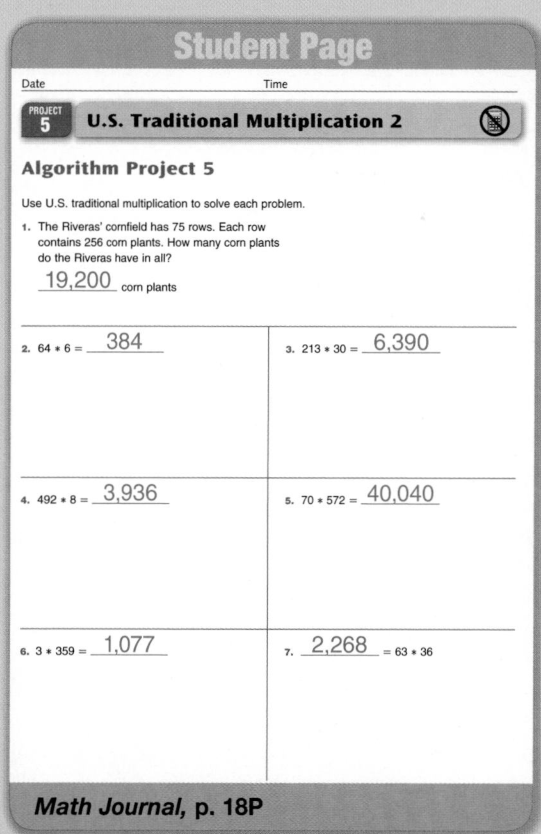
Student Page

Date Time

PROJECT 5 **U.S. Traditional Multiplication 2**

Algorithm Project 5

Use U.S. traditional multiplication to solve each problem.

1. The Riveras' cornfield has 75 rows. Each row contains 256 corn plants. How many corn plants do the Riveras have in all?
19,200 corn plants

2. 64 ∗ 6 = 384

3. 213 ∗ 30 = 6,390

4. 492 ∗ 8 = 3,936

5. 70 ∗ 572 = 40,040

6. 3 ∗ 359 = 1,077

7. 2,268 = 63 ∗ 36

Math Journal, p. 18P

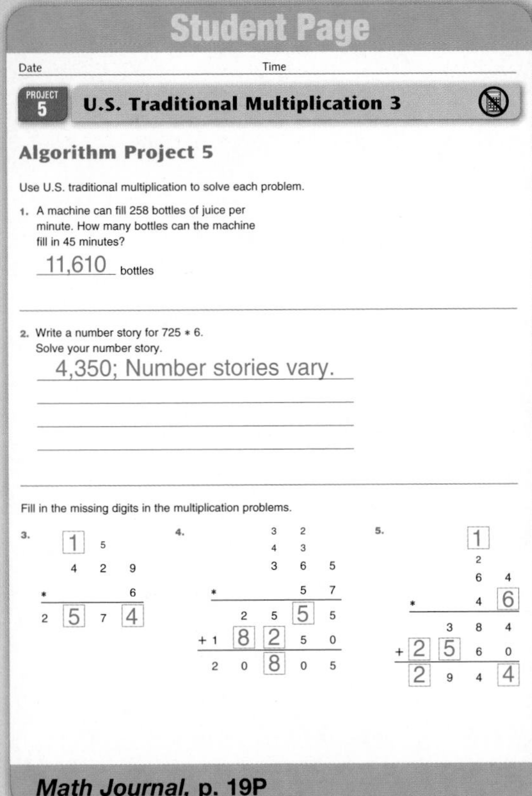
Student Page

Date Time

PROJECT 5 **U.S. Traditional Multiplication 3**

Algorithm Project 5

Use U.S. traditional multiplication to solve each problem.

1. A machine can fill 258 bottles of juice per minute. How many bottles can the machine fill in 45 minutes?
   11,610 bottles

2. Write a number story for 725 * 6. Solve your number story.
   4,350; Number stories vary.

Fill in the missing digits in the multiplication problems.

3.
1 5
4 2 9
* 6
2 5 7 4

4.
3 2
4 3
3 6 5
* 5 7
2 5 5 5
+ 1 8 2 5 0
2 0 8 0 5

5.
1
2
6 4
* 4 6
3 8 4
+ 2 5 6 0
2 9 4 4

Math Journal, p. 19P

Student Page

Date Time

PROJECT 5 **U.S. Traditional Multiplication 4**

Algorithm Project 5

Use U.S. traditional multiplication to solve each problem.

1. The zebra at the city zoo weighs 627 pounds. The hippopotamus weighs 5 times as much as the zebra. How much does the hippopotamus weigh?
   3,135 pounds

2. Write a number story for 584 * 23. Solve your number story.
   13,432; Number stories vary.

Fill in the missing digits in the multiplication problems.

3.
7 1
6 8 2
* 9
6 1 3 8

4.
3 2
4 3
2 9 7
* 4 1 5
1 4 8 5
2 9 7 0
+ 1 1 8 8 0 0
1 2 3 2 5 5

5.
1
2 2
* 3 5
1 1 0
+ 6 6 0
7 7 0

Math Journal, p. 20P

Example 2: 487 * 35

Step 1:

Multiply 487 by the 5 in 35, as if the problem were 5 * 487.

```
    4 3
    4 8 7
*     3 5
---------
  2 4 3 5  ← The partial product
             5 * 487 = 2,435
```

Step 2:

Multiply 487 by the 3 in 35, as if the problem were 3 * 487.

The 3 in 35 stands for 3 tens, so write the partial product one place to the left.

Write a 0 in the 1s place to show you are multiplying by tens.

Write the new carries above the old carries.

```
      2 2
      4 3
      4 8 7
*       3 5
-----------
    2 4 3 5
  1 4 6 1 0  ← 30 * 487 = 14,610
```

Step 3:

Add the two partial products to get the final answer.

```
      2 2
      4 3
      4 8 7
*       3 5
-----------
    2 4 3 5
+ 1 4 6 1 0
-----------
  1 7 0 4 5  ← 35 * 487 = 17,045
```

35 * 487 = 17,045

You may want to work several more examples with the whole class.

Suggestions:

▷ 12 * 43 = ? 516

▷ 509 * 6 = ? 3,054

▷ 70 * 384 = ? 26,880

▷ 9 * 500 = ? 4,500

▷ 830 * 29 = ? 24,070

▷ 67 * 30 = ? 2,010

▶ Practicing U.S. Traditional Multiplication

PARTNER ACTIVITY

(*Math Journal 1* or *2,* pp. 17P–20P; *Student Reference Book,* pp. 24C and 24D)

When students are ready, have them solve Problems 2–7 on journal page 17P. They may find the examples on *Student Reference Book,* pages 24C and 24D helpful.

Journal pages 18P–20P provide students with additional practice using U.S. traditional multiplication. Use these journal pages as necessary.

2 Extending the Project

Solving Multidigit Multiplication Problems

INDEPENDENT ACTIVITY

(Online Additional Practice, pp. 20A–20D; *Student Reference Book,* pp. 18, 19, 24C, and 24D)

Online practice pages 20A–20D provide students with additional practice solving multidigit multiplication problems. Use these pages as necessary.

Encourage students to use the focus algorithm (partial-products multiplication) to solve the problems on practice page 20A. Invite them to use any algorithm they wish to solve the problems on the remaining pages.

Students may find the examples on *Student Reference Book,* pages 18, 19, 24C, and 24D helpful.

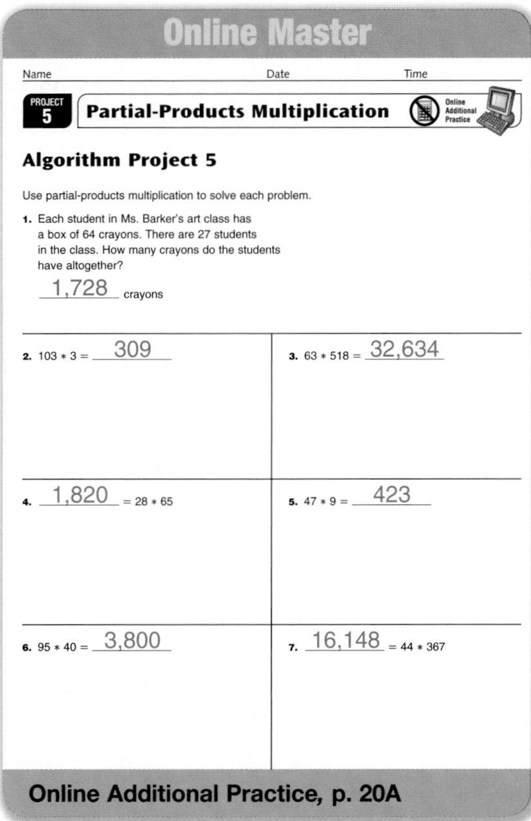
Online Master

Name Date Time

PROJECT 5 **Partial-Products Multiplication**

Algorithm Project 5

Use partial-products multiplication to solve each problem.

1. Each student in Ms. Barker's art class has a box of 64 crayons. There are 27 students in the class. How many crayons do the students have altogether?
 1,728 crayons

2. 103 * 3 = 309

3. 63 * 518 = 32,634

4. 1,820 = 28 * 65

5. 47 * 9 = 423

6. 95 * 40 = 3,800

7. 16,148 = 44 * 367

Online Additional Practice, p. 20A

Go to www.everydaymathonline.com to access the additional practice pages.

Algorithm 6 Project

U.S. Traditional Multiplication: Decimals

Objective To introduce U.S. traditional multiplication for decimals.

Technology Resources www.everydaymathonline.com

eToolkit

Algorithms Practice

EM Facts Workshop Game™

Family Letters

Assessment Management

Common Core State Standards

Curriculum Focal Points

Interactive Teacher's Lesson Guide

1 Doing the Project

Recommended Use After Lesson 9•8

Key Concepts and Skills

- Identify places in whole numbers and decimals and the values of the digits in those places.
  [Number and Numeration Goal 1]
- Use multiplication facts to calculate products of decimals and whole-number multipliers.
  [Operations and Computation Goal 3]
- Write and solve multiplication number stories with decimals.
  [Operations and Computation Goal 4]

Key Activities

Students explore and practice U.S. traditional multiplication with decimals.

Materials

- *Math Journal 1* or *2,* pp. 21P–24P
- *Student Reference Book,* p. 40C
- $1 and $10 bills (*Math Masters,* p. 428; optional)
- dimes and pennies (optional)

2 Extending the Project

Students solve decimal multiplication problems, first using the focus algorithm (partial-products multiplication) and then using any algorithm they choose.

Materials

- Online Additional Practice, pp. 24A–24D
- *Student Reference Book,* pp. 37A, 37B, and 40C

1 Doing the Project

Solving a Decimal Multiplication Problem

(*Math Journal 1* or *2,* p. 21P)

Ask students to solve Problem 1 on journal page 21P. Tell them they may use play money, paper and pencil, or any other tools they wish, except calculators.

Discussing Solutions

(*Math Journal 1* or *2,* p. 21P)

Discuss students' solutions to Problem 1 on journal page 21P. $5.98 * 4 = $23.92 Expect that students will use several different methods, which may include modeling with play money, using repeated addition, using lattice multiplication, and using partial-products multiplication. Some students may also use U.S. traditional multiplication. *Possible strategies:*

▷ Modeling with play money

$1 $1 $1 $1 $1	$1 $1 $1 $1 $1	$1 $1 $1 $1 $1	$1 $1 $1 $1 $1
(D)(D)(D)(D)(D) (D)(D)(D)(D)	(D)(D)(D)(D)(D) (D)(D)(D)(D)	(D)(D)(D)(D)(D) (D)(D)(D)(D)	(D)(D)(D)(D)(D) (D)(D)(D)(D)
(P)(P)(P)(P)(P) (P)(P)(P)	(P)(P)(P)(P)(P) (P)(P)(P)	(P)(P)(P)(P)(P) (P)(P)(P)	(P)(P)(P)(P)(P) (P)(P)(P)

Use play money to show the cost of 4 sandwiches.

5 [$1] + 5 [$1] + 5 [$1] + 5 [$1] = 20 [$1] or 2 [$10]

Combine the bills.

9 (D) + 9 (D) + 9 (D) + 9 (D) = 36 (D) or 3 [$1] and 6 (D)

Combine the dimes.

8 (P) + 8 (P) + 8 (P) + 8 (P) = 32 (P) or 3 (D) and 2 (P)

Combine the pennies.

2 [$10] + 3 [$1] + 6 (D) + 3 (D) + 2 (P) = $23.92

Combine the bills and coins.

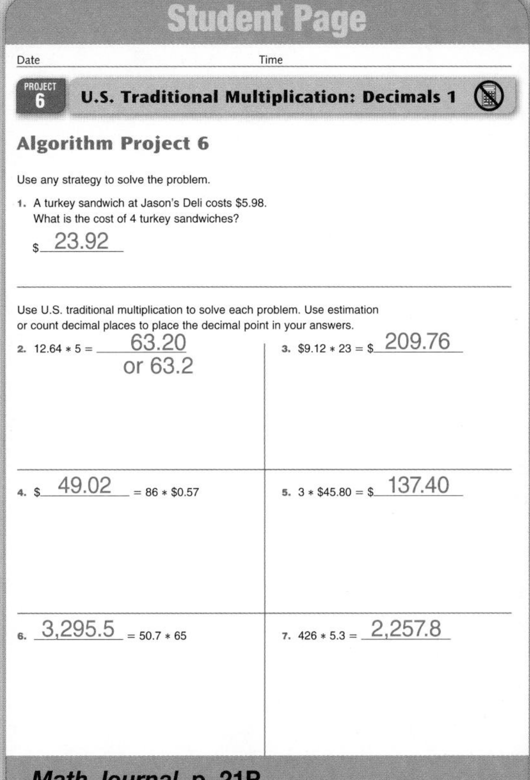

Student Page

Date Time

PROJECT 6 **U.S. Traditional Multiplication: Decimals 1**

Algorithm Project 6

Use any strategy to solve the problem.

1. A turkey sandwich at Jason's Deli costs $5.98. What is the cost of 4 turkey sandwiches?
   $ 23.92

Use U.S. traditional multiplication to solve each problem. Use estimation or count decimal places to place the decimal point in your answers.

2. 12.64 * 5 = 63.20 or 63.2
3. $9.12 * 23 = $ 209.76
4. $ 49.02 = 86 * $0.57
5. 3 * $45.80 = $ 137.40
6. 3,295.5 = 50.7 * 65
7. 426 * 5.3 = 2,257.8

Math Journal, p. 21P

▷ Using repeated addition

$5.98	$11.96
+ $5.98	+ $11.96
$10.00	$22.00
$1.80	$1.80
+ $0.16	+ $0.12
$11.96	$23.92

▷ Using lattice multiplication

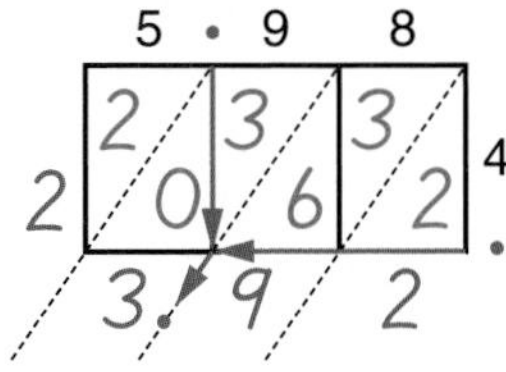

▷ Using partial-products multiplication

```
                      $5. 9 8
                    *       4
4 [$5.00]s →         2 0. 0 0
4 [$0.90]s →             3. 6 0
4 [$0.08]s →         + 0. 3 2
                      $2 3. 9 2
```

▷ Using U.S. traditional multiplication

```
   3 3
  $5. 9 8
*       4
 $2 3. 9 2
```

Introducing U.S. Traditional Multiplication for Decimals

After you have discussed students' solutions, and even if one or more students used U.S. traditional multiplication, demonstrate it again as described below.

Example 1: $5.98 * 4

Step 1:

Start with the pennies.
4 * 8 pennies = 32 pennies
32 pennies = 3 dimes + 2 pennies

```
     3
  5 . 9 8
*       4
        2
```

Step 2:

Multiply the dimes.
4 * 9 dimes = 36 dimes
Remember the 3 dimes from Step 1.
36 dimes + 3 dimes = 39 dimes in all
39 dimes = $3 + 9 dimes

```
   3 3
  5 . 9 8
*       4
      9 2
```

Step 3:

Multiply the dollars.

4 * $5 = $20

Remember the $3 from Step 2.

$20 + $3 = $23 in all

$23 = 2 [$10]s + 3 [$1]s

Remember to include the decimal point.

```
   3 3
   5.9 8
*      4
--------
  2 3.9 2
```

$5.98 * 4 = $23.92

Four turkey sandwiches cost $23.92.

One way to use U.S. traditional multiplication with decimals is to multiply the factors as though they were whole numbers and then use estimation to place the decimal point.

Example 2: 14.85 * 6

Step 1:

Multiply as though both factors were whole numbers.

```
   2 5 3
  1 4 8 5
*       6
---------
  8 9 1 0
```

Step 2:

Estimate the product: 14.85 is about 15, and 15 * 6 = 90.

Step 3:

Use the estimate to place the decimal point in the answer. The estimate is 90, so place the decimal point to make the answer close to 90: 89.10 is close to 90.

14.85 * 6 = 89.10

Another way to use U.S. traditional multiplication with decimals is to multiply as though both factors were whole numbers and then find the total number of places to the right of the decimal points of both factors to determine where to place the decimal point.

Example 3: 35 * 8.62

Step 1:

Multiply as though both factors were whole numbers.

```
        1
      3 1
      8 6 2
*       3 5
-----------
    4 3 1 0
+ 2 5 8 6 0
-----------
  3 0 1 7 0
```

Step 2:

Count the total number of places to the right of the decimal points of both factors. There are 0 places to the right of the decimal point in 35. There are 2 places to the right of the decimal point in 8.62. There are 2 decimal places in all.

Step 3:

Place the decimal point 2 places from the right.

3 0 1 . 7 0

35 * 8.62 = 301.70

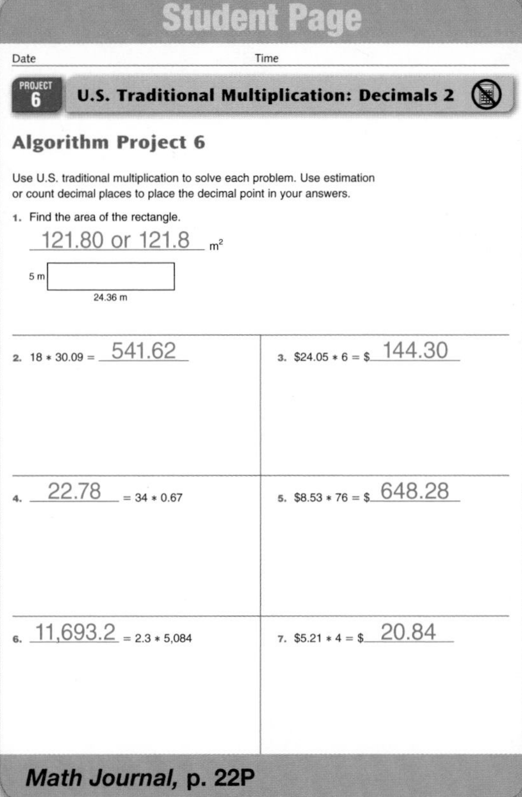

Student Page

Date Time

PROJECT 6 **U.S. Traditional Multiplication: Decimals 2**

Algorithm Project 6

Use U.S. traditional multiplication to solve each problem. Use estimation or count decimal places to place the decimal point in your answers.

1. Find the area of the rectangle.
   121.80 or 121.8 m²
   5 m, 24.36 m

2. 18 * 30.09 = 541.62

3. $24.05 * 6 = $ 144.30

4. 22.78 = 34 * 0.67

5. $8.53 * 76 = $ 648.28

6. 11,693.2 = 2.3 * 5,084

7. $5.21 * 4 = $ 20.84

Math Journal, p. 22P

NOTE This second method for multiplying decimals (used in Example 3) is useful when there are many decimal places in the factors, making it difficult to estimate the answer. For example, 0.078 * 0.029 = 0.002262.

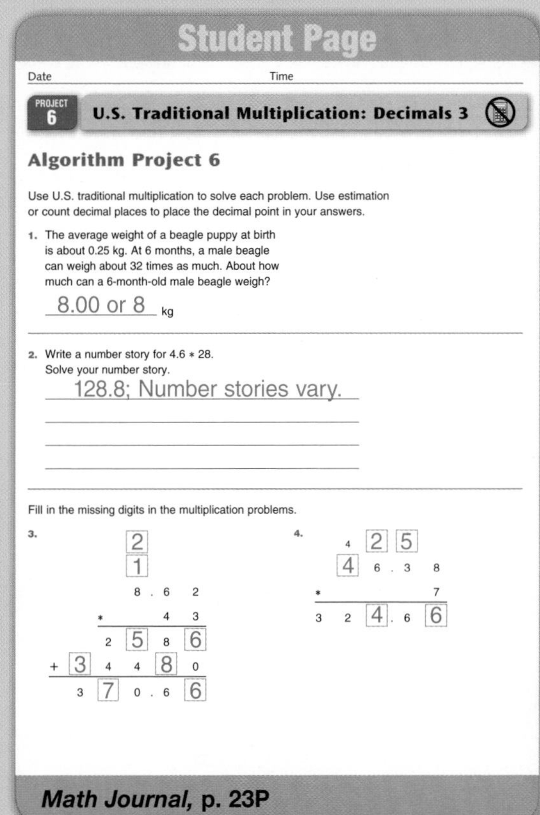

Student Page

Date Time

PROJECT 6 **U.S. Traditional Multiplication: Decimals 3**

Algorithm Project 6

Use U.S. traditional multiplication to solve each problem. Use estimation or count decimal places to place the decimal point in your answers.

1. The average weight of a beagle puppy at birth is about 0.25 kg. At 6 months, a male beagle can weigh about 32 times as much. About how much can a 6-month-old male beagle weigh?
   8.00 or 8 kg

2. Write a number story for 4.6 * 28. Solve your number story.
   128.8; Number stories vary.

Fill in the missing digits in the multiplication problems.

3.
```
        2
        1
      8.6 2
*       4 3
-----------
    2 5 8 6
+ 3 4 4 8 0
-----------
  3 7 0.6 6
```

4.
```
  4 2 5
  4 6.3 8
*       7
---------
3 2 4.6 6
```

Math Journal, p. 23P

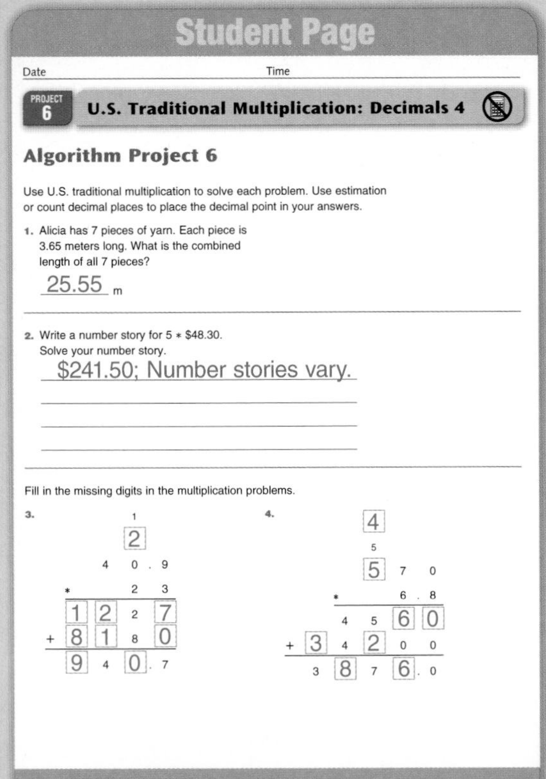

Student Page

Date Time

PROJECT 6 **U.S. Traditional Multiplication: Decimals 4**

Algorithm Project 6

Use U.S. traditional multiplication to solve each problem. Use estimation or count decimal places to place the decimal point in your answers.

1. Alicia has 7 pieces of yarn. Each piece is 3.65 meters long. What is the combined length of all 7 pieces?
   25.55 m

2. Write a number story for 5 * $48.30. Solve your number story.
   $241.50; Number stories vary.

Fill in the missing digits in the multiplication problems.

3.
```
      1
      2
    4 0 . 9
*     2   3
  1 2 2 7
+ 8 1 8 0
  9 4 0 . 7
```

4.
```
        4
        5
        5 7 0
*       6 . 8
    4 5 6 0
+ 3 4 2 0 0
  3 8 7 6 . 0
```

Math Journal, p. 24P

Go to www.everydaymathonline.com to access the additional practice pages.

Online Master

Name Date Time

PROJECT 6 **Partial-Products Multiplication: Decimals** Online Additional Practice

Algorithm Project 6

Use partial-products multiplication to solve each problem. Use estimation to place the decimal point in your answers.

1. A pack of 12 party invitations costs $8.95. Mrs. Becker bought 15 packs. How much money did she spend?
   $ 134.25

2. $0.46 * 83 = $ 38.18

3. 7 * 39.04 = 273.28

4. $ 633.15 = 63 * $10.05

5. 71.21 * 4 = 284.84

6. 60.48 = 7.56 * 8

7. 9,406 * 2.8 = 26,336.8

Online Additional Practice, p. 24A

You may want to work several more examples with the whole class.

Suggestions:

- ▷ 7.46 * 3 = ? 22.38
- ▷ 3 * $43.21 = ? $129.63
- ▷ $0.67 * 5 = ? $3.35
- ▷ 8 * 17.04 = ? 136.32
- ▷ 23 * $40.06 = ? $921.38
- ▷ 5.6 * 70 = ? 392

▶ Practicing U.S. Traditional Multiplication for Decimals

PARTNER ACTIVITY

(*Math Journal 1* or *2*, pp. 21P–24P; *Student Reference Book*, p. 40C)

When students are ready, have them solve Problems 2–7 on journal page 21P. They may find the examples on *Student Reference Book*, page 40C helpful.

Journal pages 22P–24P provide students with additional practice using U.S. traditional multiplication. Use these journal pages as necessary.

2 Extending the Project

▶ Solving Decimal Multiplication Problems

INDEPENDENT ACTIVITY

(Online Additional Practice, pp. 24A–24D; *Student Reference Book*, pp. 37A, 37B, and 40C)

Online practice pages 24A–24D provide students with additional practice solving decimal multiplication problems. Use these pages as necessary.

Encourage students to use the focus algorithm (partial-products multiplication) to solve the problems on practice page 24A. Invite them to use any algorithm they wish to solve the problems on the remaining pages.

Students may find the examples on *Student Reference Book*, pages 37A, 37B, and 40C helpful.

Algorithm 7 Project

U.S. Traditional Long Division, Part 1

Objective To introduce U.S. traditional long division.

Technology Resources www.everydaymathonline.com

eToolkit

Algorithms Practice

EM Facts Workshop Game™

Family Letters

Assessment Management

Common Core State Standards

Curriculum Focal Points

Interactive Teacher's Lesson Guide

1 Doing the Project

Recommended Use After Lesson 6•10

Key Concepts and Skills

- Subtract multidigit numbers. [Operations and Computation Goal 2]
- Apply multiplication facts to long-division situations. [Operations and Computation Goal 3]
- Solve equal-sharing division problems and number stories. [Operations and Computation Goal 4]

Key Activities

Students explore and practice U.S. traditional long division with two- and three-digit whole numbers divided by single-digit whole numbers.

Key Vocabulary

U.S. traditional long division ◆ dividend ◆ divisor ◆ quotient ◆ remainder

Materials

- ◆ *Math Journal 1* or *2,* pp. 25P–27P
- ◆ *Student Reference Book,* pp. 24E–24H
- ◆ $1 and $10 bills (*Math Masters,* p. 428; optional)
- ◆ $100 bills (optional)
- ◆ coins (optional)
- ◆ base-10 blocks (optional)
- ◆ index cards (optional)

2 Extending the Project

Students write and solve division number stories using U.S. traditional long division.

For additional practice, students solve division problems, first using the focus algorithm (partial-quotients division) and then using any algorithm they choose.

Materials

- ◆ *Student Reference Book,* pp. 22–24 and 24E–24H
- ◆ Online Additional Practice, pp. 27A–27C

Advance Preparation

If you intend to have students use coins and bills to model the division problems, you will need $100 bills. Make several copies of Grade 3 *Math Masters,* page 401. Alternatively, use index cards to create $100 bills.

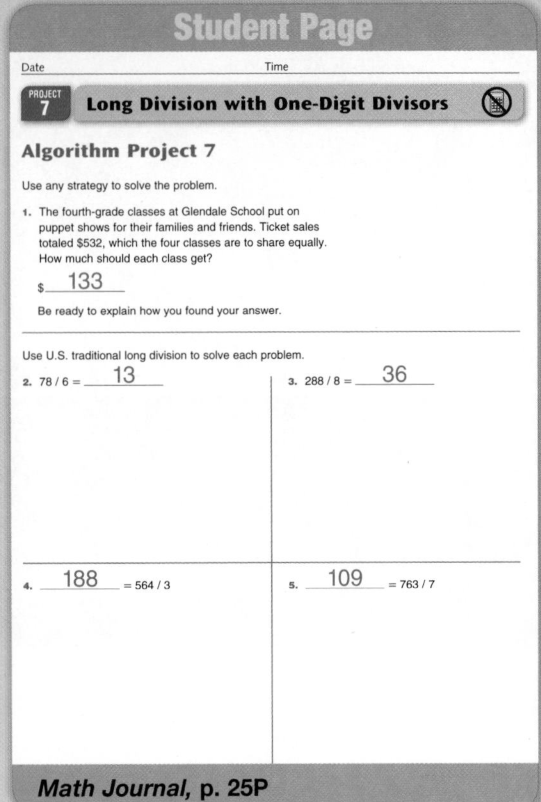

Student Page

Date Time

PROJECT 7 **Long Division with One-Digit Divisors**

Algorithm Project 7

Use any strategy to solve the problem.

1. The fourth-grade classes at Glendale School put on puppet shows for their families and friends. Ticket sales totaled $532, which the four classes are to share equally. How much should each class get?

$ 133

Be ready to explain how you found your answer.

Use U.S. traditional long division to solve each problem.

2. 78 / 6 = 13
3. 288 / 8 = 36
4. 188 = 564 / 3
5. 109 = 763 / 7

Math Journal, p. 25P

1 Doing the Project

▶ Solving a Division Problem

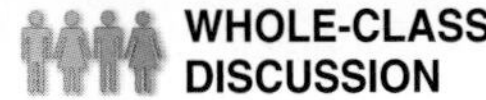

(*Math Journal 1* or *2,* p. 25P)

Ask students to solve Problem 1 on journal page 25P. Tell them they may use play money, paper and pencil, or any other tools they wish except calculators.

Discuss students' solutions. $532 / 4 = $133 Expect that students will use several different methods, including sharing or other actions with play money or other manipulatives, various informal paper-and-pencil methods, and partial-quotients division. Some students may also use U.S. traditional long division. *For example:*

▷ Sharing play money

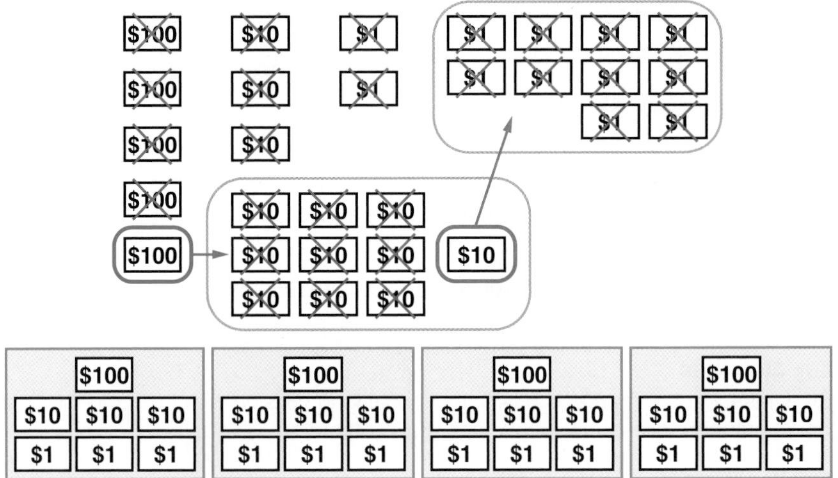

$532 / 4 = $133

▷ Sharing base-10 blocks

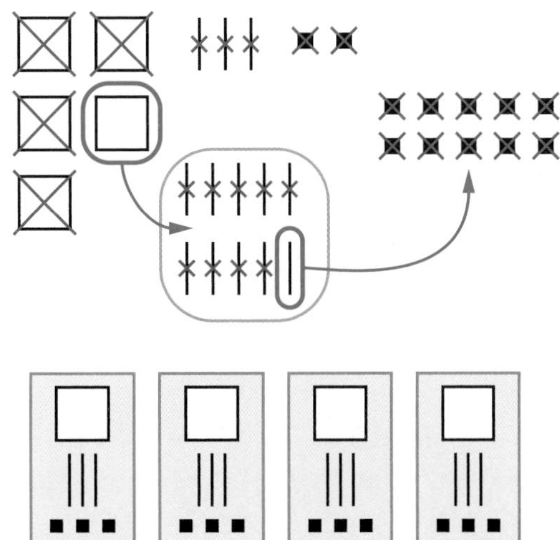

$532 / 4 = $133

▷ Using an informal paper-and-pencil method (*See margin.*)

▷ Using partial-quotients division

```
4)532
 − 400 | 100
   132 |
 −  80 |  20
    52 |
 −  40 |  10
    12 |
 −  12 |   3
     0 | 133
```

▷ Using U.S. traditional long division

```
   133
4)532
 − 4
   13
 − 12
    12
  − 12
     0
```

Introducing Long Division

WHOLE-CLASS ACTIVITY

After discussing students' solutions, regardless of whether one or more students used **U.S. traditional long division,** demonstrate it again as described below. Illustrate each step with pictures and, if possible, act out the problem using play money. Help students make connections between the steps in the algorithm and the actions of sharing the money.

Step 1:

Set up the problem. Think about sharing actual bills: 5 [$100]s, 3 [$10]s, and 2 [$1]s.

4)5 3 2 ← $532 is to be shared. We say $532 is the **dividend.** Think of $532 as 5 [$100]s, 3 [$10]s, and 2 [$1]s.

↑

The money is to be shared by four classes. We say 4 is the **divisor.**

Step 2:

Share the [$100]s. There are 5 [$100]s, so each class gets 1 [$100]. That uses up 4 [$100]s and leaves 1 [$100].

```
  1     ← Each class gets 1 [$100].
4)5 3 2
 −4     ← 1 [$100] each for 4 classes = 4 [$100]s
  1     ← 1 [$100] is left.
```

```
  532
− 100 ← $25 for each class
  432
− 100 ← $25 for each class
  332
− 100 ← $25 for each class
  232
− 100 ← $25 for each class
  132
− 100 ← $25 for each class
   32
−  32 ← $8 for each class
    0
```

$25 + $25 + $25 + $25 + $25 + $8 = $133

NOTE Long division is very demanding. Encourage students who may be overwhelmed to make a table of easy multiples of the divisor. For example:

1 * 4	4
2 * 4	8
3 * 4	12
4 * 4	16
5 * 4	20
6 * 4	24
7 * 4	28
8 * 4	32
9 * 4	36

Step 1

Money to be Shared	Ms. A's Class	Ms. B's Class	Ms. C's Class	Mr. D's Class
$100 $100 $100 $100 $100 $10 $10 $10 $1 $1				

Step 2

Money to be Shared	Ms. A's Class	Ms. B's Class	Ms. C's Class	Mr. D's Class
$100 $10 $10 $10 $1 $1	$100	$100	$100	$100

Step 3

Money to be Shared	Ms. A's Class	Ms. B's Class	Ms. C's Class	Mr. D's Class
$10 $10 $10 $10 $10 $10 $10 $10 $10 $10 $10 $10 $10 $1 $1	$100	$100	$100	$100

Step 3:

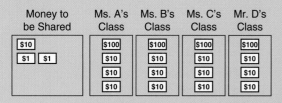

Trade the remaining [$100] for 10 [$10]s. That makes 13 [$10]s in all.

```
  1
4)5 3 2
 -4
  1 3   ← After trading the [$100] for 10 [$10]s, there are
          13 [$10]s in all.
```

Step 4

Money to be Shared	Ms. A's Class	Ms. B's Class	Ms. C's Class	Mr. D's Class
$10 $1 $1	$100 $10 $10 $10	$100 $10 $10 $10	$100 $10 $10 $10	$100 $10 $10 $10

Step 4:

Share the 13 [$10]s. Each class gets 3 [$10]s. That leaves 1 [$10] still to be shared.

```
  1 3   ← Each class gets 3 [$10]s.
4)5 3 2
 -4
  1 3
 -1 2   ← 3 [$10]s each for 4 classes = 12 [$10]s
    1   ← 1 [$10] is left.
```

Step 5

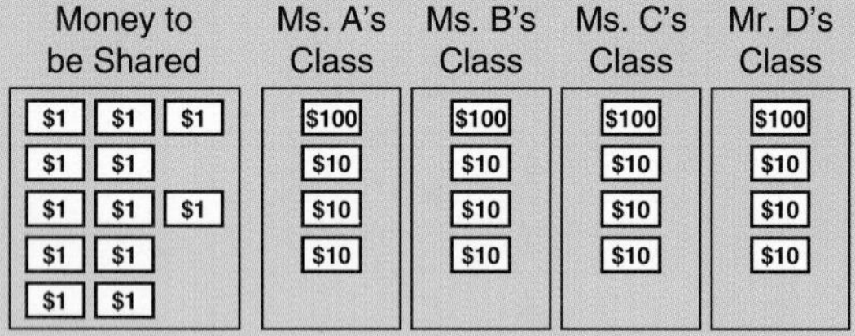

Step 5:

Trade the last [$10] to be shared for 10 [$1]s. That makes 12 [$1]s in all.

```
  1 3
4)5 3 2
 -4
  1 3
 -1 2
    1 2 ← After trading the [$10] for 10 [$1]s, there are
          12 [$1]s in all.
```

Step 6

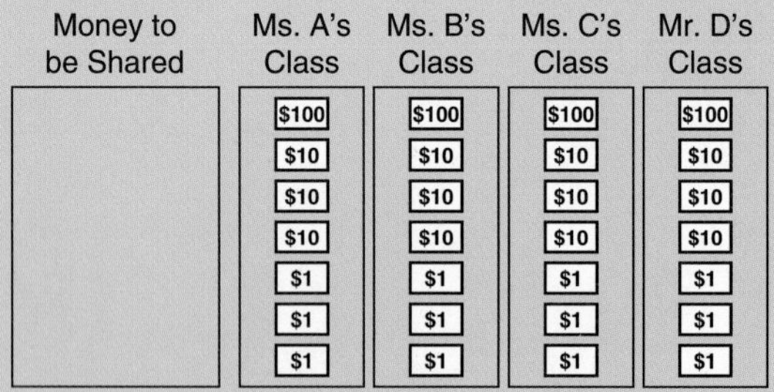

Step 6:

Share the 12 [$1]s. Each class gets 3 [$1]s.

```
  1 3 3 ← Each class gets 3 [$1]s.
4)5 3 2
 -4
  1 3
 -1 2
    1 2
   -1 2 ← 3 [$1]s each for 4 classes = 12 [$1]s
      0 ← 0 [$1]s are left.
```

Step 7:

Each class gets \$133. We say \$133 is the **quotient.** A number model is a good way to show the answer. Since there is no **remainder,** either

\$532 / 4 → \$133

or

\$532 / 4 = \$133

would be an acceptable number model for this problem.

U.S. traditional long division is complicated, so you may want to work more examples with the whole class. For now, continue to use sharing money as a context and continue drawing pictures and, if possible, acting out the problems with play money. Later, the algorithm can be generalized to non-money contexts.

Suggestions:

- ▷ \$84 / 7 \$12
- ▷ \$785 / 5 \$157
- ▷ \$122 / 8 \$15 R\$2
- ▷ \$807 / 4 \$201 R\$3
- ▷ 86 / 7 12 R2
- ▷ 468 / 5 93 R3

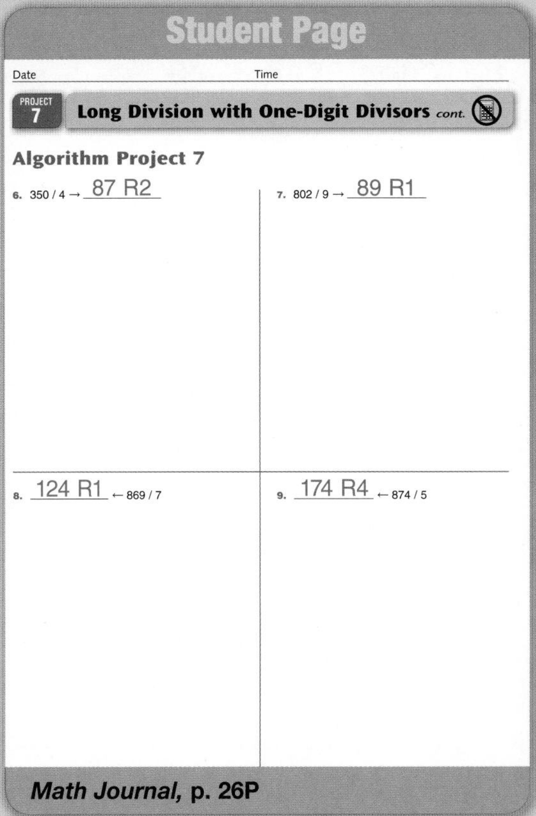
Student Page

Date Time

PROJECT 7 **Long Division with One-Digit Divisors** *cont.*

Algorithm Project 7

6. 350 / 4 → 87 R2

7. 802 / 9 → 89 R1

8. 124 R1 ← 869 / 7

9. 174 R4 ← 874 / 5

Math Journal, p. 26P

Solving Long Division Problems with One-Digit Divisors

PARTNER ACTIVITY

(*Math Journal 1* or *2,* pp. 25P–27P; *Student Reference Book,* pp. 24E–24H)

When students are ready, have them use U.S. traditional long division to solve Problems 2–13 on journal pages 25P–27P. They may find the examples on *Student Reference Book,* pages 24E–24H helpful. Students should note that Problems 6–9 involve remainders.

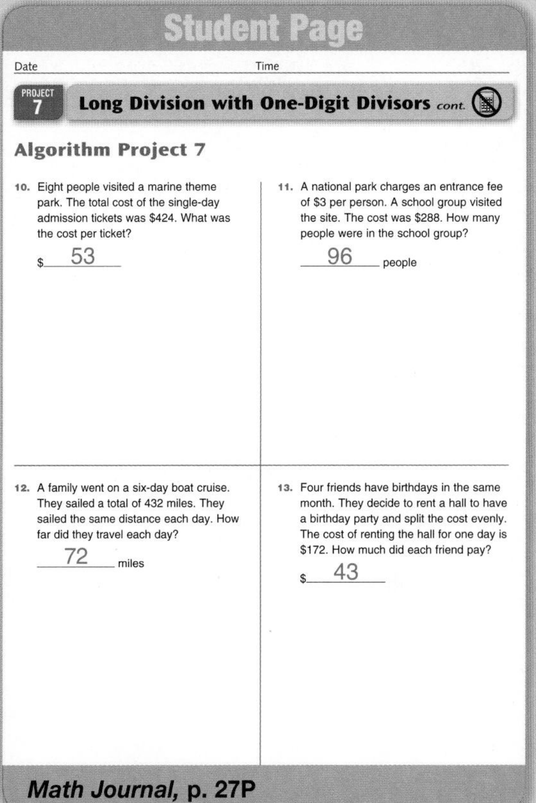
Student Page

Date Time

PROJECT 7 **Long Division with One-Digit Divisors** *cont.*

Algorithm Project 7

10. Eight people visited a marine theme park. The total cost of the single-day admission tickets was \$424. What was the cost per ticket?
\$ 53

11. A national park charges an entrance fee of \$3 per person. A school group visited the site. The cost was \$288. How many people were in the school group?
96 people

12. A family went on a six-day boat cruise. They sailed a total of 432 miles. They sailed the same distance each day. How far did they travel each day?
72 miles

13. Four friends have birthdays in the same month. They decide to rent a hall to have a birthday party and split the cost evenly. The cost of renting the hall for one day is \$172. How much did each friend pay?
\$ 43

Math Journal, p. 27P

2 Extending the Project

Writing and Solving Division Number Stories

PARTNER ACTIVITY

(*Student Reference Book,* pp. 24E–24H)

Have students write division number stories for a partner to solve using U.S. traditional long division. Again, students may find the examples on *Student Reference Book,* pages 24E–24H helpful.

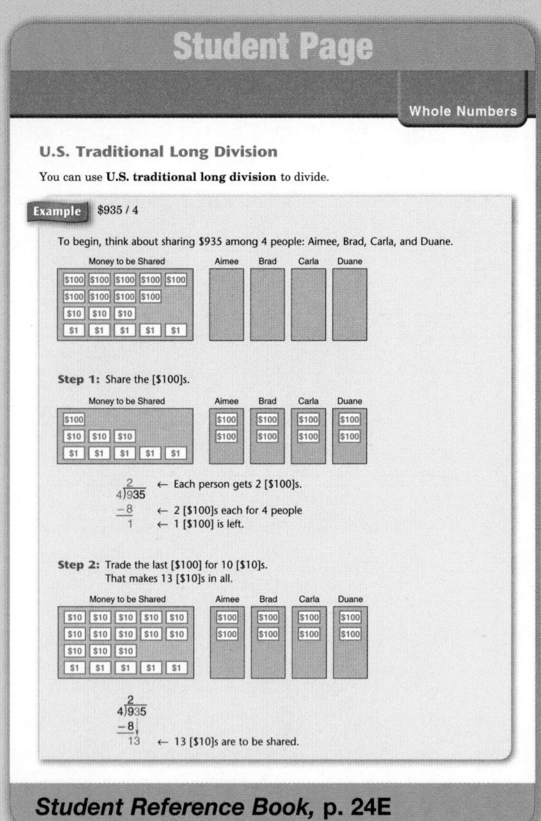
Student Page

Whole Numbers

U.S. Traditional Long Division

You can use **U.S. traditional long division** to divide.

Example $935 / 4

To begin, think about sharing $935 among 4 people: Aimee, Brad, Carla, and Duane.

Money to be Shared | Aimee | Brad | Carla | Duane

Step 1: Share the [$100]s.

Money to be Shared | Aimee | Brad | Carla | Duane

4)935 → 2 ← Each person gets 2 [$100]s.
−8 ← 2 [$100]s each for 4 people
1 ← 1 [$100] is left.

Step 2: Trade the last [$100] for 10 [$10]s. That makes 13 [$10]s in all.

Money to be Shared | Aimee | Brad | Carla | Duane

4)935 → 2
−8
13 ← 13 [$10]s are to be shared.

Student Reference Book, p. 24E

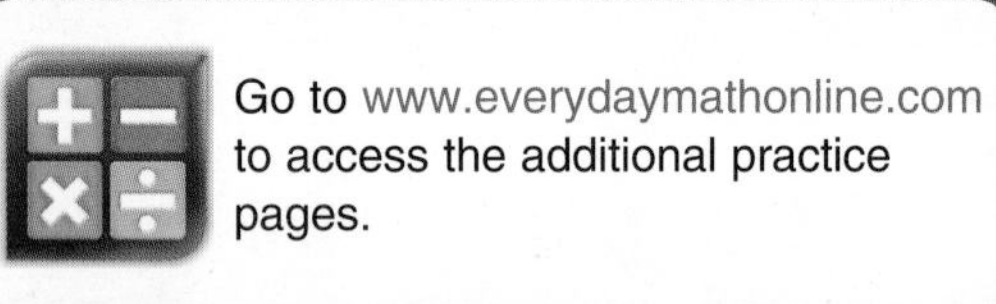

Go to www.everydaymathonline.com to access the additional practice pages.

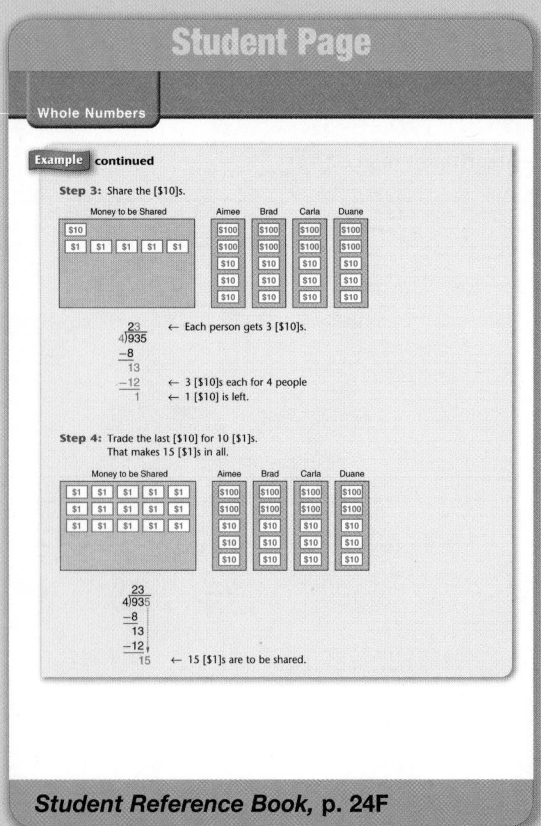
Student Page

Whole Numbers

Example continued

Step 3: Share the [$10]s.

Money to be Shared | Aimee | Brad | Carla | Duane

4)935 → 23 ← Each person gets 3 [$10]s.
−8
13
−12 ← 3 [$10]s each for 4 people
1 ← 1 [$10] is left.

Step 4: Trade the last [$10] for 10 [$1]s. That makes 15 [$1]s in all.

Money to be Shared | Aimee | Brad | Carla | Duane

4)935 → 23
−8
13
−12
15 ← 15 [$1]s are to be shared.

Student Reference Book, p. 24F

Solving Division Problems

(Online Additional Practice, pp. 27A–27C; *Student Reference Book,* pp. 22–24 and 24E–24H)

Online practice pages 27A–27C provide students with additional practice solving division problems. Use these pages as necessary.

Encourage students to use the focus algorithm (partial-quotients division) to solve the problems on practice page 27A. Invite them to use any algorithm they wish to solve the problems on the remaining pages. Students may find the examples on *Student Reference Book,* pages 22–24 and 24E–24H helpful.

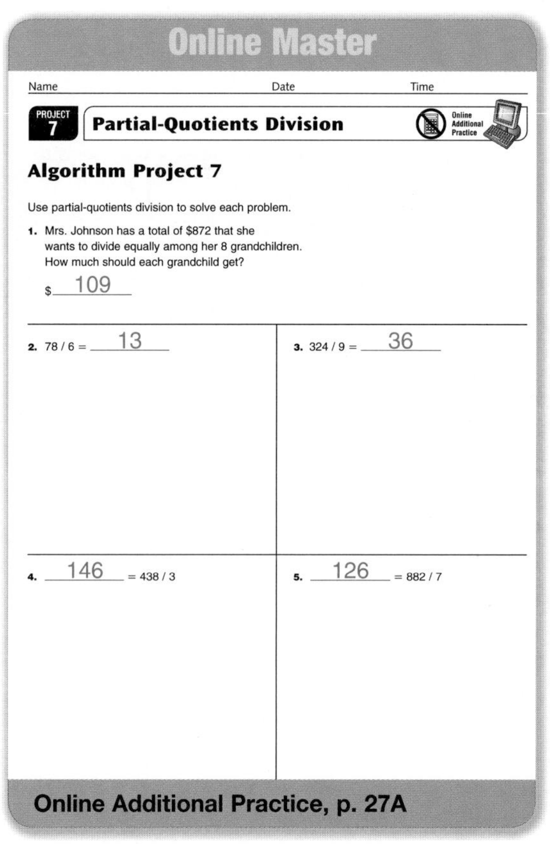
Online Master

Name Date Time

PROJECT 7 **Partial-Quotients Division**

Algorithm Project 7

Use partial-quotients division to solve each problem.

1. Mrs. Johnson has a total of $872 that she wants to divide equally among her 8 grandchildren. How much should each grandchild get?
$ 109

2. 78 / 6 = 13

3. 324 / 9 = 36

4. 146 = 438 / 3

5. 126 = 882 / 7

Online Additional Practice, p. 27A

Algorithm 8 Project

U.S. Traditional Long Division, Part 2

Objective To extend U.S. traditional long division with single-digit divisors to four- and five-digit dividends and dividends in dollars-and-cents notation.

Technology Resources www.everydaymathonline.com

eToolkit

Algorithms Practice

EM Facts Workshop Game™

Family Letters

Assessment Management

Common Core State Standards

Curriculum Focal Points

Interactive Teacher's Lesson Guide

1 Doing the Project

Recommended Use After Lesson 9•9 and after Algorithm Project 7

Key Concepts and Skills

- Subtract multidigit numbers. [Operations and Computation Goal 2]
- Apply multiplication facts to long-division situations. [Operations and Computation Goal 3]
- Solve equal-sharing division problems and number stories. [Operations and Computation Goal 4]
- Divide decimals by whole numbers. [Operations and Computation Goal 4]

Key Activities

Students explore and practice U.S. traditional long division with single-digit divisors, four- and five-digit dividends, and dividends in dollars-and-cents notation.

Key Vocabulary

quotient ◆ dividend

Materials

- *Math Journal 1* or *2,* pp. 28P–30P
- *Student Reference Book,* pp. 24E–24J and 40D–40F
- $1 and $10 bills (*Math Masters,* p. 428; optional)
- $100 and $1,000 bills (optional)
- coins (optional)
- base-10 blocks (optional)
- index cards (optional)

2 Extending the Project

Students write division number stories and use U.S. traditional long division to solve them.

For additional practice, students solve division problems, first using the focus algorithm (partial-quotients division) and then using any algorithm they choose.

Materials

- *Student Reference Book,* pp. 22–24 and 24E–24H
- Online Additional Practice, pp. 27A–27C

Additional Information

Today there are no longer any bills larger than $100 in circulation, but it was not always so. Beginning in the late 1920s and early 1930s the U.S. Treasury issued a small number of large bills, including $500, $1,000, $5,000, $10,000, and $100,000 bills. By the mid-1940s, the Treasury stopped making these bills, and in 1969 President Nixon removed them from circulation because they were rarely used and attractive to counterfeiters.

Advance Preparation

If you intend to have students use coins and bills to model the division problems, you will need $100 and $1,000 bills. Make several copies of Grade 3 *Math Masters,* page 401 for the $100 bills or use index cards to create them. Use index cards to create $1,000 bills.

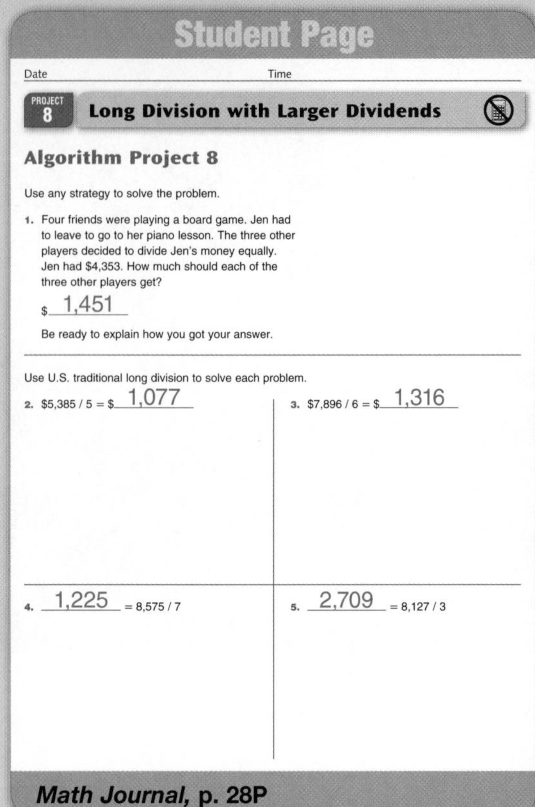

Student Page

Date Time

PROJECT 8 **Long Division with Larger Dividends**

Algorithm Project 8

Use any strategy to solve the problem.

1. Four friends were playing a board game. Jen had to leave to go to her piano lesson. The three other players decided to divide Jen's money equally. Jen had $4,353. How much should each of the three other players get?

   $ 1,451

   Be ready to explain how you got your answer.

Use U.S. traditional long division to solve each problem.

2. $5,385 / 5 = $ 1,077
3. $7,896 / 6 = $ 1,316
4. 1,225 = 8,575 / 7
5. 2,709 = 8,127 / 3

Math Journal, p. 28P

1 Doing the Project

Solving a Division Problem

WHOLE-CLASS DISCUSSION

(*Math Journal 1* or *2*, p. 28P)

Ask students to solve Problem 1 on journal page 28P. Tell them they may use paper and pencil or any tools they wish, except calculators.

Have students discuss and share solutions. $4353 / 3 = $1451 Expect a variety of approaches, including U.S. traditional long division, which was introduced in Algorithm Project 7. Have students explain why each of the steps in their procedures make sense. *For example:*

▷ Sharing play money or base-10 blocks

▷ Using an informal paper-and-pencil method

```
  4353
– 3000 ← $1000 for each player
  1353
 – 300 ← $100 for each player
  1053
 – 300 ← $100 for each player
   753
 – 300 ← $100 for each player
   453
 – 300 ← $100 for each player
   153
 – 150 ← $50 for each player
     3
   – 3 ← $1 for each player
     0
```

$1000 + $100 + $100 + $100 + $100 + $50 + $1 = $1451

▷ Using partial-quotients division (*See margin.*)

```
3)4353
 – 3000 | 1000
   1353 |
 – 1200 |  400
    153 |
  – 150 |   50
      3 |
    – 3 |    1
      0 | 1451
```

Partial-quotients division

▷ Using U.S. traditional long division

```
  1451
3)4353
 – 3
   13
 – 12
    15
  – 15
     03
    – 3
      0
```

Extending Long Division to Larger Dividends

WHOLE-CLASS ACTIVITY

After you have discussed students' solutions, regardless of whether some students used U.S. traditional long division, demonstrate it again as described on the next page. Illustrate each step in the algorithm with pictures of play money. Help students make connections between the steps in the algorithm and the actions of sharing money.

Step 1:

Set up the problem. Think about sharing actual bills: 4 [$1,000]s, 3 [$100]s, 5 [$10]s, and 3 [$1]s.

3)4 3 5 3 ⟵ $4,353 is to be shared.

↑

Three players will share Jen's money.

Step 1

Money to be Shared	Player A	Player B	Player C
$1,000 $1,000 $1,000 $1,000			
$100 $100 $100			
$10 $10 $10			
$10 $10			
$1 $1 $1			

Step 2:

Share the [$1,000]s. Each player gets 1 [$1,000]. There is 1 [$1,000] left.

1 ⟵ Each player gets 1 [$1,000].

3)4 3 5 3

– 3 ⟵ 1 [$1,000] each for 3 players = 3 [$1,000]s

1 ⟵ 1 [$1,000] is left.

Step 2

Money to be Shared	Player A	Player B	Player C
$1,000	$1,000	$1,000	$1,000
$100 $100 $100			
$10 $10 $10			
$10 $10			
$1 $1 $1			

Step 3:

Trade the 1 [$1,000] for 10 [$100]s.

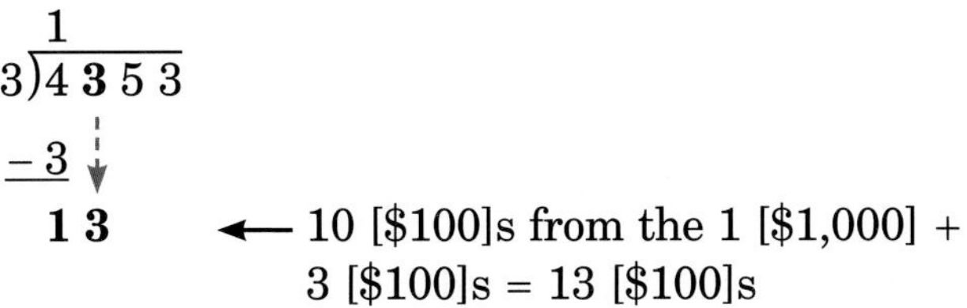

1

3)4 **3** 5 3

– 3 ↓

1 3 ⟵ 10 [$100]s from the 1 [$1,000] + 3 [$100]s = 13 [$100]s

Step 3

Money to be Shared	Player A	Player B	Player C
$100 $100 $100	$1,000	$1,000	$1,000
$100 $100			
$100 $100 $100			
$100 $100			
$100 $100 $100			
$10 $10 $10			
$10 $10			
$1 $1 $1			

Step 4:

Share the 13 [$100]s. Each player gets 4 [$100]s; 1 [$100] is left.

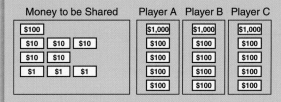

1 4 ⟵ Each player gets 4 [$100]s.

3)4 3 5 3

– 3

1 3

– 1 2 ⟵ 4 [$100]s each for 3 players = 12 [$100]s.

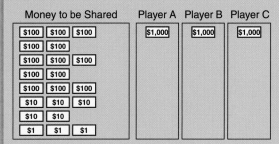

1 ⟵ 1 [$100] is left.

Step 4

Money to be Shared	Player A	Player B	Player C
$100	$1,000	$1,000	$1,000
$10 $10 $10	$100	$100	$100
$10 $10	$100	$100	$100
$1 $1 $1	$100	$100	$100
	$100	$100	$100

Step 5:

Trade the 1 [$100] for 10 [$10]s.

1 4

3)4 3 **5** 3

– 3

1 3

– 1 2 ↓

1 5 ⟵ 10 [$10]s from the 1 [$100] + 5 [$10]s = 15 [$10]s

Step 5

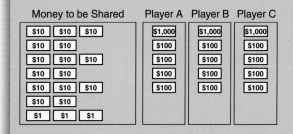

Money to be Shared	Player A	Player B	Player C
$10 $10 $10	$1,000	$1,000	$1,000
$10 $10	$100	$100	$100
$10 $10 $10	$100	$100	$100
$10 $10	$100	$100	$100
$10 $10 $10	$100	$100	$100
$10 $10			
$1 $1 $1			

Step 6

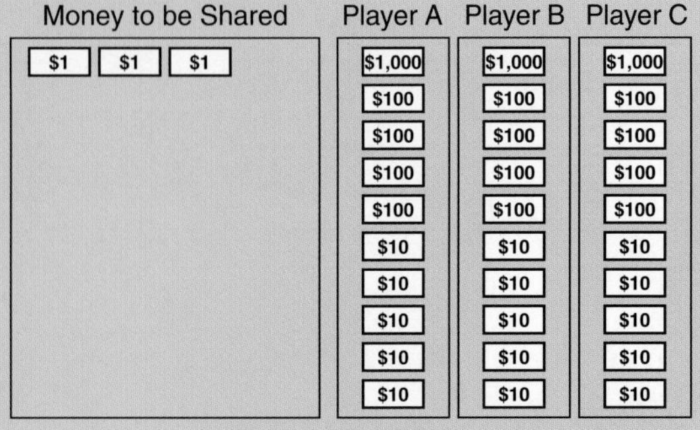

Step 7

Money to be Shared	Player A	Player B	Player C
	$1,000	$1,000	$1,000
	$100	$100	$100
	$100	$100	$100
	$100	$100	$100
	$100	$100	$100
	$10	$10	$10
	$10	$10	$10
	$10	$10	$10
	$10	$10	$10
	$10	$10	$10
	$1	$1	$1

Student Page

Date Time

PROJECT 8 **Long Division with Larger Dividends** *cont.*

Algorithm Project 8

Fill in the missing numbers.

6.
```
    1 7 3 9
 5)8 6 9 5
  - 5
    3 6
  - 3 5
      1 9
    - 1 5
        4 5
      - 4 5
          0
```

7.
```
    5 4 2
 6)3 2 5 2
  -3 0
     2 5
   - 2 4
       1 2
     - 1 2
         0
```

8. Jai is saving money to go to sleep-away camp next summer. The total cost is $1,092. He is earning money by walking dogs in his neighborhood.

a. At $4 per walk, how many dogs will Jai need to walk to earn $1,092? 273 dogs

b. At $7 per walk, how many dogs will Jai need to walk to earn $1,092? 156 dogs

Math Journal, p. 29P

Step 6:

Share the 15 [$10]s. Each player gets 5 [$10]s.

```
   1 4 5    ← Each player gets 5 [$10]s.
3)4 3 5 3
 - 3
   1 3
 - 1 2
     1 5
   - 1 5    ← 5 [$10]s each for 3 players = 15 [$10]s
       0    ← 0 [$10]s are left.
```

Step 7:

Share the 3 [$1]s. Each player gets 1 [$1].

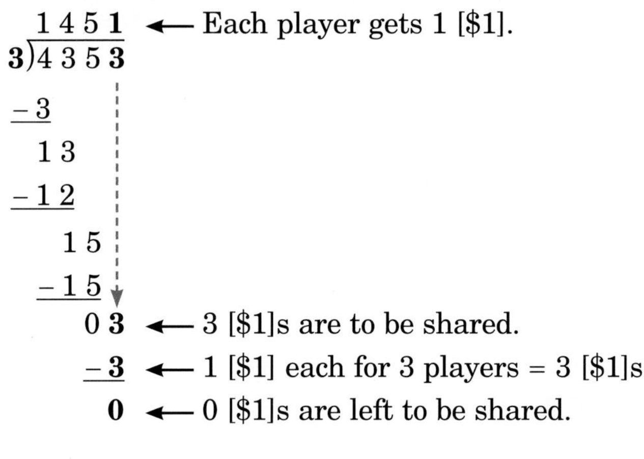

```
   1 4 5 1  ← Each player gets 1 [$1].
3)4 3 5 3
 - 3
   1 3
 - 1 2
     1 5
   - 1 5
       0 3  ← 3 [$1]s are to be shared.
       - 3  ← 1 [$1] each for 3 players = 3 [$1]s
         0  ← 0 [$1]s are left to be shared.
```

$4,353 / 3 = $1,451

Each of the continuing players gets $1,451.

▶ Solving Long Division Problems

PARTNER ACTIVITY

(*Math Journal 1* or *2,* pp. 28P and 29P; *Student Reference Book,* pp. 24E–24J)

Have partners use U.S. traditional long division to solve the problems on journal pages 28P and 29P. Students may find the examples on *Student Reference Book,* pages 24E–24J helpful.

▶ Extending Long Division to Dollars-and-Cents Notation

WHOLE-CLASS DISCUSSION

(*Math Journal 1* or *2,* p. 30P; *Student Reference Book,* pp. 40D–40F)

Have students solve Problem 1 on journal page 30P. As a class, discuss how Dennis solved the problem. Be sure to include the following points:

▷ Long division for dollars and cents looks almost exactly the same as for whole numbers.

▷ The money in Dennis's method would include dimes and pennies, not just bills as in whole-number long division with money.

▷ There are decimal points separating dollars from cents in Dennis's **quotient** and **dividend.** In whole-number long division there were no decimal points.

▷ With Dennis's method, we know exactly where the decimal point belongs. If we use partial-quotients division to solve the problem, we use estimation to place the decimal point. For example, to solve $9.45 / 7 by partial quotients:

- Estimate the answer. $9.45 / 7 would be more than $1 but less than $2.
- Divide as though the dividend were a whole number. 945 / 7 = 135
- Use the estimate to place the decimal point in the quotient. Since the answer must be between $1 and $2, the decimal point must go between the 1 and the 3; $1.35.

Have students complete Problems 2–5 on page 30P. Pose additional problems such as the following. Review *Student Reference Book,* pages 40D–40F as necessary.

▷ $1.72 / 4 $0.43	▷ $8.01 / 3 $2.67
▷ $7.05 / 5 $1.41	▷ $6.93 / 7 $0.99
▷ $9.27 / 3 $3.09	▷ $8.66 / 2 $4.33
▷ $9.42 / 6 $1.57	▷ $6.90 / 6 $1.15

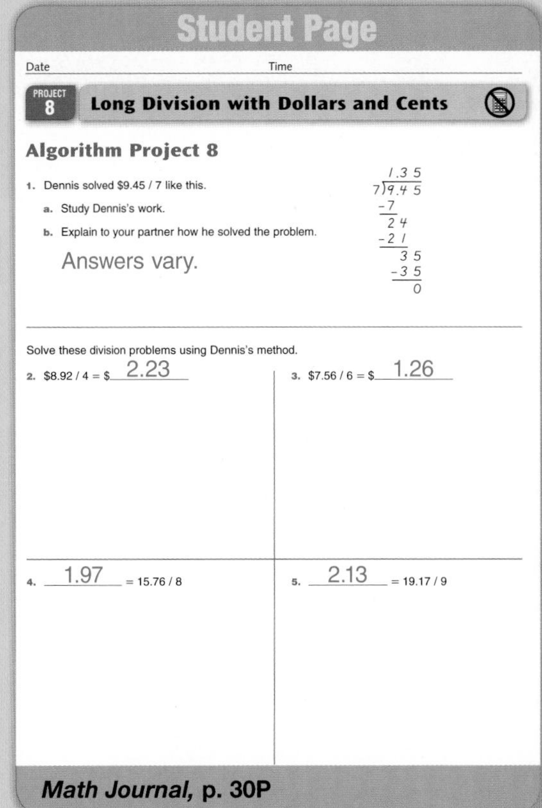
Student Page

Date Time

PROJECT 8 **Long Division with Dollars and Cents**

Algorithm Project 8

1. Dennis solved $9.45 / 7 like this.
   a. Study Dennis's work.
   b. Explain to your partner how he solved the problem.

   Answers vary.

Solve these division problems using Dennis's method.

2. $8.92 / 4 = $ 2.23
3. $7.56 / 6 = $ 1.26
4. 1.97 = 15.76 / 8
5. 2.13 = 19.17 / 9

Math Journal, p. 30P

2 Extending the Project

Writing and Solving Division Number Stories

PARTNER ACTIVITY

(*Student Reference Book,* pp. 24E–25J and 40D–40F)

Have students write division number stories that include single-digit divisors, four-and five-digit dividends, and dividends in dollars-and-cents notation. Partners use U.S. traditional long division to solve them. Students may find the examples on *Student Reference Book,* pages 24E–24J and 40D–40F helpful.

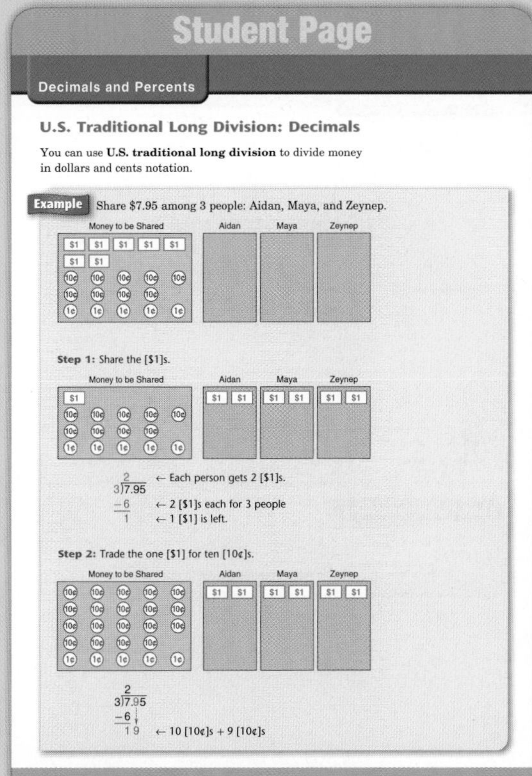
Student Page

Decimals and Percents

U.S. Traditional Long Division: Decimals

You can use **U.S. traditional long division** to divide money in dollars and cents notation.

Example Share $7.95 among 3 people: Aidan, Maya, and Zeynep.

Step 1: Share the [$1]s.

← Each person gets 2 [$1]s.
← 2 [$1]s each for 3 people
← 1 [$1] is left.

Step 2: Trade the one [$1] for ten [10¢]s.

← 10 [10¢]s + 9 [10¢]s

Student Reference Book, p. 40D

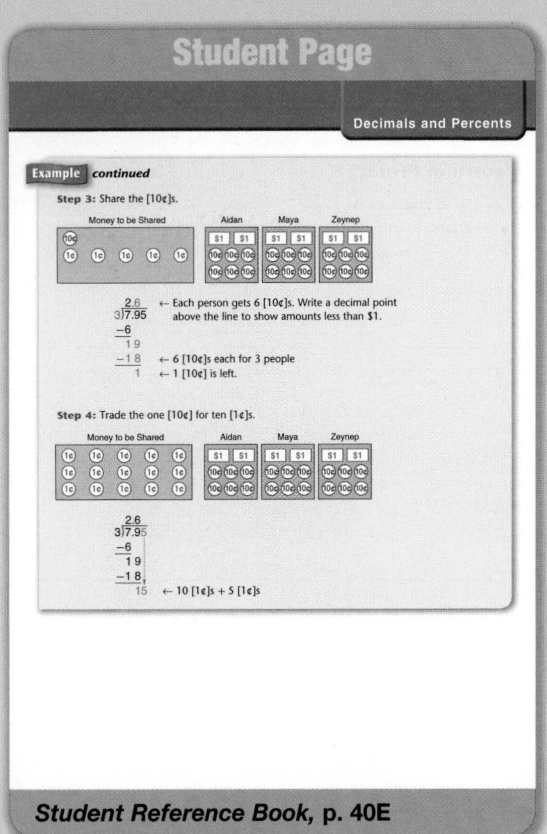
Student Page

Decimals and Percents

Example *continued*

Step 3: Share the [10¢]s.

Money to be Shared | Aidan | Maya | Zeynep

```
  2.6    ← Each person gets 6 [10¢]s. Write a decimal point
3)7.95      above the line to show amounts less than $1.
 -6
  1 9
 -1 8    ← 6 [10¢]s each for 3 people
    1    ← 1 [10¢] is left.
```

Step 4: Trade the one [10¢] for ten [1¢]s.

Money to be Shared | Aidan | Maya | Zeynep

```
  2.6
3)7.95
 -6
  1 9
 -1 8
    15   ← 10 [1¢]s + 5 [1¢]s
```

Student Reference Book, **p. 40E**

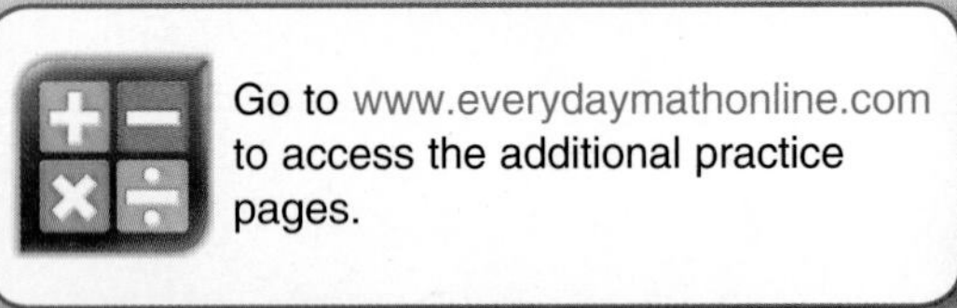

Go to www.everydaymathonline.com to access the additional practice pages.

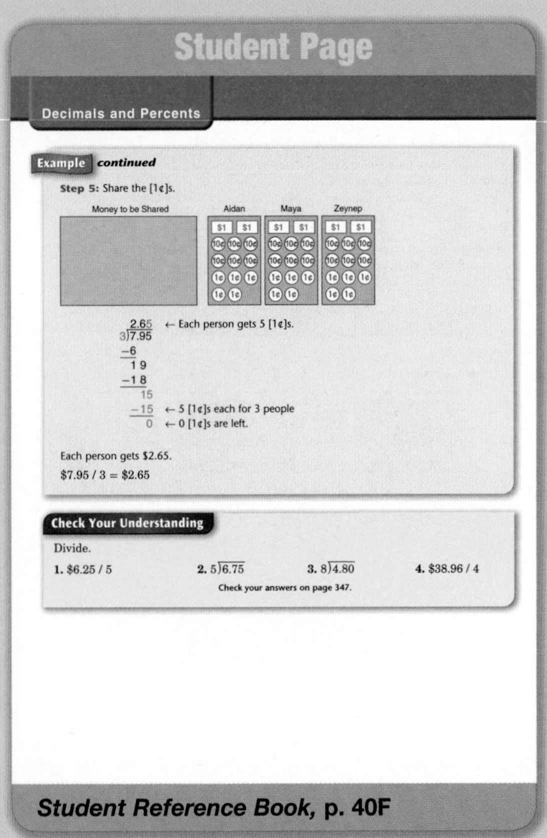
Student Page

Decimals and Percents

Example *continued*

Step 5: Share the [1¢]s.

Money to be Shared | Aidan | Maya | Zeynep

```
  2.65   ← Each person gets 5 [1¢]s.
3)7.95
 -6
  1 9
 -1 8
    15
   -15   ← 5 [1¢]s each for 3 people
     0   ← 0 [1¢]s are left.
```

Each person gets $2.65.
$7.95 / 3 = $2.65

Check Your Understanding

Divide.

1. $6.25 / 5   2. 5)6.75   3. 8)4.80   4. $38.96 / 4

Check your answers on page 347.

Student Reference Book, **p. 40F**

▶ Solving Division Problems

(Online Additional Practice, pp. 30A–30C; *Student Reference Book,* pp. 22–24, 24E–24J, and 40D–40F)

Online practice pages 30A–30C provide students with additional practice solving division problems. Use these pages as necessary.

Encourage students to use the focus algorithm (partial-quotients division) to solve the problems on practice page 30A. Invite them to use any algorithm they wish to solve the problems on the remaining pages. Students may find the examples on *Student Reference Book,* pages 22–24, 24E–24J, and 40D–40F helpful.

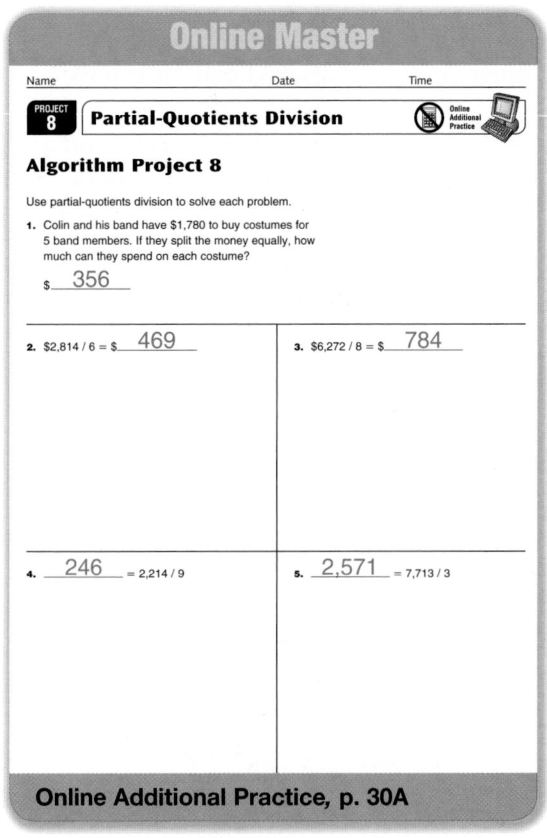
Online Master

Name Date Time

PROJECT 8 **Partial-Quotients Division**

Algorithm Project 8

Use partial-quotients division to solve each problem.

1. Colin and his band have $1,780 to buy costumes for 5 band members. If they split the money equally, how much can they spend on each costume?
$ 356

2. $2,814 / 6 = $ 469

3. $6,272 / 8 = $ 784

4. 246 = 2,214 / 9

5. 2,571 = 7,713 / 3

Online Additional Practice, p. 30A

Fourth Grade Key Vocabulary

For a more comprehensive glossary that includes additional entries and illustrations, please refer to the *Teacher's Reference Manual.*

NOTE: In a definition, terms in italics are defined elsewhere in this glossary.

A

acute angle An *angle* with a measure less than 90°.

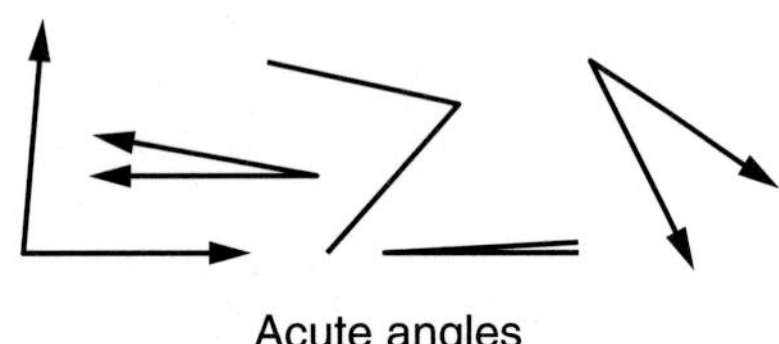

Acute angles

algorithm A set of step-by-step instructions for doing something, such as carrying out a computation or solving a problem. The most common algorithms are those for basic arithmetic computation, but there are many others. Some mathematicians and many computer scientists spend a great deal of time trying to find more efficient algorithms for solving problems.

altitude (1) In *Everyday Mathematics*, same as *height* of a figure. (2) Distance above sea level.

angle A figure formed by two *rays* or two *line segments* with a common *endpoint* called the *vertex* of the angle. The rays or segments are called the *sides* of the angle. An angle is measured in degrees between 0 and 360. One side of an angle is the *rotation* image of the other side through a number of degrees. Angles are named after their vertex point alone as in $\angle A$ below; or by three points, one on each side and the vertex in the middle as in $\angle BCD$ below.

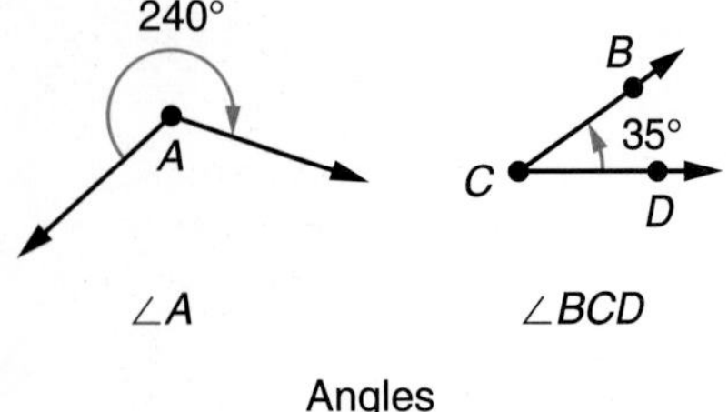

Angles

area The amount of surface inside a 2-dimensional figure. The figure might be a triangle or rectangle in a plane, the curved surface of a cylinder, or a state or country on Earth's surface. Commonly, area is measured in *square units* such as square miles, square inches, or square centimeters.

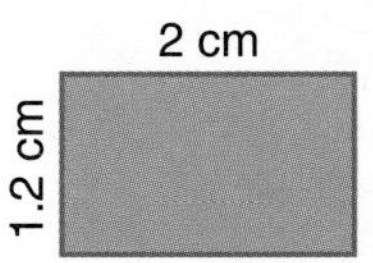

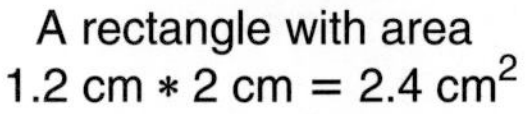

A rectangle with area 1.2 cm ∗ 2 cm = 2.4 cm²

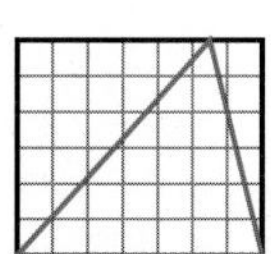

A triangle with area 21 square units

The area of the United States is about 3,800,000 square miles.

average A typical value for a set of numbers. In everyday life, average usually refers to the *mean* of the set, found by adding all the numbers and dividing by the number of numbers.

axis of a coordinate grid Either of the two number lines used to form a *coordinate grid.* Plural is axes.

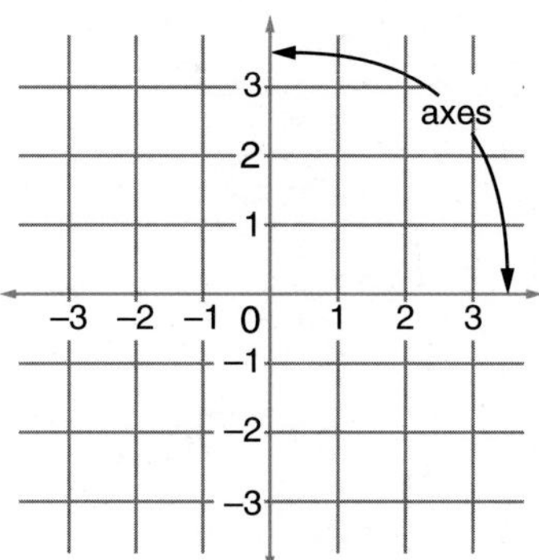

axis of rotation A *line* about which a solid figure rotates.

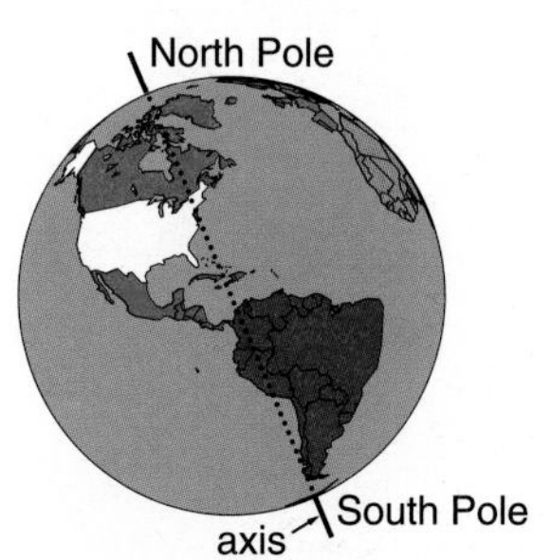

B

bar graph A graph with horizontal or vertical bars that represent data.

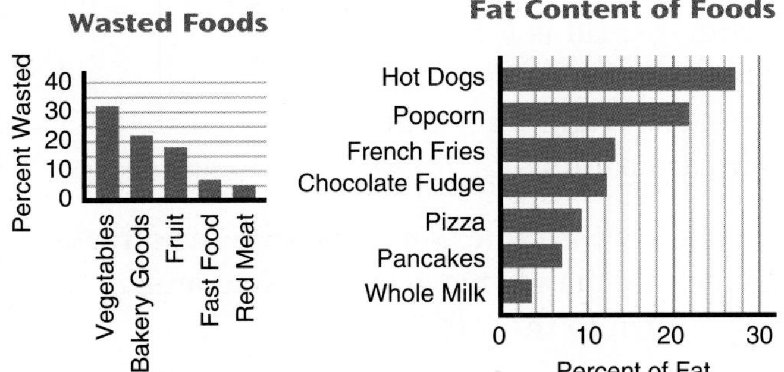

Source: The Garbage Product *Source:* The New York Public Library Desk Reference

base (in exponential notation) A number that is raised to a *power.* For example, the base in 5^3 is 5.

base of a parallelogram (1) The side of a *parallelogram* to which an altitude is drawn. (2) The length of this side. The area of a parallelogram is the base times the altitude or height perpendicular to it.

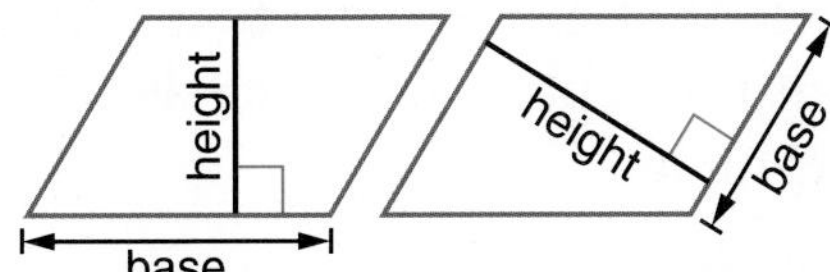

base of a prism or cylinder Either of the two parallel and congruent *faces* that define the shape of a *prism* or *cylinder.* In a cylinder, the base is a circle.

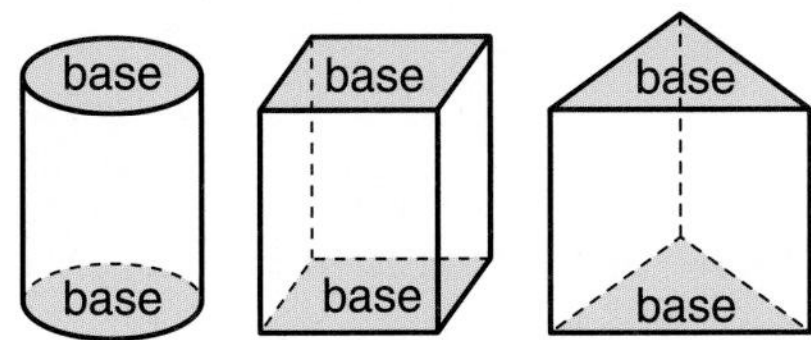

base of a pyramid or cone The *face* of a pyramid or cone that is opposite its apex (the vertex opposite the base). The base of a cone is a circle.

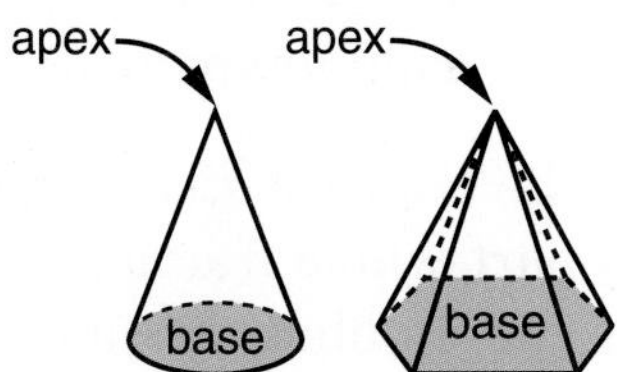

base of a rectangle (1) One of the sides of a *rectangle.* (2) The length of this side. The area of a rectangle is the base times the *altitude* or height.

base of a triangle (1) Any side of a *triangle* to which an *altitude* is drawn. (2) The length of this side. The area of a triangle is half the base times the altitude or height.

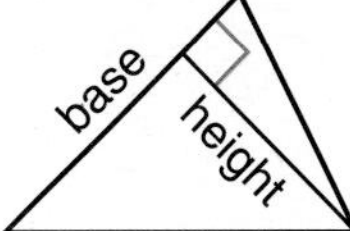

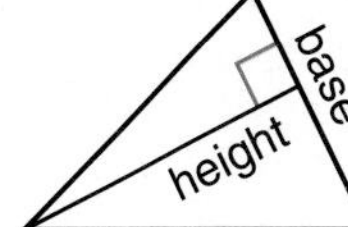

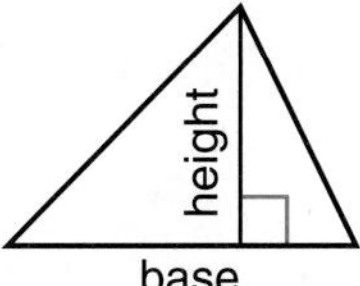

C

capacity (1) The amount of space occupied by a 3-dimensional figure. Same as *volume.* (2) Less formally, the amount a container can hold. Capacity is often measured in units such as quarts, gallons, cups, or liters.

centimeter (cm) A metric unit of *length* equivalent to 10 millimeters, $\frac{1}{10}$ of a decimeter, and $\frac{1}{100}$ of a *meter.*

circle The set of all *points* in a plane that are equally distant from a fixed point in the plane called the center of the circle. The distance from the center to the circle is the *radius* of the circle. The *diameter* of a circle is twice its radius. Points inside a circle are not part of the circle. A circle together with its interior is called a disk or a circular region.

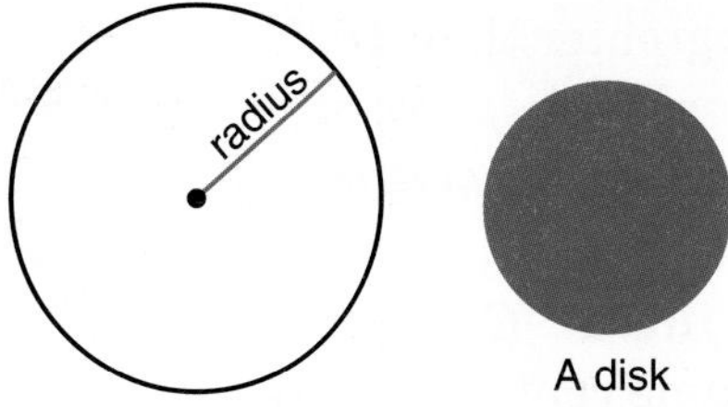

clockwise rotation The direction in which the hands move on a typical analog clock; a turn to the right.

column addition An addition *algorithm* in which the addends' digits are first added in each place-value column separately, and then 10-for-1 trades are made until each column has only one digit. Lines may be drawn to separate the place-value columns.

compass (1) A tool used to draw *circles* and arcs and copy *line segments.* Certain geometric figures can be drawn with compass-and-straightedge constructions.

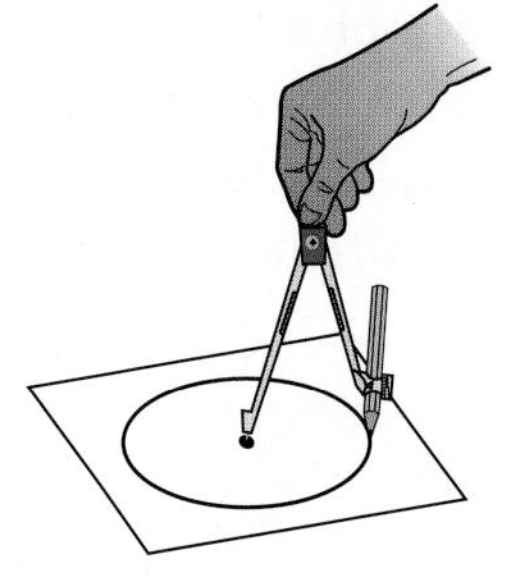

(2) A tool used to determine geographic direction.

A directional compass

composite number A *counting number* greater than 1 that has more than two *factors.* For example, 10 is a composite number because it has four factors; 1, 2, 5, and 10. A composite number is divisible by at least three whole numbers. Compare to *prime number.*

concave polygon A *polygon* on which there are at least two *points* that can be connected with a *line segment* that passes outside the polygon. For example, segment *AD* is outside the hexagon between *B* and *C*. Informally, at least one *vertex* appears to be "pushed inward." At least one interior angle has a measure greater than 180°. Same as *nonconvex polygon.* Compare to *convex polygon.*

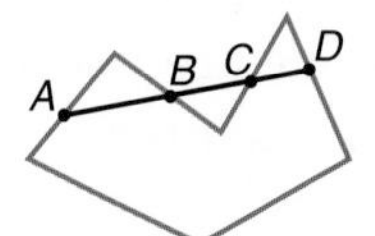

A concave polygon

concentric circles *Circles* that have the same center but have *radii* of different lengths.

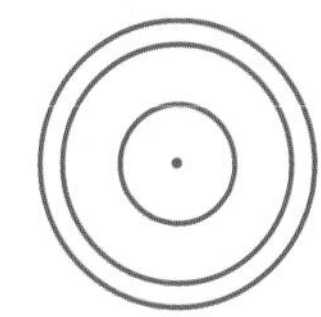

Concentric circles

convex polygon A *polygon* on which no two *points* can be connected with a *line segment* that passes outside the polygon. Informally, all *vertices* appear to be "pushed outward." Each angle in the polygon measures less than 180°. Compare to *concave polygon.*

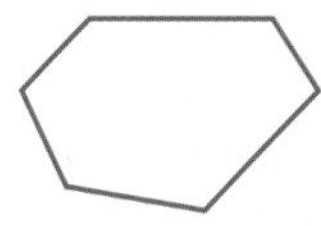

A convex polygon

coordinate (1) A number used to locate a *point* on a number line; a point's distance from an origin. (2) One of the numbers in an *ordered pair* or triple that locates a point on a *coordinate grid* or in coordinate space, respectively.

coordinate grid (rectangular coordinate grid) A reference frame for locating *points* in a plane by means of *ordered pairs* of numbers. A rectangular coordinate grid is formed by two number lines that intersect at *right angles* at their zero points.

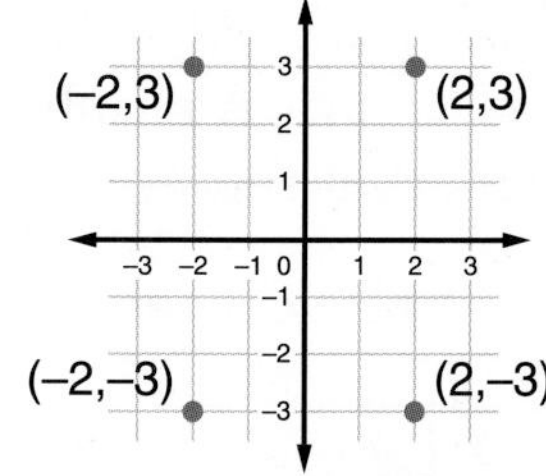

A coordinate grid

counterclockwise rotation Opposite the direction in which the hands move on a typical analog clock; a turn to the left.

counting numbers The numbers used to count things. The set of counting numbers is {1, 2, 3, 4, . . .}. Sometimes 0 is included, but not in *Everyday Mathematics.* Counting numbers are in the sets of *whole numbers,* integers, rational numbers, and real numbers, but each of these sets include numbers that are not counting numbers.

cylinder A geometric solid with two congruent, parallel circular regions for *bases* and a curved *face* formed by all the segments with an endpoint on each circle that are parallel to a segment with endpoints at the centers of the circles. Also called a circular cylinder.

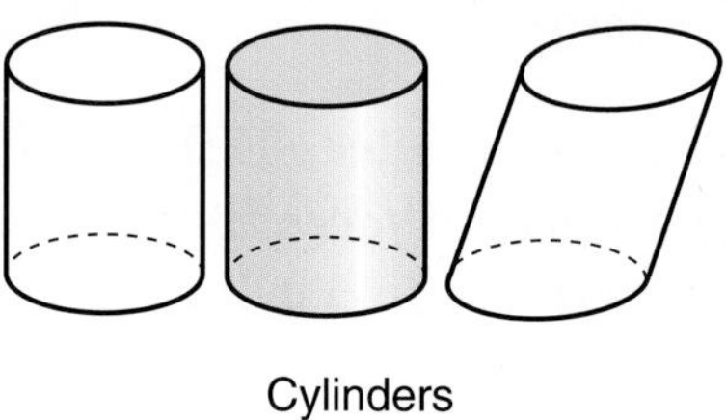

Cylinders

D

decimeter (dm) A metric unit of *length* equivalent to $\frac{1}{10}$ *meter* or 10 *centimeters.*

degree (°) (1) A unit of measure for *angles* based on dividing a *circle* into 360 equal parts. *Lines of latitude* and *longitude* are measured in degrees, and these degrees are based on angle measures. (2) A unit for measuring temperature.

denominator The nonzero *divisor b* in a fraction $\frac{a}{b}$ and *a/b*. In a part-whole fraction, the denominator is the number of equal parts into which the *whole,* or *ONE,* has been divided. Compare to *numerator*.

diameter (1) A *line segment* that passes through the center of a *circle* or *sphere* and has endpoints on the circle or sphere. (2) The length of such a segment. The diameter of a circle or sphere is twice the *radius.*

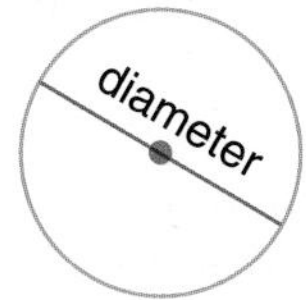

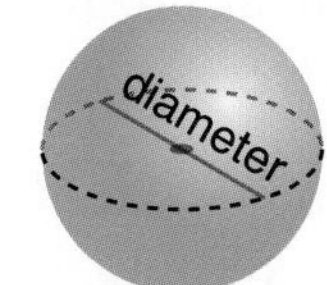

Distributive Property of Multiplication over Addition A property relating multiplication to a sum of numbers by distributing a *factor* over the terms in the sum. For example, $2 * (5 + 3) = (2 * 5) + (2 * 3) = 10 + 6 = 16$. In symbols:

For any numbers a, b, and c:

$$a * (b + c) = (a * b) + (a * c)$$

or $a(b + c) = ab + ac$

dividend The number in division that is being divided. For example, in 35 / 5 = 7, the dividend is 35.

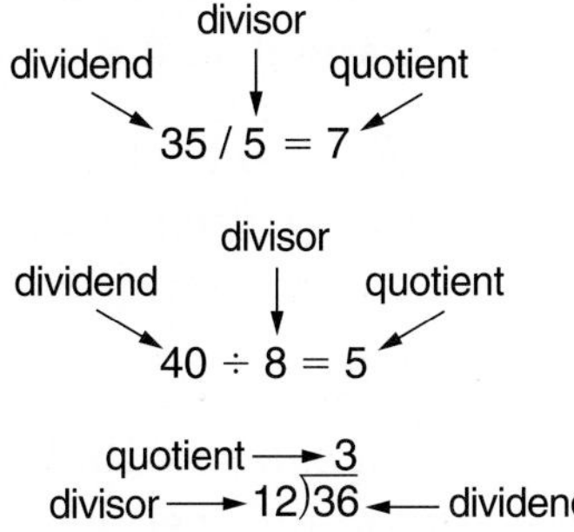

divisor In division, the number that divides another number, the *dividend.* For example, in 35 / 7 = 5, the divisor is 7. See the diagram under the definition of *dividend.*

endpoint A point at the end of a *line segment, ray,* or arc (part of a *circle* between and including two endpoints on the circle). These shapes are usually named using their endpoints. For example, the segment shown is "segment *TL*" or "segment *LT*."

endpoints

T *L*

equal-groups notation In *Everyday Mathematics,* a way to denote a number of equal-size groups. The size of each group is shown inside square brackets and the number of groups is written in front of the brackets. For example, 3 [6s] means 3 groups with 6 in each group. In general, *n* [*b*s] means *n* groups with *b* in each group.

equally likely outcomes *Outcomes* of a chance experiment or situation that have the same *probability* of happening. If all the possible outcomes are equally likely, then the probability of an event is equal to:

$$\frac{\text{number of favorable outcomes}}{\text{number of possible outcomes}}$$

equation A *number sentence* that contains an equal sign. For example, $5 + 10 = 15$ and $P = 2l + 2w$ are equations.

equator An imaginary circle around Earth halfway between the North Pole and the South Pole. The equator is the 0° *line* for *latitude.*

equilateral triangle A *triangle* with all three sides equal in length. Each angle of an equilateral triangle measures 60°, so it is also called an equiangular triangle.

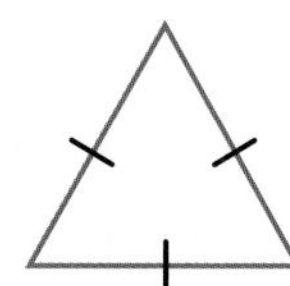

An equilateral triangle

equivalent fractions Fractions with different *denominators* that name the same number.

equivalent names Different ways of naming the same number. For example, 2 + 6, 4 + 4, 12 – 4, 18 – 10, 100 – 92, 5 + 1 + 2, eight, VIII, and 卌 /// are all equivalent names for 8. See *name-collection box.*

estimate (1) An answer close to, or approximating, an exact answer. (2) To make an estimate.

event A set of possible *outcomes* to an experiment. For example, in an experiment flipping two coins, getting 2 HEADS is an event, as is getting 1 HEAD and 1 TAIL.

expanded notation A way of writing a number as the sum of the values of each digit. For example, 356 is 300 + 50 + 6 in expanded notation.

expected outcome The average *outcome* over a large number of repetitions of a random experiment. For example, the expected outcome of rolling one die is the average number of spots landing up over a large number of rolls. Because each face of a fair die has equal probability of landing up, the expected outcome is $\frac{(1 + 2 + 3 + 4 + 5 + 6)}{6} = \frac{21}{6} = 3\frac{1}{2}$. This means that the average of many rolls of a fair die is expected to be about $3\frac{1}{2}$. More formally, the expected outcome is defined as an average over infinitely many repetitions.

exponent A small raised number used in *exponential notation* to tell how many times the *base* is used as a *factor*. For example, in 5^3, the base is 5, the exponent is 3, and $5^3 = 5 * 5 * 5 = 125$. Same as *power*.

exponential notation A way of representing repeated multiplication by the same *factor*. For example, 2^3 is exponential notation for $2 * 2 * 2$. The *exponent* 3 tells how many times the *base* 2 is used as a factor.

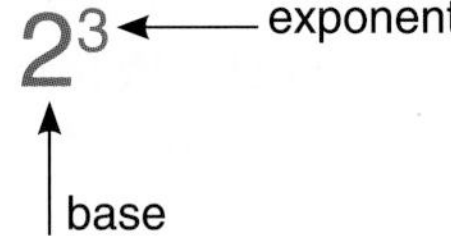

expression (1) A mathematical phrase made up of numbers, *variables*, operation symbols, and/or *grouping symbols*. An expression does not contain relation symbols such as =, >, and ≤. (2) Either side of an *equation* or inequality.

$2 + 3$
$\sqrt{2ab}$
πr^2
$9x - 2$
Expressions

extended facts Variations of basic arithmetic facts involving multiples of 10, 100, and so on. For example, $30 + 70 = 100$, $40 * 5 = 200$, and $560 / 7 = 80$ are extended facts.

face (1) In *Everyday Mathematics*, a flat surface on a 3-dimensional figure. Some special faces are called *bases*. (2) More generally, any 2-dimensional surface on a 3-dimensional figure.

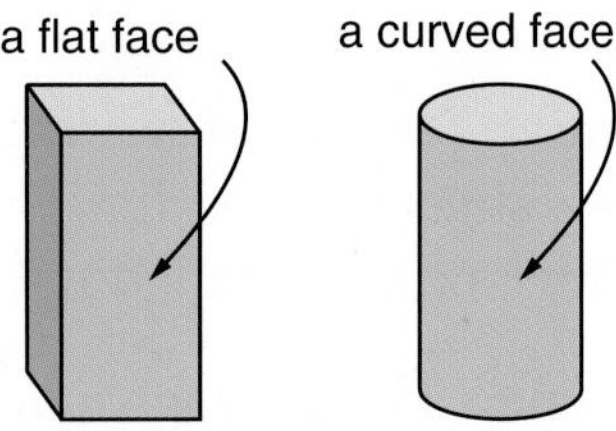

fact family A set of related arithmetic facts linking two inverse operations. For example,

$$5 + 6 = 11$$
$$6 + 5 = 11$$
$$11 - 5 = 6$$
$$11 - 6 = 5$$

are an addition/subtraction fact family.

Similarly,

$$5 * 7 = 35$$
$$7 * 5 = 35$$
$$35 / 7 = 5$$
$$35 / 5 = 7$$

are a multiplication/division fact family. Same as *number family*.

factor (1) Each of the two or more numbers in a *product*. For example, in $6 * 0.5$, 6 and 0.5 are factors. (2) To represent a number as a product of factors. For example, factor 21 by rewriting as $7 * 3$.

factor of a counting number *n* A *counting number* whose product with some other counting number equals *n*. For example, 2 and 3 are factors of 6 because $2 * 3 = 6$. But 4 is not a factor of 6 because $4 * 1.5 = 6$, and 1.5 is not a counting number.

factor pair Two *factors of a counting number* n whose product is *n*. A number may have more than one factor pair. For example, the factor pairs for 18 are 1 and 18, 2 and 9, and 3 and 6.

fair Free from bias. Each side of a fair die or coin will land up about equally often. Each region of a fair spinner will be landed on in proportion to its area.

favorable outcome An *outcome* that satisfies the conditions of an *event* of interest. For example, suppose a 6-sided die is rolled and the event of interest is "roll an even number." There are six possible outcomes: roll 1, 2, 3, 4, 5, or 6. Of these, 3 are favorable: roll 2, 4, or 6.

flip An informal name for a *reflection*.

formula A general rule for finding the value of something. A formula is usually an *equation* with quantities represented by letter *variables*. For example, a formula for distance traveled d at a rate r over a time t is $d = r * t$. The area of a triangle A with base length b and height h is given below.

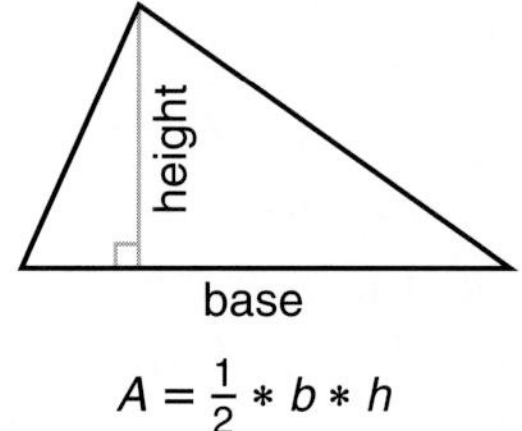

G

grouping symbols Parentheses ( ), brackets [ ], braces { }, and similar symbols that define the order in which operations in an *expression* are to be done. Nested grouping symbols are groupings within groupings, and the innermost grouping is done first. For example, in $(3 + 4) * [(8 + 2) / 5]$, the group $(8 + 2)$ is nested within $[(8 + 2) / 5]$ and is done first. So $(3 + 4) * [(8 + 2) / 5]$ simplifies as follows:

$$(3 + 4) * [(8 + 2) / 5]$$
$$(3 + 4) * [10 / 5]$$
$$7 * 2$$
$$14$$

H

height (1) A *perpendicular* segment from one *side* of a geometric figure to a *parallel* side or from a *vertex* to the opposite side. (2) The length of this segment. In *Everyday Mathematics,* same as *altitude.*

height of a parallelogram (1) The *length* of the shortest *line segment* between a *base of a parallelogram* and the *line* containing the opposite *side*. The height is *perpendicular* to the base. (2) The line segment itself.

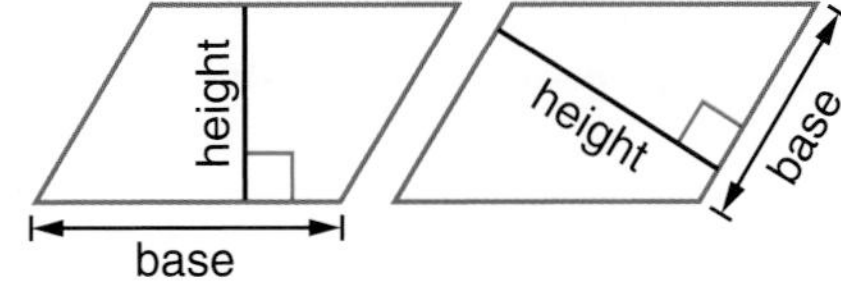

height of a prism or cylinder The *length* of the shortest *line segment* from a *base of a prism* or *cylinder* to the plane containing the opposite base. The height is *perpendicular* to the bases. (2) The line segment itself.

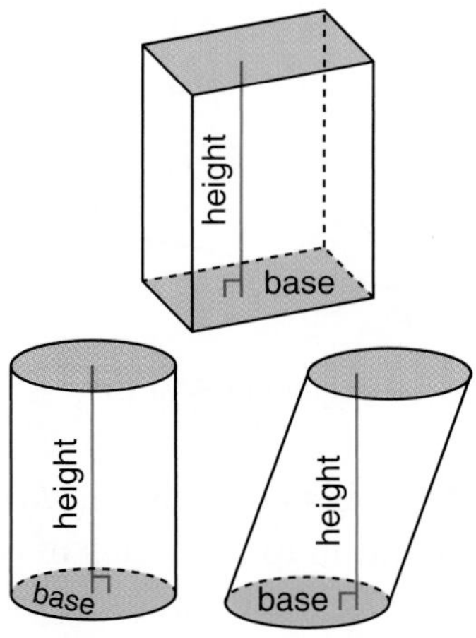

height of a pyramid or cone The *length* of the shortest *line segment* from the apex of a pyramid or cone to the plane containing the *base.* The height is *perpendicular* to the base. (2) The line segment itself.

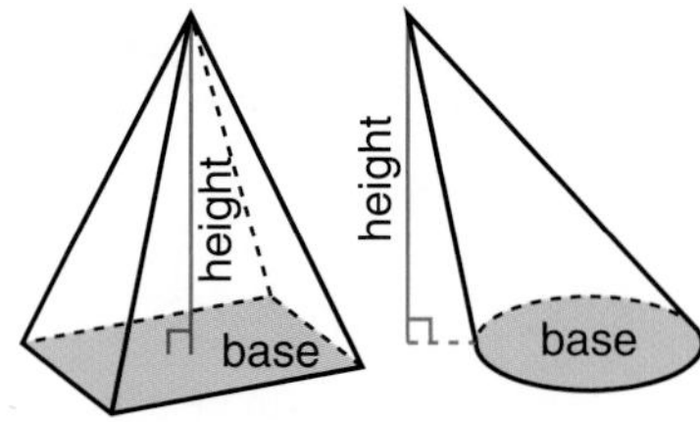

height of a rectangle The *length* of a *side perpendicular* to a *base of a rectangle.* Same as altitude of a rectangle.

height of a triangle The *length* of the shortest segment from a *vertex* of a triangle to the line containing the opposite *side.* The height is *perpendicular* to the base. (2) The line segment itself.

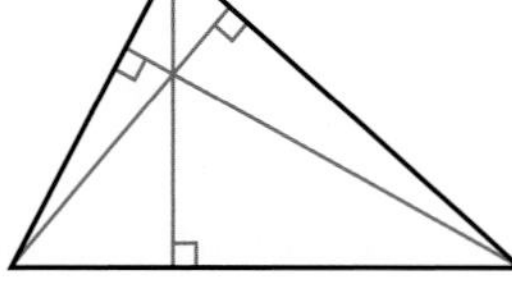

The heights of the triangle are blue.

heptagon A 7-sided *polygon.*

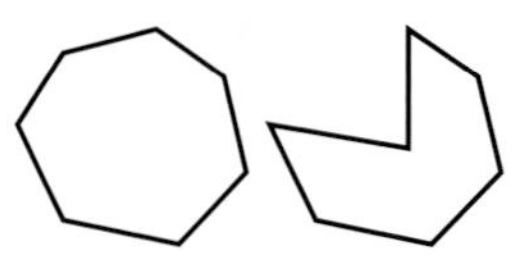

Heptagons

hexagon A 6-sided *polygon.*

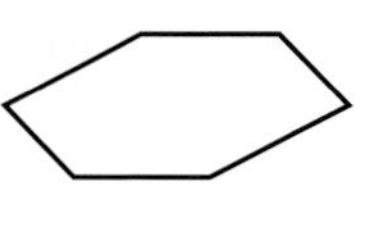

A hexagon

I

index of locations A list of places together with a reference frame for locating them on a map. For example, "Billings, D3," means that Billings is in the rectangle to the right of D and above 3 on the map below.

Section of Map of Montana

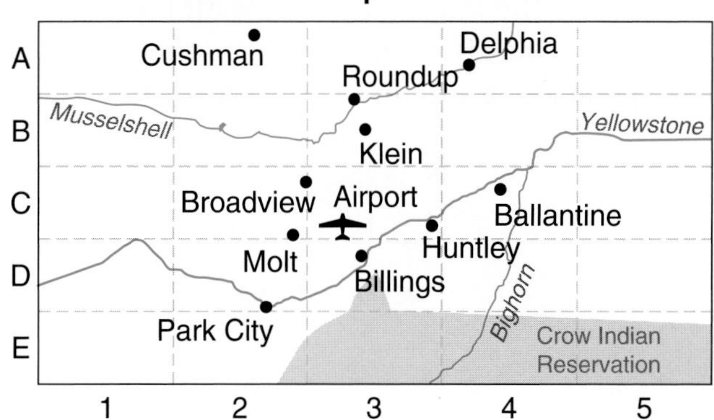

inscribed polygon A *polygon* whose vertices are all on the same *circle.*

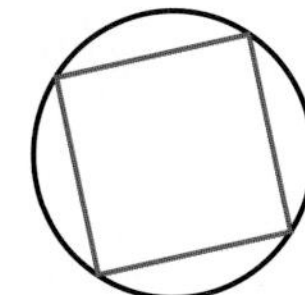

An inscribed square

interest A charge for using someone else's money. Interest is usually a *percent* of the amount borrowed.

interior of a figure (1) The set of all *points* in a plane bounded by a closed 2-dimensional figure, such as a *polygon* or *circle.* (2) The set of all points in space bounded by a closed 3-dimensional figure, such as a *polyhedron* or *sphere.* The interior is usually not considered to be part of the figure.

intersect To share a common *point* or points.

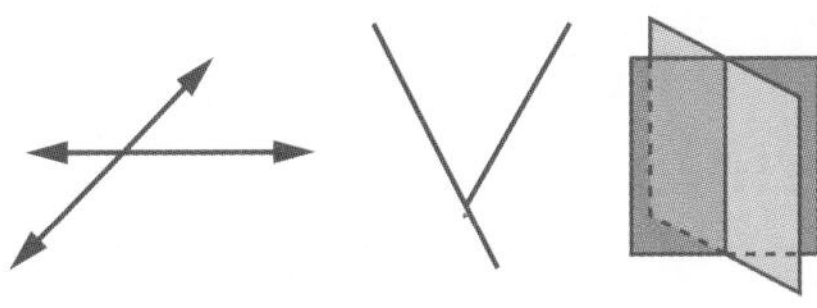

Intersecting lines and line segments   Intersecting planes

isosceles triangle A *triangle* with at least two sides equal in length. Angles opposite the congruent sides are congruent to each other.

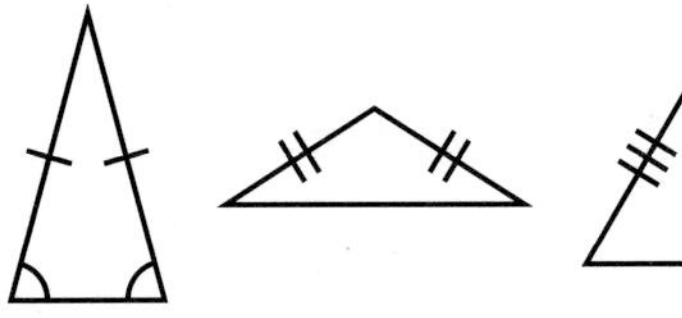

Isosceles triangles

kite A *quadrilateral* with two distinct pairs of adjacent sides of equal length. In *Everyday Mathematics,* the four sides cannot all have equal length; that is, a *rhombus* is not a kite. The diagonals of a kite are *perpendicular.*

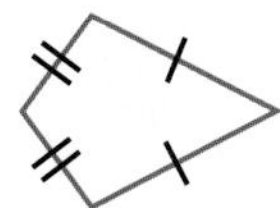

A kite

landmark In *Everyday Mathematics,* a notable feature of a data set. Landmarks include the *median, mode, mean, maximum, minimum,* and *range.*

latitude A *degree* measure locating a place on Earth north or south of the *equator.* A location at 0° latitude is on the equator. The North Pole is at 90° north latitude, and the South Pole is at 90° south latitude. Compare to *longitude.* See *lines of latitude.*

lattice multiplication A very old *algorithm* for multiplying multidigit numbers that requires only basic *multiplication facts* and addition of 1-digit numbers in a lattice diagram.

length of a rectangle Typically, but not necessarily, the longer dimension of a *rectangle.*

letter-number pair An *ordered pair* in which one of the *coordinates* is a letter. Often used to locate places on maps.

line In *Everyday Mathematics,* a 1-dimensional straight path that extends forever in opposite directions. A line is named using two *points* on it or with a single, italicized lower-case letter such as *l*. In formal Euclidean geometry, line is an undefined geometric term.

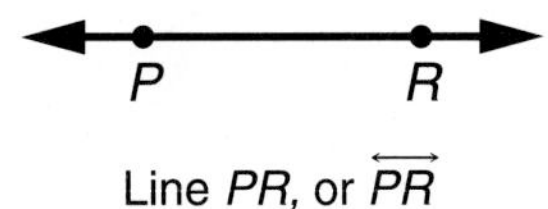

Line *PR*, or $\overleftrightarrow{PR}$

line plot A sketch of data in which check marks, Xs, or other symbols above a labeled line show the frequency of each value.

line segment (or **segment**) A part of a *line* between and including two *points,* called *endpoints* of the segment. A line segment is often named by its endpoints.

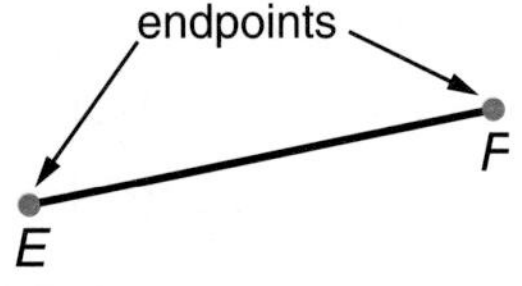

Segment *EF*, or $\overline{EF}$

lines of latitude Lines of constant *latitude* drawn on a 2-dimensional map or circles of constant latitude drawn on a globe. Lines of latitude are also called "parallels" because they are parallel to the *equator* and to each other. On a globe, latitude lines (circles) are intersections of planes parallel to the plane through the equator. Compare to *lines of longitude.*

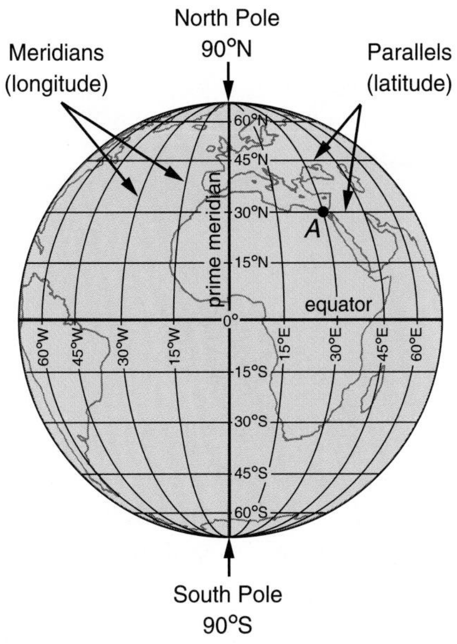

Point A is located at 30°N, 30°E.

lines of longitude Lines of constant *longitude* drawn on a 2-dimensional map or semicircles of constant longitude drawn on a globe connecting the North and South Poles. Lines of longitude are also called "meridians." Compare to *lines of latitude.*

liter (L) A metric unit of *volume* or *capacity* equal to the volume of a cube with 10-cm-long edges. 1 L = 1,000 mL = 1,000 cm^3. A liter is a little larger than a quart.

longitude A *degree* measure locating a place on Earth east or west of the *prime meridian.* A location at 0° longitude is on the prime meridian. A location at 180° east or west longitude is on or near the international date line, which is based on the imaginary semicircle opposite the prime meridian. Compare to *latitude.* See *lines of longitude.*

M

magnitude estimate A rough *estimate* of whether a number is in the tens, hundreds, thousands, or other powers of 10. For example, the U.S. national debt per person is in the tens of thousands of dollars. In *Everyday Mathematics,* students give magnitude estimates for problems such as *How many dimes are in $200?* or *How many halves are in 30?*

map scale The ratio of a distance on a map, globe, or drawing to an actual distance. For example, 1 inch on a map might correspond to 1 real-world mile. A map scale may be shown on a segment of a number line, given as a ratio of distances such as $\frac{1}{63,360}$ or 1:63,360 when an inch represents a mile, or by an informal use of the = symbol such as "1 inch = 1 mile."

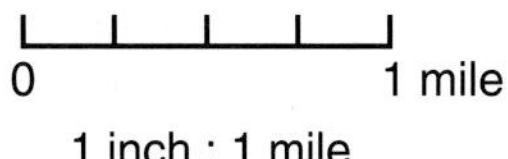

maximum The largest amount; the greatest number in a set of data. Compare to *minimum.*

mean For a set of numbers, their sum divided by the number of numbers. Often called the average value of the set. Compare to the other data *landmarks median* and *mode.*

median The middle value in a set of data when the data are listed in order from smallest to largest or vice versa. If there is an even number of data points, the median is the *mean* of the two middle values. Compare to other data *landmarks mean* and *mode.*

meridian bar A device on a globe that shows degrees of *latitude* north and south of the *equator,* called a meridian bar because it is in the same orientation as meridians (*lines of longitude*).

meter (m) The basic metric unit of *length* from which other metric units of length are derived. Originally, the meter was defined as $\frac{1}{10,000,000}$ of the distance from the North Pole to the *equator* along a meridian passing through Paris. From 1960 to 1983, the meter was redefined as 1,630,763.73 wavelengths of orange-red light from the element krypton. Today, the meter is defined as the distance light travels in a vacuum in $\frac{1}{299,792,458}$ second. One meter is equal to 10 decimeters, 100 *centimeters,* or 1,000 millimeters.

milliliter (mL) A metric unit of *volume* or *capacity* equal to $\frac{1}{1000}$ of a *liter,* or 1 cubic centimeter.

minimum The smallest amount; the smallest number in a set of data. Compare to *maximum.*

minuend In subtraction, the number from which another number is subtracted. For example, in 19 − 5 = 14, the minuend is 19. Compare to *subtrahend.*

mixed number A number that is written using both a *whole number* and a fraction. For example, $2\frac{1}{4}$ is a mixed number equal to $2 + \frac{1}{4}$.

mode The value or values that occur most often in a set of data. Compare to other *landmarks median* and *mean*.

multiple of a number *n* (1) A *product* of *n* and a *counting number*. For example, the multiples of 7 are 7, 14, 21, 28, ... (2) A product of *n* and an *integer*. For example, the multiples of 7 are . . ., –21, –14, –7, 0, 7, 14, 21, ...

multiplication/division diagram A diagram used in *Everyday Mathematics* to model situations in which a total number is made up of equal-size groups. The diagram contains a number of groups, a number in each group, and a total number. Also called a multiplication diagram for short.

rows	chairs per row	total chairs
15	25	?

A multiplication/division diagram

multiplication fact The *product* of two 1-digit numbers, such as $6 * 7 = 42$.

name-collection box In *Everyday Mathematics,* a diagram that is used for collecting *equivalent names* for a number.

25
37 – 12
20 + 5
~~////~~ ~~////~~ ~~////~~ ~~////~~ ~~////~~
twenty-five
veinticinco

***n*-gon** Same as *polygon,* where *n* is the number of sides. Polygons that do not have special names like squares and pentagons are usually named using *n*-gon notation, such as 13-gon or 100-gon.

nonagon A 9-sided *polygon.*

nonconvex polygon Same as *concave polygon.*

number family Same as *fact family.*

number model A *number sentence, expression,* or other representation that models a number story or situation. For example, the story *Sally had $5, and then she earned $8* can be modeled as the number sentence $5 + 8 = 13$, as the expression $5 + 8$, or by

$$\begin{array}{r} 5 \\ +\ 8 \\ \hline 13 \end{array}$$

number sentence Two *expressions* with a relation symbol. For example,

$$5 + 5 = 10$$
$$2 - ? = 8$$
$$16 \leq a * b$$
$$a^2 + b^2 = c^2$$

Number sentences

numerator The *dividend a* in a fraction $\frac{a}{b}$ or *a/b.* In a part-whole fraction, in which the *whole* (the *ONE* or *unit whole*) is divided into a number of equal parts, the numerator is the number of equal parts being considered. Compare to *denominator.*

obtuse angle An *angle* with measure between 90° and 180°.

octagon An 8-sided *polygon.*

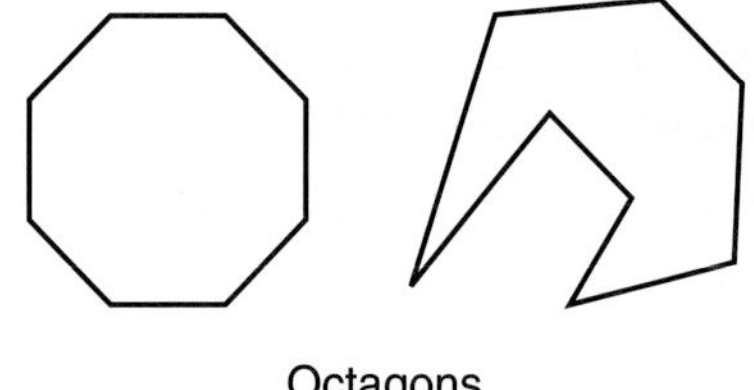

Octagons

ONE In *Everyday Mathematics,* same as *whole* or *unit whole.*

open sentence A *number sentence* with one or more *variables.* An open sentence is neither true nor false. For example, 9 + ______ = 15, $? - 24 < 10$, and $7 = x + y$ are open sentences.

ordered pair (1) Two numbers, or *coordinates,* used to locate a *point* on a rectangular *coordinate grid.* The first coordinate *x* gives the position along the horizontal axis of the grid, and the second coordinate *y* gives the position along the vertical axis. The pair is written (x,y). (2) Any pair of objects or numbers in a particular order, as in letter-number spreadsheet-cell names or map coordinates.

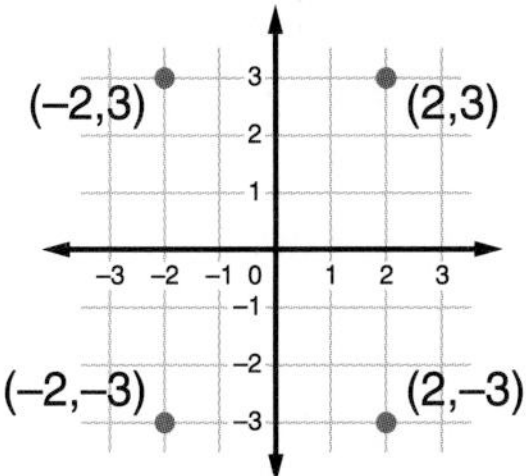

Ordered pairs

outcome A possible result of a chance experiment or situation. For example, HEADS and TAILS are the two possible outcomes of flipping a coin.

parallel lines *Lines* in a plane that never meet. Two parallel lines are always the same distance apart. *Line segments* or *rays* on parallel lines are parallel to each other.

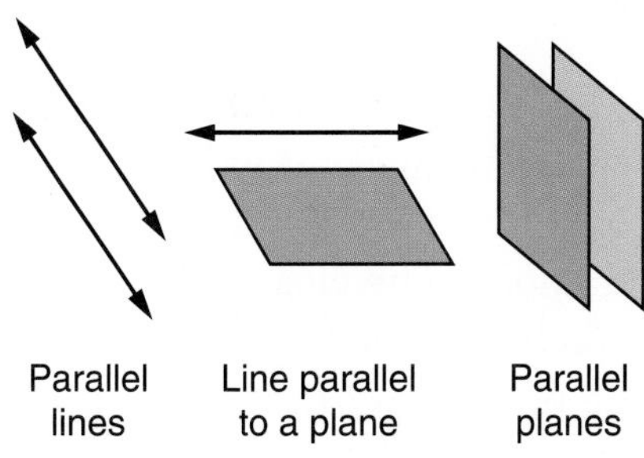

Parallel lines | Line parallel to a plane | Parallel planes

parallelogram A *quadrilateral* with two pairs of parallel sides. Opposite sides of a parallelogram have the same length and opposite *angles* have the same measure. All *rectangles* are parallelograms, but not all parallelograms are rectangles because parallelograms do not necessarily have *right angles*.

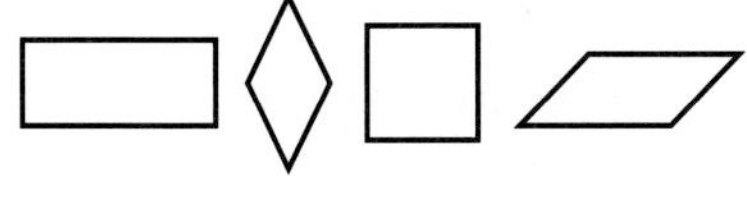

Parallelograms

partial-differences subtraction A subtraction *algorithm* in which separate differences are computed for each *place value* of the numbers and then added to get a final difference.

partial-products multiplication A multiplication *algorithm* in which partial products are computed by multiplying the value of each digit in one *factor* by the value of each digit in the other factor. The final *product* is the sum of the partial products.

partial-quotients division A division *algorithm* in which a partial quotient is computed in each of several steps. The final *quotient* is the sum of the partial quotients.

partial-sums addition An addition *algorithm* in which separate sums are computed for each *place value* of the numbers and then added to get a final sum.

pentagon A 5-sided *polygon.*

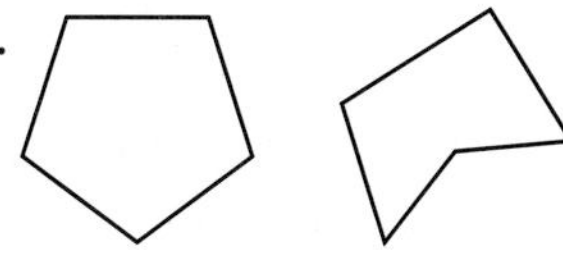

Pentagons

percent (%) Per hundred, for each hundred, or out of a hundred. $1\% = \frac{1}{100} = 0.01$. For example, *48% of the students in the school are boys* means that, on average, 48 of every 100 students in the school are boys.

perimeter The distance around the boundary of a 2-dimensional figure. The perimeter of a *circle* is called its circumference. A *formula* for the perimeter P of a *rectangle* with length l and width w is $P = 2 * (l + w)$. Perimeter comes from the Greek words for "around measure."

perpendicular ($\perp$) Two *lines* or two planes that *intersect* at *right angles. Line segments* or *rays* that lie on perpendicular lines are perpendicular to each other. The symbol $\perp$ means "is perpendicular to."

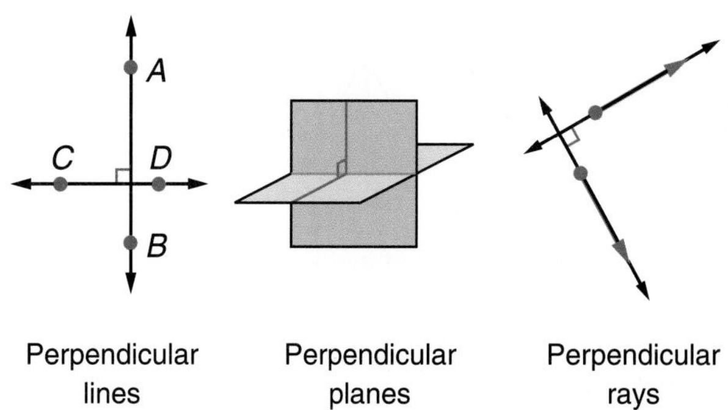

Perpendicular lines | Perpendicular planes | Perpendicular rays

place value A system that gives a digit a value according to its position, or place, in a number. In our standard, base-10 (decimal) system for writing numbers, each place has a value 10 times that of the place to its right and 1 tenth the value of the place to its left.

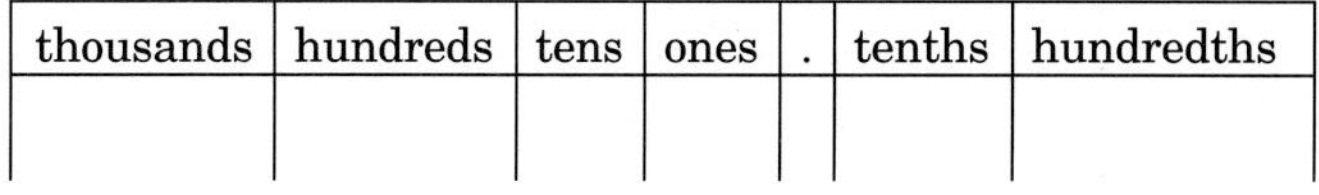

thousands	hundreds	tens	ones	.	tenths	hundredths

A place-value chart

point In *Everyday Mathematics,* an exact location in space. Points are usually labeled with capital letters. In formal Euclidean geometry, a point is an undefined geometric term.

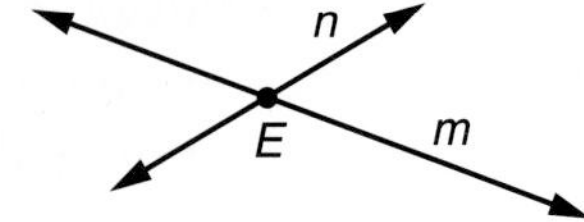

Lines *m* and *n* intersect at point *E*.

polygon A 2-dimensional figure formed by three or more *line segments* (*sides*) that meet only at their *endpoints* (*vertices*) to make a closed path. The sides may not cross one another.

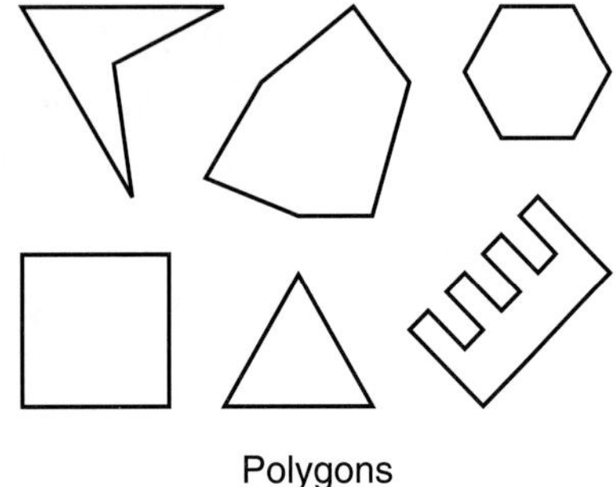

Polygons

polyhedron A 3-dimensional figure formed by *polygons* with their *interiors* (*faces*) and having no holes. Plural is polyhedrons or polyhedra.

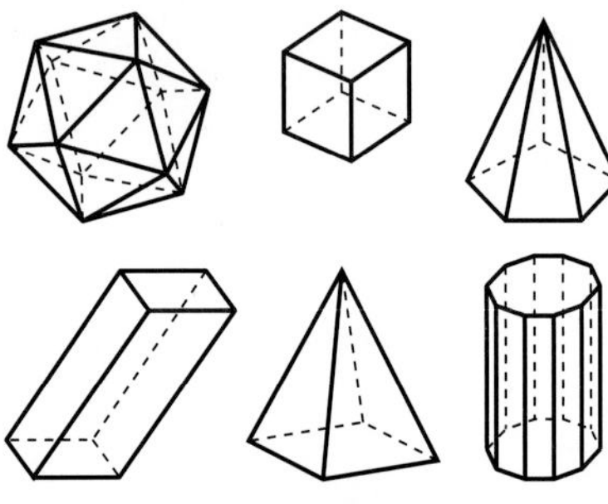

Polyhedrons

positive power of 10 A number that can be written in the form 10^a, where a is a *counting number,* that is, the numbers 10, 100, 1,000, and so on, that can be written using only 10s as factors.

prime meridian An imaginary semicircle on Earth that connects the North and South Poles through Greenwich, England. See *lines of longitude.*

prime number A *counting number* greater than 1 that has exactly two whole-number *factors,* 1 and itself. For example, 7 is a prime number because its only factors are 1 and 7. The first five prime numbers are 2, 3, 5, 7, and 11. Also simply called primes. Compare to *composite number.*

prism A *polyhedron* with two *parallel* and congruent polygonal regions for *bases* and lateral *faces* formed by all the *line segments* with *endpoints* on corresponding edges of the bases. The lateral faces are all *parallelograms*. Lateral faces intersect at lateral edges. In a right prism, the lateral faces are rectangular. Prisms get their names from the shape of their bases.

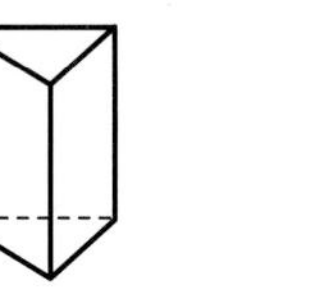

A triangular prism

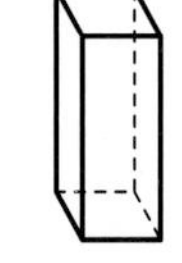

A rectangular prism

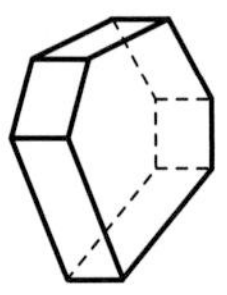

A hexagonal prism

probability A number from 0 through 1 giving the likelihood that an *event* will happen. The closer a probability is to 1, the more likely the event is to happen. The closer a probability is to 0, the less likely the event is to happen. For example, the probability that a *fair* coin will show HEADS is $\frac{1}{2}$.

product The result of multiplying two numbers, called *factors.* For example, in $4 * 3 = 12$, the product is 12.

quadrangle Same as *quadrilateral.*

quadrilateral A 4-sided *polygon.*

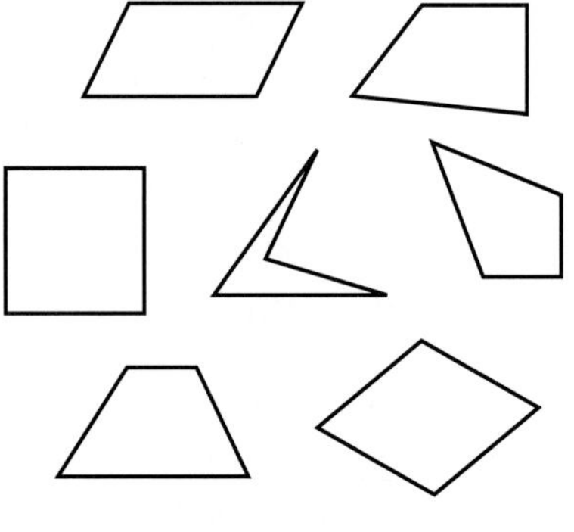

Quadrilaterals

quotient The result of dividing one number by another number. For example, in 10 / 5 = 2, the quotient is 2.

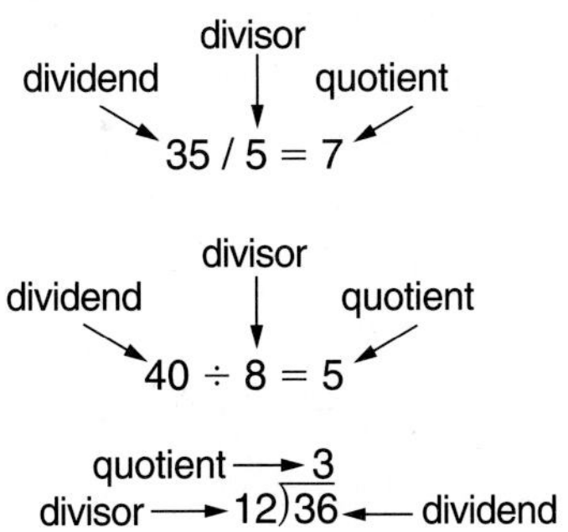

radius (1) A *line segment* from the center of a *circle* (or *sphere*) to any point on the circle (or sphere). (2) The length of this *line segment.* The length of a radius is half the length of a *diameter.* Plural is radiuses or radii.

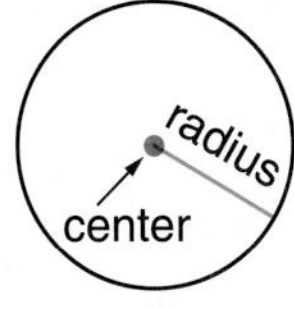

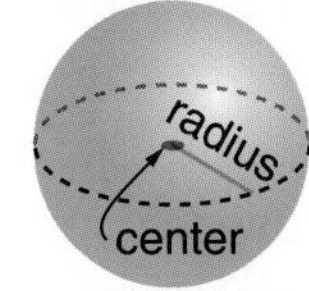

range The difference between the *maximum* and the *minimum* in a set of data. Used as a measure of the spread of the data.

rate A comparison by division of two quantities with different *units*. For example, traveling 100 miles in 2 hours is an average rate of $\frac{100 \text{ mi}}{2 \text{ hr}}$, or 50 miles per hour.

ray A part of a *line* starting at the ray's *endpoint* and continuing forever in one direction. A ray is often named by its endpoint and another *point* on it.

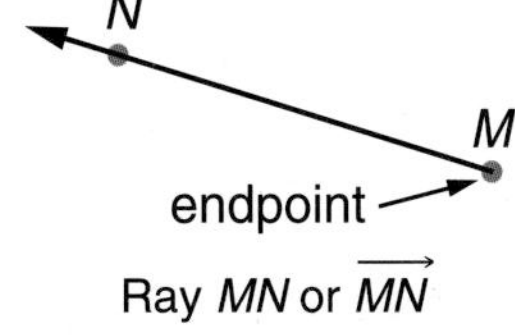

Ray *MN* or $\overrightarrow{MN}$

rectangle A *parallelogram* with all *right angles.*

reflection A point *A′* is a reflection image of a point *A* over a line of reflection *l* if *A′* and *A* are the same distance from *l* on a line *perpendicular* to it. If all *points* on one figure are reflection images of all the points on another figure over the same line, the figures are reflection images. Informally called a *flip.*

reflex angle An *angle* with a measure between 180° and 360°.

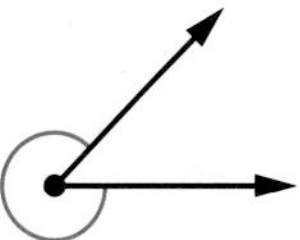

A reflex angle

regular polygon A *polygon* in which all *sides* are the same length and all *angles* have the same measure.

remainder An amount left over when one number is divided by another number. For example, in 16 / 3 → 5 R1, the *quotient* is 5 and the remainder R is 1.

rhombus A *parallelogram* with all sides the same length. All rhombuses are parallelograms. Every *square* is a rhombus, but not all rhombuses are squares. Also called a diamond. Plural is rhombuses or rhombi.

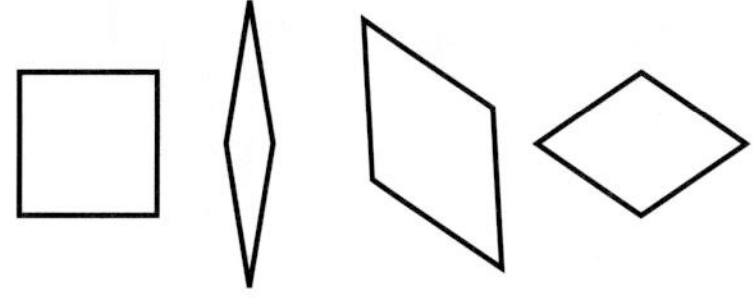

Rhombuses

right angle A 90° *angle.*

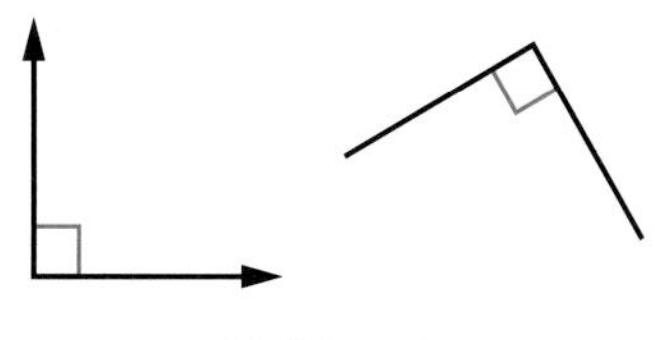

Right angles

right triangle A *triangle* with a *right angle.*

rotation (1) A point *P′* is a rotation image of a point *P* around a center of rotation *C* if *P′* is on the *circle* with center *C* and radius *CP*. If all the *points* in one figure are rotation images of all the points in another figure around the same center of rotation and with the same angle of rotation, the figures are rotation images. The center can be inside or outside of the original image. Informally called a *turn.* (2) If all points on the image of a 3-dimensional figure are rotation images around a point on a *line* called the axis of rotation, then the image is a rotation image of the original figure.

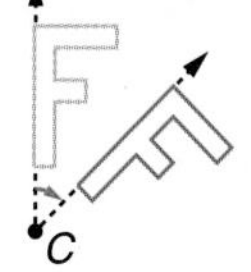

A rotation

round (1) To approximate a number to make it easier to work with, or to make it better reflect the precision of the data. "Rounding up" means to approximate larger than the actual value. "Rounding down" means to approximate smaller than the actual value. (2) Circular in shape.

S

scale (1) The relative size of something. (2) A tool for measuring weight. See *map scale.*

scale drawing A drawing of an object in which all parts are drawn to the same *scale* to the object. For example, architects and builders use scale drawings traditionally called "blueprints." A map is a scale drawing of a geographical region.

A woodpecker (8 in.) to $\frac{1}{4}$ scale

scalene triangle A *triangle* with sides of three different lengths. The three angles of a scalene triangle have different measures.

side (1) One of the *line segments* that make up a *polygon.* (2) One of the *rays* or *segments* that form an *angle.* (3) One of the *faces* of a *polyhedron.*

slide An informal name for a *translation.*

solution of an open sentence A value or values for the *variable(s)* in an *open sentence* that make the sentence true. For example, 7 is the solution of $5 + n = 12$. Although *equations* are not necessarily open sentences, the solution of an open sentence is commonly referred to as a "solution of an equation."

sphere The set of all *points* in space that are an equal distance from a fixed point called the center of the sphere. The distance from the center to the sphere is the *radius* of the sphere. The *diameter* of a sphere is twice its radius. Points inside a sphere are not part of the sphere.

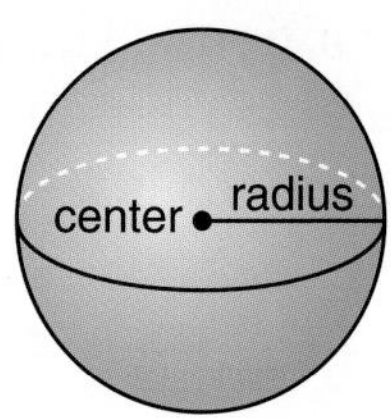

A sphere

square A *rectangle* with all sides of equal length. All angles in a square are *right angles.*

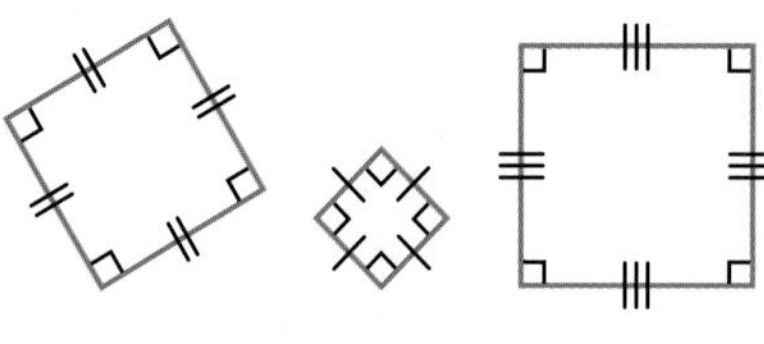

Squares

square numbers Figurate numbers (numbers that can be illustrated by specific geometric patterns) that are the product of a *counting number* and itself. For example, 25 is a square number because $25 = 5 * 5$. A square number can be represented by a square array and as a number squared, such as $25 = 5^2$.

square unit A unit to measure *area.* A model of a square unit is a square with each side a related unit of *length.* For example, a square inch is the area of a square with 1-inch sides. Square units are often labeled as the length unit squared. For example, 1 cm^2 is read "1 square centimeter" or "1 centimeter squared."

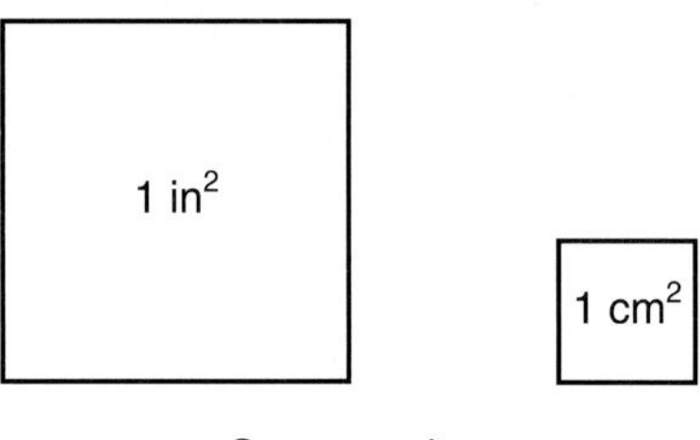

Square units

straight angle A 180° *angle.*

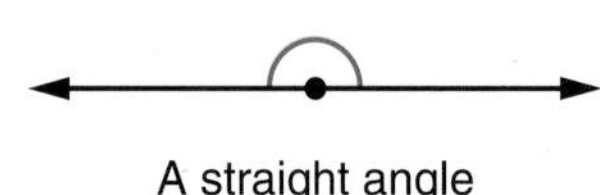

A straight angle

subtrahend The number being taken away in a subtraction problem. For example, in $15 - 5 = 10$, the subtrahend is 5.

symmetric figure A figure that exactly matches with its image under a *reflection* or *rotation.*

tally chart A table to keep track of a tally, typically showing how many times each value appears in a set of data.

Number of Pull-Ups	Number of Children
0	𝍸 /
1	𝍸
2	////
3	//

A tally chart

trade-first subtraction A subtraction *algorithm* in which all necessary trades between places in the numbers are done before any subtractions are carried out. Some people favor this algorithm because they can concentrate on one thing at a time.

translation A transformation in which every point in the *image* of a figure is at the same distance in the same direction from its corresponding point in the figure. Informally called a *slide*.

trapezoid A *quadrilateral* that has exactly one pair of *parallel* sides. In *Everyday Mathematics,* both pairs of sides cannot be parallel; that is, a *parallelogram* is not a trapezoid.

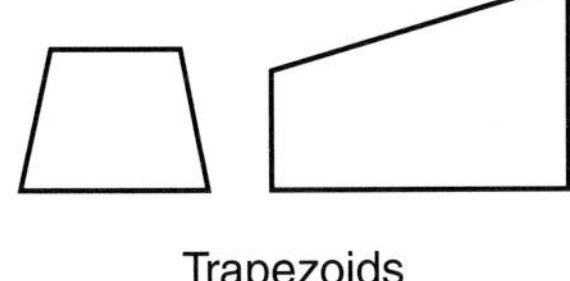

Trapezoids

triangle A 3-sided *polygon.*

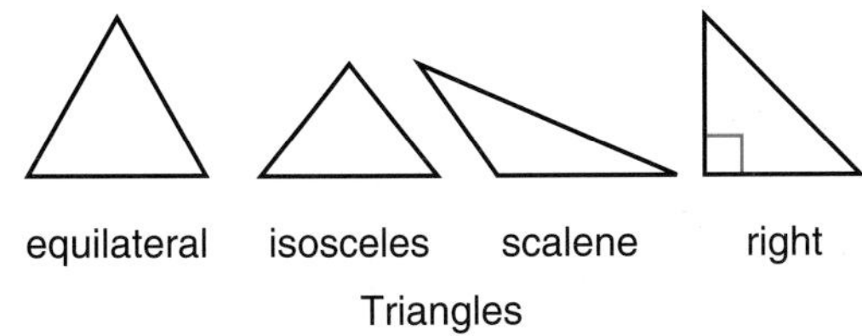

Triangles

turn An informal name for a *rotation.*

turn-around facts A pair of multiplication (or addition) facts in which the order of the *factors* (or addends) is reversed. For example, $3 * 9 = 27$ and $9 * 3 = 27$ are turn-around *multiplication facts,* and $4 + 5 = 9$ and $5 + 4 = 9$ are turn-around addition facts. There are no turn-around facts for subtraction or division. Turn-around facts are instances of the Commutative Properties of Addition and Multiplication.

unit A label used to put a number in context. In measuring length, for example, inches and centimeters are units. In a problem about 5 apples, apple is the unit. In *Everyday Mathematics,* students keep track of units in unit boxes.

unit fraction A fraction whose *numerator* is 1. For example, $\frac{1}{2}$, $\frac{1}{3}$, $\frac{1}{8}$, $\frac{1}{12}$, and $\frac{1}{20}$ are unit fractions. Unit fractions are especially useful in converting among units within measurement systems. For example, because 1 foot = 12 inches, you can multiply a number of inches by $\frac{1}{12}$ to convert to feet.

unit whole Same as *whole* or *ONE.*

variable A letter or other symbol that represents a number. A variable can represent a single number, as in $5 + n = 9$, because only $n = 4$ makes the sentence true. A variable may also stand for many different numbers, as in $x + 2 < 10$, because any number x less than 8 makes the sentence true. In *formulas* and properties, variables stand for all numbers. For example, $a + 3 = 3 + a$ for all numbers a.

vertex The *point* at which the *rays* of an angle, the *sides* of a polygon, or the edges of a *polyhedron* meet. Plural is vertexes or vertices. In *Everyday Mathematics,* same as corner.

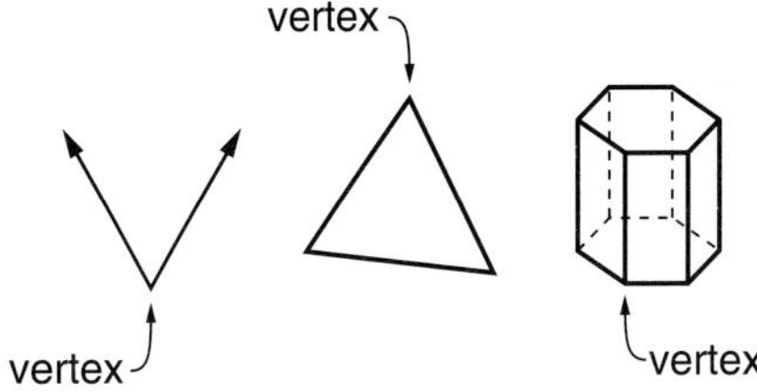

volume (1) The amount of space occupied by a 3-dimensional shape. Same as *capacity*. (2) Less formally, the amount a container can hold. Volume is often measured in cubic units, such as cm^3, cubic inches, or cubic feet.

“What’s My Rule?” problem In *Everyday Mathematics,* a problem in which two of the three parts of a function (input, output, and rule) are known, and the third is to be found out.

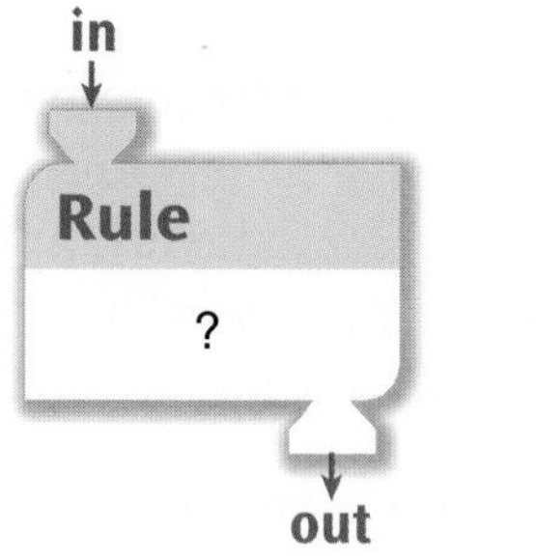

in	out
4	2
7	5
12	10
8	

A “What’s My Rule?” problem

whole An entire object, collection of objects, or quantity being considered in a problem situation; 100%. Same as *ONE* and *unit whole.*

whole numbers The *counting numbers* and 0. The set of whole numbers is {0, 1, 2, 3, . . .}.

width of a rectangle The length of one side of a *rectangle* or rectangular object, typically the shorter side.

Grade-Level Goals

Everyday Mathematics organizes content through Program Goals and Grade-Level Goals. The Grade-Level Goals Chart shows the units in which goal content is taught and then practiced and applied. For more information, see the *Assessment Handbook.*

The Grade-Level Goals are divided according to the content strands below.

Content Strands

How to Read the Grade-Level Goals Chart

Each section of the chart includes Grade-Level Goals organized by content strand. The three grade-level columns divided into units indicate in which units the goals are addressed.

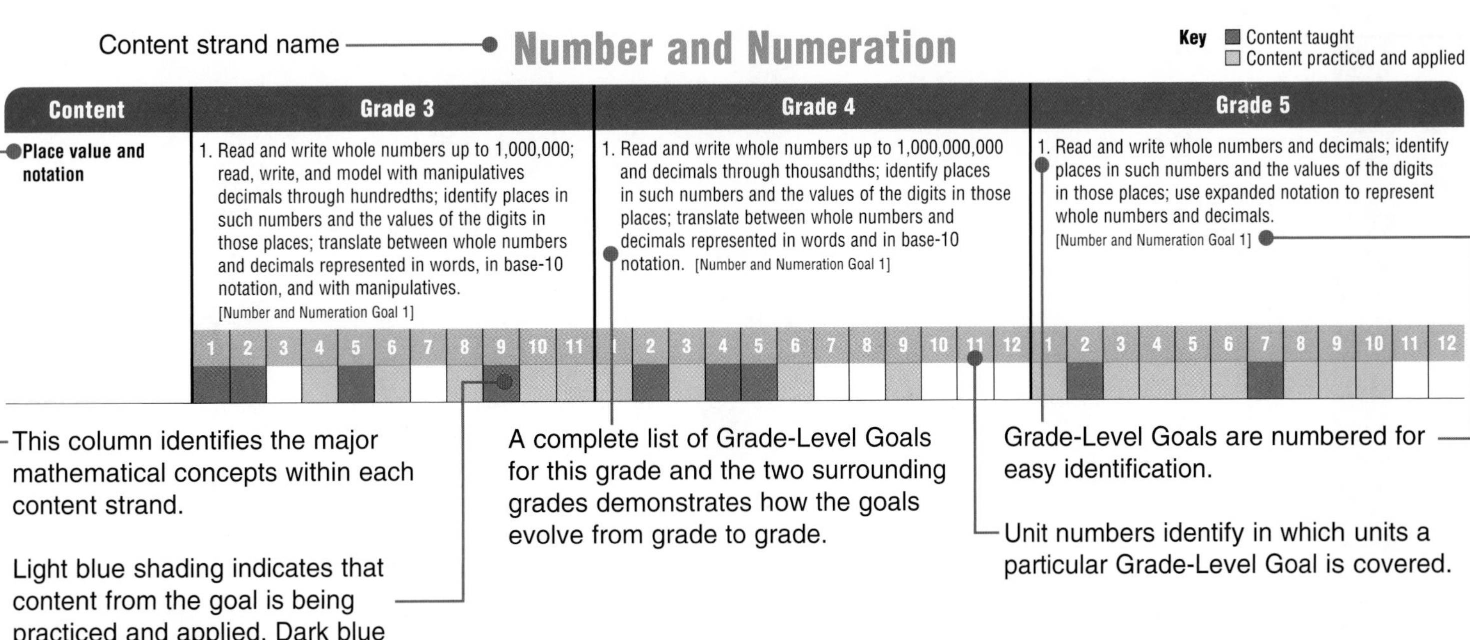

Content strand name
Number and Numeration
Key
Content taught
Content practiced and applied
Content
Grade 3
Grade 4
Grade 5
Place value and notation
1. Read and write whole numbers up to 1,000,000; read, write, and model with manipulatives decimals through hundredths; identify places in such numbers and the values of the digits in those places; translate between whole numbers and decimals represented in words, in base-10 notation, and with manipulatives. [Number and Numeration Goal 1]
1. Read and write whole numbers up to 1,000,000,000 and decimals through thousandths; identify places in such numbers and the values of the digits in those places; translate between whole numbers and decimals represented in words and in base-10 notation. [Number and Numeration Goal 1]
1. Read and write whole numbers and decimals; identify places in such numbers and the values of the digits in those places; use expanded notation to represent whole numbers and decimals. [Number and Numeration Goal 1]
1 2 3 4 5 6 7 8 9 10 11
1 2 3 4 5 6 7 8 9 10 11 12
1 2 3 4 5 6 7 8 9 10 11 12
This column identifies the major mathematical concepts within each content strand.
Light blue shading indicates that content from the goal is being practiced and applied. Dark blue shading indicates that content from the goal is being taught.
A complete list of Grade-Level Goals for this grade and the two surrounding grades demonstrates how the goals evolve from grade to grade.
Grade-Level Goals are numbered for easy identification.
Unit numbers identify in which units a particular Grade-Level Goal is covered.

Number and Numeration

Key
- Content taught
- Content practiced and applied

Content	Grade 3	Grade 4	Grade 5
Place value and notation	1. Read and write whole numbers up to 1,000,000; read, write, and model with manipulatives decimals through hundredths; identify places in such numbers and the values of the digits in those places; translate between whole numbers and decimals represented in words, in base-10 notation, and with manipulatives. [Number and Numeration Goal 1]	1. Read and write whole numbers up to 1,000,000,000 and decimals through thousandths; identify places in such numbers and the values of the digits in those places; translate between whole numbers and decimals represented in words and in base-10 notation. [Number and Numeration Goal 1]	1. Read and write whole numbers and decimals; identify places in such numbers and the values of the digits in those places; use expanded notation to represent whole numbers and decimals. [Number and Numeration Goal 1]
	1 2 3 4 5 6 7 8 9 10 11	1 2 3 4 5 6 7 8 9 10 11 12	1 2 3 4 5 6 7 8 9 10 11 12
Meanings and uses of fractions	2. Read, write, and model fractions; solve problems involving fractional parts of a region or a collection; describe strategies used. [Number and Numeration Goal 2]	2. Read, write, and model fractions; solve problems involving fractional parts of a region or a collection; describe and explain strategies used; given a fractional part of a region or a collection, identify the unit whole. [Number and Numeration Goal 2]	2. Solve problems involving percents and discounts; describe and explain strategies used; identify the unit whole in situations involving fractions. [Number and Numeration Goal 2]
	1 2 3 4 5 6 7 8 9 10 11	1 2 3 4 5 6 7 8 9 10 11 12	1 2 3 4 5 6 7 8 9 10 11 12
Number theory	3. Find multiples of 2, 5, and 10. [Number and Numeration Goal 3]	3. Find multiples of whole numbers less than 10; identify prime and composite numbers; find whole-number factors of numbers. [Number and Numeration Goal 3]	3. Identify prime and composite numbers; factor numbers; find prime factorizations. [Number and Numeration Goal 3]
	1 2 3 4 5 6 7 8 9 10 11	1 2 3 4 5 6 7 8 9 10 11 12	1 2 3 4 5 6 7 8 9 10 11 12
Equivalent names for whole numbers	4. Use numerical expressions involving one or more of the basic four arithmetic operations to give equivalent names for whole numbers. [Number and Numeration Goal 4]	4. Use numerical expressions involving one or more of the basic four arithmetic operations and grouping symbols to give equivalent names for whole numbers. [Number and Numeration Goal 4]	4. Use numerical expressions involving one or more of the basic four arithmetic operations, grouping symbols, and exponents to give equivalent names for whole numbers; convert between base-10, exponential, and repeated-factor notations. [Number and Numeration Goal 4]
	1 2 3 4 5 6 7 8 9 10 11	1 2 3 4 5 6 7 8 9 10 11 12	1 2 3 4 5 6 7 8 9 10 11 12

Content	Grade 3	Grade 4	Grade 5
Equivalent names for fractions, decimals, and percents	5. Use manipulatives and drawings to find and represent equivalent names for fractions; use manipulatives to generate equivalent fractions. [Number and Numeration Goal 5]	5. Use numerical expressions to find and represent equivalent names for fractions and decimals; use and explain a multiplication rule to find equivalent fractions; rename fourths, fifths, tenths, and hundredths as decimals and percents. [Number and Numeration Goal 5]	5. Use numerical expressions to find and represent equivalent names for fractions, decimals, and percents; use and explain multiplication and division rules to find equivalent fractions and fractions in simplest form; convert between fractions and mixed numbers; convert between fractions, decimals, and percents. [Number and Numeration Goal 5]
Comparing and ordering numbers	6. Compare and order whole numbers up to 1,000,000; use manipulatives to order decimals through hundredths; use area models and benchmark fractions to compare and order fractions. [Number and Numeration Goal 6]	6. Compare and order whole numbers up to 1,000,000,000 and decimals through thousandths; compare and order integers between –100 and 0; use area models, benchmark fractions, and analyses of numerators and denominators to compare and order fractions. [Number and Numeration Goal 6]	6. Compare and order rational numbers; use area models, benchmark fractions, and analyses of numerators and denominators to compare and order fractions and mixed numbers; describe strategies used to compare fractions and mixed numbers. [Number and Numeration Goal 6]

Operations and Computation

Key Content taught / Content practiced and applied

Content	Grade 3	Grade 4	Grade 5
Addition and subtraction facts	1. Demonstrate automaticity with all addition and subtraction facts through 10 + 10; use basic facts to compute fact extensions such as 80 + 70. [Operations and Computation Goal 1]	1. Demonstrate automaticity with addition and subtraction fact extensions. [Operations and Computation Goal 1]	
Addition and subtraction procedures	2. Use manipulatives, mental arithmetic, paper-and-pencil algorithms and models, and calculators to solve problems involving the addition and subtraction of whole numbers and decimals in a money context; describe the strategies used and explain how they work. [Operations and Computation Goal 2]	2. Use manipulatives, mental arithmetic, paper-and-pencil algorithms and models, and calculators to solve problems involving the addition and subtraction of whole numbers and decimals through hundredths; describe the strategies used and explain how they work. [Operations and Computation Goal 2]	1. Use manipulatives, mental arithmetic, paper-and-pencil algorithms and models, and calculators to solve problems involving the addition and subtraction of whole numbers, decimals, and signed numbers; describe the strategies used and explain how they work. [Operations and Computation Goal 1]

Operations and Computation (cont.)

Key
- Content taught
- Content practiced and applied

Content	Grade 3	Grade 4	Grade 5
Multiplication and division facts	3. Demonstrate automaticity with multiplication facts through 10 × 10. [Operations and Computation Goal 3] 1 2 3 4 5 6 7 8 9 10 11	3. Demonstrate automaticity with multiplication facts through 10 ∗ 10 and proficiency with related division facts; use basic facts to compute fact extensions such as 30 ∗ 60. [Operations and Computation Goal 3] 1 2 3 4 5 6 7 8 9 10 11 12	2. Demonstrate automaticity with multiplication and division fact extensions. [Operations and Computation Goal 2] 1 2 3 4 5 6 7 8 9 10 11 12
Multiplication and division procedures	4. Use arrays, mental arithmetic, paper-and-pencil algorithms and models, and calculators to solve problems involving the multiplication of 2- and 3-digit whole numbers by 1-digit whole numbers; describe the strategies used. [Operations and Computation Goal 4] 1 2 3 4 5 6 7 8 9 10 11	4. Use manipulatives, mental arithmetic, paper-and-pencil algorithms and models, and calculators to solve problems involving the multiplication of multidigit whole numbers by 2-digit whole numbers and the division of multidigit whole numbers by 1-digit whole numbers; describe the strategies used and explain how they work. [Operations and Computation Goal 4] 1 2 3 4 5 6 7 8 9 10 11 12	3. Use manipulatives, mental arithmetic, paper-and-pencil algorithms and models, and calculators to solve problems involving the multiplication of whole numbers and decimals and the division of multidigit whole numbers and decimals by whole numbers; express remainders as whole numbers or fractions as appropriate; describe the strategies used and explain how they work. [Operations and Computation Goal 3] 1 2 3 4 5 6 7 8 9 10 11 12
Procedures for addition and subtraction of fractions	1 2 3 4 5 6 7 8 9 10 11	5. Use manipulatives, mental arithmetic, and calculators to solve problems involving the addition and subtraction of fractions and mixed numbers; describe the strategies used. [Operations and Computation Goal 5] 1 2 3 4 5 6 7 8 9 10 11 12	4. Use mental arithmetic, paper-and-pencil algorithms and models, and calculators to solve problems involving the addition and subtraction of fractions and mixed numbers; describe the strategies used and explain how they work. [Operations and Computation Goal 4] 1 2 3 4 5 6 7 8 9 10 11 12
Procedures for multiplication and division of fractions	1 2 3 4 5 6 7 8 9 10 11	1 2 3 4 5 6 7 8 9 10 11 12	5. Use area models, mental arithmetic, paper-and-pencil algorithms and models, and calculators to solve problems involving the multiplication of fractions and mixed numbers; use visual models, paper-and-pencil methods, and calculators to solve problems involving the division of fractions; describe the strategies used. [Operations and Computation Goal 5] 1 2 3 4 5 6 7 8 9 10 11 12

Content	Grade 3	Grade 4	Grade 5
Computational estimation	5. Make reasonable estimates for whole number addition, subtraction, multiplication, and division problems; explain how the estimates were obtained. [Operations and Computation Goal 5]	6. Make reasonable estimates for whole number and decimal addition and subtraction problems, and whole number multiplication and division problems; explain how the estimates were obtained. [Operations and Computation Goal 6]	6. Make reasonable estimates for whole number and decimal addition, subtraction, multiplication, and division problems and fraction and mixed number addition and subtraction problems; explain how the estimates were obtained. [Operations and Computation Goal 6]
	1 2 3 4 5 6 7 8 9 10 11	1 2 3 4 5 6 7 8 9 10 11 12	1 2 3 4 5 6 7 8 9 10 11 12
Models for the operations	6. Recognize and describe change, comparison, and parts-and-total situations; use repeated addition, arrays, and skip counting to model multiplication; use equal sharing and equal grouping to model division. [Operations and Computation Goal 6]	7. Use repeated addition, skip counting, arrays, area, and scaling to model multiplication and division. [Operations and Computation Goal 7]	7. Use repeated addition, arrays, area, and scaling to model multiplication and division; use ratios expressed as words, fractions, percents, and with colons; solve problems involving ratios of parts of a set to the whole set. [Operations and Computation Goal 7]
	1 2 3 4 5 6 7 8 9 10 11	1 2 3 4 5 6 7 8 9 10 11 12	1 2 3 4 5 6 7 8 9 10 11 12

Data and Chance

Key
- Content taught
- Content practiced and applied

Content	Grade 3	Grade 4	Grade 5
Data collection and representation	1. Collect and organize data or use given data to create charts, tables, graphs, and line plots. [Data and Chance Goal 1]	1. Collect and organize data or use given data to create charts, tables, graphs, and line plots. [Data and Chance Goal 1]	1. Collect and organize data or use given data to create graphic displays with reasonable titles, labels, keys, and intervals. [Data and Chance Goal 1]
	1 2 3 4 5 6 7 8 9 10 11	1 2 3 4 5 6 7 8 9 10 11 12	1 2 3 4 5 6 7 8 9 10 11 12
Data analysis	2. Use graphs to ask and answer simple questions and draw conclusions; find the maximum, minimum, range, mode, and median of a data set. [Data and Chance Goal 2]	2. Use the maximum, minimum, range, median, mode, and graphs to ask and answer questions, draw conclusions, and make predictions. [Data and Chance Goal 2]	2. Use the maximum, minimum, range, median, mode, and mean, and graphs to ask and answer questions, draw conclusions, and make predictions. [Data and Chance Goal 2]
	1 2 3 4 5 6 7 8 9 10 11	1 2 3 4 5 6 7 8 9 10 11 12	1 2 3 4 5 6 7 8 9 10 11 12

Data and Chance (cont.)

Content	Grade 3	Grade 4	Grade 5
Qualitative probability	3. Describe events using *certain, very likely, likely, unlikely, very unlikely, impossible,* and other basic probability terms; explain the choice of language. [Data and Chance Goal 3]	3. Describe events using *certain, very likely, likely, unlikely, very unlikely, impossible,* and other basic probability terms; use *more likely, equally likely, same chance, 50-50, less likely,* and other basic probability terms to compare events; explain the choice of language. [Data and Chance Goal 3]	3. Describe events using *certain, very likely, likely, unlikely, very unlikely, impossible* and other basic probability terms; use *more likely, equally likely, same chance, 50-50, less likely,* and other basic probability terms to compare events; explain the choice of language. [Data and Chance Goal 3]
	1 2 3 4 5 6 7 8 9 10 11	1 2 3 4 5 6 7 8 9 10 11 12	1 2 3 4 5 6 7 8 9 10 11 12
Quantitative probability	4. Predict the outcomes of simple experiments and test the predictions using manipulatives; express the probability of an event by using "_____ out of _____" language. [Data and Chance Goal 4]	4. Predict the outcomes of experiments and test the predictions using manipulatives; summarize the results and use them to predict future events; express the probability of an event as a fraction. [Data and Chance Goal 4]	4. Predict the outcomes of experiments, test the predictions using manipulatives, and summarize the results; compare predictions based on theoretical probability with experimental results; use summaries and comparisons to predict future events; express the probability of an event as a fraction, decimal, or percent. [Data and Chance Goal 4]
	1 2 3 4 5 6 7 8 9 10 11	1 2 3 4 5 6 7 8 9 10 11 12	1 2 3 4 5 6 7 8 9 10 11 12

Measurement and Reference Frames

Key
- Content taught
- Content practiced and applied

Content	Grade 3	Grade 4	Grade 5
Length, weight, and angles	1. Estimate length with and without tools; measure length to the nearest $\frac{1}{2}$ inch and $\frac{1}{2}$ centimeter; draw and describe angles as records of rotations. [Measurement and Reference Frames Goal 1]	1. Estimate length with and without tools; measure length to the nearest $\frac{1}{4}$ inch and $\frac{1}{2}$ centimeter; use tools to measure and draw angles; estimate the size of angles without tools. [Measurement and Reference Frames Goal 1]	1. Estimate length with and without tools; measure length with tools to the nearest $\frac{1}{8}$ inch and millimeter; estimate the measure of angles with and without tools; use tools to draw angles with given measures. [Measurement and Reference Frames Goal 1]
	1 2 3 4 5 6 7 8 9 10 11	1 2 3 4 5 6 7 8 9 10 11 12	1 2 3 4 5 6 7 8 9 10 11 12

Key
- Content taught
- Content practiced and applied

Content	Grade 3	Grade 4	Grade 5
Area, perimeter, volume, and capacity	2. Describe and use strategies to measure the perimeter of polygons; find the areas of rectangles. [Measurement and Reference Frames Goal 2]	2. Describe and use strategies to measure the perimeter and area of polygons, to estimate the area of irregular shapes, and to find the volume of rectangular prisms. [Measurement and Reference Frames Goal 2]	2. Describe and use strategies to find the perimeter of polygons and the area of circles; choose and use appropriate methods, including formulas, to find the areas of rectangles, parallelograms, and triangles, and the volume of a prism; define *pi* as the ratio of a circle's circumference to its diameter. [Measurement and Reference Frames Goal 2]
Units and systems of measurement	3. Describe relationships among inches, feet, and yards; describe relationships between minutes in an hour, hours in a day, days in a week. [Measurement and Reference Frames Goal 3]	3. Describe relationships among U.S. customary units of measure and among metric units of measure. [Measurement and Reference Frames Goal 3]	3. Describe relationships among U.S. customary units of measure and among metric units of measure. [Measurement and Reference Frames Goal 3]
Time	4. Tell and show time to the nearest minute on an analog clock; tell and write time in digital notation.* [Measurement and Reference Frames Goal 4]		
Coordinate systems		4. Use ordered pairs of numbers to name, locate, and plot points in the first quadrant of a coordinate grid. [Measurement and Reference Frames Goal 4]	4. Use ordered pairs of numbers to name, locate, and plot points in all four quadrants of a coordinate grid. [Measurement and Reference Frames Goal 4]

*Children record their start time at the top of journal pages on a daily basis.

Geometry

Key
- Content taught
- Content practiced and applied

Content	Grade 3	Grade 4	Grade 5
Lines and angles	1. Identify and draw points, intersecting and parallel line segments and lines, rays, and right angles. [Geometry Goal 1]	1. Identify, draw, and describe points, intersecting and parallel line segments and lines, rays, and right, acute, and obtuse angles. [Geometry Goal 1]	1. Identify, describe, compare, name, and draw right, acute, obtuse, straight, and reflex angles; determine angle measures in vertical and supplementary angles by applying properties of sums of angle measures in triangles and quadrangles. [Geometry Goal 1]
	1 2 3 4 5 6 7 8 9 10 11	1 2 3 4 5 6 7 8 9 10 11 12	1 2 3 4 5 6 7 8 9 10 11 12
Plane and solid figures	2. Identify, describe, model, and compare plane and solid figures including circles, polygons, spheres, cylinders, rectangular prisms, pyramids, cones, and cubes using appropriate geometric terms including the terms *face, edge, vertex,* and *base.* [Geometry Goal 2]	2. Describe, compare, and classify plane and solid figures, including polygons, circles, spheres, cylinders, rectangular prisms, cones, cubes, and pyramids, using appropriate geometric terms including *vertex, base, face, edge,* and *congruent.* [Geometry Goal 2]	2. Describe, compare, and classify plane and solid figures using appropriate geometric terms; identify congruent figures and describe their properties. [Geometry Goal 2]
	1 2 3 4 5 6 7 8 9 10 11	1 2 3 4 5 6 7 8 9 10 11 12	1 2 3 4 5 6 7 8 9 10 11 12
Transformations and symmetry	3. Create and complete two-dimensional symmetric shapes or designs; locate multiple lines of symmetry in a two-dimensional shape. [Geometry Goal 3]	3. Identify, describe, and sketch examples of reflections; identify and describe examples of translations and rotations. [Geometry Goal 3]	3. Identify, describe, and sketch examples of reflections, translations, and rotations. [Geometry Goal 3]
	1 2 3 4 5 6 7 8 9 10 11	1 2 3 4 5 6 7 8 9 10 11 12	1 2 3 4 5 6 7 8 9 10 11 12

Patterns, Functions, and Algebra

Key: Content taught; Content practiced and applied

Content	Grade 3	Grade 4	Grade 5
Patterns and functions	1. Extend, describe, and create numeric patterns; describe rules for patterns and use them to solve problems; use words and symbols to describe and write rules for functions involving addition, subtraction, and multiplication and use those rules to solve problems. [Patterns, Functions, and Algebra Goal 1] 1 2 3 4 5 6 7 8 9 10 11	1. Extend, describe, and create numeric patterns; describe rules for patterns and use them to solve problems; use words and symbols to describe and write rules for functions that involve the four basic arithmetic operations and use those rules to solve problems. [Patterns, Functions, and Algebra Goal 1] 1 2 3 4 5 6 7 8 9 10 11 12	1. Extend, describe, and create numeric patterns; describe rules for patterns and use them to solve problems; write rules for functions involving the four basic arithmetic operations; represent functions using words, symbols, tables, and graphs and use those representations to solve problems. [Patterns, Functions, and Algebra Goal 1] 1 2 3 4 5 6 7 8 9 10 11 12
Algebraic notation and solving number sentences	2. Read, write, and explain number sentences using the symbols +, −, ×, ÷, =, >, and <; solve number sentences; write expressions and number sentences to model number stories. [Patterns, Functions, and Algebra Goal 2] 1 2 3 4 5 6 7 8 9 10 11	2. Use conventional notation to write expressions and number sentences using the four basic arithmetic operations; determine whether number sentences are true or false; solve open sentences and explain the solutions; write expressions and number sentences to model number stories. [Patterns, Functions, and Algebra Goal 2] 1 2 3 4 5 6 7 8 9 10 11 12	2. Determine whether number sentences are true or false; solve open number sentences and explain the solutions; use a letter variable to write an open sentence to model a number story; use a pan-balance model to solve linear equations in one unknown. [Patterns, Functions, and Algebra Goal 2] 1 2 3 4 5 6 7 8 9 10 11 12
Order of operations	3. Recognize that numeric expressions can have different values depending on the order in which operations are carried out; understand that grouping symbols can be used to affect the order in which operations are carried out. [Patterns, Functions, and Algebra Goal 3] 1 2 3 4 5 6 7 8 9 10 11	3. Evaluate numeric expressions containing grouping symbols; insert grouping symbols to make number sentences true. [Patterns, Functions, and Algebra Goal 3] 1 2 3 4 5 6 7 8 9 10 11 12	3. Evaluate numeric expressions containing grouping symbols and nested grouping symbols; insert grouping symbols and nested grouping symbols to make number sentences true; describe and use the precedence of multiplication and division over addition and subtraction. [Patterns, Functions, and Algebra Goal 3] 1 2 3 4 5 6 7 8 9 10 11 12
Properties of the arithmetic operations	4. Describe and apply the Commutative and Associative Properties of Addition and Multiplication, and the Multiplicative Identity; apply the Distributive Property of Multiplication over Addition. [Patterns, Functions, and Algebra Goal 4] 1 2 3 4 5 6 7 8 9 10 11	4. Describe and apply the Distributive Property of Multiplication over Addition. [Patterns, Functions, and Algebra Goal 4] 1 2 3 4 5 6 7 8 9 10 11 12	4. Describe and apply properties of arithmetic. [Patterns, Functions, and Algebra Goal 4] 1 2 3 4 5 6 7 8 9 10 11 12

Scope and Sequence Chart

Throughout *Everyday Mathematics*, students repeatedly encounter skills in each of the content strands. Each exposure builds on and extends students' understanding. They study important concepts over consecutive years through a variety of formats. The Scope and Sequence Chart shows the units in which these exposures occur. The symbol ● indicates that the skill is introduced or taught. The symbol ■ indicates that the skill is revisited, practiced, or extended. These levels refer to unit content within the *K–6 Everyday Mathematics* curriculum.

The skills are divided according to the content strands below.

Content Strands — Pages

How to Read the Scope and Sequence Chart

Each section of the chart includes a content strand title, three grade-level columns divided by units or sections, and a list of specific skills grouped by major concepts.

Number and Numeration — Content Strand

Key: ● Content taught ■ Content practiced

	Grade 4 Units												Grade 5 Units												Grade 6 Units									
Rote Counting	1	2	3	4	5	6	7	8	9	10	11	12	1	2	3	4	5	6	7	8	9	10	11	12	1	2	3	4	5	6	7	8	9	10
Count by tenths and hundredths				●																														
Place Value and Notation	1	2	3	4	5	6	7	8	9	10	11	12	1	2	3	4	5	6	7	8	9	10	11	12	1	2	3	4	5	6	7	8	9	10
Read and write numbers to hundred millions		●	■	■	■		■						■	■	●	■			■							●	■		■					
Read and write numbers to billions		●			●									■	■											●	■		■					

This row identifies the major mathematical concepts within each content strand. A list of related concepts and skills appear below this head.

Find specific skills in this list and then follow across the row to find where they appear at each grade level.

The colored circle indicates where the skill is introduced or taught.

The colored square indicates where the skill is primarily revisited, practiced, or extended.

Number and Numeration

Key ● Content taught ■ Content practiced

	Grade 4 Units												Grade 5 Units												Grade 6 Units									
Rote Counting	1	2	3	4	5	6	7	8	9	10	11	12	1	2	3	4	5	6	7	8	9	10	11	12	1	2	3	4	5	6	7	8	9	10
Count by tenths and hundredths				●																														
Place Value and Notation	1	2	3	4	5	6	7	8	9	10	11	12	1	2	3	4	5	6	7	8	9	10	11	12	1	2	3	4	5	6	7	8	9	10
Read and write numbers to hundred millions		●	■	■	■		■						■	■	●	■			■							●	■		■					
Read and write numbers to billions		●			●									■	■											●	■		■					
Explore numbers to trillions					●									●					●						■	●	■				■			
Investigate or identify place value in numbers to hundred millions		●	■	■			■						■	■	■	■			■						■	●	■						■	
Identify place value in numbers to billions		●			●									■	■								■		■	●	■						■	
Name the values of digits in numbers to billions		●			●										■										■	●	■						■	
Make exchanges among place values		●		■										■			■	■	■							■					■			
Investigate and apply powers of 10					■								■	■	■				●							●	■	■						■
Investigate and apply expanded notation		■			■									●		■		■	●							■			■	■				
Read and write numbers to trillions in standard and expanded notation		●	■		●																				●	●	■				■			■
Investigate, use, or apply exponential notation					●	■		■					●	■			■	■	●							●	■	■	■	■		■		■
Investigate and apply scientific notation																			●							●	■	■		■				■
Use dollar-and-cents notation			■	●		■	●	■	●		■	●																						
Explore uses of decimals				■																														
Model decimals with base-10 materials				●																														
Read and write decimals to ten-thousandths in standard and expanded notation				●	■				●					●	■				■						■	●			■					
Identify place value in decimals through ten-thousandths; compare decimals				●	■	■							■	●	■	■			■		■	■			●	●	■	●				●	●	
Investigate and apply expanded notation of decimals				■											■					■						●								
Translate words into numerical expressions													■		■															●				
Meanings and Uses of Fractions	1	2	3	4	5	6	7	8	9	10	11	12	1	2	3	4	5	6	7	8	9	10	11	12	1	2	3	4	5	6	7	8	9	10
Explore uses of fractions			■				●										●					■		■										

Key ● Content taught ■ Content practiced

Meanings and Uses of Fractions (cont.)	1	2	3	4	5	6	7	8	9	10	11	12	1	2	3	4	5	6	7	8	9	10	11	12	1	2	3	4	5	6	7	8	9	10
Identify fractional parts of regions					■	■	●	■	●	■							●	■		●					■			●						
Identify fractional parts of a set				●		■	●	■									●			■									■	■	■			
Decompose a fraction							●																											
Identify the whole for fractions							●		●						■		●	■	■	●								■				●		
Identify fractions on a number line						■	●	■				■					●	●									■							
Identify/find fractional parts of units of money							■													●												●		
Find a fraction of a number				●		■	●		●								●	■	■	●			■	●				●	■	■	■		■	
Use percents to describe real-life situations								■	●																							■		
Find a percent of a number								■	●			■					■	■	■	●			■	■			●	●	■	■	●	●	●	
Find the whole, given a percent of the whole									●											●				■								●	■	
Solve percent problems								■	■	■							●			●						■	●	●	■	■	●	●	●	
Estimate and calculate percent								■	●								●			●						■	●	●	■	■	●	●	●	
Find the unit fraction or unit percent to calculate unit prices												●								●		●									■	●		
Determine the better buy												●								■			●				●					●	■	
Number Theory	**1**	**2**	**3**	**4**	**5**	**6**	**7**	**8**	**9**	**10**	**11**	**12**	**1**	**2**	**3**	**4**	**5**	**6**	**7**	**8**	**9**	**10**	**11**	**12**	**1**	**2**	**3**	**4**	**5**	**6**	**7**	**8**	**9**	**10**
Identify even and odd numbers													●																	■				
Find the factors of numbers			●		■		■					■	●	■	■	■	■			■			■	●			■	■					●	
Investigate, identify, or apply the concepts of prime and composite numbers			●										●											●				●		■				
Find the prime factorization of numbers													●	■	■	■	■				■		■	●				■						
Find multiples of a number or the least common multiple of two numbers			●	■							■		●					■		■	■			●			■	●		●		■		
Find the greatest common factor of two numbers													●							■				●			■	●			●		●	
Investigate or identify square numbers, square roots, and absolute value			●										●										■				■			●			●	
Understand properties of rational numbers																					■		■			■				●	■			

Number and Numeration (cont.)

Key ● Content taught ■ Content practiced

	Grade 4 Units												Grade 5 Units												Grade 6 Units									
Equivalent Names for Whole Numbers	1	2	3	4	5	6	7	8	9	10	11	12	1	2	3	4	5	6	7	8	9	10	11	12	1	2	3	4	5	6	7	8	9	10
Find equivalent names for numbers	■	●	■	■	■	■				■		■	●	■	■	●	■	■	●		■	■			●	●		■				■	●	■
Rename numbers written in exponential notation					●	■							●						●							●	■	■	■	■		■		■
Equivalent Names for Fractions, Decimals, and Percents	1	2	3	4	5	6	7	8	9	10	11	12	1	2	3	4	5	6	7	8	9	10	11	12	1	2	3	4	5	6	7	8	9	10
Find equivalent fractions						■	●	■	■							■	●	●	■	●			■	●				●			■	●		
Rename fractions as decimals				●			●		●	■				■			●	■									■	●	●	■	■	■		
Relate fractions and decimals				●			●	■	●	■		■					●								●	●		●	■	■	■	■	■	
Convert between fractions and decimals							●	■	●	■							●			■							■	●	■	■	■	■		
Estimate equivalent percents for fractions																	●											●	●	■	■	●	■	
Rename fractions and mixed numbers in simplest forms																	■	●	■	●			■	■			■	●		■	■	■	■	
Convert between fractions, mixed numbers, decimals, and/or percents			●	●			■		●	■			■	■	■		●	●		●	■			■	●	■	■	●	■	●	●	●	■	
Use a calculator to rename any fraction as a decimal or percent									●								●	●									■	●	●		●	●		
Comparing and Ordering Numbers	1	2	3	4	5	6	7	8	9	10	11	12	1	2	3	4	5	6	7	8	9	10	11	12	1	2	3	4	5	6	7	8	9	10
Compare numbers using <, >, and = symbols	■	■	■	■	■	■	●	■			■	■	■					●	●	●	■		■	■	●	■		●		●			■	
Compare larger numbers					●	■								■					●						■	■								
Compare and order decimals			■	●	■	■			■			■	■		■	■	■		■		■			■		●	■			■		■		
Compare and order integers										●	■	■							●						●	■			■	●	■	■		
Compare and order fractions with or without benchmarks							●		■	■		■		■		■	●	●	■	●	■			■			■	●		■		■		
Plot and compare decimals on a number line																									●	■				■				
Explore uses for positive and negative numbers										●	●								●		●								■	●	■			
Use properties of positive and negative numbers										●	■	■							●							■	●		■	●	■			
Explore reference points for zero										●	■												●	●			■			■				

Operations and Computation

Key ● Content taught ■ Content practiced

	Grade 4 Units												Grade 5 Units												Grade 6 Units									
Addition and Subtraction Facts	1	2	3	4	5	6	7	8	9	10	11	12	1	2	3	4	5	6	7	8	9	10	11	12	1	2	3	4	5	6	7	8	9	10
Practice basic facts and extended facts	■	■											■	■		■			■			■	■			■			●		■	■		
Practice extensions of basic facts		■													■											■				■				
Add/subtract multiples of 10 or 100		●																																
Addition and Subtraction Procedures	1	2	3	4	5	6	7	8	9	10	11	12	1	2	3	4	5	6	7	8	9	10	11	12	1	2	3	4	5	6	7	8	9	10
Use addition/subtraction algorithms		●		●	■								■	●	■										■	●	■			■		■		
Add/subtract using a calculator		●		●																						■					■	■		
Add/subtract multidigit numbers	■	●	●		●								■	●	■										■	●		■	■		■			
Solve addition/subtraction number stories		■	●	■	●									●	■										■							■		
Add/subtract multidigit whole numbers and decimals		●	■	●	■		■							●	■	■					■	■			■	●	■			■		■		
Use estimation or algorithms to add/subtract money amounts/decimals; make change			■	●		■				●	●	●		●	■	■	■	■	■	■					■	●	■	■					■	
Solve decimal addition/subtraction number stories				●															■							●								
Add/subtract positive and negative numbers; model addition and subtraction on a number line										●	●	■							●			■	■				●	■	●	●		■		
Compute with positive and negative integers											■	■							●								■			●	■	■		
Multiplication and Division Facts	1	2	3	4	5	6	7	8	9	10	11	12	1	2	3	4	5	6	7	8	9	10	11	12	1	2	3	4	5	6	7	8	9	10
Use a Multiplication/Division Facts Table			●										■																					
Practice multiplication/division facts			●	■	■	■	■						●	■	■	●			■	■		■	■			●	●	●	■	●		●		
Practice extended multiplication/division facts			●		●	■							■	■	■	●						■				●	■					■		
Solve multiplication/division problems involving multiples of 10, 100, and 1,000					●	■							■	●	■	●									■	●	■	●	■		■	■		
Understand the relationship between multiplication and division			●			●							■			●				■			■	■						●				
Multiplication and Division Procedures	1	2	3	4	5	6	7	8	9	10	11	12	1	2	3	4	5	6	7	8	9	10	11	12	1	2	3	4	5	6	7	8	9	10
Model multiplication with arrays			■		■								●																					
Use mental arithmetic to multiply/divide		■		■	●									■	■	●		■					■	■	●	●				■		■		
Use multiplication/division algorithms					●	●	■	■	●					●	■	●					■	■		■	●	●	■	■	■		■	●		

Operations and Computation (cont.)

Key ● Content taught ■ Content practiced

	Grade 4 Units												Grade 5 Units												Grade 6 Units									
Multiplication and Division Procedures (cont.)	1	2	3	4	5	6	7	8	9	10	11	12	1	2	3	4	5	6	7	8	9	10	11	12	1	2	3	4	5	6	7	8	9	10
Relate fractions and division			■						●								■	■	●								■	●	■	■		■		
Divide by 1-digit numbers						●			■				●			●		■						■	■	●				■		■		
Divide by 2-digit numbers						●			■							●	■									●				■		■		
Use a calculator to multiply/divide					■							●	●			●		■	■			■			●	●		●	■			■	■	
Identify or investigate square numbers			●										●														■						●	
Solve multiplication/division number stories		■	■		■	●			■		■	●				●	■	■								●		■	■			■	■	
Solve multidigit multiplication/division problems					●	■								●	■	●					■	■		■	●	●	■				■			
Multiply/divide decimals by powers of 10														■	■				■			■				●	■	●		■		■		
Multiply decimals by whole numbers									●	■	■			●	■			■	■						●	●		●	■			●		
Divide decimals by whole numbers									●	■	■					●		■								●	■					■		
Multiply/divide money amounts						■			●	●		●		●		●				●	■	●				●	■					●	●	
Solve multiplication/division decimal number stories									●														■					●				■	●	
Interpret a remainder in division problems					■	●			■			●				●	■									■		●				■		
Express remainders as fractions or decimals						●						■				●										●	■	●		■		■	■	
Express quotients as mixed numbers or decimals						●											■	■								●	■	●		■		■		
Locate the decimal point in a product or quotient									●	■	■			●												●		●	■					
Round a decimal quotient to a specified place																		■			■					●		●				●		
Multiply decimals by decimals														●											■	●						●		
Multiply by positive and negative powers of 10																			●		■					●	■							
Multiply/divide positive and negative numbers																											■			●	■	■		
Use divisibility tests to determine if a number is divisible by another number													●		■	■	■	■			■	■				■	■	●						
Procedures for Addition and Subtraction of Fractions	1	2	3	4	5	6	7	8	9	10	11	12	1	2	3	4	5	6	7	8	9	10	11	12	1	2	3	4	5	6	7	8	9	10
Use benchmarks to add and subtract fractions																		●		■	■													
Use models to add/subtract fractions and mixed numbers							●		■	■	■						●	●	■	●								■						

Key ● Content taught ■ Content practiced

Procedures for Addition and Subtraction of Fractions (cont.)	1	2	3	4	5	6	7	8	9	10	11	12	1	2	3	4	5	6	7	8	9	10	11	12	1	2	3	4	5	6	7	8	9	10
Add/subtract fractions with like denominators							●	■	■	■								●		●							■	●			●	■	●	
Add/subtract fractions with unlike denominators							●	■	■	■								●		●	■			■				●	■	■	●	■	●	
Solve fraction addition/subtraction number stories; model addition and subtraction with pictures or words							●				■						●	■	■	■	■			■				●	■			■		
Use an algorithm to add/subtract mixed numbers with like denominators							●													●				■			■	●						
Use an algorithm to add/subtract mixed numbers with unlike denominators							●										■	■	■	●				■				●	■			■		
Procedures for Multiplication and Division of Fractions	**1**	**2**	**3**	**4**	**5**	**6**	**7**	**8**	**9**	**10**	**11**	**12**	**1**	**2**	**3**	**4**	**5**	**6**	**7**	**8**	**9**	**10**	**11**	**12**	**1**	**2**	**3**	**4**	**5**	**6**	**7**	**8**	**9**	**10**
Find common denominators																		●		●				■				●	■	●	●	■		
Use an algorithm to multiply fractions by whole numbers							●	■		■										●								■		■				
Use an algorithm to multiply fractions																				●	■			■				●	■	●	●	●	■	■
Use an algorithm to multiply mixed numbers																				●	■			■				●	■	●		●		■
Solve multiplication/division fraction number stories							●			■										●	■							■	■			●		
Solve “fraction-of-a-fraction” problems																				●										■	●	■	■	
Use a common denominator to divide fractions																			■	●														
Use an algorithm to multiply/divide fractions and mixed numbers; use area models to demonstrate							●													●	■							●	■	●		●	■	■
Understand the effect of multiplying fractions by a number less than 1, equal to 1, or greater than 1																				●														
Computational Estimation	**1**	**2**	**3**	**4**	**5**	**6**	**7**	**8**	**9**	**10**	**11**	**12**	**1**	**2**	**3**	**4**	**5**	**6**	**7**	**8**	**9**	**10**	**11**	**12**	**1**	**2**	**3**	**4**	**5**	**6**	**7**	**8**	**9**	**10**
Round whole numbers to a given place				■	●	■							■	■		●		■							■	●	■						●	
Use estimation to add/subtract		●	■	●	●									●						●	■							■		●		●		
Use estimation to multiply/divide					●			■						●	●	●								■	■		■	■						■
Make magnitude estimates to solve *, ÷ problems					●									●		●		●				■			■	■		■						■
Estimate sums/differences of fractions																				■	■	■						■						
Round decimals to a given place									■		■	■		●	■	●										●	■	●	■			●	■	

Operations and Computation (cont.)

Key ● Content taught ■ Content practiced

	Grade 4 Units												Grade 5 Units												Grade 6 Units									
Computational Estimation (cont.)	1	2	3	4	5	6	7	8	9	10	11	12	1	2	3	4	5	6	7	8	9	10	11	12	1	2	3	4	5	6	7	8	9	10
Estimate costs				■		■			■								■								■									
Estimate products and multiply decimals									●	■	■			●										■	■	●								■
Estimate the quotient and divide a decimal by a whole number									●	■	■					●	■									●	■	●		■				
Models for the Operations	1	2	3	4	5	6	7	8	9	10	11	12	1	2	3	4	5	6	7	8	9	10	11	12	1	2	3	4	5	6	7	8	9	10
Understand multiplicative comparisons		■	●	●	●	■		●					■		■	■				■														
Understand additive comparisons				●	●																													
Find unit rates												●										●					■				■	●	■	
Collect and compare rate data; evaluate reasonableness of rate data												●										●		●			●					●		
Use rate tables to solve problems												●										●		●			●					●		
Represent rates with formulas, tables, and graphs												●										●		●			●			■	■	●	■	
Solve rate and ratio number stories; find equivalent ratios												●								■		●		●			●				■	●	●	
Explore uses of ratios and ways of expressing ratios; differentiate between rate and ratio												●										●		●							■	●	●	
Find opposites and reciprocals of numbers																				■							●			●		■		
Solve problems involving a size-change factor																																●	●	
Write open proportions to solve model problems																								●							■	●	●	
Use cross-multiplication to solve open proportions																															■	●	■	

Data and Chance

	Grade 4 Units												Grade 5 Units												Grade 6 Units									
Data Collection and Representation	1	2	3	4	5	6	7	8	9	10	11	12	1	2	3	4	5	6	7	8	9	10	11	12	1	2	3	4	5	6	7	8	9	10
Collect data by counting/interviewing		●							●			●					●	●							●		■	■						
Collect data from print sources		●	●	■	■	■	■	■	■	■	■	■						■	■						●	■								
Collect data from a map			●	■	●	●						■			■			●					■									●		

Key ● Content taught ■ Content practiced

Data Collection and Representation (cont.)	1	2	3	4	5	6	7	8	9	10	11	12	1	2	3	4	5	6	7	8	9	10	11	12	1	2	3	4	5	6	7	8	9	10
Find locations on a map or globe		●	●		●	●	■		■		■										●													
Collect and compare rate data												●										●		●			●					●		
Conduct a survey									●									●		●					●	■								
Organize and tabulate survey data									●									●							●									
Make a tally chart		●																●													■			
Record data in a table/chart		●	●						●	■		●						●		■		●	●	●	●		●			■	■	■	●	
Record data on a map									●																									
Record/compare numerical data		●					●	■	●			●		●				●						●	●		●	●				■		
Create/interpret bar graphs		●		■	■	■			■	■	■	■		■			●	●							●	■		■			■			
Create/interpret box plots																									●	■	■							
Create/interpret broken-line graphs and line plots		■	●				■				■	■		●				●	●	■	■	●	■	●	●	■	●			■	■			
Create/interpret circle graphs with or without a Percent Circle			■	■	■	■										■	●	●		■		■	■		●	■		●	●	■		■		
Create/interpret step graphs																									●									
Create/interpret Venn diagrams	■		■		■						■						■		●				●	■					■		●	■		
Create/interpret number-line plots		●					●				●			●				●							●	■								
Create/interpret stem-and-leaf plots		■																●	■			●			●	■		■					■	
Interpret mystery graphs																						●				■	■			■			■	
Use technology to create graphs																									■									
Use a spreadsheet																											●	■				■	●	
Explore misleading ways of presenting data																									●	■								
Data Analysis	**1**	**2**	**3**	**4**	**5**	**6**	**7**	**8**	**9**	**10**	**11**	**12**	**1**	**2**	**3**	**4**	**5**	**6**	**7**	**8**	**9**	**10**	**11**	**12**	**1**	**2**	**3**	**4**	**5**	**6**	**7**	**8**	**9**	**10**
Interpret tables, graphs, and maps	■		●	■	■	■			●					●	■	■	●	●	●	●	■	●	■	●	●	■	●	■				●	■	
Use a map scale			●	■	■	●	■	●	■					●		●																●	●	
Use a mileage map					●									●		●																●		
Make and interpret scale drawings								●													■											●	●	
Identify locations for given latitudes and longitudes						●															●													

Data and Chance (cont.)

Key ● Content taught ■ Content practiced

	Grade 4 Units												Grade 5 Units												Grade 6 Units									
Data Analysis (cont.)	1	2	3	4	5	6	7	8	9	10	11	12	1	2	3	4	5	6	7	8	9	10	11	12	1	2	3	4	5	6	7	8	9	10
Find latitude and longitude for given locations						●			■												●													
Summarize and interpret data		■		■				■				●		●				●	●	●		●		●	●	■	●	■				■	■	
Compare two sets of data; compare graphical representations of the same data		■						■	■			■		●	●		●	●	●	●		●		●	●	■	■							
Make predictions about data		■					●		●			■						●				●		●	●		●	●			●			
Find/use the minimum/maximum		●		■				●		■			■	●	●	■	■	●	■		■	■	■	●	●	■	■						■	
Find/use the range		●	■	■	■		■			■			■	●	■		■	●	■		■		■	●	●	■	■						■	
Find/use the median		●	●		■		■	●		■		●	■	●	●	■	■	●	■			●	■	●	●	■	■	■					■	
Find/use the mode		●		■			■	●		■				●	■	■	■	●			■		■		●	■	■						■	
Find/use the mean		■	●	■			■					■		●	■	■	■	●			■		■		●	■	●	■	●				■	
Find/use the lower quartile, upper quartile, and the interquartile range																									●	■	■							
Understand how sample size or outliers affect results		■					■											●							●	■		■						
Determine whether the mean, median, or mode provides the most useful information in a given situation		■	■									■						●							●	■	■	■						
Use data in problem solving		■	●					■				●						●				●			●	■	●				■	■		
Qualitative Probability	1	2	3	4	5	6	7	8	9	10	11	12	1	2	3	4	5	6	7	8	9	10	11	12	1	2	3	4	5	6	7	8	9	10
Explore likelihood of events						■	●		■		■	■		●										●						■	●			
Explore fair and unfair games							●										■	●													●			
Quantitative Probability	1	2	3	4	5	6	7	8	9	10	11	12	1	2	3	4	5	6	7	8	9	10	11	12	1	2	3	4	5	6	7	8	9	10
Predict outcomes; solve problems involving chance outcomes							●	■	■					●				■						●						■	●	■		
Conduct experiments							●							●				■						●							●			
Record outcomes							●							●				■						●							●	■		
Use fractions to record probabilities of events							●		■															●						■	■	■		
Compute the probability of equally-likely outcomes							●	■	■		■			■										●						■	●	■		
Calculate and express the probability of simple events						■	●	■	■	■	■	■					■		■		■			●						■	●			

Key ● Content taught ■ Content practiced

Quantitative Probability (cont.)	1	2	3	4	5	6	7	8	9	10	11	12	1	2	3	4	5	6	7	8	9	10	11	12	1	2	3	4	5	6	7	8	9	10
Understand and apply the concept of random numbers to probability situations																															●			
Understand how increasing the number of trials affects experimental results																		●						■	●						●	■		
Investigate/apply the Multiplication Counting Principle, tree diagrams, lists, and other counting strategies to identify all possible outcomes for a situation			■																					●						■	●	■		
Explore random sampling									●									●							●						●			

Measurement and Reference Frames

	Grade 4 Units												Grade 5 Units												Grade 6 Units									
Length, Weight, and Angles	1	2	3	4	5	6	7	8	9	10	11	12	1	2	3	4	5	6	7	8	9	10	11	12	1	2	3	4	5	6	7	8	9	10
Add and subtract units of length, weight, and capacity			●		■		■				■												■											
Estimate and compare lengths/heights of objects			■	●	■		■																●										●	●
Measure to the nearest foot								●																										
Measure to the nearest inch			■				■									●								●										
Measure to the nearest $\frac{1}{2}$ inch			●																■						■							●	●	●
Measure to the nearest $\frac{1}{4}$ inch					■	■		●						■		■	●			■					■				■			●	●	
Measure to the nearest $\frac{1}{8}$ inch														■				■							■			●	■	●		●	●	
Draw or measure line segments to the nearest centimeter		●	■	●				●								■		●							■				■				■	
Measure to the nearest $\frac{1}{2}$ centimeter		●		■																														
Draw or measure line segments to the nearest millimeter				●	■	■												●		■					■				■			●	●	
Investigate the meter				●																														
Express metric measures with decimals				●																						■								
Estimate and compare distances			●	●	●	●		●						●		●					■													●
Solve length/height/distance number stories			●		■		■		■		■										■					■						●	■	
Estimate and compare weights										■	●																					■		

Measurement and Reference Frames (cont.)

Key ● Content taught ■ Content practiced

	Grade 4 Units												Grade 5 Units												Grade 6 Units									
Length, Weight, and Angles (cont.)	1	2	3	4	5	6	7	8	9	10	11	12	1	2	3	4	5	6	7	8	9	10	11	12	1	2	3	4	5	6	7	8	9	10
Estimate/weigh objects in ounces or grams											●																			■				
Use a pan balance/spring scale											●											●												
Solve weight number stories											●											●	●											
Estimate the measure of an angle			■			■	■			■					●	■												■	■					■
Use full-circle and half-circle protractors to measure and draw angles						●	■	■	■	■					●		■	●										■	●			■		
Measure angles with degree units to within 2°						●	■							■	●	■	■	●	■									■	●				■	■
Area, Perimeter, Volume, and Capacity	1	2	3	4	5	6	7	8	9	10	11	12	1	2	3	4	5	6	7	8	9	10	11	12	1	2	3	4	5	6	7	8	9	10
Investigate area and perimeter			■				■	●	■												●			■	●	■	●					■	●	
Find the areas of regular shapes								●	■	■							■			■	●	■	●		●	■	●	●		●		■	●	
Find the perimeters of regular shapes			■					●	■	■					■		■				■		■		■	■	●					■	●	
Find the areas of irregular shapes								●													●		■					■					■	
Find the perimeters of irregular shapes								■	■												■		■										■	■
Estimate area								●													●							■					●	
Compare perimeter and area								■	■			■									■		■	■	■								●	
Find the area of a figure by counting unit squares and fractions of unit squares inside the figure							■	●													●					■							■	
Use formulas to find areas of rectangles, parallelograms, and triangles; understand the relationship between these formulas								●	■												●		●		■	■	●			●		■	●	■
Find the surface areas of prisms, cylinders, and pyramids																					■		●					●					■	
Investigate/understand the concept of volume of a figure											●										●	■	■										●	■
Understand the relationships between the volumes of pyramids and prisms, and the volumes of cones and cylinders																							●										●	
Estimate volume or surface area								●			●										●												●	
Find and use an approximate value for π (pi)																						●											●	
Use a formula to find the circumference of a circle																						■	■	■									●	■

Key ● Content taught ■ Content practiced

Area, Perimeter, Volume, and Capacity (cont.)	1	2	3	4	5	6	7	8	9	10	11	12	1	2	3	4	5	6	7	8	9	10	11	12	1	2	3	4	5	6	7	8	9	10
Use a formula to find the area of a circle																						●	●	■			●					■	●	■
Distinguish between circumference and area of a circle																						●	■	■									●	
Solve cube-stacking volume problems with unit cubes and fractions of unit cubes											■										●	■	■										■	
Use formulas to calculate volumes of 3-dimensional shapes											●	■									●	■	●			■					■		●	■
Investigate/understand the concept of capacity											●	■									●		●								■		●	
Estimate and calculate capacity											●	■									●		●								■		●	■
Solve capacity number stories											●	■											●								■		●	■
Units and Systems of Measurement	1	2	3	4	5	6	7	8	9	10	11	12	1	2	3	4	5	6	7	8	9	10	11	12	1	2	3	4	5	6	7	8	9	10
Identify equivalent customary units of length	■	■	■					●	■		■			●							■	■										●	●	■
Identify equivalent metric units of length				●		■												■			■	■			■						■	■	●	
Convert between metric/customary measures			■	●				■		■	●	■						■							●	●				■		■	●	■
Use personal references for metric/customary units of length				●	■										■			●			●													
Identify equivalent customary units of weight										■	●											■	■									■		
Identify equivalent metric units of weight				■							●											■	●									■		
Identify metric units of capacity											●	■									●	■	●										●	
Identify equivalent metric units of capacity											●	■									●	■	●									■	●	
Examine the relationships among the liter, milliliter, and cubic centimeter																					●		●										●	
Use personal references for common units of area																					●				■			■					■	
Money	1	2	3	4	5	6	7	8	9	10	11	12	1	2	3	4	5	6	7	8	9	10	11	12	1	2	3	4	5	6	7	8	9	10
Compare money amounts	■		■	■					■			●																						
Temperature	1	2	3	4	5	6	7	8	9	10	11	12	1	2	3	4	5	6	7	8	9	10	11	12	1	2	3	4	5	6	7	8	9	10
Read, record, and convert units of temperature									■													■					●					■	●	
Time	1	2	3	4	5	6	7	8	9	10	11	12	1	2	3	4	5	6	7	8	9	10	11	12	1	2	3	4	5	6	7	8	9	10
Investigate 1-minute intervals						●						●																						

Measurement and Reference Frames (cont.)

Key ● Content taught ■ Content practiced

	Grade 4 Units												Grade 5 Units												Grade 6 Units									
Time (cont.)	1	2	3	4	5	6	7	8	9	10	11	12	1	2	3	4	5	6	7	8	9	10	11	12	1	2	3	4	5	6	7	8	9	10
Calculate elapsed time		■	●		■	●																●												
Convert units of time		■			●													●		■				■								■		
Solve time number stories			●		●								■																					
Coordinate Systems	1	2	3	4	5	6	7	8	9	10	11	12	1	2	3	4	5	6	7	8	9	10	11	12	1	2	3	4	5	6	7	8	9	10
Plot ordered number pairs on a one or four-quadrant coordinate grid						●	■	■	■	■		■								■	●	■		●	■	■	■		●		■		■	
Use ordered number pairs to name points in four quadrants																				■	●	■			■	■	■		■			■		■
Find distances between ordered number pairs along lines																													●	●				■

Geometry

	Grade 4 Units												Grade 5 Units												Grade 6 Units									
Lines and Angles	1	2	3	4	5	6	7	8	9	10	11	12	1	2	3	4	5	6	7	8	9	10	11	12	1	2	3	4	5	6	7	8	9	10
Identify and name points	●														■										■			■	●					■
Identify and name line segments	●		■												■					■								■	●				■	
Draw line segments to a specified length	●	●													●						■				■				●					
Identify parallel and nonparallel line segments	●				■										■														●	■		■	■	
Identify and name lines	●														■														●	■		■	■	
Identify and name intersecting lines					■										■														●	■		■	■	
Identify and name rays	●			■																														
Name, draw, and label line segments, lines, and rays	●														■										■			■	●					■
Identify and name acute, obtuse, right, straight, and reflex angles	●					●			■					■	●	■				■				■				■	●				●	
Identify and describe right angles, parallel lines, skew lines, and line segments	●													■	■													■	●			■	■	
Use full-circle and half-circle protractors to measure and draw angles						●	■	■	■	■					●		■	●										■	●			■		■
Use a compass and a protractor to draw and measure angles formed by intersecting lines															●														●					■
Solve degree problems						●	■	■	■						■														●				■	

Key ● Content taught ■ Content practiced

Lines and Angles (cont.)	1	2	3	4	5	6	7	8	9	10	11	12	1	2	3	4	5	6	7	8	9	10	11	12	1	2	3	4	5	6	7	8	9	10
Determine angle measures based on relationships among common angles					■	●	■	■	■						●													■	●					■
Find angle sums for geometric shapes						■									●														●				■	■
Apply properties of adjacent, supplementary, complementary, and vertical angles; recognize properties in real-world settings						●	■		■						●														●	■		■	●	■
Apply properties of sums of angle measures of triangles and quadrilaterals															●	■								■				■	●			■	■	■
Apply properties of angles of parallelograms															●														●				■	●
Apply properties of angles formed by two parallel lines and a transversal																													●	■		■	■	■
Explore the relationship between endpoints and midpoints																													●					
Make turns and fractions of turns; relate turns to angles						●				■					●									■					●				■	●
Solve construction problems															●														●			■		
Plane and Solid Figures	**1**	**2**	**3**	**4**	**5**	**6**	**7**	**8**	**9**	**10**	**11**	**12**	**1**	**2**	**3**	**4**	**5**	**6**	**7**	**8**	**9**	**10**	**11**	**12**	**1**	**2**	**3**	**4**	**5**	**6**	**7**	**8**	**9**	**10**
Explore shape relationships	●						●	●		●					●						■								■			●	●	■
Identify characteristics of 2-dimensional shapes; use symbolic notation to denote these characteristics	●						●	●	■	●				■	●						●					■			●			●	●	
Identify 2-dimensional shapes	●	■	■				●	●							●					■	■					■			●			■	●	■
Construct/draw 2-dimensional shapes; create designs with 2-dimensional shapes	●	■					■	●		●					●										■				●			●	●	
Use a compass and a straightedge to construct geometric figures	●	■					■	■							●														●			■		
Identify the bases and heights of triangles and parallelograms								●													●											■	●	■
Use a compass to draw a circle with a given radius or diameter, and angles formed by intersecting lines															●														●				■	
Investigate the relationship between circumference and diameter																						●					■						■	
Form shapes by combining polygons							●	■																										
Identify properties and characteristics of polygons	●	■	■	■	■			●	■	●				■	●	●					■				■	■			●			●	●	●
Classify and name polygons	●						●	●	■						●					■	■				■				●				■	■
Classify triangles and quadrilaterals according to side and angle properties	●							●							●					■					■				●				●	●

Geometry (cont.)

Key ● Content taught ■ Content practiced

	Grade 4 Units												Grade 5 Units												Grade 6 Units									
Plane and Solid Figures (cont.)	1	2	3	4	5	6	7	8	9	10	11	12	1	2	3	4	5	6	7	8	9	10	11	12	1	2	3	4	5	6	7	8	9	10
Name, draw, and label angles, triangles, and quadrilaterals	●							●							●					■					●			■	●					■
Identify types of triangles								●							●	■				■					■									
Verify and apply the Pythagorean Theorem																																	●	
Solve problems involving 2-dimensional shapes	■	■					●	●							●						●				■				●			●	●	
Identify and classify 3-dimensional shapes											●									■	●		●						■				●	
Identify characteristics of 3-dimensional shapes; compare them with their 2-D faces											●										●	■	●						■				●	
Construct 3-dimensional shapes											●										●		●										●	
Describe properties of geometric solids											●										●		●						■				●	■
Identify faces, edges, vertices, and bases of prisms and pyramids											●	■											●						■				●	
Perform and identify topological transformations																													■					●
Identify congruent figures															●					■			■					●	●	■		●		●
Draw or form a figure congruent to a given figure										●					●						■								●					■
Identify and draw similar figures								■							●														■			●	●	
Describe relationships among angles, side lengths, perimeter, and area of similar polygons								■																						■	■	●	●	
Transformations and Symmetry	1	2	3	4	5	6	7	8	9	10	11	12	1	2	3	4	5	6	7	8	9	10	11	12	1	2	3	4	5	6	7	8	9	10
Identify lines of reflection, reflected figures, and figures with line symmetry										●											●								●					■
Use a transparent mirror to draw the reflection of a figure										●																								■
Identify symmetrical figures										●											■													■
Identify lines of symmetry									■	●											■												■	■
Translate figures on a coordinate grid																					●								●					●
Rotate figures										■	■										●								●					●
Model clockwise/counterclockwise turns/rotations						●				■														■					●					
Explore transformations of geometric figures in a plane; identify preimage and image											■										●								●				■	●

Patterns, Functions, and Algebra

Key ● Content taught ■ Content practiced

	Grade 4 Units												Grade 5 Units												Grade 6 Units									
Patterns and Functions	1	2	3	4	5	6	7	8	9	10	11	12	1	2	3	4	5	6	7	8	9	10	11	12	1	2	3	4	5	6	7	8	9	10
Explore and extend visual patterns	■						●			●			●							●	●	■							●					●
Create patterns with 2-dimensional shapes	■						●			●																								■
Define and create tessellations/frieze patterns										●					●																		■	●
Identify and use notation for semiregular tessellations																																	■	●
Identify regular tessellations															●																		■	●
Find and extend numerical patterns		■	■		■						●				■			■	■	■		●				●	●	■	●			●	●	
Make/complete a sequence with a number line		●		●	■		●	■				■	●			■		■				■												
Solve "What's My Rule?" (function machine) problems; find a rule for a set of problems		■	●	■	■	■	■		■	■							●	■	●	●	■					●	■			■			■	■
Solve pan-balance problems		■																				●	■	■						●	■		●	
Describe a pattern with a number sentence that has one to three variables																											●			●		■	●	■
Find patterns in addition, subtraction, multiplication, and division facts		■	■		■								●								■					●	■	●		●	■	●	●	
Find number patterns in data; complete a table of values								●				●										●		●		●	●	●				●	●	
Solve and graph solutions for inequalities																														●	■		■	
Combine like terms to simplify expressions and equations																																	●	■
Write and identify equivalent expressions and equivalent equations													●				■	■			●								●	●			●	
Write and solve equations that represent problem situations			●		■	●	●	■	■	■						●											■			●		■	●	■
Algebraic Notation and Solving Number Sentences	1	2	3	4	5	6	7	8	9	10	11	12	1	2	3	4	5	6	7	8	9	10	11	12	1	2	3	4	5	6	7	8	9	10
Compare numbers using <, >, and = symbols	■	■	■	■	■	■	●	■			■	■						●	●	●			■	■	●			●	■	●			■	
Evaluate expressions using <, >, =, and ≈ symbols																■						■			●		●	●	■	●	■	●	●	
Translate number stories into expressions			●		■	●	●	■	■	■				●		●			●			●		●			●	■	■	●			●	
Write/solve addition and subtraction number sentences	■	●			■		■						■	●	■						■				■	■	●	■	■	●			●	
Write/solve multiplication/division number sentences			●		■	■			■				■	●		●					■				■	■	●		■	●		●	●	■
Use variables to describe general patterns																											●	■		●		●	●	

Patterns, Functions, and Algebra (cont.)

Key ● Content taught ■ Content practiced

	Grade 4 Units												Grade 5 Units												Grade 6 Units									
Algebraic Notation and Solving Number Sentences (cont.)	1	2	3	4	5	6	7	8	9	10	11	12	1	2	3	4	5	6	7	8	9	10	11	12	1	2	3	4	5	6	7	8	9	10
Determine the value of a variable		■		■		■		■		■	■	■		●	■	●		■	■	■	■	●	■	●			●	●	●	●	■	●	●	
Write and solve open sentences or number sentences with variables			●		■	●		■	■		■	■		●	■	●	■		●	●	■	●	■	●			●	●	●	●	■	●	●	
Determine if number sentences are true or false		■	●	■	■												■		●	■									■	●	■	■		
Write or evaluate algebraic expressions and formulas to describe situations			●		■	●			■													●		■			●	■		●		■	●	■
Use variables and formulas in spreadsheets																											●	■				■	●	
Evaluate formulas																					●		●			■	●	■		●		■	●	■
Use formulas to solve problems																					●		●			■	●	●		●		■	●	■
Identify dependent and independent variables																											●							
Order of Operations	1	2	3	4	5	6	7	8	9	10	11	12	1	2	3	4	5	6	7	8	9	10	11	12	1	2	3	4	5	6	7	8	9	10
Apply the use of parentheses in number sentences			●	■	■	■	■		■		■							■	●	■	■			■	■		●		■	●		■	●	■
Understand and apply the order of operations to evaluate expressions and solve number sentences																			●	■	■	●	■		■	●		■	■	●	■	■	●	■
Simplify expressions and equations that have parentheses																			●										■	●		■	●	■
Properties of Arithmetic Operations	1	2	3	4	5	6	7	8	9	10	11	12	1	2	3	4	5	6	7	8	9	10	11	12	1	2	3	4	5	6	7	8	9	10
Investigate properties of multiplication/division			●			■							●	■		●										■				●	■	■	■	
Understand and apply the Commutative Property for addition and multiplication																				■										●	■		●	
Apply the Distributive Property					●	■	■	■	■																			●		●		■	●	■
Understand and apply the Identity Property for multiplication																												●		●		●		
Understand and apply the Associative Property for addition and multiplication																	●	●			■		●					●		●			●	

Index

A

B

E

M

O

P

S

T

U

Notes